W9-BRT-269

AMERICAN COUNCIL OF LEARNED SOCIETIES

Dictionary
of Scientific
Biography
cSs

# DICTIONARY
## OF
# SCIENTIFIC BIOGRAPHY

*PUBLISHED UNDER THE AUSPICES OF*
*THE AMERICAN COUNCIL OF LEARNED SOCIETIES*

The American Council of Learned Societies, organized in 1919 for the purpose of advancing the study of the humanities and of the humanistic aspects of the social sciences, is a nonprofit federation comprising forty-two national scholarly groups. The Council represents the humanities in the United States in the International Union of Academies, provides fellowships and grants-in-aid, supports research-and-planning conferences and symposia, and sponsors special projects and scholarly publications.

*MEMBER ORGANIZATIONS*

AMERICAN PHILOSOPHICAL SOCIETY, 1743

AMERICAN ACADEMY OF ARTS AND SCIENCES, 1780

AMERICAN ANTIQUARIAN SOCIETY, 1812

AMERICAN ORIENTAL SOCIETY, 1842

AMERICAN NUMISMATIC SOCIETY, 1858

AMERICAN PHILOLOGICAL ASSOCIATION, 1869

ARCHAEOLOGICAL INSTITUTE OF AMERICA, 1879

SOCIETY OF BIBLICAL LITERATURE, 1880

MODERN LANGUAGE ASSOCIATION OF AMERICA, 1883

AMERICAN HISTORICAL ASSOCIATION, 1884

AMERICAN ECONOMIC ASSOCIATION, 1885

AMERICAN FOLKLORE SOCIETY, 1888

AMERICAN DIALECT SOCIETY, 1889

AMERICAN PSYCHOLOGICAL ASSOCIATION, 1892

ASSOCIATION OF AMERICAN LAW SCHOOLS, 1900

AMERICAN PHILOSOPHICAL ASSOCIATION, 1901

AMERICAN ANTHROPOLOGICAL ASSOCIATION, 1902

AMERICAN POLITICAL SCIENCE ASSOCIATION, 1903

BIBLIOGRAPHICAL SOCIETY OF AMERICA, 1904

ASSOCIATION OF AMERICAN GEOGRAPHERS, 1904

HISPANIC SOCIETY OF AMERICA, 1904

AMERICAN SOCIOLOGICAL ASSOCIATION, 1905

AMERICAN SOCIETY OF INTERNATIONAL LAW, 1906

ORGANIZATION OF AMERICAN HISTORIANS, 1907

COLLEGE ART ASSOCIATION OF AMERICA, 1912

HISTORY OF SCIENCE SOCIETY, 1924

LINGUISTIC SOCIETY OF AMERICA, 1924

MEDIAEVAL ACADEMY OF AMERICA, 1925

AMERICAN MUSICOLOGICAL SOCIETY, 1934

SOCIETY OF ARCHITECTURAL HISTORIANS, 1940

ECONOMIC HISTORY ASSOCIATION, 1940

ASSOCIATION FOR ASIAN STUDIES, 1941

AMERICAN SOCIETY FOR AESTHETICS, 1942

METAPHYSICAL SOCIETY OF AMERICA, 1950

AMERICAN STUDIES ASSOCIATION, 1950

RENAISSANCE SOCIETY OF AMERICA, 1954

SOCIETY FOR ETHNOMUSICOLOGY, 1955

AMERICAN SOCIETY FOR LEGAL HISTORY, 1956

AMERICAN SOCIETY FOR THEATRE RESEARCH, 1956

SOCIETY FOR THE HISTORY OF TECHNOLOGY, 1958

AMERICAN COMPARATIVE LITERATURE ASSOCIATION, 1960

AMERICAN SOCIETY FOR EIGHTEENTH-CENTURY STUDIES, 1969

# DICTIONARY

# OF

# SCIENTIFIC BIOGRAPHY

## CHARLES COULSTON GILLISPIE

*Princeton University*

*EDITOR IN CHIEF*

## Volume XIV

### ADDISON EMERY VERRILL—JOHANN ZWELFER

VINCENNES PUBLIC LIBRARY
VINCENNES, INDIANA

*CHARLES SCRIBNER'S SONS · NEW YORK*

COPYRIGHT © 1976 AMERICAN COUNCIL OF LEARNED SOCIETIES

This book published simultaneously in the
United States of America and in Canada—
Copyright under the Berne Convention

All rights reserved. No part of this book
may be reproduced in any form without the
permission of Charles Scribner's Sons.

1  3  5  7  9  11  13  15  17  19  MD/C  20  18  16  14  12  10  8  6  4  2

Printed in the United States of America
Library of Congress Catalog Card Number 69-18090
ISBN 0-684-12926-4

# Editorial Board

CARL B. BOYER, *Brooklyn College, City University of New York*

MARSHALL CLAGETT, *Institute for Advanced Study, Princeton*

ERWIN N. HIEBERT, *Harvard University*

THOMAS S. KUHN, *Princeton University*

ROBERT MULTHAUF, *Smithsonian Institution*

A. I. SABRA, *Harvard University*

CECIL J. SCHNEER, *University of New Hampshire*

LEONARD G. WILSON, *University of Minnesota*

HARRY WOOLF, *The Johns Hopkins University*

*AMERICAN COUNCIL OF LEARNED SOCIETIES*
Committee on the *Dictionary of Scientific Biography*

*CHAIRMAN*: HENRY GUERLAC, *Cornell University*

I. BERNARD COHEN, *Harvard University*

GERALD HOLTON, *Harvard University*

ERNEST NAGEL, *Columbia University*

RICHARD H. SHRYOCK, *American Philosophical Society*

CYRIL STANLEY SMITH, *Massachusetts Institute of Technology*

LYNN WHITE, JR., *University of California, Los Angeles*

FREDERICK BURKHARDT, *President, American Council of Learned Societies*

# Editorial Staff

MARSHALL DE BRUHL, *MANAGING EDITOR*

SARAH FERRELL, *Assistant Managing Editor*

LOUISE BILEBOF KETZ, *Administrative Editor*

FREDERIC C. BEIL III, *Associate Editor*

ROBERT K. HAYCRAFT, *Assistant Editor*

ROSE MOSELLE, *Editorial Assistant*

JANET BYERS, *Editorial Assistant*

ELIZABETH I. WILSON, *Associate Editor*

JOEL HONIG, *Associate Editor*

DORIS ANNE SULLIVAN, *Proofreader*

MICHAEL KNIBBS, *Proofreader*

# Panel of Consultants

GEORGES CANGUILHEM
*University of Paris*

PIERRE COSTABEL
*École Pratique des Hautes Études*

ALISTAIR C. CROMBIE
*University of Oxford*

MAURICE DAUMAS
*Conservatoire National des Arts et Métiers*

ALLEN G. DEBUS
*University of Chicago*

MARCEL FLORKIN
*University of Liège*

JOHN C. GREENE
*University of Connecticut*

MIRKO D. GRMEK
*Archives Internationales d'Histoire des Sciences*

A. RUPERT HALL
*Imperial College of Science and Technology*

MARY B. HESSE
*University of Cambridge*

BROOKE HINDLE
*Massachusetts Institute of Technology*

JOSEPH E. HOFMANN
*University of Tübingen*

REIJER HOOYKAAS
*State University of Utrecht*

MICHAEL A. HOSKIN
*University of Cambridge*

E. S. KENNEDY
*Brown University*

STEN H. LINDROTH
*University of Uppsala*

ROBERT K. MERTON
*Columbia University*

JOHN MURDOCH
*Harvard University*

SHIGERU NAKAYAMA
*University of Tokyo*

CHARLES D. O'MALLEY
*University of California, Los Angeles*

DEREK J. DE SOLLA PRICE
*Yale University*

J. R. RAVETZ
*University of Leeds*

MARIA LUISA RIGHINI-BONELLI
*Istituto e Museo di Storia della Scienza, Florence*

DUANE H. D. ROLLER
*University of Oklahoma*

KARL EDUARD ROTHSCHUH
*University of Münster/Westphalia*

S. SAMBURSKY
*Hebrew University, Jerusalem*

GIORGIO DE SANTILLANA
*Massachusetts Institute of Technology*

AYDIN SAYILI
*University of Ankara*

ROBERT E. SCHOFIELD
*Case Western Reserve University*

CHRISTOPH J. SCRIBA
*Technical University, Berlin*

NATHAN SIVIN
*Massachusetts Institute of Technology*

BOGDAN SUCHODOLSKI
*Polish Academy of Sciences*

RENÉ TATON
*École Pratique des Hautes Études*

J. B. THORNTON
*University of New South Wales*

RICHARD S. WESTFALL
*Indiana University*

W. P. D. WIGHTMAN
*King's College, Aberdeen*

L. PEARCE WILLIAMS
*Cornell University*

A. P. YOUSCHKEVITCH
*Academy of Sciences of the U.S.S.R.*

# Contributors to Volume XIV

The following are the contributors to Volume XIV. Each author's name is followed by the institutional affiliation at the time of publication and the names of the articles written for this volume. The symbol † means that an author is deceased.

**HANS AARSLEFF**
*Princeton University*
V. WEIGEL; WILKINS

**S. MAQBUL AHMAD**
*Aligarh Muslim University*
YĀQŪT AL-ḤAMAWĪ

**LUIS DE ALBUQUERQUE**
*University of Coimbra*
ZACUTO

**GARLAND E. ALLEN**
*Washington University*
E. B. WILSON

**G. C. AMSTUTZ**
*University of Heidelberg*
ZIRKEL

**HENRY N. ANDREWS**
*University of Connecticut*
W. C. WILLIAMSON

**WILBUR APPLEBAUM**
*Illinois Institute of Technology*
WING

**WILLIAM A. BARKER**
*University of Santa Clara*
A. N. WHITEHEAD

**I. G. BASHMAKOVA**
*Academy of Sciences of the U.S.S.R.*
VORONOY; ZOLOTAREV

**DONALD G. BATES**
*McGill University*
J. R. YOUNG

**HANS BAUMGÄRTEL**
J. C. W. VOIGT

**JOHN J. BEER**
*University of Delaware*
WEIZMANN

**WHITFIELD J. BELL, JR.**
*American Philosophical Society*
WISTAR

**OTTO THEODOR BENFEY**
*Guilford College*
WASHBURN

**RICHARD BERENDZEN**
*The American University, Washington, D.C.*
C. A. YOUNG

**ALEX BERMAN**
*University of Cincinnati*
VIREY

**RICHARD BIEBL†**
WIESNER

**KURT R. BIERMANN**
*Akademie der Wissenschaften der DDR*
WEIERSTRASS

**ASIT K. BISWAS**
*Department of Environment, Ottawa*
WILD

**MARGARET R. BISWAS**
*Department of Environment, Ottawa*
WILD

**L. J. BLACHER**
*Academy of Sciences of the U.S.S.R.*
ZAVADOVSKY; ZAVARZIN

**MAX BLACK**
*Cornell University*
WITTGENSTEIN

**UNO BOKLUND**
*Royal Pharmaceutical Institute, Stockholm*
WALLERIUS

**GERT H. BRIEGER**
*University of California, San Francisco*
WELCH

**T. A. A. BROADBENT†**
W. WALLACE; J. WILSON

**W. H. BROCK**
*University of Leicester*
WANKLYN; A. W. WILLIAMSON

**B. A. BRODY**
*Rice University*
WHATELY

**JOHN HEDLEY BROOKE**
*University of Lancaster*
WURTZ

**STEPHEN G. BRUSH**
*University of Maryland*
WATERSTON

**GERD BUCHDAHL**
*Whipple Science Museum*
C. WOLFF

**JED Z. BUCHWALD**
*University of Toronto*
VILLARI

**K. E. BULLEN**
*University of Sydney*
WEGENER; WIECHERT

**IVOR BULMER-THOMAS**
ZENODORUS

**WERNER BURAU**
*University of Hamburg*
WANGERIN; WEINGARTEN

**J. J. BURCKHARDT**
*University of Zurich*
J. R. WOLF

**DEAN BURK**
*National Cancer Institute*
O. H. WARBURG

**J. C. BURKILL**
*University of Cambridge*
W. H. YOUNG

**JOHN C. BURNHAM**
*Ohio State University*
YERKES

**H. L. L. BUSARD**
*State University of Leiden*
VIÈTE

**ROBERT E. BUTTS**
*University of Western Ontario*
WHEWELL

**G. V. BYKOV**
*Academy of Sciences of the U.S.S.R.*
ZININ

**JEROME J. BYLEBYL**
*University of Chicago*
WILLDENOW

**WILLIAM F. BYNUM**
*University College London*
WERNICKE; WITHERING; ZINSSER

**W. A. CAMPBELL**
*University of Newcastle Upon Tyne*
C. WINKLER

**LUIGI CAMPEDELLI**
*University of Florence*
ZUCCHI

**ROBERT CANTWELL**
A. WILSON

**GUIDO CAROBBI**
*University of Florence*
ZAMBONINI

**CARLO CASTELLANI**
*University of Parma*
ZAMBECCARI

**JOHN CHALLINOR**
*University College of Wales*
T. WEBSTER; WHITEHURST

**ALLAN CHAPMAN**
*University of Oxford*
G. WHARTON

**H. CHIARI†**
WEICHSELBAUM

# CONTRIBUTORS TO VOLUME XIV

EDWIN CLARKE
*Wellcome Institute for the History of Medicine*
C. WHITE

ALBERT B. COSTA
*Duquesne University*
WALTER; WISLICENUS

RUTH SCHWARTZ COWAN
*State University of New York at Stony Brook*
WELDON

GLYN DANIEL
*University of Cambridge*
WOOLLEY; WORM; WORSAAE

KAREL L. DE BOUVÈRE, S.C.J.
*University of Santa Clara*
A. N. WHITEHEAD

ALLEN G. DEBUS
*University of Chicago*
J. WEBSTER

SOLOMON DIAMOND
*California State University, Los Angeles*
WUNDT

J. DIEUDONNÉ
VON NEUMANN; WEYL

SALLY H. DIEKE
*Johns Hopkins University*
W. H. WRIGHT

WILLIAM DOCK
*State University of New York, Brooklyn*
W. C. WELLS

HAROLD DORN
*Stevens Institute of Technology*
WATT; WEDGWOOD

H. DÖRRIE
*University of Münster/Westphalia*
XENOCRATES OF CHALCEDON

SIGALIA DOSTROVSKY
*Barnard College*
VILLARD; VIOLLE; WHEATSTONE

A. HUNTER DUPREE
*Brown University*
WYMAN

JOY B. EASTON
*West Virginia University*
WITT

FRANK N. EGERTON III
*University of Wisconsin-Parkside*
H. C. WATSON

CHURCHILL EISENHART
*U. S. Department of Commerce, National Bureau of Standards*
WILKS; YOUDEN

VĚRA EISNEROVÁ
ZALUŽANSKÝ

GUNNAR ERIKSSON
*Umeå University*
WAHLENBERG

V. A. EYLES
J. WOODWARD

VERA N. FEDCHINA
*Academy of Sciences of the U.S.S.R.*
VYSOTSKY

A. S. FEDOROV
*Academy of Sciences of the U.S.S.R.*
VIZE

I. A. FEDOSEEV
*Academy of Sciences of the U.S.S.R.*
VOEYKOV

LUCIENNE FÉLIX
*University of Paris*
VESSIOT

JAMES W. FELT, S.J.
*University of Santa Clara*
A. N. WHITEHEAD

KONRADIN FERRARI D'OCCHIEPPO
*University of Vienna*
E. WEISS

MENSO FOLKERTS
*Technische Universität Berlin*
J. WERNER

DEAN R. FOWLER
*Center for Process Studies, Claremont, Calif.*
A. N. WHITEHEAD

ROBERT G. FRANK, JR.
*University of California, Los Angeles*
T. WILLIS

V. A. FRANK-KAMENETSKY
*Leningrad State University*
WULFF

FRITZ FRAUNBERGER
O. WIENER

ARTHUR H. FRAZIER
*U.S. Geological Survey*
WOLTMAN

H.-CHRIST. FREIESLEBEN
M. F. J. C. WOLF

HANS FREUDENTHAL
*State University of Utrecht*
N. WIENER

B. VON FREYBERG
*University of Erlangen-Nuremburg*
WALCH

KURT VON FRITZ
*University of Munich*
ZENO OF ELEA; ZENO OF SIDON

JOSEPH S. FRUTON
*Yale University*
WILLSTÄTTER

DAVID J. FURLEY
*Princeton University*
ZENO OF CITIUM

JEAN-CLAUDE GALL
*Université Louis Pasteur, Strasbourg*
VOLTZ

CHARLES C. GILLISPIE
*Princeton University*
VOLTAIRE

PAUL GLEES
*University of Göttingen*
WALDEYER-HARTZ; WIEDERSHEIM

EDWARD D. GOLDBERG
*Scripps Institution of Oceanography*
WASHINGTON

STANLEY GOLDBERG
*Hampshire College*
W. VOIGT

D. C. GOODMAN
*Open University*
W. H. WOLLASTON

I. DE GRAAF BIERBRAUWER-WÜRTZ
L. W. WINKLER

EDWARD GRANT
*University of Indiana*
VIVES

JOHN C. GREENE
*University of Connecticut*
VOLNEY

NORMAN T. GRIDGEMAN
*National Research Council of Canada*
E. B. WILSON

A. T. GRIGORIAN
*Academy of Sciences of the U.S.S.R.*
VYSHNEGRADSKY; ZHUKOVSKY; V. P. ZUBOV

N. A. GRIGORIAN
*Academy of Sciences of the U.S.S.R.*
VVEDENSKY

M. D. GRMEK
*Archives Internationales d'Histoire des Sciences*
VIEUSSENS

ERIC W. GROVES
*British Museum (Natural History)*
G. WHITE

V. GUTINA
*Academy of Sciences of the U.S.S.R.*
VINOGRADSKY

KARLHEINZ HAAS
ZEUTHEN

H. R. HAHNLOSER†
VILLARD DE HONNECOURT

A. RUPERT HALL
*Imperial College, London*
VIGANI

# CONTRIBUTORS TO VOLUME XIV

**SAMI K. HAMARNEH**
*Smithsonian Institution*
IBN WAḤSHIYYA; AL-ZAHRĀWĪ; IBN ZUHR

**RICHARD HART**
*National Academy of Sciences*
C. A. YOUNG

**J. L. HEILBRON**
*University of California, Berkeley*
VOLTA; W. WATSON; WILCKE

**DIETER B. HERRMANN**
*Archenhold Observatory*
VOGEL; WILHELM IV; ZOLLNER

**ERICH HINTZSCHE†**
VESLING

**HELMUT HÖLDER**
*University of Münster/Westphalia*
ZITTEL

**FREDERIC L. HOLMES**
*University of Western Ontario*
VOIT

**WILLIAM T. HOLSER**
*University of Oregon*
C. S. WEISS

**HO PENG YOKE**
*Griffith University*
YANG HUI

**MICHAEL A. HOSKIN**
*University of Cambridge*
T. WRIGHT

**PIERRE HUARD**
*René Descartes University*
VICQ D'AZYR

**KARL HUFBAUER**
*University of California, Irvine*
WEDEL; C. E. WEIGEL

**AARON J. IHDE**
*University of Wisconsin-Madison*
WILEY; R. R. WILLIAMS

**M. J. IMBAULT-HUART**
*René Descartes University*
VICQ D'AZYR

**DANIEL JONES**
*Oregon State University*
WIELAND

**PHILLIP S. JONES**
*University of Michigan*
WESSEL

**HANS KANGRO**
*University of Hamburg*
WEHNELT; WIEN

**GEORGE B. KAUFFMAN**
*California State University, Fresno*
WAAGE; A. WERNER

**ROBIN KEEN**
*Gillingham Technical High School*
F. WÖHLER

**MILTON KERKER**
*Clarkson College of Technology*
ZSIGMONDY

**GUNTHER KERSTEIN**
WIEGLEB

**C. G. KING**
*Columbia University*
WU

**DAVID A. KING**
*Smithsonian Institution Project in Medieval Islamic Astronomy, Cairo*
IBN YŪNUS

**LAWRENCE J. KING**
*State University of New York at Geneseo*
A. WALKER

**GEORGE KISH**
*University of Michigan*
WALDSEEMÜLLER

**MARC KLEIN†**
WICKERSHEIMER

**BRONISLAW KNASTER**
ZARANKIEWICZ

**ELAINE KOPPELMAN**
*Goucher College*
WOODHOUSE

**SHELDON J. KOPPERL**
*Grand Valley State Colleges*
WILHELMY

**HANS-GÜNTHER KÖRBER**
*Zentralbibliothek des Meteorologischen Dienstes der DDR, Potsdam*
WIEDEMANN; L. C. WIENER; WRÓBLEWSKI

**VLADISLAV KRUTA**
*Purkyně University*
WAGNER; E. H. WEBER

**WILLIAM LEFANU**
*Royal College of Surgeons*
T. WHARTON

**HENRY M. LEICESTER**
*University of the Pacific*
VIRTANEN; WALLACH; WINDAUS

**ERNA LESKY**
*University of Vienna*
WAGNER VON JAUREGG; WERTHEIM

**JACQUES R. LÈVY**
*Paris Observatory*
C. J. E. WOLF

**DAVID C. LINDBERG**
*University of Wisconsin-Madison*
WITELO

**STEN LINDROTH**
*University of Uppsala*
WARGENTIN

**R. B. LINDSAY**
*Brown University*
R. W. WOOD

**ALBERT G. LONG**
*Hancock Museum, University of Newcastle Upon Tyne*
WITHAM

**ESMOND R. LONG**
*University of Pennsylvania*
H. G. WELLS

**MARVIN W. MCFARLAND**
*Library of Congress*
WRIGHT BROTHERS

**LUDOLF VON MACKENSON**
*Astronomisch-Physikalisches Kabinett*
A. WÖHLER

**H. LEWIS MCKINNEY**
*University of Kansas*
A. R. WALLACE

**SAUNDERS MAC LANE**
*University of Chicago*
E. B. WILSON

**DANIEL MARTIN**
*University of Glasgow*
WHITTAKER

**ERNST MAYR**
*Harvard University*
WHITMAN

**OTTO MAYR**
*Smithsonian Institution*
ZEUNER

**DANIEL MERRIMAN**
*Yale University*
WALLICH

**WILLIAM J. MORISON**
*University of Louisville*
G. F. WRIGHT

**EDGAR W. MORSE**
*California State College, Sonoma*
T. YOUNG

**D. MÜLLER**
*University of Copenhagen*
WARMING

**LETTIE S. MULTHAUF**
ZACH

**R. P. MULTHAUF**
*Smithsonian Institution*
ZWELFER

**GERALD D. NASH**
*University of New Mexico*
WHITNEY

**HENRY NATHAN**
WEDDERBURN

**A. NATUCCI†**
VIVIANI

**CLIFFORD M. NELSON**
*University of California, Berkeley*
WHITFIELD

# CONTRIBUTORS TO VOLUME XIV

J. D. NORTH
*University of Oxford*
J. H. C. WHITEHEAD; F. WOLLASTON;
YULE

CHRISTOFFER OFTEDAHL
*Technical University of Norway*
J. H. L. VOGT; T. VOGT

C. D. O'MALLEY†
VESALIUS

ALEXANDER M. OSPOVAT
*Oklahoma State University*
A. G. WERNER

FRANKLIN PARKER
*West Virginia University*
A. E. WRIGHT

JEAN PELSENEER
*University of Brussels*
WENDELIN

FRANCIS PERRIN
*Académie des Sciences, Paris*
P. WEISS

P. E. PILET
*University of Lausanne*
C. VOGT; WEPFER; YERSIN

DAVID PINGREE
*Brown University*
VIJAYANANDA; YAʻQUB IBN ṬĀRIQ;
YATIVṚṢABHA; YAVANEŚVARA

A. F. PLAKHOTNIK
*Academy of Sciences of the U.S.S.R.*
N. N. ZUBOV

A. F. PLATÉ
*Academy of Sciences of the U.S.S.R.*
ZELINSKY

M. PLESSNER†
ZOSIMUS OF PANOPOLIS

HOWARD PLOTKIN
*University of Western Ontario*
A. WILSON

EMMANUEL POULLE
*École Nationale des Chartes*
WILLIAM OF SAINT-CLOUD; WILLIAM THE
ENGLISHMAN

LORIS PREMUDA
*University of Padua*
M. WIELAND

PAUL H. PRICE
*West Virginia Geological and Economic
Survey*
I. C. WHITE

J. A. PRINS
WAALS; ZERNIKE

HANS QUERNER
*University of Heidelberg*
M. W. C. WEBER

SAMUEL X. RADBILL
*College of Physicians of New Jersey*
WHYTT

HANS RAMSER
VOLKMANN; E. G. WARBURG

R. A. RANKIN
*University of Glasgow*
G. N. WATSON

NATHAN REINGOLD
*Smithsonian Institution*
R. S. WOODWARD

L. M. DE RIJK
*Filosofisch Institut, Leiden*
WILLIAM OF SHERWOOD

GUENTER B. RISSE
*University of Wisconsin-Madison*
VIRCHOW; WILBRAND

ANDRE RIVIER†
XENOPHANES

GLORIA ROBINSON
*Yale University*
WEISMAN

JACQUES ROGER
*University of Paris*
WHISTON

GRETE RONGE
WACKENRODER

B. VAN ROOTSELAAR
*State Agricultural University, Wageningen*
ZERMELO

BERNARD ROTH
*Stanford University*
R. WILLIS

K. E. ROTHSCHUH
*University of Münster/Westphalia*
VERWORN

HUNTER ROUSE
*University of Iowa*
WEISBACH

G. RUDOLPH
*University of Kiel*
WEIGERT

MICHAEL T. RYAN
*University of Chicago*
VILLALPANDO

F. SCHMEIDLER
*University of Munich Observatory*
WILSING

CHARLES B. SCHMITT
*Warburg Institute*
ZABARELLA

BRUNO SCHOENEBERG
*University of Hamburg*
H. WEBER

E. L. SCOTT
*Stamford High School, Lincolnshire*
R. WATSON; WOULFE

HAROLD W. SCOTT
*Michigan State University*
J. WALKER

J. F. SCOTT†
WARING; WREN

CHRISTOPH J. SCRIBA
*University of Hamburg*
WALLIS; WIELEITNER

A. SEIDENBERG
*University of California, Berkeley*
WILCZYNSKI

E. M. SENCHENKOVA
*Academy of Sciences of the U.S.S.R.*
VORONIN

ELIZABETH NOBLE SHOR
*Scripps Institution of Oceanography*
VERRILL; S. WATSON; WHEELER; C. D.
WHITE; WILLISTON

DIANA M. SIMPKINS
*Polytechnic of North London*
VILMORIN

NATHAN SIVIN
*Massachusetts Institute of Technology*
WANG HSI-SHAN

P. SMIT
*Catholic University, Nijmegen*
WIGAND

E. SNORRASON
*Rigshospitalet, Copenhagen*
WINSLØW

GLENN SONNEDECKER
*University of Wisconsin-Madison*
H. C. WOOD

JAMES BROOKES SPENCER
*Oregon State University*
ZEEMAN

CURT STERN
*University of California, Berkeley*
WEINBERG

SHLOMO STERNBERG
*Harvard University*
WINTNER

FRANS STOCKMANS
*University of Brussels*
ZEILLER

JANIS STRADINŠ
*Academy of Sciences of the U.S.S.R.*
WALDEN

D. J. STRUIK
*Massachusetts Institute of Technology*
VLACQ

JUDITH P. SWAZEY
*Boston University School of Music*
WALLER

FERENC SZABADVÁRY
*Technical University, Budapest*
ZEMPLÉN

GIORGIO TABARRONI
*Universities of Modena and Bologna*
ZANOTTI

# CONTRIBUTORS TO VOLUME XIV

C. H. TALBOT
*Wellcome Institute for the History of Medicine*
VIGO

M. TEICH
*University of Cambridge*
F. WALD

K. BRYN THOMAS
*Royal Berkshire Hospital*
WATERTON

PHILLIP DRENNON THOMAS
*Wichita State University*
WALTER OF ODINGTON; T. WHITE; WIED

VICTOR E. THOREN
*Indiana University*
WARD

THADDEUS J. TRENN
*University of Regensburg*
WHYTLAW-GRAY; S. YOUNG

F. G. TRICOMI
*Academy of Sciences of Turin*
VITALI

HENRY S. TROPP
*Humboldt State University*
J. W. YOUNG

G. L'E. TURNER
*University of Oxford*
B. WILSON; C. T. R. WILSON; J. WINTHROP

P. W. VAN DER PAS
*South Pasadena, Calif.*
VRIES

STIG VEIBEL
*Technical University of Denmark*
ZEISE

J. VERNET
*University of Barcelona*
IBN WAFĪD; YAḤYĀ IBN ABĪ MANṢŪR; AL-ZARQĀLI

KURT VOGEL
*University of Munich*
WIDMAN; WITTICH; WOEPCKE

E. VOLTERRA
*University of Texas*
VOLTERRA

WILLIAM A. WALLACE, O.P.
*Catholic University of America*
VINCENT OF BEAUVAIS; WILLIAM OF AUVERGNE

P. J. WALLIS
*University of Newcastle Upon Tyne*
E. WRIGHT

DEBORAH JEAN WARNER
*Smithsonian Institution*
WINLOCK

AARON C. WATERS
*University of California, Santa Cruz*
B. WILLIS

CHARLES WEBSTER
*University of Oxford*
WALTON

MARY A. WELCH
*University of Nottingham*
WILLUGHBY

JOHN W. WELLS
*Cornell University*
H. S. WILLIAMS

F. W. WENT
*University of Nevada Desert Research Institute*
WENT

JOYCE WEVERS
*State University of Utrecht*
WIDMANNSTÄTTEN

ALWYNE WHEELER
*British Museum (Natural History)*
WOTTON

RONALD S. WILKINSON
*Library of Congress*
J. WINTHROP

J. WOLFOWITZ
*University of Illinois at Urbana-Champaign*
A. WALD

A. E. WOODRUFF
*Yeshiva University*
W. E. WEBER

ELLIS L. YOCHELSON
*U.S. Geological Survey*
WALCOTT

H. S. YODER, JR.
*Carnegie Institution of Washington*
WINCHELL FAMILY; F. E. WRIGHT

A. P. YOUSCHKEVITCH
*Academy of Sciences of the U.S.S.R.*
V. P. ZUBOV

# DICTIONARY
## OF
## SCIENTIFIC BIOGRAPHY

# DICTIONARY OF SCIENTIFIC BIOGRAPHY

VERRILL – ZWELFER

**VERRILL, ADDISON EMERY** (*b.* Greenwood, Maine, 9 February 1839; *d.* Santa Barbara, California, 10 December 1926), *zoology.*

Verrill's ability to identify and remember a tremendous variety of animals, plants, and minerals appeared at a very early age. He began with rocks and minerals near his home and later collected plants, shells, and animals at Norway, Maine, where the family moved in 1853. His parents, George Washington Verrill and Lucy Hillborn, were both descended from early New England families. In preparation for his boyhood ambition to study and work under Louis Agassiz, Verrill attended Norway Liberal Institute and in 1859 entered Harvard College. Agassiz put him to work studying birds, urged him to take up zoology instead of geology, and arranged summer trips to the Bay of Fundy, Anticosti Island, and the coast of Labrador for him, in the company of Alpheus Hyatt and N. S. Shaler. Verrill's early interest in geology lasted throughout his life as a secondary profession.

Even before his graduation from Harvard in 1862, Verrill worked as assistant to Agassiz at the Museum of Comparative Zoology and continued there until 1864. A request from Yale College for recommendations to the newly established chair of zoology led Agassiz to suggest Verrill in 1864. He held the post until his retirement in 1907. He began the zoological collections of the Peabody Museum and was curator from 1865 to 1910. He also taught large classes in geology at Yale from 1870 to 1894. Simultaneously with his Yale duties, Verrill was in charge of the scientific investigations of the U.S. Commission of Fish and Fisheries, curator of the Boston Society of Natural History for ten years, and professor of comparative anatomy and entomology for one course each spring at the University of Wisconsin from 1868 to 1870. He served as associate editor of the *American Journal of Science* from 1869 to 1920.

Verrill received an honorary M.A. from Yale in 1867. He was an early member of the National Academy of Sciences, president of the Connecticut Academy of Arts and Sciences for some years, a corresponding member of the Société Zoologique de France, and a member of many American scientific societies.

Trained under Agassiz, Verrill became an outstanding taxonomist, for he considered taxonomy the foundation of biology. Until 1870 he collected marine invertebrates by dredging each summer along the Maine coast and in the Bay of Fundy, and completed the identifications of the collections during the school year. Aided by his wife's brother, Sidney I. Smith, Verrill made a detailed ecologic study of the fauna of Vineyard Sound in 1873, the first of this magnitude in the United States and the model for later ones. He was assigned to handle the invertebrates of Spencer F. Baird's Commission of Fish and Fisheries survey of the New England coast, and elected to describe and classify all the groups himself, intending to write monographs covering each major unit.

Because of his remarkable facility for distinguishing significant morphological features, he described, with few errors in judgment, at least one thousand marine invertebrates, in every phylum except Protozoa. His outstanding contribution was in the classification and natural history of corals; but his work on echinoderms, especially starfishes and the very confusing brittle stars, placed that group on a secure taxonomic foundation. He was among the first to make a phylogenetic separation of the echinoderms from the coelenterates, both of which had previously been combined into the Radiata. Verrill also completed three monographs on crustaceans, having taken over that group when the original worker, Sidney Smith, became blind. Aided by Katharine J. Bush, he wrote extensively on the mollusks, especially the cephalopods, and directed the making of a life-size model of a giant squid for the Peabody Museum. In addition to his taxonomic work, he wrote considerably on the

1

habits and natural history of each group he studied.

While participating in the dredging trips of the Commission of Fish and Fisheries, Verrill devised useful marine collecting equipment; and he enlisted students on his own weekend dredging trips by sailboat near New Haven, reaching depths of 4,000 meters. From three trips to Bermuda and extensive study he presented a painstaking report on the zoology, botany, geology, and even history and the effect of civilization on those islands. Interested in many fields of zoology, Verrill introduced new names into entomology and parasitology as well as into marine invertebrate groups; he also alerted the public to the hazards of tapeworms and similar parasites. His type specimens are at the Peabody Museum and the U.S. National Museum. He contributed most of the zoological definitions to the 1890 edition of Webster's *International Dictionary*.

### BIBLIOGRAPHY

I. ORIGINAL WORKS. The memoir by Coe, cited below, contains a detailed bibliography, by subject, of over 300 papers by Verrill and includes monographs on specific animal groups. His major report on Bermuda is "The Bermuda Islands: Their Scenery, Climate, Productions, Physiography, Natural History and Geology, With Sketches of Their Early History and the Changes due to Man," in *Transactions of the Connecticut Academy of Arts and Sciences*, **11** (1902), 413–911—further reports on the islands appeared in 1906 and 1907. The meticulous Vineyard Sound study is "Report Upon the Invertebrate Animals of Vineyard Sound and the Adjacent Waters, With an Account of the Physical Characters of the Region," in *Report of the United States Commissioner of Fisheries*, **1** (1873), 295–747.

II. SECONDARY LITERATURE. Wesley R. Coe, "Biographical Memoir of Addison Emery Verrill," in *Biographical Memoirs. National Academy of Sciences*, **14** (1932), 19–66, provides information on Verrill's childhood, personality, and scientific accomplishments. Shorter versions, also by Coe, appeared in *Science*, **66**, no. 1697 (1927), 28–29; and in *American Journal of Science*, 5th ser., **13**, no. 77 (1927), 377–387.

ELIZABETH NOBLE SHOR

**VERULAM, BARON.** See **Bacon, Francis.**

**VERWORN, MAX** (*b*. Berlin, Germany, 4 November 1863; *d*. Bonn, Germany, 23 November 1921), *physiology*.

The son of a Prussian civil servant, Verworn completed his secondary education at the Friedrich Wilhelm Gymnasium, occupying his free time with biological experiments. In 1884 he enrolled as a student of zoology and medicine at the University of Berlin, where he attended lectures by F. E. Schultze, Emil du Bois-Reymond, and Rudolf Virchow. He received the Ph.D. in zoology in 1887 and immediately began to study the medical sciences at Jena, where he met Wilhelm Preyer, Wilhelm Biedermann, and Ernst Haeckel, the latter exerting the greatest influence. In 1889, Verworn received the M.D. from Jena, where he remained until 1901, first as an assistant, then as a university lecturer (1891), and finally as associate professor at the physiological institute (1895). His marriage that year to Josephine Huse, whom he had met in Naples, was childless. In 1901 Verworn succeeded Georg Meissner at Göttingen, and in 1910 he replaced Eduard Pflüger at Bonn. In 1911, he gave the Silliman lectures at Yale University. At both Göttingen and Bonn he attracted many young research workers, including Hans Winterstein, August Pütter, and F. W. Fröhlich. He greatly influenced many Japanese students, including H. Nagai and Y. Ishikawa, who spread his teachings in Japan.

During his special experimental investigations Verworn was concerned primarily with the general basic problems of life. This preoccupation can be noticed especially in his biological-physiological studies, where he investigated the basic phenomena of life such as irritation, paralysis, narcosis, biotonus (biological base tension), hypnosis, fatigue, and recovery. In this endeavor he worked with unicellular organisms, such as Protista, or the cells of higher organisms. Verworn was a major advocate of cellular physiology; and his experimental investigations were concerned mainly with the elementary processes of muscle fibers, nerve fibers, and sensory organs. For him each analysis of function always ended with the function of the cells: for secretion, with the glandular cells; for the action of the heart, with the heart muscle cells; for psychical conduction, with the ganglion cells. In general, comparative, and microscopic physiology, Verworn followed the model of Johannes Müller, to whom he dedicated his *Allgemeine Physiologie* (1895). The book was widely read outside the field of physiology, especially since Verworn included clear statements of the controversies of the time, such as vitalism versus mechanism, psychophysical problems, and monism. In 1902 he founded *Zeitschrift für allgemeine Physiologie*; many of his articles had previously appeared in *Pflügers Archiv für die gesamte Physiologie*.

Verworn conducted his first Protista experiments during the years 1887–1891, while on research trips to the Mediterranean and Red seas and working at the Zoological Station in Naples under Anton Dohrn. His studies of one-cell animals encompassed the manifestations of regeneration (1888), the relations between cell nucleus and psyche (1890), the phenomena of stimulation and response by means of galvanic current, and, most important, the polar effects of direct current (1894, 1897). His work on irritation, irritability, and paralysis was published in 1914. Verworn differentiated spontaneous manifestations of life from the "response of stimulation" by means of various external living conditions. He did not limit his concern only to the problems of cellular physiology or theoretical biology but, rather, felt strong need to clarify the fundamental issues and therefore also investigated the relation of body and mind. In his *Psycho-physiologische Protisten-Studien* (1889), Verworn discarded the dualistic point of view in favor of the monistic—not in terms of materialism but of psychomonism. To him the final elements of the being are psychic. "The physical world exists not next to the psychic, on the contrary, within the psychic" (*Naturwissenschaft und Weltanschauung* [1904], 29).

Like Mach and Richard Avenarius, Verworn advocated the principle of conditional research rather than the usual search for causes. This multiconditionalism manifests itself especially in the basic phenomena of life, which he made the main subject of his studies (1918). He also did research on primitive cultures and anthropology, collecting artifacts from primitive cultures, specimens of ethnological importance, prehistoric subjects, and coins. Many of these were used in the writing of *Die Anfänge der Kunst* (Jena, 1909).

In the history of ideas Verworn belongs with such materialists and positivists as Ludwig Büchner, Moleschott, Haeckel, and Mach. Since he did not hesitate to establish new hypotheses—*Zellseele, Atomseele, Biotonus*—and to expound them in his works, he had many opponents in addition to supporters throughout his life.

*BIBLIOGRAPHY*

I. ORIGINAL WORKS. Verworn's books include *Psycho-physiologische Protisten-Studien. Experimentelle Untersuchungen* (Jena, 1889); *Die Bewegung der lebendigen Substanz* (Jena, 1892); *Allgemeine Physiologie. Ein Grundriss der Lehre vom Leben* (Jena, 1895); *Beiträge zur Physiologie des Centralnervensystems* (Jena, 1898); *Die Mechanik des Geisteslebens* (Leipzig, 1907); *Physiologisches Praktikum* (Jena, 1907); *Die Entwicklung des menschlichen Geistes* (Jena, 1910); *Narkose* (Jena, 1912); *Irritability* (New Haven, 1913), the Silliman lectures; and *Erregung und Lähmung. Eine allgemeine Physiologie der Reizwirkungen* (Jena, 1914).

Among his articles are "Biologische Protistenstudien," in *Zeitschrift für wissenschaftliche Zoologie*, **46** (1888), 455–470, and **50** (1890), 443–468; "Die polare Erregung . . .," in *Pflügers Archiv für die gesamte Physiologie*, **45** (1889), 1–36; **46** (1890), 267–303; **62** (1896), 415–450; and **65** (1897), 47–62; "Die physiologische Bedeutung des Zellkerns," *ibid.*, **51** (1892), 1–118; "Der körnige Zerfall. Ein Beitrag zur Physiologie des Todes," *ibid.*, **63** (1896), 253–272; "Einleitung" (as editor), in *Zeitschrift für allgemeine Physiologie*, **1** (1902), 1–18; "Die cellularphysiologische Grundlage des Gedächtnisses," *ibid.*, **6** (1907), 119–139; and "Die cellularphysiologische Grundlage des Abstraktionsprozesses," *ibid.*, **14** (1912), 277–296. He also published articles on the effect of strychnine and on fatigue, exhaustion, and recovery in the nerve center of the spinal column, in *Archiv für Anatomie und Physiologie*, Physiol. Abt. (1900), 385–414; and supp. (1900), 152–176.

II. SECONDARY LITERATURE. See Silvestro Baglioni, "Max Verworn," in *Rivista di biologia*, **4** (1922), 126–133, with bibliography; I. Fischer, in *Biographisches Lexikon der hervorragenden Ärzte der letzten 50 Jahre*, II (Berlin–Vienna, 1933), 1616–1617; Friedrich W. Fröhlich, "Max Verworn," in *Zeitschrift für allgemeine Physiologie*, **20** (1923), 185–192; R. Matthaei, "Max Verworn," in *Deutsche medizinische Wochenschrift*, **48** (1922), 102–103, with portrait; A. Pütter, "Max Verworn," in *Münchener medizinische Wochenschrift*, **68** (1921), 1655–1656; W. Thörner, "Max Verworn," in *Medizinische Klinik*, **18** (1922), 130–131; and R. Wüllenweber, *Der Physiologe Max Verworn* (Bonn, 1968), inaugural M.D. diss.

K. E. ROTHSCHUH

**VESALIUS, ANDREAS** (*b.* Brussels, Belgium, 31 December 1514; *d.* Zákinthos, Greece, 15 October 1564), *medicine.*

The date of Vesalius' birth is derived from a horoscope cast by the Milanese physician Girolamo Cardano, from which it may also be determined that he was born at a quarter to six in the morning. His father, also named Andreas, was an apothecary of the Emperor Charles V and the illegitimate son of Everard van Wesele or Vesalius and, as such, was a humble member of a family already distinguished for several generations in medical circles. The maiden name of Vesalius' mother was Isabel Crabbe, and this resemblance to the name of the English poet has given rise to the legend that she was an Englishwoman. The name Crabbe is in fact common in Brabant.

The young Vesalius received his elementary education in Brussels and matriculated at the University of Louvain in February 1530 to pursue the arts course, the necessary prerequisite for entrance into a professional school. It is not known when he decided to study medicine, but such a decision could have been related to the emperor's legitimization of the young man's father in 1531, which may have encouraged him to carry on his family's traditional profession.

Since at this time the medical school of Louvain had little repute, Vesalius chose to carry on his medical studies at the more illustrious faculty of the University of Paris, matriculating there probably in September 1533, where he studied with Guinter of Andernach, Jacobus Sylvius (Jacques Dubois), and Jean Ferne. Guinter, who in his *Institutiones anatomicae* (1536) spoke very favorably of his student, and Sylvius, an arch-Galenist and later an enemy of Vesalius, each in his own way directed the young man toward anatomical research. Since they were both supporters of the Galenic tradition, it was natural that their student, although he acquired skill in the technique of dissection, remained under the influence of Galenic concepts of anatomy.

The war between France and the Holy Roman Empire compelled Vesalius to leave Paris in 1536. He returned to Louvain, where, with the friendly support of the burgomaster, he was able to reintroduce anatomical dissection, which had not been part of the medical curriculum for many years, and in 1537 he received the degree of bachelor of medicine. While completing his studies he produced his *Paraphrasis in nonum librum Rhazae ad Regem Almansorem* (Louvain, 1537), in which he compared Muslim and Galenic therapy—to the disadvantage of the former—but sought to preserve the reputation of Rhazes and to reconcile him with the Greeks. A youthful work, of no significance except as an indication of Vesalius' continued allegiance to Galen, it was nevertheless important enough to its author for him to reprint it in Basel later in the year, on his way to Italy.

In the autumn of 1537 Vesalius enrolled in the medical school of the University of Padua, then the most famous in Europe, where, after two days of examinations, he received the degree of doctor of medicine *magna cum laude* on 5 December 1537 and on the following day accepted appointment as *explicator chirurgiae* with the responsibility of lecturing on surgery and anatomy. Immediately thereafter he gave the required annual anatomical lectures and demonstrations, which although Galenic in character were unusual because, contrary to custom, Vesalius himself performed the dissections rather than consigning that task to a surgeon. In addition, he produced four large anatomical charts representing the portal, caval, arterial, and nervous systems, based chiefly on this dissection and intended as a reference work and memory aid for his students when the cadaver was no longer available. These figures were distinctly novel both in their size, which permitted deceptively naturalistic although primarily Galenic portrayals of even the smaller structures, and in their detailed identification of the parts through an elaborately indexed anatomical terminology in Greek, Latin, Arabic, and Hebrew. The theft and subsequent publication of the drawing of the nervous system and the danger of plagiarism of the others led Vesalius to publish the three remaining drawings, together with three views of the skeleton by the Dutch artist Jan Stephen of Calcar, a student in Titian's studio. Although without a general title, they are usually referred to as *Tabulae anatomicae sex* (Venice, 1538).

In the same year Vesalius produced a dissection manual for his students, *Institutiones anatomicae secundum Galeni sententiam . . . per Ioannem Guinterium Andernachum . . . ab Andrea Vesalio . . . auctiores et emendatiores redditae* (Venice, 1538). As the title indicates, this was a revised and augmented edition of the Galenically oriented dissection manual of his former teacher in Paris, Guinter of Andernach. The revisions display a concern with the minutiae of dissection technique, and the augmentations offer several independent anatomical judgments, such as the briefly expressed but clearly anti-Galenic observation that the cardiac systole is synchronous with the arterial pulse.

Also in 1538 Vesalius visited Matteo Corti, professor of medicine in Bologna, and discussed the problems of therapy by venesection. Differences of opinion between the two men seem to have been the impulse behind Vesalius' next book, *Epistola docens venam axillarem dextri cubiti in dolore laterali secundam* (Basel, 1539), written in support of the revived classical procedure first advocated in a posthumous publication (1525) of the Parisian physician Pierre Brissot. In this procedure blood was drawn from a site near the location of the ailment, in contrast to the Muslim and medieval practice of drawing blood from a distant part of the body. As the title of his book indicates, Vesalius sought to locate the precise site for venesection in pleurisy within the framework of the classical method. The real significance of the book lay in Vesalius' attempt to support his arguments by the location and continuity of the venous system rather than by an appeal to earlier authority. Despite his own still faulty knowledge, his method may be called scientific in relation to that of others; certainly it was nontraditional and required that his opponents resort to the same method if they wished to reply effectively. With this novel approach to the problem of venesection Vesalius posed the then striking hypothesis that anatomical dissection might be used to test speculation. Here too he declared clearly, on the basis of vivisection, that cardiac systole was synchronous with arterial expansion and for the first time mentioned his initial efforts in the preparation of the anatomical monograph that was ultimately to take shape as *De humani corporis fabrica*.

These activities and the novelty of Vesalius' teaching were greatly appreciated by both the teachers and students of the university. Indeed, the official document by which the young anatomist was reappointed in 1539 to the medical faculty, with a considerable increase in salary, declared that "he has aroused very great admiration in all the students." Although the opportunities for dissection were limited by the small number of cadavers available, by 1538, from his lecturing on Galen and his own dissecting, Vesalius began to realize that there were contradictions between Galen's texts and his own observations in the human body.

In 1539 his supply of dissection material became much greater when Marcantonio Contarini, judge of the Paduan criminal court, became interested in Vesalius' investigations and made the bodies of executed criminals available to him—occasionally delaying executions to suit the convenience of the young anatomist. For the first time Vesalius had sufficient human material to make and to repeat detailed and comparative dissections. As a result, he became increasingly convinced that Galen's description of human anatomy was basically an account of the anatomy of animals in general and was often erroneous insofar as the human body was concerned. During the winter of 1539 he was sufficiently sure of his position to challenge the validity of Galenic anatomy in Padua and shortly thereafter to repeat the challenge in Bologna.

Vesalius went to Bologna in January 1540, at the invitation of the medical students of that city,

to present a series of anatomical demonstrations, in the course of which he boldly declared that human anatomy could be learned only from the dissection and observation of the human body. As proof of the nonhuman source of Galen's anatomy he articulated ape and human skeletons and demonstrated that Galen's description of the bones agreed only with the former.

On his return to Padua, Vesalius began the composition of the *Fabrica* in its final form. For the next two years, until the summer of 1542, he concentrated his efforts on this huge work, sparing no expenditure of energy or money. He hired the best draftsmen he could find to make the illustrations and the finest Venetian block cutters to reproduce them. To print the book he chose Joannes Oporinus of Basel. In the summer of 1542 Vesalius left Padua for Basel to oversee the printing of his book, and the following May he dissected the body of an executed malefactor and articulated the skeleton, which is still preserved in the University of Basel's anatomical institute.

With the publication of *De humani corporis fabrica* (Basel, 1543)—in August rather than in June as given in the colophon—and of its *Epitome* (Basel, 1543; German translation by Albanus Torinus, Basel, 1543), Vesalius, with youthful impetuosity, decided to relinquish his anatomical studies for the practice of medicine. Since there was a long tradition of imperial service in his family, he applied to the Emperor Charles V and received an appointment as physician to the imperial household. It was an unfortunate decision since much of his time was henceforth devoted to the complaints of the gluttonous emperor and, as Vesalius wrote, "to the Gallic disease, gastrointestinal disorders, and chronic ailments, which are the usual complaints of my patients." The imperial service once entered could not be abandoned; Vesalius remained the emperor's physician until the latter's abdication, thirteen years later.

Despite his renunciation of anatomical studies, it was inevitable that Vesalius would soon return to his first interest. In January 1544 he traveled to Pisa to give a series of demonstrations at the invitation of Cosimo I, grand duke of Tuscany, who sought unsuccessfully to retain his services. Thereafter, while acting as a military surgeon in the course of the emperor's wars, Vesalius never failed to visit any nearby medical school, to participate in postmortem examinations, or to take advantage of any opportunities for anatomical research. In 1546, during an extended visit to Regensburg, he wrote a long letter partly concerned with the discovery and therapeutic use of the chinaroot (*Chinae radix*) in the treatment of syphilis and partly to justify his anatomically heretical activities against the attack of the Galenic anatomists of Paris, most notably those of his former teacher Sylvius. It was published under the title *Epistola rationem modumque propinandi radicis chynae decocti pertractans* (Basel, 1546).

During his service with the imperial army Vesalius was able to apply his unrivaled anatomical knowledge to surgery. He learned the emollient treatment of gunshot wounds from the Italian surgeon Bartolomeo Maggi; and although his surgery seems to have been burdened at first by an academic quality not required or even desirable on the battlefield, he quickly learned existing surgical techniques and went on to develop others. His most notable contribution was the introduction, as early as 1547, of surgically induced drainage of empyema, and he became so proficient in this procedure that he was sufficiently confident of the outcome to recommend it to other surgeons. His account of this operation, written as a letter (1562) to Giovanni Filippo Ingrassia of Sicily, was an outstanding contribution to the surgical literature. His reputation as a surgeon became so great that in 1559, when Henry II of France received what was to be a fatal head wound in a tournament, Vesalius was summoned from Brussels and placed in charge of the patient, despite the presence of the distinguished French surgeon Ambroise Paré. Vesalius wrote the report of the case after its termination.

The qualities of mind that had been responsible for the *Fabrica* brought Vesalius the reputation of being one of the great physicians of his age; his opinion was widely sought in grave medical problems. There are a number of contemporary references to him as "that noble physician" and "the best physician in the world." An instance of what he considered the proper relation of anatomy to medicine was his remarkable diagnosis and correct prognosis in 1555 of an internal aneurysm in a living patient.

As his experience became greater and as he realized the need for correcting errors of fact and faults of composition in the *Fabrica*, Vesalius gave more thought to a new edition. It is not known when an agreement was reached with the publisher Oporinus for the costly enterprise, but it was at some time after 1547; and it seems most likely that Vesalius wrote the revised text during an extended sojourn with the emperor in Augsburg between August 1550 and October 1551. However, it was

only after a long delay that the revised edition was published in Basel in August 1555.

With the abdication of Charles V in 1555, Vesalius for unknown reasons took service with his son Philip II of Spain as physician to the Netherlanders at the Spanish court and, from time to time, to the king himself. He remained in Spain from 1559 until the year of his death.

At the close of 1561 Vesalius completed a long reply to the *Observationes anatomicae* (1561) of Gabriele Falloppio, a respectful criticism of certain aspects of the *Fabrica*, which had been sent to him by the author during the preceding summer. Vesalius' reply, later published under the title of *Anatomicarum Gabrielis Falloppii observationum examen* (Venice, 1564), is partly a defense against Falloppio's criticisms and partly an acceptance of them. In addition, it stated Vesalius' desire to return to his former chair of anatomy at Padua. During the spring of 1562, on the command of Philip II, Vesalius joined the physicians involved in the care and treatment of Don Carlos, the king's son and heir, who, as the result of a fall, had received a severe injury to his head and was for long in grave danger.

In 1564 Vesalius left Spain for a trip to the Holy Land. Contrary to various legends, the journey appears to have been undertaken with the friendly approbation of the king, although it is not entirely clear whether Vesalius intended to return to Spain. After a visit to Venice—where he apparently was invited to accept his former chair at Padua in succession to Falloppio, who had died—he set sail in March for the Holy Land by way of Cyprus. It is not known precisely when the return voyage was begun, but in any event his ship was delayed by a violent storm. After much hardship it finally reached the island of Zákinthos in October, where Vesalius died and was buried in an unidentified site.

Vesalius produced only one book of great importance, *De humani corporis fabrica* (1543), to which may be added several complementary works, the *Epitome* (1543), *Epistola rationem modumque propinandi radicis chynae* (1546), the revised edition of the *Fabrica* (1555), and the *Examen* (1564).

Several motives underlay the composition and publication of the *Fabrica*. According to Vesalius medicine was properly composed of three parts: drugs, diet, and "the use of the hands," by which last he referred to surgical practice and especially to its necessary preliminary, a knowledge of human anatomy that could be acquired only by dissecting human bodies with one's own hands. Through disdain of anatomy, the most fundamental aspect of medicine, or, as Vesalius phrased it, by refusal to lay their hands on the patient's body, physicians betray their profession and are physicians only in part.

Vesalius hoped that by his example in Padua and especially by his verbal and pictorial presentation in the *Fabrica* he might persuade the medical world to appreciate anatomy as fundamental to all other aspects of medicine and that, through the application of his principles of investigation, a genuine knowledge of human anatomy would be achieved by others, in contrast to the more restricted traditional outlook and the uncritical acceptance of Galenic anatomy. The very word "fabrica" could be interpreted as referring not only to the structure of the body but to the basic structure or foundation of the medical art as well. Thus, Vesalius directed his work toward the established physician, whom he hoped to attract to the study of anatomy as a major but neglected aspect of a true medicine and, no less important, toward those members of the medical profession who were concerned with the teaching of anatomy and might be induced to forsake their long-accepted traditional methods for those proposed by Vesalius. As anatomy was then taught, he wrote, "there is very little offered to the [students] that could not better be taught by a butcher in his shop."

The *Fabrica* was also written to demonstrate the fallacious character of Galenic anatomy and all that it implied. Since Galen's anatomy was based upon the dissection and observation of animals, it was worthless as an explanation of the human structure; and since previous anatomical texts were essentially Galenic, they likewise were worthless and ought to be disregarded. Human anatomy was to be learned only by dissection and investigation of the human body, the true source of such knowledge. Nevertheless it was desirable that human dissection be accompanied by a parallel dissection of the bodies of other animals in order to show the differences in structure and hence the source of Galen's errors. "Physicians ought to make use not only of the bones of man but, for the sake of Galen, of those of the ape and dog." It was because of Vesalius that Padua became the first great center of comparative as well as of human anatomical studies, a dual interest that continued to develop under his successors Falloppio, Fabrici, and Casserio.

According to Vesalius, the student or physician ought to carry on these activities himself and should personally dissect the human body. The professor or teacher must also descend from his *cathedra*, dismiss the surgeon who had formerly performed the actual anatomy, and undertake his own dissecting. Moreover, it was not sufficient to base judgments upon a single dissection: the same dissection should be repeated upon several bodies until the dissector could be certain that his observations did not represent structural anomaly. Even the reader of the *Fabrica* must not be content to accept Vesalius' descriptions without question but ought to test them by his own dissections and observations. For this purpose the descriptive chapters of the *Fabrica* are frequently followed by directions for making one's own dissection of the part described so as to arrive at an independent conclusion.

Vesalius regarded the *Fabrica* as the gospel of a new approach to human anatomical studies and a new method of anatomical investigation. In Padua both the gospel and its explications were presented directly by the author. For those elsewhere it was presented through the *Fabrica* with its long and complete descriptions, its illustrative and diagrammatic guides to aid recognition of details and to supplement the reader's possible shortage of dissection specimens, and even its indirect encouragement of body snatching if necessary. The work reflects fully Vesalius' method of instruction from about the end of 1539 through 1542 and represents some of it pictorially on the title page.

The presentation of a new anatomy and anatomical method raised several problems, of which the first was that of terminology. As in the *Tabulae anatomicae* (1538), Vesalius continued to use terms from several languages but stressed the Greek form wherever possible. If this was not enough for clarity, an extensive description was given to localize the part with reference to other parts, and illustrations of the particular organ or structure were provided. Additionally, as a mnemonic device and for increased comprehension, anatomical structures were related to common objects, the radius, for example, being compared to the weaver's shuttle and the trapezius muscle to the cowl of the Benedictine monks. Some of Vesalius' terms are still in use, so that this aspect of his pedagogy plays the same role today as it did in the sixteenth century. Thus the names of two of the auditory ossibles, the incus and malleus, are derived from Vesalius' description of them as "that one somewhat resembling the shape of an anvil [*incus*]" and "that one resembling a hammer [*malleus*]." The valve of the left atrioventricular orifice, the mitral valve, "you may aptly compare to a bishop's miter."

Vesalius' greatest contribution to the elucidation of anatomy is to be found in the illustrations to the *Fabrica*. With the exception of those few diagrammatic illustrations that are known to have been drawn by him there is no positive identification of individual draftsmen. The soundest theory is that they were students from Titian's studio in Venice. Possibly among them was Jan Stephen of Calcar, who drew the three figures of the skeleton for the published version of Vesalius' anatomical plates of 1538; but the three skeletons of the *Fabrica* are so greatly superior to those of the earlier work that it seems unlikely that Calcar was responsible for them.

The anatomical detail of the illustrations and their numbered and lettered explanatory legends make it clear that the drawings were made under the supervision of Vesalius for the specific purpose of clarification of a particular portion of the text. Not only is the quality of draftsmanship and precision of detail immensely superior to that of earlier books but the marginal references to the illustrations, which in some instances relate a textual description to several illustrations located in different parts of the work, are also entirely without precedent. For the first time the pedagogic purpose of illustrations was achieved—so well that unfortunately attention has more recently been centered upon the illustrations to the exclusion of the text, thereby nullifying Vesalius' purpose and even damaging his reputation. He has, for example, been criticized for the exaggerated upward extension of the rectus abdominis muscle as it appears in the fifth "muscle man," although the legend accompanying the illustration explains this as having been done deliberately to represent an error of Galenic anatomy. Several such seeming errors are in fact deliberate distortions serving pedagogical purposes; they are not appreciated, however, unless text and illustrations are studied together.

In addition to the title page the most noteworthy illustrations in the *Fabrica* are the three celebrated skeletal figures and the series of "muscle men" which through their postures were given a dynamic quality that was intentional and specifically referred to by Vesalius. The "muscle men," shown from the front, side, and back, and displaying in sequence from the surface downward the underlying layers of muscle, were a novelty, although

crudely foreshadowed by the series of figures in Berengario da Carpi's *Commentaria* (1521); the latter, however, were wholly lacking the elegance and detail to be found in the Vesalian figures.

Owing to the larger amount of dissection material available to him, Vesalius was not compelled to follow the traditional pattern of dissection and description originally established by Mondino (1316). Consequently, book I of the *Fabrica* opens with a description of the bones. This arrangement was desirable since according to Vesalius the bones are the foundation of the body, the structure to which everything else must be related; and in his anatomical demonstrations he was accustomed to sketch the position of the bones on the surface of the body with charcoal in order to orient the students. The fundamental significance of the bones was further indicated by his reference to the femur, for example, as either the bone itself or the entire leg of which the bone was the basic structure. Moreover, the bones are not only supports for the body; since by their structure and formation they assist and control movement, it is necessary to recognize in them a dynamic quality that Vesalius sought to emphasize by the suggestion of movement in the poses of the skeletons.

The teleological argument that pervades the *Fabrica*, an inheritance from Galen, is very pronounced in the description of osteology. "By not first explaining the bones anatomists . . . deter [the student] from a worthy examination of the works of God." Vesalius did not allow this doctrine of final causes to control his investigations, however, since unlike his medieval predecessors he sought to discover first structure and related function, and only then the ultimate purpose.

In his description of human osteology, the subject of book I, Vesalius made some of his strongest assaults upon Galenic anatomy. He called attention to Galen's false assertion that the human mandible is formed of two bones and demonstrated the significance of this error as reflecting a dependence upon animal sources. Likewise he pointed to the fact that the Galenic description of the sternum as formed of seven segments is true of the ape but not of the adult human sternum, which has only three. Similarly the "humerus, according to Galen, is with the exception only of the femur, the largest bone of the body. Nevertheless the fibula and tibia are distinctly of greater length than the humerus." In addition to such criticisms, there is extensive description of osteological detail, which, because much of it was wholly novel, required detailed illustrations, elaborately related by letter and number to the text. Despite some errors of description and occasional references to animal anatomy in the Galenic tradition, this first book represents Vesalian anatomy on the highest level. It concludes with a remarkable chapter on the procedure for preparation of the bones and articulation of the skeleton, since it was essential that a skeleton always be available at the dissection. Such a skeleton is a central figure of the title page.

As he had done with the bones, so Vesalius endeavored in book II to identify and give the fullest possible description of every muscle and its function; and an examination of the "muscle men" indicates the thoroughness with which that task was performed. Unfortunately, his system of identifying muscles numerically according to the part they served was cumbersome in comparison with the method of identification by origin and insertion introduced by Sylvius in 1555 and later revised and improved by the Swiss anatomist Gaspard Bauhin. The first two books represent the major Vesalian achievement in terms of accuracy of description and present the most telling blows against Galenic anatomy. In book II Vesalius also most frequently provided chapters dealing with the dissection procedure used to arrive at his conclusions. The description of the vascular system in book III is less satisfactory because of Vesalius' failure to master the complexities of distribution of the vessels and because of the close relationship of the vascular system to Galenic physiology. Vesalius was compelled to subscribe to this for lack of any other theories. The errors in the Vesalian description of the distribution of the vessels are due to his reliance on Galen, as the only other writer to have attempted such a description in detail, and to the difficulty of discovering anew the entire vascular arrangement in rapidly putrefying human material. Although Vesalius was partly successful, as, for example, in his account of the interior mesenteric and the hemorrhoidal veins, there are many indications that he was compelled to rely for much of his account on the anatomy of animals. This is clearly apparent in the illustration of the "arterial man," where the arrangement of the branchings of the aortic arch actually illustrate simian anatomy.

Book IV provides an account of the nervous system. It is introduced by an attempt to clarify and limit the meaning of the word "nerve" to the vehicle transmitting sensation and motion, because "leading anatomists declare that there are three kinds of nerve": ligament, tendon, and aponeurosis. "From dissection of the body it is clear that no nerve arises from the heart as it seemed to Aristo-

tle in particular and to no few others." Although Vesalius was obliged to accept the Galenic explanation of nervous action as induced by animal spirit distributed through the nerves from the brain, his examination of the optic nerve led him to the conclusion that the nerves were not hollow, as Galen had asserted. "I inspected the nerves carefully, treating them with warm water, but I was unable to discover a passage of that sort in the whole course of the nerve."

Vesalius accepted Galen's classification of the cranial nerves into seven pairs even though he recognized more than that number and described a portion of the trochlear nerve. To avoid confusion he declared that he would "not depart from the enumeration of the cranial nerves that was established by the ancients." Although he was not wholly successful in his efforts to trace the cranial nerves to their origins, and despite some confusion about their peripheral distribution, the level of knowledge in the text and illustrations was well above that of contemporary works and was not to be surpassed for about a generation. Vesalius was more successful in tracing the spinal nerves, but on the whole the account of the nerves must be described as being of lesser quality than some of the other books.

The description of the abdominal organs in book V is detailed and reasonably accurate. Since he knew of no alternative Vesalius accepted that aspect of Galen's physiology which placed the manufacture of the blood in the liver. Nevertheless he denied not only that the vena cava takes its origin from the liver but also that the liver is composed of concreted blood. Here his strongest blow against Galen and medieval Galenic tradition was his denial, based on human and comparative anatomy, of the current belief in the liver's multiple (usually five) lobes. According to Vesalius the number of lobes increased with the descent in the chain of animal life. In man the liver had a single mass, while the livers of monkeys, dogs, sheep, and other animals had multiple lobes that became more numerous and more clearly apparent. This difference once again proved the error of dependence upon nonhuman materials.

Vesalius also denied the erroneous Galenic belief that there was a bile duct opening into the stomach as well as one into the duodenum. In regard to the position of the kidneys, he had begun to move away from the erroneous view expressed in the *Tabulae anatomicae* that the right kidney was placed higher than the left. Although this error is illustrated in the *Fabrica*, the text declares that the reverse could also be true. Despite this partial error of traditionalism, Vesalius denied a second traditional opinion that the urine passed through the kidneys by means of a filter device. The filter theory had also been denied by Berengario da Carpi; but Vesalius went a step further by asserting that the "serous blood" was deliberately selected or drawn into the kidney's membranous body and its "branchings" to be freed of its "serous humor" in the same way that the vena cava was able to select and acquire blood from the portal vein, and that the excrement was then carried by the ureters to the bladder.

The book ends with a discussion of human generation and the organs of reproduction. Although Vesalius denied the medieval doctrine of the seven-celled uterus and declared the traditional representation of the horned uterus to result from the use of animal specimens, his description of the fetus and fetal apparatus was of less significance, reflecting, as he admitted, the lack of sufficient pregnant human specimens.

Book VI describes the organs of the thorax. It is chiefly important for the description of the heart, which Vesalius described as approaching the nature of muscle in appearance, although it could not be true muscle since muscle supplied voluntary motion and the motion of the heart was involuntary. In this instance Vesalian principle bowed to Galenic theory, and recognition of the muscular substance of the heart had to await William Harvey's investigations in the next century.

Like all his contemporaries Vesalius regarded the heart as formed of two chambers or ventricles. The right atrium was not considered to be a chamber but rather a continuation of the inferior and superior venae cavae, considered as a single, extended vessel; and the left atrium was thought to be part of the pulmonary vein. According to Galen the ventricles were divided by a midwall containing minute openings or pores through which the blood passed or seeped from the right ventricle into the left, an opinion that Vesalius strongly questioned even though by implication he was casting doubt on Galen's cardiovascular physiology. "The septum of the ventricles having been formed, as I said, of the very thick substance of the heart . . . none of its pits—at least insofar as can be ascertained by the senses—penetrates from the right ventricle into the left. Thus we are compelled to astonishment at the industry of the Creator who causes the blood to sweat through from the right ventricle into the left through passages which escape our sight." Finally Vesalius gave strong expression to his opin-

ion of ecclesiastical censorship over the question of the heart as the site of the soul. After referring to the opinions of the major ancient philosophers on the location of the soul, he continued:

> Lest I come into collision here with some scandalmonger or censor of heresy, I shall wholly abstain from consideration of the divisions of the soul and their locations, since today . . . you will find a great many censors of our very holy and true religion. If they hear someone murmur something about the opinions of Plato, Aristotle or his interpreters, or of Galen regarding the soul, even in anatomy where these matters especially ought to be examined, they immediately judge him to be suspect in his faith and somewhat doubtful about the soul's immortality. They do not understand that this is a necessity for physicians if they desire to engage properly in their art. . . .

The seventh and final book provides a description of the anatomy of the brain, accompanied by a series of detailed illustrations revealing the successive steps in its dissection. Until the time of Vesalius, illustrations of the brain and any accompanying text usually stressed the localization of intellectual activities in the ventricles, with perception in the anterior ventricles, judgment in the middle, and memory in the posterior. Sensation and motion were considered the work of animal spirit produced in a fine network of arteries at the base of the brain, the *rete mirabile*. The existence of the *rete mirabile* in the human brain had been questioned by Berengario da Carpi. It was now firmly denied by Vesalius, who showed the belief in this organ to have been the result of dissection of animals, since such an arterial network does in fact exist in ungulates. Vesalius was also the first to state that the ventricles had no function except the collection of fluid. Moreover, he denied that the mind could be split up into the separate mental faculties hitherto attributed to it. As a corollary he intimated that although animal spirit affected sensation and motion, it had nothing at all to do with mental activity—in short he suggested a divorce between the physical and mental animal. The discussion of the brain is concluded by a chapter on the procedure to be followed for its dissection and by a final, separate section on experiments in vivisection, derived and developed mostly from experiments described by Galen. The separate treatment of this latter material indicated a recognition of physiology as a discipline distinct from anatomy.

In the *Fabrica* Vesalius made many contributions to the body of anatomical knowledge, by description of structures hitherto unknown, by detailed descriptions of structures known only in the most elementary terms, and by the correction of erroneous descriptions. Despite his many errors his contribution was far greater than that of any previous author, and for a considerable time all anatomists, even those unsympathetic to him, were compelled to refer to the *Fabrica*. Its success and influence can be measured by the shrillness of Galenic apologists, by the plentiful but unacknowledged borrowings of many, and by the avowed indebtedness of the generous few, such as Falloppio. Although Colombo, Falloppio, and Eustachi corrected a number of Vesalius' errors and in some respects advanced beyond him in their anatomical knowledge, Colombo published his anatomical studies sixteen years after the appearance of the *Fabrica*, Falloppio eighteen, and Eustachi twenty. Furthermore, they relied heavily upon Vesalius' work, the detailed nature of which made it relatively easy for others to correct or to make further contributions. Although their accomplishments deserve recognition they were built upon Vesalian foundations.

More important than the anatomical information contained in the *Fabrica* was the scientific principle enunciated therein. This was beyond criticism, fundamental to anatomical research, and has remained so. It was not difficult to demonstrate Galen's errors of anatomy, but such a demonstration was only a means to an end. Its significance lay in the reason for those errors: Galen's attempt to project the anatomy of animals upon the human body. From time to time others had pointed to Galenic errors, but no one had proposed a consistent policy of doubting the authority of Galen or of any other recognized authority until the only true source of anatomical knowledge—dissection and observation of the human structure—had been tested. With the publication of the *Fabrica* all major investigators of anatomy were compelled to recognize the new principle, even though at first some paid no more than lip service to it.

For medical students and those with limited or no anatomical knowledge Vesalius composed a briefer work, the misnamed *Epitome* (1543) of the *Fabrica*. In the *Epitome* Vesalius returned to the tradition of the *Tabulae anatomicae* insofar as the illustrations in this work seem to have been considered more important than the text. The text was arranged somewhat differently from that of the *Fabrica*, since, although the first two chapters deal with bones and muscles, respectively, they are followed by chapters on the digestive system, cardio-

vascular system, nervous system (here including the brain), and finally the reproductive system. This is the simplified arrangement that Vesalius advocated "for one wholly unskilled in dissection." Although Vesalius called the work an epitome and declared it a pathway to the *Fabrica*, such is not the case; the vast text of the greater work could not be compressed into such slight dimensions, and it is certainly not, as he also wrote, a summary. At best it is a condensation of selections from the *Fabrica* and, hence, not a major scientific work.

The second edition of the *Fabrica* was considerably altered both in style and to some degree in the arrangement of the contents. The actual alterations of the contents, found chiefly in books V and VI, include the addition of accounts of autopsies performed by Vesalius from 1543 onward, revision and correction of the description of the fetal membranes, and a clear statement that the cardiac septum is impermeable.

The impact of the new Vesalian illustrations was reflected as early as 1538 in such plagiarisms of the *Tabulae anatomicae* as those published in Paris (1538), Augsburg (1539), Cologne (1539), and Strasbourg (1541). The much more remarkable illustrations of the *Fabrica* were subject to even greater plagiarism, the first instance being the excellent copperplates of the Flemish engraver Thomas Geminus (1544), published with a slightly altered text of the *Epitome* under the title *Compendiosa totius anatomie delineatio aere exarata* (London, 1545). If we except the uncompleted work of Canano, Geminus' book has the further distinction of being the first anatomical treatise to contain copper-engraved illustrations. These were republished in London in 1553 and 1559, and by Jacques Grévin in Paris in 1564, 1565, and 1569; the original plates were copied and recopied thereafter for many subsequent editions. One example of the many plagiarisms of the illustrations of the *Fabrica* is the much reduced, crude woodcut copies that are to be found in Bernardino Montaña de Monserrate's *Libro de anathomia del hombre* (1551), where they have, in fact, no relationship to the Galenic text of this first Spanish anatomical treatise in the vernacular. Somewhat better, larger, and more significant copies are to be found in Ambroise Paré's *Anatomie universelle* (1561).

More fundamentally influential were the Vesalian principle underlying anatomical investigation, the method, and the contributions to knowledge of human anatomical structures. These were somewhat slower in diffusion and occasionally met opposition, as in Jacobus Sylvius' violent attack against Vesalius' anti-Galenism, *Vaesani cujusdam calumniarum in Hippocratis Galenique rem anatomicam depulsio* (1551) and the later attack of Francesco dal Pozzo, *Apologia in anatome pro Galeno contra Andream Vessalium Bruxellensem* (1562). Advanced by the successive occupants of the anatomical chair at Padua (Realdo Colombo, Gabriele Falloppio, and Fabrici), the Vesalian principles were thence diffused through Italy and later throughout western Europe. By the beginning of the seventeenth century, with the exception of a few conservative centers such as Paris and some parts of the Empire, Vesalian anatomy had gained both academic and general support.

*BIBLIOGRAPHY*

The various editions of Vesalius' writings and most of the literature about him are to be found in Harvey Cushing, *A Bio-Bibliography of Andreas Vesalius*, 2nd ed. (Hamden, Conn., 1962); more recent papers and studies of importance, some of them the result of the Vesalian celebrations of 1964, are listed in C. D. O'Malley, "A Review of Vesalian Literature," in *History of Science*, IV (Cambridge, 1965), 1–14. M. H. Spielmann, *The Iconography of Andreas Vesalius* (London, 1925), deals with the various likenesses of Vesalius produced since the sixteenth century, although the only genuine portrait known is that in the *Fabrica*. The standard biography is C. D. O'Malley, *Andreas Vesalius of Brussels, 1514–1564* (Berkeley–Los Angeles, 1964); and particular points of importance have been dealt with by Charles Singer, *A Prelude to Modern Science* (Cambridge, 1946), and Ruben Ericksson, *Andreas Vesalius' first Public Anatomy at Bologna 1540* (Uppsala, 1959). See also Moritz Roth, *Andreas Vesalius Bruxellensis* (Berlin, 1892).

C. D. O'MALLEY

**VESLING, JOHANN** (*b.* Minden, Germany, 1598; *d.* Padua, Italy, 30 August 1649), *anatomy, botany.*

Vesling's reputation rests on his excellent powers of observation. Nothing certain is known about his parents, although it appears that the Catholic family fled to Vienna to escape religious persecution. All the biographers agree that Vesling attended secondary school and studied medicine in Venice, but his name is not found among the registration records of the university. Since Vesling stated that Everhardius Vorstius of Leiden was his teacher, an examination of the records of the university reveals that Johannes Wesling of Minden enrolled as a student at Leiden at age twenty on 15 November 1619. Vorstius had studied at German and Italian universities, including Bologna, and was especially interested in botany as well as in medicine. Vesling, too, had a predilection for botany, and he also went to Bologna, presumably on Vorstius' advice. Vesling named Fabrizio Bartoletti as his teacher in Italy. Bartoletti, who moved from Bologna to Mantua after 1675, instilled in Vesling an enthusiasm for anatomy and surgery.

The next documented fact that we have concerning Vesling's career dates from the winter of 1627–1628. He performed, in the presence of Venetian physicians, an anatomical demonstration that earned him the right to practice in the areas controlled by Venice. His teaching was so highly esteemed that even Paduan students came to hear him. The Venetian government unfairly refused to reimburse Vesling for the expenses he incurred in conducting his demonstrations. This was probably done in an attempt to drive him from the city in order to protect the much older Paduan professor Caimo from the competition of his younger colleague. For the same reason, Vesling was directed to serve as physician to the patrician Alvise Cornaro during the latter's term as Venetian representative in Cairo. The two men left for Egypt at the beginning of August 1628. Vesling studied the flora of the country with great interest. In many cases his observations were more accurate than those previously made by Prospero Alpini, and his book on the subject is also better illustrated than the latter's. Of particular interest are his comments on the coffee plant.

All of Vesling's biographers assign an earlier date to his trip to Egypt, despite the fact that Haller long ago published the correct information on the basis of letters Vesling sent to Wilhem Fabry (Hildanus Fabricius). Only Adelmann cites this reference and mentions that a date contained in Vesling's working notes makes it certain that he was still in Egypt on 7 May 1632. On that day Vesling repeated his investigations of the development of the chick embryo in artificially hatched eggs. The results of these embryological studies are very fully discussed by Adelmann, and the reader should consult his account for details. The place names that Vesling mentions in his writings show that he was familiar with only a small part of Egypt, that between Rashid (Rosetta) and Memphis. He traveled to Palestine only once, on which occasion he became a knight of the Order of the Holy Sepulcher in Jerusalem.

Because of his stay in Egypt, Vesling escaped the epidemic of plague that ravaged northern Italy in 1629–1631. During the epidemic students avoided Padua, and the chair of anatomy was vacant for a year. On 30 December 1632 Vesling was appointed professor of anatomy and surgery, and at the beginning of 1633 he returned from Egypt. Vesling proved to be a very able teacher and enlivened his lectures with drawings that he himself had prepared and that were later used in his *Syntagma anatomicum*. This textbook, characterized by a concise style, went through many editions and was translated into several languages. Of particular scientific value are his descriptions and illustrations of the chyle vessels (lacteals) and his assertion that four is the normal number of pulmonary veins emptying into the left auricle of the heart. Further, he was the first to see the *ductus thoracicus*, but he did not mention the discovery until 1649, in a letter to Thomas Bartholin.

In 1638 Vesling ceased lecturing on surgery and turned instead to botany. Under his direction the botanical garden in Padua was renovated, as several plant catalogues of the period show. In 1648 Vesling was given a leave of absence that allowed him to undertake a second botanical expedition. He went to Crete but returned ill, and he died soon after. In accordance with his wishes he was buried in the cloister of the church of St. Anthony in Padua. Vesling's posthumous papers contain much remarkable material that he would undoubtedly have formulated in more precise terms. Among the more notable things to be found in these papers (which were published by Thomas Bartholin) is a correction of his initial findings concerning the sexual organs of the viper and the scent glands of the snakes.

*BIBLIOGRAPHY*

I. ORIGINAL WORKS. Vesling's most important anatomical work is *Syntagma anatomicum, publicis dissectionibus in auditorum usum diligenter aptatum* (Padua, 1641). Along with many Latin editions, this work appeared in Dutch, German, and English translations—the last under the title *The Anatomy of the Body of Man*, N. Culpeper, trans. (London, 1653).

Vesling's most important work in botany is *De plantis aegyptiis observationibus et notae ad Prosperum Alpinum, cum additamenta aliarum eiusdem regionis* (Padua, 1638). Vesling's embryological and comparative anatomical investigations were published by Thomas Bartholin as *De pullitione Aegyptiorum et aliae observationes anatomicae et epistolae medicae posthumae* (Copenhagen, 1664).

II. SECONDARY LITERATURE. Two biographical accounts are Arturo Castiglioni, in *Enciclopedia Italiana*, XXXV (1937), p. 218; and A. Francesco La Cava, in *Castalia* (Milan, 1948). For an assessment of Vesling's contribution to the history of embryology see Howard B. Adelmann, *Marcello Malpighi and the Evolution of Embryology* (Ithaca, N.Y., 1966). Vesling's comparative anatomical studies are discussed in F. C. Cole, *A History of Comparative Anatomy* (London, 1944).

ERICH HINTZSCHE

**VESSIOT, ERNEST** (*b*. Marseilles, France, 8 March 1865; *d*. La Bauche, Savoie, France, 17 October 1952), *mathematics*.

Vessiot's ancestors were farmers near Langres, in the Haute-Marne. The family rose slowly in the social hierarchy, becoming teachers and, later, school principals. Vessiot's father was a *lycée* teacher and subsequently inspector general of primary schools. Vessiot, the third of six children, became a university professor and member of the Académie des Sciences.

A good record at the *lycée* in Marseilles enabled Vessiot to attend the École Normale Supérieure, which he entered second in his class, after Jacques Hadamard. In 1887 he obtained a teaching post at the *lycée* in Lyons. After receiving the doctorate in 1892, he taught at the universities of Lille, Toulouse, Lyons, and, finally, Paris (1910). Vessiot's first assignment at Paris was to prepare students for the *licence*. Later he taught courses in the theory of functions, in analytical mechanics, and in celestial mechanics. He became director of the École Normale Supérieure (serving in this post until his retirement in 1935) and was elected to the mechanics section of the Académie des Sciences in 1943.

Vessiot's research dealt with the application of the notion of continuous groups, finite or infinite, to the study of differential equations. Extending results obtained by Émile Picard, Vessiot demonstrated in his dissertation (1892) the existence of a group of linear substitutions with constant coefficients operating on a system of $n$ independent solutions of a differential equation. The rigor and depth of his work on groups of linear rational transformations allowed Vessiot to put into more precise form and to develop research begun by Jules Drach (1902) and to extend the results of Élie Cartan on the integration of differential systems (1907). He also completed Volterra's study of Fredholm integrals. The extension of these integrals to partial differential equations led Vessiot to obtain original results concerning perturbations in celestial mechanics, the propagation of waves of discontinuity, and general relativity. During World War I, Vessiot was assigned to work on problems in ballistics, and he corrected certain empirical formulas then in use.

A dedicated teacher, Vessiot wrote useful and well-received textbooks. As director of the École Normale Supérieure he supervised the construction of new laboratories in collaboration with his physicist colleagues Henri Abraham, Léon Bloch, and Georges Bruhat, all of whom fell victim to the Nazis during German occupation.

*BIBLIOGRAPHY*

Vessiot's writings include "Sur l'interprétation mécanique des transformations de contact infinitésimales," in *Bulletin de la Société mathématique de France,* **34** (1906), 230–269; "Essai sur la propagation des ondes," in *Annales scientifiques de l'École normale supérieure,* 3rd ser., **26** (1909), 404–448; "Sur la réductibilité et l'intégration des systèmes complets," *ibid.,* **29** (1912), 209–278; "Sur la théorie des multiplicités et le calcul des variations," in *Bulletin de la Société mathématique de France,* **40** (1912), 68–139; *Leçons de géométrie supérieure* (Paris, 1919); "Sur une théorie nouvelle des problémes d'intégration," in *Bulletin de la Société mathématique de France,* **52** (1924), 336–395; "Sur la réductibilité des équations algébriques ou différentielles," in *Annales scientifiques de l'École normale supérieure,* 3rd ser., **57** (1940), 1–60; **58** (1941), 1–36; and **63** (1946), 1–23, also in *Bulletin de la Société mathématique de France,* **75** (1947), 9–26; and *Cours de mathématiques générales,* 3 vols. (Paris, 1921–1952), written with Paul Montel.

For a discussion of Vessiot's work see Élie Cartan, "L'oeuvre scientifique de M. Ernest Vessiot," in *Bulletin de la Société mathématique de France,* **75** (1947), 1–8.

Lucienne Félix

**VICQ D'AZYR, FÉLIX** (*b.* Valognes, Manche, France, 28 April 1748; *d.* Paris, France, 20 June 1794), *anatomy, epidemiology, medical education.*

Vicq d'Azyr was a member of the Académie Française and the Académie des Sciences, as well as permanent secretary of the Société Royale de Médecine. He also was substitute professor at the Jardin du Roi and personal physician to Marie Antoinette.

After studying at Caen, Vicq d'Azyr went to Paris in 1765 and developed a marked interest in anatomy and physiology. In 1773 he gave a private course in those subjects, which attracted a large audience. He became the student of Antoine Petit (1722–1794) and of Daubenton, professor at the Jardin du Roi, whose niece he married. In 1774

Vicq d'Azyr earned his medical degree and on 16 March was elected to the Académie des Sciences as *adjoint anatomiste,* replacing Portal.[1] He soon demonstrated his considerable talents and in 1775 was sent by Turgot to stem a serious epizootic disease ravaging the Midi. The mission was successful, and in 1778 Vicq d'Azyr was named permanent secretary of the Société Royale de Médecine. On 12 December 1784 he was elected *associé anatomiste* of the Académie des Sciences, replacing Petit and became *associé* in anatomy on 23 April 1785. He received a double honor in 1788, with his election to membership of the Académie Française and his appointment as physician to the queen, who called him "mon philosophe."

During the Revolution, Vicq d'Azyr's position was ambiguous; although he continued to serve the queen, he remained a guiding spirit in the movement for medical reform, of which he had been a pioneer. Among his friends, Bailly and Lavoisier were guillotined; whereas others, such as Fourcroy, if not responsible for the executions, at least condoned them. Like his contemporary Pierre Desault, Vicq d'Azyr was obsessed by the fear that he was under suspicion and would be taken before the Revolutionary Tribunal. After attending the festival of the Supreme Being he came down with a violent fever and died in a delirium—an external manifestation (it was said) of the inner tensions and obsessions that had made rest impossible for him.

Vicq d'Azyr was greatly interested in comparative anatomy. Before the changes that he and J. F. Blumenbach made in the study of the subject, it was customary to dissect animals of different species and juxtapose their various organs. The species were poorly delimited, and Vicq d'Azyr showed that, in any case, the object of the science was different. According to him, what was most important was to decide the significant characteristics (structures of limbs, of extremities, and of pectoral and pelvic girdles; mode of remaining at rest and of moving; dentition; and so forth), to study their variations systematically throughout the animal kingdom, and to develop a nomenclature based on that used by the chemists. Toward this end he began work on *Système anatomique des vertébrés,* continued by Hippolyte Cloquet (1787–1840).

Vicq d'Azyr devoted particular attention to neuroanatomy, studying the cervical plexus and especially the vertebrate brain. In his research he introduced quantitative data, comparing the weight of the brain with body weight. In morphology he followed the majority of contemporary anatomists in neglecting the ventricles, which in the older theories had been considered reservoirs of the "animal spirits."

Like Steno before him, Vicq d'Azyr attached great importance to the structure of the fibers in the white matter of the brain. He wrote four memoirs on them, sometimes showing them in transverse and frontal sections and sometimes "scraping them without damaging the surface." (The latter technique was later perfected by Gall and Spurzheim.) He also described the mammillothalamic bundle and Reil's ribbon.

Rejecting the views of Malpighi and Vieussens, who attributed no functional importance to the cerebral cortex, Vicq d'Azyr attempted to systematize its complex morphology. In particular he isolated the convolution of the corpus callosum, the cuneus, and the sulcus separating the frontal lobe from the parietal, later described by Rolando (1829).[2]

Despite his enthusiasm for dissection, Vicq d'Azyr was not satisfied with the results obtained by this technique: "Seeing and describing are two things that everyone believes he is capable of doing; yet few people really can do them. The first requires great powers of concentration and insights in dealing with the type of object observed; the second requires method and knowledge of the terms necessary for conveying an exact idea of what one has seen" (*Oeuvres*, IV, 208). This statement probably alludes to the absence of a nomenclature for the cerebral convolutions, which at the time were no better described than those of the intestine. It also reflects a contradictory aspect of the author's thought that has been stressed by G. Lanteri-Laura.[3] Vicq d'Azyr was among those who continued to believe in a very simple neuroanatomical schema in which physiological considerations were predominant. This conception left little room for embryology, comparative anatomy, experimentation, or clinical findings, and led to some very controversial cerebral localizations. The scientists who held this view seem to have been unaware that it was rapidly being undermined by their own discoveries and methods. Paradoxically, while their research was making the complexity of brain structures increasingly evident, their theories helped to delay a thorough study of these structures.

Vicq d'Azyr was an eminent veterinarian. In the eighteenth century, animal medicine was economically important for French farmers and aristocrats. It was no less important ideologically for the two major "philosophical" groups in France: the Physi-

ocrats, who were concerned primarily with agronomic and social questions, and the Encyclopedists, who did not neglect nature but were less interested than the former group in the practical consequences of their teaching. Fortunately, Turgot and Exupère Bertin convinced the government that responsibility for dealing with epizootic diseases could not be entrusted to self-taught farriers. As a result the government founded specialized veterinary schools at Lyons (1762) and at Alfort (1765). In these schools, the term *maréchalerie* was replaced by that of *art vétérinaire* starting in 1767.

Veterinary teaching was then influenced by two contending opinions. The Physiocrats held that veterinary medicine should be allied with agriculture, while the Encyclopedists thought it more properly belonged with human medicine. The latter view, which was shared by Buffon and a number of physicians who dealt with both humans and animals (notably Nicolas Chambon de Montaux, Daubenton, and Vicq d'Azyr at Paris, and Vitet and Jacques Petetin at Lyons), temporarily triumphed following the death of Claude Bourgelat (1779) and the retirement of Bertin (1780). At this time Vicq d'Azyr taught at Alfort and wrote a number of works on comparative anatomy, since the material necessary for studying the subject was readily available. He also conceived a project for reorganizing medical studies, one aspect of which involved combining in a single overall curriculum the teaching of animal medicine (represented by the school at Alfort) and of human medicine (represented by the Faculty of Medicine, the schools of surgery, the Collège Royal, the Jardin du Roi, and the Jardin des Apothicaires).

Vicq d'Azyr was no mere theorist of veterinary medicine. He showed his ability in practice and played a particularly important part in the fight against epizootic diseases started by Turgot in 1775–1776. His *Instruction sur la manière de désinfecter une paroisse* (1775) is particularly interesting in this regard. Taking a realistic view of what was possible, the work delegates more responsibility to the government and the army than to the veterinarians. It recommends an operation encompassing diagnosis of the disease, isolation of the suspected area by a cordon of troops, quarantine, treatment, and in some cases destruction of the animals, followed by repopulation. The basic weapon in this struggle was the disinfection of hides and stables with chemicals (sulfuric acid, sulfur, gunpowder), which were substituted for the traditional perfumes with aromatic plants. This technique proved so effective that the French decrees of 1881 and 1898, which are still in effect, essentially reproduced the recommendations that Vicq d'Azyr made in 1776.

Vicq d'Azyr's publications on human medicine are of little importance. A number of them appeared under "Médecine" in the *Encyclopédie méthodique*, of which he was an editor. On the other hand, he was a pioneer in public health and medical education. As permanent secretary of the Société Royale de Médecine, Vicq d'Azyr maintained a network for exchanging information and conducting studies on a national scale for fifteen years. In this effort he was assisted by practicing physicians, medical schools, and provincial academies. The inquiries he initiated into *topographie médicale et salubrité* encouraged many provincial doctors to take a more modern and nationally oriented view of health problems and helped foster the idea that public health is one of the responsibilities of the medical profession.[4] Furthermore, while acting as medical expert for the Constituent Assembly, Vicq d'Azyr created and guided the activities of its Comité de Salubrité. He called upon the physicians who had been elected deputies to support adoption of a project for the reform of French medicine that he had completed in 1790. The project, approved by the Constituent Assembly, was adopted without major changes by the National Convention in 1794, following Fourcroy's report on it.

## NOTES

1. The archives of the Académie des Sciences contain a letter from the duke of La Vrillière, dated 13 Mar. 1774, on the election of Vicq d'Azyr and of Toussaint Bordenave to the Academy.
2. See P. Broca, "Note sur la topographie cérébrale et sur quelques points de l'histoire des circonvolutions."
3. See G. Lanteri-Laura, *L'homme et son cerveau selon Gall. Histoire et signification de la phrénologie.*
4. See D. Weiner, "Le droit de l'homme à la santé."

## BIBLIOGRAPHY

I. ORIGINAL WORKS. There is no comprehensive bibliography of the works of Vicq d'Azyr. Many of his papers are in boxes of material from the Société Royale de Médecine, now in the library of the Académie Nationale de Médecine; the catalog of these cartons has not yet been published. They contain letters and autograph memoirs of Vicq d'Azyr from the Société Royale de Médecine (fols. 159, 160; MS 33 [33]). The library of the Muséum National d'Histoire Naturelle has various notes and annotated extracts from the minute books of the Société Royale de Médecine for 1779 and 1780 (MSS 1452–1459), in 8 vols. At the Archives Nationales (ser. AF I$^{23}$) there are the original versions of the *procès verbaux* of the meetings of the Comité de Salubrité of the Constituent Assembly; cartons F$^{17}$ 1236–1239, F$^{17}$ 1245–1246, and F$^{17}$ 1094 contain reports by and correspondence from Vicq d'Azyr on various matters. The dossier on Vicq d'Azyr at the Académie des Sciences contains a dictated letter of 12 Oct. 1777 to a colleague; an autograph of June 1780, "Examens d'enfants atteints d'anomalies osseuses et de déformations"; an undated letter to a M. Perrier concerning the examination of the water of the Seine by means of a special pump (only the postscript is autograph); a letter concerning the anatomical observation of a mandrill, a callithrix, and a macaque, which was published in the *Mémoires* of the Académie des Sciences for 1780; another undated autograph; an autograph memoir on the anastomoses of Delafosse (undated); and an autograph memoir on the anatomical observation of a thirty-six-year-old woman suffering from pains in the uterus, followed by death.

Vicq d'Azyr published many articles in *Journal des sciences et des beaux-arts, Mercure de France, Clef du cabinet des souverains*, and *Journal des savants*. His most important articles were published in the *Mémoires* of the Académie des Sciences (from 1772 to 1785) and in the *Mémoires* of the Société Royale de Médecine de Paris (from 1775 to 1788). A fairly complete listing of these works is in J. D. Reuss, ed., *Repertorium commentationum*, 16 vols. (Göttingen, 1801–1821; repr. New York, 1962)—see the indexes to vols. II, III, VI, VIII, X, XV, and XVI. The Royal Society *Catalogue of Scientific Papers*, V, 152, lists two papers published in *Bulletin des sciences de la Société philomathique de Paris*, to which should be added "Observations sur un bruit singulier dans la région du coeur d'un particulier" (July 1791), 22.

A collected ed. of Vicq d'Azyr's works, with annotations and a discussion of his life and writings by J. L. Moreau, was published as *Oeuvres de Vicq-d'Azyr*, 6 vols. (Paris, 1805).

Space does not permit the listing of the many separately published works that appeared during Vicq d'Azyr's lifetime; they include translations, dissertations for which he served as chairman, and *éloges*, which are included in his *Oeuvres* (see above). Many of these works are listed in Bibliothèque Nationale, *Catalogue général des livres imprimés*, CCVIII (Paris, 1970), cols. 311–322. The following bibliography (listed in alphabetical order), although incomplete, is representative of Vicq d'Azyr's scientific publications: *Avis aux habitants des campagnes où règne la contagion* (Condom, 1774); *Avis important relativement aux bestiaux atteints de la maladie épizootique* (Condom, 1775); *Consultation sur le traitement qui convient aux bestiaux attaqués de l'épizootie* (Bordeaux, 1775); *De l'influence des marais sur la santé* . . . (Paris, 1790); *Dictionnaire de méde-cine de l'Encyclopédie méthodique*, 14 vols. (Paris, 1787–1830)—Vicq d'Azyr contributed many articles to the first six vols.; *Discours sur l'anatomie comparée* (Paris, n.d.); *Exposé des moyens curatifs et préservatifs qui peuvent être employés contre les maladies pestilen-tielles des bêtes à cornes* (Paris, 1776); *Instruction rela-tive à l'épizootie (pour les soldats)* (Rouen, 1775); *In-struction relative à l'épizootie (pour les syndics)* (Rouen, 1775); *Instruction sur la manière de désinfecter les cuirs des bestiaux morts de l'épizootie* . . . (Paris, 1775); *In-struction sur la manière de désinfecter les étables des bestiaux attaqués de l'épizootie* (Paris, 1776); *Instruc-tion sur la manière de désinfecter les villages* (Paris, 1775); *Instruction sur la manière de désinfecter une paroisse* (Paris, 1775); *Instruction sur la manière d'inventorier et de conserver. . . tous les objets qui peuv-ent servir aux arts* . . . (Paris, 1794), attributed to Vicq d'Azyr; *La médecine des bêtes à cornes*, 2 vols. (Paris, 1781); *Nouveau plan de conduite pour détruire enti-èrement la maladie épizootique* (Lille, n.d.); *Observa-tions sur les moyens que l'on peut employer pour préserver les animaux sains de la contagion* . . . (Bordeaux, 1774); *Précaution pour la purification des étables* (n.p., n.d.); *Recueil d'observations* . . . *sur dif-férentes méthodes* . . . *pour guérir la maladie épidé-mique qui attaque les bêtes à cornes* . . . (Paris, 1775); *Système anatomique. Quadrupèdes* (Paris, 1792); *Traité d'anatomie et de physiologie* (Paris, 1786); *Traité de l'anatomie du cerveau* (Paris, 1813); and *Table pour servir à l'histoire anatomique et naturelle des corps vi-vants* (n.p., n.d. [Paris, 1774]).

II. SECONDARY LITERATURE. Articles on Vicq d'Azyr are in Michaud, *Biographie universelle*, XLVIII, 374–378; *Encyclopédie méthodique*, XIII (Paris, 1830), 446–455; Dezeimeris's *Dictionnaire historique de la médecine ancienne et moderne*, IV (Paris, 1839), 330–334; Bayle and Thillaye's *Biographie médicale*, II (Paris, 1855), 718–720; and *Biographisches Lexicon*, V (Berlin–Vienna, 1934), 747–749.

Other works are L. Barbillion, "Vicq d'Azyr," in *Paris médical*, **62** (1926), 309–311 (appendix); F. G. Boisseau and C. Cavenne, "Vicq d'Azyr," in *Diction-naire des sciences médicales. Biographie médicale*, VII (Paris, 1825), 429–432; Paul Broca, "Note sur la topo-graphie cérébrale et sur quelques points de l'histoire des circonvolutions," in *Bulletin de l'Académie de méde-cine*, 2nd ser., **5** (1876), 824–834; P. J. G. Cabanis, "Éloge de Vicq d'Azyr," in his *Oeuvres complètes*, V (Paris, 1825), 177–216; G. Cuvier, *Histoire des sci-ences naturelles depuis leur origine jusqu'a nos jours*, 5 vols. (Paris, 1841–1845), IV, 297–305; V, 45, 379; J. Dobson, *Anatomical Eponyms* (Edinburgh–London, 1962); Michel Dronne, *Bertin et l'élevage français au XVIII siècle* (Alfort, 1965), 145–212; F. Dubois, "Re-cherches historiques sur les dernières années de Louis et de Vicq d'Azyr, secrétaires perpétuels de la Société royale de médecine et de la Société royale de chirurgie.

L'histoire de la guillotine," in *Journal des connaissances médicales pratiques et de pharmacologie*, **34** (1867), 17–19, 33–37, 49–51; A. J. L. M. Dufresne, *Notes sur la vie et les oeuvres de Vicq d'Azyr (1748–1794). Histoire de la fondation de l'Académie de médecine* (Bordeaux, 1906), diss. for the M.D. (no. 65); and the anonymous "Bibliographical Sketch on Vicq d'Azyr," in *Edinburgh Medical and Surgical Journal*, **3** (1807), 180–185.

See also R. L. M. Faull, D. M. Taylor, and J. B. Car-man, "Soemmering and the Substantia Nigra," in *Medi-cal History*, **12** (1968), 297–299; M. Genty, "Vicq d'Azyr commissaire pour l'extraction du salpêtre," in *Progrès médical*, supp. ill. no. 2 (1936), 9–16; C. A. de Gerville, "Vicq d'Azyr," in his *Études géographiques et historiques sur le département de la Manche*, XL (Cherbourg, 1854), 284; Lucien Hahn, "Vicq d'Azyr," in *Dictionnaire encyclopédique des sciences médicales*, 5th ser., III (Paris, 1889), 452–453; H. Hours, *La lutte contre les épizooties et l'école vétérinaire de Lyon au XVIIIᵉ siècle* (Paris, 1957), 90–92; P. Huard, "L'en-seignement médico-chirurgical," in R. Taton, ed., *Enseignement et diffusion des sciences en France au XVIIIème siècle* (Paris, 1964), 170–236; Kaime, "Une anecdote de la vie de Vicq d'Azyr," in *Revue de théra-peutique médico-chirurgicale* (1859), 249; Claude La-fisse, *Éloge de Vicq d'Azyr* . . . (Paris, 1797), also in *Recueil périodique de la Société de médecine de Paris*, III (Paris, 1798), 201–226; G. Lanteri-Laura, *L'homme et son cerveau selon Gall. Histoire et signification de la phrénologie* (Paris, 1970); and P. E. Lemontey, *Éloge historique de Vicq d'Azyr, prononcé* . . . *23 août 1825* (Paris, n.d.).

Further works are L. F. A. Maury, *Les académies d'autrefois. L'ancienne Académie des sciences* (Paris, 1864); L. Merle, "La vie et l'oeuvre du Dr. Jean Gabriel Gallot (1744–1794)," in *Mémoires de la Société des antiquaires de l'Ouest* (Poitiers), 4th ser., **5** (1962); J. L. Moreau, *Éloge de Vicq d'Azyr suivi d'un précis des tra-vaux anatomiques et physiologiques de ce célèbre méde-cin* (Paris, 1798); J. Noir, "Un savant, un innovateur et un réalisateur. Félix Vicq d'Azyr," in *Concours médical* (6 Apr. 1927), 927–929; Félix Pascalis Ouvrière, *An Exposition of the Dangers of Interment in Cities* (New York, 1824); J. Roger, *Les médecins normands*, II (Paris, 1895), 169–181; C. A. Sainte Beuve, "Notice sur Vicq d'Azyr," in *Union médicale*, **8** (1854), 355–356, 359–361, 371–372; A. C. Saucerotte, "Vicq d'Azyr," in *Nouvelle biographie générale*, XLV (Paris, 1866), 89–91; J. A. Sharp, "Alex Monro Secundus and the Interventricular Foramen," in *Medical History*, **5** (Jan. 1961), 83–89; W. A. Smeaton, *Fourcroy, Chemist and Revolutionary* (Cambridge, 1962), *passim*; and Dora Weiner, "Le droit de l'homme à la santé. Une belle idée devant l'Assemblée constituante, 1790–91," in *Clio medica*, **5** (1970), 209–223.

P. HUARD
M. J. IMBAULT-HUART

**VIDUS VIDIUS.** See **Guidi, Guido**.

**VIÈTE, FRANÇOIS** (*b.* Fontenay-le-Comte, Poitou [now Vendée], France, 1540; *d.* Paris, France, 23 February 1603), *mathematics.*

Viète's father, Étienne, was an attorney in Fontenay and notary at Le Busseau. His mother was Marguerite Dupont, daughter of Françoise Brisson and thus a first cousin of Barnabé Brisson. Viète was married twice: to Barbe Cothereau and, after her death, to Juliette Leclerc. After an education in Fontenay, Viète entered the University of Poitiers to study law. He received a bachelor's degree in law in 1560 but four years later abandoned the profession to enter the service of Antoinette d'Aubeterre, mother of Catherine of Parthenay, supervising the latter's education and remaining her loyal friend and adviser throughout his life. After Antoinette d'Aubeterre was widowed in 1566, Viète followed her to La Rochelle. From 1570 to 1573 he was at Paris, and on 24 October of that year Charles IX appointed him counselor to the *parlement* of Brittany at Rennes. He remained at Rennes for six years, and on 25 March 1580 he became *maître de requêtes* at Paris (an office attached to the *parlement*) and royal privy counselor. From the end of 1584 until April 1589 Viète was banished from the royal court by political enemies and spent some time at Beauvoir-sur-Mer. He was recalled to court by Henry III when the latter was obliged to leave Paris and to move the government to Tours, where Viète became counselor of the *parlement.* During the war against Spain, Viète served Henry IV by decoding intercepted letters written in cipher. A letter from the liaison officer Juan de Moreo to Philip II of Spain, dated 28 October 1589, fell into Henry's hands. The message, in a new cipher that Philip had given Moreo when he departed for France, consisted of the usual alphabet with homophonous substitutions, plus a code list of 413 terms represented by groups of two or three letters or of two numbers, either underlined or dotted. A line above a two-digit group indicated that it could be ignored. It was not until 15 March 1590 that Viète was able to send Henry the completed solution, although he had previously submitted parts of it. He returned to Paris in 1594 and to Fontenay in 1597. He was in Paris in 1599 but was dismissed by Henry IV on 14 December 1602.

Viète had only two periods of leisure (1564–1568 and 1584–1589). His first scientific works were his lectures to Catherine of Parthenay, only one of which has survived in a French translation: *Principes de cosmographie, tirés d'un manuscrit de Viette, et traduits en françois* (Paris, 1637). This tract, containing essays on the sphere, on the elements of geography, and on the elements of astronomy, has little in common with his "Harmonicon coeleste," which was never published but is available in manuscript (an autograph in Florence, Biblioteca Nazionale Centrale, MSS della Biblioteca Magliabechiana, cl. XI, cod. XXXVI, and a copy in cod. XXXVII; a copy by G. Borelli in Rome, Biblioteca Nazionale Centrale Vittorio Emanuele II, fondo San Pantaleone; and the Libri-Carucci copy in Paris, Bibliothèque Nationale, fonds lat. 7274. Part of the treatise is in Paris, Bibliothèque Nationale fonds Nouv. acqu. lat. 1644, fols. $67^r$–$79^v$; and a French index of the part of Bibliothèque Nationale, fonds lat. 7274, is in Bibliothèque Nationale, Nouv. acqu. franç. 3282, fols. $119^r$–$123^r$. The "Harmonicon coeleste," in five books, is Ptolemaic because Viète did not believe that Copernicus' hypothesis was geometrically valid).

All of Viète's mathematical investigations are closely connected with his cosmological and astronomical work. The *Canon mathematicus, seu ad triangula cum appendicibus*, publication of which began in 1571, was intended to form the preparatory, trigonometric part of the "Harmonicon coeleste." The *Canon* is composed of four parts, only the first two of which were published in 1579: "Canon mathematicus," which contains a table of trigonometric lines with some additional tables, and "Universalium inspectionum ad Canonem mathematicum liber singularis," which gives the computational methods used in the construction of the canon and explains the computation of plane and spherical triangles with the aid of the general trigonometric relations existing among the determinant components of such triangles. These relations were brought together in tables that allow the relevant proportion obtaining among three known and one unknown component of the triangle to be read off directly. The two other parts, devoted to astronomy, were not published. Viète certainly knew the work of Rheticus, for he adopted the triangles of three series that the latter had developed.

The *Canon* has six tables, the first of which gives, minute by minute, the values of the six trigonometric lines. For the construction of this table Viète applied the method given by Ptolemy in his *Almagest*, which was improved by the Arabs and introduced into the West through the translation of al-Zarqālī's *Canones sive regulae super tabulas astronomiae* by Gerard of Cremona; John de Lignères's *Canones tabularum primi mobilis* in the fourteenth century; and John of Gmunden's *Tractatus de sinibus, chordis et arcubus*, which inspired Peurbach and Regiomontanus. All these took as their point of departure an arc of 15° called a *kardaga*. The second table, "Canon triangulorum laterum rationalium," was based on the following proposition: "If there is a right-angled triangle having $h$ for the hypotenuse, $b$ for the base, and $p$ for the perpendicular, and the semi-difference $(h - p)/2 = 1$; then $h = (b^2/4) + 1$ and $p = (b^2/4) - 1$. If $b$ is given successive values of an arithmetical progression, the difference will be constant in the table of values of $h$ and $p$ thus formed. The third table, "Ad logisticem per $E\xi\epsilon\chi o\nu\tau\alpha\delta\alpha\varsigma$ tabella," is a multiplication table in the form of a right triangle that immediately gives, in degrees and minutes, the product $n \cdot n'/60$ for all the numbers $n$ and $n'$ included between 0 and 60. "Fractionum apud mathematicos usitarum, alterius in alterum reductionibus tabella adcommodata," the fourth table, gives the quotients obtaining by dividing the Egyptian year, the day, and the hour, and their principal subdivisions by each other and also by the most commonly used integers. The fifth table, "Mathematici canonis epitome," gives the values of the trigonometric lines from degree to degree and the length of the arc expressed in parts of the radius. The sixth table, "Canon triangulorum ad singulas partes quadranti circuli secundum $E\xi\epsilon\chi o\nu\tau\alpha\delta\omega\nu$ logisticem," gives the value of the six trigonometric lines from degree to degree, the radius 1 being divided into sixty parts, each part into sixty primes, and each prime into sixty seconds.

After the canon of triangles with rational sides, in the second part of the *Canon*, Viète gave as functions of the radius the values of the sides of inscribed polygons with three, four, six, ten, and fifteen sides and the relations that exist among these trigonometric lines, which permit easy calculation of the tables. In his solution of oblique triangles, Viète solved all the cases (except where three sides are given) by proportionality of sides to the sines of the angles opposite the sides; for the case of three sides, he follows the ancients in subdividing the triangle into right triangles. For spherical triangles he employed the same notation as for plane triangles and established that a spherical right triangle is determined by the total sine and two other elements. In spherical oblique triangles, Viète followed the ancients and Regiomontanus in subdividing the triangle into two right triangles by

an arc of a great circle perpendicular to one of the sides and passing through the vertex of the angle opposite. Also in the second part of the *Canon*, Viète wrote decimal fractions with the fractional part printed in smaller type than the integral and separated from the latter by a vertical line.

The most important of Viète's many works on algebra was *In artem analyticem isagoge*, the earliest work on symbolic algebra (Tours, 1591). It also introduced the use of letters both for known quantities, which were denoted by the consonants $B$, $C$, $D$, and so on, and for unknown quantities, which were denoted by the vowels. Furthermore, in using $A$ to denote the unknown quantity $x$, Viète sometimes employed $A$ quadratus, $A$ cubus . . . to represent $x^2$, $x^3$. . . . This innovation, considered one of the most significant advances in the history of mathematics, prepared the way for the development of algebra.

The two main Greek sources on which Viète drew appear in the opening chapter: book VII of Pappus' *Collection* and Diophantus' *Arithmetica*. The point of departure for Viète's "renovation" was his joining of facts, presented by Pappus only in reference to geometric theorems and problems, to the procedure of Diophantus' *Arithmetica*. On the basis of Pappus' exposition, Viète called this procedure *ars analytice*. In chapter 1 he undertook a new organization of the "analytic" art. To the two kinds of analysis mentioned by Pappus, the "theoretical" and the "problematical" (which he called "zetetic," or "seeking [the truth]," and "poristic," i.e.; "productive [of the proposed theorem]"), he added a third, which he called "rhetic" ("telling" with respect to the numbers), or "exegetic" ("exhibiting" in respect to the geometric magnitudes). He defined the new kind of analysis as the procedure through which the magnitude sought is produced from the equation or proportion set up in canonical form.

In chapter 2 Viète amalgamates some of the "common notions" enumerated in book I of Euclid's *Elements* with some definitions and theorems of book V, of the geometric books II and VI, and of the "arithmetical" books VII and VIII to form his stipulations for equations and proportions. In chapter 3 he gives the fundamental "law of homogeneity," according to which only magnitudes of "like genus" can be compared with each other, and in the fourth chapter he lays down "the canonical rules of species calculation." These correspond to the rules for addition, subtraction, multiplication, and division used for instruction in ordinary calculation. In this chapter he presents a mode of calculation carried out completely in terms of "species" of numbers and calls it *logistice speciosa*—in contrast with calculation using determinate numbers, which is *logistice numerosa*. Of significance for formation of the concepts of modern mathematics, Viète devotes the *logistice speciosa* to pure algebra, understood as the most comprehensive possible analytic art, applicable indifferently to numbers and to geometric magnitudes. By this process the concept of *eidos*, or species, undergoes a universalizing extension while preserving its link to the realm of numbers. In this general procedure the species represent simply general magnitudes. Viète's *logistice speciosa*, on the other hand, is understood as the procedure analogous to geometric analysis and is directly related to Diophantus' *Arithmetica*.

In chapter 5 Viète presents the *leges zeteticae*, which refer to elementary operations with equations: to antithesis (proposition I), the transfer of one of the parts of one side of the equation to the other; to hypobibasm (proposition II), the reduction of the degree of an equation by the division of all members by the species common to all of them; and to parabolism (proposition III), the removal of the coefficient of the *potestas* (conversion of the equation into the form of a proportion). The sixth chapter, "De theorematum per poristicen examinatione," deals more with synthesis and its relation to analysis than with poristics. It states that the poristic way is to be taken when a problem does not fit immediately into the systematic context.

In chapter 7, on the function of the rhetic art, Viète treats the third kind of analysis (rhetic or exegetic), which is applied to numbers if the search is for a magnitude expressible in a number, as well as to lengths, planes, or solids if the thing itself must be shown, starting from canonically ordered equations.

In chapter 8, the final one, Viète gives some definitions—such as of "equation": An equation is a comparison of an unknown magnitude with a determinate one—some rules, and some outlines of his works *De numerosa potestatum purarum, atque adfectarum ad exegesin resolutione tractatus, Effectionum geometricarum canonica recensio*, and *Supplementum geometriae*. In 1630 the work was translated into French by A. Vasset (very probably Claude Hardy) as *L'algèbre nouvelle de M. Viette* and by J. L. de Vaulezard as *Introduction en l'art analytique, ou nouvelle algèbre de François Viète*. Both also contain a translation of Viète's *Zeteticorum libri quinque*. A modern French translation of the work was published by F. Ritter in *Bullettino di bibliografia. . .*, 1 (1868), 223–244. An English version by J. W. Smith appeared as an appendix to Jacob Klein's *Greek Mathematical Thought and the Origin of Algebra* (Cambridge, Mass., 1968).

In 1593 Viète published *Zeteticorum libri quinque*, which he very probably had completed in 1591. In it he offered a sample of *logistice speciosa* and contrasted it directly with Diophantus' *Arithmetica*, which, in his opinion, remained too much within the limits of the *logistice numerosa*. In order to stress the parallelism of the two works, Viète ended the fifth book of his *Zetetics* with the same problem that concludes the fifth book of Diophantus' *Arithmetica*. In other parts of the book he also takes series of problems from the Diophantus work. References by Peletier and Peter Ramus, as well as Guilielmus Xylander's translation (1575), must certainly have introduced Viète to the *Arithmetica*, which he undoubtedly also came to know in the original.

Moreover, as K. Reich has proved in her paper "Diophant, Cardano, Bombelli, Viète, ein Vergleich ihrer Aufgaben," he was acquainted with Cardano's *De numerorum proprietatibus, Ars magna*, and *Ars magna arithmeticae* and mentioned his name in problems II,21 and II,22. According to Reich, however, it is not known whether Viète, in preparing his *Zetetics*, considered Bombelli's *Algebra*. The *Zetetics* is composed of five books, the first of which contains ten problems that seek to determine quantities of which the sum, difference, or ratio is known. The problems of the second book give the sum or difference of the squares or cubes of the unknown quantities, their product, and the ratio of this product to the sum or the difference of their squares. In the third book the unknown quantities are proportional, and one is required to find them if the sum or the difference of the extremes or means is given. This book contains the application of these problems to right triangles. The fourth book gives the solutions of second- and third-degree indeterminate problems, such as IV, 2,3, to divide a number, which is the sum of two squares, into two other squares. The fifth book contains problems of the same kind, but generally concerning three numbers: for instance (V,9), to find a right triangle in such a way that the area augmented with a given number, which is the sum of two squares, is a square.

Viète's notation in his early publications is somewhat different from that in his collected works, edited by F. van Schooten in 1646. For example, the modern $(3\ BD^2 - 3\ BA^2)/4$ is printed in the *Zetetics* as $(B$ in $D$ quadratum $3 - B$ in $A$ quadratum $3)/4$, while in 1646 it is reprinted in the form $(B$ in $Dq\ 3 - B$ in $Aq\ 3)/4$. Moreover, the radical sign found in the 1646 edition is a modification introduced by van Schooten. Viète rejected the radical, using instead the letter $l$ in the *Zetetics* — for example, $l \cdot 121$ for $\sqrt{121}$. The same holds for Viète's *Effectionum geometricarum canonica recensio*, the outline of which he had given in his *Isagoge*: "With a view to exegetic in geometry, the analytical art selects and enumerates more regular procedures by which equations of 'sides' and 'squares' may be completely interpreted" — that is, it concerns a convenient method for solving geometrical problems by using the coefficients of the equation in question, without solving the corresponding equation. All the solutions he gives in this tract have been carried out by geometric construction with the ruler and compass: for instance, the proof of proposition X, which leads to the equation $x^2 - px = q^2$, and that of proposition XVII, which leads to the equation $x^4 + p^2x^2 = p^2q^2$.

In 1593 at Tours, Jamet Mettayer edited *Francisci Vietae Supplementum geometriae, ex opere restitutae mathematicae analyseos seu algebra nova*. The following statement from proposition XXV—"Enimvero ostensum est in tractatu de aequationum recognitione, aequationes quadrato-quadratorum ad aequationes cuborum reduci"— is important because it shows that by 1593 his tract *De aequationum recognitione* had already been completed, long before its publication by Alexander Anderson (1615). The tract begins with the following postulate: A straight line can be drawn from any point across any two lines (or a circle and a straight line) in such a way that the intercept between these two lines (or the line and the circle) will be equal to a given distance, any possible intercept having been predefined. The twenty-five propositions that follow can be divided into four groups:

1. Propositions 1–7 contain the solution of the problem of the mesographicum—to find two mean proportionals between two given straight line segments—and its solution immediately yields the solution of the problem of doubling the cube.

2. Propositions 8–18 contain the solution of the problem of the trisection of an angle and the corresponding cubic equation. The trigonometric solution of the cubic equation occurs twice: in propositions 16 and 17.

3. Propositions 19–24 contain the solution of the problem of finding the side of the regular heptagon that is to be inscribed in a given circle.

4. Proposition 25 explains the importance of the applied method: the construction of two mean proportionals, the trisection of an angle, and all problems that cannot be solved only by means of the ruler and compass but that lead to cubic and biquadratic equations, can be solved with the aid of the ancient *neusis* procedure.

In 1592 Viète began a lively dispute with J. J. Scaliger when the latter published a purported solution of the quadrature of the circle, the trisection of an angle, and the construction of two mean proportionals between two given line segments by means of the ruler and compass only. In that year Viète gave public lectures at Tours and proved that Scaliger's assertions were incorrect, without mentioning the name of the author. For this reason he decided in 1593 to publish book VIII of his *Variorum de rebus mathematicis responsorum Liber VIII, cuius praecipua capita sunt: De duplicatione cubi et quadratione circuli, quae claudit πρόχειρον seu ad usum mathematici canonis methodica*. In chapters 1, 2, and 5 Viète treats the traditional problem of the doubling of the cube, that is, of the construction of two mean proportionals. In the first chapter, on the basis of Plutarch's *Life of Marcellus* (ch. 14), he calls this an irrational problem. In the fifth chapter he treats it synthetically, referring to the "ex Poristicis methodus" that he had presented in the *Supplementum geometriae*. In chapter 3 he is concerned with the trisection of an angle and, in chapter 7, with the construction of the regular heptagon to be inscribed in a given circle, proposed by François de Foix, count of Candale, the most important contemporary editor and reviser of Euclid. Chapters 6 and 14 are related to Archimedes' *On Spirals*, already known in the Latin West through the Moerbeke translation of 1269.

In chapter 8 Viète discusses the quadratrix and, in chapter 11, the lunes that can be squared. He investigates the problem of the corniculate angle in chapter 13 and sides with Peletier, maintaining that the angle of contact is no angle. Viète's proof is new: the circle may be regarded as a plane figure with an infinite number of sides and angles; but a straight line touching a straight line, however short it may be, will coincide with that straight line and will not form an angle. Never before had the meaning of "contact" been stated so plainly. In chapter 16 Viète gives a very interesting construction of the tangent to the Archimedean spiral and, in chapter 18, the earliest explicit expression for $\pi$ by an infinite number of operations. Considering regular polygons of 4, 8, 16, . . . sides, inscribed in a circle of unit radius, he found that the area of the circle is

$$2 \cdot \cfrac{1}{\sqrt{\frac{1}{2}} \cdot \sqrt{\frac{1}{2} + \frac{1}{2}\sqrt{\frac{1}{2}}} \cdot \sqrt{\frac{1}{2} + \frac{1}{2}\sqrt{\frac{1}{2} + \frac{1}{2}\sqrt{\frac{1}{2}}}} \cdots},$$

from which he obtained

$$\frac{\pi}{2} = \cfrac{1}{\sqrt{\frac{1}{2}} \cdot \sqrt{\frac{1}{2} + \frac{1}{2}\sqrt{\frac{1}{2}}} \cdots}.$$

The trigonometric portion of this treatise begins with chapter 19 and concerns right and oblique plane and spherical triangles. In regard to the polar triangle and Viète's use of it, Braunmühl in his *Vorlesungen* assures the reader that Viète's reciprocal figure is the same as the polar triangle. He arrives at this conclusion because Viète's theorems are arranged in such a manner that each theorem is the dual of the one immediately preceding it.

Since Scaliger could not defend himself against Viète's criticism, he left France for the Netherlands, where soon after his arrival in 1594 he published his *Cyclometrica elementa*, followed some months later by his *Mesolabium*. Viète responded with *Munimen adversus cyclometrica nova* (1594) and *Pseudomesolabium* (1595). In the first, through a nice consideration based on the use of the Archimedean spiral, he gives two interesting approximations of a segment of a circle. In the second he seeks those chords cutting the diameter in such a way that the four parts increase in geometric series. In the appendix Viète refutes Scaliger's assertion that in the inscribed quadrilateral the diameter and both diagonals are in arithmetical proportion.

Viète's mathematical reputation was already considerable when the ambassador from the Netherlands remarked to Henry IV that France did not possess any geometricians capable of solving a problem propounded in 1593 by Adrian Romanus to all mathematicians and that required the solution of a forty-fifth-degree equation. The king thereupon summoned Viète and informed him of the challenge. Viète saw that the equation was satisfied by the chord of a circle (of unit radius) that subtends an angle $2\pi/45$ at the center. In a few minutes he gave the king one solution of the problem written in pencil and, the next day, twenty-two more. He did not find forty-five solutions because the remaining ones involve negative sines, which were unintelligible to him.

Viète published his answer, *Ad problema, quod omnibus mathematicis totius orbis construendum proposuit Adrianus Romanus, responsum*, in 1595. In the introduction he says: "I, who do not profess to be a mathematician, but who, whenever there is leisure, delight in mathematical studies. . . ." Regarding Romanus' equation, Viète had seen at once that since $45 = 3 \cdot 3 \cdot 5$, it was necessary only to divide an angle once into five equal parts, and then twice into three, a division that could be effected by corresponding fifth- and third-degree equations. In the above problem he solved the equation $3x - x^3 = a$; using the roots $x$ he determined $y$ by $3y - y^3 = x$, and by the equation $5z - 5z^3 + z^5 = y$ he found the required roots $z$.

At the end of his work Viète proposed to Romanus, referring to Apollonius' *Tangencies*, the problem to draw a circle that touches three given circles. Romanus was acquainted with Regiomontanus' statement that he doubted the possibility of a solution by means of the ruler and compass only. He therefore solved the problem by determining the center of the required circle by means of the intersection of two hyperbolas; this solution did not, however, possess the rigor of the ancient geometry. In 1600 Viète presented a solution that had all the rigor desirable in his *Apollonius Gallus, seu exsuscitata Apollonii Pergaei* Περὶ ἐπαφῶν *geometria ad V. C. A. Romanum*, in which he gave a Euclidean solution using the center of similitude of two circles. Romanus was so impressed that he traveled to Fontenay to meet Viète, beginning an acquaintanceship that soon became warm friendship. Viète himself did not publish the book; very probably it was done by Marino Ghetaldi. A Greek letter dedicated to Viète precedes the text in the original edition. In appendix I, confronted with certain problems that Regiomontanus could solve algebraically but not geometrically, Viète provides their geometric construction and notes, by way of introduction, that these geometric constructions are important. In appendix II he vehemently attacks Copernicus, and there is also a reference to a work intended to correct the errors in the work of Copernicus and the defects in that of Ptolemy. It was to have been entitled *Francelinis* and to have contained a composition, "Epilogistice motuum coelestium Pruteniana," based on hypotheses termed Apollonian, such as the hypothesis of the movable eccentric.

In the 1591 edition of the *Isagoge*, Viète had already given the outline of the *De numerosa potestatum purarum, atque adfectarum ad exegesin resolutione tractatus*. The "numerical resolution of powers" referred to in the title means solving equations that have numerical solutions, such as $x^2 = 2916$ or $x^2 + 7x = 60750$. The work was published in 1600 at Paris, edited by Marino Ghetaldi, with Viète's consent. (All information concerning the edition is taken from a letter written by Ghetaldi to Michel Coignet, dated 15 February 1600, which is printed at the end of the work.) Viète gave some of his manuscripts to Ghetaldi when the latter was in Paris. Ghetaldi took them to Rome and allowed his friends there to make a copy. After Viète's death his heirs gave other manuscripts to his friend Pierre Alleaume, who left them to his son Jacques, a pupil of Viète's. Jacques entrusted Anderson with the treatises *De aequationum recognitione, Notae ad logisticem posteriores*, and *Analytica angularium sectionum*.

In *De numerosa potestatum*, Viète gives a method of approximation to the roots of numerical equations that resembles the one for ordinary root extraction. Taking $f(x) = k$, where $k$ is positive, Viète separates the required root from the rest, then substitutes an approximate value for it and shows that another digit of the root can be obtained by division. A repetition of this process gives the next digit, and so on. Thus, in $x^5 - 5x^3 + 500x = 7,905,504$, he takes $r = 20$, then computes $7,905,504 - r^5 + 5r^3 - 500r$ and divides the result by a value that in modern notation would be $|(f[r + s_1] - f[r])| - s_1^n$, where $n$ is the degree of the equation and $s_1$ is a unit of the denomination of the next digit to be found. Thus, if the required root is 243 and $r$ has been taken to be 200, then $s_1$ is 10; but if $r$ is taken as 240, then $s_1$ is 1. In the example above, where $r = 20$, the divisor is 878,295 and the quotient yields the next digit of the root, 4. One obtains $x = 20 + 4 = 24$, the required root.

Viète also had a role in the improvements of the Julian calendar. The yearly determination of the movable feasts had long resulted in great confusion. The rapid progress of astronomy led to the consideration of this subject, and many new calendars were proposed. Pope Gregory XIII convoked a large number of mathematicians, astronomers, and prelates, who decided upon the adoption of the calendar proposed by Clavius. To rectify the errors of the Julian calendar, it was agreed to write 15 October into the new calendar immediately after 4 October 1582. The Gregorian calendar met with great opposition among scientists, including Viète and Tobias Müller. Viète valued the studies involved in a reform of the calendar; and toward the end of his life he allowed himself to be carried away by them and to engage in unjustified polem-

ics against Clavius, the result of which was the publication with Mettayer of *Libellorum supplicum in regia magistri relatio kalendarii vere Gregoriani ad ecclesiasticos doctores exhibita pontifici maximo Clementi VIII anno Christo 1600 iubilaeo* (1600). He gave the work to Cardinal Cinzio Aldobrandini, who transmitted it to Clavius. Since Clavius rejected the proposed corrections, Viète and Pierre Mettayer, the son of Jean, published a libel against Clavius that was as vehement as it was unjust: *Francisci Vietae adversus Christophorum Clavium expostulatio* (1602).

*Francisci Vietae fontenaensis de aequationum recognitione et emendatione tractatus duo* was published in 1615, under the editorship of Viète's Scottish friend Alexander Anderson. The treatise "De emendatione" contains the subject matter of the work as announced in the *Isagoge* under the title "Ad logisticen speciosam notae posteriores" and sets forth a series of formulas (*notae*) concerning transformations of equations. In particular it presents general methods for solving third- and fourth-degree equations. This work reveals Viète's partial knowledge of the relations between the coefficients and the roots of an equation. Viète demonstrates that if the coefficient of the second term in a second-degree equation is minus the sum of two numbers the product of which is the third term, then the two numbers are roots of the equation. Viète rejected all but positive roots, however, so it was impossible for him to perceive fully the relations in question.

Viète's solution of a cubic equation is as follows: Given $x^3 + 3B^2x = 2Z^3$. To solve this let $y^2 + yx = B^2$. Since from the constitution of such an equation $B^2$ is understood to be a rectangle of which the lesser of the two sides is $y$, and the difference between it and the larger side is $x$, $(B^2 - y^2)/y = x$. Therefore $(B^6 - 3B^4y^2 + 3B^2y^4 - y^6)/y^3 + (3B^4 - 3B^2y^2)/y = 2Z^3$. When all terms have been multiplied by $y^3$ and properly ordered, one obtains $y^6 + 2Z^3y^3 = B^6$. Since this equation is quadratic with a positive root it also has a cube root. Thus the required reduction is effected. Conclusion: If, therefore, $x^3 + 3B^2x = 2Z^3$, and $\sqrt{B^6 + Z^6} - Z^3 = D^3$, then $(B^2 - D^2)/D$ is $x$, as required.

In the solution of biquadratics, Viète remains true to his principle of reduction. He first removes the term involving $x^3$ to obtain the form $x^4 + a^2x^2 + b^3x = c^4$. He then moves the terms involving $x^2$ and $x$ to the right-hand side of the equation and adds $x^2y^2 + y^4/4$ to each side, so that the equation becomes $(x^2 + y^2/2)^2 = x^2(y^2 - a^2) - b^3x + y^4/4 + c^4$. He then chooses $y$ so that the right-hand side of this equation is a perfect square. Substituting this value of $y$, he can take the square root of both sides and thus obtain two quadratic equations for $x$, each of which can be solved.

In theorem 3 of chapter VI, Viète gives a trigonometrical solution of Cardano's irreducible case in cubics. He applies the equation $(2 \cos \alpha)^3 - 3 (2 \cos \alpha) = 2 \cos 3\alpha$ to the solution of $x^3 - 3a^2x = a^2b$, when $a > b/2$, by setting $x = 2a \cos \alpha$ and determining $3\alpha$ from $b = 2a \cos 3\alpha$. In the last chapter Viète resolves into linear factors $x - x_k$ the first member of an algebraic equation $\phi(x) = 0$ from the second up to the fifth degree. Anderson's edition is the only one besides the *Opera* of 1646. There is still a manuscript that contains the text (Paris, Bibliothèque Nationale, Nouv. acqu. lat. 1644, fols. $1^r-31^v$, "De recognitione aequationum tractatus," and fols. $32^r-60^v$, "De aequationum emendatione tractatus secundus").

In 1615 Anderson published Viète's treatise on angle sections, *Ad angularium sectionum analyticem theoremata καϑολικώτερα a Francisco Vieta fontenaensis primum excogitata at absque ulla demonstratione ad nos transmissa, jam tandem demonstrationibus confirmata*. This treatise deals, in part, with general formulas of chords, sines, cosines, and tangents of multiple arcs in terms of the trigonometric lines of the simple arcs. Viète first applies algebraic transformation to trigonometry, particularly to the multisection of angles, but without proofs and calculations, which were added by Anderson. In theorem 6 Viète considers the equations for multiple angles: letting $2 \cos a = x$, he expresses $\cos na$ as a function of $x$ for all integers $n < 11$; and at the end he presents a table for determining the coefficients. In theorem 7 he expresses $2x^{n-2} \sin na$ in terms of $x$ and $y$ using $2 \sin a = x$ and $2 \sin 2a = y$. After theorem 10 Viète states: "Thus the analysis of angular sections involves geometric and arithmetic secrets which hitherto have been penetrated by no one." To the treatises of the *Isagoge* belong "Ad logisticen speciosam notae priores" and "Ad logisticen speciosam notae posteriores," the latter now lost. The first was not published during his life, because Viète believed that the manuscript was not yet suitable for publication. (It was published by Jean de Beaugrand in 1631.) It represents a collection of elementary general algebraic formulas that correspond to the arithmetical propositions of the second and ninth books of Euclid's *Elements*, as well as some interesting propositions that combine algebra with geometry. In propositions 48–51 Viète derives the

formulas for $\sin 2x$; $\cos 2x$; $\sin 3x$; $\cos 3x$; $\sin 4x$; $\cos 4x$; $\sin 5x$ and $\cos 5x$ expressed in $\sin x$ and $\cos x$ by applying proposition 46, "From two right-angled triangles construct a third right-angled triangle," to two congruent right triangles; to right triangles with simple and double angles; with simple and triple angles, and with simple and quadruple angles respectively. He remarks, that the coefficients are equal to those in the expansion $(B + D)^n$ (B being the perpendicular and D the base of the original right triangle), that the various terms must be "homogeneous" and that the signs are alternately $+$ and $-$. (A French translation of this work was published by F. Ritter in *Bullettino di bibliografia . . .*, **1** [1868], 245–276.) Besides Viète's published works there are manuscripts containing works of him or attributed to him. In addition to Nouv. acqu. lat. 1644, Bibliothéque Nationale, fonds lat., nouv. acqu. 1643, contains few new elements. The author was very well acquainted with Viète's work, particularly with his *De numerosa potestatum . . . ad exegesin resolutione . . .*; he betrays the influence of Simon Stevin's *Arithmétique* because his manner of denoting the powers of the unknown depends on the method used by Stevin and he uses the signs for equality and square root. London, British Museum, Sloane 652, fols. 1–9, contains the *Isagoge*, and fols. 10–40 the *Zetetics*.

## BIBLIOGRAPHY

I. ORIGINAL WORKS. Note references in text. Additional editions of Viète's works are *Quinque orationes philosophicae* (Paris, 1555); and *Deschiffrement d'une lettre escripte par le Commandeur Moreo au roy d'Espagne son maître* (Tours, 1590). MSS include "Mémoires de la vie de Jean de Parthenay Larchevêque," Bibliothèque Nationale, coll. Dupuy, vol. 743, fols. 189–219; "Généalogie de la maison de Parthenay," Bibliothèque de la Société d'Histoire du Protestantisme, no. 417: "Discours des choses advenues à Lyon, durant que M. de Soubise y commandait," Bibliothèque Nationale, fonds français 20783; and "Manuscrit sur la ligue," Bibliothèque Nationale, fonds français 15499. Viète's collected works were issued as *Opera mathematica* by Frans van Schooten (Leiden, 1646; repr. Hildesheim, 1970).

II. SECONDARY LITERATURE. The best survey of Viète's life and works is in F. Ritter, "François Viète, inventeur de l'algèbre moderne, 1540–1603. Essai sur sa vie et son oeuvre," in *Revue occidentale philosophique, sociale et politique*, 2nd ser., **10** (1895), 234–274, 354–415.

See also the following, listed chronologically: Florian Cajori, *A History of Mathematics* (New York, 1894;

repr. New York, 1961), 137–139, 143–144; A. von Braunmühl, *Vorlesungen über Geschichte der Trigonometrie*, I (Leipzig, 1900), 157–183; M. Cantor, *Vorlesungen über Geschichte der Mathematik*, II (Leipzig, 1900; repr. Stuttgart, 1965), 582–591, 629–641; H. G. Zeuthen, *Geschichte der Mathematik im 16. und 17. Jahrhundert* (Leipzig, 1903; repr. Stuttgart, 1966), 95–109; 115–126; M. C. Zeller, *The Development of Trigonometry From Regiomontanus to Pitiscus* (Ann Arbor, Mich., 1944), 73–85; H. Lebesgue, *Commentaires sur l'oeuvre de F. Viète*, Monographies de l'Enseignement Mathématique, No. 4 (Geneva, 1958), 10–17; P. Dedron and J. Itard, *Mathématiques et mathématiciens* (Paris, 1959), 173–185; J. E. Hofmann, "Über Vietes Beiträge zur Geometrie der Einschiebungen," in *Mathematische-physikalische Semesterberichte*, VIII (Göttingen, 1962), 191–214; H. L. L. Busard, "Über einige Papiere aus Vietes Nachlass in der Pariser Bibliothèque Nationale," in *Centaurus*, **10** (1964), 65–126; D. Kahn, *The Codebreakers, the Story of Secret Writing* (New York, 1968), 116–118; J. Klein, *Greek Mathematical Thought and the Origin of Algebra* (Cambridge, 1968), 150–185, 253–285, 315–353; K. Reich, "Diophant, Cardano, Bombelli, Viète, ein Vergleich ihrer Aufgaben," in *Rechenpfennige* (Munich, 1968), 131–150; K. Reich, "Quelques remarques sur Marinus Ghetaldus et François Viète," in *Actes du symposium international "La géométrie et l'algèbre au début du XVIIᵉ siècle"* (Zagreb, 1969), 171–174; J. Grisard, "François Viète mathématicien de la fin du seizième siècle," *Thèse de 3ᵉ cycle. École pratique des hautes études*, (Paris, 1968); and K. Reich and H. Gericke, "François Viète, Einführung in die Neue Algebra," in *Historiae scientiarum elementa*, V (Munich, 1973).

                                      H. L. L. BUSARD

**VIEUSSENS, RAYMOND** (*b.* Vigan, Lot, France, *ca.* 1635; *d.* Montpellier, France, 16 August 1715), *anatomy, medicine.*

Vieussens' father, François Vieussens, is known to have been a *bourgeois* of Vigan despite his descendants' claims to be of the nobility and their assertion that Raymond Vieussens was the son of a lieutenant-colonel, Alexandre-Gaspard, *seigneur* of Vieussens, who died at the siege of Barcelona. Vieussens never signed his name with the particle, but it is joined to his name in the posthumous editions of his writings.

Vieussens studied medicine at Montpellier, where he was awarded the doctorate on 9 October 1670, when he was about thirty-five, a surprisingly late age; the absence of information concerning his early years, however, precludes our ascertaining why he did not receive it earlier. In any case, at the time of his graduation he was already well-

known, for almost immediately he was named physician at the Hôtel Dieu St.-Éloi, then the leading hospital of Montpellier. Vieussens subsequently became chief physician there and apparently retained that post for the rest of his life. Between 1679 and 1697 twelve children were born to him and his wife, Elisabeth Peyret.

On several occasions Vieussens left Montpellier for long periods to treat important people in Paris. The publication of his books on the nervous system (1684) and on fermentation (1688) made Vieussens famous. To reward him for his writings, the king granted him the title of royal physician and an annual pension of 1,000 *livres*. Although he never treated the king, he was personal physician to the duchess of Montpensier, the Grande Mademoiselle, from 1690 until her death in 1693. Vieussens was elected to the Académie des Sciences in 1699 as correspondent of P. S. Régis, and on 15 February 1708 he was promoted to associate anatomist. In 1707 the king named him councillor of state. Although prominent in scientific medicine at Montpellier, Vieussens spent his entire career—except for his studies—outside the city's university and sometimes even in opposition to its professors. He founded a virtual dynasty of physicians: two of his sons became royal physicians, and two of his daughters married physicians. His grandson Daniel prepared the posthumous edition of his *Histoire des maladies internes.*

From the time he entered St.-Éloi, Vieussens divided his time and interest between medical practice and anatomical research. The regulations then in effect allowed him, as chief physician of the hospital, to perform a large number of autopsies. Like most of the anatomists of the time, he was as much concerned with what was called normal anatomy as with pathological changes. The study of pathological morphology, however, still lacked a satisfactory unifying theory. In this respect it is significant that while Vieussens sought quick publication of the results of his anatomical research, a large portion of his pathological observations, some of them very original, was not made public until long after his death.

Vieussens' research on the nervous system is of great importance. In *Nevrographia universalis* (1684) he sought to continue the work of Thomas Willis, which he greatly admired. The first to make good use of Steno's suggestion that the white substance in the brain should be studied by tracing the path of its fibers, Vieussens described the olivary nucleus and the centrum semiovale; the latter still bears his name. Moreover, his description of the fine structure of the cerebellum, including the discovery of the dentate nuclei, surpassed all previous publications on the subject. The most original part of the work concerns the paths of the peripheral nerves. Vieussens also studied the structure of the ear and angiology. The weak point of his work on the nervous system is his tendency to conjoin his correct morphological observations with quite fantastic physiological explanations. In his speculations on physiology, Vieussens drew inspiration from both the mechanistic philosophy of Descartes and the iatrochemical ideas of F. de la Boë (Sylvius). He believed that he had demonstrated the existence of the nervous fluid.

One of Vieussens' major areas of study was fermentation. He investigated the mechanical composition of the blood with great fervor but an equal lack of success. The discovery of an acidic salt in the blood was the source of a long and painful public polemic with the Montpellier professor Pierre Chirac, who claimed to be the first to have extracted this substance from the blood. The priority dispute was particularly unfruitful in that the discovery was erroneous. Nevertheless, until the end of his life Vieussens considered his chemical research on the blood to be his most important work.

Vieussens greatly underestimated the significance of his cardiological observations, which, in the judgment of posterity, were a truly pioneer effort. Most of his studies on the physiology and pathology of the heart and of the circulation were undertaken during the last decade of his life. While the experimental portion of the work was not published until 1755, in the posthumous *Expériences et réflexions . . .*, the clinical and anatomicopathological observations were published during his lifetime in two cardiological treatises, the more important of which is *Traité nouveau de la structure et des causes du mouvement naturel du coeur* (1715). By injecting mercury into various vessels and internal organs of living animals and fresh human cadavers, Vieussens was able to trace the exact course of the blood's flow in different parts of the body. He confirmed the hypothesis that there is a continuous vascular pathway between the arterial and venous vessels. In cardiac pathology, he was the first to describe mitral stenosis and aortic insufficiency on the basis of both clinical and anatomicopathological observation. Vieussens had already noted that a disease of the aorta manifests itself by a characteristic pulse, which was rediscovered a century later by P. J. Corrigan, whose name it now bears.

## BIBLIOGRAPHY

I. ORIGINAL WORKS. Vieussens' principal works are *Nevrographia universalis* (Lyons, 1684), also in French (Toulouse, 1774); *Tractatus duo. Primus: De remotis et proximis mixti principiis in ordine ad corpus humanum spectatis. Secundus: De natura, differentiis, subjectis, conditionibus et causis fermentationum* (Lyons, 1688); *Epistola de sanguinis humani cum sale fixo* (Leipzig, 1698); *Novum vasorum corporis humani systema* (Amsterdam, 1705), also in French (Toulouse, 1774); *Nouvelles découvertes sur le coeur* (Toulouse, 1706); *Traité nouveau de la structure de l'oreille* (Toulouse, 1714); *Traité nouveau de la structure et des causes du mouvement naturel du coeur* (Toulouse, 1715); *Traité nouveau des liqueurs du corps humain* (Toulouse, 1715); *Expériences et réflexions sur la structure et l'usage des viscères, suivies d'une explication physico-méchanique de la plupart des maladies* (Paris, 1755); and *Histoire des maladies internes*, 3 vols. (Toulouse, 1774–1775).

II. SECONDARY LITERATURE. The best biography is L. Dulieu, "Raymond Vieussens," in *Monspeliensis Hippocrates*, **10**, no. 35 (1967), 9–26. A general account can be found in C. E. Kellet, "Life and Work of Raymond Vieussens," in *Annals of Medical History*, 3rd ser., **4** (1942), 31–53. Vieussens's neurological work is discussed in B. Sachs, "Raymond de Vieussens, Noted Neuro-Anatomist and Physician of the XVIIth Century," in *Proceedings of the Charaka Club*, **3** (1910), 99–105; and in E. Clarke and C. D. O'Malley, *The Human Brain and Spinal Cord* (Berkeley–Los Angeles, 1968), 584–591, 636–641. For his cardiological discoveries, see J. J. Philipp, "Raymond Vieussens und J. M. Lancisi's Verdienste um die Lehre von den Krankheiten des Herzens," in *Janus* (Breslau), **2** (1847), 580–598; E. Schroer, *Die Förderung der Kenntnisse der Herzkrankheiten durch Vieussens und Sénac* (Düsseldorf, 1937); and C. E. Kellet, "Raymond Vieussens on Mitral Stenosis," in *British Heart Journal*, **21** (1959), 440–444.

M. D. GRMEK

**VIGANI, JOHN FRANCIS** (*b.* Verona, Italy, *ca.* 1650[?]; *d.* Newark-on-Trent, England, February 1713 [o.s.]), *chemistry, pharmacy.*

Almost every point concerning Vigani's life is doubtful, except that on 10 February 1702 [o.s.] the senate of the University of Cambridge conferred upon him the title of professor of chemistry "because he has with much praise practised the art of chemistry among us for twenty years (not without great profit to the studious)." He was the first to hold this title. Vigani therefore came to Cambridge about 1682, although he always lived in Newark with his family and had no formal association with any college. He taught at several, including Queens' (where his cabinet of materia medica is still preserved) and Trinity (where a laboratory was built for him by the master, Richard Bentley, in 1707). He was on friendly terms with John Covel and other leading men, including Isaac Newton—who took "much delight and pleasure" in his company until Vigani told him an off-color joke. Vigani described himself as *Veronensis* and mentioned a visit to Parma in 1671; otherwise nothing is known of his origins. He had no recorded degree or medical license. The years before his settlement in England are said to have been devoted to travel, study, and collecting. He ceased to teach at Cambridge in 1708 and was buried 26 February 1713 [o.s.].

The few contemporary references to Vigani's teaching on chemistry, the construction of furnaces, and materia medica are favorable; three anonymous sets of lecture notes survive (University Library, *ca.* 1700; Queens' College, 1707; and a set formerly owned by Sir C. S. Sherrington, 1705). Vigani's chemistry may be further studied in his one published work, *Medulla chemiae* (later *chymiae*; Danzig, 1682; London, 1683, later editions at London, Leiden, Nuremberg and Basel). It is not known why the first publication was at Danzig; an earlier edition (London, 1658) has been recorded and is not wholly implausible but is not now traceable. The first edition consisted of nineteen pages and the second of seventy-one and included plates of furnaces and apparatus. Vigani was above all a practical working chemist and pharmacist with no interest in theory, referring readers who desired more theoretical discussion to the writings of Robert Boyle. He attended carefully to the purity of materials and was generally cautious or even skeptical; he denied, for example, that antimony is not chemically dissolved into "antimony wine." Nevertheless, he was confused about such matters as the distillation of vinegar and the identity of gases, which signify "nothing else but a blast or Vapour," he wrote. Vigani seems to have been completely free of any alchemical tinge. His main object was to teach in a plain and reliable way the methods of preparing useful chemical compounds and pharmaceutical recipes. His cabinet contains an eclectic mixture of vegetable, mineral, animal, and chemical medicaments.

## BIBLIOGRAPHY

See L. J. M. Coleby, "John Francis Vigani," in *Annals of Science*, **8** (1952), 46–60; and E. S. Peck, "Vigani and His Cabinet," in *Cambridge Antiquarian Society Communications*, **34** (1934), 34–49.

A. RUPERT HALL

**VIGO, GIOVANNI DA** (*b.* Rapallo, Italy, 1450; *d.* 1525), *medicine.*

Vigo studied under Battista di Rapallo, surgeon to the marquis of Saluzzo. He is said to have served as surgeon at the siege of Saluzzo (1485–1486), but he makes no reference to it. Vigo practiced at Genoa, where he was befriended by Bendinelli de Saulis, later cardinal of Santa Sabina. About 1495 he went to Savona and found favor with Cardinal Giuliano della Rovere, then captain of papal armies in Umbria. When Giuliano became Pope Julius II in 1503, Vigo was summoned to the papal court as surgeon, at an annual salary of ninety-six ducats. In 1506 he served Julius II in the war against the Borgias, and at Bologna cured the pope of a hard node between two fingers. Later, in the campaign against Ferrara, he cured Julius of an ear infection. Among his patients were the duke of Urbino and many cardinals. After Julius' death (21 February 1513), Vigo became surgeon to his nephew, Sisto della Rovere, who, like his uncle, suffered from gout; his salary was then three hundred gold *scudi* a year.

After Sisto's death in 1517, Vigo retired from public life. He had at least two sons: Ambrogio, provost of Santa Maria Maddelena in Genoa and protonotary apostolic, and Luigi, a surgeon for whom he wrote *Practica in arte chirurgica copiosa* (Rome, 1514). The book, begun in 1503 and completed in 1513, treats anatomy, abscesses, wounds, ulcers, syphilis, fractures, simple medicines, and antidotes; there is also a supplement on spells, aphrodisiacs, cosmetics, cures for obesity and thinness, and a method for extracting a dead fetus. Various parts were written for different people: a *consilium* on cancer of the breast for a noblewoman, on the stone for Tommaso Regis, on syphilis for Giovanni Antracino, on gout for Cardinal Sisto della Rovere, and on antidotes for Vigo's son Luigi. Consequently the work is not well organized: diseases of the ears appear in the chapter on breasts, diseases of the teeth in the chapter on venereal disease, and diseases of the eyes in the treatise on ulcers.

Vigo's wide reading led him to copy much from others. Often overruled by physicians at the papal court, he became a timid surgeon: he left the operation for hernia and extraction of stones and cataracts to itinerant surgeons and, except for trephination and amputation, performed few operations. He relied mainly on cauterization, plasters, and ointments. For gunshot wounds, to which he attributed bruising, burning, and poisoning, his basic treatment was the application of "Egyptian" ointment, cauterization with boiling oil, and oil of roses with egg yolk.

Vigo was among the first to advocate the use of mercury ointment in treating syphilis, although Leoniceno and Cumano dismissed it as inefficacious and Juan Almenar considered it to be the cause of epilepsy and paralysis. Vigo distinguished between the primary and secondary stages of the disease, anticipating the views of Antonio Musa Brassavola of Ferrara.

In 1517, possibly stimulated by the *Compendium in chirurgia* (1514) of his pupil Mariano Santo da Barletta, Vigo published the five-book *Practica in arte chirurgica compendiosa*, in which he amplified and made more precise his teaching on certain topics, particularly on trephination. He was the first during the Middle Ages to describe the crown saw for removing a bone disk from the skull, an instrument known to Hippocrates but long fallen into oblivion. The instrument was illustrated by Andrea della Croce in *Chirurgiae universalis opus absolutum* (Venice, 1573).

Assessments of Vigo's contribution to surgery vary: the Italians consider him an innovator who anticipated many later developments; the Germans and the French are inclined to dismiss him as a mere compiler and propagandist of Arab doctrines.

*BIBLIOGRAPHY*

I. ORIGINAL WORKS. Vigo's two published works were *Practica in arte chirurgica copiosa* (Rome, 1514; Pavia, 1514), repr. at Lyons in 11 eds. between 1516 and 1582; and *Practica in arte chirurgica compendiosa* (Rome[?], 1517; Pavia, 1518; Venice, 1520; Florence, 1522, 1525); also translated into French by Nicholas Godin (1525), into Italian by Lorenzo Chrysaorio (1540), into English by Bartholomew Traheron (1543), into Spanish by Miguel Juan Pascual (1557), and into German and Portuguese in the seventeenth century. There were many eds. of each trans. at late as the eighteenth century.

II. SECONDARY LITERATURE See the following, listed chronologically: G. L. Marini, *Degli archiatri pontificii*, I (Rome, 1784), 300–303; V. Malacarne, *Delle opere de' medici, e de' cerusici che nacquero o fiorivono prima del secolo XVI negli stati della real casa di Savoia*, I (Turin, 1786), 187; G. G. Bonino, *Biografia medica Piemontese*, I (Turin, 1824), 108–121; B. Mojon, *Ritratti ed elogi di Liguri illustri* (Genoa, 1820); J.-F. Malgaigne, *Oeuvres complètes d'Ambroise Paré*, I (Paris, 1840), clxxv–clxxxii; G. B. Pescetto, *Biografia medica Ligure*, I (Genoa, 1846), 69–87; E. Gurlt, *Geschichte der Chirurgie*, I (Berlin, 1898), 919–942; V. Nicaise, "À propos de Jean de Vigo," in *Bulletin de la Société française d'histoire de la médecine*, **2** (1903), 313–347; G. Davide, "Giovanni da Vigo (1450–1525)," in *Rivista di storia delle scienze mediche e naturali*, **17** (1926), 21–35; H. Frölich, *Biographisches Lexikon der hervorragenden Aerzte*, V (Berlin, 1934), 758; and E. Razzoli, *Giovanni da Vigo, archiatro di Giulio II* (Milan, 1939).

C. H. TALBOT

**VIJAYANANDA** (or **VIJAYANANDIN**) (*fl.* Benares, India, 966), *astronomy.*

Vijayananda, the son of Jayananda, a Brāhmaṇa of Benares who followed the Saurapakṣa (see essay in the Supplement), wrote a *Karaṇatilaka* the epoch of which is 23/24 March 966; he is, then, obviously not the Vijayananda whose method of computing the longitudes of Jupiter and Saturn is referred to by Varāhamihira (*fl. ca.* 550) in his *Pañcasiddhāntikā* (XVII, 62). The *Karaṇatilaka* is known to us only in the Arabic translation with examples (some for 1025) by al-Bīrūnī, entitled *Ghurrat al-zījāt*, which survives in a unique manuscript at Ahmadabad that can be supplemented by many quotations in al-Bīrūnī's *India, Canon, Transits*, and *Shadows*.

The *Karaṇatilaka* consists of fourteen chapters:

1. On the *ahargaṇa* (lapsed time since the epoch).

2. On the mean and true longitudes of the two luminaries.

3. On the *pañcāṅga* (length of daylight; nakṣatras; tithis; yogas; and karaṇas).

4. On the mean longitudes of the five planets.

5. On the true longitudes of the five planets.

6. On the three problems relating to diurnal motion.

7. On lunar eclipses.

8. On solar eclipses.

9. On the projection of eclipses.

10. On the first visibilities of the planets.

11. On conjunctions of the planets.

12. On conjunctions of the planets with the fixed stars.

13. On the lunar crescent.

14. On the *pātas* of the sun and moon.

*BIBLIOGRAPHY*

An ed. of the *Ghurrat al-zījāt* was prepared by M. F. Quraishi of Lahore but has never been published. Sayyid Samad Husain Rizvi has edited a portion of the work (into ch. 6) with a somewhat cumbersome translation and commentary as "A Unique and Unknown Book of al-Beruni," in *Islamic Culture*, **37** (1963), 112–130, 167–187, 223–245; **38** (1964), 47–74, 195–212; **39** (1965), 1–26, 137–180.

DAVID PINGREE

**VILLALPANDO, JUAN BAUTISTA** (*b*. Córdoba, Spain, 1552; *d*. Rome, Italy, 1608), *architecture, mathematics, mechanics.*

Little is known about Villalpando's life. After entering the Jesuit order in 1575, he studied under Father Jerome Prado, who was writing a commentary on the book of Ezekiel. Evidently Villalpando's immense erudition was already apparent, and he soon joined Prado in his exegesis. In 1592 the pair moved to Rome to complete their work. Originally commissioned to provide a commentary only on chapters 40, 41, and 42 of Ezekiel, which deal with the architectural description of Solomon's temple, Villalpando suddenly found himself heir to a larger task when Prado died in 1595, having completed only the first twenty-six chapters. Although Villalpando himself died before completing the commentary, he managed to publish three volumes: *Hieronymi Pradi et Ioannis Baptistae Villalpandi e Societate Iesu in Ezechielem explanationes et apparatus urbis ac templi Hierosolymitani* (Rome, 1596–1604).

Like most Renaissance biblical commentaries, Villalpando's *Ezechiel* is the work of a polymath, containing copious information on subjects ranging from astrology, music, mathematical theories of proportion, and ornate reconstructions of Hebrew, Greek, and Roman systems of weights, measures, and currency to more orthodox etymological and scriptural preoccupations. The widely disparate topics that Villalpando considers in his attempt to re-create the temple would seem to express a Vitruvian vision of the architect. The influence of Vitruvius on Villalpando is crucial, and in this sense his work may be seen as a part of the general Renaissance revival of Vitruvius. Villalpando's great achievement was to have demonstrated in systematic fashion how Solomon's temple, as revealed by God to Ezekiel, was constructed according to Vitruvian principles of harmony and proportion, thus endowing classical architecture with divine approbation. Here, too, Villalpando was continuing an older humanist trend. In showing the celestial locus of classical architecture, he provided further evidence for the preestablished harmony between classical pagan culture and Christian civilization. It is significant that both Philip II of Spain and Pope Clement VIII expressed their approval of Villalpando's *Ezechiel* during the peak of the Counter-Reformation.

The third volume of the exegesis contains the bulk of Villalpando's mathematical and mechanical speculations. While his work on proportion and harmony (II, bk. 1, chs. 1–5) follows earlier Renaissance architectural utilizations of Euclid, his twenty-one propositions on "the center of gravity and the line of direction" (ch. 6) were deemed original enough to be reproduced by Mersenne in his *Synopsis mathematica* (1626). Duhem, who "rediscovered" Villalpando, conjectured that the Jesuit pilfered his propositions and their deductive proofs from a no longer extant manuscript by Leonardo dealing with local motion. Although Taylor has suggested that Villalpando may have had access to Leonardo's manuscripts through his mentor Juan de Herrera, other sources seem more plausible. Given Villalpando's lifelong interest in mathematics, it is highly probable that before his departure for Rome, he may have attended the Academia de Mathemáticas in Madrid, where he may have been introduced to the works of Archimedes. More interesting is the possibility that he knew Christoph Clavius, a fellow Jesuit and friend of Galileo, who was teaching in Rome at the same time. Villalpando relied heavily on Clavius' *Elements of Euclid*, speaking of it in terms of endearment, and it is possible that Clavius introduced him to the work of Commandino and Guido Ubaldo del Monte on the center of gravity. Villalpando, then, can be seen as participating in the sixteenth-century revival of Archimedes and Pappus as reconstructed by Commandino and Guido Ubaldo.

Villalpando's influence has been strongest in the history of architecture. The idea of the Escorial in Spain may have been derived from his earlier designs of the temple, and Inigo Jones certainly utilized his conceptions in introducing Palladian architecture into England. But Villalpando does touch the history of seventeenth-century science in a particularly sensitive area. No less a scientist than Isaac Newton used Villalpando's work in his own attempt to construct Solomon's temple and to determine the dimensions of the biblical cubit.

VINCENNES PUBLIC LIBRARY
VINCENNES, INDIANA

*BIBLIOGRAPHY*

I. ORIGINAL WORKS. Aside from the commentary on Ezekiel, Villalpando edited and annotated a medieval exegesis of St. Paul: *S. Remigii Rhemensis episcopi explanationes epistolarum B. Pauli Apostoli* (Rome, 1598). There is also in the Biblioteca Nacional, Madrid, a MS entitled "Relacion de la antigua Jerusalén remitida á Felippe II por el Padre J. B. Villalpando," which establishes Villalpando's connections with the royal court.

II. SECONDARY LITERATURE. The most thorough study of Villalpando's life and architectural accomplishments is René C. Taylor, "El Padre Villalpando (1552–1608) y sus ideas estéticas," in *Academia. Anales y boletín de la Real Academia de San Fernando* (1952), no. 2, 3–65. Taylor revised some of his conclusions, stressing the role of the occult in Villalpando's work, in "Architecture and Magic," in *Essays in the History of Architecture Presented to Rudolph Wittkower* (London, 1967), 81–110, and in "Hermetism and Mystical Architecture in the Society of Jesus," in R. Wittkower and I. B. Jaffe, eds., *Baroque Art: The Jesuit Contribution* (New York, 1972), 63–97, and esp. the documents printed in App. B. The mathematical and aesthetic background of Villalpando's discussion of proportion is discussed in Rudolph Wittkower, *Architectural Principles in the Age of Humanism*, 3rd ed. (London, 1962), 121 ff.

Pierre Duhem's observations on Villalpando's mechanics were first published in *Les origines de la statique*, II (Paris, 1906), 115–126; and were substantially repeated in "Léonard de Vinci et Villalpand," in his *Études sur Léonard de Vinci*, I (Paris, 1906), 53–85.

MICHAEL T. RYAN


**VILLANOVA. See Arnald of Villanova.**


**VILLARD DE HONNECOURT** (*b.* Honnecourt, Picardy, France, *ca.* 1190), *architecture.*

Villard de Honnecourt (who signed himself Wilars de Honecourt) wrote the most important known medieval source by an artist, the *Bauhüttenbuch* (Bibliothèque Nationale, Paris, MS fr. 19093) between about 1225 and 1235. Only thirty-three of the more than fifty parchment folios that he carried with him for years have been preserved. In 207 pen-and-ink drawings Villard brought together models for every type of worker enrolled in a builders' guild: architectural motifs, elements of the applied arts, machines, figures for sculpture and painting, proportion diagrams, and basic construction aids. He later added a detailed title, chapter headings, and long commentaries in the manner of illustrated treatises prepared by builders' guilds.

Hence it was not a mere "album" (Quicherat, 1849) or "sketchbook" (Willis, 1859) but, rather, a lodgebook.

Villard's technical expressions are generally the oldest in Old French and the Picard dialect; moreover, they are the only ones that are illustrated and thus can be determined precisely. The master speaks directly to his students, often expressing the most personal value judgments of the Middle Ages. Thus, he sketched the classical window at Rheims (20b)[1] "because I loved it above all else"; at Laon, "a tower such as I have never seen anywhere else," although "I was in many lands" (18), and a lectern "of the best kind I know" (13). Two successors in his guild (known as Master 2 and Master 3) completed the book with expert additions and extracts from other technical treatises.

Villard's sketches of the most important structures of the time allow us to follow his wanderings. He must have been born around 1190 at Honnecourt, for he drew the ground plan of the neighboring Cistercian abbey of Vaucelles (33a)—where he was undoubtedly a student—and later, with his neighbor Pierre de Corbie, developed a plan for a similar church (29a). At Chartres he sketched the west rose window (30c); at Laon, the west tower (18–19) of the cathedral; at Cambrai, the floor plans (28c); and at Rheims, the completed and planned structural members (20, 30, 60–64). On his way to Hungary, where he had been summoned by the Cistercians and "where I long remained," he sketched an ideal plan for a church of the order (28b) and the south rose window of the Lausanne cathedral (31a). In the Cistercian cloister at Pilis, Laszlo Gerevich discovered floorboards like those Villard sketched in Hungary;[2] and thus it is probable that he was engaged in building churches there and in constructing the tomb of Queen Agnes, who was murdered in 1213.

Important individual Christian and allegorical figures drawn by Villard have been preserved, as have scenes of the Passion and of martyrdom, purely secular scenes, and complicated studies of movements. The *Muldenfaltenstil* (style of deeply molded drapery folds) that Villard employs, which has its origins in antiquity, belongs to the classical transitional phase between high Romanesque and early Gothic that predominated from 1210 to 1235, especially at Rheims. Villard, in fact, borrowed a great number of examples from antiquity, including four partially draped nudes, a Roman tomb, lion fights, and lion-taming. On the other hand, his nature studies, including birds and a lion *peint al vif*, are unique.

VINCENNES PUBLIC LIBRARY

Villard's automatons derive in part from ancient sources, such as the spherical handwarmer (17d) and the magic fountain, and in part from Indian and Arabic sources, such as the *perpetuum mobile*. Of fundamental importance is his chapter on portraiture, in which he develops Gothic figures from abstract directrixes or geometric diagrams. His work on masonry contains the basic construction aids used by masons, such as *tierspoint* and *quintpoint*, which are *estraites de iométrie*, and—drawn from ancient sources—the fundamental procedures of bisecting the square and the circle (Plato), the Archimedean spiral, and altimetry of the Roman land surveyors. Consideration of Villard's sketches of the lectern, clock tower, and *perpetuum mobile* makes it possible to determine the laws of construction through which the medieval builders concretized their conceptual images.

*NOTES*

1. The numbers in parentheses refer to the plates in both of Hahnloser's eds. of Villard's MS.
2. Laszlo Gerevich, "Villard de Honnecourt in Ungarn," in *Müvészettörténeti értesítö*, **20** (1971), 81–104, with German abstract, 104–105.

*BIBLIOGRAPHY*

I. ORIGINAL WORKS. Eds. of Villard's *Bauhüttenbuch* are by J. B. A. Lassus and A. Darcel, *Album de Villard de Honnecourt, architecte du XIII^e siècle* (Paris, 1858), the 1st illustrated ed., with engraved plates; R. Willis, *Facsimile of the Sketch-Book of Wilars de Honecort* (London, 1859), translated from the Lassus ed., with many additional notes and articles and the same plates—a much improved ed.; H. Omont, *Album de Villard de Honnecourt, architecte du XIIIe siècle* (Paris, n.d. [1906]; 2nd ed., 1927), earliest eds. with photographic repros. but no comments; H. R. Hahnloser, *Villard de Honnecourt, kritische Gesamtausgabe des Bauhüttenbuches MS fr. 19093 der Pariser Nationalbibliothek* (Vienna, 1935), the 1st complete ed., with German trans., glossary, and complete bibliography; the 2nd ed. (Graz–Vienna, 1972), an offprint of the 1st ed. contains many new notes and plates; and T. R. Bowie, *The Sketchbook of Villard de Honnecourt* (Bloomington, Inc., 1959), with a few comments—a 2nd ed. (1962) gives the plates in iconographical order.

II. SECONDARY LITERATURE. See J. Quicherat, "Notice sur l'album de Villard de Honnecourt, architecte du XIIIe siècle," in *Revue archéologique*, **6** (1849), 65–80, 164–188, 211–216, and pls. 116–118, which contains important comments; and N. X. Willemin and A. Pottier, *Monuments français inédits pour servir à l'histoire*

*des arts*, I (Paris, 1825), 62 and pl. 106, only a few preliminary notes.

H. R. HAHNLOSER

**VILLARD, PAUL** (*b*. Lyons, France, 28 September 1860; *d*. Bayonne, France, 13 January 1934), *physics*.

Villard's main work involved the experimental study of cathode rays, X rays, and radioactivity from 1897 to 1907 or thereabouts.

Villard entered the École Normale Supérieure in 1881 and received the *agrégé* in 1884. After teaching in provincial secondary schools and in Paris, he received permission to work in the chemistry laboratory of the École Normale, where he conducted all his research. Villard received the Wilde and the La Caze prizes of the Paris Academy of Sciences and was elected a member of its general physics section in 1908. During his later years he received a *pension d'honneur* from the Caisse Nationale des Sciences.

Villard's background was in physical chemistry. During his first ten years at the chemistry laboratory of the École Normale, he worked on the hydrates of argon, methane, methylene, and acetylene, and on topics associated with change of phase. Villard retained a chemical point of view after having become involved in radiation physics, considering, for example, the "chemical action" of X rays and the "reducing action" of cathode rays.

Since Villard made all his own apparatus he was quite familiar with all of its technical details and, in addition to his research, he designed instruments and techniques that were useful to practical radiologists.

In his early work on cathode-ray tubes, Villard was interested in the nature of the material that moves in the tube. In this context he also considered the nature of canal rays, a puzzle since Goldstein had observed them in 1886. In 1898 Villard observed that positively charged material moves toward the cathode and that when there are holes in the cathode, a visible stream, causing heating, passes through it. He suggested that the positive material forms the canal rays after it passes through the cathode. He was not, however, able to deflect the stream moving through the cathode by means of electric or magnetic fields; and he assumed that it had lost its charge at the cathode. On the basis of the reducing action of various rays in the cathode tube, Villard concluded that the moving material is hydrogen. (In the same year Wien managed to deflect canal rays with electric and magnetic fields, and he found that their $e/m$ was on the order of that of the hydrogen ion.)[1]

Villard was the first to observe a penetrating radiation, which he named $\gamma$ radiation, following the pattern of Rutherford's names for $\alpha$ and $\beta$ rays. In 1900, while studying the secondary emission produced by both cathode rays and radium radiation on passing through a metal sheet, he observed that a component of the radium radiation was sufficiently energetic to pass directly through; and he associated it with the "nondeviable" (uncharged) component. As a further test Villard used a more active radium source given by the Curies and sent the radiation consecutively through two photographic plates. He concluded that the "X rays" emitted by the radium are much more penetrating than the charged rays. (At this time Villard appears already to have associated the penetrating radiation with X rays; the electromagnetic nature of the $\gamma$ rays was not proved until 1914.)

In 1906 Villard began studying the aurora experimentally by simulating the phenomenon with cathode rays in a magnetic field. (Olaf Birkeland, a Norwegian, had produced the first laboratory model of the aurora in 1896 by sending cathode rays toward a magnetized sphere.) Villard, who had been studying the properties of cathode rays produced when the cathode is in a strong magnetic field, "made some very fine experiments," according to C. Störmer, and "succeeded in producing threadlike currents of cathode rays which made it possible to follow the trajectories in detail."[2] Villard was interested in the theoretical implications of his work and, differing from others, believed the source of the aurora to be terrestrial.

### NOTES

1. W. Wien, "Untersuchungen über die electrische Entladung in verdünnten Gasen," in Wiedemann's *Annalen der Physik und Chemie*, n.s. **65** (1898), 440–452; "Die electrostatische und magnetische Ablenkung der Canalstrahlen," in *Verhandlungen der Physikalischen Gesellschaft zu Berlin* (1898), 10–12.
2. C. Störmer, *The Polar Aurora* (Oxford, 1955), 290.

### BIBLIOGRAPHY

I. Original Works. Villard's papers include "Sur les rayons cathodiques," in *Comptes rendus de l'Académie des sciences*, **126** (1898), 1339–1341, 1564–1566; **127** (1898), 173–175; **130** (1900), 1614–1616; "Sur la réflexion et la réfraction des rayons cathodiques et des rayons déviables du radium," *ibid.*, **130**

(1900), 1010–1012; "Sur le rayonnement du' radium," *ibid.*, 1178–1179; and "Sur l'aurore boréale," *ibid.*, **142** (1906), 1330–1333; **143** (1906), 143–145.

Villard's papers published before 1900 are listed in the Royal Society *Catalogue of Scientific Papers*, XIX, 352. Those published after 1900 are listed in *Science Abstracts*.

II. Secondary Literature. The discussion of Villard's work presented in connection with the award of the La Caze Prize is in *Comptes rendus . . . de l'Académie des sciences*, **145** (1907), 1002–1005. E. Borel's obituary address on Villard is *ibid.*, **198** (1934), 213–215.

Sigalia Dostrovsky

**VILLARI, EMILIO** (*b.* Naples, Italy, 25 September 1836; *d.* Naples, 20 August 1904), *physics.*

After receiving his secondary education in Naples, Villari studied at the University of Pisa, where he became professor of mathematics and medicine in 1860. Between 1860 and 1871 he lived, successively, in Florence, Berlin, and Florence again, then became professor of experimental physics at the University of Bologna. In 1900 he returned to Naples, where he taught until his death.

Villari's major interest centered on the effects of electromagnetic forces on material media. His work was not deeply mathematical; he was primarily an experimentalist who used theories qualitatively. His physical outlook was eclectic, combining elements of the Weberean action-at-a-distance school with Faraday's empirical discoveries regarding electromagnetic induction. To Villari the central element of electromagnetism was the electrical current; and his most original work consisted of an attempt to explain, from an action-at-a-distance standpoint, the peculiar effects of alternating currents on their conductors.

By 1873 Villari and others had noted that metals emit much more heat when carrying alternating currents than when bearing direct currents. Kelvin and Maxwell explained this increased heat by means of the concept of "self-induction": the continuous change in the magnitude and sign of the alternating current is supposed to produce a changing magnetic field and thus to induce an electromotive force in the conductor, a force that acts to oppose the changes in the current. In order to overcome this opposing force, more energy must be expended than if the force were absent; and this excess energy appears as heat.

To Villari, however, the problem was not one of

the action of the current, mediated by the field, upon itself. Rather he believed that the current affects the body of the conductor, which in turn reacts upon the current. He thought that all metals are composed of innately magnetic molecules that are acted on by an electric current because currents exert magnetic forces. When a circuit is first closed, the initial effect of the current as it begins to flow is to produce a realignment of the conductor's magnetic molecules. As the molecules begin to move under the action of the increasing current, they produce a changing magnetic force in the vicinity of the current. According to Faraday's law of electromagnetic induction, a changing magnetic force induces an electromotive force; as the molecules align, they therefore engender an electromotive force that opposes the force producing the current. With alternating currents the magnetic molecules will be moving constantly, and energy will be required to overcome the opposing forces induced by their motion; this energy appears as heat.

Villari's theory did not have wide influence. His experimental results, however, were well-known and extensively utilized. Nonetheless, even his theoretical opinions are important because they illustrate that, at least on the Continent, certain researchers preferred to work outside a Maxwellian context well into the 1880's. Whereas the self-induction explanation of Kelvin and Maxwell relied on the mediation of a field to produce the effects on the currents, Villari's explanation assumed a direct action between the currents and the magnetic molecules. Villari's magnetic molecules are closely related to the electrically polarizable molecules of Mossotti's dielectrics, and both were action-at-a-distance theories in that they postulated forces acting directly between various kinds of elemental electrical and magnetic fluids.

*BIBLIOGRAPHY*

Villari's more important works include "Intorno ad alcuni fatti singolari di elettro-magnetismo, ed alla ipotesi di Weber sulle elettro-calamite," in *Nuovo cimento*, **21–22** (1865–1866), 415–427; "Influenza della magnetizzazione sulla conducibilità elettrica del ferro," in *Rendiconti dell'Istituto lombardo di scienze e lettere*, 2nd ser., **1** (1868), 853–862; "Sulle correnti indotte tra il ferro ed altri metalli," in *Nuovo cimento*, 2nd ser., **1** (1869), 218–242; "Ricerche sulle correnti interrote ed invertite, studiate nei loro effetti termici ed elettro-dinamici," in *Memorie della R. Accademia delle scienze dell'Istituto di Bologna*, 3rd ser., **4** (1873), 157–195;

and "Sulla diversa tensione delle correnti elettriche indotte fra circuiti totalmente di rame od in parte di ferro," *ibid.*, 449–467. Villari's work on currents is referred to in L. Lorenz, "Ueber die Fortpflanzung der Electricität," in *Annalen der Physik und Chemie*, n.s., 7, no. 6 (1879), 141–192.

JED Z. BUCHWALD

**VILLEFRANCHE.** See **La Roche, Estienne de**.

**VILMORIN, PIERRE LOUIS FRANÇOIS LEVEQUE DE** (*b*. Paris, France, 18 April 1816; *d*. Paris, 21 March 1860), *botany*.

Vilmorin's father, Philippe André Leveque de Vilmorin, was president of the distinguished Paris seed firm Vilmorin-Andrieux et Cie; and he brought up Louis, his eldest son, to succeed him when he retired (1843). Louis was physically handicapped and appears to have been educated privately; and although he learned the business thoroughly and was capable of heading the company, he always took more interest in research. His wife, Elisa Bailly, helped him in the business and also conducted research on strawberries. Henri, the eldest of their three sons, succeeded to the business.

The firm of Vilmorin-Andrieux had already established a reputation for breeding improved stock; since 1771 it had regularly published catalogs listing available varieties with instructions for their cultivation. Under Louis de Vilmorin the firm extended and organized the work on breeding and set up an experimental farm at Verrières-le-Buisson.

Vilmorin's first important work was on the breeding of wheat. The Société d'Agriculture had asked his father to investigate the classification of cultivated wheats; but most of the work was done by Louis, who in 1850 published a classified catalog of seven species and fifty-three distinct varieties of wheat, indicating not only their characters but also their relationships. In it he showed awareness that the horticulturist's classification was not the same as the botanist's in dealing with distinct species.

From 1850 until his death Vilmorin published a series of papers on the breeding of cereal grains, potatoes, sugarbeets, and flowers. He was not isolated in the world of commerce, but was a friend of J. B. Boussingault and collaborated with Édouard Duchesne. He also edited the periodical *Bon jardinier* from 1844 until his death.

Vilmorin's work of greatest economic importance was breeding a new variety of sugarbeet with a straight taproot and a sugar content of around 20 percent, nearly double the previous maximum. In this work, published in 1856, he already showed his appreciation of the importance of finding a reliable method of assaying for the sugar content and of conducting the breeding under controlled conditions. The main part of his paper in 1856 was a record of his assay method, but he outlines his breeding techniques, and discusses his results with the frank admission that he does not understand the transmission of the "qualité sucrée." He selected plants with a high percentage of sugar and gathered and sowed the seed separately by a method originated by his father, but he does not record methods of preventing cross-fertilization. He found in the first generation three distinct groups: one of plants that were consistent high yielders, one with variable yield but including those of exceptionally high yield, and another of consistent low yielders. He then showed that the consistently high-yielding group bred true, forming a race that was high in sugar in the second generation and even more in the third. These variations were independent of culture and he believed that his rich race was permanently fixed, though of course yield would then be affected by culture.

Vilmorin's most significant work in breeding was reported by his son Henri in 1877. From 1856 to 1860 he bred plants of *Lupinus hirsutus* with pink or blue flowers, counted the progeny of each color, and tabulated the results. This was the first experimental work since Sageret to show numerical relations of the segregation of characters and was contemporary with Mendel's experiments. The lupines were generally self-fertilized, commonly blue but sometimes pink, and had no intermediate colors. From twenty-seven blue-flowered plants he obtained twenty-five blue that bred true and two pink that in later generations produced plants in ratios approximating three pink to one blue. Since Vilmorin's numbers were small, however, and since it seems likely that some cross-fertilization occurred, he concluded that there was no mathematical relationship and the segregation was due to conflict of vital forces. His theory of centripetal forces (the hereditary influence of parents) and centrifugal ones (the totality of ancestral influence), propounded in 1851, was refined to include the force of individual variation, and he considered that the proportion of pink and blue flowers measured the strength of these forces. The greatest tendency was to resemble parents, and the forces of atavism weakened with distance.

BIBLIOGRAPHY

I. ORIGINAL WORKS. Vilmorin's works include *Essai d'un catalogue méthodique et synonymique des froments qui composent la collection de L. Vilmorin* (Paris, 1850); "Note sur la création d'une nouvelle race de betteraves à sucre. Considérations sur l'hérédité dans les végétaux," in *Comptes rendus . . . de l'Académie des sciences*, **43** (1856), 871–874; *Notices sur l'amélioration des plantes par le semis et considérations sur l'hérédité dans les végétaux* (Paris, 1869); "Note sur une expérience relative à l'étude de l'hérédité dans les végétaux," in *Mémoires de la Société nationale d'agriculture de France* for 1877 (1879), 223–231, written by his son Henri; and "Tableau des effets de la rouille sur une série de variétés de froments," *ibid.*, **126**(1881), 219–226.

II. SECONDARY LITERATURE. There is a short unsigned obituary in *Gardener's Chronicle* (1860), 366; and an appreciative notice by J. A. Barral in *Revue horticole* (1860), 172–174; there is also a memorial in *Genetics*, **19** (1934), comprising a frontispiece protrait, 3 unnumbered pp. of explanatory text by John H. Parker, and text on the back cover; the note refers to, but does not locate, a bibliography of the publications of the Vilmorins by J. H. Parker, in typescript. Most information and comment on Vilmorin's work is found in surveys of the family. The most critical scientific assessment is in H. F. Roberts, *Plant Hybridization Before Mendel* (New York–London, (1965), 143–151. Also see Gustave Heuzé, "Les Vilmorin," in *Revue horticole*, **71** (1899), 453–459; and "La maison Vilmorin-Andrieux et Cie," in *Revue de l'horticulture belge et étrangère*, **36** (1910), 249–257.

There is a general history of sugarbeet genetics by J. L. de Vilmorin, *L'hérédité chez la betterave cultivée* (Paris, 1923), pp. 69–73 of which relate to the work of Louis de Vilmorin.

DIANA M. SIMPKINS

**VINCENT OF BEAUVAIS** (*b.* Beauvais, Oise, France, *ca.* 1190; *d.* Beauvais, *ca.* 1264), *natural science, transmission of knowledge.*

Vincent, known in Latin as Bellovacensis, seems to have studied at the University of Paris and to have entered the Dominican order there about 1220. Transferred to the priory in Beauvais around 1233, he became a close friend of Ralph, first abbot of the Cistercian monastery at nearby Royaumont; through Ralph he formed a lifelong friendship with Louis IX. Earlier Vincent had begun his *Speculum maius,* or "great mirror," which was to make available to one and all the hitherto inaccessible wisdom of classical and ecclesiastical authors. The king, hearing of this, desired a copy for himself and supplied the funds necessary for the work's completion. The date of composition of the *Speculum* is difficult to determine, since it went through a series of redactions and has several parts. The first version probably appeared in 1244, followed by a second some three years later and by a third in the 1250's.

Three of its components are of unquestioned authenticity: the "Speculum naturale," or "mirror of nature," an encyclopedia of nature as created by God; the "Speculum historiale," or "mirror of history," giving the history of mankind from the Creation to 1254 (in the final version); and the "Speculum doctrinale," or "mirror of teaching," summarizing all of the learned arts—liberal, mechanical, and medical, among others. To these an anonymous author, writing sometime between 1310 and 1325, added a fourth part, the "Speculum morale," or "mirror of morals," drawn mainly from the writings of Thomas Aquinas. Written in Latin, the work was translated into various vernaculars and even appeared in verse. It went through seven printings; but none of these is reliable, each containing editorial interpolations and rearrangements. Besides the *Speculum*, Vincent wrote several ascetical and theological treatises; he is especially noteworthy for his writings and influence in education (see Gabriel).

The "Speculum naturale" reflects a theological orientation in its plan, which follows the biblical account of the six days of Creation, if not in its content, which reveals it to be "a great storehouse of medieval lore" (Thorndike, 475). Its superiority to other medieval encyclopedias of nature derives from the author's access to larger and better libraries, and from his having the use of secretaries; its weakness is traceable to its being essentially a compilation of excerpts—although made with care and usually assigned to the proper authority—that shows little or no investigative originality, critical sense, or organic unity. Vincent draws heavily from Pliny, Isidore of Seville, Adelard of Bath, and Thomas of Cantimpré; and his work also is interspersed with references to Albertus Magnus and Thomas Aquinas, possibly added in subsequent revisions.

The "Speculum naturale" is composed of thirty-two books, most containing over one hundred chapters. As a preliminary, book 1 treats God, angels, and the original work of Creation; book 2 launches into the work of the first day, considering the material universe and digressing on the text "Let there be light" (Gen. 1:3) to provide thirty-four chapters on optics that deal with the nature of light, the origin of colors, and the properties of mirrors. Books 3 and 4, devoted to the work of the second day, use the formation of the firmament and the heavens to provide treatises on astronomy and meteorology, respectively. The separation of the dry land from the waters on the third day opens a treatise on geology and mineralogy that comprises 95 chapters; similarly, the creation of plants leads to 156 chapters on botany. The works of subsequent days occasion the presentation of all available information on the birds of the air, the fishes of the sea, and the animals that inhabit the dry land, man included.

The "Speculum doctrinale," composed of seventeen books divided into 2,374 chapters, duplicates some of the earlier material but is concerned more with practical matters. It deals with grammar, logic, husbandry, political affairs, trades, medicine, physics, mathematics, astrology, music, weights and measures, and surveying, and even includes a dictionary of some 3,200 entries. For the mathematical arts Vincent relies on Nicomachus of Gerasa, Boethius, and al-Fārābī; his treatment is generally brief, perfunctory, and otherwise uninteresting.

The absence of a reliable text makes it difficult to characterize and evaluate Vincent's science. His views on geography and astronomy seem to derive largely from Ibn Sīnā and are akin to those of Albertus Magnus; thus his text, at least as it has come down to us, gives basically Albertus' account of al-Biṭrūjī's theory and concludes in favor of the Ptolemaic conception of the universe. He takes his chemistry from al-Rāzī's *De aluminibus et salibus*, in the translation by Gerard of Cremona, and generally follows Ibn Sīnā's presentation of alchemical doctrines. Vincent's treatment of plants seems to be based on Alfred of Sareschel's *De plantis*. His treatise on falconry he acknowledges as being abridged from "a letter written by Aquila, Symachus, and Theodotion to Ptolemy, king of Egypt, in which they treated of noble birds and medicines for them" (*Speculum naturale*, Douai ed., I, col. 1197); Sarton notes that the original text of this letter has been lost and that apart from Vincent's excerpts it survives only in an early Catalan version, to which he gives a reference (*Introduction . . .*, p. 931). According to Cuvier, his descriptions of fishes are superior to those of Albertus Magnus. Generally, however, Vincent's excerpts are taken from classical authors and do not represent the best material available to the experts of his day; he makes little attempt to be up-to-date or to integrate the new with the old. He is somewhat credulous and occasionally intermingles superstition with verified knowledge. Yet, withal, Vincent's work is truly monumental and is the best encyclopedia to come out of the Middle Ages.

BIBLIOGRAPHY

I. ORIGINAL WORKS. Vincent's works are the *Speculum maius* (Strasbourg, 7 vols., 1473–1476; Basel, 1481 ["Speculum naturale" and "Speculum morale" only]; Nuremberg, 2 vols., 1473–1486; Venice, 1484, 1494, 1591; Douai, 4 vols., 1624, repr. Graz, 1964) and *De eruditione filiorum nobilium*, A. Steiner, ed. (Cambridge, Mass., 1938).

II. SECONDARY LITERATURE. For general accounts and bibliography see W. A. Hinnebusch, *The History of the Dominican Order*, II. *Intellectual and Cultural Life to 1500* (New York, 1973), 421–428; Michel Lemoine, "L'oeuvre encyclopédique de Vincent de Beauvais," *Cahiers d'histoire mondiale*, IX (1966), 483–518, 571–579, repr. *La pensée encyclopédique au moyen âge* (Neuchatel, 1966); G. Sarton, *Introduction to the History of Science*, II, pt. 2 (Washington, 1931), 929–932, and *passim* (see index); and L. Thorndike, *A History of Magic and Experimental Science*, II (New York, 1923), 457–476. More specialized studies are A. Gabriel, *The Educational Ideas of Vincent of Beauvais*, 2nd ed. (Notre Dame, 1962); G. Göller, "Vinzenz von Beauvais und sein Musiktraktat in Speculum doctrinale," in *Kölner Beiträge zur Musikforschung*, **15** (1959), 29–34; and P. Duhem, *Études sur Léonard de Vinci*, II (Paris, 1909), 318–319, and *Le système du monde*, III (Paris, 1915; repr. 1958), 346–348.

WILLIAM A. WALLACE, O.P.

**VINCI, LEONARDO DA.** See **Leonardo da Vinci.**

**VINOGRADSKY, SERGEY NIKOLAEVICH** (*b.* Kiev, Russia, 13 September 1856; *d.* Brie-Comte-Robert, France, 24 February 1953), *microbiology.*

Vinogradsky's father, Nikolay Konstantinovich Vinogradsky, was a member of the State Council; his mother, Natalia Viktorovna Skoropadskaya, came from a noble family. In 1866 he entered the Kiev Gymnasium and in 1873 graduated with a gold medal. The same year Vinogradsky enrolled at the Law Faculty of Kiev University. After a month, however, he transferred to the natural sciences division of the Physics and Mathematics Faculty.

An interest in music led Vinogradsky to transfer to the St. Petersburg Conservatory. In 1877, however, he entered the natural sciences department of St. Petersburg University. He graduated in 1881 with the candidate of sciences degree and re-

mained at the university to prepare for an academic career.

Vinogradsky was greatly influenced by Pasteur's ideas and experimental research and, attracted by the great opportunities, decided to devote himself to the new science of microbiology. From 1881 to 1884 Vinogradsky did his first experimental work, a study of the influence of external conditions on the development of the fungus *Mycoderma vini.*

After receiving the master's degree in 1884, Vinogradsky went in 1885 to Strasbourg, where he worked under Anton de Bary. In 1890 he moved to Zurich, where he did postgraduate study in chemistry for two years. From 1884 to 1889 Vinogradsky conducted research on the physiology and morphology of sulfur and iron bacteria, and then on nitrifying bacteria. This research brought him a wide reputation.

In 1890, Pasteur invited Vinogradsky to participate in the organization of a bacteriological laboratory at the institute he had established in Paris. In the same year the Institute of Experimental Medicine at St. Petersburg was completed, and in 1891 Vinogradsky became director of its section of general microbiology.

In 1902 he was named director of the entire institute. (He had to resign three years later, however, because of acute nephritis.) In 1903, by a decision of the scientific council of Kharkov University, Vinogradsky received a doctorate in botany without defending a dissertation. In 1912 Vinogradsky moved to the Ukraine, where for ten years he scarcely worked at experimental microbiology, concentrating on the organization of research in land use and soil science.

In 1922 Vinogradsky accepted an invitation from E. Roux to become director of the division of agricultural microbiology of the Pasteur Institute, which built a laboratory for him near Paris.

Vinogradsky's scientific and organizational work received international recognition. In 1894 he became a member of the Russian Academy of Sciences; in 1902 the Académie des Sciences of France elected him a corresponding member; and the National Society of Horticulture of France elected him an active member. Vinogradsky founded the Society of Microbiology in 1903 and was its president for the first two years. In 1923 he was elected an honorary member of the Academy of Sciences of the U.S.S.R.

Vinogradsky's interest centered on complex questions of the physiology and morphology of microorganisms and the development of culture methods for saprophytic and pathogenic microbes.

His most important studies concerned the morphological variability of microbes, the discovery of microbes' capacity for chemosynthesis, and the creation and development of the bases for ecological and soil microbiology.

During the 1870's and 1880's there was much discussion concerning the variability of microorganisms; and two trends, monomorphism and polymorphism, were apparent. Sulfur and iron bacteria were the central objects of research. Vinogradsky was the first researcher to study the morphology of microbes not by investigating fixed preparations but by observing living, normally developed cells in a microculture developed in a drop suspended under a protective glass cover. Studying the culture of sulfur bacteria, which the polymorphist Friedrich Zopf had used to confirm his views, Vinogradsky discovered a mixture of microorganisms. On the basis of these observations he showed that sulfur and iron bacteria are characterized by a strict cycle of development and do not display chaotic variability, as the advocates of polymorphism had asserted. This significantly strengthened the position of monomorphism, which, for the end of the nineteenth century, was progressive. Vinogradsky never advocated the constancy of species, however, and repeatedly criticized the monomorphists.

The study of the morphology of sulfur bacteria and iron bacteria led Vinogradsky to investigate their physiology. He determined that the sulfur appears in the cells of sulfur bacteria through oxidation of hydrogen sulfide. Relating this fact to the energy metabolism of these bacteria, Vinogradsky presented the idea that the oxidation of hydrogen sulfide is analogous to the process of respiration, which provides the cell with its necessary energy. He called this phenomenon "mineral respiration," or, in the terminology of the time (1922), anorgoxidation.

The theory of chemoautotrophic metabolism of substances received convincing proof in Vinogradsky's research on the physiology of nitrifying bacteria. His new method of studying microorganisms—selective cultures—and the concept of chemoautotrophic feeding led to the solution of the problem that had been studied by many of Vinogradsky's predecessors. Using a mineral medium without any organic substances, Vinogradsky obtained pure cultures of two autonomous stimulants of nitrification, *Nitrosomonas* and *Nitrobacter*.

In his works on nitrification, Vinogradsky presented the theory of chemosynthesis as concrete and experimentally based. The chemosynthetic activity of nitrifying bacteria was shown by means of precise quantitative determinations of the relationship of oxidized nitrogen to the assimilated carbon. The discovery of chemosynthesis, an important event in nineteenth-century biological science, is still significant. New data have introduced only corrections and additions but have not changed its scientific basis.

The ecological approach to the study of microorganisms living freely in nature helped Vinogradsky to obtain important data on the metabolism of nitrifying and cellulose-decomposing bacteria. Having created an amosphere of pure nitrogen, he became the first microbiologist to separate pure cultures of a new stimulant of anaerobic nitrogen fixation—*Clostridium pastorianum*. The study of the energy metabolism of this microbe helped to establish that it is the stimulant of oil-oxidizing fermentation.

The study of *Azotobacter* was a continuation of research on biological nitrogen fixation. Vinogradsky studied it in its natural habitats: soil or on plates of silicic acid gel.

In his work on symbiotic nitrogen fixation, Vinogradsky developed extremely accurate methods of chemical analysis that permitted him to collect nitrogen in quantities on the order of several micrograms. The use of this method led to the discovery of the formation of ammonia during the process of symbiotic nitrogen-fixation. Equally fruitful was the application of ecological research to cellulose-decomposing bacteria. Using filter paper placed in a silicic acid gel and small particles of soil as the culture medium, Vinogradsky separated three types of cellulose-composing bacteria—*Cytophaga, Cellvibrio*, and *Cellfalcicula*.

Vinogradsky's works provided a firm scientific base for the ecological approach to the study of soil microflora. His development of special methods for soil microbiology—direct study of cells in the soil, spontaneous culture in dense media, and microbe cultures in soils—were of fundamental importance in the development of that science.

*BIBLIOGRAPHY*

I. ORIGINAL WORKS. Vinogradsky's writings include *Krugovorot azota v prirode* ("The Circulation of Nitrogen in Nature"; Moscow, 1894); *O roli mikrobov v obshchem krugovorote zhizni* ("On the Role of Microbes in the General Circulation of Life"; St. Petersburg, 1897); "K morfologii organizmov protsessa obrazovania selitry v pochve" ("On the Morphology of the Process of Organisms for Producing Niter in Soil"), in *Arkhiv biologicheskikh nauk*, **1** (1922); "Sur la décomposition de la cellulose dans le sol," in *Comptes rendus . . . de l'Académie des sciences*, **183** (1926), 691–694; "Sur la morphologie et l'oecologie des azotobacter," in *Annales de l'Institut Pasteur*, **60** (1938), 351–400; and *Mikrobiologia pochvy* ("Microbiology of the Soil"; Moscow, 1952), an anthology. These and other works can be found in *Izbrannye trudy*, 2 vols. ("Selected Works"; Moscow, 1953).

II. SECONDARY LITERATURE. On Vinogradsky and his work, see A. A. Imshenstsky, "Pamyati S. N. Vinogradskogo" ("Memories of Vinogradsky"), in *Mikrobiologia*, **22**, no. 5 (1953); and "Vinogradsky. K 100-letiyu so dnya rozhdenia" (". . . on the Centenary of His Birth"), *ibid.*, **26**, no. 1 (1957); M. M. Kononova, "S. N. Vinogradsky," in *Pochvovedenie* (1953), no. 10; S. I. Kuznetsov, "Trudy vydayushchegosya russkogo mikrobiologa" ("Works of the Outstanding Russian Microbiologist"), in *Priroda* (May 1953), 119–120; D. M. Novogrudsky, "S. N. Vinogradsky. Pervy period deyatelnosti" (". . . The First Period of His Activity"), in *Mikrobiologia*, **26** (1956); and V. L. Omelyansky, "S. N. Vinogradsky (po povodu 70-letia)" (". . . on His Seventieth Birthday"), and "Zapiska ob uchenykh trudakh S. N. Vinogradskogo" ("Note on the Scientific Works of Vinogradsky"), in *Izbrannye trudy*.

V. GUTINA

**VIOLLE, JULES LOUIS GABRIEL** (*b*. Langres, France, 16 November 1841; *d*. Fixin, France, 12 September 1923), *physics*.

Most of Violle's research consisted of the experimental study of topics associated with heat radiation and with high temperatures, and developed out of Violle's interest in the temperature of the sun.

Violle entered the École Normale Supérieure in 1861. He became *agrégé* in 1868, and received the degree of *docteur-ès-sciences* in 1870. (Violle was already interested in heat; for his thesis he determined the mechanical equivalent of heat by rotating a copper disk between the poles of an electromagnet and measuring calorimetrically the heat produced by the induction currents.[1]) Violle taught at the universities of Grenoble and Lyons, and in 1884 he became *maître de conférences* at the École Normale. In 1892 he became professor of physics at the Conservatoire des Arts et Métiers, and in 1897 he was elected to the French Academy of Sciences. Violle was interested in American science and, after visiting the United States and the World's Columbian Exposition in Chicago in 1893, he published some discussions of it.[2]

Early in 1874, in Grenoble, Violle began work on his first major project, the design and use of an actinometer to measure the solar constant and, indirectly, to determine the temperature of the sun. The solar constant had been defined and first measured in 1837 by Pouillet.[3] In Violle's instrument a thermometer is kept in a container at constant temperature, and sunlight is allowed to fall onto the bulb through a small hole. The rise in temperature to an equilibrium value when the hole is opened and the subsequent fall in temperature when the hole is closed again are measured. From this information Violle calculated the initial change in the temperature of the bulb and determined the rate at which heat reaches it.

In order to obtain the solar constant, it is necessary to correct the amount of heat that the instrument actually receives by the amount of heat absorbed by the atmosphere. Before Violle, the atmospheric absorption was found by comparing measurements made at different times of day. Violle compared observations made simultaneously at different altitudes. On 16 and 17 August 1875, he took measurements at the top of Mont Blanc, while others were being taken more than 3.5 kilometers below. Violle found an empirical formula for the atmospheric absorption, and concluded that the solar constant was 2.54 cal./cm.$^2$/minute.

Without a knowledge of the relation between temperature and energy radiation, it was difficult to deduce the solar temperature from the solar constant. (It was not until 1879 that Stefan showed that the energy varies as $T^4$, and the proportionality constant was not known until much later.[4]) Violle extrapolated the empirical law of Dulong and Petit. To check on the validity of this extrapolation, Violle used his actinometer to determine the known temperature of molten steel (about 1,000° C). Violle concluded that the effective temperature of the sun is about 1,500° C.

At the time of Violle's work there was much interest in the temperature of the sun. The Paris Academy had proposed the determination of it as a problem for the Bordin prize in 1874 and in 1876. Because of the problems involved in determining atmospheric absorption and extrapolating the law of Dulong and Petit to high temperatures, Violle's work received only a recompense and not the actual prize (which was not awarded at all).[5] Some of the difficulties were solved a few years later by Samuel Pierpont Langley, who showed that the atmospheric absorption varies with frequency, and who designed a bolometer to measure the heat received across the spectrum. When Langley made his first measurements by this method (in 1881, on an expedition to Mt. Whitney), he obtained some of his data with an actinometer sent especially for the purpose by Violle.[6]

As a consequence of the work on solar temperature, Violle became involved in various questions related to the determination of high temperatures. For example, he found the specific heats of platinum, palladium, and iridium up to the highest temperatures that can be measured with a gas thermometer, and then, extrapolating the relationship between specific heats and temperature, he determined their melting points. To learn something about the relation between temperature and radiation, Violle used his actinometer to determine the heat radiation emitted by platinum at various temperatures. He found the rise in energy to be slower than the extrapolation from the law of Dulong and Petit would imply, and also that at high temperatures more of the energy is in the shorter wavelengths. Violle suggested that the light emitted by liquid platinum be used as a photometric standard, and it was adopted by the International Conference on Electrical Units and Standards in 1884.

From about 1885, and continuing for about twenty years, Violle did experiments with Théodore Vautier on the propagation of sound. Violle and Vautier were interested in obtaining an accurate determination of the velocity of sound and in studying various nonlinearities and dispersions in the propagation. They analyzed the propagation of sound along an underground cylindrical pipe built for the Grenoble water system, which provided a path length of more than 12 kilometers. They looked for effects of frequency and amplitude on the velocity and for changes in the form of the disturbance during its propagation.

## NOTES

1. "Sur l'équivalent mécanique de la chaleur," in *Annales de chimie,* **21** (1870), 64–97.
2. "L'exposition de Chicago et la science américaine," in *Revue des deux mondes,* **123** (1894), 579–611; "Court aperçu de l'état de l'astronomie aux États-Unis," in *Ciel et terre,* **15** (1894–1895), 223–232; "Le mouvement scientifique aux États-Unis," in *Annales du conservatoire des arts et métiers,* **6** (1894), 253–313.
3. C. Pouillet, "Mémoire sur la chaleur solaire, sur les pouvoirs rayonnants et absorbants de l'air atmosphérique, et sur la température de l'espace," in *Comptes rendus hebdomadaires des séances de l'Académie des sciences,* **7** (1838), 24–65.
4. Max Jammer, *The Conceptual Development of Quantum Mechanics* (New York, 1966), 6–8.
5. *Comptes rendus hebdomadaires des séances de l'Académie des sciences,* **84** (1877), 813–817. On the difficulty of determining the solar constant, S. P. Langley wrote the following:

"We are as though at the bottom of a turbid and agitated sea, and trying thence to obtain an idea of what goes on in an upper region of light and calm." *Researches on Solar Heat and Its Absorption by the Earth's Atmosphere* (Washington, D.C., 1884), 45.
6. S. P. Langley, *ibid.,* 70.

## BIBLIOGRAPHY

I. ORIGINAL WORKS. Violle's papers include "Sur la température du soleil," in *Comptes rendus hebdomadaires des séances de l'Académie des sciences,* **78** (1874), 1425–27, 1816–1820; **79** (1874), 746–749; "Mesures actinométriques au sommet du Mont Blanc," *ibid.,* **82** (1876), 662–665; "Résultats des mesures actinométriques au sommet du Mont Blanc," *ibid.,* 729–731; "Conclusions des mesures actinométriques faites au sommet du Mont Blanc," *ibid.,* 896–898; "Chaleur spécifique et chaleur de fusion du platine," *ibid.,* **85** (1877), 543–546; "Sur la loi de rayonnement," *ibid.,* **92** (1881), 1204–1206; "Sur la propagation du son à l'intérieur d'un tuyau cylindrique," in *Annales de chimie et de physique,* ser. 6, **19** (1890), 306–345, with Théodore Vautier.

The following works list publications by Violle: "Notice sur les trauvaux scientifiques de M. Jules Violle" (Paris, 1889); Royal Society *Catalogue of Scientific Papers,* VIII, 1158; XII, 757; XIX, 368–369; J. C. Poggendorff, *Biographisch-Literarisches Handwörterbuch,* III, 1393; IV, 1570–1571.

Violle summarized his work in the autobiographical essay *Notice sur les travaux scientifiques de M. Jules Violle* (Paris, 1889).

II. SECONDARY LITERATURE. P. Villard's obituary address is in *Comptes rendus hebdomadaires des séances de l'Académie des sciences,* **177** (1923), 513–515. Samuel P. Langley discussed Violle's work on the solar constant (and other earlier work) thoroughly in his *Researches on Solar Heat and Its Absorption by the Earth's Atmosphere* (Washington, D.C., 1884).

SIGALIA DOSTROVSKY

**VIRCHOW, RUDOLF CARL** (*b.* Schivelbein, Pomerania, Germany, 13 October 1821; *d.* Berlin, Germany, 5 September 1902), *pathology, social medicine, public health, anthropology.*

A strong and versatile personality equally interested in the scientific and social aspects of medicine, Virchow was the most prominent German physician of the nineteenth century. His long and successful career reflects the ascendancy of German medicine after 1840, a process that gradually provided the basic underpinnings to a discipline that was still largely clinical. Armed with great self-confidence, aggressiveness, and a deep sense of social justice, Virchow became a medical activist who engaged vigorously in political polemics and participated in social reforms. His elevation of science to the level of quasi-religious dogma and his utopian view of medicine as *the* science of man should be interpreted within the framework of his times, a period that witnessed the effective adoption of scientific method in medicine.

Virchow was born in a small town in backward and rural eastern Pomerania; he was the only son of a modest merchant. He expressed an early interest in the natural sciences and received private lessons in the classical languages. Such a background enabled Virchow to become educationally competitive and in 1835 he successfully transferred to the Gymnasium in Köslin, where he received a broad humanistic training and subsequently demonstrated high scholarly abilities.

Because of his promising aptitudes, Virchow received in 1839 a military fellowship to study medicine at the Friedrich-Wilhelms Institut in Berlin. The institution, popularly known as the "Pépinière," provided educational opportunities for those unable to afford the costs in return for subsequent army medical service.

Although contemporary German medicine was only slowly shifting away from purely theoretical concerns, Virchow had the opportunity to study under Johannes Müller and Johann L. Schönlein, thereby being exposed to experimental laboratory and physical diagnostic methods, as well as epidemiological studies.

In 1843 Virchow received his medical degree from the University of Berlin with a doctoral dissertation on the corneal manifestations of rheumatic disease. Shortly thereafter he received an appointment as "company surgeon" or medical house officer at the Charité Hospital in Berlin, where he rotated through the various services. In addition, with the hospital's prosector, Robert Froriep (1804–1861), Virchow carried on microscopic studies on vascular inflammation and the problems of thrombosis and embolism.

In 1845 two forceful speeches delivered by invitation before large and influential audiences at the Friedrich-Wilhelms Institut revealed young Virchow as one of the most articulate spokesmen for the new generation of German physicians. Rejecting transcendental concerns, Virchow envisaged medical progress from three main sources: clinical observations, including the examination of the patient with the aid of physicochemical methods; animal experimentation to test specific etiologies and study certain drug effects; and pathological

anatomy, especially at the microscopic level. Life, he insisted, was merely the sum of physical and chemical actions and essentially the expression of cell activity.

Virchow's rather provocative ideas generated considerable hostility among his older peers, but he passed his licensure examination in 1846 without difficulties and began teaching pathological anatomy. Under the auspices of Prussia's high military and civilian authorities, he traveled to Prague and Vienna in order to evaluate their programs in pathology. One of the consequences of his trip was Virchow's strong attack on Rokitansky and the Viennese Medical School, whom he indicted for their dogmatism and support of an outdated humoralism.

After completing his *Habilitationsschrift* in 1847, Virchow was officially appointed an instructor under the deanship of Johannes Müller at the University of Berlin; he also succeeded Froriep as prosector at the Charité Hospital. In the same year Virchow launched—ostensibly in order to publish his speeches of 1845—a new scientific journal with Benno Reinhardt, a colleague in pathology. The publication, named *Archiv für pathologische Anatomie und Physiologie, und für die klinische Medizin*, became one of the most prominent medical periodicals of the time; and Virchow remained its editor until his death.

The typhus epidemic that ravaged the Prussian province of Upper Silesia in early 1848 prompted the government to send a team of physicians to the area to survey the disaster. With the pediatrician and bureaucrat Stephan F. Barez, Virchow visited the afflicted region for almost three weeks and came face to face with the backward and destitute Polish minority, who were struggling precariously to survive. According to his own testimony, the impact of that encounter left an indelible mark on his already liberal social and political beliefs. Instead of merely returning with a new set of medical guidelines for the Prussian government, Virchow recommended political freedom, and sweeping educational and economic reforms for the people of Upper Silesia.

Virchow's gradual alienation from the status quo and his political radicalization led him to participate actively in the uprisings of 1848 in Berlin, where he fought alongside his friends on the barricades. As a result, Virchow was thrown into a full schedule of political activities and became a member of the Berlin Democratic Congress and editor of a weekly entitled *Die medizinische Reform.* Virchow's triumph, however, was shortlived. In early 1849 he was suspended from his academic position as prosector at the Charité Hospital because of his revolutionary activities. Although he was partially reinstated as a result of protests from medical circles and students, the defeat of liberalism imposed restrictions on Virchow and created an unfavorable climate for his activities.

Thus, in November 1849 Virchow finally left Berlin and went on to the University of Würzburg in order to assume the recently created chair in pathological anatomy, the first of its kind in Germany. He was temporarily separated from political concerns, and the ensuing years marked Virchow's highest level of scientific achievement and the establishment of the concept of "cellular pathology." He was also deeply engaged in teaching, and among his most famous Würzburg students were Edwin Klebs (1834–1913), Ernst H. P. A. Haeckel (1834–1919), and Adolf Kussmaul (1822–1902). Virchow initiated the publication of the six-volume *Handbuch der speziellen Pathologie und Therapie*, a monumental textbook of pathology and therapeutics; he also edited the famous *Jahresbericht*, a German yearbook depicting medical advances.

In 1856 Virchow accepted an invitation to return to Berlin as professor of pathological anatomy and director of the newly created Pathological Institute. Under Virchow the institution became a famous training ground for a large number of German and foreign medical scientists, including Hoppe-Seyler, Recklinghausen, and Cohnheim. In addition, for almost two decades Virchow remained in charge of a clinical section at the Charité Hospital, thereby carrying out the program of medical progress enunciated in 1845.

Two aspects of Virchow the pathologist should be distinguished: his scientific methodology and his activities in the field of cellular pathology. Without being original, Virchow stressed the importance of observation and experiment, strongly condemning his speculative predecessors. He himself, however, fell prey to the still lingering desire for an overall synthesis of medical knowledge and the establishment of first principles. Imaginative and intuitive, Virchow performed numerous inductive leaps, leaving to others, whose work he often did not acknowledge, the painstaking task of fact collecting.

Virchow expressed an early interest in "pathological physiology" and promulgated a dynamic view of disease processes, which viewed the static structural changes (pathological anatomy) sequentially. Although the idea was by no means novel, with the aid of improved microscopic and bio-

chemical techniques, Virchow applied the concept successfully. For Virchow the microscope became the central tool for reducing pathological processes to alterations occurring at the cellular level. Hence, the cell became the fundamental living unit in both health and disease—a biological rather than a mechanical entity. Virchow's notion of cellular pathology implied that all the manifestations of disease could be reduced to disturbances of living cells. Moreover, according to Virchow's famous principle, "omnis cellula e cellula," all cells originated from other cells. Cellular function, in turn, depended on intracellular physicochemical changes, which were reflected in the varying morphology. Finally, all pathological forms were to be viewed as deviations from the normal structures. Virchow's cellular pathology demolished the vestiges of humoral and neural physiopathology, and placed the field on its modern basis.

During the early years of Virchow's second period in Berlin, his interests began to shift gradually from pathology to anthropology, while he was engaged at the same time in a fair amount of political activities. Nevertheless, Virchow published in 1858 his most famous book, *Die Cellularpathologie . . .*, and in 1863 his work on tumors, *Die krankhaften Geschwülste*.

At the suggestion of an old friend, Virchow was appointed in 1859 to the Berlin City Council, where he concentrated his efforts on matters related to public health. Aided by the mayor of Berlin, Karl T. Seydel, who was his brother-in-law, Virchow was instrumental in achieving improvements in both the sewage system and water supply of the rapidly growing metropolis. In 1861 he was elected a member of the Prussian lower house and represented the new liberal Deutsche Fortschrittspartei (German Progressive Party), which he had founded with some friends. As an early leader of the opposition to Bismarck's policy of rearmament and forced unification, Virchow brought down on himself the wrath of his opponent and was challenged by Bismarck to a duel, which he was wise enough to avoid. During the ensuing Franco-Prussian War of 1870, Virchow was active in organizing military hospital facilities and establishing ambulance and train services for the wounded.

Following his experiences in Upper Silesia, Virchow stressed a sociological theory of disease, claiming that political and socioeconomic factors acted as significant predisposing factors in many ailments. He even went so far as to declare that certain epidemics arose specifically in response to some social upheavals. Virchow considered a number of diseases as "artificial" or primarily caused by conditions within society and thus liable to cure or elimination through social change. As early as 1848 Virchow insisted on the constitutional right of every individual to be healthy. Society had the responsibility to provide the necessary sanitary conditions for the unhampered development of its members. Here again, through his work in the Reichstag and the city council of Berlin, Virchow not only espoused lofty ideals but fought hard to achieve the necessary reforms in school hygiene, sewage treatment, pure water control, and hospital construction.

In proclaiming that medicine was the highest form of human insight and the mother of all the sciences, Virchow was following in the footsteps of French social thought and also expressing a postulate of the German philosophers of nature. Although his utopian hopes for medicine as the unified science of man did not materialize, Virchow's efforts were helpful in associating the rapidly developing natural sciences with medical concerns. His attempts to derive an ethical framework from the biological sciences laid the foundations of bioethics.

In his later years Virchow's skeptical attitude toward bacteriology was based, to a large extent, on his belief that there was no single cause of disease. He did not consider any germ to be the sole etiologic agent in an infectious illness. The bacterial agents were, in Virchow's view, only one factor in the causation of disease among a variety of environmental and sociological factors clearly discernible during the typhus and cholera epidemics of 1847–1849. Such broad considerations did not originate with Virchow, but they gained greater attention and significance with his prestigious support.

From 1870 onward, Virchow rather assiduously cultivated another science: anthropology. Cofounder of the German Anthropological Society a year earlier and author of several studies dealing with skull deformities, he studied the physical characteristics of the Germans, especially the Frisians. After performing a nationwide racial survey of schoolchildren, Virchow concluded that there was no pure German race but only a mixture of differing morphological types. On another matter, he questioned Darwinism as an established fact, viewing it rather as a tentative hypothesis in search of adequate proof.

The Darwinian stimulus to archaeological research also affected Virchow, and in 1870 he began his own excavations in Pomerania. His later friendship with Schliemann lent some legitimacy to this enthusiastic dilettante and eventually helped to attract the treasures to Berlin. In 1879 Virchow himself traveled with Schliemann to Hissarlik, where Homer's Troy was being excavated, and in 1888 he participated in another archaeological dig in Egypt.

In 1886 Virchow was instrumental in the erection of the Berlin Ethnological Museum, followed by the Museum of German Folklore in 1888. Throughout the 1880's he continued to play a key role in the budgetary matters of the Reichstag, and he remained chairman of the finance committee until his death.

Virchow's eightieth birthday in 1901 became the occasion for an unprecedented worldwide celebration. A torchlight parade in Berlin and numerous receptions in the leading scientific centers, even as far away as Japan and Russia, gave testimony to his unparalleled international reputation. Never seriously ill throughout his long life, Virchow suffered a broken hip in early 1902 after falling from a streetcar in Berlin. Although seemingly on the mend, the long period of inactivity seriously undermined his health, and he died several months later of cardiac insufficiency.

Virchow's great fame made him a widely respected authority in his numerous fields of endeavor. His penchant, however, for polemics and acrimonious exchanges with colleagues exerted unfavorable influences for the development of certain medical ideas and methods. An example was his opposition to the prophylactic hand washings of Semmelweis for the prevention of puerperal fever. In his later years Virchow displayed a stifling dogmatism and a certain pedantry, which in some measure detracted from his earlier popularity. In spite of these traits he was overwhelmingly self-confident and untiringly persuasive in popularizing his views. Few great men have been privileged to perceive more clearly the fruits of their labors in the autumn of their lives than Virchow. In less than half a century Germany had progressed from speculative and philosophical healing to become the world center of modern scientific medicine, and Virchow had played a decisive role in this crucial transformation.

## BIBLIOGRAPHY

I. ORIGINAL WORKS. Most of Virchow's important medical and anthropological writings are enumerated chronologically in a small "Festschrift" edited by J. Schwalbe on the occasion of the physician's 80th birthday: *Virchow-Bibliographie 1843–1901* (Berlin, 1901), which covers close to 2,000 titles, and contains a valuable subject index. Pertinent archival material can be found in the "Nachlass Rudolf Virchow" of the Literatur-Archiv, Institut für deutsche Sprache und Literatur, Deutsche Akademie der Wissenschaften, East Berlin. Thor Jager (Wichita, Kansas) has a large collection of Virchow's original MSS and letters, with many pamphlets and books.

Prominent among Virchow's publications were *Die Cellularpathologie in ihrer Begründung auf physiologische und pathologische Gewebelehre* (Berlin, 1858), representing 20 lectures that he delivered at the Pathological Institute in Berlin between February and April 1858. The 2nd ed. of the work was translated into English by F. Chance, *Cellular Pathology as Based Upon Physiological and Pathological Histology* (London, 1860). Two important collections of Virchow's writings are *Gesammelte Abhandlungen zur wissenschaftlichen Medizin* (Frankfurt, 1856), which contains, among others, articles on white cells and leukemia, thrombosis and embolism, gynecological subjects, and the pathology of the newborn; and *Gesammelte Abhandlungen aus dem Gebiet der oeffentlichen Medizin und der Seuchenlehre*, 2 vols. (Berlin, 1879), dealing with medical reform and public health; epidemics and mortality statistics; hospitals, military and urban sanitation; and legal medicine.

A collection of 30 lectures on tumors given at the University of Berlin during the winter semester 1862–1863 is in *Die krankhaften Geschwülste*, 3 vols. (Berlin, 1863–1867). For other lectures on general pathology, see *Die Vorlesungen Rudolf Virchows über allgemeine pathologische Anatomie aus dem Wintersemester 1855–56 in Würzburg*, E. Kugler, ed. (Jena, 1930).

Some of Virchow's more philosophical essays and sociopolitical speeches have received wider diffusion and have been translated into English. *Die Freiheit der Wissenschaft im modernen Staat* (Berlin, 1877) appeared as *The Freedom of Science in the Modern State* (London, 1878). *Morgagni und der anatomische Gedanke* (Berlin, 1894) was translated by R. E. Schlueter and J. Auer, "Morgagni and the Anatomical Concept," in *Bulletin of the History of Medicine*, 7 (1939), 975–989. A series of talks are in *Disease, Life and Man, Selected Essays by Rudolf Virchow*, trans. and with an introduction by L. J. Rather (Stanford, 1958), including two articles on "Standpoints in Scientific Medicine" (1847, 1877), which also appeared in *Bulletin of the History of Medicine*, 30 (1956), 436–449, 537–543.

For Virchow's critique of Rokitansky's pathology, L. J. Rather, trans., "Virchow's Review of Rokitansky's 'Handbuch' in the Preussische Medizinal Zeitung, Dec. 1846," in *Clio medica*, 4 (1969), 127–140. Virchow's Croonian lecture delivered at the Royal Society of London in 1893 was translated into English and published as "The Place of Pathology Among the Biological Sciences," in *Proceedings of the Royal Society*, 53 (1893), 114–129. Virchow also gave the second Huxley lecture at the opening of Charing Cross Hospital Medical

School, London, in 1898, which appeared first in English as "Recent Advances in Science and Their Bearing on Medicine and Surgery," in *British Medical Journal* (1898), 2, 1021–1028.

Virchow's early studies and relationships with his parents are contained in an extensive correspondence, *Rudolf Virchow, Briefe an seine Eltern, 1839 bis 1864*, M. Rabl, ed. (Leipzig, 1906).

Virchow's most notable anthropological writings are *Beiträge zur physische Anthropologie der Deutschen mit besonderer Berücksichtigung der Friesen* (Berlin, 1877) and *Crania Ethnica Americana, Sammlung auserlesener amerikanischer Schädeltypen* (Berlin, 1892). See also *Menschen und Affenschädel* (Berlin, 1870), a lecture that was translated as *The Cranial Affinities of Man and the Ape* (Berlin, 1871). For an English version of Virchow's review, see C. A. Bleismer, "Anthropology in the Last Twenty Years," in *Report of the Board of Regents of the Smithsonian Institution* (1890), 550–570. "Rassenbildung und Erblichkeit" (1896) was translated as "Heredity and the Formation of Race," in *This Is Race*, E. W. Count, ed. (New York, 1950), 176–193.

II. SECONDARY LITERATURE. The most important work on Virchow is Erwin H. Ackerknecht, *Rudolf Virchow, Doctor, Statesman, Anthropologist* (Madison, Wis., 1953), which is not primarily a biography but rather an analysis of Virchow's ideas, works, and accomplishments. Among some of the more recent biographical works in German are Ludwig Aschoff, *Rudolf Virchow* (Hamburg, 1948); Hellmuth Unger, *Virchow, ein Leben für die Forschung* (Hamburg, 1953); Curt Froboese, *Rudolf Virchow* (Stuttgart, 1953); Kurt Winter, *Rudolf Virchow* (Leipzig, 1956); and Ernst Meyer, *Rudolf Virchow* (Wiesbaden, 1956).

In 1921 a large number of speeches and articles appeared in Germany to commemorate Virchow's 100th birthday. For a list of these works, see *Virchows Archiv für pathologische Anatomie und Physiologie und für klinische Medizin*, 235 (1921), and the *Deutsche medizinische Wochenschrift*, 47, no. 40 (1921), 1185–1195. Several letters written by the young Virchow appear in G. B. Gruber, "Aus der Jungarztzeit von Rudolf Virchow," in *Virchows Archiv . . .*, 321 (1952), 462–481. Brief biographical sketches of Virchow in English are the obituary by F. Semon in *British Medical Journal*, (1902), 2, 795–802; O. Israel, "Rudolph Virchow, 1821–1902," in *Report of the Board of Regents of the Smithsonian Institution* (1902), 641–659; James J. Walsh, *Makers of Modern Medicine* (New York, 1915), 357–430; and Henry E. Sigerist, *Grosse Ärzte, eine Geschichte der Heilkunde in Lebensbildern* (Munich, 1932), English trans. by E. and C. Paul, *The Great Doctors* (Garden City, N.Y., 1958), 319–330.

Recent German works dealing with Virchow's achievements are Felix Boenheim, *Virchow, Werk und Wirkung* (Berlin, 1957); Wolfgang Jacob, *Medizinische Anthropologie im 19. Jahrhundert*; and Gerhard Hiltner, *Rudolf Virchow, ein weltgeschichtlicher Brennpunkt im Werdegang von Naturwissenschaft und Medizin*

(Stuttgart, 1970). Also noteworthy is K. Panne, "Die Wissenschaftstheorie von Rudolf Virchow" (unpublished doctoral dissertation, Univ. of Düsseldorf, 1967). Numerous articles dealing with aspects of Virchow's work are W. Pagel, "Virchow und die Grundlagen der Medizin des XIX. Jahrhunderts," in *Jenaer medizin-historische Beiträge*, **14** (1931), 1–44; P. Diepgen, "Virchow und die Romantik," in *Deutsche medizinische Wochenschrift*, **58** (1932), 1256–1258; L. J. Rather, "Virchow und die Entwicklung der Entzündungsfrage im 19. Jahrhundert," in *Verhandlungen des XX. Internationalen Kongresses für die Geschichte der Medizin* (Hildesheim, 1968), 161–177; and H. M. Koelbing, "Rudolf Virchow und die moderne Pathologie," in *Münchener medizinische Wochenschrift*, **110** (1968), 349–354.

Other valuable references to Virchow are L. S. King, "Cell Theory, Key to Modern Medicine," in *The Growth of Medical Thought* (Chicago, 1963), 207–219; and W. H. McMenemey, "Cellular Pathology, With Special Teachings on Medical Thought and Practice," in *Medicine and Science in the 1860's*, F. N. L. Poynter, ed. (London, 1968), 13–43.

Important journal articles are W. Pagel, "The Speculative Basis of Modern Pathology. Jahn, Virchow, and the Philosophy of Pathology," in *Bulletin of the History of Medicine*, **38** (1945), 1–43; J. W. Wilson, "Virchow's Contribution to the Cell Theory," in *Journal of the History of Medicine*, **2** (1947), 163–178; P. Klemperer, "The Pathology of Morgagni and Virchow," in *Bulletin of the History of Medicine*, **27** (1953), 24–38; D. Pridan, "Rudolf Virchow and Social Medicine in Historical Perspective," in *Medical History*, **8** (1964), 274–284; and L. J. Rather, "Rudolf Virchow's Views on Pathology, Pathological Anatomy and Cellular Pathology," in *Archives of Pathology*, **82** (1966), 197–204.

GUENTER B. RISSE

**VIREY, JULIEN-JOSEPH** (*b.* Hortes, Haute-Marne, France, 22 December 1775; *d.* Paris, France, 9 March 1846), *natural history, philosophy of nature, pharmacy, anthropology, hygiene, psychology, physiology.*

After serving an apprenticeship in pharmacy with an uncle in Langres, Virey entered military service in 1794 as pharmacist third class. Except for a few brief tours of duty, notably with the Army of the Rhine, his military career was spent at the Val-de-Grâce hospital in Paris, where from 1804 until his retirement in 1813, he was acting chief pharmacist. In 1814 Virey obtained an M.D. degree from the Faculty of Medicine in Paris, and in 1823 he was elected to the Academy of Medicine. He lectured on natural history at the Athénée de Paris in 1814–1815; and for some time after

1830 he represented the Haute-Marne in the Chamber of Deputies.

A remarkably prolific author, Virey produced works encompassing a wide range of interests. His *Traité de pharmacie* (1811) enjoyed considerable authority during the first half of the nineteenth century, appearing in several editions. His *Histoire naturelle des médicamens, des alimens et des poisons* (1820), as well as his numerous descriptive articles on natural products and natural history, demonstrated a high level of practical expertise. Virey also produced a large body of philosophical writings dealing with natural philosophy, anthropology, social hygiene, psychology, and physiology.

Vitalism and teleology are basic components of Virey's natural philosophy and are elaborated at length in his *De la puissance vitale* (1823) and *Philosophie de l'histoire naturelle* (1835). An "intelligence formatrice" directs the organization of life forms, and variations in fixed species are oscillations around primordial types; modification of species can come about only through cosmic change. In his *L'art de perfectionner l'homme* (1808), a work on mental health, Virey attempted to refute the sensationalism of Condillac and the materialism of Cabanis and his fellow Idéologues. Virey's lectures at the Athénée de Paris, published in 1822 as *Histoire des moeurs et de l'instinct des animaux*, sought to demonstrate how instinct and intelligence are related to the structures and functions of nervous systems. Considerable effort and erudition went into his *Histoire naturelle du genre humain* (1801; 2nd ed., 1824), a work typical of early nineteenth-century anthropology in its generalizations on types of man, customs, religion, psychology, language, infancy, women, and social organization. The status of women in society received extended treatment in *De la femme, sous ses rapports physiologique, moral et littéraire* (1823). Virey's last major work, *De la physiologie dans ses rapports avec la philosophie* (1844), attempted to construct a metaphysical foundation for physiological psychology.

But perhaps the two most significant philosophical studies undertaken by Virey concerned circadian rhythms and social hygiene. In his M.D. thesis, *Ephémérides de la vie humaine* (1814), Virey likened the daily-recurring physiological cycles in man to "une sorte d'horloge vivante" and speculated on how diurnal states of health are affected by periodic exogenous phenomena. Although some of the ideas developed in this work had already been discussed by Erasmus Darwin and others, his treatment of this subject nevertheless remains fresh and innovative. In *Hygiène philosophique* (1828), Virey explored in an original, if speculative, manner the influence of social, as well as political, institutions and events on the health of individuals and nations.

*BIBLIOGRAPHY*

I. ORIGINAL WORKS. There is no complete bibliography of Virey's publications. The most comprehensive is A. C. P. Callisen, *Medicinisches Schriftsteller-Lexicon*, XX (Copenhagen, 1834), 158–177, and XXXIII (Altona, 1845), 159–162. Some other listings are *Catalogue général des livres imprimés de la Bibliothèque nationale*, CCXI (Paris, 1972), 1036–1044; *Exposé des travaux de J.-J. Virey, dans les sciences philosophiques* (Paris, 1842); *Index-Catalogue of the Library of the Surgeon-General's Office*, XV (Washington, D.C., 1894), 768, and 2nd ser., XX (Washington, D.C., 1915), 265; J. M. Quérard, *La France littéraire*, X (Paris, 1839), 232–235; and Royal Society, *Catalogue of Scientific Papers*, VI, 166–172.

Virey wrote hundreds of articles, the bulk of them appearing in *Journal de pharmacie*, on the editorial board of which he served, and in the *Dictionnaire des sciences médicales*, 60 vols. (Paris, 1812–1824). Among the publications to which he contributed prominently were the first two eds. of *Nouveau dictionnaire d'histoire naturelle . . .*, 24 vols. (Paris, 1803–1804) and 36 vols. (Paris, 1816–1819); and to the *Dictionnaire de la conversation et de la lecture*, 52 vols. (Paris, 1832–1839).

II. SECONDARY LITERATURE. See an unsigned obituary in *Archives générales de médecine*, 4th ser., **11** (1846), 116–119; Alex Berman, "Romantic Hygeia: J. J. Virey (1775–1846), Pharmacist and Philosopher of Nature," in *Bulletin of the History of Medicine*, **39** (Mar.-Apr. 1965), 134–142; *Biographie universelle et portative des contemporains, ou dictionnaire historique des hommes morts depuis 1788 jusqu'à nos jours . . .*, V (Paris, 1834), 875–876; Maurice Bouvet, "Les origines de l'hôpital du Val-de-Grâce et ses premiers pharmaciens (de 1793 à 1815)," in *Revue d'histoire de la pharmacie*, **7** (1939), 136–145; J. H. Réveillé-Parise, "Galerie médicale (no. xxvii). Virey (Julien-Joseph)," in *Gazette médicale de Paris*, 3rd ser., **1** (1846), 847–851; [Claude Lachaise], under pseudonym C. Sachaile, *Les médecins de Paris jugés par leurs oeuvres . . .* (Paris, 1845), 628–629; and E. Soubeiran, "Discours prononcé par M. Soubeiran, aux funérailles de M. Virey," in *Journal de pharmacie et de chimie*, 3rd ser., **9** (1846), 277–282.

Virey's vitalism, as propounded in his *De la puissance vitale* (1823), is discussed in J. P. Damiron, *Essai sur l'histoire de la philosophie en France au XIXe siècle*, 3rd ed., II (Paris, 1834), 25–39.

ALEX BERMAN

**VIRTANEN, ARTTURI ILMARI** (*b*. Helsinki, Finland, 15 January 1895; *d*. Helsinki, 11 November 1973), *biochemistry*.

Virtanen, the son of Kaarlo and Serafina Isotalo Virtanen, received his elementary education at the classical lyceum in Viipuri (now Vyborg, R.S.F.S.R.), after which he entered the University of Helsinki. He received the Master of Science degree in 1916 and for a year served as first assistant in the Central Industrial Laboratory in Helsinki, then returned to the university for the doctorate, which he obtained in 1919. Virtanen did work in physical chemistry at Zurich in 1920, in bacteriology at Stockholm in 1921, and in enzymology at Stockholm with Euler-Chelpin in 1923 and 1924. Between 1918 and 1920 he was associated with laboratories for the control of butter and cheese manufacture, and from 1921 to 1931 he was director of the laboratories of the Finnish Cooperative Dairies Association. In 1931 Virtanen became director of the Biochemical Research Institute at Helsinki, a position he held for life. After 1924 he also held academic posts: *Dozent* at the University of Helsinki and professor of biochemistry at the Technical University in Helsinki, remaining at the latter until 1939. From 1939 to 1948 he was professor of biochemistry at the University of Helsinki. In 1920 he married Lilja Moisio. They had two sons.

Virtanen's broad scientific background led to his interest in theoretical biochemistry, while his experience in the dairy industry acquainted him with agricultural problems. Throughout his life he combined these interests in work that contributed greatly both to academic biochemistry and to agricultural chemistry.

Virtanen's first biochemical studies concerned bacterial fermentations. In 1924 he showed the necessity for the presence of cozymase in lactic and propionic fermentations. Convinced that most of the proteins in plant cells were enzymes, he undertook a comparison of protein content and enzyme activity of the cells. His attention was thus drawn to the nitrogenous substances of plants, and in 1925 he began to investigate their production in the root nodules of leguminous plants. Virtanen recognized that during storage much of the nitrogenous material was lost. This fact was of great practical importance in agriculture, since when fodder was kept for a long period, its value as a cattle food decreased.

These considerations led Virtanen to study methods for preserving the quality of fresh fodder. He soon learned that deterioration was slowed in an acid medium. Careful studies of various methods for producing a nutritionally safe degree of acidity that would preserve quality led him to the discovery of the AIV method of fodder storage (the name being taken from his initials). It consisted in treating the fodder with a specific mixture of hydrochloric and sulfuric acids so that silage would rapidly reach a determined degree of acidity. Fodder treated in this way retained nearly its full content of proteins, carotene, and vitamin C for prolonged periods. Cattle fed on it produced milk rich in protein and vitamin A. The method was introduced on Finnish farms in 1929, and its use gradually spread to other countries. For this discovery Virtanen was awarded the Nobel Prize for chemistry in 1945.

While this work was continuing, Virtanen was also pursuing his purely biochemical studies. He found that the synthesis of nitrogenous compounds in leguminous plant roots by bacteria required the presence of a red pigment resembling hemoglobin. He investigated the methods by which plants synthesize vitamins, and in later years he studied the chemical composition of higher plants, isolating a number of new compounds, some of considerable nutritional importance.

In addition to the Nobel Prize, Virtanen received many honorary degrees and medals, and served on the editorial boards of numerous biochemical journals. He was the Finnish representative on the United Nations Commission on Nutrition, and from 1948 to 1963 was president of the Academy of Finland.

*BIBLIOGRAPHY*

Virtanen's work on nitrogen fixation was summed up in his book *Cattle Fodder and Human Nutrition With Special Reference to Biological Nitrogen Fixation* (Cambridge, 1938). His account of his studies on the AIV system, as well as his biography, are in *Nobel Lectures in Chemistry 1942–1962* (Amsterdam–London–New York, 1964), 71–105.

HENRY M. LEICESTER

**VITALI, GIUSEPPE** (*b.* Ravenna, Italy, 26 August 1875; *d.* Bologna, Italy, 29 February 1932), *mathematics.*

Vitali was unusual, in that for most of his life he worked in relative isolation, although he lived in Genoa and thus was not cut off from intellectual life. Nevertheless, he achieved such valuable results in the theory of functions of a real variable that he is considered one of the greatest predecessors of Lebesgue.

Vitali graduated from the Scuola Normale Superiore at Pisa in 1899 and immediately became assistant to Ulisse Dini, then one of the most authoritative Italian mathematicians, whose recommendation and approval could assure a promising career to a young mathematician. Vitali left this coveted post after two years, however, possibly because of financial need, and taught at various secondary schools, ending at the Liceo C. Colombo in Genoa (1904–1923). He also became involved in politics there, as a Socialist town councillor and municipal magistrate. In 1922, after the rise to power of fascism and the dissolution of the Socialist party, Vitali returned to his studies and made such progress that at the end of 1923 he won the competition for the professorship of infinitesimal analysis at the University of Modena. The following year he moved to Padua and, in 1930, to Bologna.

In 1926 Vitali was struck by a serious circulatory disorder. Weakened in body but not in mind, he returned to research and teaching; about half his published works (of which there are not many) were composed after this illness, even though he could not write.

Vitali was essentially self-taught and accustomed to working alone. This isolation sometimes led him inadvertently to duplicate someone else's discoveries, but he also avoided well-trodden paths. He holds undisputed priority in a number of discoveries: a theorem on set-covering, the notion of an absolutely continuous function, a theorem on the analyticity of the limit of certain successions of equilimited analytical functions, and criteria for closure of systems of orthogonal functions.

In his last years Vitali confined himself to problems of less general interest, such as his new absolute differential calculus and, in collaboration with his friend and colleague A. Tònolo (1885–1962), his "geometry" of Hilbert spaces—neither of which has aroused particular interest.

After Vitali's death Giovanni Sansone published, as coauthors, Vitali's useful *Moderna teoria delle funzioni di variabile reale* (Bologna, 1935; 3rd ed., 1952), the first part of which was written mainly by Vitali.

Vitali was a corresponding fellow of the Academy of Sciences of Turin (1928), of the Accademia dei Lincei (1930), and of the Academy of Bologna (1931).

*BIBLIOGRAPHY*

See the biographies by S. Pincherle, in *Bollettino dell'Unione matematica italiana,* **11** (1932), 125–126, A. Tònolo, in *Rendiconti del Seminario matematico dell' Università di Padova,* **3** (1932), 67–81, which has a bibliography; and F. G. Tricomi, in *Memorie dell' Accademia delle scienze di Torino,* 4th ser., **4** (1962), 115–116.

F. G. TRICOMI

**VITELO. See Witelo.**

**VITRUVIUS** (*fl.* Rome, first century B.C.), *architecture.*

For a detailed account of his life and work, see Supplement.

**VIVES, JUAN LUIS** (*b.* Valencia, Spain, 6 March 1492; *d.* Bruges, Netherlands [now Belgium], 6 May 1540), *education, philosophy, psychology.*

Probably born to Jewish parents who adopted Catholicism in the oppressive religious atmosphere of fifteenth-century Spain,[1] Vives became one of the greatest Catholic humanists of sixteenth-century Europe. After early schooling in liberal Valencia, he left Spain in 1510 (never to return) and entered the University of Paris, where Spanish masters and students flourished. There, under Gaspar Lax and Jean Dullaert of Ghent, Vives received a Scholastic education that emphasized Aristotelian terminist logic, dialectic, and disputation, a program against which his developing humanist inclinations soon rebelled.

In 1512 Vives was attracted to the Low Countries, especially Bruges, where in 1514 he took up permanent residence (he married Margaret Valdaura of Bruges in 1524), and Louvain, where he attended lectures at the university in 1514 and qualified as lecturer in 1520.

Over the years Vives left Bruges intermittently. Especially significant is the period between 1523 and 1528, when he lectured at Oxford University (Corpus Christi College) and met, or continued earlier friendships with, Thomas More, John Fisher, and Thomas Linacre, and was highly regarded by Henry VIII and his queen, Catherine of Aragon. When Henry sought to divorce Catherine and relations between Henry and Spain soured, Vives fell under a cloud. His lectureship at Oxford was terminated in 1527 and he was banished from England in 1528. Frequently ill and plagued with debt, Vives produced many of his most important works during the last decade of his life.

On intimate terms with the greatest humanists of his day, including Erasmus and Budé, Vives was not only a master of classical Latin literature (he apparently cared much less for the Greek classics) but also wrote on religion, education, rhetoric, philosophy, methodology, science, and politics. Science and philosophy were not of interest for their own sakes, but only insofar as they could prove of practical use in subduing human passions and improving morality. Vives believed that original sin had weakened human reason to the extent that it could not determine nature's primary, necessary principles and was, therefore, incapable of arriving at scientific demonstration in the strict Aristotelian sense. Human knowledge was dependent on experience derived from the five fallible senses. Since the true essences of things transcended experience, knowledge of them lay beyond human reason. Man's knowledge of things was therefore based upon probability, conjecture, and approximation, which were, however, adequate because, despite original sin, God had generously allowed man sufficient reason to master nature, as evidenced by human control over the sublunar region.[2] By assuming that God guaranteed the reliability of human knowledge to whatever extent was necessary, Vives avoided falling into total skepticism. The basic empiricism described here formed the foundation of his theories of education, which emphasized observation, simple experiments, and direct experience.

Vives has been justly hailed as a major figure in the history of psychology. He held that the essence of the soul—mind—was indescribable.[3] It could be known only by its actions, as observed by the internal and external senses. Before Descartes and Francis Bacon, Vives developed an empirical psychology in which he advocated the study of mental activity introspectively and in others. He formulated a theory of association of ideas from an elaborate analysis of memory. If two ideas are implanted in the mind simultaneously, or within a short interval of time, the occurrence of one would cause the recall of the other.[4]

In commemorating the fourth centenary of

Vives' death, the Bibliothèque Nationale exhibited over five hundred editions of his works.[5] They bear witness to his great influence on his own and subsequent centuries.

## NOTES

1. Carlos G. Noreña, "Juan Luis Vives," 18–22.
2. *De prima philosophia*, bk. I, in *Opera omnia*, III, 188.
3. *De anima et vita* (Bruges, 1538), in *Opera omnia*, III, 332.
4. *Ibid.*, 349–350.
5. Noreña, *op. cit.*, 1. For the catalog of the exhibition, see J. Estelrich, *Vivès, exposition organisée à la Bibliothèque nationale, Paris, janvier–mars, 1941* (Paris, 1942).

## BIBLIOGRAPHY

I. ORIGINAL WORKS. Vives' *Opera omnia* was first published at Basel in 1555. Relying heavily on the Basel ed., Gregorio Mayans y Síscar published the only other ed. of the collected works: *Joannis Ludovici Vivis valentini Opera omnia*, 8 vols. (Valencia, 1782–1790; repr. London, 1964). Although incomplete (as in the earlier Basel ed., it lacks the *Commentaries on Saint Augustine* and perhaps a few other minor works; see Noreña, "Juan Luis Vives," 4), it does include the works relevant to science and philosophy, which appear in vols. III and VI. In addition to a number of brief treatises, vol. III contains *De Aristotelis operibus censura, De instrumento probabilitatis liber unus, De syllogismo, De prima philosophia, sive De intimo naturae opificio* (in three books), and *De anima et vita* (a lengthy treatise in three books, which treats many of the traditional topics in Aristotle's *De anima*; a photocopy repr. of the Basel ed. [1538] of this work was issued by Mario Sancipriano [Turin, 1959]); vol. VI contains the *De disciplinis*, composed of two parts, *De causis corruptarum artium* in seven bks., depicting the low state of the arts in Vives' day (especially relevant are book 3, which treats logic, and book 5, which denounces natural philosophy, medicine, and mathematics), and *De tradendis disciplinis*, in five bks., devoted to the reformation and revitalization of the fallen arts.

For a chronological list of Vives' works, see Carlos G. Noreña, *Juan Luis Vives*, which is vol. 34 in International Archives of the History of Ideas (The Hague, 1970), app. 2, 307–308; app. 1, 300–306, is "Editions of Vives' Main Works From 1520–1650" (also see Sancipriano's bibliography of eds., pp. x–xiv of his repr. ed. of *De anima et vita*, cited above). For the translations into Spanish and English, see Noreña, *op. cit.*, 310–311; and, despite the title, for English translations of Vives' Latin works, see Remigio Ugo Pane, *English Translations From the Spanish 1484–1943: A Bibliography* (New Brunswick, N.J., 1944), 201–202.

II. SECONDARY LITERATURE. Extensive bibliographies of secondary literature appear in Noreña (see above), 311–321; and Sancipriano's ed. of *De anima et vita* (see above), xiv–xviii. Noreña also includes a useful survey of the history of research on Vives in ch. 1: "The Vicissitudes of Vives' Fame," 1–14.

The standard biography and evaluation of Vives' work is Adolfo Bonilla y San Martín, *Luis Vives y la filosofía del renacimiento*, 3 vols. (Madrid, 1903). A briefer, but still substantial account of Vives' life is Lorenzo Riber's intro. to his Spanish trans. of Vives' *Opera omnia*, in *Juan Luis Vives Obras completas*, 2 vols. (Madrid, 1947–1948), 13–255. Critical of previous biographical accounts, especially on the question of Vives' Jewish parentage, is Noreña (see above), pt. 1, "The Life of Juan Luis Vives," 1–6, 1–120; a briefer biographical sketch appears in *Vives' "Introduction to Wisdom," a Renaissance Textbook*, edited, with an introduction, by Marian Leona Tobriner, S.N.J.M., which is no. 35 in the series Classics in Education (New York, 1968), 9–36.

Vives' attitudes toward Scholastic philosophy and science and his own views of science appear to have received little attention. Pierre Duhem, *Études sur Léonard de Vinci*, 3 vols. (Paris, 1906–1913), describes Vives' scornful and vivid denunciation of Scholastic education in medicine, logic, and natural philosophy at the University of Paris (III, 168–172, 180–181, 488, 490). Of substantive scientific ideas, Duhem mentions (III, 144–146) only Vives' acceptance of the much-debated Scholastic "moment of rest" (*quies media*) alleged to occur between the upward violent motion of a projectile and its subsequent downward motion. A sense of Vives' attitude to Scholastic philosophy and science can be gleaned from Noreña (see above), pt. 2, "Vives' Thought," 131–299. For Vives' role as an educational reformer, see William Harrison Woodward, "Juan Luis Vives, 1492–1540," in *Studies in Education During the Age of the Renaissance 1400–1600* (New York, 1965; original publication, 1906), 180–210, and Foster Watson, "Vives On Education," in *Vives: On Education, A Translation of the De tradendis disciplinis of Juan Luis Vives*, with an introduction by Foster Watson and a foreword by Francesco Cordasco (Totowa, N.J., 1971; original publication, 1913), ci–clvii. Contributions by Vives to education and psychology are briefly summarized by Walter A. Daly, *The Educational Psychology of Juan Luis Vives* (Ph.D. diss., Catholic University of America, 1924); and Foster Watson, "The Father of Modern Psychology," in *Psychological Review*, **22**, no. 5 (Sept. 1915), 333–353.

EDWARD GRANT

---

**VIVIANI, VINCENZO** (*b.* Florence, Italy, 5 April 1622; *d.* Florence, 22 September 1703), *mathematics.*

Viviani was the son of Jacopo di Michelangelo Viviani, a member of the noble Franchi family, and Maria Alamanno del Nente. He studied the humanities with the Jesuits and mathematics with

Settimi, a friend of Galileo's. His intelligence and ability led to his presentation in 1638 to Ferdinand II de' Medici, grand duke of Tuscany. Ferdinand introduced him to Galileo, who was so impressed by his talent that he took him into his house at Arcetri as a collaborator in 1639. After Galileo's death, Viviani wrote a historical account of his life and hoped to publish a complete edition of his works. The plan, however, could not be carried out because of opposition by the Church—a serious blow not only to Viviani's reputation but even more to the progress of science in Italy. Since he was unable to pursue the evolution of mathematical ideas that were developing during that period, Viviani turned his talent and inventiveness solely to the study and imitation of the ancients.

Although the Medici court gave him much work, Viviani studied the geometry of the ancients. His accomplishments brought him membership in the Accademia del Cimento, and in 1696 he became a member of the Royal Society of London. In 1699 he was elected one of the eight foreign members of the Académie des Sciences in Paris. He declined offers of high scientific positions from King John II Casimir of Poland and from Louis XIV.

Viviani's first project was an attempted restoration of a work by Aristaeus the Elder, *De locis solidis secunda divinatio geometrica*, which Viviani undertook when he was twenty-four. Aristaeus' work is believed to have been the first methodical exposition of the curves discovered by Menaechmus; but since it has been entirely lost, it is difficult to estimate how close Viviani came to the original work.

Viviani also undertook to reconstruct the fifth book of Apollonius' *Conics*, the first four books of which had been discovered and published. While examining the oriental codices in the grand duke's library in Florence, Borelli discovered a set of papers on which was written "Eight Books of Apollonius' *Conics*." (Actually, the manuscript contained only the first seven books.) Since the manuscript was in Arabic, Borelli obtained the grand duke's permission to take it to Rome, where he turned it over to Abraham Ecchellensis, who was competent to translate it into Latin. The contents of the work were kept secret, however, in order to give Viviani time to complete the publication of his *De maximis et minimis*, which finally appeared at Florence in 1659. Two years later the translation of Apollonius' work was published under Borelli's editorship, and it then became possible to ascertain the substantial similarity between the two works.

Another important work was *Quinto libro degli Elementi di Euclide* (1674). With the rigor and prolixity of the ancients, Viviani devoted an appendix to geometric problems, among which was one on the trisection of an angle, solved by the use of the cylindrical spiral or of a cycloid; another was the problem of duplicating the cube, solved by means of conics or of the cubic $xy^2 = k$.

Viviani also produced the Italian version of Euclid's *Elements* (1690) that was reprinted in 1867 by Betti and Brioschi, in order to raise the level of the teaching of geometry in Italy. Following the example of other learned men of the period, Viviani proposed a problem—known as the "Florentine enigma"—that received wide recognition as soon as the foremost mathematicians began to work on it.[1] The problem was to perforate a hemispheric arch, having four equal windows, in such a way that the residual surface could be squared. Viviani solved the problem by a method that became well known.[2] It is accomplished by the intersection of four right cylinders, the bases of which are tangent to the base of the hemisphere.

There is an Italian translation by Viviani of a work by Archimedes on the rectification of a circumference and the squaring of a circle. He also collected and arranged works by Torricelli after the latter's death.[3]

The search for a point in the plane of a triangle such that the sum of the distances from the vertices shall be the minimum was proposed by Fermat to Torricelli, and by Torricelli to Viviani, who solved the problem (appendix to *De maximis et minimis*, p. 144). This problem was also solved by Torricelli and Cavalieri for triangles with angles less than 120°.[4] It led to a correspondence among Torricelli, Fermat, and Roberval to which Viviani refers (*ibid*., p. 147).

*NOTES*

1. During a visit to Italy in 1689, Leibniz met Viviani and solved his problem. It was the first example of the calculation of the area of a curved surface by means of integral calculus (*Acta eruditorum* [1692], 275–279). Jakob I Bernoulli solved the problem (*ibid*.), and that work led to his study of the area of quadrics of revolution (*Acta eruditorum* [Oct. 1696]).
2. Guido Grandi demonstrated the correctness of Viviani's solution by applying the method of indivisibles. There is a reference to this solution in a letter written by Huygens to L'Hospital (*Oeuvres de C. Huygens*, X [The Hague, 1905], 829). In an appendix to this work the publishers inserted a previously unpublished passage by Huygens, in which he demonstrates that the solutions proposed by Leibniz and Viviani are identical.

3. See *Opere di Evangelista Torricelli*, I (Faenza, 1919), pt. 1, 329–407, and pt. 2, 3–43, 49–55.

4. B. Cavalieri, *Exercitationes geometricae sex* (Bologna, 1647), 504–510.

*BIBLIOGRAPHY*

I. ORIGINAL WORKS. Viviani's writings are *De maximis et minimis geometrica divinatio in quintum Conicorum Apollonii Pergaei, adhuc desideratum* (Florence, 1659); *Quinto libro di Euclide, ovvero scienza universale delle proporzioni, spiegate colla dottrina del Galileo* (Florence, 1674); *Diporto geometrico* (Florence, 1676); *Enodatio problematum universis geometricis praepositorum a D. Claudio Comiers* (Florence, 1677); *Discorso intorno al difendersi dai riempimenti e dalla corrosione dei fiumi* (Florence, 1688); *Elementi piani e solidi di Euclide agl'illustrissimi Sig. dell'Accademia de' Nobili* (Florence, 1690); *Formazione e misura di tutti i cieli* (Florence, 1692); and *De locis solidis secunda divinatio geometrica in quinque libros iniura temporum amissos, Aristaei senioris geometrae* (Florence, 1702).

II. SECONDARY LITERATURE. See L. Conte, "Vincenzo Viviani e l'invenzione di due medie proporzionali," in *Periodico di matematiche*, **25**, no. 4 (1952), 185; A. Fabroni, *Vitae italorum doctrina excellentium*, I (Pisa, 1777), 307–344; and Gino Loria, *Curve piane speciali algebriche e trascendenti*, I (Milan, 1930), 373; *Curve sghembe speciali algebriche e trascendenti*, I (Bologna, 1925), 201–233, and II, 63–65; and *Storia delle matematiche*, 2nd ed. (Milan, 1950), see index.

There are biographical articles in L. Berzolari *et al.*, eds., *Enciclopedia delle matematiche elementari*, II, pt. I (Milan, 1937), 61, 172, 193, 523, 524; and II, pt. 2 (Milan, 1938), 48; and Treccani's *Enciclopedia italiana*, XXXV, 529.

A. NATUCCI

**VIZE, VLADIMIR YULEVICH** (*b.* Tsarskoe Selo [now Pushkin], Russia, 5 March 1886; *d.* Leningrad, U.S.S.R., 19 February 1954), *oceanography, meteorology, glaciology.*

After graduating from the Gymnasium in St. Petersburg Vize studied at the universities of Göttingen and Halle, majoring in chemistry. He soon began to read books on polar expeditions and decided to become an Arctic explorer. In 1910 he returned to Russia, where he studied in the department of physics and mathematics of St. Petersburg University. While still a student (1910–1911) he traveled through the Lovozero and Khibiny tundras in northwestern Russia, studied the life of the Saamian (Lopari or Lapp) tribes, and discovered and mapped a number of lakes. In 1912–1914 he

was a member of Sedov's expedition to the North Pole. From the early 1920's to the mid-1930's he participated in the major Soviet Arctic expeditions, directing most of them.

Vize was responsible for the establishment of many polar stations in the Soviet Arctic and for the development and application of new methods of research, particularly in ice forecasting. In his works he developed the ideas of Carl Wilhelm Brennecke, Paul Gerhard Schott, Wilhelm Meinardus, and Fridtjof Nansen on the influence of atmospheric processes and hydrological conditions on the formation of ice in the Arctic seas. Continuing their work, Vize also investigated the influence of ice formation in Arctic seas on the circulation of the atmosphere. He applied the results of this research to forecast ice drift, ice conditions, hydrodynamics, temperature conditions, and other factors of substantial significance for scientific weather forecasting.

Vize strongly favored the exploitation of a sea route along the northern shore of the Soviet Union. In 1932, under his leadership, the first complete west-east through passage was made by the northern sea route. Two years later the same voyage was completed from east to west. In 1936–1937 Vize led research expeditions to high latitudes that gathered extensive material on hydrology, meteorology, glaciology, hydrochemistry, and other areas of oceanology.

Vize was a corresponding member of the Academy of Sciences of the U.S.S.R. from 1933, president of the scientific council of the Arctic Institute (later the Arctic and Antarctic Scientific Research Institute), Leningrad (1929–1950), and professor at Leningrad University from 1945. He was a member of the American and English geographical societies and the International Meteorological Committee.

*BIBLIOGRAPHY*

I. ORIGINAL WORKS. Vize's writings include *Osnovy dolgosrochnykh ledovykh prognozov dlya arkticheskikh morey* ("The Bases of Long-Term Ice Predictions for the Arctic Seas"; Moscow, 1944); *Na "Sibiryakove" i "Litke" cherez Ledovitye morya* ("On the 'Sibiryak' and 'Litka' Across the Arctic Seas"; Moscow, 1946); and *Morya Sovetskoy arktiki. Ocherki po istorii issledovania* ("The Seas of the Soviet Arctic. Sketches in the History of Research"; Moscow, 1948).

II. SECONDARY LITERATURE. See V. K. Buynitsky, *Vladimir Yulievich Vize* (Leningrad, 1969); and A. F.

Laktionov, "Vladimir Yulievich Vize," in *Otechestven-nye fiziko-geografy i puteshestvenniki* ("Native Physical Geographers and Travelers"; Moscow, 1959), 759–765.

A. S. FEDOROV

**VLACQ (VLACK, VLACCUS), ADRIAAN** (*b.* Gouda, Netherlands, 1600; *d.* The Hague, Netherlands, late 1666 or early 1667), *mathematics, publishing.*

A member of a well-to-do family, Vlacq received a good education. Interested in mathematics, he became acquainted with a local surveyor and teacher, Ezechiel De Decker (*ca.* 1595–*ca.* 1657), for whom he translated into Dutch several recent books written in Latin by British authors on the new art of reckoning, notably some by Napier and that by Briggs on logarithms. They decided to publish these and related works in Dutch. *Het eerste deel van de Nieuwe telkonst* appeared in 1626 under the name of De Decker, who in the preface praised Vlacq for his help. It contained Napier's *Rabdologia* in Dutch translation, a paper on business arithmetic by De Decker, and Stevin's *Thiende*. Also that year De Decker published the *Nieuwe telkonst*, a small table of logarithms to base 10 for the numbers from 1 to 10,000, based on Briggs's *Arithmetica logarithmica* (1624). The work promised a full table of logarithms, an accomplishment realized in *Het tweede deel van de Nieuwe telkonst* (1627), again under the name of De Decker with credit to Vlacq. It contained not only the Briggsian logarithms from 1 to 10,000 and from 90,000 to 100,000, already published by Briggs, but also those of all numbers from 1 to 100,000 (to ten decimal places). The latter, the result of Vlacq's computations, did what Briggs had planned to do.

Vlacq took out the privileges on these books and had them published by the Gouda firm of Pieter Rammaseyn, in which he seems to have had a financial interest. Having paid for the publication of tables he himself had computed, Vlacq saw no objection to republishing them under his own name in the *Arithmetica logarithmica* (1628). Although De Decker was not mentioned, there is no indication that he later resented this. Vlacq's fame rests on these tables, which were well received and contain relatively few errors. The *Tweede deel* of 1627, actually the first complete table of decimal logarithms, was long forgotten until a copy was rediscovered in 1920.

To the *Arithmetica logarithmica*, Vlacq added *Canon triangulorum sive tabula artificialium sinuum*, with the decimal logarithms of the trigonometric lines computed from Pitiscus' *Thesaurus mathematicus* (1613). In a letter to John Pell of 25 October 1628, Briggs states that the 1,000 printed copies of this book, with Latin, Dutch, and French prefaces, were almost all sold. The probable reason is that they were used by George Miller for his *Logarithmicall Arithmeticke* (London, 1631), identical with Vlacq's book except for the English preface.

From about 1632 to 1642, Vlacq had a book business in London, which he moved to Paris. After 1648 he was in The Hague, publishing many books and repeatedly involved in business or political quarrels. The books he published include Briggs and Gellibrand's *Trigonometria britannica*, containing the logarithms of the trigonometric lines with angles divided into tenths (Stevin's idea), and his own *Trigonometria artificialis*, using the traditional sexagesimal division of angles. They have log sine, log cosine, log tangent, and log secant for angles increasing by ten seconds. Both books were published by the firm of Rammaseyn (Gouda, 1633).

Since all these tables were large, Vlacq, with his keen business instincts, published the small *Tabulae sinuum, tangentium et secantium et logarithmi sin. tang. et numerorum ab unitate ad 10000* (Gouda, 1636). These tables, carried to seven decimal places, were a great success and were often reprinted and reedited, and were translated into French and German (there is a Leipzig edition of 1821).

From 1652 to 1655 Vlacq waged a pamphlet war, in which he took the English royalist side, thereby provoking an attack by John Milton. In 1654 he is mentioned as successor to Johannes Rammaseyn. Between 1651 and 1662 he was regularly listed as a visitor to the Frankfurt book fair.

*BIBLIOGRAPHY*

On Vlacq's life and work, see D. Bierens de Haan, "Adriaan Vlack en Ezechiel De Decker," in *Verslagen en mededeelingen der Koninklyke Akademie van wetenschappen*, Afd. Natuurkunde, 2nd ser., **8** (1874), 57–99; and "Adriaan Vlack en zyne logarithmentafels," *ibid.*, 163–199; C. de Waard, "Vlacq (Adriaan)," in *Nieuw nederlandsch biographisch woordenboek*, II (1912), 1503–1506; J. W. L. Glaisher, "Notice Respecting Some New Facts in the Early History of Logarithms," in *Philosophical Magazine*, 4th ser., **44** (1872), 291–

303, and **45** (1873), 376–382; and D. Bierens de Haan, "On Certain Early Logarithmic Tables," *ibid.*, 371–376. The rediscovery of the *Tweede deel* by M. van Haaften is reported in his "Ce n'est pas Vlacq, en 1628, mais De Decker, en 1627, qui a publié une table de logarithmes étendue et complète," in *Nieuw archief voor wiskunde*, **15** (1928), 49–54; he first reported it in *Verzekeringsbode*, **39** (4 Sept. 1920), 383–386. In "Quelques nouvelles données concernant l'histoire des anciennes tables néerlandaises de logarithmes," in *Nieuw archief voor wiskunde*, **21** (1942), 59–64, and in *Nieuw tydschrift voor wiskunde*, **31** (1943–1944), 137–144, van Haaften supplements his account by reference to three documents on the business relationship between De Decker and Vlacq found by P. J. T. Endenburg in the Gouda archives, reported in "De oudste nederlandsche logarithmentafels en hun makers," in *Het Boek*, **25** (1938–1939), 311–320.

D. J. STRUIK

**VOEYKOV, ALEKSANDR IVANOVICH** (*b*. Moscow, Russia, 20 May 1842; *d*. Petrograd, Russia [now Leningrad, U.S.S.R.], 9 February 1916), *geography, climatology.*

Voeykov's parents died when he was five; and he spent his childhood on an uncle's estate, where he received an excellent education that included English, French, and German. In 1860 he entered the Physics and Mathematics Faculty of St. Petersburg University; but since the university was soon closed by the government because of student disorders, he continued his education at the universities of Heidelberg, Berlin, and Göttingen. At Göttingen and Berlin he studied meteorology, and in 1865 he defended a doctoral dissertation at Göttingen, "Ueber die directe Insolation und Strahlung an verschiedenen Orten der Erdoberfläche."

On his return to Russia in 1866, Voeykov was elected to the Russian Geographical Society, in which he was active for fifty years. In 1870, while helping to outfit an expedition to northern Russia, he emphasized the necessity of studying the meteorology of that area, pointing out that atmospheric processes in the high latitudes must exert a strong influence on the climate and meteorological conditions of the middle latitudes.

A year earlier, at the request of the Geographical Society, Voeykov had visited the network of meteorological observatories in western Europe; this led to extensive ties between the Russian Geographical Society and other European scientific institutions. In the spring of 1872 he studied the chernozem in Galicia, Bukovina, Walachia,

Transylvania, and Austria; that fall and winter he traveled through western Europe, and most of 1873 was spent in the United States and Canada. Voeykov spent the last three months of 1873 in Washington, at the invitation of the secretary of the Smithsonian Institution, Joseph Henry, completing a manuscript by James Coffin entitled "Winds of the Globe," which he supplemented with data on the winds of Russia.

For almost all of 1874 and the beginning of 1875 Voeykov traveled through South America, learning Spanish and Portuguese. In June 1875 he returned to Russia, and that October he began a journey to India, Java, southern China, and Japan. Because he was a scientist, Voeykov obtained the right to travel throughout Japan, accompanied by a young Japanese who knew Russian. On the basis of information supplied by the inhabitants and from his own observations of the vegetation Voeykov compiled a general map of the climate of Japan. In January 1877 he returned to St. Petersburg and published his observations.

In 1870, Voeykov became secretary of a meteorological commission organized within the Russian Geographical Society. He undertook the organization of meteorological observations, especially on precipitation, and sought to attract a large number of volunteer observers. In 1885 Voeykov obtained a government subsidy to organize twelve meteorological stations for gathering information of special value to agriculture. From its founding in 1891 until 1916, Voeykov was editor-in-chief of *Meteorologicheskii vestnik*.

In 1884 Voeykov was elected docent, in 1885 extraordinary professor, and in 1887 ordinary professor at St. Petersburg University. He became director of the Higher Geographical Courses—the first higher educational institution for geography in Russia—in 1915. He was a member or honorary member of many Russian and foreign scientific societies but was not elected a corresponding member of the Academy of Sciences until 1910.

Voeykov's basic work was *Klimaty zemnogo shara, v osobennosti Rossii* ("Climates of the Earth, Particularly Russia"; 1884), in which he generalized achievements in meteorology, climatology, and hydrology, and his own scientific experiments. Although J. von Hann had published *Handbuch der Klimatologie* in 1883, Voeykov's work was published in German, in revised form, in 1887. This circumstance is explained by the novelty of his treatment of the subject: along with descriptions of climates, he demonstrated the reasons for their differences, described the essential meteorological phenomena and climatic processes, and examined their development and interaction with other natural factors.

Before 1884 Voeykov had published several works on the circulation of the atmosphere on the earth's surface and had shown the close relation of climate to the general circulation of the atmosphere. Emphasizing the particular importance of solar radiation as the moving force in that circulation, he believed that one of the most important problems for the physical sciences was the "introduction of an input-output table of solar heat received by the earth, with its spheres of air and water" (*Izbrannye sochinenia*, 167).

Voeykov was the first to establish the role of monsoons in the subtropics. He discovered the crest of the high barometric maximum (the Voeykov axis), formed over Asia in the cold months and extending from the Siberian anticyclone to western Europe.

In *Klimaty zemnogo shara*, Voeykov examined the most important climatic factors, indicating the primary importance of atmospheric moisture, solar radiation, and the circulation of air. He investigated all the stages of the hydrologic cycle and devoted separate chapters to atmospheric moisture, evaporation, cloud formation, precipitation, rivers, and lakes. He treated precipitation as the opposite of evaporation in the earth's hydrologic cycle, maintaining that the relation between these processes directly determines the density of the river network and the pattern of occurrence of rivers and lakes: "Under stable, even conditions, the more abundant the precipitation and the less the evaporation from the surface of the soil and water, as well as from plants, the richer in running water the country will be. Thus rivers may be regarded as the product of climate" (*Izbrannye sochinenia*, I, 243).

Voeykov demonstrated the averaging influence of lower reaches of large rivers on the climatic conditions of the entire basin. Examining certain hydraulic and hydrological aspects of river currents (particularly the influence on the drainage of the permeability of the soil, the level of the river, and the moderating influence of lakes on the level of rivers flowing through them), he classified streams in relation to the character of their sources and, as he said, established nine main types in relation to climate. He also showed that if rivers reflect the climate at a given time, then lakes reflect climatic changes.

Voeykov was one of the first to calculate the annual flow of all the rivers of the earth, although his estimate was substantially less than the actual figure. He made the first scientifically based calculation of the balance between inflow and evaporation in the Caspian Sea.

Many of Voeykov's works were devoted to the snow cover, and he was the first climatologist to detail its important influence on climate. Having established that the snow cover reflects solar radiation into space, he showed that it melts chiefly as a result of the action upon it of warm air masses. His general conclusion regarding the influence of snow on the heat balance of the earth was that for the entire planet, the warming influence of snow greatly exceeds the cooling effect; without the snow cover, the earth would be much cooler than it is. He also compared climates of present glacial regions with climate during the Ice Age.

Voeykov studied periodic and nonperiodic changes in climate; in particular, he disproved the erroneous belief that Central Asia was becoming drier.

*BIBLIOGRAPHY*

I. ORIGINAL WORKS. Voeykov published over 1,700 works, including "Ueber das Klima von ost-Asien," in *Zeitschrift der Österreichischen Gesellschaft für die Meteorologie*, **5**, no. 1 (1870), 39–42; "Die atmosphärische Circulation," Supp. 38 (1874) to *Petermanns geographischen Mitteilungen*, also in Russian in his *Izbrannye sochinenia*, II, 159–221; "Raspredelenie osadkov v Rossii" ("The Distribution of Precipitation in Russia"), in *Zapiski Imperatorskago russkago geograficheskago obshchestva po obshchei geografii*, **6**, no. 1 (1875), 1–72; "Puteshestvie po Yaponii, iyuloktyabr 1876 g." ("Journey Through Japan, July–Oct. 1876"), in *Izvestiya Gosudarstvennogo russkogo geographicheskogo obshchestva*, **13**, no. 4, sec. 2 (1877), 195–240; "Klimat oblasti mussonov Vostochnoy Azii: Amurskogo kraya, Zabaykalya, Manchzhurii, Vostochnoy Mongolii, Kitaya, Yaponii . . ." ("Climate of the Monsoon Regions of East Asia: The Amur Region, Transbaikalia, Manchuria, Eastern Mongolia, China, Japan . . ."), *ibid.*, **15**, no. 5, sec. 2 (1879), 321–410; and "Klimaticheskie uslovia lednikovykh yavleny nastoyashchikh i proshedshikh" ("Climatic Conditions of Glacial Phenomena of the Present and Past"), in *Zapiski Imperatorskago Mineralogicheskago obshchestva*, 2nd ser., pt. 16 (1881), 21–90.

See also *Klimaty zemnogo shara, v osobennosti Rossii* ("Climates of the Earth, Particularly Russia"; St. Petersburg, 1884), also in his *Izbrannye sochinenia*, I, 161–750; *Snezhny pokrov, ego vliyanie na klimat i pogodu i sposoby issledovania* ("Snow Cover, Its Influence on Climate and Weather and Methods of Research"; St. Petersburg, 1885); "O klimate Tsentralnoy

Azii na osnovanii nablyudeny chetyrekh ekspeditsy N. M. Przhevalskogo" ("The Climate of Central Asia on the Basis of Observations of N. M. Przhevalsky's Four Expeditions"), in *Nauchnye rezultaty puteshestvy Przhevalskogo po Tsentralnoy Azii* ("Scientific Results of Przhevalsky's Travels Through Central Asia"; St. Petersburg, 1895), 239–281; "Klimat polesya" ("Climate of Woodlands"), in *Prilozhenia k "Ocherku rabot Zapadnoy ekspeditsii po osusheniyu bolot za 1873–1898 gg."* ("Appendix to 'Sketch of the Work of the Western Expedition for Draining Swamps in 1873–1898'"; St. Petersburg, 1899), 1–132; "Klimat Indyskogo okeana i Indii" ("Climate of the Indian Ocean and India"), in *Zapiski po gidrografii* (1908), no. 29, 178–263; and "Oroshenie Zakaspyskoy oblasti s tochki zrenia geografii i klimatologii" ("Irrigation of the Transcaspian Region From the Point of View of Geography and Climatology"), in *Izvestia Gosudarstvennogo russkogo geografficheskogo obshchestva*, **44**, no. 3 (1908), 131–160; *Le Turkestan russe* (Paris, 1914); "Klimaty russkikh i zagranichnykh lechebnykh mestnostey" ("Climates of Russian and Foreign Therapeutic Localities"), in *Prakticheskaya meditsina* (1915), no. 6, 87–176, and no. 10, 177–180; *Izbrannye sochinenia* ("Selected Works"), 4 vols. (Moscow, 1948–1957); and *Vozdeystvie cheloveka na prirodu. Izbrannye stati* ("The Influence of Man on Nature. Selected Articles"; Moscow, 1949).

II. SECONDARY LITERATURE. See A. A. Grigoriev, "Rukovodyashchie klimatologicheskie idei A. I. Voeykova" ("Voeykov's Guiding Climatological Ideas"), in Voeykov's *Izbrannye sochinenia*, I, 10–34; K. K. Markov, "A. I. Voeykov kak istorik klimatov Zemli" ("Voeykov as Historian of the Climates of the Earth"), in *Izvestiya Akademii nauk SSSR*, Geog. ser. (1951), no. 3, 46–54; V. V. Pokshishevsky, "A. I. Voeykov i voprosy geografii naselenia" ("Voeykov and Questions of the Geography of Population"), in *Voprosy geografii* (1947), no. 5, 33–40; and "A. I. Voeykov kak ekonomiko-geograf" ("Voeykov as Economic Geographer"), in *Otechestvennye ekonomiko-geografy* ("Native Economic Geographers"; Moscow, 1957), 275–283; and G. D. Rikhter, "Zhizen i deyatelnost A. I. Voeykova" ("Voeykov's Life and Work"), in Voeykov's *Izbrannye sochinenia*, I, 35–82.

I. A. FEDOSEEV

**VOGEL, HERMANN CARL** (*b.* Leipzig, Germany, 3 April 1841; *d.* Potsdam, Germany, 13 August 1907), *astrophysics.*

Vogel was the sixth child of Johann Carl Christoph Vogel, principal of a Leipzig Gymnasium, whose friends included Alexander von Humboldt, Robert Bunsen, and Carl Ritter. Vogel's older brother Eduard, who later became an astronomer and African explorer, was a friend of Heinrich Louis d'Arrest, director of the Leipzig astronomical observatory. Through this friendship Vogel came into contact with astronomy while still young.

After graduating from his father's school, Vogel entered the Dresden Polytechnical School in 1860. Before he completed his training there, however, his parents died, leaving him with serious financial problems. He managed to support himself by doing odd jobs, supplemented by aid from his oldest brother.

Vogel returned to Leipzig in 1863 and began to study natural science at the university. He immediately became second assistant at the university observatory, directed by Karl Bruhns. Vogel's remarkable manual dexterity was very helpful in manipulating the instruments used to observe nebulae and star clusters. The Leipzig observatory was participating in the Astronomische Gesellschaft's "zone project," a great scanning operation of the northern skies, the goal of which was to ascertain the coordinates of all stars down to the ninth magnitude. At Bruhns's suggestion Vogel agreed to make his nebulae observations in the zone +9°30' to 15°30', the area assigned to the Leipzig observatory. This work formed the basis of his inaugural dissertation, which contained a report of these observations and a detailed historical survey of the observation of nebulae (Jena, 1870).

While Vogel was a student at Leipzig, J. K. F. Zöllner obtained a professorship there (1866). Scarcely seven years older than Vogel, Zöllner exerted a lasting influence on his career, especially by insistent advocacy of astrophysics (the examination of celestial objects with the then new methods of photometry, spectroscopy, and photography). The period of Zöllner's most important work in stellar photometry coincided with the years in which Vogel was working on his doctorate. At this time, for example, Zöllner proposed his ingenious design for a reversible spectroscope, with which he sought to demonstrate the existence of Doppler shifts in stellar spectra.

At the recommendation of Zöllner and Bruhns, Vogel was named director of the observatory of F. G. von Bülow at Bothkamp, near Kiel, in 1870. Bülow, an ardent amateur astronomer, wished to finance the construction of an observatory suitable for serious scientific research, even though he himself seldom did such work. Thus Vogel had complete scientific freedom and, most important, he had sole discretion in determining the program of research and in procuring the necessary technical equipment to carry it out. The observatory had a considerable number of instruments, including a relatively large refracting telescope with an aperture of 293.5 mm. (11 1/2 inches) and fitted with an automatic guiding mechanism. Vogel soon acquired additional devices for it, including a spectroscope and a camera obscura. Among the other instruments at the observatory were a comet-seeker (aperture, 136 mm.; focal distance, 1670 mm.), a Fraunhofer refracting telescope (aperture, 75 mm.; focal distance, 1160 mm.), a Zöllner photometer, a ten-inch prismatic circle, two good pendulum clocks, and meteorological measuring devices. Vogel's detailed description of the observatory's equipment was published in *Astronomische Nachrichten*, **77** (1871), cols. 289–298.

Bülow's generosity was of great significance for Vogel's scientific development, and Vogel later stated that it was at Bothkamp that he really learned astrophysics. In particular, while there he worked intensively on the spectroscopic analysis of the stars. With the eleven-inch equatorial telescope he investigated the spectra of Mercury, Venus, Mars, Jupiter, and Uranus, as well as those of various nebulae, of Comet III 1871, of the northern lights, and of the sun. In addition, with a reversible spectroscope placed at his disposal by Zöllner, he tried to ascertain the rotation of the sun. Following the attempts made by Huggins in England (1868), Vogel sought to determine spectroscopically the radial velocity of the fixed stars, a project on which he obviously was in close contact with Zöllner. The results, however, were uncertain; and Vogel, dissatisfied, temporarily abandoned this research. In the next two years he published the results he had achieved with his co-worker O. Lohse in *Beobachtungen, angestellt auf der Sternwarte des Kammerhern v. Bülow zu Bothkamp* (1872–1875). Another work on the spectra of the planets won the prize of the Royal Danish Academy of Sciences and Letters at Copenhagen. Through these publications both the Bothkamp Observatory and its director became well-known in the scientific world.

In 1871, Wilhelm Foerster, clearly grasping the importance of astrophysical research, sent a memoir to the German crown prince and the minister of education that urged the construction of an astrophysical observatory at Potsdam, near Berlin. Vogel's name naturally arose in the ensuing discussions, and in 1874 he was asked to become an observer at the future observatory. In his new post Vogel collaborated in planning the equipment for the new institution, a task for which he was well prepared by his experience at Bothkamp. In order to broaden his knowledge of recent developments in astronomy, he traveled to England, Scotland, and Ireland in 1875. On the trip he met and held scientific discussions with the leading astronomers of those countries, especially Huggins and Airy.

Even before the opening of the new observatory, Vogel pursued the astrophysical research he had begun at Bothkamp, although the time he could devote to it was limited by his responsibilities at Potsdam. It was hoped that Kirchhoff, whose research played a major role in the creation of astrophysics, would become director of the new observatory, but he refused, on the ground that the post would not allow him sufficient time for his theoretical studies because its incumbent would have sole responsibility for running the observatory. He agreed, however, to work at the observatory if he could be a codirector. His terms were accepted, and in July 1876 Kirchhoff, Wilhelm Foerster, and Arthur von Auwers (who served as business manager) were appointed codirectors of the observatory.

Vogel turned to research in spectrophotometry, a field that was to become of considerable importance. In 1876, through a study of Nova Cygni, Vogel obtained the first firm evidence of the changes that occur in a nova spectrum during the fading phase. He also began an extensive examination of the solar spectrum, intending to replace the solar spectrum tables of Kirchhoff (1861–1862) and Ångstrom (1868) with more precise ones. Vogel's painstaking measurements, the reliability of which was further increased by the new absolute wavelength measurements of Gustav Müller and Kempf, constituted an outstanding achievement for the period with regard to both exactitude and abundance of lines. Unfortunately, they were soon superseded by Rowland's tables, which were produced with diffraction gratings and therefore contained more precise measurements. In 1879, the year he completed the solar spectrum measurements, Vogel was named full professor; and on 15 March 1882 he was appointed director of the Potsdam Astrophysical Observatory, which had been officially put into service in 1879.

Vogel chose the spectroscopy of the fixed stars as his area of specialization. In response to Secchi's proposal, he sought to classify the spectra of the fixed stars; believing that these spectra would reflect the stages of development through which the stars had passed. He decided to test his classification by a spectroscopic examination of the skies, which he executed during the following years. Vogel was disappointed by the extremely uniform distribution of the individual spectral classes of his rough schema—a distribution based on his own observations (of only 4,000 objects)— for he had hoped to obtain interesting results. Such results were later obtained through a study of the Harvard classes, which were established on the basis of a greater number of objects, some of which were less bright than those Vogel had examined. Dissatisfied with his findings, Vogel abandoned work in this area.

Meanwhile, Vogel returned to a problem that had intrigued him at Bothkamp: the determination of the radial components of stellar velocities from the Doppler shifts detectable in stellar spectra. His crucial fundamental idea was to employ photography, a technique that had recently been highly developed and that he had already used to record stellar spectra. In April 1887 Vogel attended the International Congress for Astrophotography in Paris, where, presumably, he became more convinced of the correctness of his ideas. Scarcely a year later he presented to the Royal Academy of Sciences at Berlin the first results of his research, in "Über die Bestimmung der Bewegung von Sternen in Visions radius durch spektrographische Beobachtung." In it he showed that the spectrographic method yields more exact results than visual measurement of stellar spectra in the eyepiece. In a table derived from work done in collaboration with Julius Scheiner, Vogel reported the Doppler shifts of the hydrogen $\gamma$ lines in the spectra of Sirius ($\alpha$ Canis Majoris), Procyon ($\alpha$ Canis Minoris), Rigel ($\beta$ Orionis), and Arcturus ($\alpha$ Bootis). Although this initial research showed traces of haste and was conducted with instruments that were not fully adequate to the task, the results evoked great interest; for this work ended the protracted controversy over the value of Doppler's theory for the investigation of phenomena of motion in the universe and thereby gave astrophysics a new tool of immense value. Vogel worked with his collaborators to improve the observatory's apparatus, and in 1892 he published "Untersuchung über die Eigenbewegung der Sterne im Visionsradius auf spektrographischem Wege" (*Publikationen des Astrophysikalischen Observatoriums zu Potsdam*, **7**, no. 25).

Vogel's use of spectrography led to a sensational success: the discovery of the spectroscopic double stars. On the basis of periodic displacements in the spectral lines of Algol ($\beta$ Persei) and Spica ($\alpha$ Virginis), Vogel proved that these objects are actually eclipsing binary stars, the components of which could not be detected as separate entities by means of optical devices. The establishment of periodic line displacements in the Algol spectrum and their well-defined relationship with the variation of ex-

posure provided the first exact confirmation of the supposition that Algol is a component of a double star system. From the spectrographs of this system, Vogel and Scheiner derived the orbital velocity of the brighter component. Employing data on the variation of exposure and several plausible hypotheses, they also determined the dimensions of the system, the diameter of both components, the total mass of the system, and the distances of the components from each other (1889). This was the first time that important new information was logically deduced by comparing measurements of Doppler shifts with data concerning the variation of exposure of a spectrographic double star system. Vogel's introduction of these new techniques soon led to further discoveries, the first of which were Edward Pickering's findings regarding Menkalinan ($\beta$ Aurigae) and Mizar ($\zeta$ Ursae Majoris). The importance of such research is immediately evident from the relatively high number of spectrographic double stars accessible to the astronomer. (For example, probably half of the stars of spectrographic type B are of this kind.) In 1904 the spectrographic double stars played a decisive role in Hartmann's discovery of the interstellar calcium absorption lines.

As director of the Potsdam Astrophysical Observatory, Vogel had an increasing number of organizational duties, which gradually obliged him to restrict his own scientific work. On the other hand, his role in the expansion of the observatory was of considerable importance for the progress of astrophysical research. His influence and tireless efforts ensured that the observatory equipment was adequate for its ambitious research programs—for instance, a very costly photographic double refractor that was put in service in 1899 and was used to determine the radial velocities of weaker stars. The lens, achromatized for photographic work, had an aperture of 800 mm. and was the largest photographic lens ever made. Shortly after this instrument went into service, Vogel became seriously ill and had to cease working for a while. Although he never completely recovered, he was able to do a further series of studies, including one on the operational possibilities of short-focal-length reflecting telescopes for research on nebulae.

Vogel's scientific achievement brought him many international honors and assured him a place in the history of modern astronomy. The great scientific importance of the observatory he headed was due in large part to his willingness and ability to attract distinguished co-workers. Furthermore, to the extent that it was possible, given the research programs he had selected, Vogel usually assigned his co-workers to projects that corresponded to their scientific interests.

Vogel left a large sum of money to the Potsdam observatory, the interest on it to pay for study abroad and for the support of gifted children.

*BIBLIOGRAPHY*

I. ORIGINAL WORKS. The writings that Vogel published while at Potsdam are listed in W. Hassenstein, "Das Astrophysikalische Observatorium Potsdam in den Jahren 1875–1939," in *Mitteilungen des Astrophysikalischen Observatoriums (Potsdam)*, **1** (1941). This article also contains a list of all the works by Vogel's co-workers (pp. 13–55), both those that appeared in the observatory's own publications and also those that appeared elsewhere (pp. 13–53). Vogel's earlier publications and his articles in *Astronomische Nachrichten* are listed in *Generalregister der Bände 41 bis 80 der Astronomischen Nachrichten Nr. 961 bis 1920* (Kiel, 1938), col. 108; and in *Generalregister der Bände 81 bis 120 der Astronomischen Nachrichten Nr. 1921 bis 2880* (Kiel, 1891), cols. 121–122.

II. SECONDARY LITERATURE. See W. Brunner, *Pioniere der Weltallforschung* (Stuttgart, n.d. [1954?]); A. F., "Hermann Carl Vogel," in *Monthly Notices of the Royal Astronomical Society*, **68**, no. 4 (Feb. 1908), 254–257; W. Foerster, *Lebenserinnerungen und Lebenshoffnungen* (Berlin, 1911), esp. 139–140; O. Lohse, "Hermann Carl Vogel (Todes-Anzeige)," in *Astronomische Nachrichten*, **175** (1907), cols. 373–378; and G. Müller, "Hermann Carl Vogel," in *Vierteljahrsschrift der Astronomischen Gesellschaft*, **42** (1907), 323–339. See also D. B. Hermann, "Für Vorgeschichte der Astrophysikalischen Observatoriums Potsdam," in *Astronomische Nachrichten*, **296** (1975), 245–259.

DIETER B. HERRMANN

**VOGT, CARL** (*b*. Giessen, Germany, 5 July 1817; *d*. Geneva, Switzerland, 5 May 1895), *medicine, natural science.*

Vogt was the son of Philipp Friedrich Vogt, a physician, who from 1835 taught pathology and pharmacodynamics at the University of Berne. He began his studies at Giessen, where he was one of Liebig's best students and was encouraged to become a chemist. In 1835 Vogt went to Berne, where he enrolled in Valentin's courses in anatomy and physiology, and decided to study medicine. He received the medical diploma in 1839, but the natural sciences had a greater appeal for him. He enthusiastically agreed to collaborate on a major treatise on Central European freshwater fish, a project headed by Louis Agassiz; his name appears as author of the volume on Salmonidae (1842). Vogt subsequently went to Paris, where he began to write his *Lettres philosophiques et physiologiques*, intended for friends in Germany. They were published in their entirety as *Physiologische Briefe für Gebildete aller Stände* (Tubingen, 1845–1847).

After returning to Giessen, where he taught zoology and became *Reichregent* (1842), Vogt also was active in the Revolution of 1848. His involvement forced him to flee to Geneva, where he taught geology because the chair of zoology was held by F. J. Pictet de la Rive. Having become a naturalized citizen of Geneva, Vogt entered politics, becoming *conseiller aux états* and later *conseiller national*. He also was influential in transforming the Académie de Genève into a university (1872).

A work from this period, *Köhlerglaube und Wissenschaft* (Giessen, 1853), caused a great stir and went through several editions. Vogt became the staunch supporter of scientific materialism, later made famous by Ernst Haeckel. His gift for polemic and oratory enabled Vogt to exert considerable influence through both his speeches and his numerous publications. In 1872 he was appointed to the chair of zoology and became director of the Institute of Zoology, a post he held until his death.

Above all, Vogt was a distinguished zoologist whose writings did much to further the development of this science. His *Lehrbuch der praktischen vergleichenden Anatomie* (Brunswick, 1855) was long a classic. In 1840, at the age of twenty-three, Vogt published an important work, *Beiträge zur Neurologie des Reptilien*. After having begun to study the embryology of certain freshwater fish under the guidance of Agassiz, he continued this work throughout his life.

The chair of geology, assigned to him by the Geneva government, gave Vogt the opportunity to write *Lehrbuch der Geologie und Petrefaktenkunde*, the four editions of which (1846–1879) demonstrate its wide interest. It was, however, to marine biological research that Vogt devoted his energy, as is shown by his remarkable publications on hectocotyli, Cephalopoda, and Siphonophora. In 1863 Vogt published the two-volume *Vorlesungen über den Menschen, seine Stellung in der Schöpfung und in der Geschichte der Erde*, which assured his reputation as a scholar and materialist philosopher. "Mémoires sur les microcéphales ou hommes-singes" (1866) brought Vogt recognition as one of the first anthropologists. He espoused

Darwin's ideas and became a strong partisan of natural selection.

## BIBLIOGRAPHY

Vogt's autobiography is *Aus meinem Leben, Erinnerungen und Rückblicke* (Stuttgart, 1896).

See also H. Buess, *Recherches, découvertes et inventions de médecins suisses*, translated by R. Kaech (Basel, 1946), 65–66; E. Hirschman, *K. Vogt als Politiker* (Ph.D. diss., Berlin, 1924); E. Krause, "Carl Vogt," in *Allgemeine deutsche Biographie*, XL (Leipzig, 1896), 181–189; H. Misteli, *Carl Vogt. Seine Entwicklung vom angehenden naturwissenschaftlichen Materialisten zum idealen Politiker des Paulskirche* (Ph.D. diss., Zurich, 1938); and W. Vogt, *La vie d'un homme* (Paris, 1896).

P. E. PILET

**VOGT, JOHAN HERMANN LIE** (*b*. Tvedestrand, Norway, 14 October 1858; *d*. Trondheim, Norway, 3 January 1932), *geology.*

Vogt was the son of a physician and, on his mother's side, the nephew of Sophus Lie. After studying for a year at the Dresden Polytechnikum, he transferred to the University of Christiania (Oslo), where he graduated as a mining engineer–geologist in 1880. He did graduate work at Stockholm in 1882, studying geology under W. C. Brøgger, metallurgy under Richard Åkermann, and chemistry under W. Eggerts. Vogt was appointed professor of metallurgy at the University of Christiania in 1886 and in 1912 moved to the Technical University of Norway at Trondheim, where he was professor of geology, ore deposits, and metallurgy (except iron). He retained this post until his retirement in 1929.

Vogt was a pioneer in ore geology and in the physical chemistry of silicates as a basis for igneous rock petrology. His work in the latter field began with studies of slag minerals. In a series of papers, the first of which appeared in 1883, he provided the first descriptions of a number of slag minerals: enstatite, wollastonite (pseudo-wollastonite), fayalite, monticellite varieties, åkermannite, oldhamite, manganblende (alabandite), troilite, and sphalerite. Vogt soon began using the crystallization of slags as a model for silicate crystallization in igneous rocks, as shown by the title of his papers of 1888–1890: "Beiträge zur Kenntnis der Gesetze der Mineralbildung in Schmelzmassen und in den neovulkanischen Ergussgesteinen." Inspired by his mineral-

ogical studies of slags, he generalized his studies of ores and silicate rocks in "Die Silikatschmelzlösungen" (2 pts., 1902), a pioneer paper in which the crystallization relations of the different minerals and their dependence upon eutectic relations are considered. The lowering of melting points in melts with several components and the importance of eutectic compositions in binary series are discussed. The general relationships are applied to natural silicate melts and specifically to the eutectic relation between quartz and feldspars in igneous rocks. Bearing still more directly on natural relationships is "Physikalisch-chemische Gesetze der Kristallizationsfolge in Eruptiv-Gesteinen" (1905), in which the crystallization within the ternary feldspar system orthoclase-albite-anorthite and the granite system quartz-orthoclase-albite is discussed.

In another classic paper, "Über anchi-monomineralische und anchi-eutektische Eruptiv-Gesteine" (1908), Vogt discussed magmatic differentiation, on the basis of the theory proposed by Brøgger and several other leading petrographers at the turn of the century, treating the parallelism between crystallization and differentiation of silicate melts. In this work he stressed the importance of eutectic crystallization as a major factor in magmatic differentiation. Since he emphasized the physicochemical laws governing the crystallization and development of igneous rocks, Vogt was sharply critical of the static petrographic system developed by Cross, Iddings, Pirsson, and Washington (CIPW). During World War I, Vogt studied mixed systems of silicates and sulfides, stressing the importance of the low mutual solubility of such melts. This result was fundamental to his treatise on magmatic sulfide ore formation, especially nickel ore. Publications from Vogt's last ten years were marked by his continued analysis of the physicochemical laws governing magmatic differentiation.

Vogt's first paper in English appeared in *Journal of Geology*: "The Physical Chemistry of the Crystallization and Magmatic Differentiation of Igneous Rocks" (1921). Nearly the same title was used for the three-volume work published at Oslo (1924–1931). The most important part of the first volume is the discussion of the concentration of mixed crystals with high melting points in early-formed rocks and that of mixed crystals with low melting points in the magmatic end stage. The second volume deals with the relations of the ternary feldspar system orthoclase-albite-anorthite, based on many analyses; and the third, which concentrates on the rocks of the magmatic end stage, also contains a large number of chemical analyses. Not all of Vogt's main conclusions have proved correct, but he applied the principles of physical chemistry to natural silicate systems more intensely than anyone else of his generation and therefore is often called the father of modern physicochemical petrology. Among the many terms Vogt introduced is "cotectic" curves, applied to what were formerly called eutectic lines or reaction lines. His last paper was "What We May Learn from Brøgger's Essexitic Hurum Volcano Concerning Magmatic Differentiation" (*Festschrift Brøgger, Norsk geologisk tidsskrift* [1932]).

Vogt's other main field of interest was ore geology, in which he was considered a leader at that time, although his work was less original. His most important general contribution is the concept of a group of magmatic ore deposits—ilmenite, chromite, and nickeliferous pentlandite—formed early in the crystallization sequence. Vogt's early contributions (1884–1889) concerned important ore deposits in Norway. In these papers he supported the proponents of a sedimentary origin for pyritic sulfide ores. Soon afterward, Vogt changed his views on ore genesis from the syngenetic to the epigenetic theory, which in the 1870's was supported by Theodor Kjerulf and had originated with J. Durocher and Duchanoy around 1850. A magmatic, epigenetic view of sulfide ore deposits was maintained in Vogt's first well-known paper published in *Zeitschrift für praktische Geologie*: "Über die Kieslagerstätten von Typus Röros, Vigsnäs, Sulitjelma in Norwegen und Rammelsberg in Deutschland." Vogt's views were based on sharp field observations, a very good memory, and extensive travel. In the 1880's he visited European universities and observed many important ore deposits. He therefore was well qualified to write *Die Lagerstätten der nutzbaren Mineralien und Gesteine* (1910–1921) with F. Beyschlag and P. Krusch. Important at the time, this two-volume treatise remains a major handbook of ore geology.

Vogt was active in politics for several years and was always eager to apply his theoretical knowledge of ore deposits to practical purposes, seeking new ore fields and helping to develop existing ones. This interest is reflected in a work published in 1895, "Kobberets historie i fortid og nutid og om udsigterne for fremtiden, med saerligt hensyn til den norske bergverksdrift på kobber" ("The History of Copper in the Past and Present and the Prospects for the Future, with Special Regard to the Norwegian Mining of Copper").

Vogt received an honorary doctorate from the University of Aachen in 1911, the Penrose Medal of the Society of Economic Geologists (United States), and the Wollaston Medal of the Geological Society of London.

*BIBLIOGRAPHY*

There is a complete bibliography of Vogt's more than 200 published works in *Norsk geologisk tidsskrift*, **11** (1932), 454–466. The titles of his most important publications are mentioned in the text.

The only detailed biographies were published in Norwegian, some soon after his death and one commemorating the centenary of his birth—J. A. W. Bugge, in *Kongelige Norske videnskabers selskabs forhandlinger*, **31** (1958).

CHRISTOFFER OFTEDAHL

**VOGT, THOROLF** (*b*. Vang, Hedmark, Norway, 7 June 1888; *d*. Trondheim, Norway, 8 December 1958), *geology*.

The son of J. H. L. Vogt, Thorolf published his first mineralogical paper at the age of twenty. He became assistant geologist for the Geological Survey of Norway in 1909 and geologist in 1914. From 1915 to 1923 he was research associate at the University of Oslo. Vogt succeeded his father as professor of mineralogy and geology at the Technical University of Norway, at Trondheim, in 1929. In his earlier years he studied in Sweden, Denmark, Great Britain, and the United States; later he led a series of expeditions to Arctic areas, to Spitsbergen (1925, 1928), and to southeastern Greenland (1931). Of his more than 100 papers, many are short and of little importance; and his contribution to geology consists of a few major volumes. A description of the stratigraphy of the arcosic rocks (sparagmites) in central Norway and their relations to marine Lower Cambrian (1923) remains the standard treatise of Eocambrian (now called latest Precambrian) stratigraphy in Scandinavia. Vogt's main work was a monograph on a small area in northern Norway within the Caledonian zone, a petrographic-geologic description of the sulfide-rich Sulitjelma area (1927). Vogt's most important contribution was perhaps the new discussion of metamorphism on the basis of the mineral facies of Pentti Eskola. The monograph was intended as an introduction to a projected work on the description of the sulfide deposits, but the latter never appeared.

During World War II, Vogt drew upon his extensive botanical knowledge in studying plants near the sulfide deposits of Røros, in southeastern Norway. Twelve brief papers resulting from this work, collectively entitled "Geokjemisk og geobotanisk mamleting," are now considered to be a classic in geochemical prospecting. A paper of 1945 describes the stratigraphy and petrography of a small area south of Trondheim in great detail. This area is of fundamental importance for the eugeosynclinal sequence of the Scandinavian Caledonides, and the paper remained the standard reference for twenty years. At the time of his death Vogt was working several fields, including a general study of metamorphic amphiboles. The completed manuscript of the first part, "Constitution and Classification," was printed posthumously.

Vogt's importance in Norwegian geology derives from his publications and his wide-ranging activity. He taught geology and ore geology to mining students for thirty years and participated in many ore-prospecting projects. He also was active in introducing and developing geophysical methods into the practice of ore prospecting in Norway.

*BIBLIOGRAPHY*

Vogt published some 100 works from 1908 to 1958; three more papers appeared posthumously (1964–1967). The most important are "Sulitelmafeltets geologi og petrografi," which is *Norges geologiske undersøkelse*, no. 121 (1927); "Geokjemisk og geobotanisk mamleting," in *Kongelige Norske videnskabers selskabs forhandlinger*, **12–20** (1939–1947); "The Geology of Part of the Hølonda-Horg District, a Type Area in the Trondheim Region," in *Norsk geologisk tidsskrift*, **25** (1945), 449–528; and "The Amphibole Group, Constitution and Classification," in *Kongelige Norske videnskabernes selskabs skrifter*, no. 7 (1966), 1–55.

There is a short biography by Ivar Oftedal (in Norwegian) and a complete bibliography in *Norsk geologisk tidsskrift*, **39** (1959), 1–11.

                        CHRISTOFFER OFTEDAHL

**VOIGT, JOHANN CARL WILHELM** (*b.* Allstedt, Germany, 20 February 1752; *d.* Ilmenau, Germany, 1 January 1821), *geology, mining.*

Voigt came from a family of Thuringian civil servants; his father was magistrate of the district of Allstedt, which was then part of the duchy of Weimar. After studying law at the University of Jena (1773–1775), he transferred to the Freiberg mining academy (1776–1779), where he studied mainly with Abraham Gottlob Werner.

When Voigt returned to Weimar, he became acquainted with Goethe, who had already been working for a long time with his elder brother in the Weimar administration and with whom he formed a lifelong friendship. Through Voigt, Goethe learned the systematics and classification of minerals and rocks. Their friendship was of great importance to both men: through Voigt, Goethe learned the fundamentals of mineralogy and became an admirer of Werner; and through Goethe, Voigt began a career as a researcher and mining official.

Voigt was commissioned to tour the duchy of Weimar and describe it mineralogically. The result of this work, done in 1780, was the two-volume *Mineralogische Reisen durch das Herzogthum Weimar und Eisenach*, which Goethe published (1781–1785). At Goethe's behest Voigt traveled through the Fulda region in 1781 and the Harz Mountains in 1782, preparing mineralogical maps of these areas. In 1783 he became mining secretary and later mining director. Much of his time was subsequently devoted to running the silver mine at Ilmenau, which was reopened on Goethe's initiative in 1784 but had to be abandoned by 1800. Voigt's works on the petrography and geology of Thuringia and his contributions to the science of mineral deposits brought him considerable renown. He became known more widely, however, through his geological works, especially his contribution to the debate concerning the origin of basalt.

In his *Mineralogische Reisen* Voigt had presented the Thuringian basalts as being of volcanic origin. This approach provoked a protest from Werner, who had become the leader of the "neptunist" party, which considered basalt to be a marine sediment. The "neptunist controversy" lasted in its public, and sometimes quite sharply conducted, form until about 1795, at which time the neptunists appeared to have won. In the course of this dispute Voigt became the leader of the volcanists in Germany. His interpretation of the basalt mountains as the remnants of the erosion of the eruptions of great volcanoes was almost correct; but he then allowed himself to be influenced by the incorrect views of William Hamilton and August Veltheim, who considered the basalt mountains to be groups of volcanoes exposed by erosion. Voigt did, however, make a number of enduring contributions to scientific volcanism and was the first to draw attention to the phenomena of contact metamorphism.

BIBLIOGRAPHY

I. ORIGINAL WORKS. Voigt's publications include *Mineralogische Reisen durch das Herzogthum Weimar und Eisenach*, 2 vols. (Weimar, 1781–1785); *Petrographische Landkarte des Hochstifts Fulda* (Frankfurt, 1782); *Mineralogische Reise von Weimar über den Thüringer Wald und Meiningen bis Hanau* (Leipzig, 1787); *Mineralogische und bergmännische Abhandlungen*, 3 vols. (Leipzig, 1789–1791); *Praktische Gebirgskunde* (Weimar, 1792); *Kleine mineralogische Schriften* (Weimar, 1799); *Mineralogische Reise nach den Braunkohlenwerken und Basalten in Hessen wie auch nach den Schieferkohlenwerken des Unterharzes* (Weimar, 1802); and *Geschichte des Ilmenauischen Bergbaues* (Sondershausen–Nordhausen, 1821).

II. SECONDARY LITERATURE. There is no full-length biography, but Voigt is often mentioned in biographies of Werner and Goethe, and in works on the controversy over Neptunism—for instance, Walther Herrmann, *Goethe und Trebra*, which is Freiberger Forschungshefte, ser. D., no. 9 (Berlin, 1955), 36, 48–52, 62–64; and Otfried Wagenbreth, *Abraham Gottlob Werner und der Höhepunkt des Neptunistenstreits um 1790*, which is Freiberger Forschungshefte, ser. D, no. 11 (Berlin, 1955), see 183–241. A short biography is Carl Schiffner, *Aus dem Leben alter Freiberger Bergstudenten*, I (Freiberg, 1935), 16–17.

HANS BAUMGÄRTEL

**VOIGT, WOLDEMAR** (*b.* Leipzig, Germany, 2 September 1850; *d.* Göttingen, Germany, 13 December 1919), *physics.*

Voigt graduated from the Nikolaischule at Leipzig in 1868. He then entered the University of Leipzig, but in 1870 his studies were interrupted by service in the Franco-Prussian War. He resumed his studies in 1871, this time at Königsberg. At first Voigt was undecided between a career in physics and a career in music, for the latter had always played a large role in his life: Felix Mendelssohn and Robert Schumann had been frequent visitors to his parents' house. His musical ear was highly trained; and while in the army he would often pass the time while marching by reciting, note for note, the complete orchestration of entire symphonic pieces. He finally decided on a career in physics, on the ground that, unlike music, in physics there is a reasonable mean, not simply highs and lows.

While at Königsberg, Voigt came under the influence of Franz Neumann, his deep respect and love for whom largely determined his career, in terms of subject matter, the style of his research, and the manner in which he presented his work to the physics community. His dissertation on the elastic constants of rock salt was completed in 1874. He then returned to Leipzig, where he taught at the the Nikolaischule, but in 1875 was called back to Königsberg as extraordinary professor of physics. In 1883 Voigt was appointed ordinary professor of theoretical physics at Göttingen, with the promise that he and Eduard Reike were to have a new physical institute (which was not ready until 1905). His chief research interests centered on the understanding of crystals, but near the turn of the century he became more and more concerned with the Zeeman effect and the electron theory.

Voigt's interest in crystals was closely related to Neumann's work. At Königsberg, Neumann had worked in both the physics department and the department of mineralogy, so it was quite natural that he should do extensive work on the optical properties of crystals. Neumann had developed a mechanical theory of light propagation that assumed that light oscillations had a mechanical-elastic nature. The oscillations were transmitted through an ether conceived of as an elastic solid. He had not restricted his activities in physics to theoretical work, however, and had initiated a great number of experimental studies; his students spent many hours in his laboratories studying the properties of crystals.

Voigt brought this tradition of theoretical and experimental work to Göttingen. Although for many years he was hampered by lack of adequate facilities, he not only pursued theoretical studies of the properties of crystals but also undertook a host of very delicate experimental investigations in which the physical properties of many crystalline substances were measured.

According to the theories of Poisson and Cauchy, which were based on special molecular assumptions, certain relationships must exist between the constants of a crystal regardless of its classification. Voigt determined the elastic constants for a wide variety of crystals and showed that the predicted relationships were not at all satisfied. While some felt that this work vindicated those who objected to forming special hypotheses about the nature of crystals, Voigt did not accept this point of view and in many of his publications indicated the direction that must be taken in amending the molecular hypothesis.

In 1887, in a paper on the Doppler effect in which he analyzed the differential equations for oscillations in an incompressible elastic medium, Voigt established a set of transformation equations that later became known as the Lorentz transformations.

Voigt's extensive theoretical and physical researches on the nature of crystals were summarized in *Magneto- und Elektro-Optik* (1908) and *Kristallphysik* (1910). These treatises reveal the elegance of his mathematical treatments and the great orderliness that his research had brought to the understanding of crystals. The elastic, thermal, electric, and magnetic properties of crystals were ordered in magnitudes of three types: scalar, vector, and tensor. In fact, it was Voigt who in 1898 had introduced the term "tensor" into the vocabulary of mathematical physics.

Even though Voigt devoted considerable time to his research and his students, and even though he acquired more administrative responsibility at Göttingen, he never gave up an active interest in music and musicology. He was recognized as an expert on Bach's vocal works and in 1911 published a book on Bach's church cantatas. Voigt often referred to the study of physics in musical terms. To him the region of science that represented the highest degree of orchestration and that possessed the utmost in rhythm and melody was crystal physics. It was altogether fitting that on 15 December 1919 his funeral bier was carried from his house to its final resting place to the strains of a Bach chorale.

## BIBLIOGRAPHY

I. ORIGINAL WORKS. There is no comprehensive catalog of Voigt's more than 200 publications. Among his most significant works are "Allgemeine Formeln für die Bestimmung der Elasticitäts Constanten von Krystallen durch die Beobachtung der Biegung und Drillung von Prismen," in *Annalen der Physik*, **16** (1882), 273–310, 398–415; "Volumen und Winkeländerung krystallinischen Körper bei all-oder einseitigen Druck," *ibid.*, 416–426; "Theorie des Lichtes für vollkommen durchsichtige Media," *ibid.*, **19** (1883), 873–908; "Zur Theorie des Lichtes," *ibid.*, **20** (1883), 444–452; "Theorie der absorbirenden isotropen Medien insbesonder Theorie der optischen Eigenschaften der Metalle," *ibid.*, **23** (1884), 104–147; "Theorie der electromagnetischen Drehung der Polarisationsebene," *ibid.*, 493–511; "Zur Theorie des Lichtes für absorbirende isotrope Medien," *ibid.*, **31** (1887), 233–242; and "Zur Erklärung der elliptischen Polarisation bei Reflexion an durchsichtigen Medien," *ibid.*, **32** (1887), 526–528.

Also see "Ueber das Doppler'sche Princip," in *Nachrichten von der Königlichen Gesellschaft der Wissenschaften zu Göttingen* (1887), 44–51; "Theorie des Lichtes für bewegte Medien," in *Annalen der Physik*, **35** (1888), 370–396; 524–551; "Zur Theorie des Lichtes," *ibid.*, **43** (1891), 410–437; "Ueber einen einfachen Apparat zur Bestimmung der thermischen Dilation fester Körper, speciel der Krystalle," *ibid.*, 831–834; "Bestimmung der Elasticitätsconstanten einiger quasi-isotroper Metalle durch langsame Schwingungen von Stäben," *ibid.*, **48** (1893), 674–707; "Bestimmung der Constanten der thermische-Dilation und des thermische-Druckes für einige quasi-isotrope Metalle," *ibid.*, **49** (1893), 697–708; "Die specifischen Wärmen $c_p$ und $c_v$ einiger quasi-isotroper Metalle," *ibid.*, 709–718; "Beiträge zur moleculären Theorie der Piëzoelectricität," *ibid.*, **51** (1894), 638–660; "Ueber Medien ohne innere Kräfte und über eine durch sie gelieferte mechanische Deutung der Maxwell-Hertz'schen Gleichungen," *ibid.*, **52** (1894), 665–672; and "Beiträge zur geometrischen Darstellung der physikalischen Eigenschaften der Krystalle," *ibid.*, **63** (1897), 376–385.

Additional works are "Zur kinetischen Theorie idealer Flüssigkeiten," in *Nachrichten von der Königlichen Gesellschaft der Wissenschaften zu Göttingen* (1897), 19–47, 261–272; "Lässt sich die Pyroelectricität der Krystalle vollständig auf piëzoelectrische Wirkungen zuruckführen?" in *Annalen der Physik*, **66** (1898), 1030–1060; "Doppelbrechung von im Magnetfelde befindlichen Natriumdampf in der Richtung normal zu den Kraftlinien," in *Nachrichten von der Königlichen Gesellschaft der Wissenschaften zu Göttingen* (1898), 355–359; "Ueber das bei der sogenannten totalen Reflexion in des zweite Medium eindringende Licht," in *Annalen der Physik*, **67** (1899), 185–200; "Zur Theorie der magneto-optischen Erscheinungen," *ibid.*, 345–365; "Ueber die Proportionalität von Emissions- und Absorptionsvermögen," *ibid.*, 366–387; "Weiteres zur Theorie der Zeemaneffectes," *ibid.*, **68** (1899), 352–364; "Neuere Untersuchungen über die optischen Wirkungen eines Magnetfeldes," in *Physikalische Zeitschrift*, **1** (1899), 116–120, 128–131, 138–143; "Zur Festigkeitlehre," in *Annalen der Physik*, **4** (1901), 567–591; "Beiträge zur Elektronentheorie des Lichtes," *ibid.*, **6** (1901), 459–505; "Elektronenhypothese und Theorie des Magnetismus," in *Nachrichten von der Königlichen Gesellschaft der Wissenschaften zu Göttingen* (1901), 169–200; and "Ueber einige neuere Beobachtungen von magneto-optischen Wirkungen," in *Annalen der Physik*, **8** (1902), 872–889.

Further, see "Ueber das optische Verhalten von Kristallen der hemiëdrischen Gruppe des monokinen Systemes," in *Physikalische Zeitschrift*, **7** (1906), 267–269; "Betrachtungen über die komplizierteren Formen des Zeemaneffektes," in *Annalen der Physik*, **24** (1907), 193–224; "Beobachtungen über natürliche und magnetische Drehung der Polarisationsebene in Krystallen von K. Honda," in *Physikalische Zeitschrift*, **9** (1908), 585–590; *Magneto- und Elektro-Optik* (Leipzig, 1908); *Kristallphysik* (Leipzig–Berlin, 1910; 2nd ed., 1926); "Zur Theorie der komplizierteren Zeemaneffecte," in

*Annalen der Physik*, **36** (1911), 873–906; "Allgemeines über Emission und Absorption in zusammenhang mit der Frage der Intensitätsmessungen beim Zeeman-Effect," in *Nachrichten von der Königlichen Gesellschaft der Wissenschaften zu Göttingen* (1911), 71–97; "Ueber Emission und Absorption schichtenweise stetig inhomogener Körper," in *Annalen der Physik*, **39** (1912), 1381–1407; "Weiteres zur Polarisation des Rowland Gittern gebeugten Lichtes," in *Nachrichten von der Königlichen Gesellschaft der Wissenschaften zu Göttingen* (1912), 385–417, written with P. Collet; "Ueber die anormalen Zeeman-effekte der Wasserstofflinien," in *Annalen der Physik*, **40** (1913), 368–380; "Weiteres zum Ausbau der Koppelungstheorie der Zeeman-effekte," *ibid.*, **41** (1913), 403–440; "Ueber die Zeeman-effekte bei mehrfachen Serienlinien besonders auch bei dem O-Triplet λ =3947," *ibid.*, **43** (1914), 1137–1164; and "Ueber sekundäre Wirkungen bei piëzoelektrischen Vorgängen, insbesondere im Falle der Drillung und Biegung eines Krieszylinders," *ibid.*, **48** (1915), 433–448.

II. SECONDARY LITERATURE. See E. T. Whittaker, *A History of the Theories of Aether and Electricity*, 2 vols. (New York, 1960), I, 333, 415; II, 33, 160, 238–239. Obituary notices are by H. L[amb?], in *Proceedings of the Royal Society*, **99A** (1921), xxix–xxx; and by C. Runge, in *Physikalische Zeitschrift*, **21** (1920), 81–82; and in *Nachrichten von der Königlichen Gesellschaft zu Göttingen: Geschäftliche Mitteilungen aus dem Jahre 1920* (Göttingen, 1920), 47–52.

                                        STANLEY GOLDBERG

**VOIT, CARL VON** (*b*. Amberg, Bavaria, 31 October 1831; *d*. Munich, Germany, 31 January 1908), *physiology*.

Voit was the son of August Voit, a well-known architect. He entered medical school in Munich, in 1848, and completed his training there in 1854, after spending the year 1851 at Würzburg. In 1855 he studied chemistry in Göttingen with Wöhler, and the following year became an assistant to Theodor Bischoff at the Physiological Institute in Munich. In 1859 he became a lecturer at the University of Munich, and in 1863 he was named professor of physiology, a position he held for the rest of his career. During the next three decades Voit became the leader of the dominant school investigating metabolism. He acquired an authoritative position through the technical mastery with which he refined previously developed procedures, and by means of which he was able to resolve fundamental problems into which his predecessors had fallen.

When Voit returned to Munich in 1852, he attended Liebig's chemistry course, and was inspired by Liebig's writings on "animal chemistry" to investigate the "laws" of animal nutrition. For many years Voit was guided by Liebig's theory that the organized parts of the body are formed exclusively by nitrogenous "albuminoid" nutrient substances (plastic aliments), and that non-nitrogenous nutrients (respiratory aliments) are oxidized in the blood to produce animal heat. He also adhered to Liebig's belief that all mechanical work is produced by the "metamorphosis" of the nitrogenous tissue constituents. Liebig's contention that one could measure the amount of tissue metamorphosis by the formation of urea provided the research program to which Voit devoted much of his career. At the time Voit entered this field, Jean-Baptiste Boussingault, Friedrich Bidder and Carl Schmidt, and Bischoff had already carried out extensive comparative measurements of the intake and output of the elements (carbon, hydrogen, oxygen, and nitrogen) constituting the bulk of the food, excretions, and respiratory gases of animals. Their results had created several theoretical and practical dilemmas. They realized that one should ideally measure the composition of the food and excrements simultaneously with the gaseous exchanges, but the differing experimental conditions appropriate respectively to the collection of the excrements and to that of the respiratory gases had prevented this. In 1852 Bischoff encountered another serious setback. Using a simple and reliable new method developed by Liebig for measuring urea, Bischoff found that large portions of the dietary nitrogen were unaccounted for in the urine; this unexplained nitrogen "deficit" seemed to preclude direct measurements of the turnover of nitrogenous tissue constituents.

When he became Bischoff's assistant, Voit continued Bischoff's feeding experiments on dogs. Taking care to assure that the nitrogen content of the meat that was fed to the dogs was uniform, and to collect the feces and urine without losses, Voit found that the nitrogen absorbed in the meat was always nearly equal to that in the urea, or could be accounted for by the weight changes in the animal. This outcome reassured Voit that under rigorously controlled conditions one could rely on the quantity of urea excreted as a measure of nitrogenous metabolism.

Encouraged by this success, Voit carried out extensive further investigations with Bischoff, determining the quantities of urea formed by a dog under various dietary conditions. Between 1857 and 1860 they tried pure meat diets, in which they systematically increased and decreased the daily quantities, and combinations of meat with varying quantities of sugar, starch, fat, and gelatin. The changes in the urea production under these conditions led them to conclude that the rate of decomposition of nitrogenous matter in an animal does not depend directly upon the quantity of nitrogenous nutrient but upon the nutritive condition of the animal. As the nitrogenous mass of the body increases or decreases, so does the rate of metamorphosis of these constituents. The same diet might at one time supply enough nitrogen and at another time not, because the requirement itself varies with the changing condition of the animal. Additions of sugar, starch, or fat decrease the output of urea by a relatively small amount. In 1860 they published their results in a lengthy treatise entitled *The Laws of the Nutrition of Carnivorous Animals.* Practically, they believed they had established methods that could be used for determining the most economical quantitative combination of nitrogenous and non-nitrogenous foods, which would maintain a given animal. Theoretically, they thought they had confirmed Liebig's distinction between plastic and respiratory nutrients.

Then Voit took up on his own the question of whether other factors can influence the rate of decomposition of organic substances. He began by examining the effects of coffee but concluded that it does not significantly affect the nitrogenous metabolism. During this series of experiments, Voit realized that he could distinguish effects of an added factor most clearly if the animal were in a condition of equilibrium between the intake and output of nitrogenous substances. He learned that if a dog is fed a steady nitrogenous daily diet, the nitrogen consumption gradually rises or falls until it balances the intake, and the nutritional condition of the animal thereafter remains constant.

From Liebig's assertion that the metamorphosis of nitrogenous tissue substance is the sole source of motion and his claim that the urea formed is a measure of that metamorphosis, it followed that muscle activity ought to increase the amount of urea excreted. To test that inference, Voit trained a dog to run rapidly, for ten minutes at a time, on a large treadmill. He compared the urea output over three days on which the dog had run six times daily, with the output over three days of rest. He found that the performance of a great amount of mechanical work produced only very small increments of urea excretion. These unexpected results seemed to him at first completely incompatible with his previous conceptions. In order to reconcile the results he assumed that the energy released by nitrogenous decomposition during rest is converted into an "electromotive force," which can be transformed in turn into muscle motion. There is therefore a store of energy available, limited by the amount of nitrogenous matter that decomposes each day. This theory explained why an animal can do only a certain amount of work in a day. Thereafter Voit considered the urea production as a measure not of the muscle activity at any particular time, but of the capacity for such activity over a longer time period.

The rigor and comprehensiveness of Bischoff and Voit's investigations quickly won them a leading position in the field of nutrition, and after 1860 their experimental results were featured in influential physiological textbooks. Their interpretations of their results, however, were not generally accepted. Carl Vogt published a sweeping polemic review in which he tried to show that their analytical foundations were not adequate to support their theories concerning internal processes. In a more penetrating critique, Moritz Traube argued in 1861 that Voit's treadmill experiment repudiated the doctrine that organized muscle is decomposed by its work, and that urea gives a measure of the muscle force expended. Of all the objections that Voit's views encountered, that which caused him the most trouble was the repeated denial of his claim that all of the nitrogen of the substances decomposed in the body is excreted in the urine and feces. From 1860 to 1870 Voit devoted much of his effort to the defense of his methods and conclusions from such criticisms.

In their joint experiments Voit and Bischoff calculated indirectly the quantities of carbon, hydrogen, and oxygen exhaled, by subtracting the amounts of these elements excreted from the amounts ingested. From these differences and a rough estimate of the daily heat production, they judged whether the substances gained or lost, in addition to the nitrogenous constituents, were likely to be fat, water, or both. In order to obviate the uncertainties arising from such estimates, Voit afterward sought means to measure directly the respiratory products. His colleague and former teacher Pettenkofer constructed a respiration chamber large enough to accommodate either a man or an animal for a day. In 1861 they began combined feeding-respiration experiments. In the first group of experiments they measured the carbonic acid exhaled, but not the water, so that they could not calculate the oxygen consumption. The quantity of carbonic acid exhaled daily varied widely and, like urea production, seemed to depend on changes in the nutritional conditions. With a large pure meat diet, less carbon was exhaled than ingested, a result that led Pettenkofer and Voit to think that after the decomposition of the "flesh" in the body, a portion of the non-nitrogenous residue may be deposited as fat. This and similar subsequent results led Voit to question the prevailing view that the fat formed in animals is derived from carbohydrate.

Beginning in 1862 Pettenkofer and Voit measured the water vapor as well as the carbonic acid exhaled. They were then able to calculate the absorbed oxygen from the difference between the initial weight of the dog—together with the food and water it ingested—and its final weight plus the excretions and the expired carbonic acid and water. Their first experiments produced anomalous ratios between the oxygen absorbed and that contained in the exhaled carbonic acid. In February 1863, after making various refinements, they succeeded in attaining a complete balance of the incoming and outgoing elements for their dog at equilibrium on a pure meat diet. The difference between the total measured daily input of carbon, hydrogen, nitrogen, and oxygen, and the totals contained in the excretions and exhaled gases, was less than one percent of the total mass of material exchanged. As Pettenkofer and Voit pointed out, this was the first measurement of the intake and output of an animal for which every single value was ascertained by experiment. They had reached a goal that numerous investigators had pursued for nearly twenty-five years. To do so they had had to combine two types of experiment—nutritional and respirational measurements—which had previously been carried out separately because the conditions required for accurate measurements of one type of experiment seemed incompatible with those required for the other. It had been difficult to extend respirational experiments beyond a few hours, whereas nutritional experiments had appeared reliable only if they lasted several days. Pettenkofer's large, accurate respiration apparatus, in addition to the precise control Voit had attained over the diets and analysis of excretions, enabled the two collaborators to make both sets of measurements on one animal over the same time period.

Throughout the 1860's Voit kept up the same kind of measurements of the nitrogenous *Stoffwechsel* of dogs that he had been making since 1857. In the later experiments he elucidated in closer detail the variables affecting the consumption of nitrogenous substances in particular nutritional states, and he further refined his control over the analytical factors. By 1866 he could show that

the excretion of urea by a dog on a uniform diet is so regular that the daily quantities deviate from the mean by less than three grams. Voit increasingly stressed the primacy of method over theories concerning the internal nature of nutritional phenomena. Gradually he lost his commitment to the central theoretical ideas for the support of which he had originally devised his methods. Yet he never gave up the goal of understanding the intermediate steps in the metamorphosis of nutrient materials within animals.

In 1866 Voit showed that the daily urea production of a dog in periods of hunger declined in diminishing decrements until after the sixth day, when the rate remained nearly steady. The initial decrease was largest when the animal had been best nourished just before the period of abstinence. When he subtracted the nearly constant amount secreted after the fifth day from the amount excreted during the first day of hunger, the remainder was proportional to the quantity of "flesh" stored up in the animal during its preceding period of nourishment. These patterns led Voit to propose that there are two types of protein in the body—a large proportion derived directly from the nourishment, of which about 70 percent undergoes decomposition daily, and a much smaller amount, of which only about 1 percent can decompose during one day. He called the two types storage protein and organ protein, and in his later investigations he sought to determine the effects of various kinds of nourishment on their proportions.

Using the respiration chamber, Voit also continued his collaborative work with Pettenkofer. In August 1865 they applied their methods to a diabetic patient in order to see how the rates of the nutritional decomposition processes are changed by this disease. In 1866 they carried out similar investigations on a leukemia patient. They then realized that they needed bases of comparison with the rates of decomposition in normal humans. Therefore, over the next twelve months they carried out investigations on two healthy men. The papers that resulted from these and their subsequent experiments provided the foundation for the many studies on metabolism in health and disease that were carried out over the rest of the century.

During the 1860's a number of events, including especially the experiments of Fick and Wislicenus, undermined Liebig's theory that the decomposition of nitrogenous substances is the sole source of muscle work. With Pettenkofer, Voit confirmed his own earlier treadmill experiments showing that exercise produces no increase in the formation of urea. With the respiration chamber they also observed the large augmentation in the expiration of $CO_2$ and water, which they and others linked with the increased consumption of fat or carbohydrate. Voit continued to resist the conclusion that the combustion of non-nitrogenous substances provided mechanical work, for that view ignored the obvious influence of the protein content of the nourishment and of the body on the sustained capacity of the organism for work. Nevertheless, his own belief that there are two sources of urea—organ and storage protein—had rendered nearly meaningless Liebig's definition of nitrogenous nutrients as "plastic" aliments. By 1867 Voit acknowledged that there was no evidence for Liebig's idea that proteins are decomposed only during the activity of the organs, or that nitrogenous nutrients must become part of organized tissue before they are decomposed. The old concept of the *Stoffwechsel* which represented this view had, he said, lost its meaning. At the same time Voit was developing further support for his theory that animal fat was produced from the decomposition products of nitrogenous substances rather than from carbohydrate. Liebig strongly disagreed with Voit's view. By 1869, when Voit presented all of the accumulated evidence for his own position, he had dissociated himself from most of Liebig's theories concerning nutrition. In that year Liebig wrote a defense of his concepts of the source of muscle motion and of the conversion of carbohydrate to fat. In his article he referred to Voit's demonstration of the formation of fat from protein as worthless. Deeply offended, Voit wrote in 1870 a long reply in which he relentlessly exposed the inadequacies of Liebig's theories on nutrition.

Voit's own nutritional theories remained controversial. Pflüger and others opposed his distinction between organ and storage, or "circulating," protein and his arguments for the conversion of protein into fat. Voit's laboratory nevertheless became increasingly the center of activity in the field. Because the methods he had developed were crucial to his success, those hoping to enter the field found it important to work under his direction. A large proportion of the leaders of the era in which metabolic balance investigations reached their high point came out of Voit's laboratory. They included Max Rubner, Joseph Bauer, Friedrich von Müller, Alexander Ellinger, Edward Cathcart, Max Cremer, Graham Lusk, and Voit's successor, Otto Frank.

The work in the Munich laboratory continued along the lines Voit had established during the 1860's. In later investigations purified protein preparations replaced the trimmed whole meat, which Voit had earlier used. Attention focused on defining an adequate nourishment and on determining whether substances such as asparagine and peptones have nutritive value—that is, whether their addition to a non-nitrogenous diet can substitute for protein, and whether their addition to a diet including protein can "spare" protein. Beginning in the 1880's some of the experiments were done on white rats, the small size and omnivorous habits of which made them particularly convenient for such investigations.

In later years Voit spent much of his time on official university duties, and served as secretary for the mathematics and physical sciences section of the Bavarian Academy of Sciences. Voit continued to deliver memorable course lectures up until the last year of his life, when ill health finally forced him to forgo his "greatest pleasure."

*BIBLIOGRAPHY*

I. ORIGINAL WORKS. Major articles or monographs by Voit include *Physiologisch-chemische Untersuchungen*, I (Augsburg, 1857); *Untersuchungen über den Einfluss des Kochsalzes, des Kaffee's und der Muskelbewegungen auf den Stoffwechsel* (Munich, 1860); "Physiologie des Allgemeinen Stoffwechsels und der Ernährung," in *Handbuch der Physiologie*, L. Hermann, ed., VI, pt. 1 (Leipzig, 1881), and *Die Gesetze der Ernährung des Fleischfressers durch neue Untersuchungen festgestellt* (Leipzig, 1860), written with T. L. W. Bischoff.

The germinal articles by Pettenkofer and Voit using the respiratory chamber are "Untersuchungen über die Respiration," in *Annalen der Chemie und Pharmacie*, supp. 2 (1863), 52–70; and "Ueber die Producte der Respiration des Hundes bei Fleischnährung und über die Gleichung der Einnahmen und Ausgaben des Körpers dabei," *ibid.*, 361–377. For a detailed description of a later, smaller version of the Pettenkofer respiration apparatus, including detailed drawings, see "Beschreibung eines Apparates zur Untersuchung der gasförmigen Ausscheidungen des Thierkörpers," in *Abhandlungen der Bayerischen Akademie der Wissenschaften*, **12** (1876), 219–271.

Beginning in 1865, articles by Voit and his students reporting the research carried out in the Munich Institute of Physiology appeared regularly in the *Zeitschrift für Biologie*, of which he was a founding editor. Preliminary communications were often published in the *Sitzungsberichte der Bayerischen Akademie der Wissenschaften zu München*.

II. SECONDARY LITERATURE. Otto Frank, *Carl von Voit, Gedächtnisrede* (Munich, 1910), a eulogy by

Voit's successor, contains a long, but not exhaustive bibliography of Voit's publications. Graham Lusk, *Nutrition* (New York, 1969), contains a lengthy summary of Voit's contributions, and "Carl von Voit, Master and Friend," in *Annals of Medical History*, **3** (1931), 583–594, is a very informal reminiscence, with four photographs of Voit, two photographs of the Physiological Institute, and transcriptions of letters from Voit to Lusk.

FREDERIC L. HOLMES

**VOLKMANN, PAUL OSKAR EDUARD** (*b.* Bladiau, near Heiligenheil, Germany, 12 January 1856; *d.* Königsberg, Germany [now Kaliningrad, R.S.F.S.R.], 20 April 1938), *physics, epistemology, history of science.*

The son of a minister, Volkmann attended the Friedrichkollegium in Königsberg from 1864 to 1875. He began to study mathematics and physics in 1875 at the University of Königsberg, where his most important teachers were Heinrich Weber and Woldemar Voigt. He assisted Voigt while still a student; after receiving the doctorate in 1880, he became Voigt's regular assistant.

Volkmann remained at the University of Königsberg throughout his career. He qualified as a lecturer in 1882 and in 1886 succeeded Voigt as assistant professor of theoretical physics; he became full professor in 1894. Volkmann was assigned not only to teach theoretical physics but also to direct the laboratory of thermodynamics and optics that was part of the institute of theoretical physics. Besides providing an introduction to theoretical physics, Volkmann offered seminars in theoretical mathematical physics, practical laboratory periods in mathematical physics, and occasional sessions to perfect the manual skills required in the laboratory.

Volkmann's early publications were devoted exclusively to theoretical and experimental physics; later they dealt increasingly with epistemology, the history of science, and pedagogy. Most of his publications on physics concerned the determination of the surface tension of water and aqueous solutions on the basis of their height in capillary tubes and between flat plates. His careful investigations on this topic found recognition in two papers by Niels Bohr (1909, 1910), who pointed out the agreement between his own results—reached by a different method—and Volkmann's earlier findings. Volkmann also studied the theory of physical systems of measurement, Green's expression for the potential of the luminiferous ether, Mac-

Cullagh's theory of the total reflection of light, the measurement of soil temperatures, and Ohm's law.

Volkmann took a position on the atomic theory in the third thesis of his dissertation: "The acceptance of the absolute indivisibility of the atom is philosophically quite conceivable and leads to no contradiction." In 1897, stimulated by Boltzmann's "Ueber die Unentbehrlichkeit der Atomistik in der Naturwissenschaft," he set forth his own moderate views in "Ueber notwendige und nicht-notwendige Verwertung der Atomistik in der Naturwissenschaft," which was favorably received.

Volkmann considered axiomatics in "Hat die Physik Axiome?" (1894), in which he rejected the idea of axiomatizing physics but clearly grasped the essential aspects of the subject and recognized its importance five years before the publication of David Hilbert's *Die Grundlagen der Geometrie*, through which this method first entered mathematics.

Volkmann presented his epistemological views in *Erkenntnistheoretische Grundzüge der Naturwissenschaft . . .* and *Einführung in das Studium der theoretischen Physik . . ..* His theory states that because of man's limited intellect and understanding, he necessarily has a subjective comprehension of experience. This comprehension is flawed by errors, which must be detected and eliminated; the goal is an objective knowledge of experience. The means to this end is the introduction of postulates, hypotheses, and natural laws, which permit the construction of a system of knowledge that transcends sense perception and enables man to use mathematics to solve physical problems. Once these foundations are laid, an "oscillation" begins between subjective perception and objective reality. There will always be a difference between the object and the subjective conception of it, but man seeks to narrow the gap by constantly reformulating and adapting his ideas.

In his studies on the history of science, Volkmann dealt most fully with Newton and Franz Neumann. *Franz Neumann, Beiträge zur Geschichte der deutschen Wissenschaft* (1896) contains abundant material on nineteenth-century physics and physicists. The essays "Kant und die theoretische Physik der Gegenwart" and "Studien über Ernst Mach vom Standpunkt eines theoretischen Physikers der Gegenwart," both of which appeared in *Annalen der Philosophie* (1924), were Volkmann's last publications.

In 1887, with Ferdinand Lindemann, Volkmann published *Ratschläge für die Studierenden der reinen und angewandten Mathematik*, a work that explicitly presumed four or five years of study by its readers. He also considered his *Einführung in das Studium der theoretischen Physik* as a contribution to the teaching of physics. In 1912 he instituted a refresher course for Gymnasium teachers, which led to the publication *Fragen des physikalischen Schulunterrichtes*, in which Volkmann advocated the principle of teaching by example.

Despite his interest in education, Volkmann exerted only a limited influence as a teacher. His reticent and careful manner offered little excitement to young physicists hoping to hear him discuss new theories and concepts. He found satisfaction in immersing himself in the fund of existing knowledge, so he had little to communicate to students like Hilbert and Sommerfeld. The limited impact of Volkmann's teaching may well account for the fact that, following his death, none of his former students published an obituary of him or a tribute to his work.

*BIBLIOGRAPHY*

I. ORIGINAL WORKS. Volkmann's writings are listed in Poggendorff, III, 1400; IV, 1578; V, 1317–1318; and VI, 2772. They include *Ueber den Einfluss der Krümmung der Wand auf die Constanten der Capillarität bei benetzenden Flüssigkeiten* (Leipzig, 1880), his doctoral dissertation; *Vorlesungen über die Theorie des Lichtes (unter Rücksicht auf die elastische und die electromagnetische Anschauung)* (Leipzig–Berlin, 1891); *Erkenntnistheoretische Grundzüge der Naturwissenschaften und ihre Beziehungen zum Geistesleben der Gegenwart* (Leipzig–Berlin, 1896; 2nd ed., enl., 1910); *Franz Neumann, Beiträge zur Geschichte der deutschen Wissenschaft* (Leipzig–Berlin, 1896); *Einführung in das Studium der theoretischen Physik, insbesondere das der analytischen Mechanik, mit einer Einleitung in die Theorie der physikalischen Erkenntnis* (Leipzig–Berlin, 1900; 2nd ed., 1913); and *Fragen des physikalischen Schulunterrichtes, Vier Vorträge* (Leipzig–Berlin, 1913).

II. SECONDARY LITERATURE. There is a short biography in *Deutsche Senioren der Physik* (Leipzig, 1936), Karte 19, with portrait. See also B. Bavink, "Formalistisches und realistisches Definitionsverfahren in der Physik," in *Zeitschrift für den physikalischen und chemischen Unterricht*, **31** (1918), 161–172; Niels Bohr, "Determination of the Surface-Tension of Water by the Method of Jet Vibration," in *Philosophical Transactions of the Royal Society*, **209** (1909), 282–317, esp. 315–316; and "On the Determination of the Tension of a Recently Formed Water-Surface," in *Proceedings of the Royal Society*, **A84** (1910), 395–403, esp. 402–403; L. Boltzmann, "Ueber die Unentbehrlichkeit der Atomistik in der Naturwissenschaft," in *Annalen der Physik*, 3rd ser., **60** (1897), 231–247; and "Nochmals über die Atomistik," *ibid.*, **61** (1897), 790–793; A. Höfler, "Zur physikalischen Didaktik und zur physikalischen Philosophie," in *Zeitschrift für den physikalischen und chemischen Unterricht*, **31** (1918), 1–9, 37–46; W. Lorey, *Das Studium der Mathematik an den deutschen Universitäten seit Anfang des 19. Jahrhunderts* (Leipzig–Berlin, 1916), esp. 262, 282, 299; and F. Poske, "Galilei und der Kausalbegriff," in *Archiv für die Geschichte der Naturwissenschaften und der Technik*, **6** (1913), 288–293; "Das Ohmsche Gesetz im Unterricht," in *Aus der Natur* (Leipzig), **14** (1917–1918), 49–59; and "Studien zur Didaktik des physikalischen Unterrichts," in *Zeitschrift für den physikalischen und chemischen Unterricht*, **31** (1918), 191–193.

HANS RAMSER

**VOLNEY, CONSTANTIN-FRANÇOIS CHASSEBOEUF, COMTE DE** (*b.* Craon, France, 3 February 1757; *d.* Paris, France, 20 April 1820), *geography, linguistics, sociology.*

As a student in Paris, Volney learned from Holbach, Mme Helvétius, and other French Idéologues the principles and outlook that were to dominate his thought and action. He then embarked on a voyage to the Levant (1783–1785) to gather data for a systematic account relating the political and social state of the Near East to the physical environment. His *Voyage en Égypte et en Syrie . . .* (1787) was a pioneer work in physical and human geography, distinguished from earlier travel accounts by its systematic method and high standards of accuracy. Volney later used similar methods in producing his *Tableau du climat et du sol des États-Unis d'Amérique* (1803), based on his travels in America (1795–1798). This work contained the first colored geological map of the United States and the first general account of the geology of the trans-Allegheny region.

During the French Revolution, Volney won literary fame for his deistic work *Les ruines, ou méditations sur les révolutions des empires* (1791) and served as a delegate to the Constituent Assembly. Imprisoned during the Reign of Terror, he was later appointed professor of history at the École Normale Supérieure, where he urged the study of history as a social science. Elected to the Institut de France in 1797 and made senator and count by Napoleon, Volney became increasingly disaffected with the Napoleonic regime. Gradually he withdrew from public life to devote himself to linguistic and historical studies.

In linguistics Volney pursued the idea of developing a universal alphabet, an idea embodied in his *Simplification des langues orientales . . .*

(1795), *L'alphabet européen appliqué aux langues asiatiques* (1819), and *L'hébreu simplifié* . . . (1820), and in his bequest of 24,000 francs to establish a prize for work in this field. His studies of Greek, Jewish, and Egyptian chronology, collected in *Recherches nouvelles sur l'histoire ancienne* (1813–1814), were erudite but overambitious.

The scholar, the sociologist, the scientific traveler, and the Idéologue were united in Volney. A pioneer in several fields of inquiry, he was master of none. In all he endeavored to liberate the human mind and to rationalize human institutions by means of an *enquête des faits*.

*BIBLIOGRAPHY*

Incomplete collections of Volney's works are *Oeuvres complètes de Volney . . . mise en ordre et précédées de la vie de l'auteur* [by A. Bossange], 8 vols. (Paris, 1820–1822); and *Oeuvres complètes, avec notice de Bossange et buste de Volney par David d'Angers*, 4 pts. (Paris, 1837), both of which underwent subsequent eds.

The most comprehensive study of Volney, containing an extensive account of the primary sources, a chronological list of some of the eds. of his various works, and a selection of the most useful secondary literature, is Jean Gaulmier, *L'Idéologue Volney (1757–1820). Contribution à l'histoire de l'orientalisme en France* (Beirut, 1951). Gaulmier has also published Volney's *Voyage en Égypte et en Syrie* in a modern ed. with intro. and notes (Paris–The Hague, 1959). See also Gilbert Chinard, *Volney et l'Amérique d'après des documents inédits et sa correspondance avec Jefferson*, Johns Hopkins Studies in Romance Literatures and Languages, I (Baltimore, 1923). George W. White's intro. to the Hafner ed. of Charles Brockden Brown's trans. of Volney's *Tableau du climat et du sol des États-Unis d'Amérique — A View of the Soil and Climate of the United States of America by C. F. Volney Translated With Occasional Remarks by C. B. Brown* . . . (New York–London, 1968) — gives a critical evaluation of Volney's contributions to early American geology.

                                        JOHN C. GREENE

**VOLTA, ALESSANDRO GIUSEPPE ANTONIO ANASTASIO** (*b.* Como, duchy of Milan, Italy, 18 February 1745; *d.* Como, 5 March 1827), *physics.*

Volta came from a Lombard family ennobled by the municipality of Como and almost extinguished, in his time, through its service to the church. One of his three paternal uncles was a Dominican, another a canon, and the third an archdeacon; his father, Filippo (1692–*ca.* 1752), after eleven years as a Jesuit, withdrew to propagate the line. Filippo

Volta's marriage in 1733 with Maddelena de' conti Inzaghi (*d.* 1782) produced seven children who survived childhood; three girls, two of whom became nuns; three boys who followed precisely the careers of their paternal uncles; and Alessandro, the youngest, who narrowly escaped recruitment by his first teachers, the Jesuits.

The doctrines, social life, and observances of the church of Rome consequently made up a large part of Volta's culture. He chose clerics as his chief friends, remained close to his brothers the canon and archdeacon, and actively practiced the Catholic religion. Examples of his religiosity include a flirtation with Jansenism in the 1790's; a confession of faith in 1815 to help defend religion against scientism (*Epistolario*, V, 290–292); and an appeal in 1794 to his brothers and to the professor of theology at the University of Pavia for advice about marriage. Not that Volta was prudish or ascetic. He was a large, vigorous man, who, in the words of his friend Lichtenberg, "understood a lot about the electricity of women" (*Epistolario*, II, 269). For many years he enjoyed the favors of a singer, Marianna Paris, whom he might have married but for the weight of theological, and family, opinion.

Volta was about seven when his father died. His uncle the canon took charge of his education, which began in 1757 at the local Jesuit college, where his quickness soon attracted the attention of his teachers. In 1761 the philosophy professor, Girolamo Bonensi, tried to recruit him; his suit, sweetened by gifts of chocolates and bonbons, alarmed Volta's uncle, who took him from school. Bonensi continued his campaign in letters (*Epistolario*, I, 6–33) carried secretly by Volta's eccentric friend, the future canon Giulio Cesare Gattoni (1741–1809), until Volta's uncle the Dominican, who shared his order's opinion of Jesuits, put an end to the affair.

Volta continued his education at the Seminario Benzi, where Lucretius' *De rerum natura* made a powerful impression upon him, and at the so-called Gattoni tower, a disused redoubt rented by his richer and older friend as a laboratory and museum. This cabinet, begun about 1765, won a reputation for its collections in natural history. It also sheltered some physics: a joint study by Gattoni and Volta of the electricity brought down by its lightning rod, said to be the first erected in Como, and experiments of Volta's made possible by books, instruments, and encouragement generously supplied by Gattoni. The first fruit of these mixed studies was a Latin poem of some 500 hexameters in which Volta celebrated the discoveries of

Priestley, Nollet, Symmer, and Musschenbroek (*Aggiunte*, 123–135). Several other poems by Volta in French and Italian survive (*Aggiunte*, 136–158); according to Gattoni, he was always "an excellent judge of all kinds of literature,"[1] which, however, did not save his own style from prolixity.

Volta's uncles wished to make him an attorney, a profession well represented on his mother's side of the family. Volta preferred to obey what he called his genius, which directed him, at the age of eighteen, to the study of electricity.

**Electrostatics.** The chief authorities on electricity in the early 1760's were Nollet and Beccaria, to whom Volta would write whenever questions or suggestions occurred to him. His first letter to Beccaria, inspired in part by Bošković's ideas, announced that electrical phenomena arose entirely from an attractive force operating between the electrical fluid and common matter (*Epistolario*, I, 4). Beccaria, a testy man who held to the original Franklinist theory of a self-repulsive electrical fluid, took a year to reply, and did so only after Volta had apologized for his "very frivolous chatter." As a cure for frivolity Beccaria recommended reading Beccaria and doing experiments (*Epistolario*, I, 33–36; *Opere*, III, 23). Volta followed the advice, without access to the usual apparatus; forced to invent cheap substitutes, he began to develop that genius for inexpensive, effective instrumentation that determined his career.

His earliest results, communicated to Beccaria in April 1765, derived from the discovery, which Volta fancied new, that silk rubbed by hand became plus, and silk rubbed by glass, minus. He designed a machine to capitalize on the electrical properties of silk and drew up a schematic triboelectric series, doubtless independent of Wilcke's. The correspondence lasted until 1769, when Volta published a Latin dissertation, *De vi attractiva*, which boldly reinterpreted Franklin's theory and Beccaria's latest experiments in terms of the unique attractive principle (*Epistolario*, I, 36–43, 64–65; *Opere*, III, 6–7, 10–11, 19–20, 23–24).

Volta observed that Franklinist electrical matter cannot itself be the cause of electrical motions because it courses unidirectionally, from excess to defect, while in the most common of experiments, as Nollet had emphasized, the same electrified body simultaneously imposes both attractions and repulsions. Nor can the effluvia operate indirectly, by impelling the air, for electrical attraction takes place between bodies immersed in oil (an experiment Volta lifted without acknowledgment from Cigna). We must therefore admit short-range attractive forces. To the usual objection that multiplying such forces clutters matter with special nonmechanical powers, Volta countered that, since only "mixed bodies" are electric, one need imagine no special virtue of electricity, but merely a net macroscopic force compounded from the different microscopic forces possessed by the particles of pure substances, or from the universal, elemental, multipurpose force of Bošković. Nor should one falter at the great range of electrical attraction: we have, on the one hand, the patent example of magnetism and, on the other, the existence of electrical atmospheres. These, according to Volta's evenhanded compromise, consist of surplus electrical fluid, the attraction of which extends a little way beyond their physical limits. "However that might be, for present purposes it need only be granted that attractive forces really exist in bodies" (*Opere*, III, 25–29, 85).

Volta's fundamental concept is that there exists for each body a state of saturation in which the integrated attractions of its particles for electric fluid are precisely satisfied. This integrated attraction may be altered by any process, mechanical or chemical, that displaces the particles relative to one another; friction, pressure, and, perhaps, evaporation electrify bodies by destroying the existing pattern of saturated forces and redistributing the electrical fluid (*Opere*, III, 30–34). In this proposition one sees the seeds of the experiment of Volta, Lavoisier, and Laplace on electrification by evaporation, and, perhaps, of Volta's consequential concept of contact charge. As for the notion of saturation, it vaguely foreshadowed the concept of tension, Volta's qualitative equivalent of the modern potential: the condition of electrical equilibrium between two bodies being not equality of quantity of electric fluid, but of degree of departure from saturation.

For the rest, *De vi attractiva* is an exercise in reducing the standard phenomena—attraction, "repulsion" (really attraction away from the "repelling" body), the Leyden experiment, and the effects of Beccaria's vindicating electricity—to the single attractive force. Again one can see fruitful tendencies, particularly in Volta's analysis of induction in an insulated conductor *B* under the influence of a positively charged body *A*: *A*'s atmosphere supersaturates *B* without altering *B*'s integrated positive force; *B* therefore sheds fluid, which surrounds its far side in an atmosphere. Touch *B*: it loses its surplus, but shows no electrical signs because its residual fluid and *A*'s atmosphere exactly saturate it (bring it to zero potential). Now remove $A$: $B$ is no longer saturated, and shows itself negative (*Opere*, III, 36–50). Here one sees seeds of the electrophore and the condensator. Although Volta soon acknowledged that the single attractive force could not account for many simple phenomena—for example, the difference between insulators and conductors, and the charging of a Leyden jar—he continued to be guided by it and to ascribe most electrical effects to it, until 1784 or even later (*Opere*, III, 56–71, 85; IV, 410–413).

The reluctance to change or discard a once-useful theory was characteristic of Volta. As he said when describing his slowness to accept Lavoisier's chemistry, he wished to be neither too open nor too resistant to novelties. He remained faithful to the Franklinist hypothesis of a single electrical fluid, "la nostra cara dottrina" (*Opere*, IV, 359, 380), while most important physicists of the Continent preferred the dualistic system of Symmer. Volta eventually was brought to agree that all known electrical effects could be explained on either system; but he preferred the singlist, partly (as he said) because of a reluctance to multiply entities unnecessarily, and mainly because of his scientific conservatism (*Opere*, IV, 269; *Epistolario*, II, 278).

To concoct the electrophore, the most intriguing electrical device since the Leyden jar, Volta had only to combine the insight that resin retained its electricity longer than glass with the fact, emphasized by Cigna and Beccaria, that a metal plate and a charged insulator properly maneuvered can produce many flashes without enervating the electric. Beccaria inspired the combination. In 1772 he published a lengthy, difficult, updated version of *Elettricismo artificiale*, which emphasized more strongly than before his odd view that the contrary electricities destroy one another in the union of a charged insulator with a momentarily grounded conductor, only to reappear, "revindicated," in subsequent separations. Beccaria also criticized the hypothesis of the unique attractive force, without deigning to mention Volta, who in return conceived that, if he could greatly increase the duration of the effects ascribed to vindicating electricity, the implausible theory of alternate destructions and incomplete recuperations would fall to the ground. After many trials Volta found that an insulator made of three parts turpentine, two parts resin, and one part wax answered perfectly; and in June 1775 he informed Priestley of the invention of an *elettroforo perpetuo*, which "electrified but once, briefly and moderately, never loses its electricity,

and although repeatedly touched, obstinately preserves the strength of its signs" (*Opere*, III, 96).

The device consisted of a metal dish containing a dielectric cake, and a light wooden shield covered with tin foil rounded to remove all corners and joined to an insulating handle. The cake is first charged, say negatively, by rubbing. The shield is then set upon it, and momentarily grounded, thereby charging positively by induction. The shield may then be removed and its charge given to, say, the hook of a Leyden jar; then replaced, touched, and again brought to the hook; and so on until the condenser is moderately charged. Any number of jars and electrophores may be electrified without regenerating the original; and if it should decline, it can be reinvigorated by lightly rubbing its cake with the coating of a Leyden jar that the shield had charged through the hook. Volta set great store by this last property, which did seem to vouchsafe eternal life to the electrophore and to justify the term *elettricità vindice indeficiente*, with which he proposed to celebrate his victory over Beccaria (*Opere*, III, 98–105).

The triumph was clouded. Beccaria thundered that the "perpetuity" of the charge of the electrophore proved nothing and that he and Cigna had already described the necessary manipulations. Other claimants came or were thrust forward: Stephen Gray, Aepinus, Wilcke, and the Jesuits of Peking. With his customary good sense (*Opere*, III, 120, 137–143), Volta acknowledged the role of Cigna, but insisted, quite rightly, that he alone had made a usable instrument, and had developed the cake, the armatures, and the play with the bottle. Even Wilcke, who had fully grasped the theory, had not embodied it in the sort of apparatus—sturdy, useful, powerful, intriguing—characteristic of Volta's designs.

The electrophore killed off not only vindicating electricity but also the last vestiges of the old doctrine of literal atmospheres (*Opere*, III, 140n; *Epistolario*, I, 275–280). The only successful theories of the device, for example, those of Ingen-Housz and Wilcke, employed actions at a distance between electrical fluids confined by the surfaces of conductors. Accordingly, as contemporaries recognized,[2] the electrophore caused electricians to take seriously the neglected approach of Aepinus. Volta himself first met with a copy of Aepinus' "incomparably profound book" (*Opere*, III, 210n, 236) in the 1770's, too late to guide his invention but in time to assist his own revision of the concept of atmospheres.

The mid-1770's marked the beginning of Volta's

career. In October 1774 he took his first academic job, principal or regent of the state Gymnasium in Como (*Epistolario*, I, 66–68), then recently taken over from the Jesuits. Next came the electrophore and, at Volta's request, the professorship of experimental physics at the Gymnasium, which he garnered in 1775 without the usual examination (*Epistolario*, I, 99, 100). A sally into pneumatics brought the discovery of methane (1776) and a greater reputation, which helped him in 1777 to obtain state support for a trip to the chief centers of learning in Switzerland and Alsace (*Epistolario*, I, 149–150, 178). There Volta met several savants—particularly H. B. de Saussure and Jean Senebier of Geneva—both of whom would advertise and encourage his work, and help keep him informed about transalpine physics (*Epistolario*, I, 192–193).

Volta's travel grant came from the Austrian government, which then controlled the duchy of Milan, including Como, and which, through its minister Count Carlo di Firmian, was modernizing the educational institutions of the region. Chief among these was the University of Pavia, where the Austrians had been encouraging science, particularly since 1769, when Spallanzani came to the chair of natural history.

In 1777 Pavia had two professorships of physics, both occupied by clerics: a "general" held by Francesco Luini (Jesuit) and an "experimental" held by Carlo Barletti (Scolopian). In 1778 Firmian, the "immortal Maecenas, benefactor and greatest protector of the university" (*Epistolario*, II, 285), sent Luini to Mantua, translated Barletti to general physics, and gave Volta the post he would hold for almost forty years, the professorship of experimental physics at Pavia (*Epistolario*, I, 298). Volta proved a very popular professor (*Epistolario*, II, 41, 283–284). A new lecture hall was built to house his auditors and the university's ever-increasing collection of instruments, many of which Volta bought at state expense on state-financed trips to France and England in 1781–1782 (*Epistolario*, II, 51–141) and to Germany in 1784 (*Epistolario*, II, 225–273).

As Volta's professional opportunity and acquaintance increased, his style of physics altered, at least in its public form. The change was manifest in 1778 in a published letter to his new friend Saussure on electrical capacity. While *Di vi attractiva* developed a microscopic model of electrical action, which explained but did not guide, and while the account of the electrophore was primarily a description of laboratory manipulations, the letter to Saussure applied new theoretical concepts to the design and explanation of new experiments. These powerful concepts, the macroscopic quantities capacity and tension, also appear in Cavendish's now famous memoir of 1771. There is reason to believe that Volta read this memoir, which most contemporary electricians ignored or misunderstood, and that he derived from it—and perhaps also from the works of Aepinus and even of Barletti, who first acquainted him with Aepinus[3]—the clue for the transformation of his otiose notion, "natural saturation," into a serviceable substitute for the concept of potential.

Volta's thought is that the capacity $C$ of a conductor and the tension $T$ of its charge $Q$ alter with its distance from other conductors (*Opere*, III, 201–229; *Epistolario*, I, 275, 280). For example, as the charged shield is raised from the electrophore cake, electrometer threads attached to it spread, owing to an increase in the tension of its charge; since the quantity of charge does not change, the tension grows because the shield becomes less capacious, less able to hold its naturally expansive charge as it moves farther from the opposite electricity of the cake. The reverse effect occurs with a pair of similarly charged conductors: the capacity of each is enlarged, and its tension lessened, as the distance between them increases. Volta deduced that the "atmospheres" of the various surface elements of the same conductor might inhibit one another, and that, for a given surface area, the longer the conductor the greater the capacity. Perhaps, as Cavendish had suggested, the capacity of a single conductor could be increased to that of a Leyden jar. It was just this expectation that Volta confirmed in his letter to Saussure, who had earlier doubted its possibility (*Opere*, III, 213–215).

In describing the experiment Volta used the old term "electrical atmosphere," by which, however, he now no longer meant an envelope of electrical fluid but, as was becoming commonplace, merely a "sphere of activity" (*Opere*, III, 155, 160, 166–167, 182, 206, 236–240). The point is important, as many commentators, perhaps misled by Biot, have ascribed to Volta a belief in the retrograde literal atmospheres that his work helped to destroy. It is plain from Volta's manuscripts—for example, the beautiful and exact theory of the slow-motion charging of a Leyden jar (*Opere*, III, 248–258), or the *Lezioni compendiose sull'elettricità* (*Opere*, IV, 419)—that soon after, if not before, the letter to Saussure, Volta had freed himself of the ideas that "anything real" passed between bodies interacting electrically beyond sparking range, and that the surplus electrical fluid of a positively charged body resided in the air about it (*Opere*, III, 236, 273; IV, 65–68, 71–74; *Epistolario*, II, 213). Occasionally he represented this sphere of activity as a state of the space or air surrounding charged bodies (*Epistolario*, I, 296, 326–327, 376, 411); a representation not of literal atmospheres but of a crude field theory, which may be traced from Canton and Beccaria through Avogadro and on to Faraday.

Volta embodied the quantities capacity and tension, and the implicit relation that he had established between them ($Q = CT$), in a new instrument, a "condensator" for rendering sensible atmospheric electricity otherwise too weak for detection (*Opere*, III, 271–300). This famous device is nothing but an electrophore with a poor conductor like polished marble or oiled wood as its cake. One runs a wire from an apparently unelectrified atmospheric probe to the shield, waits, removes the wire and raises the shield, which can then affect an electroscope. Volta explained that owing to its great capacity the electrophore soaks up the electricity of the probe as often as it becomes charged, while the separated shield, being of small capacity, can reveal the weak collected electricity. He emphasized that the quantity of charge on a conductor increases as the product of its tension and its capacity, the former being the quantity measured by electrometers (*Opere*, IV, 71–74). Others soon incorporated this insight into ingenious multipliers of weak charges, such as the well-known "doubler" invented by William Nicholson.

**Meteorology.** Volta's interest in meteorology centered on atmospheric electricity, the study of which began in 1752 with the apparent confirmation of Franklin's hypothesis about the electrical character of lightning. It was quickly discovered, by Beccaria and Canton among others, that the atmosphere exhibited electricity even in fair weather, and that, contrary to Franklin's expectation, it was more often negative than positive. This information was at first deduced from the electrical state of the lower end of an insulated pointed pole or wire, which was thought to exchange electrical fluid with the surrounding air. In fact such probes charge partly by conduction but mainly by induction, and their electricity does not give an unambiguous index of the electrical state of the atmosphere. Among the few to understand and to evade this ambiguity was Saussure, whose work directly inspired Volta's.[4]

Saussure employed not a long pole but a form of the bottle electrometer invented by Cavallo, with silver wires ending in pith balls as the indicator. Saussure would touch the stem and case of the electrometer to the ground and suddenly raise the instrument above his head; the consequent spread of the wires indicated, as he said, the electrical tension of the atmosphere at the site of the electrometer. Saussure carried this device on his famous attempt at Mont Blanc in 1787, which Volta, who was then visiting Geneva, commemorated in no fewer than sixty-six *terzini* (*Aggiunte*, 146–152). When he returned to Pavia, Volta undertook to make Saussure's instrument "more obedient" (*Opere*, V, 88–90). In 1787 he began to announce his results in letters to G. L. Lichtenberg, professor of physics at the University of Göttingen, whom he had met on his trip to Germany in 1784. The nine Lichtenberg letters constitute Volta's chief writings on meteorology.

Alerted to the problematic operation of the pointed pole, Volta hit on a solution quite different from Saussure's: bathing the point in flame, which promoted the exchange of electric fluid and brought the point quickly to the potential of the atmosphere just outside it (*Opere*, V, 88–92, 152–156). Volta found that electrometers armed with flames registered four times the electricity recorded by Saussure's detector under identical circumstances (*Opere*, IV, 71–74). The device was widely used, although probably not fully understood, until William Thomson gave its theory in the 1850's and replaced it by his ingenious waterdripper.[5]

The next business was to make of Saussure's electrometer a sensitive, uniformly calibrated, international standard. Volta improved the sensitivity by replacing Saussure's wires with light straws with large effective repelling surfaces (*Opere*, V, 35–42, 68, 71); the result was an inexpensive form of the exactly contemporaneous gold-leaf electrometer (1786) invented by Abraham Bennet. Uniform calibration, which Volta deemed essential, was obtained by giving the electrometer successive sparks from a capacious Leyden jar kept at a constant potential by a small electrophore (*Opere*, V, 39–42). Taking the intercomparability of thermometers and of hygrometers as his model, Volta proposed the adoption of a fundamental unit of tension, namely that of a standard metal disk hung from one arm of a balance a distance *d* above a conducting surface, and counterbalanced by a certain weight *W*. The unit, equivalent to a spread of 350 degrees of Volta's straw electroscope, is about 13,350 volt in modern measure.[6]

In experiments with the unit, Volta found that

the "force of attraction" measured by the weight $W$ was proportional to $(T/d)^2$, $T$ being the tension of the disk according to his straw electrometer. It is most interesting that he took this result, which is correct, as evidence against the universality of Coulomb's law, which gives the same dependence on distance, but for a different geometry (*Opere*, V, 78–79, 81–83). Moreover, other geometries yielded "diverse other laws, as curious as they are novel." Like many of his colleagues, Volta did not have mathematics enough to work from a hypothetical law of interaction of electrical elements to the observed electrical forces between macroscopic bodies.

Volta accepted the Franklinist presumption that the instruments of atmospheric electricity measured the surplus (or deficiency) of electrical fluid in the lower atmosphere; and he had suggested in *De vi attractiva* that the fluid enters (or leaves) the air during evaporation. One of the first tasks he assigned his condensator was the detection of the supposititious electrification during change of state. He was then (1782) in France, and undertook the experiments in collaboration with Lavoisier and Laplace. At first they failed, as they should have, there being no such effect; but shortly before Volta left Paris for London they succeeded, or believed they had, and made much of their success. According to Volta, everything depended on a change in electrical capacity suffered by water droplets in going from the liquid to the vapor state (*Opere*, III, 33–34, 301–305, 364; V, 173–187, 196–197; *Epistolario*, II, 104–105; *Aggiunte*, 21–24). They had probably detected electricity generated by the friction of bubbles against the evaporating pan. The subject was to remain confused for over a century.

Volta's explanation, which differed from that in *De vi attractiva*, doubtless owed something to his adherence to the doctrine of latent heat (*Opere*, VI, 313–316), which became widely known in the early 1780's. It remained the basis of his speculations about meteorological phenomena. For example, according to his much admired theory of hail, evaporation abstracts both heat and electricity from vaporizing droplets, creating charged microscopic ice seeds, which dance about under electrical forces in their parent cloud, growing at the expense of surrounding droplets until they become too heavy for the ballet, and fall to the ground (*Opere*, V, 201–206, 283–307, 421–462).

**Pneumatics**. Volta's work on gases shows the same genius for instrumentation and measurement,

and the same failure or reluctance to establish general principles, that characterize his work on electrostatics. His first pneumatic studies concerned "inflammable air from marshes" (chiefly methane), which he discovered in November 1776 in Lago Maggiore. It was not a chance find. Inflammable air from metals (hydrogen released from acids) had been known since its isolation by Cavendish in 1766, and Franklin's description of a natural source of inflammable air had just been published by Priestley in a book quickly known in Italy.[7] In the autumn of 1776 Volta's friend P. Carlo Giuseppe Campi had found a natural source near Pavia; and Volta himself, intrigued by the "ever more remarkable and interesting subject of the different kinds of air" (*Opere*, VI, 19), had scoured the countryside for telltale bubbles. The testing of his new gas—new in source, flame color, and combustibility (*Opere*, VI, 30)—led him into the faddish field of eudiometry.

In 1772 Priestley had isolated a "nitrous air," which, when combined with common air over water, left a volume of gas less than the sum of the volumes of the ingredients. He found the reduction to be less the more the common air had been vitiated by respiration or combustion; and he proposed to take the degree of reduction as a measure of the "goodness" of the common air. Priestley's procedure was improved, and his interpretation adopted by two of Volta's friends: Marsilio Landriani, who introduced the term "eudiometry," and Felice Fontana, whose nitrous-air eudiometer won wide acceptance in northern Europe (*Epistolario*, I, 218–219; 258–260; III, 4–8). Both hoped that the instrument would help to identify malarial and other insalubrious regions; and for almost thirty years physicists visited swamps, cesspools, dung heaps, prisons, and hospitals hoping to correlate the reading of their eudiometers with the evident foulness of the air. No consistent correlations emerged. In 1805 Humboldt and Gay-Lussac put an end to the search by showing that the percentage of oxygen in unvitiated air was independent of its source. They succeeded by employing a device of Volta's, who had never believed that the eudiometer could measure the salubrity—as opposed to the respirability (oxygen content)—of the air (*Opere*, VI, 9).

Ever interested in large, reproducible effects, Volta had shifted his attention to hydrogen upon discovering that, when mixed with common air and sparked, Cavendish's inflammable air ignited more readily and burnt more fiercely than his own (*Opere*, VI, 50); whence Volta's famous "inflammable air pistol," filled with hydrogen and air or oxygen, and fired by a portable electrophore (*Opere*, VI, 134–135). To perfect this artillery (which could fire a lead ball with force enough to dent wood at fifteen feet [*Opere*, VI, 155]), he looked for the mixture that destroyed the greatest quantity of gas (*Opere*, VI, 146). He thereby came to the problem of the eudiometer, but from a new side, and with a new eudiometric fluid, hydrogen, which could be obtained purer than the standard nitric oxide (*Opere*, VI, 180–181), and acted much more vigorously (*Opere*, VI, 159–160). Volta's first eudiometric technique was to find the minimum volume of the air under test in which a standard amount of inflammable air could be ignited by a spark; the larger the volume, the poorer the air. As for the optimum explosive mixture, it turned out to be four parts inflammable to eleven parts unvitiated common air (*Opere*, VI, 179), or two parts inflammable to one part dephlogisticated air (oxygen) (*Opere*, VI, 190n). In the definitive form of his eudiometer (*Opere*, VII, 173–213), Volta mixed equal volumes of hydrogen and common air, exploded them, and determined the diminution; the maximum contraction, for the best air, fell out just under 3/5 volume, confirming that, as other of his measurements suggested, the maximum possible reduction in unit volume of common air was about 1/5 (*Opere*, VII, 197).[8] Volta's numerical results were fully confirmed by Humboldt and Gay-Lussac, who found oxygen to occupy about 21 percent of the volume of common air. This should be compared to the results obtained by Humboldt, Lavoisier, and Scheele, using the Fontana nitrous-oxide eudiometer, namely 26 to 28 percent.

Volta's eudiometer set up one of the most important discoveries of the eighteenth century, the composition of water, detected by Lavoisier, among others, by sparking oxygen and hydrogen over mercury (1783). As early as the spring of 1777 Volta had been looking for the residue of the reaction. In his version of phlogistic chemistry, inflammable air ($H_2$) was phlogiston ($\phi$) combined with an unknown "base," which he supposed to be of an "acid" or "saline" character (*Opere*, VI, 150, 342, 400–401). He recognized that, since the base might be soluble in water, the sparking should be done over mercury, but he had not enough for the task (*Opere*, VI, 196–197, 303, 410–411; *Epistolario*, I, 267–270). While working to obtain more, he sparked inflammable and common air over water, and noticed (in 1778) that the walls of the test vessel fogged (*Opere*, VI, 382). While in

Paris in 1782 he told Lavoisier about the fogging; and later in the year Lavoisier, Laplace, and Monge obtained water over mercury by Volta's method (*Opere*, VI, 410–411).

The French, following Lavoisier's ideas, thought they had synthesized water; Volta, remaining faithful to phlogiston, believed that they had analyzed the gases (*Opere*, VI, 342, 411; VII, 87–88, 101, 103):

Inflammable air (water + $\phi$) + dephlogisticated air (water + caloric) = water + heat.

Volta did not adopt the new chemistry for many years, perhaps not definitively until after 1800, although he began to speak of it more favorably in the 1790's (*Opere*, VII, 246, 269–270, 284; *Epistolario*, III, 61–62). He later said that the decisive proof was his own calcification of metals in closed vessels by burning mirrors. Calcification proceeded until the volume of the air fell by 1/5, precisely the amount of dephlogisticated air that, according to Volta's earlier measurements, would be available to support the combustion (*Opere*, VII, 285).

Volta's later pneumatic studies centered on the action of heat on gases and vapors. His general conception of heat followed the fluid theories of Crawford and Kirwan (*Opere*, VI, 315; VII, 45–47), with one characteristic exception: whereas his sources ascribed the phenomenon of latent heat to a chemical combination responsible for change of state, Volta made the change primary, and the latent heat the result of a consequent jump in specific heat capacity. This concept, developed in notes to the Italian edition of Macquer's *Dictionnaire de chymie* (1783–1784), derived from Volta's mature conception of electrical capacitance and from an assimilation of the properties of the two fluids: since nothing analogous to latency—the supposed inability of accumulated caloric to affect a thermometer—occurred in electricity, it was difficult for Volta to credit it in the case of heat (*Opere*, VII, 19–20). Consequently he once again opposed Lavoisier, now regarding his claim that evaporation arose from the chemical combination of heat and water (*Opere*, VII, 87–93). Volta also opposed the older theory, already under attack, that evaporation consisted of the "solution" of water in the bases of the atmosphere.

Against this last proposition Volta could adduce his own experiments on what we would now call partial pressures. Already in 1784, in a letter to Lichtenberg, Volta sketched the law usually attributed to Dalton for the case of water vapor. Volta also stated clearly in letters obscurely published in 1795 and 1796 that "the quantity of elastic vapor is the same in a space either void of air or filled with air at any density, and depends only upon the degree of heat" (*Opere*, I, 301; VII, 441). Hence he easily derived an argument fatal to the theory of evaporation by solution. Moreover, Volta anticipated and even went beyond Dalton in measuring the dependence of the density and pressure of water vapor on temperature. The laborious and difficult measurements, made in a heated Torricelli space, gave results in very rough agreement with modern determinations.[9]

Volta was more successful in measuring the dilation of air as a function of heat, or rather of temperature indicated on a mercury thermometer. The proportionality of heat and temperature so measured had been established, to Volta's satisfaction, by Deluc, "a most knowledgeable and accurate experimenter" (*Opere*, VII, 414), whose thermometric example had probably encouraged Volta's comparative electrometry. Between 1772 and 1790, when Volta took up the subject, many physicists had tried to measure $\alpha$, the percentage increase in volume of a gas per degree of temperature. In his masterful memoir published in 1793 (*Opere*, VII, 347–375), Volta pointed to values of $\alpha$ ranging from 1/85 (Priestley) to 1/235 (Saussure) per degree Réaumur, and to uncertainty whether $\alpha$ varied with temperature between the freezing and boiling points. Volta cut through the uncertainty by observing that the dilation produced when heating a gas over water derives from two causes: (1) the true expansion of the gas and the water vapor it contains, and (2) the generation of additional vapor from the walls of the experimental vessel and from the water used to measure the dilation. Dry the vessel carefully, conduct the experiment over mercury or oil, and, according to Volta, you should get an $\alpha$ for air independent of temperature and equal to about 1/216. This value, which agreed perfectly with those obtained by Deluc and by Lambert from less systematic measurements, differs very little from that now accepted.

The journal to which Volta confided these results had little circulation outside Italy. Once again his priority was ignored, this time in favor of Gay-Lussac, who in 1802 deduced a value of $\alpha$ (1/213) poorer than his predecessor's and based on flimsier data, albeit for more gases. (Gay-Lussac obtained $\alpha$ from the total dilation between freezing and boiling points; Volta had measured it for each degree.) It is possible that Gay-Lussac did not obtain his

number in total ignorance of Volta's.[10] In any case, the proposition, "the coefficient of expansion of air is constant," was restored to Volta by unanimous vote of the international congress of physicists meeting at Como in 1927 in observance of the centennial of his death (*Opere*, VII, 346).

**Animal Electricity and Galvanism**. In 1791 Galvani, professor of anatomy at the University of Bologna, published his now famous study of the electrical excitation of disembodied frog legs. He explained the jerking of a leg upon completing a circuit through the crural nerve and the leg muscle as the direct result of the discharge of a "nerveo-electrical fluid" previously accumulated in the muscle, which he supposed to act like a Leyden jar. The analogy between muscle and jar did not rest only on the need for a complete discharge circuit. Consider also the following phenomenon: the internal electrode of a charged grounded Leyden jar is pointed and brought near a large electrified insulated conductor; when a spark is drawn from the conductor, a "penicillum" of light flashes from the pointed electrode. According to Galvani, precisely the same sort of discharge occurred during the chance observation that had led him into his odd studies: a freshly prepared frog's leg jumped (that is, its muscle discharged, in analogy to the penicillum) if the circuit were completed at the instant that a spark was drawn from a nearby electrical machine. In Galvani's opinion the structure of the muscle, like the peculiar anatomy of the torpedo or electric eel, effected and retained the accumulation of the nerveo-electrical fluid. As for the fluid, it was similar to but distinct from frictional electricity, an "animal" electricity sui generis.

When Volta learned of Galvani's experiments he dismissed them as "unbelievable" and "miraculous." He had a low opinion of physicians, whom he found to be generally "ignorant of the known laws of electricity"; and he recognized "animal electricity" only in electrical fish, to which, however, he ascribed only the power of manipulating common electrical fluid (*Opere*, I, 10–11, 21–23, 26; *Epistolario*, III, 143–145). Moreover, even as late as 28 March 1792, just after he had first tried the experiments, "with little hope of success," under the urging of his colleagues in pathology and anatomy, his immediate research plans included only meteorology and the dilation of gases. But by 1 April the experiments had succeeded, and Volta had begun the brilliantly planned and executed experiments that step by step brought him to the invention of the pile.

Volta's first instinct was to measure the minimum tension of "artificial" or "frictional" electricity that would cause the frog to jerk: "How can causes be found if one does not determine the quantity as well as the quality of the effects?" (*Opere*, I, 27). Frog legs prepared as directed by Galvani proved to be by far the most sensitive electroscope yet discovered. When placed in a discharge train of a Leyden jar, they responded to a tension of as little as 5/100 degree of Volta's straw electrometer, an amount he could only detect after manipulation by the condensator. He also succeeded in inducing convulsions in a live frog by joining its leg and back externally by a circuit made of dissimilar metals. (Galvani had discovered by chance that prepared frog legs kicked violently and reliably when nerve and muscle were joined by a circuit composed of two kinds of metals.) Volta's discovery, probably made in April 1792, required modification of Galvani's theory. While agreeing that the electrical imbalance detected by the spasms arose from action of the animal, Volta doubted the appropriateness of the analogy to the Leyden jar; rather, it seemed to him that a weak animal electricity constantly circulated through the body of a normal frog, and that artificial circuits brought about convulsions by disturbing the natural flow (*Opere*, I, 15, 30–33).[11]

Volta's use of the whole frog—a move unnatural for an anatomist like Galvani—proved consequential. When the animal was intact it could be made to tremble only when struck by a discharge from a Leyden jar or when part of a bimetallic circuit. Volta inferred that the electricity put in action in the second case arose from the mere contact of dissimilar bodies (*Opere*, I, 55, 64–66, 73–74), a property he had already identified in "electrics" (insulators) but was surprised to meet in metals (*Opere*, I, 136). The fact, however, was plain, as well as the conclusion that animal electricity played no part in spasms inspired by bimetallic arcs. The only true galvanic effect, according to Volta, was the convulsion of a freshly prepared specimen in a circuit completed by a single metal (*Opere*, I, 116–118, 156–157, 180). And even this "beautiful and great discovery" (*Opere*, I, 175), this "truly astonishing experiment" (*Opere*, I, 178), could not occur as Galvani thought; for, as Volta showed, the muscle need not be included in the circuit. Electricity excited the nerve, and the nerve the muscle; there was no room for a Leyden jar fabricated of muscle tissue. To illustrate the office of the nerve Volta thought to excite the sense of taste by a bimetallic arc. With great satisfaction he experienced an unpleasant taste by joining a bit of tin on the tip of his tongue to a silver spoon resting further back (*Opere*, I, 56–57, 62–63, 73–74). It happened that, unknown to Volta, this experiment had been described many years earlier by J. G. Sulzer, who, however, did not associate it with electricity and doubtless—again in contrast to Volta—did not design it as a test of theory (*Opere*, I, 152–154, 196).

The tendency of Volta's results was to restrict more and more the domain of animal electricity. By November 1792, after countless trials on diverse unlucky creatures from insects ("it is very amusing to make a [headless] grasshopper sing" [*Opere*, I, 190–191]) to mammals, Volta had concluded that all galvanic excitations arose from external electrical stimulation. As for the classic case (a freshly killed and stripped frog, highly excitable, joined crural nerve to leg muscle by a single metal), Volta supposed that the electricity came not from animal power but from the contact between the metal and unobserved impurities in it (*Opere*, I, 147, 156–157). Nothing remained of the theory of animal electricity, or so Volta told Galvani's nephew and defender, Giovanni Aldini, professor of physics at the University of Bologna, in an open letter published early in 1793 (*Opere*, I, 149–159).

While the Galvanists pondered their response, Volta ranked the metals according to their electromotive power (*Opere*, I, 214, 234, 304) and tried to determine the seat of the electromotive force. He recognized that an effective circuit contained, besides a bimetallic joint, at least one "moist conductor," namely, the nerve to be excited, and he thought it more probable that the electrical imbalance occurred in the contact between the metals and the moist conductor than in the joint between the metals (*Opere*, I, 205, 212–213, 231–232). This proposition gained plausibility by his discovery in 1793 that the electromotive power of a chain of dissimilar metals depends only upon the nature of the two extreme links, precisely those touching the moist conductor, and that nothing happens if each metal is in contact only with moist conductors (*Opere*, I, 226–227).

Volta was accordingly prepared to answer the counterattack launched in 1794 by Galvani, Aldini, and a resourceful physician, Eusebio Valli, who had always thought the contact theory "ridiculous"; for "how [he said] is it possible for a single shilling to contain electricity sufficient to move the leg of a horse?"[12] Their strongest and most worrisome new evidence was Valli's excitation of spasms in freshly prepared frogs using himself as arc. It appeared that convulsions could be induced without the metallic contact which, in his reply to Galvani and Aldini, Volta had just asserted to be necessary (*Opere*, I, 274, 279, 295n, 308). Although many people conceived that Valli's stroke had saved animal electricity, Volta had no trouble turning it to his advantage. He observed that, as Valli had reported, the experiment worked best when the nerves and muscles were moistened with blood or saliva. As he explained to Sir Joseph Banks in March 1795, and then to A. M. Vassalli, professor of physics at the University of Turin, in a letter printed in 1796, a sequence of dissimilar moist conductors could generate an electrical current by contact forces without the intervention of metals (*Opere*, I, 255–256; 295–297).

Volta's next, and characteristic, step was to determine the "electromotive force" (his words) of various combinations of conductors. He tried to rank moist conductors ("conductors of the second kind") as he had the metals ("conductors of the first kind") (*Opere*, I, 371, 405–406). He confirmed that an electromotive force occurred only via the contact of dissimilar conductors (*Opere*, I, 372, 397, 411–413), and he sought the most powerful combination of "electromotors." The results, in order of decreasing power, expressed in Volta's notation (where capital and small letters signify conductors of the first and second kind, respectively [*Opere*, I, 230, 379–382]); *rABr* (where *r*, the frog, is both a conductor of the second kind and the electroscope); *raAr; rabr; rAr* and *rar*, both zero (*Opere*, 396–397, 401–402). What about *ABCA*? Volta thought that analogy favored the possibility of a weak finite current in such a circuit. But how to detect it when the only electroscope sensitive enough to register galvanic electricity was itself a conductor of the second kind (*Opere*, I, 377–378)? The difficulty instanced a much more serious one, which had long bothered Volta: that his claim of the identity of galvanic and common electricity rested on experiments in which pieces of animals played an indispensable part (*Opere*, I, 490, 540–555).

The contact of zinc and silver develops about 0.78 volt. Volta's most sensitive straw electrometer marked about 40 volt/degree.[13] By the summer of 1796 he had managed to multiply the charges developed by touching dissimilar metals together enough to stimulate his electrometer (*Opere*, I, 525; *Epistolario*, III, 349, 359). He first succeeded with a Nicholson doubler (*Opere*, I, 420–424) and then with an unaided gold-leaf electroscope (*Opere*, I, 435–436); and he later rendered contact electricity easily sensible by a "condensing electroscope," a straightforward combination of the condensator and the straw electrometer (*Epistolario*, III, 438). All these devices, including the doubler, came directly or indirectly from Volta's earlier work. Note that to obtain contact charges that he could multiply Volta had to change his mind about the principal seat of the electromotive force, which he now located in the junction of metals and not in their union with moist conductors (*Opere*, I, 419, 472). In 1797 he published a full account of his detection of galvanic electricity by electrostatic means (*Opere*, I, 393–447).

It remained to find a way to multiply galvanic electricity directly. Volta discovered soon enough that piling metal disks on one another (say *aABAB* · · · *a*) did not help, and that a circuit made only of metals gave no electromotive force. These results led to the useful rule, a precise version of his result of 1793, that the electromotive force of a pile of disks is equal to what its extreme disks would generate if put into immediate contact (*Opere*, II, 61). How or when Volta hit on the far from obvious artifice of repeating the apparently unimportant secondary conductors in his generator is not known; an anticipation appears in one of the combinations published by Gren in 1797 (*Opere*, I, 398, fig. 13, 400). The definitive pile, *AZaAZaAZa* · · · *AZ*, consisting of pairs of silver and zinc disks separated by pieces of moist cardboard, was first made public in 1800, in a letter addressed to Banks, president of the Royal Society of London, and published in its *Philosophical Transactions* (*Opere*, I, 563–582). The letter also describes an alternative arrangement, a "crown of cups" consisting of a circle of glasses filled with salty or alkaline water and connected by bimetallic arcs dipping into the liquid (*Opere*, I, 568, 571; see also *Opere*, I, 399, 403–404).

Volta represented his discovery as an "artificial electric organ," an apparatus "fundamentally the same" as the natural electrical equipment of the torpedo (*Opere*, I, 556, 582). A medium-size pile, with forty or fifty pairs, gave anyone who touched its extremities about the same sensation he could enjoy grasping an electric fish. In both cases, Volta said, a constant current running externally from top to toe of the electromotor passed through the arms and breast, and agitated the sense of touch. Were it directed at the senses of vision, taste, or hearing, the current would cause light, taste, or sound instead (*Opere*, I, 578–580). Neither the pile nor the torpedo give electrostatic signs because, as Cavendish had argued long before, they operate at too low a tension; their effects derive rather from the quantity of electrical matter they move. The analogy to the torpedo played little part in Volta's discovery; the emphasis upon it in the letter to Banks was intended to silence the Galvanists. As for the cause and continuance of the electricity generated by the contact of dissimilar conductors, Volta feigned no hypothesis: "This perpetual motion may appear paradoxical, perhaps inexplicable; but it is nonetheless true and real, and can be touched, as it were, with the hands" (*Opere*, I, 576; see also *Opere*, I, 489).

It appears that Volta possessed most of the ingredients of the pile by 1796, including even an anticipation of the outstanding key discovery, the constructive combination of the generating pairs. The delay in completing the invention may be explained by external circumstances. First, Volta's marriage, in 1794, to Teresa Peregrini, daughter of a government official in Como, quickly brought him a sizable family (three sons between 1795 and 1798) and many new demands upon his time. Second, during just these years, 1796 to 1800, Volta, like many of his colleagues, was distracted by the French invasion of Italy. In May 1796 he was chosen by the city of Como as one of a delegation to honor Napoleon, then fresh from driving the Austrians from the Milanese. Shortly thereafter he became an official of Como's new government (*Epistolario*, III, 291). But he was not comfortable in the position, which he resigned as soon as possible (*Epistolario*, III, 309–310); for although he did not, like Galvani, refuse to take an oath to the new Cisalpine Republic, he had a lingering loyalty, or rather gratitude, toward the Austrian regime, whose favor he had enjoyed. Moreover, the French authorities had not recommended themselves by allowing their soldiers to sack Pavia and to damage Volta's laboratory (*Epistolario*, III, 294). His coldness toward the French and open opposition to Jacobin colleagues, and also the accusation that he favored a proposal to move the university from Pavia to Milan, led to harassment that drove him from Pavia for some months. These opinions did him no harm when the Austrians returned in 1799 and shut up the university; for the victors only took away his job, and not—as in the case of Barletti, who had welcomed the French—his liberty. Thirteen months later the French were back. Napoleon immediately opened the university, and Volta, having recovered his professorship (*Epistolario*, IV, 8), resigned himself to citizenship in the revived Cisalpine Republic. Indeed, he proposed that he and a colleague,

L. Brugnatelli, professor of chemistry, go to Paris to express the gratitude of the university directly to the First Consul (*Epistolario*, IV, 16–17).

The trip, proposed in September 1800, was put off for a year because of war (*Epistolario*, IV, 24–25). It then turned into more than a mission to "cement an alliance of talent and science for the immortality of the two republics" (*Epistolario*, IV, 52–53); for in the interim Volta's letter to Banks had been published, and the chemical power of the pile discovered. The political mission became a triumphal march. Volta showed his experiments in Geneva, at the home of his friend Senebier; in Arcueil; in Paris, in the laboratories of Fourcroy, Seguin, Lamétherie, and above all, of Charles, where a special commission on galvanism of the Paris Academy met four times to see Volta's electricity; and at the Academy itself, where he performed at three sessions, each attended by Napoleon.[14] These demonstrations brought nothing new. They emphasized the electrostatic detection of the contact tension via a condensator and straw electroscope; used the old value of 1/60 degree of the latter (0.67 volt) as the tension of a single silver-zinc pair (*Opere*, II, 39–40, 50–61); and insisted on distinguishing between high tension/low current devices, like the standard electrical machine, and low tension/high current ones, like the pile, the crown of cups, and the torpedo (*Opere*, II, 72–83). When Volta concluded, Napoleon proposed the award of a gold medal; that, providentially, was also the recommendation of the commission on galvanism, which endorsed Volta's identification of galvanic and common electricity, and showed how to compute the tensions of various arrangements of disks and condensators (*Opere*, II, 113–115).

Napoleon continued to patronize Volta, giving him a pension and raising him to count and senator of the kingdom of Italy. In this there was more than politics. Volta's discoveries captured the imagination of Napoleon, who, to ensure continuance of similar inventions, authorized the Academy of Sciences to award a medal "for the best experiment made each year on the galvanic fluid" and a prize of 60,000 francs "to whoever by his experiments and discoveries makes a contribution to electricity and galvanism comparable to Franklin's and Volta's" (*Opere*, II, 122). But there was politics too. Just before leaving Paris in November 1801, Volta received what amounted to orders (*Epistolario*, IV, 88–89) to go to Lyons, to grace, and so endorse, a meeting at which selected Italian delegates were to be inspired to elect Napoleon president of the Cisalpine Republic. The republic soon disappeared into the kingdom of Italy, of which Napoleon became king. Volta played a small part in the kingdom as president of the Consiglio del Dipartimento del Lario (from 1803) and of the Comense Collegio Elettorale (1812). He retained sufficient confidence in French administration to cast his senatorial vote in 1814 in favor of offering the crown of Italy to Napoleon's stepson, Eugène de Beauharnais.

Napoleon was quite right in predicting that the pile presaged a new era in science. Its chemical power, employed in electrolyzing alkali salts, soon revealed the existence of sodium and potassium, a discovery for which Davy won the medal established by Napoleon. Studies of the properties of the current led to the laws of Oersted, Ohm, and Faraday, and to the beginnings of electrotechnology. In all of this Volta played no part. He was not much interested in the chemical effects of the pile, which he considered to be secondary phenomena (*Opere*, II, 37, 91). What effort he devoted to galvanism after his triumph in Paris went toward refuting the old doctrine of animal electricity, still very much alive. His last memoir on the subject, a lengthy review of his reasons for identifying galvanic and common electricity, was submitted under the name of a student in a prize competition announced in 1805 by the Società Italiana delle Scienze as follows: "Explain with clarity and dignity, and without offending anyone, the question of galvanism disputed by our worthy members Giovanni Aldini and Alessandro Volta" (*Opere*, II, 206). None of the papers submitted won the prize. Volta's memoir, which indeed contained little that was new, was printed in 1814 by his student and successor Pietro Configliachi (*Opere*, II, 205–307). After this competition Volta cut down his academic work. He sought and was refused retirement by the French ("a soldier," Napoleon told him, "should die on the field of honor" [*Epistolario*, IV, 455]); the Austrians, who returned in 1814, let him go in 1819. He spent his retirement chiefly in Como, where he died in 1827.

Volta received many honors besides those bestowed by Napoleon. The Royal Society of London elected him a member in 1791 and three years later gave him its highest prize, the Copley Medal, for setting right the Galvanists. He became a correspondent of the Berlin Academy of Sciences in 1786, and a foreign member of the Paris Academy in 1803. His fame also brought tangible rewards. In 1795 his university salary, 5,000 lire, was only double what he had during his last year at the Como Gymnasium. In 1805 he received an addi-

tional annuity of 4,000 lire from Napoleon, which survived the emperor's fall; and in 1809 he began to enjoy a senatorial salary of 24,000 lire. During the last twenty years of his life he had the income of a wealthy man.

As a scientist, Volta was conservative, yet alert to novelties; a strong theoretician, a "raisonneur sans pareil" (*Epistolario*, II, 268), as Lichtenberg said, yet an exceedingly careful and painstaking experimentalist, who constantly improved and varied his apparatus to exclude adventitious special cases. His uncommon imagination for effective instrumentation extended to anticipations of important practical devices such as the electrical telegraph (*Opere*, III, 194) and the incandescent gas lamp (*Opere*, VI, 150; VII, 155). He was no mathematician. His published work contains little mathematics beyond the rule of three and no evidence (according to Biot) that its author had a "mind fit for establishing rigorous theories"; while his lectures customarily skipped the mathematical parts of physics and omitted optics altogether. For these omissions Volta was bitterly attacked by Barletti in the early 1790's, no doubt partly for political reasons, and perhaps out of jealousy as well. The episode cost Volta much time and annoyance, and ended in an elaborate letter to the ministry in defense of his practice.[15] But despite his preference for the nonmathematical branches of physics, Volta fully understood the need for measurement: "Nothing good can be done in physics [he said] unless things are reduced to degrees and numbers" (*Opere*, I, 27). His mixture of precision in experiment and of indifference to—or ineptness at—general mathematical formulations also characterized several of his close colleagues, notably Saussure and Deluc. For the rest Volta went his own way, an autodidact seldom influenced by the work of others except at the beginning of an investigation.

NOTES

1. Quoted by Volpati, *Alessandro Volta*, 119; see *Epistolario*, V, 387–389.
2. For example, F. K. Achard, *Vorlesungen über die Experimentalphysik*, III (Berlin, 1791), 60.
3. *Epistolario*, I, 121; cf. Barletti, *Dubbi e pensieri* (Milan, 1776), 61–63, 103–119.
4. H. B. de Saussure, *Voyages dans les alpes*, II (Geneva–Neuchâtel, 1786), 212–219; see *Opere*, V, 154–155.
5. W. Thomson, *Reprint of Papers on Electricity and Magnetism*, 2nd ed. (London, 1884), 206–208, 227–229.
6. *Opere*, V, 55–56, 75–79; see Polvani, *Alessandro Volta*, 145.
7. *Opere*, VII, 228; Gliozzi, ed., *Opere scelte*, 248n.

8. The 2 vols. contain about 0.2 vol. $O_2$ and 1 vol. $H_2$; the total, therefore, falls by 0.6 vols., or 30 percent.

9. Grassi, "I lavori . . .," 562–563; Polvani, *Alessandro Volta*, 221–231; *Opere*, VII, 423–425.

10. Grassi, "I lavori . . .," 528–533.

11. The spasm occurring during discharge of a neighboring electrical machine brought nothing new; as Volta observed (*Opere*, I, 46–48, 175), it arose from the discharge of electricity induced in the specimen analogous to the return stroke in the case of lightning.

12. According to T. Cavallo in a letter to J. Lind, 23 Nov. 1792, British Museum Add. MS 22898, f. 25–26.

13. One degree of Volta's most sensitive straw electrometer equaled 1/10 of a degree of the Henley quadrant electrometer (*Opere*, V, 37, 52, 81; I, 486), 35 degrees of which marked about 13,350 volt (see note 6 above). Hence, one degree of the straw electrometer indicated about 40 volt. Volta later estimated the tension between zinc and silver at 1/60 degree straw (*Opere*, II, 39), or about 0.7 volt.

14. Z. Volta, *Alessandro Volta a Parigi*, 18–19, 41–47, 53–57, 96–97.

15. L. Magrini, "Notizie biografiche e scientifiche su A. Volta dai suoi autografi recentemente rinvenuti e inediti," in *Atti dell'Istituto lombardo di scienze e lettere*, 2 (1861), 254–283, on pp. 260–262, 272; C. Volpati; "Momenti d'amarezza sul camino della gloria," in *Voltiana*, 1 (1926), 437–447.

## BIBLIOGRAPHY

I. COLLECTED WORKS. The best bibliography is F. Scolari, *Alessandro Volta* (Rome, 1927), which incorporates F. Fossatti, "Bibliografia degli scritti editi di Alessandro Volta," in *Memorie dell'Istituto lombardo di scienze e lettere*, cl. sci. mat. nat., 18 (1900), 181–217. See also "Scritti del Volta o che lo riguardano stampati negli *Atti* del R. Istituto lombardo di scienze e lettere," in *Rendiconti dell'Istituto lombardo di scienze e lettere*, 60 (1927), 580–583. There are two collected works: *Collezione dell'opere*, V. Antinori, ed., 3 vols. in 5 (Florence, 1816), which is incomplete; and the magnificent national edition, *Le opere*, 7 vols. (Milan, 1918–1929), which is referred to in this article. There are also several anthologies: *Briefe über thierische Elektrität (1792)* and *Untersuchungen über den Galvanismus, 1796 bis 1800*, A. J. von Oettingen, ed., which are Ostwalds Klassiker der exakten Wissenschaften, nos. 114 and 118 (Leipzig, 1900); *L'opera di Alessandro Volta*, F. Massardi, ed. (Milan, 1927); and the excellent *Opere scelte*, M. Gliozzi, ed. (Turin, 1967).

Volta's correspondence is available in a national edition, *Epistolario*, 5 vols. (Bologna, 1949–1955), which, with the *Opere* and *Aggiunte alle opere e all'epistolario* (Bologna, 1966), supersedes all earlier editions. For the location of Volta's MSS, see *Opere*, I, x–xxi; Scolari, *Alessandro Volta*, pp. 171–462; and the unsigned "La nuova sede del Cartellario voltiano e la annessa biblioteca," in *Rendiconti dell'Istituto lombardo di scienze e lettere*, 60 (1927), 567–579. For Volta's instruments, most of which perished in a fire in 1899, see Società Storica Comense, *Raccolta voltiana* (Como, 1899) and *Il tempio voltiano in Como* (Como, 1939, 1973). Volta's library of printed books, unfortunately unannotated, is now at the Burndy Library, Norwalk, Connecticut.

II. IMPORTANT INDIVIDUAL WORKS. For electrostatics, see *De vi attractiva ignis electrici* (Como, 1769), in *Opere*, III, 21–52; Italian trans. in *Opere scelte*, M. Gliozzi, ed., 49–90; *Novus ac simplicissimus electricorum tentaminum apparatus* (Como, 1771), in *Opere*, III, 53–76; "Lettera . . . al dott. Giuseppe Priestley [sull'elettroforo perpetuo]," in *Scelta d'opuscoli interessanti*, 9 (1775), 91–107; 10 (1775), 87–113, in *Opere*, III, 93–108; "Lettera . . . a Giuseppe Klinkosch . . . sulla teoria dell'elettricità vindice e sull'elettroforo perpetuo," *ibid.*, 20 (1776), 32–67, in *Opere*, III, 131–151; "[Lettera al Saussure] Osservazioni sulla capacità de' conduttori elettrici," in *Opuscoli scelti sulle scienze e sulle arti . . .*, 1 (1778), 273–280, in *Opere*, III, 201–229; "Del modo di render sensibilissima la più debole elettricità," in *Philosophical Transactions of the Royal Society*, 72 (1782), 237–280 (English trans. in Appendix, vii–xxxiii), also in *Opere*, III, 271–300; and "Mémoire sur les grands avantages d'une espèce d'isolement très imparfait," in *Journal de physique*, 22 (1783), 325–350; 23 (1783), 3–16, 81–99, and in *Opere*, III, 313–377.

Volta's works on meteorology include "[Lettere a G. C. Lichtenberg] Sulla meteorologia elettrica," in *Biblioteca fisica d'Europa*, 1 (1788), 73–137; 2 (1788), 103–142; 3 (1788), 79–122; 5 (1788), 79–134; 6 (1788), 137–147; 7 (1789), 81–111; 9 (1789), 129–148; 10 (1789), 39–69; 11 (1789), 33–53; 14 (1790), 61–112; in *Opere*, V, 29–228, 239–307; "Sopra la grandine," in *Istituto nazionale italiano, Memorie*, Cl. fis. mat., 1, pt. 2 (1806), 125–190, also in *Opere*, V, 421–462, and in *Journal de physique*, 69 (1809), 333–360.

On pneumatics, see *Lettere [al p. Campi] sull'aria infiammabile nativa delle paludi* (Milan, 1777), in *Opere*, VI, 17–102; "Lettere . . . al marchese Castelli sulla costruzione di un moschetto e di una pistola ad aria infiammabile," in *Scelta d'opuscoli interessanti*, 30 (1777), 86–109; 31 (1777), 3–24; and in *Opere*, VI, 123–150; "[Lettres à Priestley] Sur l'inflammation de l'air inflammable," in *Journal de physique*, 12 (1778), 365–373; 13 (1779), 278–303, and in *Opere*, VI, 173–215; "[Contributions to the Italian edition of P. G. Macquer, *Dizionario di chimica* (Pavia, 1783–1784)]," in *Opere*, VI, 349–436; VII, 3–105; "Descrizione dell'eudiometro al aria infiammabile," in *Annali di chimica e storia naturale*, 1 (1790), 171–213; 2 (1791), 161–186; 3 (1791), 36–45; and in *Opere*, VII, 173–213; and "Della uniforme dilazione dell'aria per ogni grado di calore," *ibid.*, 4 (1793), 227–294, in *Opere*, VII, 345–375.

Volta's works on animal electricity and galvanism include "[Memorie] sull'elettricità animale," in *Giornale fisico-medico*, 2 (1792), 146–187, 241–270; 3 (1792), 35–73; 4 (1793), 63–81; in *Opere*, I, 13–35, 41–74, 149–159; "Account of Some Discoveries Made by Mr. Galvani of Bologna . . . in Two Letters . . . to Mr. Tiberius Cavallo [in French]," in *Philosophical Transactions of the Royal Society*, **83**, pt. 1 (1793), 10–44, also in *Opere*, I, 171–197; "Nuove osservazioni sull'elettricità animale," in *Giornale fisico-medico*, **5** (1792), 192–196, and also in *Opere*, I, 143–147; "Nuova memoria sull'elettricità animale . . . in alcune lettere al sig. ab. Anton Maria Vassalli," in *Annali di chimica e storia naturale*, **5** (1794), 132–144; **6** (1794), 142–166; **11** (1796), 84–128, also in *Opere*, I, 261–281, 287–301; "[Lettere al prof. Gren] Sul galvanismo ossia sull'elettricità eccitata del contatto de' conduttori dissimili," *ibid.*, **13** (1797), 226–274; **14** (1797), 3–74, in *Opere*, I, 393–447; excerpted in German in *Neues Journal der Physik*, **3** (1797), 479–481; **4** (1797), 107–135; and in French in *Annales de chimie*, **23** (1797), 276–315; **29** (1798), 91–93; "[Lettere al cittadino Aldino] Intorno alla pretesa elettricità animale," in *Annali di chimica e storia naturale*, **16** (1798), 3–88, in *Opere*, I, 519–555; "On the Electricity Excited by the Mere Contact of Conducting Substances of Different Kinds [in French]," in *Philosophical Transactions of the Royal Society*, **90**, pt. 2 (1800), 403–431, in *Opere*, I, 563–582, and *Journal de physique*, 51 (1800), 344–354; English trans. in *Philosophical Magazine*, **7** (1800), 288–311; "Sur les phénomènes galvaniques," in *Journal de physique*, **53** (1801), 309–316, and in *Opere*, II, 35–43; "Memoria sull' identità del fluido elettrico col fluido galvanico," in *Ann. chim. stor. natur.*, **19** (1802), 38–88; **21** (1802), 163–211; in *Opere*, II, 45–84 (in part in *Annales de chemie*, **40** [1802], 225–256); *L'identità del fluido elettrico col cosi detto fluido galvanico* [1805] (Pavia, 1814), in *Opere*, II, 205–307.

III. BIOGRAPHY. The best general assessment of Volta is C. Volpati, *Alessandro Volta nella storia e nell'intimità* (Milan, 1927). Giovanni Cau, *Alessandro Volta: L'uomo, la scienza, il suo tempo* (Milan, 1927), is also useful. Older influential notices are J. B. Biot, in *Biographie universelle*, XLIV, 2nd ed., 78–81; F. Arago, *Oeuvres*, J. A. Barral, ed., 2nd ed., I (Paris, 1865), 187–240; M. Monti, *Biografia degli italiani illustri*, F. de Tipalso, ed., IX (Venice, 1844), 258–288; and C. Cantù, *Italiani illustri*, 3rd ed., III (Milan, 1879), 567–602.

On Volta's family and early years, see G. Gemelli, "Geneologia ed arma gentilizia della famiglia Volta," *Raccolta voltiana*, no. 6 (Como, 1899); and Z. Volta, *Alessandro Volta. Parte prima . . . Della giovinezza* (Milan, 1875), and the review *Voltiana* (1926–1927). For Volta's travels, see A. Verrechia, "Lichtenberg und Volta," in *Sudhoffs Archiv für Geschichte der Medizin und der Naturwissenschaften*, **51** (1967), 349–360; C. Volpati, "Amici e ammiratori di Alessandro Volta in Germania," in *Nuova rivista storica*, **11** (1927), 535–570; G. Bilancioni, "Alessandro Volta e Antonio Scarpa," in *Archeion*, **8** (1927), 351–363; M. Cermenati, *Alessandro Volta alpinista* (Turin, 1899); and Z. Volta, *Alessandro Volta a Parigi* (Milan, 1879). For politics, see G. Gallavresi, "Alessandro Volta e l'epopea napoleonica," in *Nuova antologia*, **334** (1927) 201–208; and

Z. Volta, "Alessandro Volta e l'università di Pavia dal 1778 al 1799," in *Archivio storico lombardo*, 24 (1899), 393–447. For Volta's honors, see S. Ambrosoli, "Le medaglie di Alessandro Volta," in *Raccolta voltiana*, no. 7 (Como, 1899); and F. Frigerio, "Saggio di iconografia voltiana," in *Como ad Alessandro Volta* (Como, [1945]), 143–156. There is additional bibliography in Scolari, *Alessandro Volta*, 30–44.

IV. WORK. By far the best general account of Volta's work is G. Polvani, *Alessandro Volta* (Pisa, 1942). On electricity, see also M. Gliozzi, *L'elettrologia fino al Volta*, 2 vols. (Naples, 1937), and "Consonanze e dissonanze tra l'elettrostatica di Cavendish e quella di Volta," in *Physis*, **11** (1969), 231–248; F. Massardi, "Sull'importanza dei concetti fondamentali . . . [in Volta's] *De vi attractiva*," in *Rendiconti dell'Istituto lombardo di scienze e lettere*, **59** (1926), 373–381, and "Concordanza di risultati e formule emergenti da manoscritti inediti del Volta con quelli ricavati della fisicomatematica," *ibid.*, **56** (1923), 293–308; and W. C. Walker, "The Detection and Estimation of Electric Charges in the Eighteenth Century," in *Annals of Science*, **1** (1936), 66–99.

On meteorology, see L. Volta, "Alessandro Volta e la meteorologia, specialmente elettrica," in *Rendiconti dell'Istituto lombardo di scienze e lettere*, **60** (1927), 471–482; and C. Volpati, "L'ultimo episodio della vita scientifica di Alessandro Volta (La questione della difesa contra la grandine)," in *Como ad Alessandro Volta* (Como, 1945), 113–142.

On pneumatics, see R. Watermann, "Eudiometrie," in *Technikgeschichte*, **35** (1968), 293–319; V. Broglia, "Alessandro Volta und die Chemie," in *Chemikerzeitung*, **90** (1966), 628–640; W. A. Osman, "Alessandro Volta and the Inflammable Air Eudiometer," in *Annals of Science*, **14** (1958), 215–242; C. Pirotti, "La pistola di Volta e il motore a scoppio," in *Nuovo cimento*, **4:10** (1927), cxxviii–cxxxv; and F. Grassi, "I lavori del Volta e del Gay-Lussac per l'azione del calore," in *Rendiconti dell' Istituto lombardo di scienze e lettere*, **60** (1927), 505–534, and "I lavori del Volta e del Dalton su le tensione dei vapori," *ibid.*, 535–566.

On animal electricity and galvanism, see P. Sue, *Histoire du galvanisme*, 2 vols. (Paris, 1802); G. Carradori, *Istoria del galvanismo in Italia* (Florence, 1817); A. Mauro, "The Role of the Voltaic Pile in the Galvani-Volta Controversy," in *Journal of the History of Medicine*, 24 (1969), 140–150; and T. M. Brown, "The Electrical Current in Early 19th Century French Physics," in *Historical Studies in the Physical Sciences*, 1 (1969), 61–103.

J. L. HEILBRON

**VOLTAIRE, FRANÇOIS MARIE AROUET DE** (*b.* Paris, France, 21 November 1694; *d.* Paris, 30 May 1778), *literature*.

Voltaire's importance for the history of science lies particularly in his having composed a famous popularization of Newton, *Éléments de la philosophie de Newton* (1738), while also collaborating with his companion and mistress, Émilie, marquise du Châtelet, on her translation of the *Principia* into French, and more generally in his having referred, with the lightness of touch that made him a serious critic of the human condition, his moral philosophy to what he took to be the Newtonian, and hence the correct, account of physical reality.

Born François Arouet, his father having been a lawyer of the middling bourgeoisie and a notary, he took the pen name Voltaire when setting up as a young poet and playwright prior to 1725, one who soon had a certain success in the world of letters and fashion with his *Oedipe* and *Henriade*. The footing there proved slippery when Voltaire exchanged man-about-town insults in January 1726 with a young nobleman whom he had unrealistically thought to be a friend, the chevalier de Rohan. Instead of being accorded the satisfaction of a duel, Voltaire was beaten in the street by lackeys and was then incarcerated as a nuisance in the Bastille. He was released on condition that he exile himself until the embarrassment that his temerity had caused a great and noble family should be forgotten.

It was thus in the wake of shocking injustice and humiliation that Voltaire was in London between 1726 and 1729. He was present for Newton's funeral in Westminster Abbey in 1727. The first mention of scientific matters in his published work occurs in the *Lettres philosophiques*, or *Lettres sur les Anglais*, which he drafted during his English period, although it did not appear until 1734. Among the many merits of life in England that it celebrates, to the disadvantage by comparison of life in France, was the dignity that Voltaire there found accorded in society to men of science and letters. A well-known passage contrasts the physical picture of Paris, where the world is full of Cartesian vortices, to that of London, where it is empty of all but Newtonian attraction. Voltaire discussed Bacon, Locke, Newton, and inoculation against smallpox approvingly in letters 11 through 17, after praising religious pluralism, commercial enterprise, and representative government, and before turning to the theater and literature.

Voltaire had thus already adopted Newtonianism in principle, and had read in and about science, before his association with Mme du Châtelet, which began in 1733. Both were also friendly with Maupertuis, who had verified what he said about

Newton in the *Lettres philosophiques*, and with Clairaut. Fearful of arrest again, Voltaire took up residence at Mme du Châtelet's château at Cirey near the border of Champagne and Lorraine in 1734. They lived there until her death in 1749, and it was there that he undertook intensive study and correspondence with experts preparatory to writing the *Éléments*, in which (he wrote to a friend) he proposed "to reduce this giant to the measure of the dwarfs who are my contemporaries." A frequent visitor to Cirey was Francesco Algarotti, the success of whose *Il Newtonianismo per le dame* (1737) is often said to have inspired Voltaire to write a more serious work.

Voltaire's title is accurate, whether designedly or no, in that the book is about the philosophy that he read out of (or into) Newton and is not a technical guide to the science, whether mathematics, mechanics, or optics. Part I handles the metaphysical and theological issues of the Leibniz-Clarke correspondence, part II the theory of light and colors, and part III gravity and cosmology. Even in the optical part, only four out of fourteen chapters discuss Newton's actual work. The rest of it consists of an overview of seventeenth-century optics in general, so presented as to make it appear that color perception supports the associationist psychology. It is not perfectly clear from the chapters on the *Opticks* itself that Voltaire had grasped the distinction in Newton's mind between the phenomena of refraction, which established the composite character of white light, and the production of colors in thin transparent media, which exhibited the interaction of light and matter and which were later called interference effects. In any case, it was the latter aspect that Voltaire emphasized, probably for the reason that it could more easily be discussed in connection with his favorite among Newton's principles, the principle of attraction.

The transition that Voltaire made from color to gravity would lead the reader to suppose that Newton had extended this cardinal principle from optics to cosmology and had thus come to explain the system of the world. Discussing the *Principia*, Voltaire did give a qualitative sketch of that last topic, which occupies its third book. Newton had himself advised readers that, in addition to Book III, the minimum requisites for comprehending the *Principia* consisted in a command of the definitions and laws of motion and the first three sections of Book I (motion in conic sections under the influence of central forces). Of that Voltaire gave his readers only a verbal summary of proposition 1.

There is no discussion of physical quantities and no statement of the laws of motion. In general, the technical level is indicated by a remark apropos of the *Opticks* which informs the reader that there is a constant proportion between the sines of the angles of incidence and refraction but dispenses him from an explanation of what a sine is, since that would surpass the mathematical demands to be placed on him.

Evidently Voltaire's book may be taken as an index to what a clever writer thought could be expected scientifically of the literate public. It cannot be supposed to have told technically proficient readers anything substantive about Newton's work. The point needs emphasis since something more positive is often attributed to Voltaire's transmission of Newtonian physics in works of general history, which usually credit him with having converted French opinion—whatever that may mean—from Cartesianism to Newtonianism, and also since Voltaire himself does seem to have entertained briefly the desire to make some small contribution to science. He and Mme du Châtelet installed a laboratory at Cirey and made experiments. In 1736 the Académie des Sciences set the problem of the nature of fire for the prize it proposed to award in 1738. Both partners entered memoirs in the competition, which was won by Euler. Voltaire also wrote a piece defending the Newtonian measure of force in the vis viva controversy (on which issue he disagreed with Mme du Châtelet), composed several essays of natural history, and published clarifications and corrections of the cosmological discussion in the *Éléments*. Errors had found their way into the first edition, he explained, because the Dutch printer had made changes in the text without his knowledge.

None of that made any significant difference, however, either to science or probably to Voltaire, who did not persist in these researches. What really mattered to him about science was the vantage point he thought it offered to intelligence in the battle that did count, that of fact against dogma and illusion, which he waged throughout his life. Scholarship has established that it was almost certainly in 1739 that he composed *Micromégas* (not published until 1752 in London). It was his first fully successful venture in the genre of the *conte philosophique*, the form that he brought to its highest state of perfection. The observations of the extraplanetary visitor from Sirius light-heartedly reduce man to his true proportions in the scheme of things. Voltaire wrote it when his head was full of the information he had assembled for the *Éléments*. As for his masterpiece, *Candide*, there is nothing of science in that famous tale. But we need to appreciate the reason for Voltaire's admiration of Newton in order to take the full thrust of his scorn for Leibniz in the caricature of Dr. Pangloss. For Pangloss is the personification of mealy-mouthed dogma, denaturing every fact and justifying every illusion, however absurd, in the name of principles—"All is for the best in the best of possible worlds"—that will leave untroubled the beneficiaries of the systematic deceptions that rule in society.

Throughout part I of the *Éléments*, Leibniz is the obstacle to enlightenment in metaphysics, as Descartes had been in physics, and for similar reasons: both had presumed to project their doctrines upon God or nature in the guise of necessities. Not so Newton, who had generalized his laws from phenomena, confirmed them by experience, and restricted them within the scope of mathematical formulation. Nothing pleased Voltaire more than repeating how Newton had made no pretense of stating the cause of attraction and had confined himself to demonstrating its quantity. The modern reader who expects to encounter eighteenth-century skepticism in Voltaire may be surprised to find that the *Éléments* opens with the argument that Newton gave in the General Scholium of the *Principia* for the existence and dominion of God. In further chapters Voltaire developed Newton's view that space and time are attributes of God, who, all unconstrained by Leibniz' principle of sufficient reason, had been perfectly free to constitute things as he saw fit. Thus the Newtonian philosophy, in consequence of which it followed that God had accorded a portion of his infinite liberty to man in the form of free will. Now then, all this about God may very well have been tongue-in-cheek on Voltaire's part, but not the part about liberty. For what he really cared about was improving the possibility that an informed man may have to make reasoned choices in a world of events that are largely indifferent to his wishes. The enemy of such a liberty was dogma and never fact. "Droit au fait" was a favorite among his sayings, fortified by what he understood of science; and as for dogma, reinforced by prejudice and tradition and armed by authority, that was the infamy to be scotched in the injunction "Écrasez l'infâme!" yet more regularly repeated in his later, more political, more moral, and (in the highest sense) more journalistic years.

*BIBLIOGRAPHY*

I. ORIGINAL WORKS. *Éléments de la philosophie de Newton mis à la portée de tout le monde* (Amsterdam, 1738) was published in a revision in 1741 and in a 2nd ed. in 1745. The latter is the version included in vol. XXXI of the Kehl ed. of his works (1784–1789) and in most later collections. Other writings on "Physique" include (1) the letters and a "Défense" of Newtonianism (1739); (2) the "Essai sur la nature du feu et sur sa propagation" and "Doutes sur la mesure des forces mortices et sur leur nature" (1741); (3) an abstract of Mme du Châtelet's memoir on fire, "Mémoire sur un ouvrage de physique de Madame la Marquise du Châtelet" (1739), and a lengthy commentary on her book about Leibniz, "Exposition du livre des Institutions Physiques" (1740); and (4) writings on natural history: "Relation touchant un Maure blanc amené d'Afrique à Paris en 1744," "Dissertation . . . sur les changements arrivés dans notre globe, et sur les pétrifactions qu'on prétend en être les témoignages" (it was in this essay, sent to the Academy in Bologna in 1746, that Voltaire advanced the opinion that it was more probable that fossils found in the Alps had been dropped by travelers than that revolutionary changes have occurred in the order of nature), "Des singularités de la nature" (1768), and "Les colimaçons du Révérend Père l'Escarbotier . . ." (1768). Voltaire reprinted much of ch. 9, pt. III, of the *Éléments* in the article "Figure de la terre," in his *Questions sur l'Encyclopédie* (1770), taking the occasion to make several corrections. Three further fragments appear in the *Mélanges littéraires* of the Kehl ed., "A.M.***" (1739) and "Courte réponse aux longs discours d'un docteur allemand" (1740), both about Newtonianism, and finally, "Lettre sur la prétendue comète" (1773), the appearance of which was vulgarly supposed to herald the end of the world. The 1827 ed. of *Oeuvres complètes* includes these fugitive pieces in its second *Physique* volume (XLII). Theodore Besterman has edited *Voltaire's Correspondence*, 107 vols., Institut et Musée Voltaire (Geneva, 1953–1965). A convenient modern ed. of the *Leibniz-Clarke Correspondence* is that by H. G. Alexander (Manchester, 1956).

II. SECONDARY LITERATURE. The important work on Newtonianism in France, Pierre Brunet, *L'introduction des théories de Newton en France au XVIII<sup>e</sup> siècle avant 1738* (Paris, 1931), was never completed. Ira O. Wade, *The Intellectual Development of Voltaire* (Princeton, 1969), draws on the author's earlier, more specialized studies dealing with scientific themes in Voltaire's work. See, especially, Wade's ed. of *Micromégas* (Princeton, 1950), where the 1739 date of composition is convincingly argued. There is a valuable discussion of *Candide* in Peter Gay, *The Enlightenment: An Interpretation*, I (New York, 1966), 197–203. Robert Walters, "Voltaire and the Newtonian Universe," an unpublished dissertation (1954) in the Princeton Univ. library, is a study of the *Éléments*. See also Martin S. Staum, "New-

ton and Voltaire: Constructive Skeptics," in *Studies on Voltaire and the Eighteenth Century*, **62** (1968), 29–56; and two articles by Henry Guerlac, "Three 18th-Century Social Philosophers: Scientific Influences on Their Thought," in *Daedalus*, **88** (1958), 12–18; and "Where the Statue Stood: Divergent Loyalties to Newton in the 18th Century," in Earl Wasserman, ed., *Aspects of the 18th Century* (Baltimore, 1965), 317–334. The interpretation of the present article is developed more fully in an essay by the undersigned, "Science and the Literary Imagination: Voltaire and Goethe," in David Daiches and A. K. Thorlby, eds., *Literature of the Western World*, IV (London, 1975), 167–194.

CHARLES C. GILLISPIE

**VOLTERRA, VITO** (*b.* Ancona, Italy, 3 May 1860; *d.* Rome, Italy, 11 October 1940), *mathematics, natural philosophy.*

Volterra was the only child of Abramo Volterra, a cloth merchant, and his wife Angelica Almagià. His ancestors had lived in Bologna, whence at the beginning of the fifteenth century one of them had moved to Volterra, a small city in Tuscany—the origin of the family's present name. In 1459 this ancestor's descendants opened a bank in Florence. Volterras are remembered as fifteenth-century writers and travelers and as collectors of books and ancient codices. In the following centuries branches of the family lived in various Italian cities, including Ancona in the 1700's.

Volterra was two years old when his father died. He and his mother, left amost penniless, were taken into the home of her brother, Alfonso Almagià, an employee of the Banca Nazionale. Later they lived in Turin and in Florence. Volterra spent the greater part of his youth in Florence and considered himself almost a native of that city. He attended the Scuola Tecnica Dante Alighieri and the Istituto Tecnico Galileo Galilei, both of which had excellent teachers, including the physicist Antonio Roiti, who played an important part in Volterra's career.

Volterra was a very precocious child. At the age of eleven he began to study Bertrand's *Traité d'arithmétique* and Legendre's *Éléments de géométrie*. He formulated original problems and tried to solve them. At thirteen he worked on ballistic problems and, after reading Jules Verne's novel *From the Earth to the Moon*, tried to determine the trajectory of a gun's projectile in the combined gravitational field of the earth and the moon—a restricted version of the three-body problem. In his solution the time is partitioned into small intervals, for each of which the force is considered as a constant and the trajectory is given as a succession of small parabolic arcs. Almost forty years later, at the age of fifty-two, Volterra demonstrated this solution in a course of lectures given at the Sorbonne. The idea of studying a natural phenomenon by dividing into small intervals the time in which it occurs, and investigating the phenomenon in each such interval by considering the causes that produce it as invariable, was later applied by Volterra to many other kinds of problems, such as differential linear equations, theory of functionals, and linear substitutions.

Although Volterra was greatly interested in science, his family, which had little money, urged him to follow a commercial career. There followed a struggle between his natural inclination and practical necessity. The family appealed to a distant cousin, Edoardo Almagià, a civil engineer with a doctorate in mathematics, hoping that he would persuade the boy to interrupt his studies and devote himself to business. The cousin, however, who later became Volterra's father-in-law, was so impressed by his mathematical ability that he tried to persuade the family to let the boy pursue his scientific studies. Roiti, having learned that his most able student was being urged to become a bank clerk, immediately nominated him as assistant in the physics laboratory at the University of Florence, an unusual occurrence since Volterra had not enrolled at the university.

Volterra completed high school in 1878 and enrolled in the department of natural sciences at the University of Florence. Two years later he won the competition to become a resident student at the Scuola Normale Superiore in Pisa. At the University of Pisa he enrolled in the mathematics and physics courses given by Betti, Dini, and Riccardo Felici. At first he was very interested in Dini's work in analysis. In one of Volterra's early papers, published while he was still a student, he was the first to present examples of derivable functions the derivatives of which are not reconcilable with Riemann's point of view. This observation was used much later as a starting point for Lebesgue's research on this subject. Volterra was fascinated most by Betti's lectures, and under his influence he devoted his research to mechanics and mathematical physics.

In 1882 Volterra graduated with a doctorate in physics and was immediately appointed Betti's assistant. The following year, at the age of twenty-three, he won the competition for a professorship

of mechanics at the University of Pisa. After Betti's death Volterra succeeded him in the chair of mathematical physics. In 1892 Volterra was appointed professor of mechanics at the University of Turin, and in 1900 he succeeded Eugenio Beltrami in the chair of mathematical physics at the University of Rome. In the same year he married Virginia Almagià, who for over forty years was his devoted companion.

In recognition of his scientific achievements, Volterra was made a senator of the kingdom of Italy in 1905. Although he was never attracted by politics, he spoke frequently in the Senate on important issues concerning university organization and problems. He was active in Italian political life during World War I and, later, in the struggle against Fascist oppression.

When World War I broke out, Volterra felt that Italy should join the Allies; and when Italy entered the war, Volterra, although he was fifty-five, enlisted as an officer in the army corps of engineers, joining its air branch. He perfected a new type of airship, studied the possibility of mounting guns in it, and was the first to fire a gun from an airship. He also experimented with airplanes. For these accomplishments he was mentioned in dispatches and decorated with the War Cross.

At the beginning of 1917 Volterra established the Italian Office of War Inventions and became its chairman. He made frequent trips to France and to Great Britain in the process of wartime scientific and technical collaboration among the Allies. He was the first to propose the use of helium as a substitute for hydrogen in airships.

In October 1922 Fascism came to power in Italy. Volterra was one of the few to understand, from the beginning, its threat to the country's democratic institutions. He was one of the principal signatories of the "Intellectuals' Declaration" against Fascism, an action he took while president of the Accademia dei Lincei. When the proposed "laws of national security" were discussed by the Italian Senate, a small group of opposition senators, headed by Volterra and Benedetto Croce, appeared—at great personal risk—at all the Senate's meetings and always voted against Mussolini. By 1930 the parliamentary government created by Cavour in the nineteenth century was abolished, and Volterra never again attended sessions of the Italian Senate.

In 1931, having refused to sign the oath of allegiance imposed upon professors by the Fascist government, Volterra was dismissed from the University of Rome; and in 1932, for the same reason, he was deprived of all his memberships in Italian scientific academies. In 1936, however, on the nomination of Pope Pius XI he was elected to the Pontifical Academy of Sciences.

After 1931 Volterra lectured in Paris at the Sorbonne, in Rumania, in Spain, in Belgium, in Czechoslovakia, and in Switzerland. He spent only short periods in Italy, mainly at his country house at Ariccia, in the Alban Hills south of Rome. From December 1938 he was afflicted by phlebitis, but his mind remained clear and he continued his passionate pursuit of science until his death.

Volterra's scientific work covers the period from 1881, when he published his first papers, to 1940 when his last paper was published in the *Acta* of the Pontifical Academy of Sciences. His most important contributions were in higher analysis, mathematical physics, celestial mechanics, the mathematical theory of elasticity, and mathematical biometrics. His major works in these fields included the foundation of the theory of functionals and the solution of the type of integral equations with variable limits that now bear his name, methods of integrating hyperbolic partial differential equations, the study of hereditary phenomena, optics of birefringent media, the motion of the earth's poles and elastic dislocations of multiconnected bodies, and, in his last years, placing the laws of biological fluctuations on mathematical bases and establishing principles of a demographic dynamics that present analogies to the dynamics of material systems.

Volterra received numerous honors, was a member of almost every major scientific academy and was awarded honorary doctorates by many universities. In 1921 he received an honorary knighthood from George V of England.

Scientific research did not, however, occupy all of Volterra's activity. He was an intimate friend of many well-known scientific, political, literary, and artistic men of his time. He has been compared to a typical man of the Italian Renaissance for the variety of his interests and knowledge, his great scientific curiosity, and his sensitivity to art, literature, and music.

## BIBLIOGRAPHY

I. ORIGINAL WORKS. Volterra's works were collected as *Opere matematiche. Memorie e note*, 5 vols. (Rome, 1954–1962).

His writings include *Trois leçons sur quelques progrès récents de la physique mathématique* (Worcester, Mass., 1912), also in *Lectures Delivered . . . by V. Volterra, E. Rutherford, R. W. Wood, C. Barus* (Worcester, Mass., 1912), and translated into German (Leipzig, 1914); *Leçons sur les équations intégrales et les équations intégro-différentielles*, M. Tomassetti and F. S. Zarlatti, eds. (Paris, 1913); *Leçons sur les fonctions de lignes*, collected and edited by Joseph Pérès (Paris, 1913); "Henri Poincaré: L'oeuvre mathématique," in *Revue du mois*, **15** (1913), 129–154; *Saggi scientifici* (Bologna, 1920); and *Leçons sur la composition et les fonctions permutables* (Paris, 1924), written with J. Pérès.

Additional works are *Theory of Functionals and of Integral and Integro-Differential Equations*, Luigi Fantapié, ed., M. Long, trans. (London–Glasgow, 1930), repr. with a preface by Griffith C. Evans and an almost complete bibliography of Volterra's works and a biography by Sir Edmund Whittaker (New York, 1959); *Leçons sur la théorie mathématique de la lutte pour la vie*, Marcel Brelot, ed. (Paris, 1931); *Les associations biologiques au point de vue mathématique* (Paris, 1935), written with U. D'Ancona; *Théorie générale des fonctionnelles* (Paris, 1936), written with J. Pérès; and *Sur les distorsions des corps élastiques (théorie et applications)* (Paris, 1960), written with E. Volterra, preface by J. Pérès.

II. SECONDARY LITERATURE. Biographies of Volterra and descriptions of his scientific work were published immediately after his death in 1940. A year later Sir Edmund Whittaker published a biography in *Obituary Notices of Fellows of the Royal Society of London*, **3** (1941), 691–729, with a bibliography; an abridged version appeared in *Journal of the London Mathematical Society*, **16** (1941), 131–139.

Other biographies and commemorations of Volterra, listed chronologically, include *Enciclopedia italiana di scienze, lettere ed arti*, XXXV (Rome, 1938), 582–583; Émile Picard, in *Comptes rendus . . . de l'Académie des sciences*, **211** (1940), 309–312; S. Mandelbrojt, in *Yearbook. American Philosophical Society* (1940), 448–451; D'Arcy W. Thompson and Sir Sydney Chapman, in *Nature*, **147** (22 Mar. 1941), 349–350; C. Somigliana, in *Acta Pontificiae Accademiae scientiarum*, **6** (1942), 57–86; C. Somigliana, in *Rendiconti del Seminario matematico e fisico di Milano*, **17** (1946), 3–61, with bibliobraphy; Guido Castelnuovo and Carlo Somigliana, "Vito Volterra e la sua opera scientifica," in *Atti dell' Accademia nazionale dei Lincei* (1947), session of 17 Oct.; and J. Pérès, in *Ricerca scientifica*, **18** (1948), 1–9.

See also *Enciclopedia italiana di scienze, lettere ed arti, seconda appendice 1938–1948* (Rome, 1949); and G. Armellini, *Discorso pronunciato . . . per le onoranze a V. Volterra . . .* (Ancona, 1951); Guido Corbellini, *Vito Volterra nel centenario della sua nascita* (Rome, 1960); Accademia Nazionale dei Lincei, *Vito Volterra nel I centenario della nascita* (Rome, 1961); and Francesco G. Tricomi, "Matematici italiani del primo secolo dello stato unitario," *Memorie dell'Accademia delle scienze di Torino*, Cl. di scienze fisiche, matematiche e naturali, 4th ser., no. 1 (1962), 118.

E. VOLTERRA

**VOLTZ, PHILIPPE LOUIS** (*b.* Strasbourg, France, 15 August 1785; *d.* Paris, France, 30 March 1840), *geology.*

Voltz came from a poor family, and his parents had to make great sacrifices for his education. He entered the École Polytechnique in 1803 and the École des Mines in 1806. After serving as a mining engineer in the Belgian provinces, he held the post of chief engineer of the Strasbourg mineralogical district from August 1814 until 1836. In this capacity he advised industrialists in eastern France, made an inventory of the mineral resources of Alsace, and began the surveys needed to establish a geological map of the province. Only the map of the southern region (the Haut-Rhin department) was completed, however; it was published in 1833. Greatly interested in minerals and fossils, Voltz devoted much time to the development of Strasbourg's museum of natural history, which, as a result, soon possessed one of France's largest collections concerning stratigraphic paleontology.

Voltz's publications on the stratigraphy of eastern France, particularly on the Triassic, display his remarkable gifts as an observer. "Aperçu de la topographie minéralogique de l'Alsace" (1828), which appeared simultaneously in German, treats of the stratigraphy and paleontology of the province, as well as of its mineralogy. Paleontology increasingly attracted Voltz, who published several studies of fossil mollusks, notably belemnites and Nerinea.

Because of his fame as a paleontologist, new fossil forms were frequently named after Voltz: for example, Adolphe Brongniart's genus *Voltzia*, a gymnosperm abundant in the Triassic.

Voltz was fluent in German and encouraged contact between scientists on both sides of the Rhine. In December 1828 he and some of his friends founded the Société d'Histoire Naturelle de Strasbourg. He was also a member of the Geological Society of London and a corresponding member of the Société Industrielle de Mulhouse.

In 1830 Voltz began to give a free course of lectures in geognosy at the Strasbourg Faculty of Sciences. Among his students were Jules Thurmann and Amanz Gressly, the latter of whom apparently took up the notion of facies that Voltz had introduced into geology in 1828. Voltz organized and presided at the special meeting of the French Geological Society held at Strasbourg and in the Vosges 6–14 September 1834, which was attended by many French and foreign geologists.

Voltz's activities went far beyond geology. He was a municipal councillor of Strasbourg and *counseiller général* of the Bas-Rhin department. While holding these offices he became concerned about the conditions of the poor, and he seems to have been an enthusiastic supporter of the July Revolution of 1830.

Named inspector-general of mines in December 1836, Voltz moved to Paris, where, besides handling his administrative duties, he enriched the paleontological collection of the École des Mines. His health began to deteriorate, however, and he died four years later.

*BIBLIOGRAPHY*

I. ORIGINAL WORKS. Voltz's writings include "Aperçu de la topographie minéralogique de l'Alsace," in J. F. Aufschlager, ed., *Nouvelle description historique et topographique de l'Alsace* (Strasbourg, 1828), 1–66; "Observations sur les bélemnites," in *Mémoires de la Société du Muséum d'histoire naturelle de Strasbourg*, **1**, no. 1 (1830), 1–70; "Carte géologique du département du Haut-Rhin," *Statistiques générales du département du Haut-Rhin*, no. 46 (1833); and "Notice sur le grès bigarré de la grande carrière de Soultz-les-Bains," in *Mémoires de la Société du Muséum d'histoire naturelle de Strasbourg*, **2**, no. 3 (1836), 1–9.

II. SECONDARY LITERATURE. See G. Dubois, "L'enseignement de la géologie à l'Université de Strasbourg avant 1870," in *Revue d'Alsace*, **85**, no. 552 (1938), 1–60; and W. Fischer, *Gesteins- und Lagerstättenbildung im Wandel der wissenschaftlichen Anschauung* (Stuttgart, 1961), 102, 217.

JEAN-CLAUDE GALL

**VON NEUMANN, JOHANN** (or **JOHN**) (*b.* Budapest, Hungary, 28 December 1903; *d.* Washington, D.C., 8 February 1957), *mathematics, mathematical physics.*

Von Neumann, the eldest of three sons of Max von Neumann, a well-to-do Jewish banker, was privately educated until he entered the Gymnasium in 1914. His unusual mathematical abilities soon came to the attention of his teachers, who pointed out to his father that teaching him conventional school mathematics would be a waste of time; he was therefore tutored in mathematics under the guidance of university professors, and by the age of nineteen he was already recognized as a professional mathematician and had published his first paper. Von Neumann was *Privatdozent* at Berlin from 1927 to 1929 and at Hamburg in 1929–1930, then went to Princeton University for three years; in 1933 he was invited to join the newly opened Institute for Advanced Study, of which he was the youngest permanent member at that time. At the outbreak of World War II, von Neumann was called upon to participate in various scientific projects related to the war effort; in particular, from 1943 he was a consultant on the construction of the atomic bomb at Los Alamos. After the war he retained his membership in numerous government boards and committees, and in 1954 he became a member of the Atomic Energy Commission. His health began to fail in 1955, and he died of cancer two years later.

Von Neumann may have been the last representative of a once-flourishing and numerous group, the great mathematicians who were equally at home in pure and applied mathematics and who throughout their careers maintained a steady production in both directions. Pure and applied mathematics have now become so vast and complex that mastering both seems beyond human capabilities. In von Neumann's generation his ability to absorb and digest an enormous amount of extremely diverse material in a short time was exceptional; and in a profession where quick minds are somewhat commonplace, his amazing rapidity was proverbial. There is hardly a single important part of the mathematics of the 1930's with which he had not at least a passing acquaintance, and the same is probably true of theoretical physics.

Despite his encyclopedic background, von Neumann's work in pure mathematics had a definitely smaller range than that of Poincaré or Hilbert, or even of H. Weyl. His genius lay in analysis and combinatorics, the latter being understood in a very wide sense, including an uncommon ability to organize and axiomatize complex situations that a priori do not seem amenable to mathematical treatment, as in quantum mechanics and the theory of games. As an analyst von Neumann does not belong to the classical school represented by the French and English mathematicians of the early 1900's but, rather, to the tradition of Hilbert, Weyl, and F. Riesz, in which analysis, while being as "hard" as any classical theory, is based on extensive foundations of linear algebra and general topology; however, he never did significant work in number theory, algebraic topology, algebraic geometry, or differential geometry. It is only in

comparison with the greatest mathematical geniuses of history that von Neumann's scope in pure mathematics may appear somewhat restricted; it was far beyond the range of most of his contemporaries, and his extraordinary work in applied mathematics, in which he certainly equals Gauss, Cauchy, or Poincaré, more than compensates for its limitations.

**Pure Mathematics.** Von Neumann's work in pure mathematics was accomplished between 1925 and 1940, which might be called his *Sturm und Drang* period, when he seemed to be advancing at a breathless speed on all fronts of logic and analysis at once, not to speak of mathematical physics. This work, omitting a few minor papers, can be classified under five main topics.

*Logic and Set Theory.* Von Neumann's interest in set theory arose very early: in his second paper (1923) he gave an elegant new definition of ordinal numbers, and in the third (1925) he introduced an axiomatic system for set theory quite different from the one proposed by Zermelo and Fraenkel (it was later adopted by Gödel in his research on the continuum hypothesis). In the late 1920's von Neumann also participated in the Hilbert program of metamathematics and published a few papers on proofs of noncontradiction for parts of arithmetic, before Gödel shattered the hopes for a better result.

*Measure Theory.* Although it was not in the center of von Neumann's preoccupation, he made several valuable contributions to measure theory. His knowledge of group theory enabled him to "explain" the Hausdorff-Banach-Tarski "paradox," in which two balls of different radii in $\mathbf{R}^n$ ($n \geq 3$) are decomposed into a finite number of (nonmeasurable) subsets that are pairwise congruent (such decompositions cannot exist for $n = 1$ or $n = 2$); he showed that $n = 1$ or $n = 2$ is impossible because the orthogonal group in three or more variables contains free non-Abelian groups, whereas it does not for $n \leq 2$.

Another highly ingenious paper established the existence of an algebra of bounded measurable functions on the real line that forms a complete system of representatives of the classes of almost-everywhere-equal measurable bounded functions (each class contains one, and only one, function of the algebra). This theorem, later generalized to arbitrary measure spaces by Dorothy Maharam, holds the key to the "disintegration" process of measures (corresponding to the classical notion of "conditional probability"). It is a curious coincidence that in "Operator Methods in Classical

Mechanics" von Neumann was the first to prove, by a completely different method, the existence of such disintegrations for fairly general types of measures.

On the borderline between this group of papers and the next lies von Neumann's basic work on Haar's measure, which he proved to be unique up to a constant factor; the first proof was valid only for compact groups and used his direct definition of the "mean" of a continuous function over such a group. The extension of that idea to more general groups was the starting point of his subsequent papers, some written in collaboration with Solomon Bochner, on almost-periodic functions on groups.

*Lie Groups.* One of the highlights of von Neumann's career was his 1933 paper solving Hilbert's "fifth problem" for compact groups, proving that such a group admits a Lie group structure once it is locally homeomorphic with Euclidean space. He had discovered the basic idea behind that paper six years earlier: the fact that closed subgroups of the general linear group are in fact Lie groups. The method of proof of that result was shown a little later by E. Cartan to apply as well to closed subgroups of arbitrary Lie groups.

*Spectral Theory of Operators in Hilbert Space.* This topic is by far the dominant theme in von Neumann's work. For twenty years he was the undisputed master in this area, which contains what is now considered his most profound and most original creation, the theory of rings of operators. The first papers (1927) in which Hilbert space theory appears are those on the foundations of quantum mechanics (see below). These investigations later led von Neumann to a systematic study of unbounded hermitian operators, which previously had been considered only in a few special cases by Weyl and T. Carleman. His papers on unbounded hermitian operators have not been improved upon since their publication, yet within a few years he realized that the traditional idea of representing an operator by an infinite matrix was totally inadequate, and discovered the topological devices that were to replace it: the use of the graph of an unbounded operator and the extension to such an operator of the classical "Cayley transform," which reduced the structure of a self-adjoint operator to that of a unitary operator (known since Hilbert). At the same time this work led him to discover the defects of a general, densely defined hermitian operator, which later were seen to correspond to the "boundary conditions" for opera-

tors stemming from differential and partial differential equations.

The same group of papers includes another famous result from von Neumann's early years, his proof in 1932 of the ergodic theorem in its "$L^2$ formulation" given by B. D. Koopman a few months earlier. With G. D. Birkhoff's almost simultaneous proof of the sharper "almost everywhere" formulation of the theorem, von Neumann's results were to form the starting point of all subsequent developments in ergodic theory.

*Rings of Operators.* Most of von Neumann's results on unbounded operators in Hilbert space were independently discovered a little later by M. H. Stone. But von Neumann's ideas on rings of operators broke entirely new ground. He was well acquainted with the noncommutative algebra beautifully developed by Emmy Noether and E. Artin in the 1920's, and he realized how these concepts simplified and illuminated the theory of matrices. This probably provided the motivation for extending such concepts to algebras consisting of (bounded) operators in a given separable Hilbert space, to which he gave the vague name "rings of operators" and which are now known as "von Neumann algebras." He introduced their theory in the same year as his first paper on unbounded operators, and from the beginning he had the insight to select the two essential features that would allow him further progress: the algebra must be self-adjoint (that is, for any operator in the algebra, its adjoint must also belong to the algebra) and closed under the strong topology of operators and not merely in the finer topology of the norm.

Von Neumann's first result was the "double commutant theorem," which states that the von Neumann algebra generated by a self-adjoint family $\mathscr{F}$ of operators is the commutant of the commutant of $\mathscr{F}$, a generalization of a similar result obtained by I. Schur for semisimple algebras of finite dimension that was to become one of the main tools in his later work. After elucidating the relatively easy study of commutative algebras, von Neumann embarked in 1936, with the partial collaboration of F. J. Murray, on the general study of the noncommutative case. The six major papers in which they developed that theory between 1936 and 1940 certainly rank among the masterpieces of analysis in the twentieth century. They immediately realized that among the von Neumann algebras, the "factors" (those with the center reduced to the scalars) held the key to the structure of the general von Neumann algebras; indeed, in his last major paper on the subject (published in 1949 but dating from around 1940), von Neumann showed how a process of "direct integration" (the analogue of the "direct sum" of the finite dimensional theory) explicitly gave all von Neumann algebras from factors as "building blocks."

The evidence from classical study of noncommutative algebras seemed to lead to the conjecture that all factors would be isomorphic to the algebra $\mathscr{B}(H)$ of all bounded operators in a Hilbert space $H$ (of finite or separable dimension). Murray and von Neumann therefore startled the mathematical world when they showed that the situation was far more complicated. As in the classical theory, their main tool consisted of the self-adjoint idempotents in the algebra, which are simply orthogonal projections on closed subspaces of the Hilbert space; the novelty was that, in contrast with the classical case (or the case of $\mathscr{B}[H]$), minimal idempotents may fail to exist in the algebra, which implies that all idempotents are orthogonal projections on infinite-dimensional subspaces. Nevertheless, they may be *compared*, the projection on a subspace $E$ being considered as "smaller" than one on a subspace $F$ when the algebra contains a partial isometry $V$ sending $E$ onto a subspace of $F$. This is only a "preorder"; but when one considers the corresponding order relation (between equivalence classes), it turns out that in a factor this is a total order relation that may be described by a "dimension function" that attaches to each equivalence class of projections a real number $\geq 0$ or $+\infty$. Murray and von Neumann showed that after proper normalization the range of the dimension could be one of five possibilities: $\{1, 2, \cdots, n\}$ (type $I_n$, the classical algebras of matrices), $\{1, 2, \cdots, +\infty\}$ (type $I_\infty$, corresponding to the algebras $\mathscr{B}[H]$), the whole interval $[0, 1]$ in the real line (type $II_1$), the whole interval $[0, +\infty]$ in the extended real line (type $II_\infty$), and the two-element set $\{0, +\infty\}$ (type $III$).

It may be said that the algebraic structure of a factor imposes on the set of corresponding subspaces of $H$ (images of $H$ by the projections belonging to the factor) an order structure similar to that of the subspaces of a usual projective space, but with completely new possibilities regarding the "dimension" attached to these subspaces. Intrigued by this geometric interpretation of his results, von Neumann developed it in a series of papers on "continuous geometries" and their algebraic satellites, the "regular rings" (which are to continuous geometries as rings of matrices are to vector spaces). This classification, which required

great technical skill in the handling of the spectral theory of operators, immediately led to the question of existence for the new "factors." Murray and von Neumann devoted many of their papers to this question; and they were able to exhibit factors of types $II_1$, $II_\infty$, and $III$ by using ingenious constructions from ergodic theory (at a time when the subject of actions of groups on measure spaces was still in its infancy) and algebras generated by convolution operators. They went even further and initiated the study of isomorphisms between factors, succeeding, in particular, in obtaining two nonisomorphic factors of type $II_1$; only very recently has it been proved that there are uncountably many isomorphism classes for factors of types $II_1$ and $III$.

**Applied Mathematics.** *Mathematical Physics.* Von Neumann's most famous work in theoretical physics is his axiomatization of quantum mechanics. When he began work in that field in 1927, the methods used by its founders were hard to formulate in precise mathematical terms: "operators" on "functions" were handled without much consideration of their domain of definition or their topological properties; and it was blithely assumed that such "operators," when self-adjoint, could always be "diagonalized" (as in the finite dimensional case), at the expense of introducing "Dirac functions" as "eigenvectors." Von Neumann showed that mathematical rigor could be restored by taking as basic axioms the assumptions that the states of a physical system were points of a Hilbert space and that the measurable quantities were Hermitian (generally unbounded) operators densely defined in that space. This formalism, the practical use of which became available after von Neumann had developed the spectral theory of unbounded Hermitian operators (1929), has survived subsequent developments of quantum mechanics and is still the basis of nonrelativistic quantum theory; with the introduction of the theory of distributions, it has even become possible to interpret its results in a way similar to Dirac's original intuition.

After 1927 von Neumann also devoted much effort to more specific problems of quantum mechanics, such as the problem of measurement and the foundation of quantum statistics and quantum thermodynamics, proving in particular an ergodic theorem for quantum systems. All this work was developed and expanded in *Mathematische Grundlagen der Quantenmechanik* (1932), in which he also discussed the much-debated question of "causality" versus "indeterminacy" and concluded that no introduction of "hidden parameters" could keep the basic structure of quantum theory and restore "causality."

Quantum mechanics was not the only area of theoretical physics in which von Neumann was active. With Subrahmanyan Chandrasekhar he published two papers on the statistics of the fluctuating gravitational field generated by randomly distributed stars. After he started work on the Manhattan project, leading to atomic weapons, he became interested in the theory of shock waves and wrote many reports on their theoretical and computational aspects.

*Numerical Analysis and Computers.* Von Neumann's uncommon grasp of applied mathematics, treated as a whole without divorcing theory from experimental realization, was nowhere more apparent than in his work on computers. He became interested in numerical computations in connection with the need for quick estimates and approximate results that developed with the technology used for the war effort—particularly the complex problems of hydrodynamics—and the completely new problems presented by the harnessing of nuclear energy, for which no ready-made theoretical solutions were available. Dissatisfied with the computing machines available immediately after the war, he was led to examine from its foundations the optimal method that such machines should follow, and he introduced new procedures in their logical organization, the "codes" by which a fixed system of wiring could solve a great variety of problems. Von Neumann devised various methods of programming a computer, particularly for finding eigenvalues and inverses of matrices, extrema of functions of several variables, and production of random numbers. Although he never lost sight of the theoretical questions involved (as can be seen in his remarkably original papers with Herman Goldstine, on the limitation of the errors in the numerical inversion of a matrix of large order), he also wanted to have a direct acquaintance with the engineering problems that had to be faced, and supervised the construction of a computer at the Institute for Advanced Study; many fundamental devices in the present machines bear the imprint of his ideas.

In the last years of his life, von Neumann broadened his views to the general theory of automata, in a kind of synthesis of his early interest in logic and his later work on computers. With his characteristic boldness and scope of vision, he did not hesitate to attack two of the most complex questions in the field: how to design reliable machines using unreliable components, and the construction of self-reproducing machines. As usual he brought remarkably new ideas in the approach to solutions of these problems and must be considered one of the founders of a flourishing new mathematical discipline.

*Theory of Games.* The role as founder is even more obvious for the theory of games, which von Neumann, in a 1926 paper, conjured—so to speak—out of nowhere. To give a quantitative mathematical model for games of chance such as poker or bridge might have seemed a priori impossible, since such games involve free choices by the players at each move, constantly reacting on each other. Yet von Neumann did precisely that, by introducing the general concept of "strategy" (qualitatively considered a few years earlier by E. Borel) and by constructing a model that made this concept amenable to mathematical analysis. That this model was well adapted to the problem was shown conclusively by von Neumann in the same paper, with the proof of the famous minimax theorem: for a game with two players in a normalized form, it asserts the existence of a unique numerical value, representing a gain for one player and a loss for the other, such that each can achieve at least this favorable expectation from his own point of view by using a "strategy" of his own choosing; such strategies for the two players are termed optimal strategies, and the unique numerical value, the minimax value of the game.

This was the starting point for far-reaching generalizations, including applications to economics, a topic in which von Neumann became interested as early as 1937 and that he developed in his major treatise written with O. Morgenstern, *Theory of Games and Economic Behavior* (1944). These theories have developed into a full-fledged mathematical discipline, attracting many researchers and branching into several types of applications to the social sciences.

*BIBLIOGRAPHY*

Von Neumann's works were brought together as *Collected Works of John Von Neumann*, A. H. Taub, ed., 6 vols. (New York, 1961). His books include *Mathematische Grundlagen der Quantenmechanik* (Berlin, 1932); and *Theory of Games and Economic Behavior* (Princeton, 1944), written with O. Morgenstern. A memorial volume is "John von Neumann, 1903–1957," which is *Bulletin of the American Mathematical Society*, **64**, no. 654 (May 1958).

J. DIEUDONNÉ

**VORONIN, MIKHAIL STEPANOVICH** (*b.* St. Petersburg, Russia [now Leningrad, U.S.S.R.], 2 August 1838; *d.* St. Petersburg, 4 March 1903), *mycology, phytopathology.*

Voronin entered the natural sciences section of the Faculty of Physics and Mathematics of St. Petersburg University in 1854 and specialized in botany, which he studied under L. S. Tsenkovsky, who influenced him to investigate the lower plants. After graduating in 1858 with a candidate's degree, Voronin worked in Holle's laboratory in Heidelberg and in de Bary's laboratory at Freiburg. His acquaintance with de Bary developed into a close friendship and collaboration, and they later published the journal *Beiträge zur Morphologie und Physiologie der Pilze.* It was in de Bary's laboratory that Voronin did his first botanical work, on the anatomy of the stalk of *Calycanthus.* In 1860 he moved to the Antibes laboratories of the French algologists G. A. Thuret and Édouard Bornet. The results of his research there on the marine plants *Acetabularia* and *Espera* were presented in his master's thesis, which he defended at St. Petersburg University in 1861.

Voronin continued his studies of marine plants after returning to Russia but devoted his later work primarily to fungi. Because he was independently wealthy, he was not obliged to seek paid employment. He was *Privatdozent* in mycology at St. Petersburg University in 1869–1870 and taught general cytology and mycology at the St. Petersburg University for Women from 1873 to 1875 without fee. He used his wealth to organize and support scientific institutions and to publish scientific works.

Novorossysk University in Odessa awarded Voronin the doctorate in 1874 without his having defended a dissertation; and in 1898 he was elected a member of the Russian Academy of Sciences, of which he subsequently headed the section of cryptogamous plants. Although he conducted his research in a modest home laboratory, using only the simplest equipment (a Hartnack microscope, a razor, and needles), his results were included in standard Russian and foreign textbooks of botany and mycology. His work was concerned mainly with the lower plants: he discovered and studied their cycle of development and described many that are biologically, as well as botanically, important. His most important research in algology dealt with *Botrydium* and *Chromophyton.*

It was for his mycological research, however, which was of great practical and theoretical importance, that Voronin acquired an international reputation. He discovered and studied the causal organisms of clubroot, sunflower rust, the mold on apples, and ergotism. The cause of clubroot, which ravaged huge areas and destroyed the harvest, had previously been ascribed to insects. Voronin's study (1874–1877) led him to determine that the causal organism was a slime mold, which he named *Plasmodiophora brassicae*; and he proposed concrete measures for combating the disease. His earlier study of the life history of sunflower rust (1869–1875) resulted in the discovery that it was caused by the fungus *Puccinia helianthi.* While investigating "drunken" rye bread from the southern Ussuri region (1890), which induced headache, vomiting, and vertigo, Voronin isolated fifteen fungi, identifying four as those that cause ergotism. It was for these and related discoveries that many consider Voronin the founder of phytopathology in Russia.

Voronin's most important theoretical works were in mycology, to which he contributed knowledge of a new form of basidiomycete, *Exobasidium vaccinii*, which has no fruiting body; and he provided the basis for classifying the smut fungi (Ustilagineae) according to the germination of the chlamydospores. The outstanding results of his research on *Sclerotinia*, which attacks bilberry plants, was his discovery of the parasite of the ascomycete *Sclerotinia heteroica*, which grows successively on two plants; the parasite had previously been considered only a rust fungus.

Voronin also studied the slime mold *Ceratium* (similar in form to higher fungi) and the ascomycetes in the development of ascous fruiting bodies. While examining the latter, he discovered a peculiar structure of the female sex organ (an archicarp) in the form of a thick curved hypha, now known as Voronin's hypha. He also investigated *Chytridium* (Archimycetes) and *Mucorales* (Mucoraceae). With de Bary he established the genus *Synchytrium*, and in 1867 he described the cycle of development of *Synchytrium mercurialis.* In the last year of his life Voronin investigated the development and the sexual and asexual reproduction of three species of the aquatic fungus *Monoblepharis*, which he discovered in Finland.

*BIBLIOGRAPHY*

I. ORIGINAL WORKS. Many of Voronin's writings were brought together in *Izbrannye proizvedenia* ("Selected Works"; Moscow, 1961), which includes a bibliography of his works (271–274). They include *Mikologicheskie issledovania* ("Mycological Research";

St. Petersburg, 1869); *Issledovania nad razvitiem rzhavchinnogo gribka Puccinia helianthi, prichinyayushchego bolezn podsolnechnika* ("Research on the Development of the Rust Fungus *Puccinia helianthi*, Which Causes the Sunflower Disease"; St. Petersburg, 1871); *Plasmodiophora brassicae. Organizm, prichinyayushchy kapustnym rasteniam bolezn, izvestnuyu pod nazvaniem kily* (". . . Organism Causing the Disease of Cabbage Known as 'Kila' [Clubroot]"; St. Petersburg, 1877); "O 'pyanom khlebe' v Yuzhno-Ussuryskom krae" ("On 'Drunken Bread' in the Southern Ussuri Region"), in *VIII sezd russkikh estestvoispytatelei v Peterburge* ("VIII Congress of Russian Natural Scientists in St. Petersburg"; St. Petersburg, 1890), 13–21; and "*Sclerotinia heteroica*," in *Trudy Imperatorskago S.-Peterburgskago obshchestva estestvoispytatelei*, Botany sec., **25** (1895), 84–91.

II. SECONDARY LITERATURE. See I. P. Borodin, "Pamyati nezabvennogo M. S. Voronina" ("Recollections of the Unforgettable M. S. Voronin"), in *Trudy Botanicheskogo sada. Yurevskogo universiteta*, **4**, no. 4 (1903), 286–292; M. S. Dunin, "M. S. Voronin—klassik mikologii i fitopatologii" ("M. S. Voronin—a Classic of Mycology and Phytopathology"), in Voronin's *Izbrannye proizvedenia* (see above), 3–16; which also includes a list of secondary literature (275); A. S. Famintsyn, "Nekrolog M. S. Voronina" ("Obituary of M. S. Voronin"), in *Trudy Imperatorskago S.-Petersburgskago obshchestva estestvoispytatelei*, **34** (1903), 210–222; N. A. Komarnitsky, "Voronin, M. S.," in S. Y. Lipshits, ed., *Russkie botaniki. Biografo-bibliograﬁchesky slovar* ("Russian Botanists. Biographical-Bibliographical Dictionary"), II (Moscow, 1947), 163–168, with lists of Voronin's works (106 titles) and secondary literature (16 titles); N. I. Kuznetsov, "Sorokaletie nauchnoy deyatelnosti M. S. Voronina" ("Fortieth Anniversary of the Scientific Career of Voronin"), in *Trudy Botanicheskogo sada. Yurevskogo universiteta*, **1**, no. 1 (1900), 47–51; and S. Navaschin, "Michael Woronin," in *Berichte der Deutschen botanischen Gesellschaft*, **21**, no. 1 (1903), 36–47.

E. M. SENCHENKOVA

**VORONOY, GEORGY FEDOSEEVICH** (*b.* Zhuravka, Poltava guberniya, Russia, 28 April 1868; *d.* Warsaw, Poland, 20 November 1908), *mathematics.*

Voronoy's father was superintendent of Gymnasiums in Kishinev and in other towns in the southern Ukraine. After graduating from the Gymnasium in Priluki in 1885, Voronoy enrolled in the mathematics section of the Faculty of Physics and Mathematics of the University of St. Petersburg. He graduated in 1889 and was retained to prepare for a teaching career. In 1894 he defended his master's dissertation, on algebraic integers associated

with the roots of an irreducible third-degree equation. He then became professor in the Department of Pure Mathematics at the University of Warsaw. He defended his doctoral dissertation, on a generalization of the algorithm of continued fractions, at St. Petersburg in 1897; both dissertations were awarded the Bunyakovsky Prize of the St. Petersburg Academy of Sciences.

Voronoy subsequently elaborated his own ideas on the geometry of numbers and conducted investigations on the analytic theory of numbers. In 1904 he participated in the Third International Congress of Mathematicians in Heidelberg, where he met Minkowski, who was then working on topics closely related to those in which Voronoy was interested.

Voronoy's work, all of which concerns the theory of numbers, can be divided into three groups: algebraic theory of numbers, geometry of numbers, and analytic theory of numbers.

In his doctoral dissertation Voronoy gave the best algorithm known at the time for calculating fundamental units of a general cubic field, for both a positive and negative discriminant.

Voronoy completed two of a planned series of memoirs in which he intended to apply the principle of continuous Hermite parameters to problems of the arithmetical theory of definite and indefinite quadratic forms. In the first of these works, which dealt with certain characteristics of complete quadratic forms, he solved the question posed by Hermite concerning the precise upper limit of the minima of the positive quadratic forms of a given discriminant of $n$ variables. E. I. Zolotarev and A. N. Korkin had given solutions for $n = 4$ and $n = 5$; with the aid of the methods of the geometrical theory of numbers Voronoy gave a full algorithmic solution for any $n$. In the second paper, which concerned simple parallelepipeds, Voronoy dealt with the determination of all possible methods of filling an $n$-dimensional Euclidean space with identical convex nonintersecting polyhedra having completely contiguous boundaries (parallelepipeds). A solution of this problem for three-dimensional space had been given by the crystallographer E. S. Fedorov, but his proofs were incomplete. In 1896 Minkowski demonstrated that the parallelepipeds must have centers of symmetry and that the number of their boundaries did not exceed $2(2^n - 1)$. Voronoy imposed the further requirement that $n + 1$ parallelepipeds converge at each summit and completely solved the problem for these conditions.

In a memoir concerning a problem from the theories of asymptotic functions Voronoy solved Dirichlet's problem concerning the determination of the number of whole points under the hyperbola $xy = n$. Dirichlet had found that the number of such points lying in the area $x > 0$, $y > 0$, $xy \leq n$ was expressed by the formula $F(n) = n(\log n + 2C - 1) + R(n)$, where $R(n) = O(\sqrt{n})$. By introducing series similar to a Farey series and by dividing the area of summation into the subsets associated with these series, Voronoy substantially improved the evaluation, obtaining $R(n) = O(\sqrt[3]{n} \cdot \log n)$. His paper served as the starting point for the work of I. M. Vinogradov, and the Farey series that he introduced was employed in the investigation of problems in the additive theory of numbers by Vinogradov, G. H. Hardy, and J. E. Littlewood.

*BIBLIOGRAPHY*

Voronoy's collected works were published as *Sobranie sochineny*, 3 vols. (Kiev, 1952–1953). Papers mentioned in the article are "Sur un problème du calcul des fonctions asymptotiques," in *Journal für die reine und angewandte Mathematik*, **126** (1903), 241–282; "Sur quelques propriétés des formes quadratiques positives parfaites," *ibid.*, **133** (1908), 97–178; and "Recherches sur les paralleloèdres primitifs," *ibid.*, **136** (1909), 67–179. These papers are reprinted in *Sobranie sochineny*, II, 5–50, 171–238, 239–368. On his work, see B. N. Delone, *Peterburgskaya shkola teorii chisel* ("The St. Petersburg School of the Theory of Numbers"; Moscow–Leningrad, 1947).

I. G. BASHMAKOVA

**VRIES, HUGO DE** (*b.* Haarlem, Netherlands, 16 February 1848; *d.* Lunteren, Netherlands, 21 May 1935), *plant physiology, genetics, evolution.*

The ancestors of Hugo de Vries[1] had been Baptists since the Reformation. As dissenters they were not eligible for public office, but they found an outlet for their talents and energy in trade; during the seventeenth and eighteenth centuries they were prosperous merchants. When the drastic political changes at the end of the eighteenth century brought more liberal views, the activities of the family also changed; they became professors, lawyers, and statesmen.

Hugo de Vries's paternal grandfather, Abraham de Vries, was a Baptist minister and librarian for the city of Haarlem; he was a noted expert on the history of printing. His maternal grandfather, Caspar Jacob Christiaan Reuvens, was the first professor of archaeology at the University of Leiden and founder of its archaeological museum. An uncle, Matthias de Vries, was professor of Dutch literature at Leiden and a pioneer in Dutch philology. The dictionary he started with Lambert A. te Winkel (1863), completed in 1888, was the authoritative source for Dutch spelling for half a century.

Hugo de Vries's father, Gerrit de Vries, studied law and literature at the University of Leiden. He served as a representative in the Provincial States of North Holland for many years and became the leading expert on legislation concerning water management. In 1862 he was appointed to the Council of State, a position he held until his death. Ten years later he was asked by William III to form a cabinet, and he took the post of minister of justice. De Vries's mother, Maria Everardina Reuvens, came from a family of scholars and statesmen.

De Vries was educated in Haarlem at a private Baptist grammar school and subsequently at the municipal Gymnasium. The area around Haarlem was a botanist's paradise, and it awakened in him a deep love for plants at an early age. During his vacations he roamed the entire country on foot, in search of plants for his herbarium. When he entered the university, he felt that his collection of dried phanerogams of the Netherlands was complete.

In 1862 the family moved to The Hague, where de Vries attended the Gymnasium for four years. Since there was no Baptist community in The Hague, he was sent to Leiden on weekends to receive religious instruction. Here he was soon invited by Willem Suringar, a professor of botany, to help classify the plants in the herbarium of the Netherlands Botanical Society.

Consequently, when de Vries matriculated at the University of Leiden in 1866, he was already an expert on the flora of the Netherlands. He therefore turned to other fields of interest. These he found after reading Sachs's *Lehrbuch der Botanik* (1868), to which he owed his interest in plant physiology, and Charles Darwin's *Origin of Species*, which aroused his interest in evolution. The University of Leiden was ill-equipped for the pursuit of either of these studies; plant physiology was not taught there, and there was no laboratory for experimental work. The experimental work for his doctoral dissertation on plant physiology was done in his attic. Suringar was hostile to the theory of evolution; and this hostility, combined with de Vries's youthful enthusiasm, caused a permanent estrangement between them.

De Vries was not happy with the education he

had received at Leiden, and he decided to continue his studies in Germany. In the autumn of 1870 he went to Heidelberg, where he studied with Hofmeister. In the spring and summer of 1871 he was at Sachs's laboratory in Würzburg, where he finally found what he had been seeking. Sachs took a keen interest in his progress and considered him his best pupil.

Although he intended to work in Würzburg for several years, in September 1871 de Vries accepted an appointment as teacher of natural history at the First High School in Amsterdam.[2] He was still able to spend most of the long summer vacations in Sachs's laboratory at Würzburg; the reports of his experimental work there are found in *Arbeiten des botanischen Instituts in Würzburg*, Sachs's journal.

De Vries's teaching duties became more and more demanding, and began to interfere with his studies. Sachs then recommended him for a position at the Prussian Ministry of Agriculture. In January 1875 de Vries was given the task of writing monographs on agricultural plants that were published in the *Landwirtschaftliche Jahrbücher*. The necessary experimental work was done at Würzburg, in space provided by Sachs in his laboratory. Here de Vries wrote monographs on red clover, the potato, and the sugar beet. In addition, he carried out extensive studies on osmosis in plant cells during this period. He frequently traveled to other university towns to meet with the leading professors of botany.

Sachs showed his continued interest in de Vries's future by recommending him for the post of *Privatdozent* in the physiology of cultivated plants at the University of Halle. To be eligible for the appointment, de Vries had to pass a doctoral examination. He defended a dissertation based on his work on the stretching of cells and received the appointment on 12 February 1877.

The lectures at Halle were not a success. Attendance was poor, and there was no real interest in the subject. Thus de Vries was much relieved when he was appointed lecturer in plant physiology at the newly constituted University of Amsterdam. The Amsterdam Athenaeum was founded in 1632 but did not have the authority to grant degrees; it was necessary for students to pass examinations at an accredited university, usually Leiden or Utrecht. In 1877 the Athenaeum was given university status, and many new teachers were needed. De Vries was the first instructor in plant physiology in the Netherlands. In the summer of 1877, he traveled to England to meet the botanists of that

country. The highlight of the trip was a visit with Darwin.

In the autumn of 1878 de Vries was appointed extraordinary professor and, on his birthday in 1881, ordinary professor. Until about 1890 he conducted research on osmosis in plant cells—the famous experiments on plasmolysis. In addition to his teaching and research, he sponsored the research of his pupil J. H. Wakker on the diseases of bulb plants; he investigated the causes of the contamination of the water mains of Rotterdam; and he served on the committee to study the future water supply of the city of Amsterdam. During this period Wakker, J. M. Janse, F. A. Went, H. P. Wijsman, and H. W. Heinsius earned their doctorates under de Vries's guidance.

In addition to his experimental work in plant physiology, de Vries made extensive studies of the theories and literature on heredity and variation in plants. About 1890 he abruptly abandoned the study of plant physiology and devoted himself exclusively to heredity and variation. This period in his career began with his *Intracellular Pangenesis* (1889), in which he reviewed critically the work of Spencer, Darwin, Nägeli, and Weismann, and proposed his own theory that "pangenes" were the carriers of hereditary traits. One of the most important books in the history of genetics, it attracted little attention at the time.

De Vries's experimental work in the 1890's led to the rediscovery of Mendel's laws and the discovery of the phenomenon of mutation. The rediscovery of Mendel's laws was announced almost simultaneously by de Vries, Correns, and Tschermak-Seysenegg—in that order. De Vries certainly knew the segregation laws in 1896, and he deduced these laws from his own experimental work and not from reading Mendel's paper or any reference to Mendel's work in the literature.

The results of his more than ten years of experimentation and study were laid down in de Vries's *Die Mutationstheorie . . .* (1901–1903), in which he described in detail his work on the segregation laws, on phenomena of variation, and on plant mutations. The book made him famous, and he was recognized as one of the foremost botanists of his time.

During the 1890's no doctorates were earned under de Vries's guidance. These were years of hard personal work, but apparently they were not happy ones. In 1896 he succeeded C. A. J. A. Oudemans as senior professor of botany at Amsterdam. He was charged with teaching systematic botany and genetics; instruction in plant physiology and pharmacology was turned over to Eduard Verschaffelt.

De Vries's physiological work was well known on the continent of Europe, less so in England, and hardly at all in the United States. His rediscovery of Mendel's laws and the formulation of the mutation theory, however, became widely known, especially in the United States. During the summers of 1904 and 1906, de Vries was invited to lecture at the University of California at Berkeley; in 1912 he was invited to participate at the opening of the Rice Institute in Houston, Texas. He wrote books about each of his American journeys.

After 1900 a number of students earned their doctorates under de Vries: C. J. J. van Hall, T. Weevers, P. J. S. Cramer, J. A. Lodewijks, A. R. Schouten, J. M. Geerts, J. A. Honing, T. J. Stomps, and H. H. Zeylstra. In that period de Vries received many honors. Eleven honorary doctorates were conferred upon him; he was awarded seven gold medals, and was made a regular or honorary member of most of the major academies and societies.

In 1918 de Vries reached mandatory retirement age. He had already bought a house at Lunteren, a remote village, where the soil was suitable for an experimental garden. He also built a laboratory, and he remained professionally active until his death. He also produced a large number of scientific papers during this time. His rather lonely life in Lunteren was relieved by visits from former pupils, friends, and admirers from all over the world, and several students from the the universities of Amsterdam and Utrecht came to Lunteren to do the experimental work for their dissertations.

**Scientific Work.** In his doctoral dissertation de Vries reviewed the literature concerned with the influence of temperature on the vital processes of plants. Based on an essay that received a gold medal, the dissertation was supported by original experimental data that affirmed or refuted the statements of various authors.

At Würzburg, Sachs studied plant physiology from a mechanical point of view. Initially he assigned de Vries subjects for study, but later he gave him a free hand in the choice of subjects. In 1871 de Vries discovered that stalks and isolated ribs of leaves usually have a greater growth capability on the upper side than on the underside. He called this phenomenon "epinasty" and the reverse phenomenon, which is sometimes found in young organs, "hyponasty." He claimed that these two phenomena, together with the already recognized phenomena of geotropism and heliotropism, are sufficient to explain all growth patterns of plants. In 1872 he studied the mechanism of tendril curving and found it to be almost exclusively the result of increased growth in the outer region of the tendril. In the same year he studied the mechanism of the movements of climbing plants and established that the nutating shoots of such plants are not irritable and that the nutation is caused by the shoots' having a zone of increased growth parallel to the axis, with the zone slowly rotating around the axis of the organ. Darwin greatly admired this work and praised it in his *Climbing Plants*,[3] which started the correspondence between Darwin and de Vries. The next year de Vries investigated the rate of cell growth at various points on the growing shoot and found that the zone of fastest growth is not located at the tip but farther back on the organ.

As a student in Leiden and in Hofmeister's laboratory, de Vries had shown that the contraction of the protoplast of a plant cell, caused by its introduction into a salt solution of appropriate concentration, did not kill the cell, as was generally believed. In addition, he established that the protoplast is permeable only by water. At Würzburg, while writing his monographs on agricultural plants, de Vries continued this research. He wanted to decide how much of the increase of the cell wall of a growing plant organ was the result of the growth of the cell and how much was the result of the stretching of the cell wall caused by the pressure of the cell fluid—turgor. Annulling the turgor by submerging the plant organ in a suitable salt solution, de Vries found that in young, growing cells the expansion caused by turgor amounts to some 10 percent of the total length. In mature cells there was no turgor expansion. He described this work in the *Habilitationsschrift* submitted at Halle.

As a professor at Amsterdam, de Vries continued his research on the function of the cell contents. He theorized that calcium is a waste product in plants, absorbed for the sake of the needed elements with which it is combined and stored in cells as an organic salt (often calcium oxalate). He formulated a growth theory, stating that growth in plants is caused primarily by extension of the cell walls by turgor, with the extension fixed later. He conjectured that organic acids are the chemical compounds that contribute most to the turgor, a conjecture that he qualified later when he had analyzed the cell fluid of some plants. He applied his growth theory to explain many forms of plant movement, including the movement of tendrils, the erection of lodged grain, and the contraction of roots of biennial plants in autumn.

These and other investigations posed questions. How great is the pressure caused by the turgor in the cell? How much does each of the components of the cell fluid contribute to this pressure? What is the cause of an increase of this pressure in cells? In order to answer these questions, de Vries returned to his observations of the effect of salt solutions on plant cells. In previous experiments he had found that if a plant cell is immersed in successively stronger salt solutions, the cell initially contracts; subsequently the protoplast starts contracting and frees itself from the cell wall until it becomes a globular body within the cell. De Vries called this process "plasmolysis." In the new research he used the plant cell as an indicator, immersing the cell in solutions of increasing strength until he found the concentration at which the protoplast just starts to free itself from the cell wall. At this concentration the osmotic pressures of the solution and of the cell contents are equal or—in de Vries's terminology—"isotonic." He determined the isotonic concentration for the solution to be tested and for a reference solution; three times the concentration of the reference solution, divided by the concentration of the solution to be tested, was called the "isotonic coefficient." Saltpeter ($KNO_3$) was always used as a reference solution.

After determining the isotonic coefficients of a great many chemicals, de Vries found that isotonic coefficients always have a near integer value—ranging from 2 to 5. Generalizing this, he stated the following rules: for neutral organic compounds and organic acids, the isotonic coefficient is 2; for salts with one alkali atom, 3; with two alkali atoms, 4; with three alkali atoms, 5; with one alkaline earth atom, 2; and with two alkaline earth atoms, 4. This is known as the law of isotonic coefficients. Using this law, de Vries was able to determine the proportional contribution to the total osmotic pressure in the cell for each component of the cell fluid. It appears that for different species, different chemicals in the cell fluid account for the largest part of the osmotic pressure: in *Rheum* it is oxalic acid, in *Rosa* it is glucose, and in *Gunnera* it is calcium chloride.

De Vries's work on the isotonic coefficients of solutions led van't Hoff to his formula for the osmotic pressure of solutions, one of the first results in physical chemistry. Van't Hoff's law in turn enabled de Vries to determine the total osmot-

ic pressure in plant cells. At about the same time, Arrhenius discovered the dissociation of molecules in solution. This explained why de Vries had to use a factor of 3 in his computation of the isotonic coefficient. Even under laboratory conditions the reference solution was only about 50 percent ionized, and different salt solutions dissociate to different degrees. The phenomenon of ionization indicates that de Vries's law of isotonic coefficients cannot be exactly true.

The law of isotonic coefficients enabled de Vries to determine the molecular weight of raffinose during a discussion of that weight at a meeting of the Royal Netherlands Academy of Sciences and, in a few minutes, to settle this long-standing question.

During the late 1880's de Vries studied protoplasm. He found that the inner lining of the cell wall, the protoplast, consists of three layers, not two, as was currently believed. He discovered the innermost of these, the tonoplast. He also established that the vacuoles in the cell have a lining of their own, investigated the aggregation of the protoplasm of insectivorous plants, and studied the ribbon-shaped parietal chloroplasts of *Spirogyra*.

In addition to his physiological research on plants, de Vries conducted an extensive study of the literature on variability and heredity. Based on this research, he wrote nineteen articles for a Dutch agricultural journal. This series, "Thoughts on the Improvement of the Races of Our Cultivated Plants" (1885–1887), resembles Darwin's *Origin of Species* and *Variation of Animals and Plants Under Domestication* in its organization and approach. The study probably was of no great use to the farmers for whom it was written, but it was of great importance to de Vries as a means of formulating a program for future research.

In his first work in this new field of interest, *Intracellulare Pangenesis* (1889), de Vries presented his own theory. He considered the hereditary characteristics of living organisms as units that manifest themselves independently of each other and that can, therefore, be studied separately. Each independent characteristic is associated with a material bearer, which de Vries called a "pangene." The pangene is a morphological structure, made up of numerous molecules, that can take nourishment, grow, and divide to yield two new pangenes. After cell division, each daughter cell receives one set of pangenes from the mother cell. A pangene can be either active or latent. Some characteristics may be represented by more than one pangene. Where conflicting characteristics are possible—for example, red or white flowers—the characteristic represented by the largest number of pangenes is dominant. In each reproductive cell at least one of the representative pangenes, either active or latent, is present.

Using these concepts, de Vries explained all the vital phenomena of an organism: how a cell develops into an organ, how metamorphosis is brought about, and how an offspring becomes and remains uniform with the parents. The characteristics of the genus are caused by large aggregates of pangenes, which remain unchanged in the offspring. It is possible that one (or more than one) pangene starts to multiply in an extraordinary way or is changed during cell division. In such a case the different pangene that is created results in a new characteristic of the organism. This is, according to de Vries, the principal mechanism of evolution.

De Vries's pangene theory is remarkably close to the theory formulated later by geneticists, including T. H. Morgan. The concept that a characteristic is represented by two pangenes, each of which may be active or latent, and the concept that the pangenes are linked in groups (later called chromosomes) were not part of de Vries's theory.

De Vries called his material units pangenes to honor Charles Darwin, whose gemmule theory he rejected, however. The name "gene," given to the hereditary unit by Johannsen, was derived from de Vries's pangene.[4]

The research undertaken by de Vries to follow up his theoretical considerations covered several fields. He studied the causes and hereditary properties of many kinds of monstrosities, including forced tensions (Zwangsdrehungen—on which he wrote a monograph), fasciations, symphysis, and virescence. Jules MacLeod, professor at the University of Ghent, may have introduced him to the statistical methods of Quetelet and Galton. They had shown that in the animal kingdom the magnitude of variations (for example, the body length of soldiers) was distributed according to a probability curve (Gauss curve; de Vries used the term Galton curve). De Vries demonstrated that this is often true for the plant kingdom as well. This distribution manifested what he called the normal fluctuation of the considered characteristics. There were many cases where a symmetrical curve was not obtained. In some cases only a half Galton curve was obtained; de Vries expressed the opinion that such a curve shows the emergence of a discontinuous variation. In other cases the distribution curve showed two peaks; de Vries conjectured that such a curve indicates that a mixture of two races is

present, and he succeeded in isolating these races by selection.

Because of his pangenesis theory and his work on variability, de Vries decided that experimental work in heredity should be performed with closely allied races or varieties, differing in only one characteristic or, at most, a few characteristics. In 1896 he demonstrated to his advanced students the segregation laws, now known as Mendel's laws, in Papaver somniferum var. Mephisto and var. Danebrog. He examined many species belonging to several families, and found the segregation laws confirmed in each case. He did not publish these results, however, reserving them, with his work on mutations, for a single large book. When he accidentally came across a reprint of Mendel's paper early in 1900, de Vries felt obliged to publish in order to protect his priority. This publication triggered the publications of Correns and Tschermak-Seysenegg. The work of de Vries did not quite parallel the work of Mendel, who had studied only two species, Pisum and Hieracium, and whose work with the latter had been unsuccessful. De Vries demonstrated the segregation laws in some twenty species. On the other hand, Mendel examined not only monohybrids but also dihybrids and trihybrids, and followed the offspring through a great many generations. In his rediscovery papers, de Vries reported on only two dihybrid experiments, and he followed the offspring of a cross through two generations at most. L. C. Dunn correctly states; "It is clear that de Vries was not a 'rediscoverer' but a creator of broad general principles."[5]

After the rediscovery of Mendel's laws, many investigators took up the subject. De Vries was not among them, however. He believed that hybridization only causes redistribution of existing characters and for that reason cannot explain the appearance of new species. Therefore, he concentrated on the phenomenon of mutation, which he believed explained the origin of new species and therefore gave necessary support to the theory of evolution.

One difficulty in studying the origin of new species was that the concept of "species" was ill-defined. Plants recognized as belonging to the same species often showed marked differences. The French botanist Alexis Jordan had found that, among plants recognized as belonging to the same species, there are subgroups of which the members are exactly alike and breed true under self-fertilization. These subgroups were later called "jordanons," while the traditional species, "which a good naturalist intuitively recognizes,"[6] were later called "linneons." De Vries claimed that the jordanon is the true species. Among specimens of the same jordanon, individual differences, including size of leaves and weight of seeds, are still possible; these "individual variations" follow Galton's law.

In 1886, near Hilversum, de Vries noticed on a plot of formerly cultivated land, overgrown with *Oenothera lamarckiana* (evening primrose), a number of specimens that differed markedly from the others. He took seeds of the normal form and of two differing ones for planting in his experimental garden. He went through considerable trouble to discover the origin of these *Oenotheras* (which had escaped from a nearby garden) and to ascertain the history of the introduction of the species into Europe. Although it was said that the plant had originally been introduced from Texas and was known to Lamarck in 1796 under the name *O. grandiflora*, the plant was unknown in the United States. De Vries was convinced that *O. lamarckiana* was a pure species.

New forms that appeared suddenly and unexpectedly were called "single variations" by de Vries; he later called them "mutations." The *Oenotheras* that he had collected near Hilversum soon started to produce new forms, which he judged to differ sufficiently from the parent species for him to consider them a new species, and hence to give them a binomial name. He obtained a giant form, which he named *O. gigas*; a form with pale-green, delicate, narrow leaves, which he named *O. albida*; one with red veins in the leaves, *O. rubinervis*; one with narrow leaves on long stalks, *O. oblonga*; and a dwarf form, *O. nanella*. These mutants appeared to be constant or almost constant under self-fertilization. Another mutant showed only female flowers and still another yielded, after self-fertilization, the original *lamarckiana* plus some mutants. The two mutants found in Hilversum also produced *lamarckianas* as well as mutants, including some new ones.

In order to explain why only the *Oenothera lamarckiana* produced so rich a harvest of mutants, while only a very few other species were known to product mutants (and then only a few mutants at a time), de Vries postulated that in its evolutionary life a species produces mutants over discrete, comparatively short periods of time only—their mutation periods. In addition, he conjectured that these periods are preceded by premutation periods, during which the latent characters are formed.

On the basis of his *Oenothera* research, de Vries

distinguished mutations that supply a useful characteristic, which he called "progressive," and those that supply a useless or even harmful characteristic, which he called "retrogressive." Only the progressive characteristics contribute to the evolution of the species.

De Vries carried out extensive crossings between his *Oenothera* mutants. On the basis of this work and additional work on variability, he distinguished two kinds of crosses: bisexual and unisexual. In bisexual crosses the parents differ in at least one characteristic. These characteristics are all active in one parent and latent in the other. In unisexual crosses only one parent possesses a certain characteristic. De Vries associated these concepts with earlier terminology as follows: variety crossings are bisexual, exhibit a Mendel split, and produce fertile offspring; species crossings are unisexual, do not exhibit a Mendel split, and produce less fertile or even infertile offspring. It must be remembered that these concepts date from before the discovery that a characteristic is represented in the somatic cell by two genes, each of which can be either dominant or recessive.

De Vries's work on variability and mutation, necessarily only briefly sketched above, was reported in *Die Mutationstheorie . . .* (1901–1903), a heroic effort to correlate and explain the existing knowledge in this field and his own discoveries. De Vries's 1904 lectures at Berkeley were published as *Species and Varieties* (1905), a book that is much easier to read than *The Mutation Theory*. In his 1906 lectures in Berkeley, his topic was the application of his doctrines to agricultural and horticultural practice. These lectures were published in *Plant Breeding* (1907).

In 1906 de Vries considered his mutation research finished, and he prepared to study, as his next research project, the adaptation of plants to an adverse environment, such as a desert. That year, however, his *Oenothera* cultures showed "twin hybrids" for the first time; to gather information to explain this phenomenon, he decided to continue his *Oenothera* research for a few years. Circumstances forced him to continue the *Oenothera* study for the rest of his life.

Although the mutation theory was generally enthusiastically received, there were critics. The first of these was William Bateson, who suggested as early as 1902 that the *O. lamarckiana* might well be a hybrid. This idea was vigorously advocated by B. M. Davis, who questioned de Vries's arguments for the provenance and the purity of the *lamarckiana*. Davis tried, without notable success, to synthesize a *lamarckiana* by crossing *O. biennis* with *O. grandiflora* and *O. franciscana*. Zeylstra, a student of de Vries's, declared that *O. nanella* was nothing but a diseased *lamarckiana*; another of his students, J. A. Honing, gave a critique that anticipated the later work of O. Renner.

From about 1908 Morgan, Sturtevant, Hermann J. Muller, and Calvin B. Bridges had been studying the genetics of the fruit fly *Drosophila*. This work, which was first summarized in *The Mechanism of Mendelian Heredity* (1915), provided the essentials of the chromosome theory of heredity as it is known today. In this theory de Vries's pangenes, which he had described as single material units existing in a free state in the cell nucleus, became the genes, grouped on the chromosomes in the cell nucleus.

The first mutant to be explained was *O. gigas*. In 1907 Anne M. Lutz found that this mutant is a tetraploid; it has twenty-eight chromosomes in the somatic cells instead of fourteen, as is common with the *Oenotheras*. In 1912 Lutz discovered that *O. lata* is a triploid and that it has fifteen chromosomes.

In the course of time, new anomalies in *Oenothera* were added to those described by de Vries in his *Mutation Theory*. He himself discovered the "twin hybrids": two true-breeding parents yield two different types in the first-generation offspring. Another phenomenon, the significance of which was not realized until 1914, was the fact that often a large percentage of the seeds obtained in *Oenothera* cultures were infertile. These and other phenomena were studied by Renner, who discovered that *O. lamarckiana* is a permanent heterozygote (hence a hybrid) containing two chromosome complexes, which are transmitted as a whole and which he called "gaudens" and "velans." They are balanced lethals. Hence, of the four combinations formed in equal numbers during the first generation of the offspring of self-fertilized *lamarckianas*— that is, *gv*, *vg*, *vv*, *gg*—the latter two (half the total number of seeds) were not viable, the others having the same phenotype as the parent and hence creating the illusion that the plant breeds true. When a *lamarckiana* was crossed with another *Oenothera* species—for example, *O. muricata*— half of the offspring contained the *mg* combination and the other half the *mv* combination, hence the twin hybrids.

Studies by Renner and others showed that the genetic makeup of *Oenothera* is very unusual and complicated; few genera show such phenomena, and those to a much lesser extent. Because of the

work of a large number of investigators, the genetic properties of *Oenothera* are now quite well known. Among these investigators were de Vries himself and his students T. J. Stomps, D. J. Broekens, K. Boedijn, H. Dulfer, and J. A. Leliveld. Much of the *Oenothera* work was done at the Station for Experimental Evolution at Cold Spring Harbor, New York. De Vries gave the keynote speech at the opening of the station in 1904. A. F. Blakeslee and R. E. Cleland, who showed that the chromosome complexes are ring formations, were leaders in this work. The *Oenothera* problem was solved finally by Sturtevant and Sterling Emerson.

The fact that de Vries's mutants were superseded does not mean that his work on the phenomenon of mutation was valueless. Many true mutations have been discovered in the animal and plant kingdoms and mutation is still the cornerstone of the theory of evolution. Next to the *Drosophila* experiments, the work with *Oenothera* has contributed most to the chromosome theory of heredity.

### NOTES

1. Sometimes—for example, in *Isis Cumulative Bibliography*, II, 603—the name is given as Hugo Marie de Vries. The addition of Marie is not justified, for no member of the de Vries family ever had more than one Christian name.
2. A secondary school that emphasized modern languages and science.
3. Charles R. Darwin, *The Movements and Habits of Climbing Plants* (London, 1876), see 9, 22, 160, 165, 181.
4. Wilhelm L. Johannsen, *Elemente der exakten Erblichkeitslehre* (Jena; 1909; 2nd ed., 1913). In the 1st ed. (p. 124) Johannsen ignored the use of "pangene" by de Vries; in the 2nd ed. (p. 143) he corrected this omission. Johannsen made the change from pangene to gene to express his opinion that the hereditary unit to be named, formerly designated by the German *Anlage*, is nonmaterial. When the materiality of the hereditary unit was confirmed, the name gene was retained.
5. L. C. Dunn, *A Short History of Genetics* (New York, 1965), 43.
6. In determining whether a form should be ranked as a species or a variety, the opinion of naturalists having sound judgment and wide experience seems the only guide to follow. Darwin, *The Origin of Species* (London, 1859), 47.

### BIBLIOGRAPHY

I. ORIGINAL WORKS. A complete bibliography of de Vries's works contains more than 700 entries. About half of these were contributions to popular literature. The most important scientific papers, selected by de Vries himself, are collected in *Opera e periodicis collata*, 7 vols. (Utrecht, 1918–1927).

His most important scientific books and papers are *De invloed der temperatuur op de levensverschijnselen der planten* (The Hague, 1870); "Sur la perméabilité du protoplasme des betteraves rouges," in *Archives néer-*

landaises des sciences exactes et naturelles, **6** (1871), 117–126; "Sur la mort des cellules végétales par l'effet d'une température élevée," ibid., 245–295; "Ueber einige Ursachen der Richtung bilateral symmetrischer Pflanzentheile," in Arbeiten des botanischen Institutes in Würzburg, **1** (1872), 223–277; "Längenwachsthum der Ober- und Unterseite sich krümmender Ranken," ibid., **1** (1873), 302–316; "Zur Mechanik der Bewegung von Schlingpflanzen," ibid., 317–342; "Ueber die Dehnbarkeit wachsender Sprosse," ibid., **1** (1874), 519–545; "Ueber Wundholz," in Flora, oder allgemeine botanische Zeitung, **59** (1876), 2–6, 17–25, 38–42, 49–55, 81–88, 97–108, 113–121, 129–139; "Ueber longitudinale Epinastie," in Flora, oder allgemeine botanische Zeitung, **60** (1877), 385–391; and Untersuchungen über die mechanischen Ursachen der Zellstreckung, ausgehend von der Wirkung von Salzlösungen auf den Turgor wachsender Pflanzenzellen (Leipzig, 1877): "Ueber die Ausdehnung wachsender Pflanzenzellen durch ihren Turgor," in Botanische Zeitung, **35** (1877), 2–10; "Beiträge zur speziellen Physiologie landwirtschaftlicher Kulturpflanzen, I. Rother Klee," in Landwirtschaftliche Jahrbücher, **6** (1877), 465–514, 893–956; "II. Kartoffeln," ibid., **7** (1878), 19–39, 217–249, 591–682; "III. Zuckerrüben," ibid., **8** (1879), 13–35, 417–498.

Other works include De ademhaling der planten (Haarlem, 1878); "Ueber die Verkürtzung pflanzlicher Zellen durch Aufnahme von Wasser," in Botanische Zeitung, **37** (1879), 649–654; "Ueber die inneren Vorgänge bei den Wachsthumskrümmungen mehrzelliger Organe," ibid., 830–838; "Ueber die Bedeutung der Pflanzensäuren für den Turgor de Zellen," ibid., 847–853; "Over de bewegung der ranken van Sicyos," in Verslagen en mededeelingen der Koninklijke Akademie van Wetenschappen, Afdeeling Natuurkunde, 2nd ser., **15** (1880), 51–174; "Ueber den Antheil der Pflanzensäuren an der Turgorkraft wachsender Organe," in Botanische Zeitung, **41** (1883), 849–854; "Ueber die periodische Säurebildung der Fettpflanzen," ibid., **42** (1884), 337–343, 353–358; "Eine Methode zur Analyse der Turgorkraft," in Jahrbüchern für wissenschaftliche Botanik, **14** (1884), 427–601; "Beschouwingen over het verbeteren van de rassen onzer cultuurplanten," in Maandblad van de Hollandsche Maatschappij van Landbouw, 19 articles (May 1885–July 1887).

Also see "Ueber die Bedeutung der Circulation und der Rotation des Protoplasma für den Stofftransport in den Pflanzen," in Botanische Zeitung, **43** (1885), 1–6, 17–24; "Plasmolytische Studien über die Wand der Vacuolen," in Jahrbücher für wissenschaftliche Botanik, **16** (1885); 464–598; "Ueber die Periodicität im Säuregehalt der Fettpflanzen," in Verslagen en mededeelingen der Koninklijke Academie van Wetenschappen, Afdeeling Natuurkunde, 3rd ser., **1** (1885), 58–123; "Ueber die Aggregation im Protoplasma von Drosera rotundifolia," in Botanische Zeitung, **44** (1886), 1–11, 17–26, 33–43, 57–64; "Ueber den isotonischen Coefficient des Glycerin," ibid., **46** (1888), 229–235, 245–253;

"Osmotische Versuche mit lebenden Membrane," in Zeitschrift für physikalische Chemie, **2** (1888), 415–432; "Détermination du poids moléculaire de la raffinose par la méthode plasmolytique," in Comptes rendus . . . de l'Académie des sciences, **106** (1888), 751–753; "Isotonische Koeffizienten einiger Salze," in Zeitschrift für physikalische Chemie, **3** (1889), 103–109; and Intracellulare Pangenesis (Jena, 1889), English trans. as Intracellular Pangenesis (Chicago, 1910), Dutch trans. as Intracellulaire pangenesis (Amsterdam, 1918).

Further works are Die Pflanzen und Thiere in den dunklen Räumen der Rotterdamer Wasserleitung (Jena, 1890); Monographie der Zwangsdrehungen (Berlin, 1891), also in Jahrbücher für wissenschaftliche Botanik, **23** (1892), 13–206; "Ueber halbe Galtonkurven als Zeichen diskontinuierlicher Variation," in Berichte der Deutschen botanischen Gesellschaft, **12** (1894), 197–207; "Sur l'introduction de l'Oenothera lamarckiana dans les Pays Bas," in Nederlandsch kruidkundig archief, 2nd ser., **6** (1895), 579–583; "Eine zweigipfliche Variationskurve," in Archiv für Entwicklungsmechanik der Organismen, **2** (1895), 52–64; "Eenheid in veranderlijkheid," in Album der Natuur, **47** (1898), 65–80; "Over het omkeeren van halve Galtonkurven," in Botanisch Jaarboek, **10** (1898), 27–61; "Alimentation et sélection," in Volume jubilaire de la Société de biologie de Paris (1899), 17–38; "Ueber Curvenselektion bei Chrysanthemum segetum," in Berichte der Deutschen botanischen Gesellschaft, **17** (1899), 84–98; and "On Biastrepsis in Its Relation to Cultivation," in Annals of Botany, **13** (1899), 395–420.

Subsequent writings include "Sur la loi de disjonction des hybrides," in Comptes rendus . . . de l'Académie des sciences, **130** (1900), 845–847; "Das Spaltungsgesetz der Bastarde," in Berichte der deutschen botanischen Gesellschaft, **18** (1900), 83–90; "Sur les unités des charactères spécifiques et leur application à l'étude des hybrides," in Revue générale de botanique, **12** (1900), 257–271; "Sur l'origine expérimentale d'une nouvelle espèce végétale," in Comptes rendus . . . de l'Académie des sciences, **131** (1900), 124–126; "Ueber erbungleiche Kreutzungen (vorläufige Mittheilung)," in Berichte der Deutschen botanischen Gesellschaft, **18** (1900), 435–443; "Hybridizing of Monstrosities," in Journal of the Royal Horticultural Society, **24** (1900), 69–75; "Over het ontstaan van nieuwe soorten in planten," in Verslagen van de zittingen der wis- en natuurkundige afdeeling van de Koninklijke Academie van wetenschappen, **9** (1900), 246–248; Die Mutationstheorie, Versuche und Beobachtungen über die Entstehung von Arten im Pflanzenreich, 2 vols. (Leipzig, 1901–1903), English trans. as The Mutation Theory, Experiments and Observations on the Origin of Species in the Vegetable Kingdom, 2 vols. (Chicago, 1909–1910), from which translation all discussions of Mendel's segregation law have been omitted, and Die Mutationen und die Mutationsperioden bei der Entstehung der Arten (Leipzig, 1901).

Also see "Ueber tricotyle Rassen," in Berichte der

*Deutschen botanischen Gesellschaft*, **20** (1902), 45–54; "La loi de Mendel et les charactères constants des hybrides," in *Comptes rendus . . . de l'Académie des sciences*, **136** (1903), 321–323; "On Atavistic Variation in *Oenothera cruciata*," in *Bulletin of the Torrey Botanical Club*, **30** (1903), 75–82; "Anwendung der Mutationslehre auf die Bastardierungsgesetze," in *Berichte der Deutschen botanischen Gesellschaft*, **21** (1903), 45–82; "Sur la relation entre les charactères des hybrides et leurs parents," in *Revue générale de botanique*, **15** (1903), 241–252; "Bastaardeering en bevruchting," in *De Gids*, 4th ser., **21** (1903), 403–450; "Experimenteele evolutie," in *Onze Eeuw*, **4** (1904), 282–309, 362–393; "The Evidence of Evolution," in *University Record of the University of Chicago*, **9** (1904), 202–209; *Naar Californië, Reisherinneringen* (Haarlem, 1905; 2nd ed., 1906); *Het Yellowstone Park; Experimenteele evolutie* (Amsterdam, 1905); *Species and Varieties* (Chicago, 1905); "Aeltere und neuere Selektionsmethoden," in *Botanisches Zentralblatt*, **26** (1906), 385–395; "Die Neuzuchtigungen Luther Burbanks," *ibid.*, 609–621; and "Burbank's Production of Horticultural Novelties," in *Open Court*, **20** (1906), 641–653.

Additional works are "Evolution and Mutation," in *Monist*, **17** (1907), 6–22; "New Principles in Agricultural Plantbreeding," *ibid.*, 209–219; *Naar Californië II* (Haarlem, 1907); *Plant Breeding, Comments on the Experiments of Nilsson and Burbank* (Chicago, 1907; 2nd ed., 1919), Dutch trans. as *Het veredelen van kultuurplanten* (Haarlem, 1908); "On Twin Hybrids," in *Botanical Gazette*, **44** (1907), 401–407; "Bastarde von *Oenothera gigas*," in *Berichte der Deutschen botanischen Gesellschaft*, **26a** (1908), 754–762; "On Triple Hybrids," in *Botanical Gazette*, **47** (1909), 1–8; "Ueber doppelt reziproke Bastarde von *Oenothera biennis* L. und *Oenothera muricata* L.," in *Botanisches Zentralblatt*, **31** (1911), 97–104; "The Evening Primroses of Dixie Landing," in *Science*, n.s. **35** (1912), 599–601, written with H. H. Bartlett; *Die Mutationen in der Erblichkeitslehre* (Berlin, 1912); "*Oenothera Nanella*, Healthy and Diseased," in *Science*, n.s. **35** (1912), 753–754; *Van Texas naar Florida* (Haarlem, 1913); *Gruppenweise Artbildung* (Berlin, 1913); "L'*Oenothera grandiflora* de l'herbier de Lamarck," in *Revue générale de botanique*, **25b** (1914), 151–166; and "The Probable Origin of *Oenothera lamarckiana*," in *Botanical Gazette*, **57** (1914), 345–361.

Further, see "Ueber künstliche Beschleunigung der Wasseraufnahme in Samen durch Druck," in *Botanisches Zentralblatt*, **35** (1915), 161–176; "The Coefficient of Mutation in *Oenothera biennis* L.," in *Botanical Gazette*, **59** (1915), 169–196; "*Oenothera nanella*, a Mendelian Mutant," *ibid.*, **60** (1915), 337–345; "Die Grundlagen der Mutationstheorie," in *Naturwissenschaften*, **4** (1916), 593–598; "Ueber die Abhängigkeit der Mutations Koeffizienten von äusseren Einflüssen," in *Berichte der Deutschen botanischen Gesellschaft*, **34** (1916), 1–7; "New Dimorphic Mutants of the *Oenotheras*," in *Botanical Gazette*, **62** (1916), 249–280; "Die

endemischen Pflanzen von Ceylon und die mutierenden Oenotheren," in *Botanisches Zentralblatt*, **36** (1916), 1–11; "Gute, harte und leere Samen von *Oenothera*," in *Zeitschrift für induktive Abstammungs- und Vererbungslehre*, **16** (1916), 239–292; "The Origin of the Mutation Theory," in *Monist*, **27** (1917), 403–410; "*Oenothera lamarckiana mut. velutina*," in *Botanical Gazette*, **63** (1917), 1–25; "Halbmutanten und Zwillingsbastarde," in *Berichte der Deutschen botanischen Gesellschaft*, **35** (1917), 128–135; and "Ueber monohybride Mutationen," in *Botanisches Zentralblatt*, **37** (1917), 139–148.

Additional works by de Vries are "Kreutzungen von *Oenothera lamarckiana mut. velutina*," in *Zeitschrift für induktive Abstammungs- und Vererbungslehre*, **19** (1918), 1–13; "Mass Mutations and Twin Hybrids of *Oenothera grandiflora* Ait.," in *Botanical Gazette*, **65** (1918), 377–422; "Twin Hybrids of *Oenothera hookeri*, T. and G.," in *Genetics*, **3** (1918), 397–421; "Mutations of *Oenothera suaveolens*, Desf.," *ibid.*, 1–26; "Mass Mutations in *Zea mais*," in *Science*, **47** (1918), 465–467; *Van amoebe tot mensch* (Utrecht, 1918); "*Oenothera lamarckiana mut. simplex*," in *Berichte der Deutschen botanischen Gesellschaft*, **37** (1919), 65–73; "*Oenothera Rubinervis*, a Half Mutant," in *Botanical Gazette*, **67** (1919), 1–26; "*Oenothera lamarckiana erythrina*, eine neue Halmutante," in *Zeitschrift für Induktive Abstammungs- und Vererbungslehre*, **21** (1919), 91–118; "Ueber die Mutabilität von *Oenothera lamarckiana mut. simplex*," *ibid.*, **31** (1923), 313–357; "Ueber sesquiplex Mutanten von *Oenothera lamarckiana*," in *Zeitschrift für Botanik*, **15** (1923), 369–408; "*Oenothera lamarckiana mut. perennis*," in *Flora, oder allgemeine botanische Zeitung*, **116** (1923), 336–345; "Ueber die Entstehung von *Oenothera lamarckiana mut. velutina*," in *Botanisches Zentralblatt*, **43** (1923), 213–224; and "On the Distribution of Mutant Characters Among the Chromosomes of *Oenothera lamarckiana*," in *Genetics*, **8** (1923), 233–238, written with K. Boedijn.

Also see "Die Gruppierung der Mutanten von *Oenothera lamarckiana*," in *Berichte der Deutschen botanischen gesellschaft*, **42** (1924), 174–178, written with K. Boedijn; "Doubled Chromosomes of *Oenothera semigigas*," in *Botanical Gazette*, **78** (1924), 249–270, written with K. Boedijn; "Die Mutabilität von *Oenothera lamarckiana gigas*," in *Zeitschrift für induktive Abstammungs- und Vererbungslehre*, **35** (1924), 197–237; "Sekundäre Mutationen von *Oenothera lamarckiana*," in *Zeitschrift für Botanik*, **17** (1925), 193–211; "Mutant Races, Derived From *Oenothera lamarckiana*," in *Genetics*, **10** (1925), 211–222; "Brittle Races of *Oenothera lamarckiana*," in *Botanical Gazette*, **80** (1925), 262–275; "Die latente Mutabilität von *Oenothera biennis*," in *Zeitschrift für induktive Abstammungs- und Vererbungslehre*, **38** (1927), 141–197; "A Survey of the Cultures of *Oenothera lamarckiana* at Lunteren," *ibid.*, **47** (1928), 275–286, written with R. R. Gates; "Ueber das Auftreten von Mutanten aus *Oenothera lamarck-*

iana," *ibid.*, **52** (1929), 121–190; and "Ueber semirezessive Anlagen in *Oenothera lamarckiana*," *ibid.*, **70** (1935), 222–256.

II. SECONDARY LITERATURE. Discussions of de Vries and his work include G. E. Allen, "Hugo de Vries and the Reception of the 'Mutation Theory,'" in *Journal of the History of Biology*, **2** (1969), 55–87; F. M. Andrews, "Hugo de Vries," in *Plant Physiology*, **5** (1930), 175–180; Annelén [pseud.], "Professor Hugo de Vries en de Amsterdamsche Universiteit," in *Algemeen Handelsblad* (15 Oct. 1927); A. F. Blakeslee, "The Work of Professor Hugo de Vries," in *Scientific Monthly*, **36** (1933), 378–380; and "Hugo de Vries, 1848–1935," in *Science*, **81** (1935), 581–582; J. H. van Burkom, "In Memoriam Prof. Hugo de Vries," in *Natura*, **34** (1935), 161; F. Chodat, "Hugo de Vries, 1848–1935," in *Comptes rendus des séances de la Société de physique et d'histoire naturelle de Genève*, **54** (1937), 7–10; R. Cleland, "Hugo de Vries, 1848–1935," in *Journal of Heredity*, **26** (1935), 289–297; and "Hugo de Vries," in *Proceedings of the American Philosophical Society*, **76** (1936), 248–250; J. C. Costerus, "Professor Hugo de Vries," in *Eigen Haard*, **21** (1895), 261–264; C. F. Cox, "Hugo de Vries on the Origin of Species and Varieties by Mutation," in *Journal of the New York Botanical Garden*, **6** (1905), 66–70; E. O. Dodson, "Mendel and the Rediscovery of His Work," in *Scientific Monthly*, **58** (1955), 187–195; and P. Fröschel, "Einige Briefe von Hugo de Vries," in *Acta botanica neerlandica*, **10** (1961), 202–208.

Also see S. S. Gager, "De Vries and His Critics," in *Science*, n.s. **24** (1906), 81–89; R. R. Gates, "Prof. Hugo de Vries, For. Mem. R. S.," in *Nature*, **136** (1935), 133–134; G. C. Gerrits, *Grote Nederlanders bij de opbouw der natuurwetenschappen* (Leiden, 1947); A. D. Hall, "Hugo de Vries," in *Obituary Notices of Fellows of the Royal Society of London*, **4** (1935), 371–373; J. Heimans, "Hugo de Vries," in *Hugo de Vries, Voordrachten ter herdenking van zijn honderdste geboortedag op 16 Februari 1948* (Amsterdam, 1948), 1–9; *Zeventig jaar pangenenleer* (Amsterdam, 1959); "De herontdekking," in *Honderd jaar Mendel* (Wageningen, 1965), 62–80; and "Gregor Mendel and Hugo de Vries on the Species Concept," in *Acta botanica neerlandica*, **18** (1969), 95–98; H. W. Heinsius, "Hugo de Vries, 16 Februari 1848–1918," in *De Amsterdammer* (16 Feb. 1918); J. van der Hoeven, "In Memoriam Hugo de Vries," in *Verslagen en mededeelingen der Koninklijke Akademie van Wetenschappen, Afdeeling Natuurkunde*, **44** (1935), 59–62; A. A. W. Hubrecht, "Hugo de Vries' mutatietheorie," in *De Gids*, 4th ser., **19** (1901), 492–519; H. T. A. Hus, "The Work of Hugo de Vries," in *Sunset Magazine*, **13** (1904), 39–42; and "Hugo de Vries," in *Open Court*, **20** (1906), 713–725; and W. van Itallie-van Embden, "Sprekende portretten," in *Haagsche post* (19 Dec. 1925), an interview with Hugo de Vries.

Other works on de Vries are Ilse Jahn, "Zur Geschichte der Wiederentdeckung der Mendelschen Ge-

setze," in *Wissenschaftliche Zeitschrift der Friedrich Schiller-Universität Jena*, **7** (1957–1958), 215–227; E. Lehmann, *Die Theorien der Oenotheraforschung* (Jena, 1922); and "Die Entwicklung der Oenotheraforschung," in *Hugo de Vries, sechs Vorträge zur Feier seines 80 Geburtstages, gehalten im botanischen Institut, Tübingen* (Stuttgart, 1929), 36–42; (D. Manassen), "Prof. Hugo de Vries," in *Algemeen handelsblad* (18 Nov. 1910); M. Moebius, "Hugo de Vries und sein Lebenswerk," in *Revista sudamericana de botánica*, **2** (1935), 162–168; J. W. Moll, "Hugo de Vries, 16 Februari 1848–1918," in *De nieuwe Amsterdammer* (16 Feb. 1918); and D. Müller, "Drei Briefe über reine Linien, von Galton, de Vries und Yule und Wilhelm Johannsen in 1903 geschrieben," in *Centaurus*, **16** (1972), 316–319.

Further works are H. R. Oppenheimer, "Hugo de Vries als Pflanzenphysiologe," in *Palestine Journal of Botany and Horticultural Science*, **1** (1935–1936), 51–69; P. van Oye, "Julius MacLeod en Edward Verschaffelt," in *Mededelingen van de Koninklijke Vlaamsche academie voor wetenschappen, letteren en schoone kunsten van België*, **23** (1961), 3–20; P. W. van der Pas, "Hugo de Vries als taxonoom," in *Scientiarum historia*, **11** (1969), 148–166; "The Correspondence of Hugo de Vries and Charles Darwin," in *Janus*, **57** (1970), 173–213; "Hugo de Vries visits San Diego," in *Journal of San Diego History*, **17** (1971), 12–23; and "Hugo de Vries in the Imperial Valley," *ibid.*; O. Renner, "Hugo de Vries," in *Erbarzt*, **3** (1935), 177–184; and "Hugo de Vries, 1848–1935," in *Naturwissenschaften*, **24** (1936), 321–324; H. F. Roberts, *Plant Hybridization Before Mendel* (New Haven, 1929); and Elisabeth Schiemann, "Hugo de Vries," in *Züchter*, **7** (1935), 159–161; and "Hugo de Vries zum hundertsten Geburtstage," in *Berichte der Deutschen botanischen Gesellschaft*, **62** (1948), 1–15.

In addition, see A. Schierbeek, "De pangenesis theorie van Hugo de Vries," in *Bijdragen tot de geschiedenis der geneeskunde*, **24** (1943), 64–67; G. H. Schull, "Hugo de Vries at Eighty-five," in *Journal of Heredity*, **24** (1933), 1–6; Sinotō Yositō, "Tabi ni ahishi hitobito," in *Kagaku zassan*, **3** (8), (1933), 295–297, a pilgrimage to famous men; T. J. Stomps, "Aus dem Leben und Wirken von Hugo de Vries," in *Hugo de Vries, Sechs Vorträge zur Feier seines 80 Geburtstages, gehalten im botanischen Institut, Tübingen* (Stuttgart, 1929), 7–16; *Vijf en twintig jaren Mutatietheorie* (The Hague, 1930); "Hugo de Vries," in *Berichte der Deutschen botanischen Gesellschaft*, **53** (1936), 85–96; "Hugo de Vries et la cytologie," in *Revue de cytologie et de cytophysiologie végétales*, **2** (3) (1937), 281–285; and "On the Rediscovery of Mendel's Work by Hugo de Vries," in *Journal of Heredity*, **45** (6) (1954), 293–294; E. Von Tschermak-Seysenegg, "Hugo de Vries, der Begründer der Mutationstheorie," in *Reichspost* (2 Feb. 1936); and "Historischer Rückblick auf die Wiederentdeckung der Gregor Mendelschen Arbeit," in *Verhandlungen der Zoologisch-botanischen Gesellschaft in Wien*, **92** (1951), 25–35.

Also see F. J. van Uildriks, "Professor Hugo de Vries zeventig jaar," in *Aarde en haar volken*, **54** (1918), 45–46; T. W. Vaughan, "The Work of Hugo de Vries and Its Importance in the Study of Problems of Evolution," in *Science*, n.s. **23** (1906), 681–691; J. H. Verduyn de Boer, "Hugo de Vries, de groote Nederlandsche geleerde drie en tachtig jaar," in *Huisgenoot* (6 Feb. 1931); J. H. de Vries, *De Amsterdamsche doopsgezinde familie de Vries* (Zutphen, 1911); T. Weevers, "Hugo de Vries als plantenphysioloog," in *Hugo de Vries, Voordrachten ter herdenking van zijn honderdste geboortedag op 16 Februari 1948* (Amsterdam, 1948), 11–15; and F. A. F. C. Went, "Hugo de Vries," in *Mannen en vrouwen van beteekenis in onze dagen*, **31** (7) (1900), 263–320; "Hugo de Vries en de mutatietheorie," in *Elsevier's maandschrift*, **39** (1905), 35–42; and "Herinneringen aan Hugo de Vries," in *Natura*, **27** (1928), 19–21.

PETER W. VAN DER PAS

**VULF, YURI VIKTOROVICH.** See **Wulff, Georg.**

**VVEDENSKY, NIKOLAY EVGENIEVICH** (*b.* Kochkovo, Vologodskaya gubernia, Russia, 28 April 1852; *d.* Kochkovo, 16 September 1922), *physiology.*

After graduating from the Vologod religious seminary, Vvedensky entered St. Petersburg University in 1872. Two years later he was arrested for participation in student revolutionary activities and spent more than three years in prison. He graduated from the university in 1879, having studied physiology with I. M. Sechenov, then worked in physiology laboratories in Germany (1881–1882), Austria (1884), and Switzerland (1887).

After defending his master's thesis in 1884, Vvedensky became *Privatdozent* in the department of physiology; in 1889, after Sechenov moved to Moscow, he became extraordinary professor, and in 1895, professor at St. Petersburg University.

Vvedensky's research was devoted to clarifying the regularities in the reaction of living tissue to various irritants. Having applied the method of telephonic auscultation of the excited nerve, he showed that a living system changes not only under the influence of irritation but also during its normal activity; he thus introduced the time factor into physiology. In his master's thesis, "Telefonicheskie issledovania nad elektricheskimi yavleniami v myshechnykh i nervnykh apparatakh" ("Telephonic Research on Electrical Phenomena in Muscle and Nerve Apparatus"), Vvedensky provided a thorough analysis of the literature on muscle con-

traction and nerve fatigue. In his doctoral dissertation, "O sootnosheniakh mezhdu razdrazheniem i vozbuzhdeniem pri tetanuse" ("On the Relationship Between Stimulus and Excitation in Tetanus"; 1886), he formulated the theory of the optimum and pessimum irritation, on the basis of which he established the law of relative functional movement (lability) of tissue. Vvedensky examined nerve-muscle preparations as heterogeneous formations (consisting of nerve tissue, nerve ends, and muscles), the parts of which possess different lability.

Vvedensky's outstanding achievement was his theory of parabiosis, developed in *Vozbuzhdenie, tormozhenie i narkoz* ("Excitation, Inhibition, and Narcosis"; 1901), in which he generalized his ideas on the nature of the processes of excitation and inhibition, showing their identity.

*BIBLIOGRAPHY*

Vvedensky's writings were brought together in *Polnoe sobranie sochineny* ("Complete Collected Works"), 7 vols. (Leningrad, 1951–1963).

Secondary literature includes I. A. Arshavsky, *N. E. Vvedensky, 1852–1922* (Moscow, 1950); Y. M. Ufland, *Osnovnye etapy razvitia uchenia N. E. Vvedenskogo* ("Basic States in the Development of the Theory of N. E. Vvedensky"; Moscow, 1952); and E. K. Zhukov, "Evolyutsionny metod v shkole Vvedenskogo-Ukhtomskogo" ("The Evolutionary Method in the School of Vvedensky and Ukhtomsky"), in *Uchenye zapiski Leningradskogo . . . universiteta . . .*, Ser. biolog. nauk, **12**, no. 77 (1944), 437–468.

N. A. GRIGORIAN

**VYSHNEGRADSKY, IVAN ALEKSEEVICH** (*b.* Vyshni Volochek, Tver gubernia [now Kalinin oblast], Russia, 20 December 1831; *d.* St. Petersburg, Russia, 6 April 1895), *mechanics, engineering.*

The son of a priest, Vyshnegradsky enrolled at the Tver Ecclesiastical Seminary in 1843; but after three years he moved to St. Petersburg and enrolled at the Physics and Mathematics Faculty of the Central Pedagogical Institute, where Ostrogradsky's lectures aroused his interest in mathematics and physics. He graduated in 1851 and began teaching mathematics at the St. Petersburg Military School. Vyshnegradsky received his master's degree at St. Petersburg University in 1854 and became instructor in mathematics at the Mikhaylovsky Artillery Academy, where he taught special technical courses.

In 1860 the Artillery Academy sent Vyshnegradsky abroad to study mechanical engineering and to prepare for a professorship in applied mechanics. He spent about two years in Germany, France, Belgium, and England. In 1862, upon his return to Russia, he was appointed professor of applied mechanics at the Mikhaylovsky Artillery Academy and, shortly thereafter, professor of mechanics at the St. Petersburg Technological Institute as well. Vyshnegradsky was both an outstanding theoretician and a gifted design engineer; he was responsible for the reconstruction of many Artillery Department factories and for the construction of railroads. From 1867 to 1878 he was the mechanics and engineering specialist of the Central Artillery Administration. In 1875 he was appointed director of the St. Petersburg Technological Institute. Vyshnegradsky was elected an honorary member of the St. Petersburg Academy of Sciences in 1888.

Vyshnegradsky taught a generation of Russian mechanical engineers and was the head of the first Russian school of mechanical engineering. His students included N. P. Petrov, the founder of the theory of hydraulic friction; V. L. Kirpichev, engineer and scholar who organized higher technical education in Russia; and A. P. Borodin, who introduced a number of improvements in the steam locomotive. He was named a deputy minister of the Russian Ministry of Finance in 1887 and was minister of finance from 1888 until 1892.

Vyshnegradsky's most significant scientific contributions were in the theory of automatic regulation. Before him, many scholars had studied the regulation of industrial processes, but the regulators that they developed were created experimentally and were not explained on a theoretical basis. Through his research Vyshnegradsky established the mathematical bases for the general scientific principles of automatic regulation. Prior to his work the machine and the regulator had been examined individually, and only the statics of the regulator had been studied.

In 1877 Vyshnegradsky published "O regulyatorakh pryamogo deystvia" ("On Direct-Action Regulators"), in which the conditions of stability of a steam engine equipped with a direct-action centrifugal regulator were explained. The stability condition for a regulating system, as established by Vyshnegradsky, is known in the technical literature as the Vyshnegradsky criterion. His article greatly influenced subsequent development of the theory of regulation. Published in several languages, it received great attention in Germany, France, and the United States.

## BIBLIOGRAPHY

I. ORIGINAL WORKS. Vyshnegradsky's writings include *O dvizhenii sistemy materialnykh tochek, opredelyaemoy polnymi differentsialnymi unravneniami* ("On the Motion of a System of Material Points, Which [System] Is Defined by Complete Differential Equations"; St. Petersburg, 1854), his master's thesis; *Publichnye populyarnye lektsii o mashinakh* ("Public Popular Lectures on Machines"; St. Petersburg, 1859); "Neskolko zamechany o parovykh pressakh" ("Some Remarks on Steam [Powered] Presses"), in *Artillerysky zhurnal,* **4** (1860), 237–259; *Mekhanicheskaya teoria teploty* ("The Mechanical Theory of Heat"; St. Petersburg, 1873); *Lektsii o parovykh mashinakh, chitannye v Tekhnologicheskom institute* ("Lectures on Steam Engines Read at the Technological Institute"; St. Petersburg, 1874); "Sur la théorie générale des régulateurs," in *Comptes rendus . . . de l'Académie des sciences,* **83** (1876), 318–321: "Über direktwirkende Regulatoren," in *Civilingenieur,* n.s. 22 (1877), 95–131; "O regulyatorakh pryamogo deystvia" ("On Direct-Action Regulators"), in *Izvestiya Peterburgskogo prakticheskogo tekhnologicheskogo instituta,* **1** (1877), 21–62; "Mémoire sur la théorie générale des régulateurs," in *Revue universelle des mines . . .,* 2nd ser., **4** (1878), 1–38; and **5** (1879), 192–227; and *O regulyatorakh nepryamogo deystvia* ("On Indirect-Action Regulators"; St. Petersburg, 1878).

II. SECONDARY LITERATURE. See A. A. Andronov, *I. A. Vyshnegradsky i ego rol v sozdanii teorii avtomaticheskogo regulirovania* ("Vyshnegradsky and His Role in the Creation of the Theory of Automatic Regulation"; Moscow–Leningrad, 1949); A. T. Grigorian, *Ocherki istorii mekhaniki v Rossii* ("Essays on the History of Mechanics in Russia"; Moscow, 1961), 119–131; and V. L. Kirpichev, "I. A. Vyshnegradsky, kak professor i ucheny" ("Vyshnegradsky as Professor and Scholar"), in *Vestnik Obshchestva tekhnologov,* **6** (1895), 307–322.

A. T. GRIGORIAN

**VYSOTSKY, GEORGY NIKOLAEVICH** (*b.* Nikitovka, Chernigov gubernia, Russia, 19 February 1865; *d.* Kharkov, U.S.S.R., 6 April 1940), *soil science, forestry.*

Vysotsky entered the Petrovsky Agricultural Academy in 1886 and studied forestry, botany, and soil science. He began his scientific career in 1890 at the Berdyansk forest reserve, studying steppe forestry. In May 1892 he joined Dokuchaev's expedition to Poltava and was manager of the Great Anadolian forest reserve in the Ukraine. The ideas of Dokuchaev and Morozov decisively influenced the formation of Vysotsky's scientific views.

From 1904 to 1913 Vysotsky headed the reorganization in St. Petersburg of experimental forestry and also conducted field research in the region near Samara. In 1913 he directed projects for forestation of an artificial forest reserve on the steppe at Kiev. From 1918 Vysotsky taught at and worked for scientific organizations in Kiev, Simferopol, Minsk, and Kharkov; organized and headed experimental forestry research in Byelorussia and the Ukraine; and created and headed departments of forestry and forest management.

Vysotsky's main achievement was the establishment of the scientific foundations of steppe forestry and forest improvement; in particular, he determined that the vegetation of steppes is primarily a combination of oak and shrubbery and showed that what were then considered "normal" types of steppe forests, with a predominance of elms, involved intensive transpiration of soil moisture. Vysotsky demonstrated the influence of a forest on the microclimate of planted areas and adjacent localities, and classified steppe conditions for local growth according to the degree of suitability for forests, and in relation to topography, snow accumulation, depth of groundwater, and presence of subsoil salts.

Vysotsky revealed why steppes are without forests, and in "Ergenya" he showed the evolution of steppe vegetation under human influence and demonstrated experimentally the influence of steppe forest cultivation on the agricultural harvest. He wrote general works on the moisture cycle in nature and on the main questions of forest hydrology, also elucidating the role of forest in the water cycle of the plains in European Russia. Vysotsky pointed out the regularities of the moisture cycle and the movement of salts in the soil in the steppe and underforest, and developed the theory of gley—the formation of sticky clay layers—as a biochemical oxidation-reduction process.

## BIBLIOGRAPHY

I. ORIGINAL WORKS. Vysotsky's more than 200 writings include "Rastitelnost Veliko-Anadolskogo uchastka" ("Vegetation of the Great Anadolian District"), in *Trudy ekspeditsii V. V. Dokuchaeya* ("Works of the Dokuchaev Expedition"), II, pt. 2 (St. Petersburg, 1898); "Biologicheskie, pochvennye i fenologicheskie nablyudenia i issledovania v Veliko-Anadole 1892–1893 gg." ("Biological, Soil, and Phenological Observations and Research in Great Anadolia 1892–1893"), in *Trudy opytnykh lesnichestv* ("Works in Experimental Forestry"; St. Petersburg, 1901); *Lesnye kultury v Mariupolskom opytnom lesnichestve, 1886–1900* ("Forest Culture in the Mariupol Forest Reserve . . ."; St. Petersburg, 1901); "O nauchnykh issledovaniakh, kasayushchikhsya stepnogo lesorazvedenia" ("On Scientific Investigations Concerning Steppe Forest Culture"), in *Lesnoy zhurnal* (1901), no. 2; "Stepnoy illyuvy i struktura stepnykh pochv" ("Steppe Illuvium and the Structure of Steppe Soils"), in *Pochvovedenie* (1901), nos. 2–4, and (1902), no. 2; "Mikorizy dubovykh i sosnovykh seyantsev" ("Mycorrhizae of Oak and Pine Seedlings"), in *Lesopromyshlennyi vestnik* (1902), no. 29; and "O stimulakh, prepyatstviakh i problemakh razvedenia lesa v stepyakh Rossii" ("On the Incentives, Obstacles, and Problems of Forest Culture on the Steppes of Russia"), in *Trudy II Sezda deyateley selskokhozyaystvennogo opytnogo dela* ("Works of the II Congress of Workers in Experimental Agriculture"), I (St. Petersburg, 1902).

See also "O karte tipov mestoproizrastania" ("On a Map of Types of Local Growth"), in *Sovremennye voprosy russkogo selskogo khozyaystva* ("Contemporary Questions in Russian Agriculture"; St. Petersburg, 1904); "O vzaimnykh sootnosheniakh mezhdu lesnoy rastitelnostyu i vlagoyu, preimushchestvenno v yuzhno-russkikh stepyakh" ("On the Mutual Relations Between Forest Vegetation and Moisture, Primarily on the Southern Russian Steppes"), in *Trudy opytnykh lesnichestv* ("Works in Experimental Forestry," II; St. Petersburg, 1904); "K voprosu o vlianii lesa na nadzemnuyu vlazhnost v Rossii" ("On the Influence of the Forest on Underground Moisture in Russia"), in *Trudy III Sezda deyateley selskokhozyaystvennogo opytnogo dela* ("Works of the III Congress of Workers in Experimental Agriculture"; St. Petersburg, 1905); "Gley," in *Pochvovedenïe* (1905), no. 7, also in *Lesnoy zhurnal* (1906), no. 3; "Ob oroklimaticheskikh osnovakh klassifikatsii pochv" ("On the Oroclimatic Bases of Soil Classification"), in *Pochvovedenie* (1906), **8**, no. 1; "Pochvenno-botanicheskie issledovania v yuzhnykh Tulskikh zasekakh" ("Soil-Botanical Research in the Southern Tula Abatis"), in *Trudy opytnykh lesnichestv* ("Works in Experimental Forestry"; St. Petersburg, 1906); and "Ob usloviakh lesoproizrastania i lesorazvedenia v stepyakh Evropeyskoy Rossii" ("On the Conditions of Forest Growth and Forest Culture on the Steppes of European Russia"), in *Lesnoy zhurnal* (1907), nos. 1–2.

Additional works are *O lesorastitelnykh usloviakh rayona Samarskogo udelnogo okruga* ("On Forest Growth Conditions of the Samara Region in a Specific District"), 2 vols. (St. Petersburg, 1908–1909); "Buzuluksky bor i ego okrestnosti" ("The Buzuluk Pine Forest and Its Surroundings"), in *Lesnoy zhurnal* (1909), no. 8; "Pochvoobrazovatelnye protsessy v peskakh" ("Soil-Forming Processes in Sands"), in *Izvestiya Russkogo geograficheskogo obshchestva*, **47**, pt. 6 (1911); "Lesnye kultury stepnykh opytnykh lesnichestv s 1893 po 1907 gg." ("Forest Cultures of the Steppe Experimental Forest Reserves 1893–1907"), in *Trudy po lesnomu opytnomu delu v Rossii* ("Works on Experimental Forestry in Russia"), no. 41 (St. Petersburg, 1912); "O dubravakh v Evropeyskoy Rossii" ("Oak Groves in European Russia"), in *Lesnoy zhurnal* (1913), nos. 1–2; "Ergenya, kulturno-fitologichesky ocherk" ("Ergenya, a Cultural-Phytological Sketch"), in *Trudy byuro po prikladnoi botanike* (1915), **10–11**; "Izokarbonaty" ("Isocarbonates"), in *Russki pochvoved* (1915); and *Lesa Ukrainy i uslovia ikh proizrastania i vozobnovlenia* ("The Forests of the Ukraine and the Conditions of Their Growth and Renewal"; Kiev, 1916).

Also see "Lesovodnye ocherki" ("Forestry Culture Notes"), in *Zapiski Belorusskogo gosudarstvennogo instituta selskogo i lesnogo khozyaistva*, **3** (1924); "Ocherki o pochve i rezhime gruntovykh vod" ("Sketches on Soil and Groundwater Conditions"), in *Byulleten pochvoveda* (1927), nos. 1–8; "O roli lesa v povyshenii urozhaynosti" ("On the Role of the Forest in Increasing the Harvest"), in *Lesnoe khozyaistvo* (1929), 10–11; "Uchenie o lesnoy pertinentsii" ("Theory of Forest"), in *Lesovedenia i lesovodstvo* ("Forestry and Forest Culture"; Leningrad, 1930); *Materialy po izucheniyu vodookhrannoy i vodoreguliruyushchey roli lesov i bolot* ("Materials for the Study of the Water-Retaining and Water-Regulating Roles of Forests and Swamps"; Moscow, 1937); *O gidrogeologicheskom i meteorologicheskom vlianii lesov* ("On the Hydrological and Meteorological Influence of Forests"; Moscow, 1938); and his autobiography, in *Pochvovedenie* (1941), no. 3.

II. SECONDARY LITERATURE. See E. A. Danilov, "G. N. Vysotsky i stepnoe lesorazvedenie" ("Vysotsky and Steppe Forest Culture"), in *Pochvovedenie* (1935), no. 4; A. G. Isachenko, *G. N. Vysotsky – vydayushchysya otechestvenny geograf* ("Vysotsky – Outstanding Native Geographer"; Moscow, 1953); E. M. Lavrenko, "G. N. Vysotsky," in *Russkie botaniki, biografo-bibliografichesky slovar* ("Russian Botanists, Biographical-Bibliographical Dictionary"), II (Moscow, 1947); P. S. Pogrebnyak, "G. N. Vysotsky," in *Vydayushchiesya deyateli otechestvennogo lesovodstva* ("Outstanding Native Workers in Forest Culture"; Moscow, 1950); and "Georgy Nikolaevich Vysotsky, 1865–1940," in *Lyudi russkoy nauki* ("People of Russian Science"; Moscow, 1963); S. S. Sobolev, "G. N. Vysotsky i ego nauchnaya deyatelnost" ("Vysotsky and His Scientific Career"), in *Pochvovedenie* (1935), no. 4; M. E. Tkachenko, "Veliky agrolesomeliorator, pamyati akademika G. N. Vysotskogo" ("Great Improver of Forest Agriculture, Recollections of Academician G. N. Vysotsky"), in *Lesnoe khozyaistvo* (1940), no. 9; and A. A. Yarilov, "G. N.

Vysotsky – sledopyt-geograf" ("Vysotsky – Pathfinder-Geographer"), in *Pochvovedenie* (1941), no. 3.

VERA N. FEDCHINA

**WAAGE, PETER** (*b.* island of Hitterø [now Hidra], near Flekkefjord, Norway, 29 June 1833; *d.* Christiania [now Oslo], Norway, 13 January 1900), *chemistry, mineralogy.*

The son of Peter Pedersen Waage, a shipmaster and shipowner, and Regine Lovise Wattne, Waage was raised on the island of Hitterø, where his forebears had lived as seamen for hundreds of years. Since his father was usually at sea, he grew up mainly under the supervision of his mother, who was his first teacher. When his precocity became known (he was able to read at the age of about four), it was decided that rather than follow the traditional family occupation, he was to have further education.

Waage's first regular schooling, at Flekkefjord, began when he was eleven. The school principal persuaded him to go to the University of Christiania, and to prepare for this he entered the fourth year of the Bergen Grammar School in 1849. He passed his matriculation examination *cum laudabilis* in 1854 and studied medicine during his first three years at the university. In 1857 he turned to mineralogy and chemistry. (As a boy, he had an extensive collection of minerals, plants, and insects, and some of his first publications dealt with mineralogy and crystallography.) In 1858 Waage was awarded the Crown Prince's Gold Medal for "Udvikling af de surstofholdige syreradikalers theori," which was published in 1859, the same year as his book *Outline of Crystallography*, written with H. Mohn.

In 1859, after graduation, Waage received a scholarship in chemistry that enabled him to make a year's study tour in France and Germany, beginning in the following spring. Most of his time was spent with Bunsen at Heidelberg. In 1861 Waage was appointed lecturer in chemistry, and in 1866 he was promoted to the only chair of chemistry then existing at the University of Christiania.

C. M. Guldberg and Waage, whose names are linked for their joint discovery of the law of mass action, were related through marriages to daughters of cabinet minister Hans Riddervold; Waage married Johanne Christiane Tandberg Riddervold, by whom he had five children. His wife died in 1869, and in 1870 he married one of Guldberg's sisters, Mathilde Sofie Guldberg; they had six children.

Their collaboration on the studies of chemical affinity that led to the law of mass action began immediately after Guldberg's return from abroad in 1862. The first report of their results, published in 1864 in *Forhandlinger i Videnskabs-selskabet i Christiania*, remained almost completely unknown to scientists, a fate also suffered by a more detailed description of their theory published in French in 1867. The theory did not become generally known until Ostwald, in a paper published in 1877, adopted the law of mass action and proved its validity by new experiments. In 1878 van't Hoff, apparently without any knowledge of Guldberg and Waage's work, derived the law from reaction kinetics. Although the law had several forerunners, the combined efforts of the theorist Guldberg and the empiricist Waage led to the first general mathematical and exact formulation of the role of the amounts of reactants in chemical equilibrium systems.

After completing his studies with Guldberg on the law of mass action, Waage increasingly concentrated on practical problems and on social and religious work, much of which dealt with nutrition and public health. For example, he discovered a method for preserving milk and developed a process for producing unsweetened condensed milk and sterilized canned milk. Waage also devoted considerable time to the industrial exploitation of the large quantities of fish caught along the Norwegian coast, developing a highly concentrated and excellent fish meal that was used on Norwegian ships and expeditions and was exported to Sweden, Finland, Denmark, and Germany. In Waage's time beer was taxed according to the amount of malt used in the brewing; he proposed, however, that taxation be based on alcoholic content and developed a method for determining the concentration of alcohol in beer by measurement of the boiling point.

Religious work with young people was a major interest of Waage's. He was active in the founding and management of the Christiania Ynglingeforening (later the Oslo YMCA) and the Norwegian Christian Youth Association. He was co-editor of the *Polyteknisk tidsskrift*, an active member and officer of scientific societies, and the recipient of many honors.

*BIBLIOGRAPHY*

I. ORIGINAL WORKS. Guldberg and Waage's papers on the law of mass action were abridged and translated into German by Richard Abegg as *Untersuchungen über die chemischen Affinitäten*, Ostwald's Klassiker der Exakten Wissenschaften no. 104 (Leipzig, 1899). Their first paper, "Studier over Affiniteten," in *Forhandlinger i Videnskabs-selskabet i Christiania*, 7 (1864), 35–45, appears in facs., along with a number of articles on the law, in Haakon Haraldsen, ed., *The Law of Mass Action: A Centenary Volume 1864–1964* (Oslo, 1964), 7–17.

II. SECONDARY LITERATURE. A biography of Waage and a discussion of his work by Haakon Haraldsen are in *The Law of Mass Action*, 26–32, 32–34; and in *Untersuchungen . . . Affinitäten*, 174–178. For a brief obituary see W. Ramsay, in *Journal of the Chemical Society*, 77 (1900), 591–592.

GEORGE B. KAUFFMAN

WAALS, JOHANNES DIDERIK VAN DER (*b.* Leiden, Netherlands, 23 November 1837; *d.* Amsterdam, Netherlands, 8 March 1923), *physics.*

The son of a carpenter, van der Waals became a primary-school teacher. After training for secondary-school teaching (1866), while a headmaster in The Hague, he studied physics at the University of Leiden. On the basis of his knowledge of the work of Clausius and other molecular theorists, he wrote his dissertation, *Over de continuiteit van den gasen vloeistoftoestand* (1873). As Maxwell said, "this at once put his name among the foremost in science." Using rather simple mathematics, the dissertation gave a satisfactory molecular explanation for the phenomena observed in vapors and liquids by Thomas Andrews and other experimenters, especially the existence of a critical temperature, below which a gas can be condensed to a two-phase system of vapor and liquid; while above it there can be only a homogeneous vapor phase. This was one of the first descriptions of a collective molecular effect, although the kinetic theory of gases was already well known.

The law of corresponding states, which van der Waals developed some years later, allows a somewhat better fit with experimental data and in succeeding years was a useful guide in the work on liquefaction of the "permanent" gases. In 1875 he was elected to the Royal Netherlands Academy of Sciences and Letters; and two years later, after the Amsterdam Athenaeum had become the University of Amsterdam, he occupied the chair of physics. As a teacher van der Waals was much admired, and he inspired his pupils to do both experimental and theoretical work. His scientific publications were mostly on molecular physics and thermody-

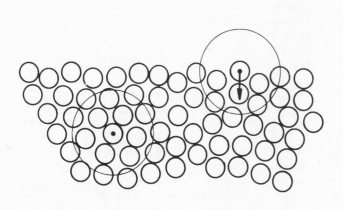

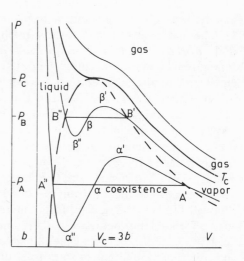

FIGURE 1.   In the surface layer the van der Waals attraction sphere is only filled below and so causes a pressure, proportional to $1/V^2$ because both the number of surface molecules and the resultant force on each of them are proportional to the density $\rho = 1/V$.

FIGURE 2.   Schematic van der Waals isotherms, one above and two below the critical isotherm $T_c$. In the coexistence region (inside broken curve) are two horizontal isothermal coexistence line segments, $A'A''$ and $B'B''$, at the two sides of which the surfaces (such as $A''\alpha''\alpha$ and $\alpha\,\alpha'A'$) included by the van der Waals isotherm are equal. (This is Maxwell's rule.)

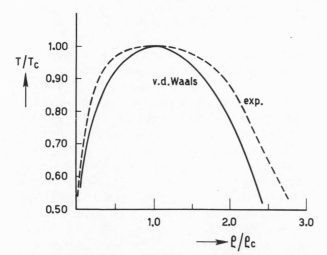

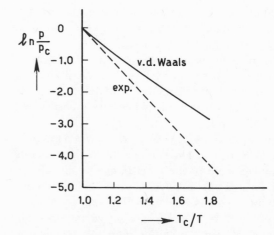

FIGURE 3.   Coexistence region in reduced variables according to the van der Waals equation and to experiment for noble gases, and similar substances.

FIGURE 4.   Natural logarithm of saturated vapor pressure plotted versus inverse temperature, according to van der Waals equation and to experiment, in reduced variables.

namics. He retired in 1907 and was succeeded by his son, who was named for him. In 1910 he was awarded the Nobel Prize for physics.

The van der Waals equation of state links the pressure $P$, absolute temperature $T$, and volume $V$, using three constants $a$, $b$, and $R$ (the last four quantities being proportional to the amount of substance or its square):

$$\left(P+\frac{a}{V^2}\right)(V-b)=RT.$$

The term $a/V^2$ accounts for the molecular attraction, determined by integrating over the "attraction sphere" (Figure 1). It is supposed (and at medium densities it is sufficiently true) that in the average over time the attraction sphere, outside its central part, is filled rather homogeneously with molecules with a local density equal to the overall density. With very close packing $a$ would no longer remain constant, but gradually increase (by less than a factor of 2). Likewise $b$, accounting for the nonoverlapping of molecules, is equal at low density to four times the "proper" volume of all molecules together, but gradually decreases (by a factor not smaller than 0.5) for very close packing. Moreover, the temperature also affects $a$ and $b$, since it influences the radial distribution of the molecules around an arbitrary one.

These detailed and, even for modern methods, rather difficult complications were rightly disregarded by van der Waals, although he was aware of them. With constant $a$ and $b$, the isotherms may be calculated (see Figure 2), giving for the critical point

$$V_c=3\,b,\,P_c=\frac{a}{27b^2},\,RT_c=\frac{8a}{27b}.$$

Below the critical point the assumption of one homogeneous phase no longer holds, except perhaps for very short moments. Energy relations are such that it is more favorable here for some of the molecules to move closer together (liquid), leaving the other molecules to fill the rest of the volume in a much sparser distribution (vapor). This two-phase system is represented by horizontal line tracks in Figure 2. Most thermodynamic quantities can now be calculated: saturated vapor pressure curve, Joule-Kelvin effect, supercooling, and so on. The comparison with experiment is given in Figures 3 and 4 for noble and pseudo-noble gases (hydrogen, carbon monoxide, nitrogen). The falling of all experimental points for these different substances, in reduced variables, on the same curve is an expression of the law of corresponding

states. For other kinds of molecules the divergences from van der Waals's findings may be smaller or larger.

Van der Waals scarcely could have had adequate ideas about the nature of the attractive forces between molecules, so it is historically rather inexact that the London forces (energy proportional to $r^{-6}$) should often be called "van der Waals forces." It would be somewhat more reasonable to give this name to all forces not of ionic origin, but so loose a terminology would not be useful.

*BIBLIOGRAPHY*

I. ORIGINAL WORKS. Van der Waals's writings include *Over de continuiteit van den gas- en vloeistoftoestand* (Leiden, 1873), his dissertation; articles in *Versl. Kon. Akademie van Wetenschappen*; and *Lehrbuch der Thermodynamik* (Leipzig, 1912), written with P. A. Kohnstamm. See also "The Equation of State for Gases and Liquids," in *Nobel Lectures in Physics, 1901–1921* (Amsterdam, 1967), which also contains a biography.

II. SECONDARY LITERATURE. See an article in *Physica* (Amsterdam), **4** (1937); S. G. Brush, *Nobel Prizes in Physics* (Milan, 1970); and W. Leendertz, "J. D. van der Waals," in *Gids*, **87** (1923), 151.

J. A. PRINS

**WACKENRODER, HEINRICH WILHELM FERDINAND** (*b.* Burgdorf, near Hannover, Germany, 8 March 1798; *d.* Jena, Germany, 4 September 1854), *pharmacy.*

Wackenroder was the son of Heinrich Wackenroder, a physician and apothecary in Burgdorf, and Charlotte Rougemont. He completed his apothecary's training in nearby Celle and worked for a time in his father's shop. In 1819 he went to Göttingen, where, in addition to pharmacy and natural science, he studied mathematics and medicine. After two and a half years he returned to Burgdorf and in 1824 passed the pharmacy examination. In 1825 Wackenroder became assistant to Friedrich Stromeyer in the pharmacy institute at Göttingen, where he gained experience in teaching and, by accompanying Stromeyer, in the inspection of apothecary shops. In 1827 he received a doctor of philosophy degree at Erlangen. In 1828 Wackenroder became a *Privatdozent* at Göttingen and in the same year accepted an offer to succeed Carl Göbel, as extraordinary professor, at the University of Jena. He was promoted to professor in 1836 and for the rest of his life was director of the pharmacy institute and inspector of apothecary shops for the grand duchy of Saxe-Weimar-Eisenach.

Wackenroder was exceptionally successful as a teacher, researcher, and scientific writer, and, most important, he made pharmacy an independent science. Besides the principal subjects of the curriculum he instituted special courses in forensic chemistry, phytochemistry, zoochemistry, toxicology, pharmaceutical technology, and merchandizing. He was the author of several textbooks, and his *Chemische Tabellen zur Analyse der unorganischen Verbindungen* (1829) went through five editions by 1843. From 1838 to 1854 he was coeditor of *Archiv der Pharmazie*. In this and in other specialized journals he reported on his many experimental investigations, chief among which was his work on phytochemistry. He discovered corydaline in the bulbs of *Corydalis tuberosa*, carotene in carrots, and solanine in potato sprouts. His name is commemorated by "Wackenroder's solution," a solution of polythionic acids formed when diluted sulfurous acid is treated with hydrogen sulfide.

*BIBLIOGRAPHY*

I. ORIGINAL WORKS. Wackenroder's books include *Chemische Tabellen zur Analyse der unorganischen Verbindungen* (Jena, 1829; 5th ed., 1843); *Anleitung zur qualitativen chemischen Analyse* (Jena, 1836); *Ausführliche Charakteristik der stickstofffreien organischen Säuren nebst Anleitung zur qualitativen chemischen Analyse* (Jena, 1841); and *Chemische Classification der einfachen und zusammengesetzten Körper* (Jena, 1851). For his journal articles, see Royal Society *Catalogue of Scientific Papers*, VI, 219–221; VIII, 1177; and XII, 763–765.

II. SECONDARY LITERATURE. On Wackenroder and his work, see *Allgemeine Deutsche Biographie*, XL, 443–444; Kurt Brauer, "Goethe und die Chemie," in *Zeitschrift für angewandte Chemie*, 37 (1924), 185–189; Fritz Chemnitius, *Die Chemie in Jena von Rolfinck bis Knorr* (Jena, 1929) 32–33; Fritz Ferchl, ed., *Chemisch-Pharmazeutisches Bio- und Bibliographikon* (Mittenwald, 1938), 561–562; H. Ludwig and E. Reichardt, "Biographisches Denkmal für Heinrich Wilhelm Ferdinand Wackenroder," in *Archiv der Pharmazie*, 135 (1856), 101–111; Poggendorff, II, 1237; Eduard Reichardt, "Bericht über die Jubelfeier des Geheimen Hofraths und Professors Dr. H. Wackenroder. . .," in *Archiv der Pharmazie*, 126 (1853), 321–341; Wolfgang Schneider, "Wackenroders Jubiläum," in *Die pharmazeutische Industrie*, 15 (1953), 403–405; and Otto Zekert, *Berühmte Apotheker* (Stuttgart, 1955), 151.

GRETE RONGE

**IBN WĀFID, ABŪ AL-MUṬARRIF ʿABD AL-RAHMAN**, also known as **Abenguefit, Abenguéfith, Albenguéfith, Abel Nufit** (*fl.* Toledo, Spain, *ca.* 1008–1075), *pharmacology.*

Ibn Wāfid studied the works of Aristotle, Dioscorides, and Galen. At the demand of the king of Toledo, Al-Ma'mūn, he planted a botanical garden in the king's orchard, which extended between the Galiana and Tajo palaces in front of the bridge of Alcántara. Ibn Luengo, a disciple of Ibn Wāfid, and possibly Ibn Baṣṣal studied in the king's garden.

For twenty years Ibn Wāfid worked on the *Kitāb al-adwiya al-mufrada* ("Book of the Simple Medicines"), a synthesis, with some new data, of Dioscorides and Galen. The structure of the book confirms what Ibn Ṣāʿid (Ibn Wāfid's friend and bibliographer) had stated, that is, that Ibn Wāfid did not like to prescribe compound medicines, but simple ones; and, if possible, he abstained from prescribing the latter and tried to cure his patients by following a dietary treatment.

Ibn Wāfid's *Kitāb al-rashshād fī al-ṭibb* ("Guide to Medicine") is a pharmacopoeia and manual of therapeutics. On account of an incorrect reading of the title by Casiri, who confused the letter *rāʾ* for *wāw* thereby reading *wisād*, the title was translated as "Book of the Pillow."

Ibn Wāfid's other works are the following: *Mudjarrabāt fī al-ṭibb* ("Medical Experiences"); *Tadqīq al-naẓar fī ʿilal ḥāssat al-baṣar* ("Observations on the Treatment of Eye Illnesses"), which might be the one preserved in the anonymous manuscript 876 at El Escorial; *Kitāb al-mugīth* ("Book of Assistance"), the title of which alludes to the drug *mugīth*, valuable for the treatment of many diseases; and *Madjmūʿal-filāḥa* ("A Compendium of Agriculture"), which is in a medieval Castilian translation and fragment.

J. M. Millás Vallicrosa found various Arabic manuscripts, in which Ibn Wāfid avoids discussing the pharmacologic properties of plants, and insists on his proper method of tillage. This book was made good use of by Gabriel Alonso de Herrera in his *Agricultura General* (Madrid, 1513; repr., 1819). Ibn Wāfid also wrote a treatise on balneology preserved in a Latin version as *De balneis* (Venice, 1553).

*BIBLIOGRAPHY*

On Ibn Wāfid and his work, see J. M. Millás Vallicrosa, "La traducción castellana del 'Tratado de Agricultura' de ibn Wāfid," in *Al-Andalus*, **8** (1943), 281–332; and G. Sarton, *Introduction to the History of Science*, I (Baltimore, 1927), 728.

J. VERNET

**WAGNER, RUDOLPH** (*b*. Bayreuth, Germany, 30 July 1805; *d*. Göttingen, Germany, 13 May 1864), *comparative anatomy, physiology, anthropology.*

Wagner was the son of Lorenz Heinrich Wagner, a Bavarian court councillor and Gymnasium director. He studied at the Gymnasiums in Bayreuth and Augsburg before beginning his medical education at the University of Erlangen in 1822. Two years later he transferred to the University of Würzburg, from which he graduated M.D. in 1826. His interest in the natural sciences then led him to spend eight months studying with Cuvier in Paris, where he received an excellent grounding in comparative anatomy. Returning to Germany, Wagner became a prosector in anatomy at Erlangen; he was made *Privatdozent* in 1829, and professor of comparative anatomy and zoology in 1832. In 1840 he accepted an appointment at Göttingen, where he succeeded J. F. Blumenbach as professor of physiology, comparative anatomy, and general natural history; he also served as curator of Blumenbach's craniological collection and lectured on anthropology.

Wagner conducted research in a number of areas. His most important work concerned mammalian ova and sperm. Purkyně had already, in 1825, discovered the nucleus in the avian egg, while K. E. von Baer had discovered the mammalian ovum (1827), and J. V. Coste had identified its nucleus (1833). It remained for Wagner to discover (1835) an important formation in the ovum of several species of mammals, which he called the *macula germinativa*—later known as the nucleolus. With Dujardin, Wagner was one of the first to use the achromatic microscope to examine sperm; in 1837 he published highly accurate illustrations of spermatozoa, showing the structures that he had actually seen, which he called "seminal threads." His accomplishment was the more noteworthy in that at the same time a number of other biologists believed that spermatozoa were parasitic animals, and even attempted to identify a visceral system in them.

In a series of other microscopical researches, Wagner demonstrated, in 1833, that red blood corpuscles have no nuclei. He made significant contributions to the study of the retina and the choroidea of the eye (1835) and of the electric organ of the torpedo fish (1847), as well as sharing in George Meissner's discovery of the tactile corpuscles of the skin (1852). In 1853 and 1854, Wagner also conducted investigations of the nervous system, by which he was able to show the relation between the peripheral nerve fibers and the ganglion cells of the brain.

Wagner's most important physiological work was his edition of the five-volume *Handwörterbuch der Physiologie mit Rücksicht auf physiologische Pathologie*, published between 1842 and 1853. He intended this work to be a compendium of all the physiological knowledge of the day; it consists of sixty-three extensive review articles by thirty authors, including Lotze, Berzelius, E. H. Weber, Purkyně, Carl Ludwig, Valentin, A. W. Volkmann, and Bidder. Wagner himself contributed a single article on the microscopic structure of the nervous system and an addendum to R. Leuckart's article on reproduction.

In his physiological work, Wagner emphasized the value of microscopic observation. As a leading representative of the histophysiological trend, he considered the microscope to be an essential means of elucidating physiological function, and tended to be somewhat critical of experimentation and pure mensuration. "What the scales are for the chemist, the telescope for the astronomer, so the microscope is for the physiologist," he wrote. His own work exemplifies his theory; his study of the structure of the electric organ of the torpedo fish was designed to explain the production of electric potential, while the discovery of the tactile corpuscles in the skin contributed to the knowledge of the mechanics of the stimulation of sensory nerve endings. A number of Wagner's students worked under similar principles; an investigation of the structure of nerve endings in muscle performed by his pupil W. F. Kühne, for example, led to clarification of the functional transmission of impulses in the motor nerve endings.

In his teaching, Wagner was a captivating lecturer, who emphasized practical instruction. He had an ability to stimulate and help young scientists, and a number of his collaborators, including R. Leuckart, Billroth, Meissner, and Julius Vogel, became prominent in a variety of specialties. He was also able to further his views through the foundation of the Göttingen Physiological Institute.

In addition to his work in anatomy and physiology, Wagner was strongly interested in philosophical problems concerning mind and body, science and society, and morality and materialism. These interests deepened after he suffered a severe pulmonary hemorrhage in 1845, and began to confine his work to the study of the nervous system and to anthropology. His philosophical views were first published in 1851; highly conservative, they proved a source of annoyance to younger scientists. In 1854 Wagner addressed a meeting of German scientists and physicians at Göttingen, and his speech initiated an unpleasant controversy about materialism, in which his chief opponent, Carl Vogt, published a witty and sarcastic critique of Wagner's views on the creation of man and the nature of his soul. The discussion soon thereafter degenerated into personal insult from both sides, and Wagner thereafter confined his attention to more strictly scientific matters.

*BIBLIOGRAPHY*

I. ORIGINAL WORKS. A chronological list of Wagner's writings, including their translations, is in E. Ehler's paper (see below), 484–488. They include *Zur vergleichenden Physiologie des Blutes. Untersuchungen über Blutkörperchen, Blutbildung und Blutbahn, nebst Bemerkungen über Blutbewegung, Ernährung und Absonderung* (Leipzig, 1832–1833) with *Nachträge* (Leipzig, 1838); *Lehrbuch der vergleichenden Anatomie* (Leipzig, 1834–1835); "Einige Bemerkungen und Fragen über das Keimbläschen," in Müller's *Archiv für Anatomie . . .*, **2** (1835), 373–384; *Prodromus historiae generationis hominis atque animalium* (Leipzig, 1836); "Fragmente zur Physiologie der Zeugung, vorzüglich zur mikroskopischen Analyse des Spermas," in *Abhandlungen der k. Bayerischen Akademie der Wissenschaften*, **2** (1837), 381–416; *Icones physiologicae. Tabulae physiologiam et geneseos historiam illustrantes*, 3 fascs. (Leipzig, 1839), also supp., *Bau und Endigungen der Nerven* (Leipzig, 1847); *Icones zootomicae* (Leipzig, 1841); *Lehrbuch der Physiologie für Vorlesungen und Selbstunterricht*, I. *Specielle Geschichte der Lebensprocesse* (Leipzig, 1839, 1843, 1845); *Elements of Physiology for the Use of Students, and With Special Reference to the Wants of Practitioners*, translated by Robert Willis (London, 1841); *Samuel Thomas von Soemmerings, Leben und Verkehr mit seinen Zeitgenossen*, 2 vols. (Leipzig, 1844); "Ueber den feineren Bau des elektrischen Organs im Zitterrochen," in *Abhandlungen der k. Gesellschaft der Wissenschaften zu Göttingen*, **3** (1848), 141–166; "Semen," in *Todd's Cyclopedia of Anatomy and Physiology*, 1V (London, 1848), written with R. Leuckart; *Neurologische Untersuchungen* (Göttingen, 1854); *Menschenschöpfung und Seelensubstanz* (Göttingen, 1854); *Über Wissen und Glauben mit beson-*

*derer Beziehung zur Zukunft der Seelen* (Göttingen, 1854); *Der Kampf um die Seele vom Standpunkt der Wissenschaft* (Göttingen, 1857); and *Bericht über die Zusammenkunft einiger Anthropologen im September 1861 in Göttingen . . .* (Leipzig, 1861), written with K. E. von Baer.

II. SECONDARY LITERATURE. "Nekrolog von Rudolph Wagner," by his eldest son, Adolph Wagner, was published in *Nachrichten von der k. Gesellschaft der Wissenschaften zu Göttingen* (1864), 375–399. An interesting critical biography is in E. Ehler, "Göttinger Zoologen," in *Festschrift zur Feier des hunderfünfzigjährigen Bestehens der Königlichen Gesellschaft der Wissenschaften zu Göttingen* (Berlin, 1901), 431–447. Wagner's conception of physiology is discussed in K. E. Rothschuh, *Physiologie. Der Wandel ihrer Konzepte, Probleme und Methoden vom 16. bis 19. Jahrhundert* (Freiburg–Munich, 1968), 260–261, 296–297. On the controversy over materialism, see E. Nordenskiöld, *The History of Biology* (New York, 1928), 450; and H. Degen, "Vor hundert Jahren. Die Naturforscher Versammlung in Göttingen und der Materialismusstreit," in *Naturwissenschaftliche Rundschau*, **7** (1954), 271–277. On anthropology, see Benno Ottow, "K. E. von Baer als Kraniologe und die Anthropologen-Versammlung 1861 in Göttingen," in *Sudhoffs Archiv . . .*, **50** (1966), 43–68.

VLADISLAV KRUTA

**WAGNER VON JAUREGG** (or **WAGNER-JAUREGG**), **JULIUS** (*b.* Wels, Austria, 7 March 1857; *d.* Vienna, Austria, 27 September 1940), *psychiatry*.

Wagner von Jauregg was the son of a civil servant. He entered the University of Vienna medical school in 1874 and, while still a student, worked under Salomon Stricker at the Institut für Allgemeine und Experimentelle Pathologie. After receiving the doctorate in 1880, he became an assistant in Stricker's laboratory, where he met Sigmund Freud, one year his junior. The two young men established a lifelong friendship strong enough to withstand not only the great differences in their personalities and temperaments, but also their later profound disagreements on a number of scientific questions.

Wagner von Jauregg came to psychiatry by chance when, after failing to obtain an assistantship at either of Vienna's teaching hospitals, he seized upon an opportunity to work under Max von Leidesdorf at the university psychiatric clinic in 1883. Although his decision had been a hasty one, he later observed that it had "harmed neither myself nor psychiatry." He quickly found his way in the new subject and by 1885 qualified as a teacher of neurology and, two years later, as a teacher of psychiatry.

During his years as Leidesdorf's assistant, Wagner von Jauregg established the two basic areas of his later research: the pathology of the thyroid gland, and the treatment of general paresis. In 1884 he had observed the remarkable behavior— including aggressive lunging, convulsions, and spasms—of cats that had been subjected to thyroidectomy. In 1889, upon succeeding Krafft-Ebing as professor of psychiatry at the University of Graz, Wagner von Jauregg undertook further studies of the function of the thyroid gland and stated his view that the phenomena of cretinism were caused by the impairment or failure of thyroid function. (These findings were later published in *Jahrbuch für Psychiatrie*, **12** [1894], 102–107, and **13** [1895], 17–36.) He also traveled throughout Styria studying goiter and assessing the effects of treatment by iodine tablets. By 1898 he had become convinced that the regular intake of small amounts of iodine was prophylactic against the disease, and proposed that iodized salt be sold in areas in which goiter was endemic—a measure that the Austrian government put into force in 1923, some years after Switzerland had taken similar measures.

Wagner von Jauregg's work in the treatment of general paresis began in 1887. He then noted that when psychiatric patients contracted infectious, febrile diseases, such as erysipelas or typhus, their mental state was substantially improved after the fever abated. He was consequently led to wonder if psychoses might be treated by inducing fever, and undertook a series of methodical sickbed observations. At this same early date he also speculated whether malarial infection might be used to treat general paresis, or creeping paralysis, as it was then known. In a series of experiments, he began infecting patients with tuberculosis, since Koch had, in 1890, made public his findings on tuberculin, and Wagner von Jauregg thought it too dangerous to induce malaria itself. He had some success, but achieved permanent remission in only a minority of patients.

In 1893 Wagner von Jauregg was called back to Vienna as full professor of psychiatry and director of the Psychiatric and Neurological Clinic. In this post he served as a member of the Austrian board of health, advising on all legislation concerning the mentally ill. It was during his tenure that modern laws, providing exemplary protection to the men-

tally incompetent, were formulated. At the same time, he carried on his own research on the febrile treatment of general paresis, utilizing staphylococci, streptococci, and typhus vaccines, but was unable to improve upon his results.

Despite the advances in the treatment of syphilis made in the early years of the twentieth century, the treatment of general paresis remained uncertain. Ehrlich's Salvarsan was not effective against the disease in its most advanced form, in which it attacked the central nervous system, and paretics still constituted, in the 1910's, some 15 percent of all patients in mental institutions. The life expectancy of such patients was, moreover, only three to four years. Wagner von Jauregg therefore decided to resume his experiments with the malarial treatment of paretics, especially since a number of studies had shown that malaria could be cured by the use of quinine. On 14 June 1917 he for the first time injected a paralytic patient with blood taken from a patient with tertian malaria; this and subsequent trials led to significant improvement of paretic patients and, in some instances, to complete remissions.

The method of fever-therapy was developed systematically from Wagner von Jauregg's findings, and applied from 1919 on. A number of hypotheses were put forward to explain its effectiveness, but Wagner von Jauregg himself believed that the injected malaria acted primarily by strengthening the defense of the organism against the *Spirochaeta pallida* that causes syphilis, thereby increasing its resistance to the poisonous substances produced. The malaria fever-therapy was widely used throughout the 1920's and 1930's, and in 1927 Wagner von Jauregg received the Nobel Prize for his part in its development. It was superseded in the mid-1940's with the introduction of antibiotics, particularly penicillin.

In addition to providing a remedy for a previously incurable disease, Wagner von Jauregg's work served as the basis for the acquisition of new knowledge about the biology of the malarial parasites. Through his experiments it was, for example, learned that *Plasmodium vivax*, the agent of benign tertian malaria, which normally produces the first attack of fever about fourteen days after infection, can have a latency period of as long as forty weeks should the infection occur in autumn, so that the first onset of fever then occurs the following spring or summer.

Wagner von Jauregg retired as director of the Vienna Psychiatric and Neurological Clinic in

1928. He left behind him a great school of psychiatry and neurology; it is characteristic of his generosity of mind that during his tenure the most widely divergent trends in modern psychiatry developed within it. He was tolerant of approaches to which he was not personally sympathetic (as, for example, Freudian psychoanalysis), and the richness and diversity of the psychiatric thinking that flourished in his school is reflected in the names of his students, including Konstantin von Economo, Hans Hoff, Johann Paul Karplus, Otto Kauders, Otto Pötzl, Emil Raimann, Paul Ferdinand Schilder, and Erwin Stransky.

## BIBLIOGRAPHY

I. ORIGINAL WORKS. Wagner von Jauregg's works include "Über die Einwirkung fieberhafter Erkrankungen auf Psychosen," in *Jahrbuch für Psychiatrie und Neurologie,* 7 (1887), 94–134; "Zur Reform des Irrenwesens," in *Wiener klinische Wochenschrift,* 14 (1901), 293–296, *passim; Beiträge zur Ätiologie und Pathologie des endemischen Kretinismus* (Vienna, 1910), with Friedrich Schlagenhaufer; *Myxödem und Kretinismus* (Vienna–Leipzig, 1912); "Über die Einwirkung der Malaria auf die progressive Paralyse," in *Psychiatrisch-neurologische Wochenschrift,* 20 (1918–1919), 132–134; *Fieber und Infektionstherapie* (Vienna–Leipzig, 1936); and *Lebenserinnerungen,* L. Schönbauer and M. Jantsch, eds. (Vienna, 1950).

II. SECONDARY LITERATURE. On Wagner von Jauregg and his work, see J. Gerstmann, *Die Malariabehandlung der progressiven Paralyse* (Vienna, 1925); H. Hoff, in *Wiener klinische Wochenschrift,* 62 (1950), 888–889; J. P. Karplus, "Experiment und Klinik," in *Wiener medizinische Wochenschrift,* 82 (1932), 373–375; O. Pötzl, in *Wiener klinische Wochenschrift,* 50 (1937), 277; L. Schönbauer and M. Jantsch, "Julius Wagner Ritter von Jauregg," in K. Kolle, ed., *Grosse Nervenärzte* (Stuttgart, 1956), 254–266, with partial bibliography and secondary literature; E. Stransky, in *Wiener medizinische Wochenschrift,* 77 (1927), 1515–1516; and W. Weygandt, in *Münchener medizinische Wochenschrift,* 74 (1927), 547–548.

ERNA LESKY

**WAHLENBERG, GÖRAN (Georg)** (*b.* Skarphyttan, Sweden, 1 October 1780; *d.* Uppsala, Sweden, 22 March 1851), *botany.*

Wahlenberg began his studies at Uppsala University at the age of twelve under the guidance of a tutor. He soon decided to study medicine and natural history; botany became his major interest, and under Thunberg he acquired a thorough knowledge of plants. In 1806 Wahlenberg received his medical degree, having defended a dissertation on the sites of medically active substances within the plant body. He advanced very slowly in his career, and his financial situation was correspondingly poor for many years. From 1801 he had several positions, all at very low salaries, at the natural history collections of the university; and in 1814 he was promoted to the poorly paid post of botanical demonstrator. By 1828, when Wahlenberg succeeded Thunberg as professor of botany, he had acquired an international reputation and had completed almost all of his botanical work; his interest now centered on homeopathic cures.

Of the greatest importance for Wahlenberg's scientific development were the many voyages he made during his younger years. In 1799 he traveled to Gotland, in the Baltic Sea, which has remarkable calcareous flora; and he visited Lapland in 1800, 1802, 1807, and 1810. Through these journeys he gained an extensive knowledge of Scandinavian plants and their geographical distribution. In 1811–1814 Wahlenberg traveled in Germany, Switzerland, Austria, and Hungary, comparing the flora of the Alps and the Carpathians with that of the mountains of northern Europe. While visiting Berlin in 1811 he became friends with the botanist C. L. Willdenow and the geologist Leopold von Buch.

Wahlenberg seems to have considered his steadfast defense of the Linnaean tradition in its most limited sense as his most important contribution to botany. His declared ambition was never to alter the limit of a Linnaean species or name and never to abandon the Linnaean sexual system in any detail—however trifling; and his judgment of those whom he considered heretics was severe. His main scientific works were floras, based on his travels, in which he expounded these principles: *Gotlands flora* (1805–1806), *Flora lapponica* (1812), *Flora Carpathorum principalium* (1814), *Flora upsaliensis* (1820), and *Flora suecica* (1824–1826; second edition, 1831–1834). He is better known today, however, for the introductions of these floras than for the works themselves. The introductions place him among the pioneers of plant geography, worthy of comparison with Humboldt.

Wahlenberg's interest in geography dates from early in his career, and his love of cartography is reflected in the beautiful maps included in his works, which he drew. His geographical writings include *Geografisk och ekonomisk beskrifning om Kemi lappmark* (1804), *Berättelse om lappska fjällens höjd och temperatur* (1808; also in German,

1812), *Rön om springkällors temperatur* (1811), and *De vegetatione et climate in Helvetia septentrionali* (1813). Together with his botanical works they constitute his considerable contribution to phytogeography.

A keen observer of the distribution of plants, Wahlenberg made a definitive analysis of the stratification of vegetation on mountains with summits above the snow line and with treeless strata above regions dominated successively by different species of trees. His knowledge of the Alps, Carpathians, and mountains of Lapland enabled him to make comparisons that emphasized both the similarities and the differences in stratification. In Scandinavia, especially in Sweden, Wahlenberg also distinguished the main regions of the lower parts of the country, both those in the north-south succession and those oriented to the east or west according to their distance from or nearness to the coast.

In discussing the causes and circumstances of the differentiation of vegetation, Wahlenberg considered the most important factors to be the influence of climate (temperature and precipitation) and its dependence on latitude, altitude, and nearness to the sea; thus he was aware of oceanic as well as continental floreal elements. According to Wahlenberg the distribution of temperature during the seasons—not the mean annual temperature—was what determined the vegetation of a region. He also indicated the importance of soil temperature, which he measured in springs that did not freeze in winter, together with its difference from the temperature of the air—a difference varying, for instance, in relation to altitude.

Wahlenberg's awareness of the influence of climate on vegetation did not preclude his ascribing great importance to the soil. He also considered the complicated relationship between climate and soil, noting, for instance, that certain calcareous plants of the Carpathians could be found in noncalcareous soil of the Alps and Lapland.

Wahlenberg was also conscious of the time factor in phytogeography and maintained that the present distribution of plants is due to migrations occurring at various times and originating from different sites. Many areas were once submerged and consequently were invaded by their present vegetation only after emerging from the water. The distribution in other countries of Swedish plants indicated to Wahlenberg their migration either from the south, over the Danish islands, or from the vast forests of Finland and Siberia to the northeast. It is difficult to assess Wahlenberg's true impor-

tance. His views on plant history were obviously influenced by Willdenow, who in his *Grundriss der Kräuterkunde* had stressed mountain regions (considered as former islands on an otherwise submerged earth) as centers of distribution of the plants found in lower regions. Priority for the idea of the influence of climate and geology on vegetation must be shared by Wahlenberg, Humboldt, and Buch. Their ideas, soon disseminated among younger phytogeographers, came to be considered so self-evident that few cared who had introduced them.

Wahlenberg had great difficulty in collaborating with other botanists. Considered odd and egocentric, he went his solitary way, isolated during his last twenty years from botany as well as from others. He never married. No student was allowed to enter the botanical garden, and in winter he forbade skating on the pond. Iron from the skates, he believed, would remain in the water when the pond thawed. His grazing cows would then ingest the iron with their water and thus, according to his homeopathic convictions, render the milk dangerous to drink.

*BIBLIOGRAPHY*

I. ORIGINAL WORKS. There is a complete list of Wahlenberg's botanical works in T. O. B. N. Krok, *Bibliotheca botanica suecana* (Uppsala–Stockholm, 1925), 741–745. An MS on phytogeography is in S. Borgman, "Göran Wahlenbergs handskrift 'Svensk växtgeografi,' " in *Svensk botanisk tidskrift*, **49** (1955), 337–347. Many letters and MSS are at the library of the University of Uppsala.

II. SECONDARY LITERATURE. There is a biography by E. Wikström in *Kungliga Svenska vetenskapsakademiens handlingar* (1851), 431–505, with bibliography. See also H. Krook, "Den siste linneanen," in his *Angår oss Linné?* (Stockholm, 1971), 104–115; and "Den unge Göran Wahlenberg," in *Nationen och hembygden*, **8** (1960), 188–211. Further works are A. Engler, "Die Entwickelung der Pflanzengeographie in den letzten hundert Jahren und weitere Aufgaben derselben," in *Wissenschaftliche Beiträge zum Gedächtniss der hundertjährigen Wiederkehr des Antritts von Alexander von Humboldt's Reise nach Amerika* (Berlin, 1899), 9–10, 164; and S. Lindroth, in *Kungliga Svenska Vetenskapsakademiens historia*, II (Stockholm, 1967), 424–429.

GUNNAR ERIKSSON

**IBN WAHSHIYYA, ABŪ BAKR AHMAD IBN ᶜSALĪ IBN ĀL-MUKHTĀR** (*b.* Qussīn, near Janbalā, Iraq, *ca.* 860; *d.* Baghdad, *ca.* 935), *agronomy*, *botany, alchemy, astrology, mysticism, medicine, toxicology, sorcery.*

Little is known about Ibn Waḥshiyya's life except that he was descended from the Nabataeans, the ancient inhabitants of Iraq (known in Arabic as the Nabaṭī). He was skilled and eloquent in their language, one of the West Aramaic group, and very proud of their culture and intellectual contributions. In view of their accomplishments in agriculture, commerce, arts, and applied sciences, Ibn Waḥshiyya said, the Nabataeans for centuries enjoyed a high degree of prestige.

He also practiced astrology in Baghdad during the period when it was a great cosmopolitan city that was a center of both intellectual and economic activity. He used talismans, charms, and incantations to tell fortunes and to heal the sick, and he wrote several books in this field.

Ibn Waḥshiyya was a contemporary of al-Rāzī, who, like him, upheld the art of the alchemist. They make no mention of each other in their writings, however. This is understandable because al-Rāzī was of a different class and a much more skillful physician, alchemist, and philosopher. As is evident from the titles of his books, Ibn Waḥshiyya's alchemical writings were full of sorcery, magic, symbolism, and talismans; while al-Rāzī's books, such as *Sirr al-asrār* and *al-Asrār*, were objective and free from magic and jugglery. Some doubt on Ibn Waḥshiyya's veracity and integrity is cast by his practice of legerdemain, expulsion of devils, and humbug—in addition to his exaggerated statements about the accomplishments of his forebears, the nicknames he included in his family tree (ibn Galatia, ibn Britania, and so on), and his contempt for other civilizations, even the Islamic. Ibn al-Nadīm listed his biobibliography under the section devoted to sorcerers who practiced "bad methods."

Ibn Waḥshiyya's best-known works are *al-Filāḥa al-nabaṭiyya*, on agriculture (allegedly claimed to be a translation from ancient Nabataean writings), and *al-Sumūm wa'l-tiryāqāt*, on poisons and their antidotes. The *Filāḥa* supposedly was completed in 904; but it was not dictated or copied until 930 by a student and associate, Aḥmad ibn al-Ḥusayn ibn ʿAlī ibn Aḥmad ibn Muḥammad ibn ʿAbd al-Malik al-Zayyāt (*d. ca.* 978), who also disseminated it. It is not clear whether al-Zayyāt contributed to the final copy of the *Filāḥa* as well as to *al-Sumūm*.

Both works supposedly were translations from ancient Aramaic texts, the author of which seems to have known similar, earlier writings in Sanskrit, Greek, and Persian. These two works contained significant ideas on agricultural practice and toxicology, and influenced later works on these topics in medieval Islam. The reference by Thomas Aquinas to the works of Ibn Waḥshiyya suggests that one or more of his writings, translated into Latin in the late twelfth or early thirteenth century, were influential in the West as well.

## BIBLIOGRAPHY

I. ORIGINAL WORKS. Ibn Waḥshiyya's two best-known works, *al-Filāḥa* and *al-Sumūm*, exist in several MSS, some incomplete; at the national libraries in Algiers, Berlin, Cairo, and Paris, the Süleymaniye Library at Istanbul, the Bodleian Library at Oxford, and the British Museum library. Ernest Renan, in *An Essay on the Age and Antiquity of the Book of Nabathaean Agriculture* (London, 1862), explained that Thomas Aquinas referred to Ibn Waḥshiyya's work in a Latin trans. (possibly *al-Filāḥa*), of which abstracted copies were known in Arabic.

His other important work, *al-Sumūm wa'l-tiryāqāt*, was translated into English with useful introduction and indexes by Martin Levey as "Medieval Arabic Toxicology, the Book on Poisons of Ibn Waḥshiyya and Its Relation to Early Indian and Greek Texts," which is *Transactions of the American Philosophical Society*, **56**, pt. 7 (Nov. 1966). I personally examined MSS of the *Sumūm* in Br. Museum, Add. 23, 604—see Charles Rieu, *Catalogus codicum manuscriptorum Orientalium qui in Museo Britannico asservantur*, II, *codices arabicos amplectens*, II (London, 1871), 461–462, 630–631—and in Zahiriyah Library, Damascus, gen. no. 9575, containing chs. 2–17.

The first to list Ibn Waḥshiyya's works was Ibn al-Nadīm of Baghdad, in his *Fihrist*, completed in 987 (Cairo, 1929), 447, 518–519. He mentioned some nine books on sorcery, talismans, and idol worship, most of which are lost (one is preserved in the Bodleian Library). Ibn Waḥshiyya's treatise *al-Asmā*', or *al-Shawq al-mustahām fī ma'rifat rumūz al-aqlām*, was edited by J. Hammer as *Ancient Alphabets and Hieroglyphic Characters Explained* (London, 1806) and reprinted by Sylvestre de Sacy in Millins *et al.*, eds., *Magasin Encyclopédique*, XVI (1810), 145–175. Most of Ibn Waḥshiyya's approximately five books on alchemy and symbolism are extant in rare MSS and await evaluation.

His book on mysteries of planets and the firmament, attributed to Tankalūshā the Chaldean (Babylonian), is described in D. Chwolson, "Über die Überreste der altbabylonischen Literatur," in *Mémoires de l'Académie impériale des sciences de St.-Pétersbourg*, 6th ser., **8** (1859), 329–524; and Carlo Nallino, *Arabian Astronomy, Its History During the Medieval Times* (Rome,

1911), 198–210. The "Nabataean Agriculture" is discussed in A. von Gutschmid, "Die nabatäische Landwirtschaft und ihre Geschwister," in *Zeitschrift der Deutschen morgenländischen Gesellschaft*, **15** (1861), 82–89, and his *Kleine Schriften*, II (Leipzig, 1890), 677–678, 686–688. Three other works by Ibn Waḥshiyya on medical therapy, natural history, and theology are mentioned; but no extant MSS are known.

II. SECONDARY LITERATURE. Ibn Abī Uṣaybiʿa alludes to Ibn Waḥshiyya's works on sorcery, specifically the *al-Adwār*, and on alchemy, in his *ʿUyūn al-Anbāʾ*, Būlāq ed., II (Cairo, 1882), 181, 203–204. Much later Ḥājjī Khalīfa, in his *Kashf al-ẓunūn*, II (Cairo, 1893), 101, 203, referred to Ibn Waḥshiyya's work on agriculture and on sorcery. Interest was renewed in Ibn Waḥshiyya's writings in the nineteenth century. See Lucien Leclerc, *Histoire de la médecine arabe*, I (Paris, 1876), 307–315; Ernst Meyer, *Geschichte der Botanik*, III (Königsberg, 1856), 43–88; and T. Nöldeke, "Noch Einiges über die nabatäische Landwirthschaft," in *Zeitschrift der Deutschen morgenländischen Gesellschaft*," **30** (1875), 445–455.

Later biobibliographies besides Levey's "Medieval Arabic Toxicology" (see above) are Carl Brockelmann, *Geschichte der arabischen Litteratur*, I (Leiden, 1943), 279–281, and *Supplement*, I, 430–431; and George Sarton, *Introduction to the History of Science*, I (Baltimore, 1927), 634–635.

On mathematics see L. C. Karpinski, "Hindu Numerals Among the Arabs," in *Bibliotheca mathematica*, n.s. **13** (1913), 97–98; and on his alleged translation of the "Nabataean Agriculture," see E. Wiedemann, "Zur nabatäischen Landwirtschaft," in *Zeitschrift für Semitistik*, **1** (1922), 201–202; and *Encyclopaedia of Islam*, II (Leiden, 1931), 427. Regarding his influence on medical botany and pharmacy see Sami Hamarneh, *Catalogue of Arabic Manuscripts on Medicine and Pharmacy at the British Library* (Cairo, 1975), 60–64.

SAMI K. HAMARNEH

**WALCH, JOHANN ERNST IMMANUEL** (*b.* Jena, Germany, 29 August 1725; *d.* Jena, 1 December 1778), *theology, philology, paleontology*.

Walch was the son of Johann Gottlob Walch, professor of theology at Jena, and Charlotte Katharina Buddeus. He received private instruction at home until the age of seventeen, when he entered the University of Jena to study theology and philology. He received his master's degree in 1745 and began lecturing on theology the following year. During 1747 and 1748 he traveled throughout Europe and met scholars from many universities. In 1750 he became assistant professor and in 1755 full professor of logic and metaphysics. Appointed professor of oratory and poetry in 1759, he was twice rector and eight times dean of the university, becoming privy councillor in Weimar in 1770. He declined appointments offered by several other universities.

Walch has been described as a friend of everything beautiful and good, a lecturer who aroused the enthusiasm of his large audiences, and a scholar who spent his life in the service of noble endeavor and scientific work. He was a member of many German and foreign scientific societies. Most of his scholarly publications concern the classical languages; and his work in this field has frequently been valuable in New Testament exegesis, his *Introductio in linguam graecam* being of especial importance. As crucial as these studies were for the advance of philology, however, they are rarely consulted nowadays.

The situation is different with regard to Walch's paleontological works, which are of continuing value. How little progress the subject had made toward specialization at that time is confirmed by the disparate subjects that he was able to examine simultaneously. In his travels Walch had visited natural history collections and had begun to assemble one himself, composed primarily of rocks and fossils, for which he outlined an exact system that he published in 1761–1764. During this period a copperplate engraver in Nuremberg, Georg Wolfgang Knorr (1705–1761), had become famous for his magnificent illustrations, including some in the natural sciences, and had contributed to science even though he was not a scientist. Before his death he had published, with an unscientific text, the first part of a work on fossils. On behalf of Knorr's heirs and using the plates Knorr had prepared, Walch continued its publication under its original title and later with the title *Die Naturgeschichte der Versteinerungen* (1762–1773; the index [1774] is by Johann Samuel Schröter).

In this work Walch presented the first comprehensive paleontology ordered according to the zoological system; it is still occasionally consulted. For him the fossils were not—as had previously been assumed—evidence of the Flood but, rather, of the displacements of the seas. Moreover, in addition to a basic systematics of all the forms known to him, Walch provided a general paleontology (deposition, sedimentary facies, facies distribution), and a history of paleontology that is still worth reading. His recognition that fossils are members of a sequence linked by historical descent was a fundamental perception. Walch made the previously muddled study of fossils into a science.

In the journal *Naturforscher*, which he founded and which continued publication until 1804, Walch rounded out his chief work with many studies of particular problems and findings.

*BIBLIOGRAPHY*

I. ORIGINAL WORKS. Walch's major publications are *Commentationes quibus antiquorum christianorum doctorum de jureiurando sententiae percensentur et deiudicantur* (Jena, 1744); *De vinculis Paulli apostoli* (1746); *Einleitung in die Harmonie der Evangelisten* (1749); *Marmor Hispaniae antiquum* (Jena, 1750); *Antiquitates Herculanenses litterariae* (Jena, 1750); *Dissertationes in Acta Apostolorum* (1756; 2nd ed., 1759; 3rd ed., 1761); *De arte critica veterum Romanorum* (Jena, 1757); *Die Naturgeschichte der Versteinerungen zur Erläuterung der Knorrischen Sammlung von Merkwürdigkeiten der Natur*, 3 vols. (Nuremberg, 1762–1774); *Das Steinreich systematisch entworfen*, 3 vols. (Halle, 1762–1764); *Introductio in linguam graecam* (1763; 2nd ed., 1772); "Neue lithologische Entdeckungen," in Schröters *Journal für die Liebhaber des Steinreichs . . .*, **1**, no. 2 (1773), 310–320; and "Von dem Schwerdt- oder Sägefisch des Herrn Bürgermeister Bauder in Altdorf," *ibid.*, **2** (1775), 376–378.

II. SECONDARY LITERATURE. Biographical material is in von Dobschütz, "Johann Ernst Immanuel Walch," in *Allgemeine deutsche Biographie*, XL (Leipzig, 1896), 652–655. His importance as a paleontologist is treated in B. von Freyberg, *Die geologische Erforschung Thüringens in älterer Zeit* (Berlin, 1932); and "Johann Friedrich Bauder (1713–1791) und seine Bedeutung für die Versteinerungskunde in Franken," in *Geologische Blätter für Nordost-Bayern . . .*, **8** (1958), 76–106; and K. A. von Zittel, *Geschichte der Geologie und Paläontologie* (Munich–Leipzig, 1899).

B. VON FREYBERG

**WALCOTT, CHARLES DOOLITTLE** (*b.* New York Mills, New York, 31 March 1850; *d.* Washington, D.C., 9 February 1927), *paleontology.*

Walcott contributed significantly to knowledge of Cambrian faunas and rocks, and was an exceptionally able administrator of science for the federal government. The leader during his time in studies of Cambrian rocks and fossils, he began his scientific career, without benefit of college training, when he moved near Trenton Falls, New York. There he found one of the first occurrences of trilobites with appendages preserved. His work (1875–1881) on trilobites, amplified forty years later, contributed substantially to establishing the zoological importance and position of this group.

After a year's work under James Hall in Albany, New York, Walcott joined the newly formed U.S. Geological Survey in 1879. Although it was here that he made his reputation with studies of the Cambrian, he engaged in other stratigraphic studies as well. His *Paleontology of the Eureka District* (Nevada) (1884) was a standard reference for western fossils.

During the mid-1880's Walcott became involved in the "Taconic" question, concerning the age of rocks at the eastern boundary of New York state. By finding new fossil localities and reinterpreting earlier data, he resolved some problems controversial for half a century. Shortly afterward, he was able to establish that Cambrian rocks at St. John, New Brunswick, had been affected by structural complications. This interpretation brought Cambrian fossil zones of North America into harmony with those established earlier in Europe.

During the 1890's Walcott's fieldwork took him throughout the country, but this period is best marked by a major work on fossil jellyfish (1898). During this and the subsequent decade he completed a number of papers on Cambrian Brachiopoda. This work culminated in the two-volume *Cambrian Brachiopoda* (1912), a worldwide study that considered their biology as well as their stratigraphic position.

Starting in 1907, Walcott extended his fieldwork to the high mountains of Alberta and British Columbia, a rugged area he visited almost annually for the next two decades. His contributions to Cambrian geology and paleontology from this area fill five volumes of *Smithsonian Miscellaneous Collections*. The most significant event was the discovery in 1909 of the Middle Cambrian Burgess shale deposit. Three years of hard work quarrying these rocks resulted in a spectacular collection of numerous soft-bodied organisms of the sort that are almost never preserved as fossils. This has been described by some authorities as the single most important find of fossils, and its discovery and study would certainly have brought him worldwide fame even if it had been the only work in Walcott's career. His work was so voluminous, however, that at the time of his death he had described about one-third of all Cambrian fossils then known; he was probably the second or third most prolific student of American paleontology.

Besides his scientific career, Walcott had a remarkable record as an administrator. He rose through the ranks of the U.S. Geological Survey and in 1894 succeeded John Wesley Powell, becoming the third director of the Survey. From 1902 to 1907 he headed both the Survey and the U.S. Reclamation Service, and for eighteen months (1897–1898) he served as acting assistant secretary of the Smithsonian Institution.

Following the death of S. P. Langley, Walcott was appointed secretary of the Smithsonian Institution in 1907 and resigned as director of the Geological Survey. During the early years of his secretaryship the Museum of Natural History opened; and in the later years he was able to convince C. L. Freer to allow construction of the gallery to house his art collection. This change of plans—Freer had wished to wait until after his death—was in large measure an indication of his confidence in Walcott.

In 1915 Walcott founded the National Advisory Committee for Aeronautics. He was also one of a small group who approached Andrew Carnegie to request support for basic research. This effort eventually led to the founding of the Carnegie Institution of Washington, with Walcott as one of the original incorporators.

F. G. Cottrell had offered his patents to the Smithsonian in 1911. Although they could not legally be accepted, Walcott and Cottrell conceived the idea of a foundation to supply the Smithsonian and other organizations with funds for scientific research, an idea that was developed into the Research Corporation. He also was active in the organization of the National Park Service.

Walcott was president of the National Academy of Sciences from 1917 to 1923 and was a founder of the National Research Council. His scientific accomplishments brought him the presidencies of, and medals from, several societies and a dozen honorary degrees from universities.

*BIBLIOGRAPHY*

A complete bibliography of Walcott's works may be found in Ellis L. Yochelson, "Charles Doolittle Walcott, 1850–1927," in *Biographical Memoirs. National Academy of Sciences,* **39** (1967), 516–540.

ELLIS L. YOCHELSON

**WALD, ABRAHAM** (*b.* Cluj, Rumania, 31 October 1902; *d.* India, 13 December 1950), *mathematical statistics, mathematical economics, geometry.*

Wald was born into a family which had considerable intellectual interests but had to earn its livelihood in petty trade because of anti-Jewish restrictions. These restrictions made his education

at the University of Cluj, and later at the University of Vienna, very difficult. After Hitler occupied Austria in 1938, Wald moved to the United States, which saved him from death in a German concentration camp—the fate of all but one other member of his numerous family. He later married Lucille Lang, an American, who died with him in an airplane crash.

At Vienna, Wald was a student and a protégé, and later a friend, of Karl Menger. His work in pure mathematics was largely, although not wholly, in geometry. Menger later directed Wald toward mathematical statistics and mathematical economics, so that he was able to find employment with the distinguished economist Oskar Morgenstern.

It seems reasonable to say that Wald's most important work was in statistics, both because of his relative importance in the field and because of the current assessment of the field's importance. One of his great contributions to statistics was to bring to it mathematical precision in the formulation of problems and mathematical rigor in argument. These qualities, which were often lacking when he began his statistical career in 1938, have transformed the subject—although not necessarily to the satisfaction of everyone. It should be emphasized, however, that these accomplishments were a by-product and consequence of his extraordinary ability and the breadth of his statistical interests. Wald wrote lucidly and unambiguously on many statistical subjects, and there is scarcely a branch of modern statistics to which he did not contribute. His writings and lectures were so lucid and so unambiguous because of this precision, and he achieved so much in the way of results, that the superiority of mathematical precision became apparent to all. It is impossible to discuss Wald's statistical results in detail; rather, we shall single out the two most important fields of his work, which he founded and in which his results still dominate: sequential analysis and the theory of decision functions.

In sequential analysis one takes observations seriatim until the evidence is sufficiently strong, bearing in mind certain previously imposed bounds on the probabilities of error. When there are only two possible hypotheses, the "Wald sequential probability ratio test" has the property that it requires the smallest average number of observations under either hypothesis. This famous "optimum property of the sequential probability ratio test" was brilliantly conjectured by Wald in 1943 and proved jointly by him and a colleague in 1948. Wald proved many theorems on the distribution of the required number of observations and obtained many approximations on probabilities of error and average required numbers of observations, that are still used in applications. Most, although not all, of his results were summed up in *Sequential Analysis* (1947). With minor exceptions, the entire contents of this book were obtained by him. Such a phenomenon is rare in mathematical books and indicates the extent to which he founded and dominated the field of sequential analysis.

When Wald began his work in statistics, a large part of the field was concerned with the theory of testing hypotheses. He regarded this theory as, at best (when properly interpreted), one of deciding between exactly two courses of action. Consequently very many statistical problems actually fall outside the scope of this theory. There was no consistent theory for deciding among more than two courses of action, and attempts to force such problems into the framework of the theory of testing hypotheses had yielded very unsatisfactory results. It is interesting that these objections were clearly realized by a theoretician like Wald and not by the practical statisticians in industrial and agricultural laboratories who applied the theory. (For a recent criticism of the theory see Wolfowitz, "Remarks on the Theory of Testing Hypotheses.") Wald's theory of statistical decision functions considers the problem of deciding among any number of (possibly infinitely many) courses of action, both sequentially and nonsequentially. The statistician introduces a loss function that measures the consequences of various actions under different situations. With each statistical procedure (decision function) there is associated a vector, or function, of average loss under the various possible situations (the risk function). The statistical procedures of which the risk functions are not inferior to those of any other form a "complete" class, and the statistician can properly ignore the procedures not in the complete class.

At Wald's death the theory of statistical decision functions was far from the point of application to everyday, practical statistical problems; and little progress has been made in this direction since then. The theory is still of great conceptual and theoretical importance, and provides a logical basis for the formulation of many research problems. Recent research in the theory itself has, however, been chiefly in the direction of very technical mathematical refinements and has not achieved any essential breakthroughs.

Some of Wald's work in statistics originated in economic problems and properly belongs to both subjects. One such example is his work on the identification of economic relations—roughly speaking, the problem whether the distributions, which result from a model of the observed chance variables, uniquely determine all or certain specified parameters of the model. Also included in this category is his work on stochastic difference equations—models involving sequences of chance variables connected by difference equations with "error" chance variables. Wald also proved theorems on the existence of unique solutions for systems of equations for several types of economic systems and studied cost-of-living index numbers, the empirical determination of indifference surfaces, and the elimination of seasonal variation in time series. In all these his methods were ingenious and his contributions very important.

In pure mathematics, Wald's first three published papers and "Zur Axiomatik des Zwischenbegriffes" dealt with the characterization of "betweenness" in metric spaces. He also extended Steinitz's theorem to vectors with infinitely many elements; the theorem states that a divergent series, the elements of which are finite vectors, can, by a permutation of its terms, be made to converge to any element of a linear manifold. Perhaps his best result was the development of a differential geometry that starts from the assumption of a convex, compact metric space that at every point admits what should be called a Wald curvature. From this he was able to derive properties of differential geometry that are postulated in other systems.

Relatively uninterested in mathematical elegance, Wald spent little time in polishing a paper after a problem was solved to his satisfaction. In his masterly hands simple methods sometimes yielded the most amazing results. Although he was readily accessible, he had very few students. With one of these, J. Wolfowitz, who became his friend and colleague, he wrote fifteen joint papers. His American, and largely statistical, period was relatively brief (1938–1950) and extraordinarily productive. During this time he learned mathematical statistics, contributed deeply to it, changed it essentially, and dominated the subject. It has borne his impress since, and the paths he opened are still being pursued.

## BIBLIOGRAPHY

I. ORIGINAL WORKS. A comprehensive bibliography of Wald's writings follows Tintner's memoir (see below). His works include "Zur Axiomatik des Zwischenbegriffes," in *Ergebnisse eines mathematischen Kollo-quiums*, **4** (1933), 23–24; *Sequential Analysis* (New York–London, 1947); and "Optimum Character of the Sequential Probability Ratio Test," in *Annals of Mathematical Statistics*, **19** (1948), 326–339, written with J. Wolfowitz.

II. SECONDARY LITERATURE. On Wald and his work, see J. Wolfowitz, "Abraham Wald, 1902–1950," in *Annals of Mathematical Statistics*, **23** (1952), 1–13; Karl Menger, "The Formative Years of Abraham Wald and His Work in Geometry," *ibid.*, 14–20; G. Tintner, "Abraham Wald's Contributions to Econometrics," *ibid.*, 21–28; and "The Publications of Abraham Wald," *ibid.*, 29–33, which lists 103 works (1931–1952).

See also J. Wolfowitz, "Remarks on the Theory of Testing Hypotheses," in *New York Statistician*, **18**, no. 7 (Mar. 1967), 1–3.

J. WOLFOWITZ

**WALD, FRANTIŠEK** (*b.* Brandýsek, near Slaný, Czechoslovakia, 9 January 1861; *d.* Vítkovice [now part of Ostrava], Czechoslovakia, 19 October 1930), *chemistry*.

Wald's father came from Chemnitz (now Karl-Marx-Stadt, D.D.R.) and became foreman in the workshops of the Austrian State Railways at Slaný. His mother was a native German from the Karlovy Vary (Karlsbad) district. Although of German origin, Wald adopted Czech nationality. He attended a Czech municipal school at Kladno, a center of the iron industry, to which his parents moved after the Austro-Prussian War (1866). The thorough grounding in elementary mathematics that he received prepared him well for his essentially nonclassical secondary education at a Czech school in Prague. When he obtained a grant from the Austrian State Railways, Wald was obliged to leave the Czech school and attend its German counterpart. After finishing school he studied chemistry at the German technical university in Prague until 1882 without formally taking a degree, because it was not required for appointment as a technician in industry.

Wald joined the laboratory of Pražská železářská společnost, a leading ironworks at Kladno, and in 1886 he was appointed chief chemist. Although a gifted analytical chemist—he devised ingenious gasometric and other methods of making mining and metallurgical practice more scientific—he gradually came to devote himself to an examination of the theoretical basis of chemistry. Several efforts to procure Wald an appointment to a professorship by, among others, Ostwald and Mach,

were unsuccessful. Finally the chair of theoretical and physical chemistry and metallurgy at the Czech Technical University in Prague was offered to him (1908), and he held it until his retirement twenty years later. During his tenure Wald was twice elected dean of the Faculty of Chemical Technology and was rector of the university (1920–1921).

Dissatisfied with the atomic-molecular interpretation of chemical phenomena, Wald initially turned his attention to the first two laws of thermodynamics. Summarizing his views in *Die Energie und ihre Entwertung* (Leipzig, 1888), he argued that it was an error to elaborate the second law of thermodynamics on the assumption that processes encountered in nature were reversible when actually they were not. For Wald the second law of thermodynamics was based on experience (*Erfahrungsgesetz*) and could be deduced logically, without the aid of mathematics. As for the first law, he believed in the quantitative principle of the conservation of energy but questioned the qualitative equivalence between work and heat. The amount of heat into which a certain amount of work was transformed was not really equivalent to the original amount of work, since it did not possess the same quality or effectiveness (*Wirkungsfähigkeit*). Energy did not disappear, but degenerated; and Wald accepted the inference that heat that could not be usefully transformed into work or other forms of energy was accumulating in the universe. He supposed, however, that the state of uniform temperature or "heat death" to which the universe was tending would be reached only in infinite time.

Wald disapproved of the accepted theoretical basis of chemistry, on the ground that it was too hypothetical. He believed that natural compounds had rather a varying composition. Apparently never conceding the general validity of atomic considerations for chemical theory, Wald attempted to work out a system in which the atom was replaced by the more tangible "phase" as the fundamental concept. He treated the subject extensively in his second book, *Chemie fází* (Prague, 1918). Wald's efforts to establish a general chemical theory on the basis of the phase concept clearly had some relation to his familiarity with problems of phase equilibrium in metallurgical practice. The Russian chemist N. S. Kurnakov, who was thinking along similar lines, valued Wald's work very highly. Wald was deeply impressed by the predictive and controlling faculty of scientific chemistry, which made the chemist as powerful as nature.

Unlike many contemporary scientists, Wald thought that philosophy could not be kept out of science and criticized theoretical chemistry because of its philosophical shallowness. As a convinced idealist he rejected the mechanist interpretation of natural phenomena but, interestingly, admitted both free will and necessity. He recognized the existence of both and did not feel compelled to choose either one or the other. In an article on the theory of chemical operations, written only a year before his death, he proclaimed that this choice, imposed upon man, was unnecessary because each—natural law and human will—had its domain of influence, with conscious practical activity as the mediator. Although it was an insoluble puzzle to many, Wald had no difficulty in reconciling the two seemingly exclusive conceptions and in perceiving the link between them.

## BIBLIOGRAPHY

I. ORIGINAL WORKS. A list of Wald's publications, compiled by A. Šimek, in *Collection of Czechoslovak Chemical Communications*, **3** (1931), 3–8, does not include Wald's notices and popular articles on scientific and technical topics. "The Foundations of a Theory of Chemical Operations" appeared in Czech in *Přírodovědecký sborník*, **6** (1929); an English trans. appeared in *Collection* (see above), 32–48, and a condensed version in G. Druce, *Two Czech Chemists*, 57–61 (see below).

II. SECONDARY LITERATURE. Originally planned as a *Festschrift* in honor of Wald's seventieth birthday, *Collection* (see above) contains articles by J. Baborovský on Wald's life (in English), by A. Kříž on Wald's theory of phases and of chemical stoichiometry (in English), and by Q. Quadrát on Wald's contribution to analytical chemistry (in French). These articles served as the main source of information for G. Druce, *Two Czech Chemists: Bohuslav Brauner (1855–1935) František Wald (1861–1930)* (London, 1944). M. Teich discusses Wald's place in the history of chemical thought and practice in Bohemia in *Dějiny exaktních věd v českých zemích*, L. Nový ed. (Prague, 1961), 334–335, 347–351 (in Czech, with Russian and English summaries). See also M. Teich, "Der Energetismus bei Wilhelm Ostwald und František Wald," in *Naturwissenschaft, Tradition, Fortschritt-Beiheft zur Zeitschrift für Geschichte der Naturwissenschaften, Technik und Medizin*, supp. (1963), 147–153. Although neglected it is not quite correct that Wald's work has been almost completely ignored, as Joachim Thiele maintains in "Franz Walds Kritik der theoretischen Chemie (nach Arbeiten aus den Jahren 1902–1906 und unveröffentlichten Briefen)," in *Annals of Science*, **30** (1973), 417–433.

M. TEICH

**WALDEN, PAUL** (also known as **PAVEL IVANOVICH VALDEN**) (*b*. Rosenbeck parish, Wenden district [now Latvian S.S.R.], Russia, 26 July 1863; *d*. Gammertingen, Germany, 22 January 1957), *chemistry*.

The son of Latvian farmers, Walden was orphaned as a child and was obliged to earn his living as a private tutor. In 1882 he entered the chemistry department of the Riga Polytechnical School, where he began his scientific work under F. W. Ostwald. His first scientific work led to the discovery of the Ostwald-Walden empirical rule, which makes it possible to determine the basicity of multiatomic acids and bases according to molar (gram molecular) electroconductivity (1887). After Ostwald moved to Leipzig, Walden became Carl A. Bischoff's assistant and turned his interest to organic stereochemistry. However, he did not abandon his initial work in electrochemistry; his first doctoral dissertation (1891) was devoted to the determination of the affinities of organic acids by conductometric methods. After graduating in 1889, Walden remained at the Polytechnicum as an assistant (since 1888), becoming professor in 1894. His work with Bischoff, his visit to Adolf von Baeyer, and his frequent visits to Ostwald's laboratory in Leipzig enabled him to combine the viewpoints of organic and physical chemistry, and Walden set as his lifework the synthesis of these two disciplines. He became one of the founders of physical organic chemistry.

Walden's stereochemical research led him to the discovery of "Walden's inversion" (1896), so named by Emil Fischer, in which one optical isomer is converted into its optic antipode by the action of specific reagents so that a change in absolute configuration occurs. Because it did not coincide with existing representations of substitution reactions, the Walden inversion elicited an extended discussion. The mechanism of Walden inversion was clarified in 1934–1937 by E. D. Hughes and C. K. Ingold. They demonstrated that inversion is always involved in nucleophilic substitution reactions involving two steps ($S_N2$-mechanism).

Walden also conducted detailed studies of autoracemization, sought to relate the degree of specific rotatory power to the chemical structure of an organic molecule, and attempted to substantiate the presence of optically active compounds in crude oil (an argument for biogenesis of petroleum, first mentioned by Walden). These data formed the basis for his second doctoral dissertation, on optical isomerism. After defending it in St. Petersburg in 1899 and becoming professor of inorganic and analytical chemistry at the Riga Polytechnical Institute, Walden embarked upon a study of the electrochemistry of nonaqueous solutions. Between 1900 and 1934 he determined the degree of ionization of about fifty polar nonaqueous solvents, including liquified $SO_2$, $SO_2Cl_2$, $SOCl_2$, chlorosulfonic acid, anhydrous sulfuric acid, formamide, nitromethane, esters, and acid anhydrides. He introduced the concepts of solvation and solvolysis, and pioneered in the representation of the ionic mechanism of several organic reactions. In 1906 he introduced a formula, relating the viscosity of the solvent $\eta$ and the equivalent electroconductivity of a given electrolyte $\lambda$, $\lambda_\infty \cdot \eta_\infty = $ constant, where $\lambda_\infty$ is the equivalent electroconductivity at infinite dilution of a certain ion (electrolyte), and where $\eta_\infty$ is the viscosity of the solvent at infinite dilution of a certain ion (electrolyte). Walden's work facilitated the rapprochement of the physical and chemical theories of solutions, and the rules that he discovered furthered the construction of the modern theory of acids and bases, the theory of electrolytes, and the study of the mechanism of organic reactions.

Walden earned international recognition for having established empirical laws relating surface tension, critical parameters, and hidden heat of fusion to the molecular weight (degree of association) of liquids, thereby contributing to the study of intermolecular forces in liquids.

Elected a member of the St. Petersburg Academy of Sciences in 1910, Walden combined his professorial duties in Riga with his directorship of the Academy's chemistry laboratory in St. Petersburg (since 1911). He devised a project for establishing an academic institute of chemistry in St. Petersburg; and he was active in scientific education in Russia, furthering the rational use of the nation's natural resources. He wrote the first extensive work on the history of chemistry in Russia (1914, printed in 1917). A founder of Latvia University in Riga, he became its first rector in 1919.

Following the establishment of the postwar nationalist regime in Latvia, Walden emigrated to Germany in August 1919 and became professor of chemistry at the University of Rostock. He continued his research on the electrochemistry of nonaqueous solutions, on which he wrote several monographs. After retiring in 1934 he devoted himself almost exclusively to the history of chemistry. During World War II he moved to Frankfurt-am-Main, and then to Tübingen, where until the age of ninety he lectured on the history of chemistry at the university. His later writings were dedicated to the history, psychology, and logic of chemistry; several were of an autobiographical character. He received honorary doctorates from several universities, was elected a member of scientific academies, and was an honorary member of the Chemical Society of London.

*BIBLIOGRAPHY*

I. ORIGINAL WORKS. Walden published more than 300 scientific papers. His writings include "Ocherk istorii khimii v Rossii" ("Essay on the History of Chemistry in Russia"), intro. to A. Ladenburg, *Lektsii po istorii razvitia khimii ot Lavuazie do nashikh dney* ("Lectures on the History of the Development of Chemistry From Lavoisier to the Present"; Odessa, 1917, pp. 361–654); *Nauka i zhizn* ("Science and Life"), 3 pts. (Petrograd, 1919–1921); *Optische Umkehrerscheinungen (Waldensche Umkehrung)* (Brunswick, 1919); "Elektrochemie nichtwässriger Lösungen," in *Handbuch der angewandten physikalischen Chemie*, XIII (Leipzig, 1924); "Leitvermögen der Lösungen" (3 pts.), in F. W. Ostwald *et al.*, *Handbuch der allgemeinen Chemie*, IV a, IV b (Leipzig, 1924); *Chemie der freien Radikale* (Leipzig, 1924); and *Geschichte der organischen Chemie seit 1880* (Berlin, 1941).

II. SECONDARY LITERATURE. See W. Hückel, "Paul Walden, 1863–1957," in *Chemische Berichte*, **91** (1958), xix–lxv, with complete bibliography of Walden's writings; J. Stradiņš, *Cilvēki, eksperimenti, idejas* (Riga, 1965), 217–258; *Materialy dlya biograficheskogo slovarya deystvitelnykh chlenov imperatorskoy Akademii nauk* ("Materials for a Biographical Dictionary of Members of the Imperial Academy of Sciences"), I (Petrograd, 1915); J. Stradiņš, "K biografii Paula Valdena" ("On the Biography of Paul Walden"), in *Iz istorii estestvoznania i tekhniki Pribaltiki*, **1** (1968), 157–167; Y. Soloviev and J. Stradiņš, "Paul Valden kak istorik khimii" ("Paul Walden as a Historian of Chemistry"), *ibid*, **5** (1976); and I. Walden-Hollo, "Vospominania ob ottse" ("Recollections of My Father"), in *Nauka i tekhnika* (Riga, 1975), no. 3, 33–35; no. 4, 33–35.

JANIS STRADIŅŠ

**WALDEYER-HARTZ, WILHELM VON** (*b.* Hehlen, Germany, 6 October 1836; *d.* Berlin, Germany, 23 January 1921), *anatomy.*

Waldeyer was the son of Johann Gottfried Waldeyer, an estate manager, and Wilhelmine von Hartz, the daughter of a schoolteacher. He received his early education at Paderborn, then in 1856 entered the University of Göttingen to study natural sciences. Having attended the lectures of the great anatomist Friedrich Gustav Jacob Henle, however, he changed his course to medicine; indeed, Johannes Sobotta, Waldeyer's best-known student, stated his belief that Waldeyer not only studied medicine but also became an anatomist under Henle's influence. Waldeyer was unable to complete his studies at Göttingen, since it was the university of the kingdom of Hannover and did not, at that time, grant examination certificates to Prussians; he therefore transferred to Greifswald, where he remained until he went to Berlin to qualify. He was drawn there by the reputation of Karl Reichert, the anatomist and embryologist. Believing that a sound knowledge of embryology was essential to an anatomist, Waldeyer finished his studies with Reichert, under whose direction he prepared a doctoral dissertation of the structure and function of the clavicle, published in 1862.

Waldeyer then went to the University of Königsberg as an assistant in the department of physiology. He also taught histology, and became acquainted with the anatomist Friedrich Leopold Goltz. In 1864 he moved on to the University of Breslau, where he had been appointed lecturer in physiology and histology and was also responsible for a service department in pathology. This marked the beginning of his interest in that subject, and he published a number of papers on pathology, including one on the histological changes in muscles following typhoid fever, that led to his appointment, at the age of twenty-nine, as professor of pathology and director of a department of postmortem investigations. In 1866, soon after he received this post, Waldeyer married; in 1868, when he was thirty-two, he was appointed to the chair of pathology. His work at this time was chiefly concentrated on the diagnosis of early cancer, and won him considerable renown; in 1887 he was one of the German doctors called upon to diagnose the Emperor Frederick III's tumor of the vocal cords.

In 1872 Waldeyer went to the University of Strasbourg. The conquest of Alsace by Prussia in the preceding year had resulted in the forced resignation of French professors from that university, and both Waldeyer, who was appointed to the chair of anatomy, and Goltz, who became professor of physiology, were among the Germans who were installed in their stead. Waldeyer remained at Strasbourg for eleven years, then returned to Berlin to succeed Reichert. At Berlin he found an outdated laboratory and a large number of students, but he proved to be a highly successful administra-

tor and teacher, and remained there as director of the anatomy department for over thirty-three years. His academic duties required his full time and energies, and after his relocation in Berlin Waldeyer performed little original research; he was an excellent teacher of both anatomy and histology, however, and he and his student Sobotta offered courses that must remain unsurpassed in their careful and varied presentation.

Indeed, Waldeyer's fame as an anatomist derives largely from his brilliant, lucid, and systematic (as they were styled by his contemporaries) lectures. He nevertheless published a significant number of papers on a wide variety of morphological subjects, including studies of the urogenital system, anthropology, the spinal cord of the gorilla, and topographical observations of the pelvis. He was receptive to new ideas, and quickly grasped the importance of, for example, the neurohistological studies of Ramón y Cajal; he himself coined the word "neuron," and helped to lay the foundation upon which the neuron doctrine was established. (He also coined the term "chromosome" to describe the bodies in the nucleus of cells and invented a number of embryological terms, including those that describe the structure of developing teeth, that are still in use.) Waldeyer also published the first description—both embryological and functional—of the naso-oro-pharyngeal lymphatic tissue; Waldeyer's tonsillar ring, the ring of lymphoid tissue formed by the lingual, pharyngeal, and faucial tonsils that encircles the throat or pharynx, is named for him.

Waldeyer remained at the University of Berlin until he was eighty years old, carrying out all the duties that his position imposed. He remained physically and mentally fit until his death, following a stroke, five years later. Of the four children who survived him, none entered medicine or science.

*BIBLIOGRAPHY*

I. ORIGINAL WORKS. Waldeyer's works include his inaugural dissertation, *De claviculae articulis et functione* (Berlin, 1862); "Untersuchungen über den Ursprung und den Verlauf des Achsenzylinders bei Wirbellosen und Wirbeltieren, sowie über dessen Endverhalten in der quergestreiften Muskelfaser," in *Zeitschrift für rationelle Medicin*, **20** (1863), 193–256; "Über die Endigung der motorischen Nerven in den quergestreiften Muskeln," in *Zentralblatt für die medizinischen Wissenschaften*, **24** (1863), 369–372; *Untersuchungen über die*

*Entwicklung der Zähne* (Danzig, 1864); "Anatomische und physiologische Untersuchungen über die Lymphherzen der Frösche," in *Zeitschrift für rationelle Medicin*, **21** (1864), 103; "Die Veränderungen der quergestreiften Muskelfasern beim Abdominaltyphus," in *Zentralblatt für die medizinischen Wissenschaften*, **7** (1865), 97–100; *Eierstock und Ei. Ein Beitrag zur Anatomie und Entwicklungsgeschichte der Sexualorgane* (Leipzig, 1870), written with W. Engelmann; "Diffuse Hyperplasie des Knochenmarkes: Leukaemie," in *Virchows Archiv für pathologische Anatomie und Physiologie und für klinische Medizin*, **52** (1871), 305–317; "Die Entwicklung der Carcinome," *ibid.*, **55** (1872), 67–159; "Über die Beziehungen der Hernia diaphragmatica congenita zur Entwicklungsweise des Zwerchfells," in *Deutsche medizinische Wochenschrift*, **14** (1884), 211–212; and "J. Henle. Nachruf," in *Archiv für mikroskopische Anatomie und Entwicklungsmechanik*, **26** (1885), 1–32.

See also "Beiträge zur normalen und vergleichenden Anatomie des Pharynx mit besonderer Beziehung auf dem Schlingweg," in *Sitzungsberichte der Königlich Preussischen Akademie der Wissenschaften zu Berlin*, **12** (1886), 233–250; "Über Karyokinese und ihre Beziehungen zu den Befruchtungsvorgängen," in *Archiv für mikroskopische Anatomie und Entwicklungsmechanik*, **32** (1888), 1–122; "Das Rückenmark des Gorilla, vergleichen mit dem des Menschen," in *Korrespondenzblatt der Deutschen Gesellschaft für Anthropologie, Ethnologie und Urgeschichte*, **19**, no. 10 (1888), 112–113; "Das Gorillarückenmark," in *Abhandlungen der Preussischen Akademie der Wissenschaften* (1889); "Bemerkungen über den Bau der Menschen- und Affenplacenta," in *Archiv für mikroskopische Anatomie und Entwicklungsmechanik*, **35** (1890), 1–51; "Das Gibbongehirn," in *Internationale Beiträge zur wissenschaftliche Medizin*, **1** (1891), 1–40; "Ueber einige neuere Forschungen im gebiete der Anatomie des Centralnervensystems," in *Deutsche medizinische Wochenschrift* (1891), 1213–1219, 1244–1246, 1267–1269, 1287–1289, 1331–1332, 1350–1356; *Beiträge zur Kenntnis der Lage der weiblichen Beckenorgane nebst Beschreibung eines frontalen Gefrierschnittes des Uterus gravidus in situ* (Bonn, 1892), written with F. Cohen; *Das Becken, topographisch-anatomisch mit besonderer Berücksichtigung der Chirurgie und Gynäkologie dargestellt*, II (Bonn, 1899); and "Hirnfurchen und Hirnwindungen, Hirnkommissuren, Hirngewicht," in *Ergebnisse der Anatomie und Entwicklungsgeschichte*, **8** (1899), 362–401.

II. SECONDARY LITERATURE. On Waldeyer and his work, see J. Sobotta, "Zum Andenken an Wilhelm v. Waldeyer-Hartz. Anatomischer Anzeiger," in *Zentralblatt für die gesamte wissenschaftliche Anatomie*, **56**, nos. 1 and 2 (Vienna, 1922); and W. von Waldeyer-Hartz, *Lebenserinnerungen*, 2nd ed. (Bonn, 1921).

PAUL GLEES

**WALDSEEMÜLLER, MARTIN** (*b*. Radolfzell, Germany, 1470; *d*. St.-Dié, France, 1518 [?]), *geography.*

Waldseemüller (he also used the Greek form, Ialocomylus) studied theology at Freiburg im Breisgau, was ordained, and later became canon of St.-Dié, when he settled at the court of Duke René II of Lorraine. The duke's secretary, Gauthier Lud (or Ludd), gathered a small circle of humanists at the court during the opening years of the sixteenth century; calling themselves "Gymnasium Vosagense," they collected and published information on the new world then becoming known through the voyages of discovery. A writer, cartographer, and printer, Waldseemüller appears to have been the most versatile member of the group.

The first, and most important, publication of Lud's group was a slender volume dated 25 April 1507: *Cosmographiae introductio cum quibusdam geometriae ac astronomiae principiis ad eam rem necessariis*. It consisted of a general introduction to cosmography and a Latin translation of the report on Amerigo Vespucci's four voyages. The volume also contained a map and globe gores, representing knowledge gained through the latest discoveries. In a passage appearing on the verso of leaf 103, Waldseemüller suggested that the fourth part of the world should be called the land of Amerigo, or America, since it was discovered by Amerigo Vespucci. To reinforce his suggestion, his maps printed at the time had the name "America" on the southern part of the New World. The maps were soon sold out and lost from view, the sole surviving copy not being discovered until 1901; but the little book made a lasting impression, and Waldseemüller did indeed christen the New World "America."

During the rest of his life, Waldseemüller continued to produce maps, including one of Europe; a world map entitled "Carta marina navigatoria" (1516); and, most important, a set of maps for a new edition of Ptolemy's *Geographia*. Printed at Strasbourg in 1513, this edition is justly called the first modern atlas, for in addition to the traditional Ptolemaic maps, it included twenty *novae tabulae* that brought the *Geographia* up to date. Of these Waldseemüller designed eleven, including an important world map showing the New World but naming it "Land of the Holy Cross," as if the cartographer recognized that Vespucci was not the discoverer of America after all.

*BIBLIOGRAPHY*

A facs. ed. of the *Cosmographiae introductio*, with English trans. by J. Fischer, F. von Wieser, and C. G. Herbermann, was published as monograph 4 of the U.S. Catholic Historical Society (New York, 1907). An excellent facs. of the 1507 world map was published by J. Fischer and F. R. von Wieser: *Die älteste Karte mit dem Namen Amerika . . . 1507 und die Carta marina . . . 1516 des M. Waldseemüller* (Innsbruck, 1905).

Waldseemüller's "Carta marina," repr. after his death, is the subject of a monograph by Hildegard Binder Johnson, *Carta marina—World Geography in Strassburg, 1525* (Minneapolis, 1963).

GEORGE KISH

**WALKER, ALEXANDER** (*b.* Leith, Scotland, 20 May 1779; *d.* Leith, 7 December 1852), *physiology.*

Walker probably matriculated at the medical school of the University of Edinburgh in 1797 and certainly studied anatomy with John Barclay.[1] He seems not to have completed his studies, since no record of his receiving a medical degree exists.[2] At the age of twenty he went to London, where he was associated with the well-known John Abernethy at St. Bartholomew's Hospital. Following some difficulties there Walker returned in 1808 to Edinburgh,[3] where he lectured in the Assembly Rooms to mixed audiences on general and particular science; his lectures in the Lyceum and elsewhere were well attended by students and medical practitioners. He attracted considerable notice by instructing the students on the mode of cutting down arteries, for which he gave exact mathematical directions. Walker is listed as a lecturer in the "Extra-academical School of Medicine and Surgery" only for the year 1808.[4]

Walker was the founder and editor of *Archives of Universal Science* (1809). Perhaps his earliest writings on neuroanatomy are the two articles published in the *Archives* in April and July 1809. The final issue (July 1809), divided into major sections—sciences, arts, and reviews—contained twelve articles by Walker.[5]

Walker's principal training was in anatomy and his publications in this area are the most controversial; they also are most frequently associated with his name, at least in the medical community. According to P. F. Cranefield, in 1809 Walker suggested that the roots of the spinal nerves differ in function, the anterior root being sensory and the dorsal root being motor—the reverse of the actual state of affairs.[6] Throughout his life Walker maintained his original views, which were proclaimed in

*The Nervous System* (1834) and *Documents and Dates of Modern Discoveries in the Nervous System* (1839).[7] Cranefield concludes that Walker was the first to conjecture that one root is sensory and the other motor, while François Magendie was the first to assign the functions correctly and to provide the experimental evidence.

Historian W. T. Buckle cites Walker and others in the use of the deductive method in physiology, although in the case noted it led to erroneous conclusions. Thus Walker was in no sense an experimentalist, as his refusal to learn from the experiments of Magendie well illustrates.[8]

Some years later Walker returned to London, where his major efforts were literary. J. Struthers records that he was connected with several newspapers and was an active founder of the *Literary Gazette*.[9] Walker as a person has remained obscure; but his many books were widely read and reviewed, and many editions appeared both in Britain and in the United States. He pioneered as an authoritative and popular writer on subjects that in the Victorian era received little if any careful attention in print. *Beauty in Woman* (1836) still remains a striking and scholarly work, illustrated with plates from drawings by Henry Howard of the Royal Academy of Arts.[10] This book, together with *Intermarriage* (1838)[11] and *Women Physiologically Considered* (1839), was issued in 1843 as a three-volume collection under the general title *Anthropological Works*. His *Physiognomy Founded on Physiology* (1834) is an excursion into a curious but then popular subject.[12]

In surviving letters Walker refers to his wife and family, but children are not specifically mentioned.[13] Two poignant letters of 1850 have been preserved from the correspondence of Richard Owen, both relating to Owen's support of Walker's request for a Civil List pension from Lord John Russell, the British prime minister.[14]

In 1842 Walker returned to Leith in weakened health and was cared for by James Struthers until his death ten years later.[15] The few surviving records indicate that his final years were extremely difficult.

Walker's dogged determination is evident in much of his writing, particularly in that on the Bell-Magendie controversy. Contributions in the medical area have been well documented, but efforts in other areas are little known. His interests ranged widely, and his literary efforts to popularize science (as then understood) were considerable. Walker's creative nature and sensibility to the arts are revealed in a group of works and articles. His lifelong fighting spirit sustained him during many protracted struggles with creditors and other adversaries.

*NOTES*

1. "Alexander Walker" appears on the matriculation roll of the University of Edinburgh medical school for 1797–1798, 1798–1799, and 1799–1800. Photocopies of the 1797–1798 signature, those from the nine letters of 1809–1812, and two letters of 1850 have been carefully studied (letters, Jean R. Guild, University of Edinburgh library). There are differences as well as similarities; since the latter predominate, the current judgment favors the possibility that it was the subject of this article who signed the matriculation roll. In 1797 Walker was eighteen, certainly an acceptable age for a beginning medical student. The name Alexander Walker is very common in Scotland, however, so caution is essential in the attribution of publications and other materials bearing this name (see P. F. Cranefield, *Alexander Walker*, vii). A. C. P. Callisen, *Medicinisches Schriftsteller—Lexicon*, XX, 329, notes to Alexander Walker 2, "Med. Dr. Edinb. 1832; geb. in Schottland," and his dissertation title: "De calore animali," dated 12 July 1832 at Edinburgh.

   Biographical data are extremely meager for Walker; the only account, by John Struthers (1867), provides no information on lineage or on Walker's immediate family. John Walker (1731–1803) was a professor of natural science at Edinburgh who married late and died without issue (*Fasti ecclesiae scoticanae*, as noted by Jean R. Guild, University of Edinburgh library, letter, 15 Feb. 1974)—thus any connection with Alexander Walker seems unlikely. Extensive searches for obituary accounts have yielded only the brief *Lancet* note at the time of his death. Searches of Edinburgh newspapers of that date (*The Scotsman*, and others) revealed no obituary (letter, Margaret Deas, National Library of Scotland, 22 Jan. 1974), nor was one found in *Art Journal* for 1852 (letter, A. P. Burton, Victoria and Albert Museum library, 28 Jan. 1974).

   The illustrious Alexander Walker LL.D. (1825–1903) of Aberdeen apparently was not related to the physiologist (obituary, *Aberdeen Daily Journal*, 11 Feb. 1903; letter, Ian M. Smith, (Aberdeen Art Gallery and Museum, 8 Jan. 1975); also see *In Memoriam* (Aberdeen, 1903), 152–161 (letter, C. A. McLaren, Aberdeen University library, 16 Apr. 1975).

2. Walker recognized that the lack of a medical degree reduced his ability to attract students to his lectures. He desired one from "St. Andrews," but no record of receiving it exists (Walker letters, University of Edinburgh, 1809; letter, R. N. Smart, University Library, St. Andrews, 8 Jan. 1974).

3. "In London he had had to leave the school in consequence of showing the students, after lecture, that Abernethy, instead of tying the subclavian artery, had put the ligature round the neighboring nerve-trunk. What position he had occupied at St. Bartholomew's, or in Abernethy's class, I am unaware, but the incident of the nerve being tied instead of the artery (on the dead subject), and Mr. Walker's giving offence and having to leave there, in consequence of pointing it out, I have on good authority" (J. Struthers, *Historical Sketch* . . . 77; also Cranefield, *op. cit.*, v).

4. Struthers, *loc. cit.*; also Cranefield, *loc. cit.*; J. D. Comrie, *History* . . ., 628, 629.

5. Only three issues of *Archives of Universal Science* appeared: Jan., Apr., July 1809. The title pages all state: "By

Alexander Walker, Esq., Lecturer on Physiology, Etc." The Journal was printed by Charles Stewart, university printer and a good friend and benefactor to Walker. Most of Walker's surviving letters are to Stewart, and they detail his financial woes.

6. The complicated story of this controversy has been ably analyzed by P. F. Cranefield (1973) in the introductory pages to the reprint of Walker's principal work on this topic, *Documents and Dates* . . . (1839). Cranefield has also published *The Way in and the Way out, François Magendie, Charles Bell and the Roots of the Spinal Nerves* (Mt. Kisco, N.Y., 1974), which reprints all of Walker's writings on the subject.

7. In reference to his controversy with Bell, one reviewer in 1833 stated: "You are a bold man Mr. Walker, and it is to be feared that you think too favorably of yourself. It may be true what you say, but modesty and genius are very usually twins." (*London Monthly Review*, in reference to Walker's priority claims against Bell and Magendie; cited in Allibone, *Critical Dictionary* . . ., 160).

8. H. T. Buckle, *On Scotland* . . . (1970), 23.

9. An examination of early issues of *Literary Gazette* does not record Walker's name among the editorial or other staff listings. He did contribute a letter (signed "W") in **1**, no. 9 (22 Mar. 1817); also in **1**, no. 10 (29 Mar. 1817).

10. *Beauty in Woman* is an admirable work and, following the 1st ed. (1836), was issued in at least six other printings or eds., the last being the 5th ed. by T. D. Morison (Glasgow, 1892). An exquisitely bound and deluxe copy with extra plates, prepared by the Paris bookbinder Petrus Ruban, is now in the New York Public Library. Ruban may have been active until about 1910 (see *Catalogue de beaux livres . . . de Mr. Petrus Ruban* [Paris, 1910]). Such a specially bound work with extra illustrations was a custom of certain nineteenth-century collectors, and the process is also referred to as grangerizing (letter, P. Needham, Pierpont Morgan Library, New York, 26 Feb. 1975).

11. Alexander Walker was a very early writer on heritable variation in man and in domestic animals. *Intermarriage . . . and . . . and Account of Corresponding Effects in the Breeding of Animals . . .* (1838) includes both a dedicatory letter by Walker to "Thomas Andrew Knight, Esq., F.R.S., F.L.S., President of the Horticultural Society, etc. . . ." and a letter to Walker ". . . respecting his work from George Birkbeck, Esq., M.D., F.G.S."

12. The following has been attributed—perhaps erroneously—to Walker: *Natural System of the History, Anatomy, and Physiology and Pathology of Man, Adapted to the Use of Professional Students, Amatorie, and Artists* (London, 1813), in 4 vols. with atlas of copperplates. No copies of this work are known (listed only in Callisen, *op. cit.*, xxxiii, 328–329). An inquiry failed to locate a copy of the work or to verify Walker's authorship (letter, P. A. Christiansen, University Library, Copenhagen, 3 Sept. 1974).

13. From this period one may note "Mrs. A. Walker" as the author of *Female Beauty as Preserved and Improved by Regimen, Cleanliness and Dress* . . . (London, 1836), also in an American ed. (New York, 1840). The title page of the 1837 ed. reads "by Mrs. A. Walker," yet most book catalogs and library catalog cards list this under "Mrs. Alexander Walker." Among the advertising pages at the end of the 1837 ed. of the work (p. 355) a book is listed by Donald Walker, *Exercises for Ladies*. The 1837 title page also states, "All that regards hygiene and health being furnished by medical friends, and revised by Sir Anthony Carlisle, F.R.S., Vice President of the College of Surgeons. . . ."

   It is possible that this was written by Alexander Walker and issued under his wife's name, although no direct evidence exists for this supposition. The publisher, Hurst, was never utilized by Walker for his many works. One association is interesting, however; in Walker's *Intermarrige* (1839 ed.) a paragraph is quoted from "Sir A. Carlisle in a letter to the author." Anthony Carlisle was professor of anatomy at the Royal Academy of Arts, London, from 1808 to 1824.

One puzzling work is the listing *Walker's Observations on the Constitution of Women* in *The London Catalogue of Books* (London, 1811). The author's full name is not given, but the title reads like a work by Alexander Walker. The title is suggestive of both *Beauty . . . in Woman* and *Female Beauty. . . .*

14. The first is a small handwritten note sent from Seafield, Leith, Scotland, on 16 Jan. 1850 to "Professor Owen": "In kindly & generously supporting my memorial with Lord John Russell it is not to be forgotten that philosophers & medical men have been enlightened by my discoveries during the last forty years; that I am consequently overwhelmed with debts contracted during so long a period; and that a suitable allowance can alone support me in satisfying these, and in closing my life in peace and honour. See the three volumes of Archives of Universal Science, 1809, in the Library of the British Museum, as well as many subsequent publications from which I never deviated. I am, My Dear Sir, Your Most Respectful, Obedient and Obliged Servant, Alexander Walker."

"Professor Owen" almost certainly was Sir Richard Owen, distinguished anatomist and former conservator of the Hunterian Museum at the Royal College of Surgeons. E. H. Cornelius (letter, Royal College of Surgeons, 11 Mar. 1975) notes that this would have been a Civil List pension, that is, a government pension awarded by Queen Victoria on the recommendation of Lord John Russell, prime minister, for services to the nation. It would have been very natural for Owen, as a leading scientist of the day, to support an application on Walker's behalf. The letter, in the collections of the British Library (British Museum) bears a stamp mark "Ex Litt. Ricardi Owen."

The second letter, also to Owen and dated 1 Mar. 1850, was sent from Seafield and is in the Owen Collection, British Museum (Natural History). It further reveals Walker's dire straits and again refers to the pension request.

The pension apparently was not granted, for no record exists in *The Register of Warrants for Civil List Pensions*, T.38/824, or *The Civil List Ledger* (1850) T.38/252. *The Register of Treasury Papers* (1849), T.2/208, records two such requests by Walker. Other funds, however, were made available to him, care of Rev. T. Laing of Leith (*The Minute Book of the Treasury Board* [1849], T.29/539; letter, D. Crook, Public Record Office, London, 24 Apr. 1975).

15. James Struthers M.D. was the brother of John Struthers M.D., author of *Historical Sketch . . .* (1867), which included some biographical notes on A. Walker. John Struthers' information on this point is at variance with a published record: *Edinburgh and Leith Post Office Directory* for 1850–1851 and 1851–1852 listed Alexander Walker as living in Seafield, but there is no mention of his living there in earlier issues of the *Directory* (letter, Margaret Deas, National Library of Scotland, Edinburgh, 14 Apr. 1975).

*BIBLIOGRAPHY*

I. ORIGINAL WORKS. A bibliography of Walker's publications is provided in the intro. to P. F. Cranefield's facs. repr. (1973) of Walker's *Documents and Dates . . .*, vii–xi; additional items and notes are provided in Cranefield's *The Way in and the Way Out . . .* (Mt. Kisco, N.Y., 1974), 1–3, 24–25. The former lists works of questionable Walker authorship and provides a record of the many eds. and printings. Only principal works are listed below; those marked with an asterisk are newly revealed (and hence are not listed by Cranefield).

The earliest include *Prospectus of Lectures on the Natural System of Universal Science* (Edinburgh, 1808[?]), a pamphlet; *Prospectus of Two Courses of Lectures; One on Anatomy and Physiology; the Other on Pathology and the Practice of Medicine* (Edinburgh, 1808), a pamphlet; *Result of the Operation, Publicly Performed, in Order to Refute or to Confirm the Principle of Surgical Operation Proposed by . . .* (Edinburgh, 1808), a pamphlet; "Theory of Phonics, Hearing, etc. Physiological Dissertation on the Functions of the *Ossicula auditus*, and on the Tympanic Muscles in Particular, and on those of the Ear in General," in *London Medical and Physical Journal*, **19** (1808), 385–414; "General Physiology of the Intellectual Organs," in *Archives of Universal Science*, no. 2 (1809), 167–205; "New Anatomy and Physiology of the Brain," *ibid.*, no. 3, 172–179; *"A Critique on the Antique Statues and Those of Michael Angelo, in Which Not Only the Defects in Their Attitudes, but Also the Errors Which They Present With Regard to the Particular Muscles Brought Into Action, Are Pointed out," *ibid.*, no. 3 (July 1809), 224–234; "Sketch of a General Theory of the Intellectual Functions of Man and Animals, Given in Reply to Drs. Cross and Leach," in Thomson's *Annals of Philosophy*, **6** (1815), 26–34, 118–124; and *"An Attempt to Systematise Anatomy, Physiology and Pathology," *ibid.*, 283–292.

Further works are "A Simple Theory of Electricity and Galvanism; Being an Attempt to Prove That the Subjects of the Former Are the Mere Oxygen and Azote of Air, and the Subjects of the Latter the Mere Oxygen and Hydrogen of Water," in Thomson's *Annals of Philosophy*, **8** (1816), 182–189; *a probable Walker letter in *Literary Gazette* (London), **1**, no. 10 (29 Mar. 1817), 146, which refers to the last number of *Thomson's Annals of Philosophy* concerning an article by "Mr. Magendie" on physiological experiments on animals and criticizing Thomson for having published this article, signed "W."; *"Character of the French," in *Blackwood's*, **26** (1829), 309–314; *"Comparison of the Modern With the Ancient Romans," *ibid.*, 314–317; *"Character of the English, Scots, and Irish," *ibid.*, 818–824; *"The Picturesque," in *Arnold's Magazine of the Fine Arts*, n.s. **1**, no. 2 (June 1833), 105–106; *"Cause of the Fine Arts in Greece," *ibid.*, **1**, no. 6 (Oct. 1833), 491–493; and "On the Cause of the Direction of Continents and Islands, Peninsulas, Mountain Chains, Strata, Currents, Winds, Migrations, and Civilization," in *Philosophical Magazine*, 3rd ser., **3** (1833), 426–431.

Also see *Physiognomy Founded on Physiology, and Applied to Various Countries, Professions, and Individuals . . .* (London, 1834), reviewed in *Arnold's Magazine of the Fine Arts*, **4**, no. 9 (July 1834), 255; *The Nervous System, Anatomical and Physiological . . .*

(London, 1834); *Beauty; Illustrated Chiefly by an Analysis and Classification of Beauty in Woman . . .* (London, 1836); *Influence of Natural Beauty, and of Its Defects on Offspring, and Law Regulating the Resemblance of Progeny of Parents* (London, 1837), a pamphlet; *Intermarriage: Or, the Mode in Which, and the Causes Why, Beauty, Health, and Intellect Result From Certain Unions; and Deformity, Disease, and Insanity From Others . . .* (London, 1838); *The New Lavater, or an Improved System of Physiognomy Founded Upon Strictly Scientific Principles . . .* (London, 1839); *Women Physiologically Considered as to Mind, Morals, Marriage, Matrimonial Slavery, Infidelity, Divorce* (London, 1839); the unsigned *Documents and Dates of Modern Discoveries in the Nervous System* (London, 1839), about which Cranefield (1973), in his reprint of this work, notes ". . . it has always been taken for granted that it is by Walker, and there is not the slightest reason to doubt that assumption" (p. iii); *Pathology Founded on the Natural System of Anatomy and Physiology . . .*, 2nd ed. (London, 1841); and "Purification of Edinburgh, etc.," in *Letters on the Sanitary Condition of Edinburgh* (Edinburgh, 1842), cited by Cranefield (1973, p. x) from a copy in the British Museum.

Archival items include a printer's proof of an Edinburgh lecture schedule with markings, and eleven MS letters. Nine MS letters from Walker to Charles Stewart, university printer, are held by the University of Edinburgh library; photocopies have been made available for study (letters, Jean R. Guild, reference librarian, 7 Nov. 1973, 18 Dec. 1973, 15 Feb. 1974). They consist largely of pleas for funds, but a few other matters may be gleaned from them. Only a few letters are dated, but the time span appears to be about 1809–1812. They generally are not individually cited here but are referred to as the "Walker letters."

A possible early signature (1797) occurs on the matriculation rolls of Edinburgh University medical school. No authenticated portrait is known. The National Portrait Gallery (London) notes that a portrait of an Alexander Walker by C. Ambrose was exhibited at the Royal Academy of Arts (London) in 1829 (Walker would have been fifty) and that there is a drawing by Alphonse Legros of a sitter of the same name in the Aberdeen Art Gallery and Museum (letter, M. Rogers, assistant keeper, 2 Dec. 1974). A. Graves, *The Royal Academy of Arts (Exhibitors, 1769–1904)* (1905), 30, lists the works by C. Ambrose exhibited in 1829: no. 24, Alderman Walker; no. 274, David Walker, Esq.; no. 344, Alexander Walker, Esq.; no. 425, Portrait of a Lady. The Scottish National Portrait Gallery (Edinburgh) has no Walker portrait (letter R. E. Hutchinson, keeper, 25 Nov. 1974).

II. SECONDARY LITERATURE. See S. A. Allibone, *A Critical Dictionary of English Literature and British and American Authors . . .*, III (Philadelphia, 1898), 1539, which cites a review of Walker's *Intermarriage* (Philadelphia, 1851) in *Medical Examiner and Record of Medical Science*, **14** (n.s. 7) (1851), 371–372; an anony-

mous death notice of Walker in *Lancet* (1852), **2**, 583, dated Leith, Scotland, 7 Dec. 1852; British Museum, *Catalogue of Additions to the Manuscripts, 1931–1935* (London, 1967)—see 843, listing of letter from Alexander Walker, physiologist, to R. Owen (1850), item 42577, F. 273; and *Catalogue of Printed Books*, XXVI, microprint ed. (New York, 1967), 553–554; H. T. Buckle, *On Scotland and the Scotch Intellect*, H. J. Hanham, ed. (Chicago, 1970), 23, taken from *History of Civilization in England*, I (London, 1857); and A. C. P. Callisen, *Medicinisches Schriftsteller-Lexicon*, XX (Copenhagen, 1834), 205–206, and *Nachtrag*, XXXIII (Altona, 1845), 328–329, valuable for the citations to reviews of Walker's many works in the medical journals.

Further works are J. D. Comrie, *History of Scottish Medicine*, 2nd ed., II (London, 1932), 628, 629; P. F. Cranefield, *Alexander Walker, Documents and Dates of Modern Discoveries in the Nervous System*, facs. of the London ed. (1839), with intro. by Cranefield (Metuchen, N.J., 1973)—in notes, p. vi: "Nor should one overlook, in all the polemic and eccentricity, the fact that Walker had a brilliant mind and a wry sense of humor and appears to have begun life as a first rate anatomist, while the many editions of his popular books testify to his skill as a writer"; A. Durel, *Catalogue de beaux livres modernes en éditions de luxe, recouverts de riches reliures composant la bibliothèque de Mr. Petrus Ruban exrelieur* (Paris, 1910), in which Walker's works are not listed; A. Graves, *The Royal Academy of Arts (Exhibitors, 1769–1904)*, I (London, 1905), 30; and Sir N. Moore, *The History of St. Bartholomew's Hospital*, II (London, 1918), which makes no mention of A. Walker.

Also see *The New Statistical Account of Scotland*, I, *List of Parishes—Edinburgh* (Edinburgh, 1845), 760–782; J. M. D. Olmsted, *François Magendie—Pioneer in Experimental Physiology and Scientific Medicine in XIX Century France* (New York, 1944), 119, 265; J. Russell, *The Story of Leith* (London, 1922), 334–335, passim; J. Struthers, *Historical Sketch of the Edinburgh Anatomical School* (Edinburgh, 1867), 76–78—these pages quoted verbatim in Cranefield's ed. of Walker's *Documents and Dates . . .*, v–vi; J. Thornton, *John Abernethy. A Biography* (London, 1953), in which no reference to A. Walker is included; University of Edinburgh, *Catalogue of the Library*, III (Edinburgh, 1923), 1106; and W. Wright, "Alexander Walker—Who Was He?" in *Notes and Queries*, 8th ser., **3** (1893), 329; no reply or comment was ever published.

LAWRENCE J. KING

**WALKER, JOHN** (*b*. Edinburgh, Scotland, 1731; *d*. Edinburgh, 31 December 1803), *geology, botany, religion.*

Walker was born into a family firmly convinced of the value of education. His father was rector of the Canongate Grammar School; and as a youth

Walker was trained in Latin and Greek, reading in those languages at an early age. In addition to his ability in the classics, he developed an interest in minerals before he was fifteen. After finishing studies at his father's school, Walker studied at the University of Edinburgh, where he prepared for the ministry in the (Presbyterian) Church of Scotland.

In the course of his work, Walker became especially interested, through the influence of William Cullen, in chemistry and mineralogy. He soon realized that the classification of minerals had been sadly neglected and therefore traveled throughout the British Isles, sometimes with Cullen, collecting minerals from mines and rock outcrops. Using his own collection as well as that at the University Museum, he had established an "elementa mineralogiae" by the 1750's; this classification was later modified to include 323 genera. Among the most interesting of the minerals that he collected in the 1760's was strontianite, from the mines of Leadhills.

Licensed to preach in 1754, Walker was assigned to his first post at Glencorse in September 1758. He soon met Henry Home, Lord Kames, who became his enthusiastic sponsor. Through this relationship Walker was commissioned to make an extensive study of the Hebrides in 1764. This was neither his first nor his last study of the Hebrides or the Highlands; and it was directly responsible for the preparation of a two-volume book printed posthumously in 1808 by his friend Charles Stewart.

From his first ministry in 1758 until his appointment in 1779 to the chair of natural history at the University of Edinburgh, Walker spent all of his spare time in the study of botany and geology; and his knowledge of Latin and Greek permitted him to read the significant literature in those fields. Walker was greatly influenced by the works of Cronstedt and especially by the contributions of Linnaeus, with whom he corresponded in the 1760's.

Most of Walker's botanical and geological papers were published or prepared between 1758 and 1779. A new phase in his life commenced with his appointment as regius professor at the University of Edinburgh, where his first class was enrolled at least as early as 1781.

Walker was an organizer of the Royal Society of Edinburgh and was appointed first secretary of the Physical Section in 1783; he also was active in the organization of the Natural History Society of Edinburgh in 1782. He was a long-time member of the Highland Society of Scotland and, as a result of his great interest in agriculture, formed the Agriculture Society of Edinburgh in 1792. These groups gave him an opportunity to participate in scientific discussions and provided an outlet for the publication of some of his articles.

In his initial lecture to his first class, Walker said: "I am to teach a science I never was taught." He then proceeded to organize a set of lectures on geology "or the Natural History of the Earth." From then until the end of his life he gave regular lectures on the various aspects of geology and had a great influence in establishing the science as a discipline in higher education. Three of his most famous students were James Hall, John Playfair, and Robert Jameson. In addition, he influenced the early development of geology in America through his student Samuel Latham Mitchill, who became one of the leading men of American science upon his return to the New York area. Walker was a contemporary of James Hutton, and both were members of the Royal Society.

One of Walker's chief contributions was the establishment of geology as an organized classroom subject in an institution of higher learning, and he therefore has a legitimate claim to the title of "Father of Geological Education." Walker's classroom methods were essentially those used today: he lectured; distributed syllabuses; established a laboratory; and brought in rocks, minerals, and fossils, which were studied with a microscope. The laboratory work included the study of polished surfaces and a large suite of minerals and fossils. In the study of minerals he used a hardness scale similar to that devised by Mohs thirty years later.

In his lectures Walker discussed the origin of carbonates and differentiated between limestone and marble. In addition, he considered the origin of igneous and sedimentary rocks. Among the common rocks, he paid particular attention to the origin of basalt and granite and to the environment of deposition of such sediments as sand.

One of his classic works was his essay on peat, in which he made an exhaustive analysis of the organic content and origin of this substance. In other papers he affirmed that petroleum occurred in rocks as a natural substance. His discussion of rock structures included accurate definitions of strike and dip as well as recognition of horizontal strata overlying tilted beds, a condition to which he referred as offlap. Walker described the work of both surface and subsurface water and recognized density stratification of lake water. He wrote about till but did not know of its glacial origin.

Walker collected fossils and used them for demonstration purposes in the laboratory. He classified the methods of fossilization and strongly supported the Linnaean system of binomial nomenclature. He believed that fossils could be used to determine rock chronology and maintained that animals and plants were linked in a common evolutionary chain from the "lowest subject up to the human species . . . all being linked . . . by the most beautiful and regular gradation."

*BIBLIOGRAPHY*

Walker's writings include "An Essay on Peat, Containing an Account of Its Origin, of Its Chymical Principles and General Properties," in *Prize Essays and Transactions of the Highland Society of Scotland*, **2** (1803), 1–137; *An Economical History of the Hebrides and Highlands of Scotland*, 2 vols. (Edinburgh, 1808); *Essays on Natural History and Rural Economy* (Edinburgh, 1808; repr. London, 1812), published by Charles Stewart; and Harold W. Scott, ed., *Lectures on Geology by John Walker* (Chicago, 1965), with a complete bibliography, including MSS.

Two short biographies of Walker are W. Jardine, "Memoir of John Walker, D.D." in *The Birds of Great Britain and Ireland*, III (London, 1842), 3–50; and George Taylor, "John Walker, D.D., F.R.S.E., 1731–1803, A Notable Scottish Naturalist," in *Transactions of the Botanical Society of Edinburgh*, **38** (1959), 180–203. A portrait is in John Kay, *A Series of Original Portraits and Caricature Etchings*, III (Edinburgh, 1840), 178.

HAROLD W. SCOTT

**WALLACE, ALFRED RUSSEL** (*b.* Usk, Monmouthshire, Wales, 8 January 1823; *d.* Broadstone, Dorset, England, 7 November 1913), *natural history.*

Wallace was the eighth of nine children born to Thomas Vere Wallace and Mary Anne Greenell. Suffering from constant economic setbacks and having six children to support at the time, his parents had moved across the Severn River to the inexpensive rural environs of Wales less than a mile from the small village of Usk. In the beautiful surroundings beside the Usk River Wallace spent the first five carefree years of his life before moving to Hertford, where he first attended school. In the one-room Hertford Grammar School he studied Latin, French, geography, mathematics, and history. Wallace later had a low opinion of his only formal education, which seems to have been quite pedestrian and dull. More important for his intellectual development, apparently, was the extensive reading of travel works, biographies, novels, classics, and anything else he could find at home.

Early in 1837 Wallace went to London to live temporarily with his brother John. While there he attended lectures at the "Hall of Science" and became acquainted with Robert Owen's socialistic ideas as well as the ideas of religious skeptics. (His agnosticism began at this point and prevented him at a later time from seriously considering orthodox views, largely with religious overtones, on the formation of new species.) The following summer he was apprenticed to his brother William, a surveyor, with whom he worked for the most part until mid-December 1843.

During his survey work, Wallace first began to experience the lure of nature, but not until 1841 did he timidly pursue interests which had barely been awakened in him. The purchase of a cheap book on botany (to assist in beginning a herbarium) marks the beginning of his scientific career, and his interests in botanical explorations and reading continued to grow from that point onward.

About December 1843 his brother's surveying business diminished severely, and Wallace was forced to go to work in 1844 as a master at the Collegiate School in Leicester, where he taught English, arithmetic, surveying, and elementary drawing. At Leicester during 1844–1845, Wallace read widely in the natural sciences; indeed, during the period from 1842 to 1846, he consumed various works by Alexander von Humboldt, T. R. Malthus, Charles Darwin, Robert Chambers, Charles Lyell, and William Swainson. These books profoundly influenced his subsequent intellectual development as did his amateurish explorations in Charnwood Forest in Leicester with his new friend, Henry Walter Bates.

In 1845 his brother William's death forced Wallace to return briefly to surveying and construction work, but he continued reading, collecting, and corresponding with Bates. In 1847 he audaciously suggested to Bates that they transfer their collecting efforts to the forbidding continent of South America and support themselves by collecting objects of natural history. W. H. Edward's *A Voyage up the River Amazon* (1847) prompted them to journey to the Amazon basin, where Wallace explored from 1848 until 1852.

Although he established a scientific reputation for his excellent work in the Amazon, Wallace lost most of his materials, and almost his life, when his ship caught fire and sank in the Atlantic during his return voyage. After his rescue and arrival in

England, Wallace decided to embark on another lengthy expedition, this time to the Malay Archipelago (now Indonesia and Malaysia). During that period of extensive exploration (1854–1862), Wallace formulated the principle of natural selection and made many other fundamental discoveries in biology, geology, geography, ethnography, and other natural sciences.

Upon returning to England in 1862, Wallace enjoyed an enviable reputation as a naturalist. He spent the rest of that decade publishing more articles, culminating with his classic *The Malay Archipelago* (1869), which went through countless editions and was translated into many foreign languages. His interests also began to extend into other nonbiological areas.

During the 1860's Wallace was converted to Spiritualism, which affected his views about natural selection and man. In the late 1870's he became involved in the land nationalization movement and was the first president of the Land Nationalization Society in 1881. In 1890 he publicly announced his acceptance of socialism, which he had thought about since the late 1830's. Early in the twentieth century he supported women's liberation movements through various articles. All these diverse interests were concurrent with his scientific activities, which may be divided into the following categories: natural history exploration, evolutionary biology, ethnology, zoogeography, mimicry and other means of protective colorations, geology, vaccination, and astronomy.

After arriving at Pará (Belém), Brazil, late in May 1848, Wallace and Bates immediately commenced exploring and eventually covered a sizeable portion of the Amazon basin. During the first two years they concentrated their work around Pará, the Tocantins River, and the banks of the Amazon itself as far as Barra (Manaus), where the Amazon and Rio Negro converge. To increase coverage, the young naturalists had already explored a great deal by themselves; and at Barra in March 1850 they separated permanently, with Wallace going to the Rio Negro and Uaupés rivers, and Bates eventually going to the upper Amazon region, where he assembled a spectacular natural history collection before returning to England in 1859.

Wallace penetrated as far north as Javíta in the Orinoco River basin and as far west as Micúru (Mitú) on the Uaupés River. He was deeply impressed by the grandeur of the virgin forest, by the variety and beauty of the butterflies and birds, and by his first encounter with primitive Indians on the Uaupés River area, an experience he never forgot.

The explorations of Wallace were recounted in his fascinating book *A Narrative of Travels on the Amazon and Rio Negro* (1853). Although most of his splendid collections and much else had been lost at sea when his ship sank on 6 August 1852, the book nevertheless displays the keen eyes and mind of a naturalist, by then a mature professional. His notes and drawings on the palm trees of the Amazon fortunately were rescued and appeared in a small but charming book, often quoted in botanical literature on palms.

A major reason for the expedition to South America was to collect information on the variation and evolution of species. In 1845 after reading Chambers' *Vestiges of the Natural History of Creation* (1844), a controversial but extremely stimulating and valuable Victorian work on evolution, Wallace was converted to the belief that species arise through natural laws, rather than by divine fiat. From this point onward he never seriously entertained commonly held views on species, and he apparently convinced Bates that Chambers was right in principle. Their task was to supply scientific details and perhaps uncover a satisfactory evolutionary mechanism.

Since his collections had been lost, Wallace hesitated to declare his views publicly, although glimpses of his ideas may be observed in his early comments on the geographical distribution of monkeys, birds, and insects, as published in articles and in his travel narrative. Also in his narrative are references to the "marvellous adaptation of animals to their food, their habits, and the localities in which they are found" (*A Narrative of Travels on the Amazon and Rio Negro* ([1853], p. 83). He explicitly rejected the orthodox explanations for these phenomena, saying that naturalists were seeking new explanations for species variations. He definitely thought evolution was the explanation but wisely refrained from further comment until 1855.

Since he had not solved the perplexing question of how species evolve while in the Amazon region, Wallace decided to venture once more to the tropics, this time to Southeast Asia and the Malay Archipelago. Securing passage on a government vessel, Wallace departed in 1854 for explorations that lasted eight years and covered between 14,000 and 15,000 miles. The boundaries of the range of his explorations were the Aru Islands to the east; Malacca, Malaya, to the west; the northern tip of Celebes to the north; and as far south as southern Timor.

The enormous quantity of materials gathered

there—about 127,000 specimens of natural history—enabled him to publish scores of fundamental scientific papers on a broad range of topics. These works alone would have established him as one of the greatest English naturalists of his age, but his classic natural history travel book, *The Malay Archipelago* (1869), earned him an international reputation that has endured to this day. On the basis of artistic format, literary style, and scientific merit, it is clearly one of the finest scientific travel books ever written.

From his first arrival in the Malayan region Wallace had decided to gather precise scientific data on groups of animals in order to work out their geographical distribution and consequently to throw light on their origins through evolutionary processes. He kept a notebook on evolution, here designated as his "Species Notebook." His first explicit, published evolutionary statements drew on those materials.

An article by the English naturalist Edward Forbes, Jr., in which he emphatically denied "organic progression" (1854), provoked Wallace to publish a concise synthesis of his ideas on the subject. Like many brilliant works, his "On the Law Which Has Regulated the Introduction of New Species" (September 1855) was based on well-known, acceptable scientific information combined with many personal observations, although he had transformed the mass of facts into an unusually persuasive argument. The evidence was drawn from geology and geography—the distribution of species in time and space—and following nine acceptable generalizations (axioms), Wallace concluded: "*Every species has come into existence coincident both in space and time with a pre-existing closely allied species*" (McKinney, *Lamarck to Darwin: Contributions to Evolutionary Biology, 1809–1859* [1971], pp. 71–72). He claimed that he had explained "the natural system of arrangement of organic beings, their geographical distribution, their geological sequence," as well as the reason for peculiar anatomical structures of organisms. Although the article was carefully worded, Wallace had definitely announced that he was an evolutionist.

Despite this excellent presentation, there were no public replies, although the private comments were quite another matter. Indeed, Edward Blyth, Charles Lyell, and Charles Darwin all read Wallace's article and were greatly impressed by his arguments, but in particular Lyell, who began a complete reexamination of his long-held ideas on species. On 16 April 1856 Lyell discussed Wallace's paper with Darwin, urging him to publish his own views on species as soon as possible. Darwin then began what we now call the long version of the *Origin*, and that version was used as a basis for the *Origin* as published in 1859.

The immediate stimulus for Darwin, however, was a paper written by Wallace entitled "On the Tendency of Varieties to Depart Indefinitely From the Original Type." After publishing his evolutionary paper in 1855, Wallace had continued to search for an evolutionary mechanism. Very ill with malaria while on the large island of Gilolo (Halmahera), some ten miles from Ternate, he formulated the principle of natural selection, the now famous mechanism of evolution; and upon returning to Ternate, he mailed a paper (and covering letter) to Darwin expounding his long-sought discovery (9 March 1858). Evidence now suggests that the "bombshell" arrived at Down House on the third (or fourth) day of June 1858.

Determined that their friend Darwin should receive recognition of priority, Lyell and Hooker decided that Wallace's paper should be presented before the Linnean Society of London along with an excerpt from an essay by Darwin on natural selection and a letter from Darwin to Asa Gray discussing divergence (1 July 1858). Prefatory remarks by Hooker and Lyell emphasized Darwin's priority of discovery, and Wallace's paper was presented last. Wallace was never consulted on these matters and did not learn about the presentation until after the papers were published (20 August 1858). These items focused on natural selection and divergence, not the general arguments for evolution. Darwin's *Origin* appeared late in November 1859.

Wallace subsequently published numerous articles and books supporting evolution with many original and forceful arguments. In 1864 after his return to England he read a paper before the Linnean Society on the variation and distribution of the Papilionidae butterflies of the Malayan region, which demonstrated evolution occurring in nature. In 1870 he published a collection of his evolutionary essays entitled *Contributions to the Theory of Natural Selection*, and in 1876 his monumental *Geographical Distribution of Animals* appeared. He summarized current knowledge of zoogeography and explained the data "by means of established laws of physical and organic change." His *Island Life* (1880) applied evolutionary concepts to insular flora and fauna.

During the 1880's Wallace had given a number of lectures on evolution by means of natural selection, including many while touring the United States in 1886–1887. These mature reflections finally appeared in elaborated form in his important *Darwinism* (1889), which carefully reviewed thirty years of evolutionary biology. While pointing out differences between himself and Darwin, the book actually elaborates a pure form of Darwinian evolution, devoid of Lamarckian elements, and therefore represents (except for the last chapter on man) perhaps the authoritative statement on the subject in the late nineteenth century. The work went through many printings.

From the 1860's onward one of the forceful arguments used by Wallace to support evolution was mimicry. Initially discovered by his traveling companion in South America, Henry Walter Bates, who first published on the subject in 1862, the theory of mimicry was immediately accepted by Wallace since it had been explained in terms of natural selection. Batesian mimicry stated that relatively scarce, unprotected specific forms may resemble other species that are protected by strong smell and bad taste. Resemblance affords protection, and the closer the resemblance, the greater the survival value. In his 1864 paper on the Papilionidae (swallowtailed butterflies) Wallace described mimetic complexes in the Indo-Malayan region, thus forcefully supporting what Bates had observed in South America. Wallace added to those arguments the following two points: a species may have two or more very different forms, and each one may mimic a different model. In the female only, these tend to be polymorphic (Remington [1963], p. 146).

To these views on mimicry Wallace soon added his ideas about numerous other protective resemblances among animals (1867). He observed that resemblances depend upon utility of characters, need for protective concealment, extreme variability of color, and the fact that concealment can most easily be obtained through color modification.

Problems remained, however, for no one had explained why two or more seemingly protected species resemble one another. From a German expatriate living in Brazil came the explanation. In 1878–1879 Fritz Müller observed that if a number of different species are protected chemically or physically in some way, then it is to their advantage in the struggle for existence to resemble one another. Their mutual color patterns warn predators to stay away, and losses during the predator education period are absorbed by a larger group. Wallace had observed but not understood these resemblances, which he thought were due to "unknown local causes." After a second article by

Müller (1881), Wallace heard about these explanations, which had not been enthusiastically supported, and published an article in *Nature* (1882), supporting and accepting Müller's arguments, which afterward gained broad acceptance.

In 1889 Wallace summarized the various ideas on mimicry and proposed an extension of Müller's explanation: that in the same locality several members of the same protected genus may resemble each other; and a scarce edible species can obtain some protection from predators by resembling and intermingling with an abundant edible species (Remington, p. 148). Others, including E. B. Poulton, *The Colours of Animals* (1890), continued the work of Bates, Müller, and Wallace.

While Wallace was one of the founders of modern evolutionary biology, his views on man underwent significant alteration during the 1860's after his return from the Malay Archipelago. Before 1862 he was concerned with man as an animal who had a close kinship with other primates, and his ethnological interests had deep roots, extending back into the 1840's. In a letter to Bates, dated 28 December 1845, Wallace discussed man in an evolutionary context and continued to think of him in the same way for almost twenty years. Immediately before discovering natural selection in 1858, he recalled the work of Malthus, while reflecting on the origins and variations of the indigenous tribes of the Indo-Malayan region.

After returning to England, Wallace's ideas on man underwent modification. The reasons involve his new views about deity and spiritual beings and his decision that natural selection could not adequately explain all aspects of man's development. Although certain points are still unclear, we do know that in 1864 Wallace announced his new view of natural selection, namely that at some point during man's history, his body ceased to change, while his head and brain alone continued to undergo modifications. Man had therefore partially escaped the power of natural selection and could himself influence organic change by selection. Eventually, on land, human selection would supplant natural selection: man's superior intellect had unchained him from an inexorable law of nature, natural selection. As man's social, moral, and intellectual faculties developed, he became a being apart from the ordinary (see Wallace, in *Journal of the Anthropological Society of London*, **2** [1864], clvii–clxxxvii; and Smith [1972], 178–199).

This theme was further developed in 1869 in his review of Lyell's *Principles of Geology* (10th ed., 1867–1868) and *Elements of Geology* (6th ed.,

1865), in which he observed that man's "intellectual capacities and his moral nature were not wholly developed by the same process [natural selection]." Neither natural selection nor evolution can explain the origin of man's intellect. The "moral and higher intellectual nature of man is as unique" as the origin of life on earth. Furthermore, man's brain, speech apparatus, hand, and external form demonstrate that a "Higher Intelligence" had a part in the development of the human race (Wallace, *Contributions to the Theory of Natural Selection*, chapter 10).

This conclusion referring to the necessity of a higher intelligent being agreed at least in principle with the final two pages of Lyell's *Geological Evidences of the Antiquity of Man* (1863) and was a conscious attempt by Wallace to reconcile science with theology, which shocked Darwin, who marked and annotated his copy from Wallace. At one point there are four exclamation marks in the margin (p. 392, lines 6–8). Before reading the review, Darwin had commented to Wallace, "I hope you have not murdered too completely your own and my child." In exactly the reverse direction of a common trend since the eighteenth century, Wallace had *added* deity to his mechanistic, self-regulating universe ("Creation by Law" [October 1867], repr. in *Contributions to the Theory of Natural Selection* [1870]). A watchmaker was necessary after all. These views received full expression in his article "The Limits of Natural Selection as Applied to Man" (*ibid.*, 332–371).

During the early 1860's—clearly no later than 1865—Wallace's statements on man's development (and other topics as well) must be examined within a religious context. What, then, were his religious views and what led him to those views? Wallace's parents were orthodox believers, as was he until 1837 when he lived with his brother John in London and then with his brother William, who was "of advanced liberal and philosophical opinions." While at Leicester in 1844, experiments with phrenology and mesmerism impressed him deeply, leading him to believe in extrasensory phenomena. During his twelve years of natural history exploration, he had heard about Spiritualism and decided to investigate the subject upon his return to England in 1862. Until then, by his own admission, he was an agnostic, a materialist, a philosophical skeptic. That was the situation, he has told us, "up to the time when I first became acquainted with the facts of Spiritualism," that is, July 1865. In two other specific places in this same book, *On Miracles and Modern Spiritualism* (1875), however, Wallace claimed that he had been an agnostic for "twenty-five years" (thus 1837–1862), and there is additional evidence that appears to support his explicit references to twenty-five years.

In a highly praised paper, "On the Physical Geography of the Malay Archipelago" (read 8 June 1863), Wallace urged that governments and scientific institutions immediately set about assembling the best possible collections of natural history for the purposes of study and interpretation. He then concluded in a manner quite foreign to him in the past:

> If this is not done, future ages will certainly look back upon us as a people so immersed in the pursuit of wealth as to be blind to higher considerations. They will charge us with having culpably allowed the destruction of some of those records of *Creation* which we had in our power to preserve; and *while professing to regard every living thing as the direct handiwork and best evidence of a Creator*, yet, with a strange inconsistency seeing many of them perish irrecoverably from the face of the earth, uncared for and unknown [*Journal of the Royal Geographic Society*, **33** (1863), 234, italics added].

It is therefore possible that Wallace's religious views began to alter as early as 1862/1863, although he claimed emphatically that various facts, "not any preconceived or theoretical opinions," led him in 1865 to accept Spiritualism, but not orthodox Christianity, which he frequently criticized. In 1866 he published a fifty-seven-page booklet, *The Scientific Aspect of the Supernatural*, thereby publicly announcing his support of Spiritualism.

At the moment it must remain a moot point whether he questioned the all-sufficiency of natural selection on purely empirical, scientific grounds or because embryonic religious views had caused him to doubt. Seeds of doubt are evident in Wallace's "The Origin of Human Races and the Antiquity of Man Deduced From the Theory of Natural Selection," but we may be involved in the chicken-egg syndrome. In any event, doubt once raised in Wallace's mind for whatever reason was like an incurable itch until a satisfactory solution was found. Later it was necessary to convince scientists of the weaknesses of natural selection (using the argument of utility) in explaining the evolution of natural phenomena in order to persuade them to consider, as an alternative, psychic phenomena (Smith [1972], pp. 178–199).

Considering his previous history, it is curious that Wallace found satisfaction in Spiritualism, which shocked Darwin and Huxley, but which may have had a profound effect on those scientists with religious views who were unable to resolve their own doubts. Wallace, a discoverer of natural selection, had rescued man from the degradation of evolution and had returned to him his God-given "soul" (intellect). Later elaborations on this theme appeared in *Darwinism* (1889) and particularly *The World of Life* (1910). The full impact of Wallace's conversion has never been assessed.

It has been incorrectly asserted that the facts of geographical distribution led both Darwin and Wallace to accept evolution. In the case of Wallace, the reverse is true. He went to the Amazon to collect facts establishing the case for evolution, but as an amateur naturalist, what facts was he capable of collecting? The answer is clear, especially when we understand that Lyell in his *Principles of Geology* and Chambers in his *Vestiges of the Natural History of Creation*, two major influences on Wallace, stressed the importance of distributional phenomena.

While in South America, he observed variation and the struggle for existence, which he had read about in Lyell, but Wallace's foremost contributions from his Amazon experience originated from observations on the distribution of the palm trees, insects, birds, and monkeys. This evidence substantiated his belief in evolution, and he used it in his important paper "On the Law Which Has Introduced the Introduction of New Species" (1855). Generally speaking, he observed that certain species on opposite sides of river barriers are closely related, but not identical. Since the physical conditions were almost the same, biologists believing in special creation were hard pressed to explain why an omniscient God had created different species on opposite sides of rivers within sight of each other. Wallace thought that after the barriers had been established, evolution had led to the formation of new, but similar, species from the divided parent stock.

Once evolution had been accepted, the facts of geographical distribution could be used to good effect. For example, arguments for the creationist's belief in centers of creation were quickly enlisted as evidence for the evolutionists. Wallace used this technique to good advantage as did Darwin in chapters 11 and 12 on geographical distribution in the *Origin* (1859). Both Wallace and Darwin were able to cite much of their own evidence on this topic in their evolutionary works.

Indeed, it is significant that their works up to

1859 interpreted and applied these facts in a distinctly modern way. Before 1859 most works on natural history had been extremely vague and imprecise in citing the geographical distribution of a specimen. It was not unusual to find merely South America or Brazil as the only locality given. Only after the case for evolution by means of natural selection was presented, particularly in Darwin's *Origin*, did other naturalists begin to give this matter the attention it deserved.

In 1858, however, Wallace was already preparing an announcement of an important zoogeographical discovery, which proposed a boundary line dividing the archipelago into Indo-Malayan (Oriental) and Australian zoological regions. In a paper on the geographical distribution of birds ("Letter From *Mr. Wallace* on the Geographical Distribution of Birds," *Ibis* [1859], 449–454), he first suggested this line and accepted the zoogeographical provinces recommended by P. L. Sclater (1858) on the basis of the zoogeography of bird populations. In 1860 Wallace published a much more elaborate discussion of the zoological geography of the archipelago, before announcing explicitly in 1863 what became known as Wallace's Line, the zoogeographical line that extended between Bali and Lombok in the south and farther north between Borneo and Celebes, and continuing eastward around the Philippines. This line has been shifted many times since 1863 as more zoogeographical information has been accumulated.

Wallace's investigations made it quite clear that zoogeography should be based on a wide range of geographical and geological facts interpreted by evolutionary doctrines. He was also one of the few early zoogeographers to rely on a statistical approach.

The culmination of Wallace's approach was achieved in his monumental two-volume *The Geographical Distribution of Animals* (1876). Relying on data he had collected on families and genera of terrestrial vertebrates, Wallace established evolutionary zoogeography on its modern foundation. While an enormous amount of subsequent data has improved our knowledge and determination of the zoogeographical provinces, few, if any, subsequent works have been more important to the subject.

As was previously the case, Wallace's evolutionary approach to zoogeography provided a rock-solid factual basis for evolutionary biology. While he hoped that his two volumes would elaborate Darwin's two chapters in the *Origin* in much the same way as Darwin's own two-volume work

*Animals and Plants Under Domestication* extended the first chapter, Wallace's work actually transformed the subject and became the standard authority for many years.

In 1880 Wallace further applied his approach in evolutionary zoogeography to island flora and fauna. Whereas his great work in 1876 dealt with large groups of animals, in his *Island Life* (1880) he focused on species to examine variation, distribution, and dispersal. His discussion of the relevance of the ice ages was extremely important, as was his reemphasis on the interaction and "complete interdependence of organic and inorganic nature." His later works on zoogeography represent summaries of these two great books.

Before going to South America, Wallace knew little about geology except what he had learned from books and what he casually observed as a surveyor. After his two expeditions he published many works utilizing geological information. In his *Geographical Distribution of Animals* Wallace interpreted animal distributions on the basis of geological principles, especially paleontological data. In *Island Life* Wallace presented advanced views on the causes of ice ages, showing the cumulative effects of snow and ice in lowering temperature. He also discussed the general permanence of oceanic and continental areas with a wide range of data. In 1893 Wallace argued vigorously for the action of glaciers in the formation of lake basins.

Early in the 1870's Wallace became acquainted with a group that opposed vaccination, but he did not join the movement until William Tebb introduced him to statistical studies attacking vaccination. Upon personal investigation, Wallace found apparently cogent evidence to renounce his former belief in the efficacy of vaccination, whereupon he published a thirty-eight-page pamphlet "Forty-five Years of Registration Statistics, Proving Vaccination to Be Both Useless and Dangerous" (1885).

Wallace and the anti-vaccination movement forced the appointment of the Royal Commission on Vaccination, and he spent three days presenting evidence (1890). Disregarding his statistical evidence, the commission published a report in 1896 supporting vaccination, which led him in turn to publish a longer work in 1898 (96 pages and 12 diagrams) denouncing the "ignorance and incompetence" of the commission and reiterating his previous opposition with extensive data. In his *The Wonderful Century* (1898), Wallace reprinted his arguments, which he thought would eventually be judged as "one of the most important and truly

scientific of my works." It is perhaps ironic that today we have discontinued smallpox vaccination because more patients die from the vaccination than die from the disease itself.

In *The Wonderful Century* (1898) Wallace had written the chapter "Astronomy and Cosmic Theories," and after the turn of the century he expanded the subject into his *Man's Place in the Universe* (1903). The primary purpose was to establish with extensive scientific data that life as we know it cannot exist elsewhere in the universe. In 1907 he reiterated this theme in his *Is Mars Habitable?*, which was written to refute Lowell's *Mars and Its Canals* (1906). Lowell had presented arguments for advanced life on Mars. Wallace was of course only an intelligent layman, but he corresponded with professional astronomers and presented a strong argument for his views.

Wallace summed up his work on biology in 1910 with his *The World of Life*, in which he accepted the chromosome theory of inheritance and Galton's numerical law of inheritance. Numerical phytogeography and zoogeography also are stressed, and the continuing influence of Spiritualism is evident. This was his last extensive work on scientific matters; his last two books were rehashings of his social ideas.

In April 1866 at the age of forty-three, Wallace married Annie Mitten, the teenage daughter of the English botanist William Mitten. They had three children: Herbert (died age four), Violet, and William.

During his distinguished career Wallace received numerous recognitions of merit, including the Royal Medal of the Royal Society (1868); the Gold Medal, Société de Géographie (1870); LL.D., Dublin, (1882); D.C.L., Oxford (1889); the Darwin Medal, Royal Society (1890); the Founder's Medal of the Royal Geographical Society (1892); election to the Royal Society (1893); the Gold Medal of the Linnean Society of London (1892); the Copley Medal of the Royal Society (1908); Order of Merit (1908); and the first Darwin-Wallace Medal, Linnean Society of London (1908).

Few naturalists have made more important contributions to so many subjects, and yet his views on Spiritualism, vaccination, land nationalization, women's rights, and socialism have combined to diminish his reputation in science. Those who dismiss him as a "crank" forget that cranks often make the machinery go, and in whatever he did, Wallace was one who made things happen. He rarely avoided controversy; indeed, he was at his very best while marshaling evidence for an argument. His brilliant imaginative mind, however, frequently offended lesser spirits, for he did not easily tolerate ignorant, pompous arguments; and while others refrained from the lists, Wallace charged into battle. That he did so greatly enriched science. Ironically, many of his social views, which have long detracted from his scientific contributions, are now widely accepted.

*BIBLIOGRAPHY*

I. ORIGINAL WORKS. Wallace published more than twenty books. James Marchant, ed., *Alfred Russel Wallace. Letters and Reminiscences* (New York, 1916), 477, provides an incomplete bibliography. Some editions of Wallace's book-length scientific publications (excluding translations) are *Palm Trees of the Amazon and Their Uses* (London, 1853; repr., Lawrence, Kans., 1971); *A Narrative of Travels on the Amazon and Rio Negro* (London, 1853; 2nd ed., 1889; repr. 1971); *The Scientific Aspect of the Supernatural* (London, 1866); *The Malay Archipelago: The Land of the Orang-Utan, and the Bird of Paradise. A Narrative of Travel with Studies of Man and Nature* (London–New York, 1869); *Contributions to the Theory of Natural Selection. A Series of Essays* (London, 1870; 2nd ed., 1871); *The Geographical Distribution of Animals*, 2 vols. (London–New York, 1876; repr., 1962); *Tropical Nature, and Other Essays* (London, 1878); *Australasia. Stanford's Compendium of Geography and Travel*, edited and extended by Wallace (London, 1879; rev., 1893); *Island Life or the Phenomena and Causes of Insular Faunas and Floras Including a Revision and Attempted Solution of the Problem of Geological Climates* (London–New York, 1880; 2nd. ed., 1892); *Darwinism. An Exposition of the Theory of Natural Selection With Some of Its Applications* (London–New York, 1889; 3rd ed., 1912); *Natural Selection and Tropical Nature. Essays on Descriptive and Theoretical Biology* (London–New York, 1891); *Vaccination a Delusion, Its Penal Enforcement a Crime: Proved by the Official Evidence in the Reports of the Royal Commission* (London, 1898); *The Wonderful Century. Its Successes and Its Failures* (London–New York, 1898, 1925); *Studies Scientific & Social*, 2 vols. (London–New York, 1900); *The Wonderful Century Reader* (London, 1901); *Man's Place in the Universe. A Study of the Results of Scientific Research in Relation to the Unity or Plurality of Worlds* (London–New York, 1903; 4th ed., 1904); *My Life, A Record of Events and Opinions*, 2 vols. (London–New York, 1905; 2nd ed., 1908); *Is Mars Habitable?* (London, 1907); Richard Spruce, *Notes of a Botanist on the Amazon and Andes*, 2 vols. (London, 1908), ed. by Wallace; and *The World of Life. A Manifestation of Creative Power, Directive Mind and Ultimate Purpose* (London, 1910; New York, 1911).

Wallace published about 400 articles and reviews, many of which are listed in Marchant (1916), 478–486. Errors and important omissions abound, and no citation should ever be based on Marchant. The Royal Society *Catalogue of Scientific Papers* adds a few missing articles but is still very incomplete. H. Lewis McKinney is doing a bibliography of all of Wallace's works. Wallace's two important evolutionary articles of 1855 and 1858 are reprinted in H. Lewis McKinney, ed., *Lamarck to Darwin: Contributions to Evolutionary Biology, 1809–1859* (Lawrence, Kans., 1971; repr. 1975), 69–82, 89–98.

Many of Wallace's letters appeared in *My Life* (1905). James Marchant, *Alfred Russel Wallace. Letters and Reminiscences*, 2 vols. (London, 1916; American ed., in one vol., New York–London, 1916), is the only other collection of published correspondence, although one by H. Lewis McKinney is in progress. Other letters appear in the lives and letters of Charles Lyell, J. D. Hooker, and Charles Darwin. The most complete list of MSS is in McKinney (1972), 177–179, cited below.

II. SECONDARY LITERATURE. For Wallace's early work up to 1858, concentrating on evolution and natural selection, see H. Lewis McKinney, *Wallace and Natural Selection* (New Haven–London, 1972), which cites most secondary literature up to 1972. For a comparison of Wallace's scientific ideas with currently held ideas, especially in zoogeography, see Wilma George, *Biologist Philosopher. A Study of the Life and Writings of Alfred Russel Wallace* (London–Toronto–New York, 1964). See also Roger Smith, "Alfred Russel Wallace: Philosophy of Nature and Man," in *British Journal for the History of Science*, **6** (1972), 178–199; and M. J. Kottler, "Alfred Russel Wallace, the Origins of Man, and Spiritualism," in *Isis*, **65** (1974), 145–192. For references to mimicry, see Charles Remington, "Historical Backgrounds on Mimicry," in *Proceedings of the XVI International Congress of Zoology*, **4** (1963), 145–149.

H. LEWIS McKINNEY

**WALLACE, WILLIAM** (*b*. Dysart, Scotland, 23 September 1768; *d*. Edinburgh, Scotland, 28 April 1843), *mathematics.*

Wallace had no schooling after the age of eleven, when he was apprenticed to a bookbinder; he subsequently taught himself mathematics and became a teacher at Perth. In 1803 he was appointed to the Royal Military College at Great Marlow and in 1819 became professor of mathematics at the University of Edinburgh, where he remained until his retirement in 1838. Wallace wrote many articles for encyclopedias and numerous papers in *Proceedings of the Royal Society of Edinburgh*, including some on mechanical devices. He also played a large part in the establishment of the observatory on Calton Hill, Edinburgh.

The feet of the perpendiculars to the sides of a triangle from a point P on its circumcircle are collinear. This line is sometimes called the pedal line but more often, incorrectly, the Simson line of the triangle relative to P. It was stated by J. S. Mackay that no such theorem is in Simson's published works. The result appears in an article by Wallace in Thomas Leybourn's *Mathematical Repository* (2 [1799–1800], 111), and Mackay could find no earlier publication. In the preceding volume Wallace had proved that if the sides of a triangle touch a parabola, the circumcircle of the triangle passes through the focus of the parabola, a result already obtained by Lambert. To demonstrate this, Wallace showed that the feet of the perpendiculars from the focus to the sides of the triangle lie on the tangent at the vertex of the parabola, which is equivalent to saying that the pedal line of the triangle is the tangent at the vertex. The close connection of this theorem with the pedal line suggests that Wallace was led to the property of the pedal line from the parabolic property.

In 1804 the following result was proposed for proof in *Mathematical Repository* (n.s. 1, 22): If four straight lines intersect each other to form four triangles by omitting one line in turn, the circumcircles of these triangles have a point in common. The proposer was "Scoticus," which Leybourn later said was a pseudonym for Wallace. Two solutions were given in the same volume (170). Miquel later proved that five lines determine five sets of four lines, by omitting each in turn; and the five points, one arising from each such set, lie on a circle. Clifford proved that the theorems of Wallace and Miquel are parts of an endless chain of theorems: $2n$ lines determine a point as the intersection of $2n$ circles; taking one more line, $2n + 1$ lines determine $2n + 1$ sets of $2n$ lines, each such set determines a point, and these $2n + 1$ points lie on a circle.

*BIBLIOGRAPHY*

Two articles by J. S. Mackay in *Proceedings of the Edinburgh Mathematical Society*—9 (1891), 83–91, and 23 (1905), 80–85—give the bibliography of Wallace's two theorems and later extensions and generalizations with scholarly thoroughness.

For a full account of Wallace's life, see the unsigned but evidently authoritative obituary in *Monthly Notices of the Royal Astronomical Society*, 6 (1845), 31–36.

T. A. A. BROADBENT

**WALLACH, OTTO** (*b*. Königsberg, Prussia [now Kaliningrad, R.S.F.S.R.], 27 March 1847; *d.* Göttingen, Germany, 26 February 1931), *chemistry*.

Wallach came from a family of lawyers, but his father was a Prussian state official, who was transferred from Königsberg to Stettin and, in 1855, to Potsdam. The boy was educated at the Potsdam Gymnasium, where he acquired his two major interests: chemistry and the history of art. Although he became a professional chemist, he remained an art collector throughout his life and spent many vacations visiting the art galleries of Europe.

In the spring of 1867 Wallach entered the University of Göttingen, where he attended Wöhler's lectures. A short stay in Berlin with A. W. von Hofmann convinced him that Göttingen was a better place for him to work, and he returned there to study for his doctorate with Hans Hübner. He received the degree in 1869 with a dissertation on position isomerism in the toluene series. Wallach worked for a short time in Berlin; but in the spring of 1870 he was called to Bonn as assistant to Kekulé, who was then gradually withdrawing from active laboratory work. He remained at Bonn for nineteen years, with a short interlude of industrial experience at the Aktien Gesellschaft für Anilin-Fabrikation (Agfa) plant in Berlin. His health was never good, and the noxious fumes at the plant soon drove him back to Bonn. In 1889 Wallach succeeded Victor Meyer at Göttingen, where he served as director of the Chemical Institute until his retirement in 1915. He continued experimental work until he was eighty.

Wallach's early work included a number of studies in general organic chemistry. In 1879 he was assigned to teach pharmacy, with which he had had little experience. In teaching this course his attention was drawn to the chemistry of natural compounds. He found in a cupboard at Bonn a number of bottles of plant essential oils that Kekulé had collected but never studied. Wallach decided to investigate these substances, and the rest of his life was devoted to the study of such compounds, on which he published 126 papers.

At the time Wallach began this work, the field was in a state of extreme confusion. No one had obtained truly pure compounds from the natural mixtures; and various names had been proposed for many of the substances thought to be pure. A skilled and patient experimentalist, Wallach set himself the task of characterizing individual compounds beyond doubt and then of determining their relationships. For this purpose he separated the pure substances by careful distillations and studied their reactions with a series of relatively simple reagents.

After three years Wallach had distingished eight pure terpenes, as he called this class of compounds. He suggested that they were composed of five carbon atom fragments known as isoprene units and showed that in many cases it was possible to rearrange one terpene into another by the action of strong acids and high temperatures. He was particularly interested in the relations among the various compounds and was less concerned with preparing new substances, the chief occupation of most organic chemists of the time. Wallach often left the task of synthesizing and determining structures of his compounds to others, for he realized that the field of terpene chemistry was so large that one man could not cover it completely. His methods were so successful and had progressed so far by 1895 that when, in that year, he and others determined the structure of α-terpineol, the structures of an entire series of terpenes were at once established. This accomplishment was an outstanding example of the value of Wallach's experimental methods. After he had made the fundamental discoveries, a number of chemists continued his work, and terpene chemistry became an important branch of organic chemistry. It was soon extended to the biologically important carotenoids and steroids.

Wallach received wide recognition for his work, becoming an honorary member of many universities and scientific societies. These honors culminated in the award of the Nobel Prize in chemistry in 1910.

*BIBLIOGRAPHY*

I. Original Works. Among Wallach's important papers were his suggestion of isoprene units in terpenes, "Zur Kenntniss der Terpene und ätherischen Oele. IV," in *Justus Liebigs Annalen der Chemie*, **238** (1887), 78–89; and his work on terpineol, "Zur Constitutionsbestimmung des Terpineols," in *Berichte der Deutschen chemischen Gesellschaft*, **28** (1895), 1773–1777. He summarized his work in *Die Terpene und Campher* (Leipzig, 1909; 2nd ed., 1914).

II. Secondary Literature. The longest account of Wallach is the Pedlar lecture by L. Ruzicka, "The Life and Work of Otto Wallach," in *Journal of the Chemical Society* (1932), 1582–1597, repr. in Eduard Farber, ed., *Great Chemists* (New York, 1961), 833–851. A shorter account is William S. Partridge and Ernest R. Schierz, "Otto Wallach: The First Organizer of the Terpenes," in *Journal of Chemical Education*, **24** (1947), 106–108.

An account of the industrial significance of Wallach's work is Albert Eller, "Otto Wallach und seine Bedeutung für die Industrie der ätherischen Öle," in *Zeitschrift für angewandte Chemie . . .*, **44** (1931), 929–932.

Henry M. Leicester

**WALLER, AUGUSTUS VOLNEY** (*b.* Faversham, England, 21 December 1816; *d.* Geneva, Switzerland, 18 September 1870), *neurophysiology, neurohistology.*

Waller, the son of William Waller, was raised at Nice until his father's death in 1830. He then returned to England, living with Dr. Lacon Lambe and then with William Lambe, a noted vegetarian. Following early training in the physical sciences, Waller studied medicine at Paris, receiving the M.D. degree in 1840. The following year he became a licentiate of the Society of Apothecaries in London and began a successful general practice in Kensington. In 1842 Waller married Matilda Walls; they had two daughters and one son, the physiologist Augustus D. Waller.

The publication of two papers in the *Philosophical Transactions* (1849, 1850) led to Waller's election as a fellow of the Royal Society in 1851. That same year he abandoned his general practice and moved to Bonn in order to devote full time to research; he spent five years there, working principally with the ophthalmologist Julius Budge. The investigations begun in England and continued in Bonn brought Waller the Monthyon Prize of the French Academy of Sciences in 1852 and 1856, and a Royal Society medal in 1860.

After leaving Bonn in 1856 Waller worked in Pierre Flourens's laboratory at the Jardin des Plantes but developed a chronic fever that invalided him for two years. He returned to England and in 1858 was appointed professor of physiology at Queen's College, Birmingham, and physician to the college hospital. A heart condition soon forced him to relinquish these posts, and in the same year he retired to Bruges. Ten years later he moved to Geneva, where he hoped to resume general practice. In the spring of 1870 Waller went briefly to London to deliver the Royal Society's Croonian lecture; he returned to Geneva, where he died suddenly on 18 September.

Waller is best remembered for pioneering a major technique for unraveling the complex structure of the nervous system, the method of secondary or Wallerian degeneration. His interest in the functional anatomy of the nervous system began while he was a medical student in Paris, when he began to study the histology of the frog's tongue. Like other neurohistologists and physiologists in the first half of the nineteenth century, Waller must have found the processes of nerve degeneration and regeneration to be one of the most difficult problems he confronted in trying to elucidate the structure of the nerve fiber. In retrospect, we know today that the large body of erroneous belief about the fine structure of nerve fibers and nerve cells that arose in the eighteenth and nineteenth centuries resulted in part from mistaking the products of nerve degeneration—the structures seen after a nerve was sectioned or otherwise injured—as normal structures. Our knowledge that the nerve cell body is a trophic center, and that a detached nerve cell process consequently will degenerate and die, began with Waller's studies of the frog's tongue.

Using the simple technique of cutting the nerves in the tongue, Waller found in 1849 that degeneration occurred throughout the axon's distal segment and concluded that the nerve cell body is the axon's source of nutriment. His belief that the proximal part of the nerve process and the cell body itself did not degenerate following sectioning of the fiber was subsequently modified through the development of improved staining methods. Waller's study, first reported in the *Philosophical Transactions* (1840), added to the growing evidence that nerve cell bodies and processes were somehow interconnected. By the 1880's, when the origin of nerve fibers from nerve cells had been firmly established with the development of better methods for fixing and staining tissues, the Wallerian method became a major means of tracing the origin and course of nerve fibers and tracts; and in the hands of such investigators as Forel, it helped to establish the neuron theory.

Fundamental studies of the autonomic nervous system, conducted during his five years in Bonn, formed the second major area of Waller's researches. In 1851 and 1852, Budge and Waller published three memoirs in the *Comptes rendus* of the Paris Academy, examining the role of the nervous system on the motion of the eye's iris. In a series of well-designed and carefully executed experiments, they showed the influence of the cervical portion of the sympathetic nerve in dilation of the pupil. They then used the Wallerian method to trace the pathway of the pupillary dilator fibers in the dog, following them in the sectioned sympathetic nerve trunk to the first and second thoracic segments of of the spinal cord. When this region was then stimulated in the intact animal, the pupils of the

eye dilated. When in turn the cervical part of the sympathetic nerve was sectioned unilaterally, electrical stimulation in the thoracic area no longer caused pupillary dilation on the side that had been sectioned. Budge and Waller termed the area of the sympathetic nerve trunk controlling dilation of the pupils the "ciliospinal center."

After receiving the Monthyon Prize for the work on the ciliospinal center, Waller went on to demonstrate the action of the cervical sympathetic nerves on the constriction of blood vessels in the head. His experiments on the vasoconstrictor properties of the nerves from the ciliospinal region confirmed and extended the discoveries of Claude Bernard in 1851 and of Brown-Séquard in 1852.

Waller's work was not confined to the definition of neural structure and function. The readers of *Philosophical Magazine* in the 1840's, for example, found that Waller had turned his microscope upon a variety of objects: "The Microscopic Observations on the Perforation of the Capillaries by the Corpuscles of the Blood" (November 1846), "Origin of Mucus and Pus" (November 1846), and "Microscopic Investigations on Hail" (July and August 1846, March 1847).

## BIBLIOGRAPHY

I. ORIGINAL WORKS. Waller's writings include "Experiments on the Section of the Glossopharyngeal and Hypoglossal Nerves of the Frog, and Observations of the Alterations Produced Thereby in the Structure of Their Primitive Fibres," in *Philosophical Transactions of the Royal Society*, **140** (1850), 423–429; "Nouvelle méthode pour l'étude du système nerveux, applicable à l'investigation de la distribution anatomique des cordons nerveux, et au diagnostique des maladies du système nerveux, pendant la vie et après la mort," in *Comptes rendus . . . de l'Académie des sciences*, **33** (1851), 606–611; "Recherches sur le système nerveux. Première partie. Action de la partie cervicale du nerf grand sympathétique et d'une portion de la moelle épinière sur la dilatation de la pupille," *ibid.*, 370–374, written with J. L. Budge; "Recherches expérimentales sur la structures et les fonctions des ganglions," *ibid.*, **34** (1852), 524–527—also papers by Waller on 582–587, 675–679, 842–847; "Septième mémoire sur le système nerveux," *ibid.*, **35** (1852), 301–306; "Huitième mémoire . . .," *ibid.*, 561–564; and "On the Results of the Method Introduced by the Author of Investigating the Nervous System, More Especially as Applied to the Elucidation of the Functions of the Pneumogastric and Sympathetic Nerves," in *Proceedings of the Royal Society*, **18** (1869–1870), 339–343, the Croonian lecture.

II. SECONDARY LITERATURE. See D. Denny Brown, "Augustus Volney Waller," in W. Haymaker, ed., *Foun-*

ders of Neurology (Springfield, Ill., 1953), 95–98; R. Gertler-Samuel, Augustus Volney Waller (1816–1870) als Experimentalforscher (Zurich, 1965); and D'Arcy Power, "Waller, Augustus Volney," in Dictionary of National Biography, XX, 579–580.

JUDITH P. SWAZEY

**WALLERIUS, JOHAN GOTTSCHALK** (*b.* Stora Mellösa, Nerke, Sweden, 11 July 1709; *d.* Uppsala, Sweden, 16 November 1785), *chemistry, mineralogy.*

Wallerius was the son of Erik Wallerius, a Lutheran minister, and Elisabet Tranaea. At the age of five he studied Latin, Greek, and Hebrew at home with his older brothers. Wallerius entered the Gymnasium in Strängnäs in 1722, enrolled at the University of Uppsala in 1725, and received a master's degree in philosophy in 1731. He next studied medicine and in the same year defended a thesis in anatomy, receiving an assistant professorship in medicine at Lund in 1732. He defended his doctoral dissertation there in 1735; but toward the end of the year he returned to Uppsala, where the Medical Faculty granted him the degree *venia docendi.* Wallerius practiced medicine and in 1737 was appointed superintendent at Danemarks, a spa near Uppsala, where he analyzed the spring water. As early as 1732 he had shown an interest in mining science and mineraology: en route to Lund through the Swedish mining district he studied mines and blast furnaces and collected mineral specimens. These latter formed the base of his private mineral collection, which ultimately amounted to over 4,000 specimens.

While at Lund, Wallerius studied the extensive mineral collection of Kilian Stobaeus and the famous royal collections in Copenhagen. This experience proved valuable when, at Uppsala, he had to teach chemistry to students of mining science as well as of medicine. For this purpose he installed a small private laboratory when he demonstrated chemical and pharmaceutical reactions for the medical students and where the future mining chemists could practice assaying. All participants in the course were free to ask questions and discuss the experiments. This attitude was new, and the number of students taking the course increased. The interest in chemistry at Uppsala during this period owed much to Wallerius' method of teaching.

In November 1741, Wallerius was appointed assistant professor of medicine at Uppsala, with responsibility for lectures on materia medica and later on physiology and anatomy as well. He also continued his lectures and experiments in chemistry and mineralogy. His research led to *Mineralogia eller Mineralriket* (1747), his first great work, which was received as an outstanding handbook of contemporary knowledge; never before had such a wealth of minerals been presented so systematically. Wallerius' clear and precise descriptions, which gave more weight to essential chemical properties than to exterior appearance, opened a new epoch in mineralogy. The book became widely known in Europe through translations into German, French, Russian, and (later) Latin, and served as a model for later works. The following year Wallerius published *Hydrologia eller Wattu-Riket* (1748), in which he tried to classify different kinds of water.

Wallerius was appointed the first professor of chemistry in Sweden, at Uppsala, in 1750; he continued to be responsible for metallurgy and pharmacy. Although chemistry had been taught at Uppsala for more than a century, it remained a minor subject within the Medical Faculty and lacked a spokesman of its own. The authorities used this situation as an excuse not to build a laboratory. When the chair of chemistry was placed within the Philosophical Faculty and the curriculum became part of the examination for the candidate's degree in philosophy, however, the professor also was obliged to examine the medical students and to give courses for future mining chemists. Rooms suitable for lectures had therefore to be furnished, and this need led to the construction of the university's first chemical institute.

Wallerius' courses included laboratory periods, experiments, and lectures. These were later published as *Chemia physicae*, in three volumes, which represents a summary of contemporary knowledge about chemical substances: acids, alkalies, salts, sulfur, bitumen and other combustible materials, semimetals, and metals. The work begins with a brief history of chemistry and presents the system of chemical symbols then in use, as well as a detailed description of the available chemical apparatus and the procedures. He also published his lectures on metallurgy as *Elementa metallurgiae, speciatim chemicae* (Stockholm, 1768), "which . . . has cost me innumerable experiments and much trouble."

In accord with the utilitarian tendencies of the time, Wallerius, as professor of chemistry, was called upon to show what his knowledge could contribute to economic life. Mining chemists had already demonstrated the advantages of chemistry applied to mining; and Wallerius' interest in agriculture naturally led him to pursue agricultural chemistry, especially since agriculture was of great importance for the national economy. His research proved so basic and of such scope that he was called the father of agricultural chemistry. His principal work in this field was *Agriculturae fundamenta chemica, Åkerbrukets kemiska grunder* (1761), which was published in Latin and Swedish, in parallel columns, and was later translated into German, French, Spanish, and English. Wallerius established as a fundamental, necessary principle that agricultural chemistry should be based on comparative study of the chemical composition not only of plants but also of the earth in which they grow.

Unsatisfactory working conditions in the laboratory undermined Wallerius' health; and deafness that had begun when he was young increasingly worsened. Finally, serious symptoms of illness forced him to request early retirement, which was granted in 1767. He was allowed to retain his salary in recognition of his thirty-four years devoted to the teaching of chemistry.

After his retirement Wallerius bought a farm outside Uppsala and, by actively applying his chemical theories concerning agriculture, established a model farm. These experiences are collected in *Rön, rörande landtbruket. Om svenska åkerjordarternas egenskaper och skiljemerken samt deras förbättring genom tienlig jordblanning* ("Observations of Agriculture"; 1779), which contains an essay on the qualities and differences of Swedish soils and their improvement by suitable mixing that was awarded a prize by the Royal Swedish Academy of Sciences in Stockholm.

Wallerius was by no means infatuated with innovation in chemistry, and he stubbornly held outdated beliefs. In *Tankar om verldenes, i synnerhet jordenes danande och ändring* ("Thoughts on the Creation and Change of the World, Particularly of the Earth"; 1776), which was translated into many languages, he assigned the highest authority to the biblical account of the history of creation. In chemistry he never entirely freed himself from the Becher-Stahl philosophical-chemical doctrine. Thus he became known not through new discoveries but, rather, for the new ways in which he applied chemistry to agriculture.

## BIBLIOGRAPHY

I. Original Works. Wallerius' numerous publications have appeared in various eds., and some were translated into several languages. J. R. Partington has compiled a good and extensive bibliography in *A History of Chemistry*, III (1962), 169–170, which also includes the titles of the many dissertations over which Wallerius presided and that have been printed in *Disputationum academicarum fasciculus primus cum annotationibus* (Uppsala, 1780) and . . . *fasciculus secundus* (Uppsala, 1781). It can be completed from Wallerius' autobiography, *Curriculum vitae Johan. Gotschalk Wallerii*, which ends with a bibliography that he compiled. This autobiography has been published in its entirety, with intro. and English summary, by Nils Zenzén, in *Lychnos* (1953), 235–259.

II. Secondary Literature. See C. E. Bergstrand, *Johan Gottschalk Wallerius som landtbrukskemist och praktisk jordbrukare* (". . . Wallerius as Agricultural Chemist and Practical Farmer"; Stockholm, 1885); T. Frängsmyr, *Geologi och skapelsetro* ("Geology and the Belief in Creation"; Uppsala, 1969); Hugo Olsson, *Kemiens historia i Sverige intill år 1800* (Uppsala, 1971), 108–115, 179–182, 319–321; C. W. Oseen, "En episod i den svenska kemiens historia," in *Lychnos* (1940), 73–85; J. R. Partington, *A History of Chemistry*, III (London, 1962), 169–172; E. Svedmark, "Några anteckningar om Johan Gottschalk Wallerius" ("Some Notes on . . . Wallerius"), in *Geologiska föreningens i Stockholm förhandlingar*, 7 (1885); and Nils Zenzén, "Johan Gottschalk Wallerius and Axel Fredrik Cronstedt," in Sten Lindroth, ed., *Swedish Men of Science* (Stockholm, 1952), 92–104.

Uno Boklund

**WALLICH, GEORGE CHARLES** (*b*. Calcutta, India, November 1815; *d*. Marylebone, London, England, 31 March 1899), *medicine, zoology.*

Wallich was the eldest son of Nathaniel Wallich, superintendent of the botanical gardens at Calcutta from 1815 to 1850. He was sent to Beverley (Yorkshire) and, later, to Reading Grammar School. After attending the arts classes at King's College, Aberdeen, he received an M.D. at Edinburgh University in 1836. Ironically, a classmate was Edward Forbes, proponent of the azoic theory, which held that the absolute depth to which life extended in the seas was 300 fathoms.

Wallich entered the Indian army in 1838, served in the Sutlej (1842) and Punjab (1847) campaigns with distinction, and was field surgeon during the Sonthal rebellion (1855–1856). He was invalided to England in 1857 and spent two years recuperating on Guernsey before settling in Kensington.

In 1860 Wallich shipped as naturalist on H.M.S. *Bulldog*, under the command of Sir Francis Leopold McClintock, to survey the proposed north Atlantic telegraph route between Great Britain and America (2 July–11 November). A single sounding during October in 1,260 fathoms (lat. 59° 27'N., long. 26°41'W.) brought up thirteen living starfishes (*Ophiocomae*) from the bottom—incontrovertible, although at the time generally disregarded, evidence that "The conditions prevailing at great depths . . . are not incompatible with the maintenance of animal life" as well as ". . . the inference that the deep sea has its own special fauna." Although he wrote extensively on this discovery, the majority of Wallich's scientific publications dealt with the Protozoa. He entered the *Bathybius* controversy with trenchancy, correctly opposing Huxley, who, in the course of examining a ten-year-old collection of sea-bottom samples, found a gelatinous substance that he took to be a primitive form of life and named after Ernst Haeckel. The substance was later determined by J. Y. Buchanan to be a precipitate of calcium sulfate caused by the alcohol in which the samples were preserved.

The year before his death, Wallich was awarded the gold medal of the Linnean Society of London "in recognition of his researches into the problems connected with bathybial and pelagic life."

*BIBLIOGRAPHY*

I. Original Works. Wallich's writings include *Notes on the Presence of Animal Life at Vast Depths in the Sea* (London, 1860); "Results of Soundings in the North Atlantic," in *Annals and Magazine of Natural History*, 3rd ser., **6** (1860), 457–458; "On the Existence of Animal Life at Great Depths in the Sea," *ibid.*, **7** (1861), 396–399; *The North Atlantic Sea-Bed* (London, 1862); "On the Value of the Distinctive Characters in Amoeba," in *Annals and Magazine of Natural History*, 3rd ser., **12** (1863), 111–151; "On the Vital Functions of the Deep-Sea Protozoa," in *Monthly Microscopical Journal*, **1** (1869), 32–41; "On the Radiolaria as an Order of the Protozoa," in *Popular Science Review*, **17** (1878), 267–281, 368–382; "The Threshold of Evolution," *ibid.*, **19** (1880), 143–155; and "Critical Observations on Prof. Leidy's 'Freshwater Rhizopods of North America,' and Classification of the Rhizopods in General," in *Annals and Magazine of Natural History*, 5th ser., **16** (1885), 317–334, 453–473.

II. Secondary Literature. See "Surgeon-Major G. C. Wallich, M.D.," in *Nature*, **60** (4 May 1899), 13; and obituaries in *Indian Medical Gazette*, **34** (1899), 227–228; *Lancet* (8 Apr. 1899), 997; *Journal of the Royal Microscopical Society* (1899), 263–264; and *Transactions and Proceedings of the Botanical Society of Edinburgh*, **21** (1900), 222–224.

Daniel Merriman

**WALLINGFORD.** See **Richard of Wallingford.**

**WALLIS, JOHN** (*b*. Ashford, Kent, England, 3 December 1616; *d*. Oxford, England, 8 November 1703), *mathematics*.

Wallis was the third child of John Wallis and his second wife, Joanna Chapman. His father studied at Trinity College, Cambridge, and after having taken holy orders became minister at Ashford, about 1603. Standing in great esteem and reputation in his town and parish, he died when John was barely six.

Young John grew up, together with his two older sisters and two younger brothers, in the care of his mother. After he had received his first education, he was sent in 1625 to a grammar school at Tenterden, Kent, where, according to his autobiography,[1] he enjoyed a thorough training in Latin. In 1631–1632 Wallis attended the famous school of Martin Holbeach at Felsted, Essex. Besides more Latin and Greek he also learned some Hebrew and was introduced to the elements of logic. As mathematics was not part of the grammar school curriculum, he obtained his first insight into this field during a vacation; he studied what a brother of his had learned in approximately three months as preparation for a trade.

Wallis entered Emanuel College, Cambridge, the "Puritan College," about Christmas 1632 as a pensioner. He not only took the traditional undergraduate courses (obtaining his bachelor of arts degree early in 1637), followed by studies in theology, but he also studied physic, anatomy, astronomy, geography, and other parts of natural philosophy and what was then called mathematics—although the latter "were scarce looked upon, with us, as Academical Studies then in fashion." He was the first student of Francis Glisson to defend the doctrine of the circulation of the blood in a public disputation.

In 1640 Wallis received the degree of master of arts and was ordained by the bishop of Winchester. For some years he earned his living as private chaplain and as minister in London. From 1644, after the outbreak of the Civil War, he also acted as secretary to the Assembly of Divines at Westminster, which was charged with proposing a new form of church government. For about a year he also held a fellowship at Queens' College, Cambridge, in consequence of a Parliamentary ordinance. He gave up this position when he married Susanna Glyde of Northiam, Sussex, on 14 March 1645.

Wallis' appointment as Savilian professor of geometry at Oxford on 14 June 1649 must have come as a surprise to many; his accomplishments thus far, with one exception, had had little to do with mathematics. His predecessor, Peter Turner, was a Royalist who had been dismissed by an order of Parliament; Wallis had rendered valuable services not only as a secretary to the Assembly of Divines but also by his skill in deciphering captured coded letters for the Parliamentarians. Few people in 1649 could have foreseen that within a few years the thirty-two-year-old theologian would become one of the leading mathematicians of his time.

This appointment determined Wallis' career; he held the chair until his death more than half a century later. In addition, in 1657–1658 he was elected—by a somewhat doubtful procedure—custos archivarum (keeper of the archives) to the university, an office he also held for life. In 1654 he had been admitted doctor of divinity. At the Restoration Wallis was confirmed in his offices for having possessed the courage to sign the remonstrance against the execution of King Charles I; he also received the title of royal chaplain to Charles II. When in 1692 Queen Mary II offered Wallis the deanery of Hereford, he declined, hinting that favors for his son and his son-in-law Blencowe would be more welcome signs of recognition of his services to his country.

These achievements include the mathematical works, helping found the Royal Society; his work in the decipherment of code letters for the government; logic; teaching deaf mutes to speak and the related grammatical and phonetical writings; archival studies and his assistance to the university in legal affairs; theological activities as a preacher and author of treatises and books; and the editions (many of them first editions) of mathematical and musical manuscripts of ancient Greek authors.

The first two decades of the Savilian professorship were the most creative period in Wallis' life. He later increasingly turned to editing works of other scientists (J. Horrox, W. Oughtred, and Greek authors) and his own earlier works, and to the preparation of historical and theological discourses. His *Opera mathematica* appeared between 1693 and 1699, financed by and printed at the university.

Wallis enjoyed vigorous health throughout his life. His powers of intellect were remarkable, and he was renowned for his skill in public disputations. But he also possessed a highly contentious disposition and became involved in many violent controversies—the more so since modesty does not seem to have been one of his virtues. Nevertheless he had many devoted friends. It was for Thomas Smith, vice-president of Magdalen College, Oxford, and librarian at the Cottonian Library, London, that Wallis wrote his autobiography in 1697; and Samuel Pepys commissioned Sir Godfrey Kneller to paint a full-length portrait of "that great man and my most honoured friend, Dr. Wallis, to be lodged as an humble present of mine (though a Cambridge-man) to my dear Aunt the University of Oxford."[2] Wallis was interred in St. Mary's, the university church, and an epitaph by his son was placed in the wall near his burial place: "Joannes Wallis, S.T.P., Geometriae Professor Savilianus, et Custos Archivarum Oxon. Hic dormit. Opera reliquit immortalia . . ." ("Here sleeps John Wallis, Doctor of Theology, Savilian Professor of Geometry, and Keeper of the Oxford Archives. He left immortal works. . . ."[3])

**Mathematics.** Wallis reports in his *Algebra*[4] that his interest in mathematics (beyond the little that he may have learned at Cambridge) was first aroused in 1647 or 1648, when he chanced upon a copy of William Oughtred's *Clavis mathematicae*. After having mastered it in a few weeks, he rediscovered Cardano's solution of the cubic equation (not given by Oughtred) and, continuing where Oughtred had left off, composed in 1648 a *Treatise of Angular Sections*, which remained unpublished until 1685. In the same year, at the request of Cambridge professor of mathematics John Smith, the Platonist (1618–1652), he gave an explanation of Descartes's treatment of the fourth-degree equation. The basic idea, to write the equation as a product of two quadratic factors, could be derived from Harriot's *Artis analyticae praxis* (published posthumously in 1631); yet Wallis repeatedly claimed not to have known this book in 1648. Such was the total evidence of his mathematical talents that Wallis presented when he was made Savilian professor of geometry in 1649.

With a rare energy and perseverance, he now took up the systematic study of all the major mathematical literature available to him in the Savilian and the Bodleian libraries in Oxford. According to the statutes of his chair, Wallis had to give public lectures on the thirteen books of Euclid, on the *Conics* of Apollonius, and on all of Archimedes' work. He was also to offer introductory courses in practical and theoretical arithmetic—with a free choice of textbooks therein. Lectures on other subjects such as cosmography, plane and spherical trigonometry, applied geometry, mechanics, and the theory of music were suggested but not obligatory according to the statutes.

An outcome of his elementary lectures was the *Mathesis universalis, seu opus arithmeticum* (1657). Its treatment of notation, including a historical survey, stressed the great advantages of a suggestive and unified symbolism; yet the influence of Oughtred (who had developed a rather special notation) sometimes makes itself felt—to no great advantage. On the whole, this work reflects the rather weak state of mathematical learning in the universities at the time.

In the treatise *De sectionibus conicis* (1655) Wallis dealt with a classical subject in a new way.[5] He considered the conic sections merely as plane curves, once he had obtained them by sections of a cone, and subjected them to the analytical treatment introduced by Descartes rather than to the traditional synthetic approach. In addition, he employed infinitesimals in the sense of Cavalieri and Torricelli. Here he also first introduced the sign for infinity and used $1/\infty$ to represent, for example, the height of an infinitely small triangle. Although Mydorge in adherence to the ancient methods had obtained a certain simplification of the treatment in 1631, Wallis was rather proud of his achievement; he may not have known Mydorge's *De sectionibus conicis* at the time of writing. Shortly afterward, in 1659, Jan de Witt's valuable treatise *Elementa curvarum linearum*, also employing the analytic symbolism, appeared in Amsterdam. Yet, on the whole, the new viewpoint was accepted only slowly by mathematicians.

Together with his conic sections Wallis published the book on which his fame as a mathematician is grounded, *Arithmetica infinitorum*; the title page is dated 1656, but printing had been completed in the summer of 1655. It resulted mainly from his study of Torricelli's *Opera geometrica* (1644), for Cavalieri's basic work on the methods of indivisibles was unavailable. At first Wallis' attempts to apply these methods to the quadrature of the circle met with failure; and not even a study of the voluminous *Opus geometricum* (1647) of Gregory of St. Vincent, which was devoted to this subject, would help. But then, by an ingenious and daring sequence of interpolations, he produced his famous result[6]

$$\frac{4}{\pi} = \frac{3}{2} \cdot \frac{3}{4} \cdot \frac{5}{4} \cdot \frac{5}{6} \cdot \frac{7}{6} \cdots.$$

Although the method was mistrusted by such eminent mathematicians as Fermat and Huygens, the result was ascertained by numerical computation.

Wallis' main interest lay not with the demonstration, but with the investigation. Actually searching for the value of

$$\int_0^1 (1-x^2)^{\frac{1}{2}} \, dx = \frac{\pi}{4},$$

he considered the generalized integral

$$I(k, n) = \int_0^1 (1 - x^{1/k})^n \, dx.$$

Its reciprocal $1 : I(k, n)$ he tabulated first for integral values of $k$ and $n$ (receiving the symmetric array of the binomical coefficients or figurated numbers), then for the fractions $k = \frac{1}{2}, \frac{3}{2}, \frac{5}{2}, \cdots$; for, with $k = n = 1/2$, this should yield $1 : I\left(\frac{1}{2}, \frac{1}{2}\right) = \frac{4}{\pi}$, for which he wrote the symbol $\square$. Then each second value of the row and column which met at $\square$ was a certain (fractional) multiple of $\square$. Assuming that all rows and columns in his table would continually increase, Wallis was able to derive two sequences of upper and lower bounds for $\square$, respectively. When these sequences are continued indefinitely, they yield his famous infinite product. William Brouncker soon transformed it into a regular continued fraction, which Wallis included in his book.

Wallis' method of interpolation—he himself gave it this name, which has become a *terminus technicus*—is based on the assumption of continuity, and, incidentally, seems closely related to the procedure he had to apply when he deciphered coded letters. To preserve this continuity and thereby the underlying mathematical law in his table, Wallis went to the utmost limit. He admitted fractional multiples of the type $A \cdot \frac{0}{1} \cdot \frac{2}{3} \cdot \frac{4}{5} \cdot \frac{6}{7} \cdots$, claiming that $A$ here should be infinite so that the value of the product was a finite number. One must emphasize the kind of "functional thinking" revealed here—not on the basis of geometric curves but of sequences of numerical expressions, that is, tabulated functions.

There are many more remarkable results of a related nature in the *Arithmetica infinitorum*, in the tracts on the cycloid and the cissoid, and in the *Mechanica*.[7] The integral $I(k, n)$ may in fact, by the substitution $x \to y^k$, be transformed into the normal form of the beta integral. He soon derived analytically the integral for the arc length of an ellipse and reduced other integrals to the elliptic one. But more important than the individual problems that Wallis mastered was the novelty of his approach—his analytic viewpoint, in contrast to the traditional geometric one—at a time when the symbolism of analysis had not yet been properly developed. The best documentation of his new "functional thinking" is provided in the *Arithmetica infinitorum*; he finally plots the graphs of the family of functions the values of which he had so far evaluated only for a sequence of distinct points. There he considers not so much the single curves as the sequence of them, since the parameter changes from one integral value to the next. The answer to his question of what the equations of these curves would be for fractional values of the parameter—another type of interpolation and example of "continuous thinking"—was given by Euler by means of the gamma function, the generalized factorial.

The *Arithmetica infinitorum* exerted a singularly important effect on Newton when he studied it in the winter of 1664–1665.[8] Newton generalized even more than Wallis by keeping the upper limit of the integrals $I(k, n)$ variable. He thus arrived at the binomial theorem by way of Wallisian interpolation procedures. In a few cases the binomial expansion could be checked by algebraic division and root extraction; but, just as in the case of Wallis' product, a rigorous justification had to wait until mathematical techniques had been much refined.

The publication of the *Arithmetica infinitorum* immediately provoked a mathematical challenge from Fermat. He directed "to Wallis and the other English mathematicians," some numerical questions: To find a cube, which added to all its aliquot parts will make a square (such as $7^3 + 7^2 + 7 + 1 = 20^2$), and to find a square number, which added to all its aliquot parts, will make a cube.[9] Fermat, lawyer and councillor of the *parlement* in Toulouse, had added: "We await these solutions, which, if England or Belgic or Celtic Gaul do not produce, Narbonese Gaul will." Besides Wallis, Brouncker, later the first president of the Royal Society, participated in the contest on the side of the English. On the Continent, Frenicle de Bessy applied his great skill in handling large numbers. Wallis at first highly underestimated the difficulty as well as the theoretical foundation of Fermat's questions; and Fermat added further problems in 1657–1658. Wallis maintained the number 1 to be a valid solution, and in return drew up some superficially similar questions. His method of solution was more or less that of trial and error, based on intelligent guessing, and in some ways was not unrelated to the procedures employed in his *Arithmetica infinitorum*. Until the end of his life Wallis

had no idea of the number-theoretical insights that Fermat had obtained—nor could he, since his challenger did not reveal them. Afraid that the French mathematicians might reap all the glory from this contest, Wallis obtained permission to publish the letters: the *Commercium epistolicum* appeared in 1658. The last chapter of his *Discourse of Combinations, Alternations, and Aliquot Parts* (1685) deals with "Monsieur Fermat's Problems Concerning Divisors and Aliquot Parts." Finally, among his manuscripts there are also a number of attempts to solve some of Fermat's problems, including the "Theorema Fermatianum Negativum" that $a^3 + b^3 = c^3$ is not possible in integral or rational numbers and another negative theorem that there does not exist a right triangle with square area.[10]

But number theory had no special appeal to Wallis—nor to any other mathematician of the time, Frenicle excepted. This was so partly because it was hardly applicable, as Wallis himself emphasized and partly because it did not suit the taste of seventeenth- and eighteenth-century mathematicians, Euler being a notable exception. Fermat, who had glimpsed the treasures of number theory and had recognized its intrinsic mathematical value, did little to introduce his fellow mathematicians to the subject. Thus the general judgment about the contest had to be based on Wallis' *Commercium epistolicum*, and the editor did not hesitate to underline the achievements he and Brouncker had made. No wonder that his fame was now firmly established throughout Europe.

Wallis also participated in the competition in which Pascal in the summer of 1658 asked for quadratures, cubatures, and centers of gravity of certain figures limited by cycloidal arcs.[11] Neither Wallis nor Lalouvère, who also competed for the prize, satisfied Pascal, and no prize was awarded. This was not quite fair, and in 1659 Wallis replied with *Tractatus duo . . . de cycloide et . . . de cissoide*. Here, as well as in the second part of his voluminous *Mechanica, sive de motu tractatus geometricus* (1669–1671), he again relied on his analytic methods. This second part, on the calculation of centers of gravity, is the major part of the *Mechanica*, and in it Wallis carried on the analytical investigations of the 1650's.

The first part deals with various forms of motion in a strictly "geometrical," that is, Euclidean, manner, starting with definitions followed by propositions. The motion of bodies under the action of gravity is covered in particular. The final chapter of the first part is devoted to a treatment of the balance and introduces the idea of moment, which is essential for the inquiries into the centers of gravity. In the third part, Wallis returns not only to the elementary machines, according to ancient tradition, but above all to a thorough treatment of the problems on percussion. In 1668 percussion and impact were a major topic of discussion at the Royal Society, and Wallis, Wren, and Huygens submitted papers.[12] In the *Mechanica*, Wallis extended his investigations, studying the behavior of both elastic and inelastic bodies. Although in style and subject matter it is not a uniform book, at the time it certainly was one of the most important and comprehensive in its field. It represents a major advance in the mathematization of mechanics, but it was superseded in 1687 by a much greater one—Newton's *Principia*.

Wallis' last great mathematical book was *Treatise of Algebra, Both Historical and Practical* (1685), the fruit of many years' labor.[13] As its title suggests, it was to combine a full exposition of algebra with its history, a feat never previously attempted by any author. The book was Wallis' only major mathematical work to be published in the vernacular. (In 1693 an augmented Latin translation was issued as vol. II of his *Opera mathematica*.)

Of the 100 chapters, the first fourteen trace the history of the subject up to the time of Viète, with emphasis on the development of mathematical notation. The subsequent practical introduction to algebra (chapters 15–63) was based almost entirely on Oughtred's *Clavis mathematicae*, Harriot's *Artis analyticae praxis*, and *An Introduction to Algebra* (1668), Thomas Brancker's translation of J. H. Rahn's *Teutsche Algebra* (1659), with numerous additions by John Pell, Rahn's former teacher. This fact alone signals the great bias Wallis had developed in favor of his countrymen. It becomes even more obvious in the passages where the author claimed that Descartes had obtained his algebraical knowledge from Harriot. Criticisms of Wallis' one-sided account were raised immediately and have continued since. After an insertion concerning the application of algebra to geometry and geometrical interpretations of algebraic facts (chapters 64–72, including an attempt to give a representation of imaginary numbers),[14] Wallis devoted the final twenty-eight chapters to a subject that one would hardly look for in a book on algebra today: a discussion of the methods of exhaustion and of indivisibles, again with reference to the *Arithmetica infinitorum*. Thus the new methods were

still considered as an extension of an old subject rather than as a wholly new field of mathematics.

The *Algebra* also includes an exposition of the method of infinite series and the first printed account, much augmented in the second edition, of some of Newton's pioneering results. Wallis had long been afraid that foreigners might claim the glory of Newton's achievements by publishing some of his ideas as their own before Newton himself had done so. He therefore repeatedly warned his younger colleague at Cambridge not to delay but to leave perfection of his methods to later editions.[15] (Volume III of the *Opera* [1699] contains an *Epistolarum collectio*, of which the most important part is the correspondence between Newton and Leibniz, in particular Newton's famous "Epistola prior" and "Epistola posterior" of 1676.)

Apart from some editions of Greek mathematical classics, the *Algebra* with its several supplementary treatises—*Cono-Cuneus* (a study in analytic three-dimensional geometry), *Angular Sections*,[16] *Angle of Contact*, and *Combinations, Alternations, and Aliquot Parts*—marked the end of the stream of mathematical works. Even without the polemics against Hobbes and some minor pieces, they fill three large volumes.

Wallis helped shape over half a century of mathematics in England. He bore the greatest share of all the efforts made during this time to raise mathematics to the eminence it enjoyed on the Continent. The center of mathematical research and of the "new science" in Galileo's time lay in Italy. It then shifted northward, especially to France and the Netherlands. Because of Wallis' preparative work and Newton's genius, it rested in Britain for a while, until through the influence of Leibniz, the Bernoullis, and Euler it moved back to the Continent.

**Nonmathematical Work.** Wallis first exhibited his mental powers early in the Civil War (1642 or 1643), when by chance he was shown a letter written in cipher and succeeded in decoding it within a few hours.[17] Because more letters were given to him by the Parliamentarians, rumors were later spread that he had deciphered important royal letters that had fallen into their hands. Wallis strenuously denied the accusation, and it is very unlikely that he revealed anything harmful to the royal family or the public safety—if indeed he came across such information. On the contrary, the confirmation of his offices at the Restoration may well have been a sign of gratitude to him by Charles II. For many years Wallis continued to decipher intercepted letters for the government, especially after the Revolution. In old age he taught the art to his grandson William Blencowe but refused to disclose it when Leibniz on behalf of his government requested information on it.

In his autobiography, written in January 1697, when he was over eighty, Wallis referred to one of his first successes more than half a century earlier:

> Being encouraged by this success, beyond expectation; I afterwards ventured on many others (some of more, some of less difficulty) and scarce missed of any that I undertook, for many years, during our civil Wars, and afterwards. But of late years, *the French Methods of Cipher* are grown so intricate beyond what it was wont to be, that I have failed of many; tho' I did have master'd divers of them.[18]

Of great importance for much of his later scientific work was his introduction, while living in London, to a group interested in the "new" natural and experimental sciences—the circle from which the Royal Society emerged soon after the Restoration.[19] To Wallis we owe one of the few reports on those early meetings that give direct evidence.

> About the year 1645, while I lived in *London* (at a time, when, by our Civil Wars, Academical Studies were much interrupted in both our Universities:) beside the Conversation of divers eminent Divines, as to matters Theological; I had the opportunity of being acquainted with divers worthy Persons, inquisitive into Natural Philosophy, and other parts of Humane Learning; and Particularly of what hath been called the *New Philosophy* or *Experimental Philosophy*.
>
> We did by agreement, divers of us, meet weekly in *London* on a certain day, to treat and discours of such affairs. . . .
>
> These meetings we held sometimes at *Dr. Goddards* lodgings in *Woodstreet* (or some convenient place near) on occasion of his keeping an Operator in his house, for grinding Glasses for Telescopes and Microscopes; and sometime at a convenient place in *Cheap-side*; sometime at *Gresham College* or some place near adjoyning.
>
> Our business was (precluding matters of Theology and State Affairs) to discours and consider of *Philosophical Enquiries*, and such as related thereunto; as *Physick, Anatomy, Geometry, Astronomy, Navigation, Staticks, Magneticks, Chymicks, Mechanicks*, and *Natural Experiments*; with the State of these Studies, as then cultivated, at home and abroad. We there discoursed of the *Circulation of the Blood, the Valves in the Veins, the Venae Lacteae, the Lymphatick vessels, the Copernican Hypothesis, the Nature of Comets, and New Stars, the Satellites of Jupiter, the Oval Shape* (as it then appeared) *of Sat-*

*urn, the spots in the Sun, and its Turning on its own Axis, the Inequalities and Selenography of the Moon, the several Phases of Venus and Mercury, the Improvement of Telescopes, and grinding of Glasses for that purpose, the Weight of Air, the Possibility or Impossibility of Vacuities, and Natures Abhorrence thereof; the Torricellian Experiment in Quicksilver, the Descent of heavy Bodies, and the degrees of Acceleration therein;* and divers other things of like nature. Some of which were then but New Discoveries, and others not so generally known and imbraced, as now they are; With other things appertaining to what hath been called *The New Philosophy;* which from the times of *Galileo* at *Florence*, and *S$^r$ Francis Bacon (Lord Verulam)* in *England*, hath been much cultivated in *Italy, France, Germany*, and other Parts abroad, as well as with us in *England*.

> About the year 1648, 1649, some of our company being removed to *Oxford* (first *D$^r$ Wilkins*, then I, and soon after *D$^r$ Goddard*) our company divided. Those in *London* continued to meet there as before (and we with them, when we had occasion to be there;) and those of us at *Oxford* . . . continued such meetings in *Oxford*; and brought those Studies into fashion there. . . .
>
> Those meetings in *London* continued, and (after the Kings Return in 1660) were increased with the accession of divers worthy and Honorable Persons; and were afterwards incorporated by the name of *the Royal Society*, etc. and so continue to this day.

While the Royal Society of London did indeed grow and continue, the Oxford offspring suffered a less happy fate. After a period of decline and interruption it seems to have flourished again in the 1680's when Wallis was elected its president and tried to establish closer contacts with the mother society and similar groups in Scotland. But Oldenburg, secretary of the London society, initiated publication of the *Philosophical Transactions* and thereby provided a more permanent means of scientific exchange than personal intercourse and weekly discussions.[20] Wallis made ample use of the *Transactions*; and between 1666 and 1702 he published more than sixty papers and book reviews. The reviews concerned mathematical books, but the papers were more wide-ranging.[21] One of the leading scientists among the early fellows of the Royal Society, he was also one of the most energetic in promoting it and helping it to achieve its goals, at a time when not a few of these virtuosi were men without a real understanding of the scientific experiments conducted and of the complex theories behind them.

Wallis' most successful work was his *Grammatica linguae anglicanae*, with a *Praxis grammatica* and a treatise, *De loquela*, on the production of the sounds of speech. First published in 1652, the sixth, and last, edition in England appeared in 1765; it was also published on the Continent.

In his *History of Modern Colloquial English*, H. C. Wyld emphasized that Wallis "has considerable merits as an observer of sounds, he has good powers of discrimination, nor is he led astray by the spelling like all the sixteenth-century grammarians, and Bullokar, Gill, and Butler in the seventeenth."[22] He then continued to discuss some of Wallis' more noteworthy observations. A much more detailed account is given in M. Lehnert's monograph.[23]

Wallis' *Treatise of Speech* formed a useful theoretical foundation for his pioneering attempts to teach deaf-mutes how to speak. In 1661 and 1662 Wallis instructed two young men, Daniel Whaley and Alexander Popham; the latter had previously been taught by Dr. William Holder. Wallis presented Whaley to the Royal Society on 21 May 1662 and in 1670 reported on his instruction of Popham in the *Philosophical Transactions* — failing to mention Holder's teaching.[24] This unfair act eventually (1678) led to a bitter attack by Holder, to which Wallis replied in no less hostile words.[25]

This was one of the many violent quarrels in which Wallis became involved. Although readily inclined to boast of his achievements and to appropriate the ideas of others for further development, he did not always acknowledge his debt to his predecessors. Furthermore he was often carried away by his temper and would reply without restraint to criticism. He thus quarreled with Holder, Henry Stubbe, Lewis Maydwell, and Fermat; and his longest and most bittered dispute, with Thomas Hobbes, dragged on for over a quarter of a century.[26] Despite, or rather because of, his limited mathematical knowledge, Hobbes claimed in 1655 to possess an absolute quadrature of the circle. Somewhat later he also purported to have solved another of the great mathematical problems — the duplication of the cube. Hobbes's chief transgression, however, was in having dared to criticize Wallis' *Arithmetica infinitorum*. The controversy soon degenerated into the most virulent hostility, which gave rise to wild accusations and abusive language. The quarrel ended only with Hobbes's death in 1679. J. F. Scott has suggested that Wallis' relentless attacks may have been partly motivated by Hobbes's increasing influence, especially as author of the *Leviathan*, and by Wallis' fear that Hobbes's teachings would undermine respect for the Christian religion.

As keeper of the archives, Wallis rendered considerable services to his university. In his brief account of Wallis' life, David Gregory said, "He put the records, and other papers belonging to the University that were under his care into such exact order, and managed its lawsuits with such dexterity and success that he quickly convinced all, even those who made the greatest noise against this election, how fitt he was for the post."[27] A successor as keeper, Reginald L. Poole, also praised Wallis' work: "He left his mark on the Archives in numerous transcripts, but above all by the Repertory of the entire collection which he made on the basis of Mr. Twyne's list in 1664 and which continues to this day the standard catalogue."[28] Wallis' catalogue was not replaced until even later in the twentieth century. Although not a practicing musician, Wallis composed some papers on musical theory that were published in the *Philosophical Transactions*,[29] and he edited works on harmony by Ptolemy, Porphyrius, and Bryennius. One of his papers reports his observation of the "trembling" of consonant strings, while others contain a mathematical discussion of the intervals of the musical scale and the resulting need for temperament in tuning an organ or other keyboard instrument. In an appendix to Ptolemy's *Harmonics*, Wallis attempted to explain the surprising effects attributed to ancient music (which he rendered in modern notation); and he also dealt with these effects in a separate paper. Finally he contributed extended remarks on Thomas Salmon's *Proposal to Perform Musick, in Perfect and Mathematical Proportions* (London, 1688), the forerunner of which, *An Essay to the Advancement of Musick* (London, 1672), had aroused great interest as well as conflicting views.

**Theology.** From 1690 to 1692 Wallis published a series of eight letters and three sermons on the doctrine of the Holy Trinity, directed against the Unitarians. In order to explain this doctrine he introduced an analogous example from mathematics: a cubical body with three dimensions, length, breadth, and height; and compared the mystery of the Trinity with the cube:

> This *longum, latum, profundum,* (Long, Broad, and Tall), is but *One* Cube; of *Three Dimensions,* and yet but *One Body.* And this *Father, Son,* and *Holy-Ghost*: Three Persons, and yet but One God.[30]

Wallis' discourses on the Trinity met with marked approval from various theological quarters. It was even used in Pierre Bayle's famous *Diction-*

*naire historique et critique* in a note to the article on Abailard. Bayle wished to vindicate Abailard of the charge of Tritheism,[31] which had been raised against him for having used an analogy between the Trinity and the syllogism that consists of proposition, assumption, and conclusion. Just as nobody doubts the orthodoxy of Wallis on the basis of his geometrical example, Bayle argued, there was no reason to attack Abailard for his analogy of the syllogism.

Wallis' sermons and other theological works, often praised for their simple and straightforward language, testify that his religious principles were Calvinist, according to the literal sense of the Church of England. He never denied the Puritanism in which he had grown up, although he remained a loyal member of the official church.

From his student days, Wallis sided with the Parliamentarians, and Cromwell is said to have had a great respect for him. As secretary to the Assembly of Divines at Westminster during the Civil War, Wallis became thoroughly familiar with the controversial issues within the Episcopal Church and between the Church and Parliament. Included in his autobiography is a rather long intercalation about this assembly, which was convened to suggest a new form of church government in place of the episcopacy.[32] His interpretation of proceedings carried on half a century earlier might have been somewhat colored by the actual events that followed. The episcopacy was, after all, not abolished; and Wallis had tried to stay on good terms with the bishops and archbishops. Toward the end of the century he strongly opposed the introduction of the Gregorian calendar in England, considering it a kind of submission to Rome. The new calendar was not in fact adopted in Britain until 1752. Some of Wallis' friends and colleagues in the Royal Society exchanged their university posts for careers in the church, but Wallis himself was never given the opportunity. Obviously his trimming politics had made him not totally acceptable to the monarchy, although he did enjoy signs of royal favor. As he himself expressed it, he was "willing whatever side was upmost, to promote (as I was able) any good design for the true Interest of Religion, of Learning, and the publick good."[33]

## NOTES

1. C. J. Scriba, "The Autobiography . . .," 24.
2. J. R. Tanner, ed., *Private Correspondence and Miscellaneous Papers of Samuel Pepys, 1679–1703*, II (London, 1926), 257.

3. "S.T.P." is the usual abbreviation for Doctors of Divinity in inscriptions; Wallis was never created professor of theology.
4. J. Wallis, *Algebra*, ch. 46.
5. See H. Wieleitner, "Die Verdienste."
6. For a more detailed description, see Sir T. P. Nunn, "The Arithmetic"; J. F. Scott, *The Mathematical Work*, ch. 4; and D. T. Whiteside, "Patterns of Mathematical Thought in the Later Seventeenth Century," in *Archives for History of Exact Sciences*, 1 (1961), 179–388, esp. 236–243.
7. See W. Kutta, "Elliptische," and A. Prag, "John Wallis," esp. 391–395.
8. D. T. Whiteside, "Newton's Discovery of the General Binomial Theorem," in *Mathematical Gazette*, 45 (1961), 175–180; and *The Mathematical Papers of Isaac Newton*, D. T. Whiteside, ed., I (Cambridge, 1967), 96–111.
9. See G. Wertheim, "P. Fermats Streit . . .," and J. E. Hofmann, "Neues über Fermats. . . ."
10. See C. J. Scriba, *Studien . . .*, chs. 2–3.
11. See K. Hara, "Pascal et Wallis . . .," and J. Hofmann and J. E. Hofmann, "Erste Quadratur der Kissoide," in *Deutsche Mathematik*, 5 (1941), 571–584.
12. See A. R. Hall, "Mechanics and the Royal Society, 1668–1670," in *British Journal for the History of Science*, 3 (1966–1967), 24–38.
13. See J. F. Scott, "John Wallis."
14. See G. Eneström, "Die geometrische Darstellung."
15. See C. J. Scriba, "Neue Dokumente zur Entstehungsgeschichte des Prioritätsstreites zwischen Leibniz und Newton um die Erfindung der Infinitesimalrechnung," in *Akten des Internationalen Leibniz-Kongresses Hannover, 14.–19. November 1966*, II. *Mathematik-Naturwissenschaften* (Wiesbaden, 1969), 69–78.
16. See C. J. Scriba, *Studien*, ch. 1.
17. See D. E. Smith, "John Wallis," and D. Kahn, *The Codebreakers* (New York, 1967), 166–169.
18. See C. J. Scriba, "The Autobiography," 38.
19. Different opinions have been expressed as to whether the Royal Society emerged from the London group described by Wallis or from an independent Oxford group in existence before Wallis came to Oxford in 1649. For a champion of the latter view, see M. Purver, *The Royal Society: Concept and Creation* (London, 1967). A brief review of this is C. J. Scriba, "Zur Entstehung der Royal Society," in *Sudhoffs Archiv für Geschichte der Medizin und der Naturwissenschaften*, 52 (1968), 269–271. There is an extended debate, in three articles by P. M. Rattansi, C. Hill, and A. R. Hall and M. B. Hall, in *Notes and Records. Royal Society of London*, 23 (1968), 129–168, where further references are given. It seems to be without doubt that the London group cannot be ignored. Wallis' report is taken from "The Autobiography," 39–40.
20. Wallis' correspondence with Oldenburg is printed in *The Correspondence of Henry Oldenburg*, A. R. Hall and M. Boas Hall, eds. (Madison, Wis., 1965–     ).
21. For a not quite complete list of Wallis' publications in the *Philosophical Transactions of the Royal Society*, see J. F. Scott, *The Mathematical Work*, 231–233; paper no. 62 is not by Wallis.
22. H. C. Wyld, *A History of Modern Colloquial English*, 3rd ed. (Oxford, 1936; repr. 1953), 170.
23. M. Lehnert, in *Die Grammatik*, criticizes the older work by L. Morel, *De Johannis Wallisii*, as insufficient. See also A. B. Melchior, "Sir Thomas Smith and John Wallis," in *English Studies*, 53 (1972), and his review of John Wallis, "Grammar of the English Language," in *English Studies*, 55 (1974), 83–85.
24. *Philosophical Transactions of the Royal Society*, 5, no. 61 (18 July 1670), 1087–1097 (pagination repeated).
25. W. Holder. *A Supplement*; J. Wallis, *A Defense*.
26. See J. F. Scott, *The Mathematical Work*, ch. 10.
27. Bodleian Library Oxford, MS Smith 31, p. 58; J. Collier, *A Supplement*.

28. R. L. Poole, *A Lecture on the History of the University Archives* (Oxford, 1912), 25.
29. *Philosophical Transactions of the Royal Society*, **12**, no. 134 (23 Apr. 1677), 839–842; **20**, no. 238 (Mar. 1698), 80–84; **20**, no. 242 (July 1698), 249–256; **20**, no. 243 (Aug. 1698), 297–303. See L. S. Lloyd, "Musical Theory in the Early *Philosophical Transactions*," in *Notes and Records. Royal Society of London*, **3** (1940–1941), 149–157.
30. Quoted from R. C. Archibald, "Wallis on the Trinity," 36.
31. See the query by E. H. Neville, "Wallis on the Trinity," 197, who quotes the 5th ed., I (Amsterdam, 1734), 30. In the new ed. (Paris, 1820), it is I, 59–60, note M.
32. See Scriba, "The Autobiography," 31–37.
33. *Ibid.*, 43.

## BIBLIOGRAPHY

I. ORIGINAL WORKS. Most of Wallis' publications (including pamphlets and sermons) are listed in the British Museum catalog, but a complete bibliography is still a desideratum. Wallis collected his more important books and some articles in his *Opera mathematica*, 3 vols. (Oxford, 1693–1699), repr. with intro. by C. J. Scriba (Hildesheim–New York, 1972). The table of contents in vol. I contains a list of books that were originally not planned for inclusion in the *Opera mathematica*, which was to consist of two volumes only. A selection of mathematical and nonmathematical works taken from this list and augmented by additional material is included in vol. III.

The *Opera mathematica* should not be confused with the *Operum mathematicorum pars prima* and *pars secunda*, published in 1657 and 1656 [sic], respectively. Vol. I contains *Oratio inauguralis*; *Mathesis universalis, sive arithmeticum opus integrum*; *Adversus Meibomii De proportionibus dialogum, tractatus elenctibus*; and *M. Mersenni locus notatur*. Vol. II contains *De angulo contactus et semicirculo disquisitio geometrica*; *De sectionibus conicis, nova methodo expositis, tractatus*; *Arithmetica infinitorum* (already printed and in some copies distributed in 1655), and the brief *Eclipsis solaris observatio*.

Works cited in the text and in the notes include the reply to W. Holder, *A Supplement to the Philosophical Transactions of July 1670, With Some Reflexions on Dr. John Wallis, His Letter There Inserted* (London, 1678), which Wallis issued under the title *A Defence of the Royal Society, and the Philosophical Transactions, Particularly Those of July 1670, in Answer to the Cavils of Dr. William Holder* (London, 1678); and the voluminous *Treatise of Algebra, Both Historical and Practical, Showing the Original, Progress, and Advancement Thereof, From Time to Time; and by What Steps It Hath Attained to the Height at Which Now It Is* (London, 1685; enl. Latin version in vol. II of the *Opera mathematica*). There is a facs. ed. of the *Grammatica linguae anglicanae* of 1653 (Menston, 1969), and a new ed. with translation and commentary by J. A. Kemp, *Grammar of the English Language* (London, 1972).

Wallis' autobiography was reprinted in C. J. Scriba, "The Autobiography of John Wallis, F.R.S.," in *Notes and Records. Royal Society of London*, **25** (1970), 17–46; this includes a survey of other early biographies of Wallis, including that by David Gregory, which is printed in J. Collier, *A Supplement to the Great Historical, Geographical, Genealogical and Poetical Dictionary . . . Together With a Continuation From the Year 1688, to 1705, by Another Hand* (London, 1705; 2nd ed., 1727).

II. SECONDARY LITERATURE. The book-length monographs on Wallis the mathematician are J. F. Scott, *The Mathematical Work of John Wallis, D.D., F.R.S. (1616–1703)* (London, 1938); and C. J. Scriba, *Studien zur Mathematik des John Wallis (1616–1703). Winkelteilungen, Kombinationslehre und zahlentheoretische Probleme* (Wiesbaden, 1966). Scott surveys Wallis' life and his main published mathematical works; Scriba concentrates on the topics stated in his title, making use also of unpublished MSS, and includes a list of books owned by Wallis, which are now in the Bodleian, as well as a brief survey of the MS material. An index to the correspondence is C. J. Scriba, "A Tentative Index of the Correspondence of John Wallis, F.R.S.," in *Notes and Records. Royal Society of London*, **22** (1967), 58–93.

Wallis the grammarian and phonetician is the subject of L. Morel, *De Johannis Wallisii grammatica linguae anglicanae et tractatu de loquela thesis* (Paris, 1895), which is superseded by M. Lehnert, *Die Grammatik des englischen Sprachmeisters John Wallis (1616–1703)* (Wrocław, 1936). The following articles deal with Wallis or his work: R. C. Archibald, "Wallis on the Trinity," in *American Mathematical Monthly*, **43** (1936), 35–37, and in *Scripta mathematica*, **4** (1936), 202; L. I. Cherkalova, "Sostavnye otnoshenia u Vallisa," in *Doklady na nauchnykh konferentsiakh*, **2**, no. 3 (1964), 153–160; G. Eneström, "Die geometrische Darstellung imaginärer Grössen bei Wallis," in *Bibliotheca mathematica*, 3rd ser., **7** (1906–1907), 263–269; K. Hara, "Pascal et Wallis au sujet de la cycloïde," in *Annals of the Japanese Association of the Philosophy of Science*, **3** (1969), 166–187; J. E. Hofmann, "Neues über Fermats zahlentheoretische Herausforderungen von 1657," in *Abhandlungen der Preussischen Akademie der Wissenschaften*, Math. naturwiss. Kl. (1943), no. 9 (Berlin, 1944); M. Koppe, "Die Bestimmung sämtlicher Näherungsbrüche einer Zahlengrösse bei John Wallis (1672)," in *Sitzungsberichte der Berliner mathematischen Gesellschaft*, **2** (1903), 56–60; F. D. Kramar, "Integratsionnye metody Dzhona Vallisa," in *Istoriko-matematicheskie issledovaniya*, **14** (1961), 11–100; W. Kutta, "Elliptische und andere Integrale bei Wallis," in *Bibliotheca mathematica*, 3rd ser., **2** (1901), 230–234; E. H. Neville, "Wallis on the Trinity," in *Scripta mathematica*, **2** (1934), 197; T. F. Nikonova, "Pervy opyt postroeni istorii algebry anglyskim matematikom Dzhonom Vallisom," in *Uchenye zapiski. Moskovskoi oblastnoi pedagogicheskii institut*, **202** (1968), 379–392; T. P. Nunn, "The Arithmetic of Infinites," in *Mathe-*

*matical Gazette*, **5** (1910–1911), 345–357, 378–386; H. C. Plummer, "Jeremiah Horrocks and his *Opera posthuma*," in *Notes and Records. Royal Society of London*, **3** (1940–1941), 39–52. Wallis was instrumental in selecting the material for the posthumous ed. of Horrocks' astronomical work.

See also A. Prag, "John Wallis. 1616–1703. Zur Ideengeschichte der Mathematik im 17. Jahrhundert," in *Quellen und Studien zur Geschichte der Mathematik, Astronomie und Physik*, Abt. B, **1** (1931), 381–412, mainly devoted to the *Arithmetica infinitorum* and the *Algebra*, but with many astute remarks on the general state of seventeenth-century mathematics; J. F. Scott, "John Wallis as a Historian of Mathematics," in *Annals of Science*, **1** (1936), 335–357; and "The Reverend John Wallis, F.R.S. (1616–1703)," in *Notes and Records. Royal Society of London*, **15** (1960), 57–67, with selected bibliography by D. T. Whiteside, 66–67; C. J. Scriba, "Wallis and Harriot," in *Centaurus*, **10** (1964), 248–257; "John Wallis' *Treatise of Angular Sections* and Thâbit ibn Qurra's Generalization of the Pythagorean Theorem," in *Isis*, **57** (1966), 56–66; "Das Problem des Prinzen Ruprecht von der Pfalz," in *Praxis der Mathematik*, **10** (1968), 241–246; "Wie läuft Wasser aus einem Gefäss? Eine mathematisch-physikalische Aufzeichnung von John Wallis aus dem Jahr 1667," in *Sudhoffs Archiv*, **52** (1968), 193–210; and "Eine mathematische Festvorlesung vor 300 Jahren," in *Janus*, **56** (1969), 182–190; D. E. Smith, "John Wallis as a Cryptographer," in *Bulletin of the American Mathematical Society*, **24** (1917), 82–96; L. Tenca, "Giovanni Wallis e gli italiani," in *Bollettino dell' Unione matematica italiana*, 3rd ser., **10** (1955), 412–418; G. Wertheim, "P. Fermats Streit mit J. Wallis," in *Abhandlungen zur Geschichte der Mathematik*, **9** (1899), 555–576; H. Wieleitner, "Die Verdienste von John Wallis um die analytische Geometrie," in *Weltall*, **29** (1929–1930), 56–60; and G. U. Yule, "John Wallis, D.D., F.R.S. 1616–1703," in *Notes and Records. Royal Society of London*, **2** (1939), 74–82.

Christoph J. Scriba

**WALTER BURLEY.** See **Burley, Walter.**

**WALTER OF EVESHAM.** See **Walter of Odington.**

**WALTER OF ODINGTON** (*fl.* Evesham and Oxford[?], England, 1280[?]–1330[?]), *alchemy, music.*

As is the case with many medieval alchemists, the details of Walter's life are obscure. There is confusion as to where and when he lived. Astronomical observations in his treatise "Motion of the Eighth Sphere" indicate that he probably was ac-

tive in the last half of the thirteenth century (*ca.* 1280), but manuscript sources refer to him as having lived in the early fourteenth century. In his manuscripts he is referred to as either Walter of Odington or Walter of Evesham. Odington probably refers to his birthplace, which may be the Oddington in northern Oxfordshire, while Evesham is clearly a reference to the Benedictine abbey at Evesham. Several sources testify to his being a Benedictine monk. Since he was a member of a regular order, it is difficult to explain the sources that place him at Merton College, Oxford, for an extensive period in the early fourteenth century.

Odington wrote treatises on alchemy, optics, arithmetic, and geometry, and a famous work on medieval music, *De speculatione musice*, in which he treated acoustics, the division of the monochord, musical notation, mensurable music, and rules for composition. His most important scientific study was his alchemical investigation *Icocedron* (from "icosahedron").

As the title indicates, the *Icocedron* is divided into twenty chapters; and it follows the general Islamic alchemical-medical-pharmaceutical tradition of the period. The first fourteen chapters present standard alchemical information outlining the basic principles of the art, the methods of preparing the materials, techniques for perfecting the "medicine," and steps to be followed in mixing the elements. In the concluding chapters Walter became more alchemically sophisticated, discussing in some detail metals, the intension and remission of qualities, and the four basic elements of alchemical composition—earth, air, fire, and water. Seeking to present a way of accurately describing alchemical change quantitatively, he assigned quantitative distinctions to each element. Fire is thus hot in the fourth degree and dry near the end of the third degree. Since each degree has sixty minutes, fire therefore has 240 minutes of calidity and 180 minutes of aridity. Through an elaborate procedure of combining the qualities, the secondary quality in a given element could be destroyed and the element reduced to its simplest form.

The most important feature of Walter's alchemical work was his attempt to quantify qualitative intensities. Distinguishing between temperature and (quantity of) heat, he sought to interpret the relationships between qualitative intensities and quantitative amounts. He conceived of qualitative intensity as a magnitude. In the *Icocedron* he presented six rules for these relationships—one stated implicitly, four in tabular form, and one verbally. His verbal rule utilizes functions similar to those of

Bradwardine in his famous "law of motion," while its mathematical expression is similar to that used in the pharmaceutical tradition of al-Kindī by the scholars of Montpellier.

*BIBLIOGRAPHY*

I. ORIGINAL WORKS. There is no collective ed. of Walter's works. The *Icocedron* is extant in the following MSS: British Museum, Add. MS 15549, fols. $4^r$–$20^v$; Cambridge University, Trinity College MS 1122, fols. $177^v$–$183^r$; Bodleian Library, Digby MS 119, fols. $142^r$–$147^v$; and Murhardsche Bibliothek der Stadt Kassel und Landesbibliothek, Handschrift 2° MS Chem. 8, fols. $240^r$–$253^v$. British Museum, Add. MS 15549 has been edited by Phillip Drennon Thomas as "David Ragor's Transcription of Walter of Odington's *Icocedron*," in *Wichita State University Studies*, no. 76 (Aug. 1968), 3–24. The incipits and locations for Walter's other scientific works are in Lynn Thorndike and Pearl Kibre, *A Catalogue of Incipits of Mediaeval Scientific Writings in Latin* (Cambridge, Mass., 1963). *De speculatione musice* has been edited in E. Coussemaker, *Scriptorium de musica medii aevi*, I (Paris, 1864).

II. SECONDARY LITERATURE. For a brief biographical sketch, see Henry Davey, "Walter of Evesham or Walter of Odington," in *Dictionary of National Biography*, XX, 702–703. Lynn Thorndike presents a cursory examination of Odington's career and works in *A History of Magic and Experimental Science*, III (New York, 1960), 127–135. For an examination of his alchemical rules, see Donald Skabelund and Phillip Thomas, "Walter of Odington's Mathematical Treatment of the Primary Qualities," in *Isis*, **60** (1969), 331–350; and Phillip D. Thomas, "The Alchemical Thought of Walter of Odington," in *Actes du XII$^e$ Congrès international d'histoire des sciences* (Paris, 1968), 141–144.

PHILLIP DRENNON THOMAS

**WALTER, PHILIPPE** (*b.* Cracow, Poland, 31 May 1810; *d.* Paris, France, 9 April 1847), *chemistry.*

After completing his doctoral studies at Cracow, Walter took part in the unsuccessful popular uprising of 1830–1831 against the Russian rulers of Poland. He subsequently found refuge in Paris, where he joined the group associated with Dumas. In 1829 Dumas had been a founder of the École Centrale des Arts et Manufactures, a school for advanced study in the applied sciences; and Walter became a teacher of analytical chemistry there.

Most of Walter's investigations concerned natural plant products. In 1838 he and Pierre Joseph Pelletier isolated toluene as a product of the de-

structive distillation of pine resin. They called it retinaphtha and correctly determined its composition, noting that it contained the benzoic radical and represented a hydrocarbon sought by chemists, since it was the hypothetical hydrocarbon formed through the replacement of the oxygen atoms of benzoic acid by hydrogen.

In 1840 Pelletier and Walter discovered another important hydrocarbon. By fractional distillation of naphtha they isolated an analogue of ethylene. Determination of its vapor density gave them a formula of $C_8H_{16}$. Originally named naphthene, it subsequently came to be known as caprylene, after caprylic alcohol, from which it also could be prepared (the modern name is octene).

In 1839 Walter had distinguished between menthol and camphor, finding the molecular formula of menthol by determining its vapor density. This information, together with Dumas's determination of its composition, enabled him to show that menthol was a compound distinct from camphor.

In 1842 Walter observed that the reaction of camphoric anhydride and sulfuric acid yielded sulfocamphoric acid and carbon monoxide. This reaction was the first indication that carbon could be replaced in organic compounds by other elements. Walter noted the importance of this fact, and in an 1843 paper he quoted from a work in which Dumas had suggested that substitution in organic compounds might not be restricted to hydrogen; perhaps oxygen, nitrogen, and even carbon might be replaced. The composition of sulfocamphoric acid clearly showed that an $SO_2$ group had replaced a carbon atom in the camphoric anhydride. Walter claimed that this work supported Dumas's substitution (1834) and type (1839) theories. In the latter theory organic molecules were considered to be unitary types with properties depending less on the nature of the elements than on their position and arrangement. Thus, the replacement of carbon in camphoric anhydride bolstered Dumas's attempt to establish a novel and controversial theory of organic compounds.

*BIBLIOGRAPHY*

I. ORIGINAL WORKS. Walter wrote a treatise on Polish chemical nomenclature, *Wyklad nomenklatury chemicznej poskiej i porównanie jej z nomenklaturami lacińską, francuską, angielską i niemiecką* (Cracow, 1842; 2nd ed., 1844). His papers are listed in the Royal Society *Catalogue of Scientific Papers*, VI, 256–257. The more important include "Examen des produits provenant du traitement de la résine dans la fabrication du gaz pour l'éclairage," in *Annales de chimie et de physique*, 2nd ser., **67** (1838), 269–303, written with P. J. Pelletier; "Mémoire sur l'essence de menthe poivrée cristallisée," *ibid.*, **72** (1839), 83–109; "Mémoire sur l'action qu'exerce l'acide sulfurique anhydre sur l'acide camphorique anhydre," *ibid.*, **74** (1840), 38–52; "Recherches chimiques sur les bitumes," in *Journal de pharmacie*, **26** (1840), 549–568, written with P. J. Pelletier; and "Mémoire sur l'acide camphorique anhydre," in *Annales de chimie et de physique*, 3rd. ser., **9** (1843), 177–200.

II. Secondary Literature. There is a biography of Walter by S. Sekowski and S. Szostkiewicz, *Serce i retorta, czyli zywot chemiiposwiecony* (Warsaw, 1957). See also *Wielka Encyklopedia Powszechna PWN*, XII (Warsaw, 1969), p. 96, and J. R. Partington, *A History of Chemistry*, IV (London, 1964), 340, 367, 558, and 868.

Albert B. Costa

**WALTON, IZAAK** (*b.* Stafford, England, 9 August 1593; *d.* Winchester, England, 15 December 1683), *zoology.*

Although Walton made no great claims to scientific originality, no author better illustrates the attitude toward natural philosophy in mid-seventeenth-century England. Religion and natural history were then so closely connected and their interactions so numerous that separation must involve severe historical distortion.

Walton's early life is obscure. Son of Gervase Walton of Stafford, a yeoman, Walton probably attended a local grammar school before settling with his sister in London. There he served an apprenticeship and in 1618 gained admission to the Ironmongers' Company. As a prosperous tradesman he was married twice, to Rachel Floud (*d.* 1640) and to Anne Ken (d. 1662), both of whom came from well-connected Anglican families, thereby enhancing Walton's social status and literary connections. His life was long, comfortable, and uneventful, even during the civil wars, which left him untouched in spite of his strong Royalist sympathies.

Walton is primarily remembered as author of *The Compleat Angler*, but his more long-term and extensive literary activity was as a biographer. His valuable contribution to literature and Anglican apologetics developed as a result of a friendship with John Donne, Walton's parish priest. His biographies of Donne (1640) and of another friend, Sir Henry Wotton (1651)—like the subsequent biographies of Thomas Hooker (1665), George Herbert (1670), and Robert Sanderson (1678)—provide a valuable source about a group of figures who considerably influenced the outlook of natural

philosophers in the later seventeenth century. The biographies also contain significant information about Bacon, Savile, and Boyle.

Walton's Anglican associations are important for appreciating the origin and bias of *The Compleat Angler*. Angling was a favorite pastime for a whole stream of Anglican divines, from the Elizabethan Dean Alexander Nowell to Walton's friend Archbishop Gilbert Sheldon. Nowell's catechism may even have prompted Walton to adopt the didactic dialogue form for his book. Direct instigation to write on this subject came from Wotton, who himself had intended to compose a treatise in praise of fishing. Composed at a time when the established church greatly needed support, *The Compleat Angler* was a vehicle for many favorite themes in Anglican theology.

Walton's enthusiasm for fishing gave him the keen eye of a naturalist, his knowledge being particularly sound on a wide range of freshwater fish. Contrasting with the stereotyped compendiums on natural history, Walton introduced a wide range of "observations of the nature and breeding, and seasons, and catching of Fish." His own observations were compared with scrupulously acknowledged information drawn from such authors as Gesner, Scala Johann Dubravius, and Bacon. He was much less familiar with authors unavailable in translation, perhaps a reflection on his limited classical education and a notable contrast with the similarly disposed Sir Thomas Browne. Walton also drew material from the small vernacular literature on angling; his debt to the dialogue *The Arte of Angling* (1577) is obvious but extremely difficult to establish precisely. Walton far exceeded his precursors in attaining a balance between natural history and practical advice. A final component of religious, moral, and philosophical digression gave *The Compleat Angler* an extremely wide appeal. Among the topical scientific references was a consideration of Helmont's willow tree experiment, which was cited to support the contention that water was the prime element in nature. After the first modest edition of 1653, the book was revised four times by Walton. Since then almost three hundred editions and translations have appeared, making Walton one of the best-known authors in the English language.

BIBLIOGRAPHY

I. Original Works. Walton's *Lives* appeared separately between 1640 and 1678; subsequently they appeared in collected editions. The *Lives* and their revisions are discussed in great detail in D. Novarr, *The Making of Walton's Lives* (Ithaca, N.Y., 1958). *The Compleat Angler, or the Contemplative Man's Recreation* was published anonymously in 1653; it was greatly revised and augmented in 1655, and minor revisions were made in 1661, 1668, and 1678. The most detailed edition of *The Compleat Angler* is that of George Washington Bethune (New York–London, 1847). B. S. Horne, *The Compleat Angler 1653–1967* (New York, 1970), lists the editions. For a collected edition of Walton's works, see G. Keynes, *The Compleat Walton* (London, 1929).

II. SECONDARY LITERATURE. No biography is adequate, but see Andrew Lang, "Izaak Walton," in *Dictionary of National Biography*; and Stapleton Morton, *Izaak Walton and His Friends*, 2nd ed. (London, 1904). A more critical evaluation is A. M. Coon, "The Life of Izaak Walton," unpublished Ph.D. diss., Cornell University (1937). On natural history, see R. B. Marston, *Walton and Some Writers on Fish and Fishing* (London, 1894). *The Arte of Angling (1577)*, which was discovered recently, has been edited by G. E. Bentley (Princeton, 1956); its relevance to Walton is examined critically by M. S. Goldman, in *Studies in Honor of T. W: Baldwin*, D. C. Allen, ed. (Urbana, Ill., 1958), 185–204. J. R. Cooper, *The Art of the Compleat Angler* (Durham, N.C., 1968), examines the stylistic sources for *The Compleat Angler*.

CHARLES WEBSTER

**WANGERIN, ALBERT** (*b.* Greiffenberg, Pomerania, Germany, 18 November 1844; *d.* Halle, Germany, 25 October 1933), *mathematics*.

Wangerin studied mathematics and physics from 1862 to 1866 at the universities of Halle and Königsberg, receiving the Ph.D. from the latter in 1866. Until 1876 he taught in high schools in Posen (now Poznan, Poland) and Berlin. He began to teach on the university level at Easter 1876, when he assumed the post of extraordinary professor at the University of Berlin. In 1882 he was named full professor at the University of Halle, where he remained until his retirement in 1919.

At Königsberg, Wangerin studied under Richelot, a supporter of the Jacobian tradition, and under Franz Neumann. It was Neumann who suggested the subject of his dissertation, and Wangerin later wrote a book (1907) and a highly appreciative article on his former teacher. Wangerin's admiration for Neumann remained an important influence on his choice of research problems. He became an expert on potential theory, spherical functions, and the fields of mathematical physics related to these subjects. For example, in one of his papers he calculated the potential of certain ovaloids and sur-

faces of revolution. Wangerin also worked, although less intensely, in differential geometry. In 1894 he wrote an article showing how to determine many bending surfaces of a given surface of revolution of constant curvature without knowing its geodetic lines.

Wangerin's importance, however, does not lie in the authorship of enduring scientific works but, rather, in his astonishingly varied activities as university teacher, textbook author, contributor to encyclopedias and journals, editor of historical writings, and president of a scientific academy. While at Berlin he directed his lectures to a fairly broad audience, and even at Halle he continued to be greatly interested in the training of high school teachers. He also wrote a two-volume work on potential theory and spherical functions for the series Sammlung Schubert.

Wangerin wrote two articles for *Encyklopädie der mathematischen Wissenschaften*. The first (1904) deals with the theory of spherical and related functions, especially Lamé and Bessel functions. The second, "Optik; ältere Theorien" (1907), appeared in the physics volume of the *Encyklopädie*. In it Wangerin displays a familiarity with the history of physical theory that is unusual for a mathematician. His sensitivity to historical questions evokes his study, four decades earlier, under Neumann. Wangerin's historical interests are also evident in his editing of works by Gauss, Euler, Lambert, and Lagrange for *Ostwalds Klassiker der exakten Wissenschaften*.

From 1869 to 1924 Wangerin was a coeditor of *Fortschritte der Mathematik*, then the only periodical devoted to reviewing mathematical literature. In this capacity he reviewed almost all the works in his special field published during this period. For 1906 to 1921 Wangerin was president of the Deutsche Akademie der Naturforscher Leopoldina in Halle.

*BIBLIOGRAPHY*

Wangerin's writings include "Über die Abwicklung von Flächen konstanten Krümmungsmasses sowie einiger anderer Flächen aufeinander," in *Festschrift zur 200-jährigen Jubelfeier der Universität Halle* (Halle, 1894), 1–21; "Theorie der Kugelfunktionen und der verwandten Funktionen, insbesondere der Laméschen und Besselschen (Theorie spezieller, durch lineare Differentialgleichungen definierter, Funktionen)," in *Encyklopädie der mathematischen Wissenschaften*, II, pt. 1 (Leipzig, 1904), 699–759; *Franz Neumann und sein Wirken als Forscher und Lehrer* (Brunswick, 1907);

"Optik, ältere Theorien," in *Encyklopädie der mathematischen Wissenschaften*, V, pt. 3 (Leipzig, 1907), 1–93; *Theorie des Potentials und der Kugelfunktionen*, 2 vols., nos. 58 and 59 in Sammlung Schubert (Leipzig, 1908–1921); "Franz Neumann als Mathematiker," in *Physikalische Zeitschrift*, **11** (1910), 1066–1072; and "Über das Potential gewisser Ovaloide," in *Nova acta Leopoldina*, **6**, no. 1 (1915), 1–80.

Secondary literature includes W. Lorey, "Zum 70. Geburtstag des Mathematikers A. Wangerin," in *Zeitschrift für mathematischen und naturwissenschaftlichen Unterricht*, **46** (1915), 53–57; and "Bericht über die Feier der 80. Wiederkehr des Geburtstages des Herrn Geh. Rats Prof. Dr. Wangerin," in *Jahresberichte der Deutschen Mathematiker-vereinigung*, **34** (1926), 108–111.

WERNER BURAU

**WANG HSI-SHAN**[1] (*b*. 23 July 1628, registered at Wu-chiang,[2] Soochow prefecture, China; *d*. 18 October 1682), *astronomy*.

Wang was the son of Wang P'ei-chen[3] and his wife, whose maiden name was Chuang.[4] Wang Hsi-shan's epitapher, who would have been expected to cite distinguished ancestors in the preceding few generations, was unable to do so. Wang was designated to continue the family line of a childless uncle, which suggests that he was not the eldest child. Nothing is known of his education except that he was self-taught in mathematics and astronomy. He had no son to arrange for posthumous publication of his writings. One of his few disciples sketched, in twenty-five Chinese characters, the impression Wang made: "emaciated face, protruding teeth, tattered clothes, and shoes burst through the heels. His character made him aloof, as though no one could suit him; but when someone inquired about a scholarly topic, he was forthcoming as a river in flood."[a]

The conventional road to social advancement for the son of an obscure gentry family was the civil service examinations, which required many years of special preparation. This path was clouded by the Manchu conquest. The invaders from the north overran Wang's district in 1645. Whether to collaborate with the alien government was an issue for all Chinese. Wang was only sixteen, but he made it clear that he did not wish to live with the new order: "In a burst of passion, wanting to die, he jumped repeatedly into the river. It always happened that someone was there to save his life. He then refused to take food for seven days, but still did not die. His parents were persistent; he had no choice but to resume eating. Renouncing worldly ambition, he dedicated all of his powers to learning." Hopes for a Ming restoration soon faded, but in letters and manuscripts he never acknowledged the new Ch'ing dynasty. His friends, who included the great transitional figure of neo-Confucianism, Ku Yen-wu[5] (1613–1682), were Ming loyalists.

Wang was not widely traveled; he never met Mei Wen-ting[6] (1633–1721) of Anhwei or the northerner Hsueh Feng-tso[7] (*d*. 1680), now considered the other two great astronomical scholars of the time. Mei acknowledged Wang's preeminence, however, and wrote commentaries (never published) on several of his books.[b]

Wang apparently made an indifferent living by teaching a few disciples. He was supported for a time by a wealthy scholar of his district who was compiling a history of the Ming dynasty (another act of devotion to the lost cause). Wang's career was short, impeded by isolation, and hampered by illness, including partial paralysis of the extremities in his later years. The year before he died, he wrote, in connection with the prediction of a solar eclipse: "Whenever there is a conjunction I have always checked the precision of my computations against that of my observations, despite sickness, cold, or heat, for thirty years and more."[c]

Wang's technical writings circulated in manuscript among astronomers after his death. Their preservation was not guaranteed until a major composition was included in the enormous imperial manuscript collection of rare texts, the *Ssu k'u ch'üan shu*[8] ("Complete Library in Four Repositories," compiled 1773–1785). The descriptive and critical catalog of this collection was printed and brought Wang's contribution to general attention.

**The Setting of Wang Hsi-shan's Career.** From about 1600 until the papal suppression of the Society of Jesus in 1773, missionaries of that order were practically the sole source of Chinese knowledge about Western astronomy. The Astronomical Bureau was the one part of the Chinese court where groups of foreigners had been employed in positions of trust for some centuries. Indians since the eighth century and Muslims (mostly Central Asians) since the thirteenth century had applied geometrical and trigonometric methods, which the Chinese lacked, to critical computational tasks, especially the prediction of eclipses. Appointments in the Bureau provided the Jesuits with access to the ruling elite, whose conversion was their main object. Mathematical and astronomical treatises demonstrated high learning and proved that the missionaries were civilized and socially acceptable, although religion was not part of the conventional discourse of gentlemen and attempts to convert one's friends were considered bad form. Science was of no direct concern to the missionaries of other orders, who gradually began to proselytize in China, since their clientele was predominantly the poor and forsaken.

The missionaries began publishing on astronomy in the first decade of the seventeenth century. Their earliest writings did not provide what was needed to predict the celestial motions, but merely demonstrated the usefulness of Aristotelian-Ptolemaic cosmology and astronomy as then practiced in Europe. It was mainly the series of treatises presented to the throne in 1631–1635, as part of the campaign to gain operational control of the Astronomical Bureau and institute a calendar reform based on Western techniques, that set out the mathematical rudiments of the calendrical art. The principles of calendar reform were accepted by the government only on the eve of defeat by the Manchus, but the alien dynasty promptly accepted the Jesuits' offer of services. Compiling a new system of calendrical computation was one of many steps usually taken to assert ritually the legitimacy of a new regime. The astronomical treatises, earlier printed individually by the missionaries, were published together by imperial order as *Hsi-yang hsin fa li shu*[9] ("Astronomical Treatises According to the New Methods of the West," presented to the throne in 1646). The prestige of official sponsorship assured them fairly wide distribution, although, unlike other imperial publications, they were never privately reprinted as a set.

Once the Jesuits were established in a secure position to protect their religious activities, there was no need to continue reporting on European developments in astronomy and cosmology—until a series of attacks by their enemies temporarily deposed them from the Astronomical Bureau (1665–1669) and even closed their churches in the provinces. During that time of crisis, the Flemish Jesuit Ferdinand Verbiest wrote several important new books, comprising tables and accounts of instruments and of predictions. The Tychonic cosmology of most of the "New Methods" treatises was not modified until the Keplerian ellipse was quietly introduced—for the solar orbit only—in 1742. The heliostatic world system was not introduced until 1760, after Copernicus' *De revolutionibus* had been removed from the Index (1757), and even then it was only described, without a new computational scheme.

In sum, Chinese astronomers had to form their impression of European astronomy and cosmology from writings that, about 1630, were not untypical of textbooks and handbooks current in the church's educational institutions in Europe but that, as time passed, failed increasingly to reflect the emergence of modern astronomy. It was with this in mind that the distinguished historian of science, Hsi Tse-tsung, remarked, "We can imagine, if Wang Hsi-shan had only come upon [Copernicus' *De revolutionibus*, Galileo's *Dialogo*, and Kepler's *Epitome astronomiae Copernicanae*, all of which the missionaries kept for their private use in Peking], how much greater his contribution to astronomy would have been."[d]

Wang, Mei Wen-ting, and Hsueh Feng-tso were the first scholars in China to respond to the new exact sciences and to shape their influence on their successors. They were, in short, responsible for a scientific revolution. They radically reoriented the sense of how one goes about comprehending the celestial motions. They shifted from using numerical procedures for generating successive angular orientations to using geometric models of successive locations in space. They changed the sense of which concepts, tools, and methods are centrally important, so that geometry and trigonometry largely replaced numerical algebra, and such issues as the absolute sense of rotation of a planet and its relative distance from the earth became important for the first time. They convinced Chinese astronomers that mathematical models can have the power to explain the phenomena as well as to predict them.

This revolution did not reach the same pitch of tension as the one going on in Europe at the same time. It did not burst forth in as fundamental a reorientation of thought about nature. The new ideas and techniques did not arouse in Wang and others a need to cast doubt on all the traditional ideas of what constitutes an astronomical problem and what significance astronomical prediction can have for the ultimate understanding of nature. The traditional idea persisted that explaining the astronomical phenomena could not by itself lead to a synthetic comprehension of the inherent pattern of the cosmos, the Tao.

The limited character of the seventeenth-century breakthrough is perhaps not surprising. The decree of the Congregation of the Index in 1616 denied Chinese access to the fruits of the Copernican revolution and its aftermath in Europe, at least as long as Catholic missionaries were the only foreigners who had reason to write on astronomy in Chinese. Still, the reorientation determined a new style for Chinese astronomy until finally, between 1870 and 1920, that science ceased to exist apart from modern astronomy as an international enterprise.

This train of events has drawn little sympathetic attention, largely because it confounds the widespread assumption that in the encounter between cultures, Western science must assert its dominance by a process so automatic that one need not trouble oneself with a critical examination of instances. On the contrary, in China the new tools were used to rediscover and recast the lost mathematical astronomy of the past and thus to perpetuate traditional values rather than to replace them.[e] The "imperatives of modernization" appear universal to the uncritical merely because the encounter between traditional and modern science in one society after another has been resolved by social change and political fiat, in view of which the comparative appropriateness of each system of science to the cultural environment is beside the point. The same may even be said for early modern technology, which was clearly superior to that of traditional societies, but was superior mainly in applications that did not exist until it generated them.

In a word, there has seldom been a direct encounter between traditional and modern science in East or West. Seventeenth-century China was an exception of great interest because European civilization had no appreciable political or social impact, and astronomy had to make its way on its own merits. Not on its abstract intellectual merits alone, to be sure, for what constituted merit was largely defined by the use the court traditionally made of astronomy.

At the time there were no socially marginal students of astronomy alienated from traditional values and protected by association with privileged foreigners, as would be the case in late nineteenth-century China and elsewhere in the heyday of imperialism. The only astronomers who could respond to the Jesuits' writings were members of the old intellectual elite, who were bound to evaluate innovations in the light of established ideals that they felt an individual responsibility to strengthen and perpetuate.

In order to assure acceptance of the Western methods among people of his own kind, Mei Wen-ting created the myth that European mathematics evolved out of certain techniques that had originated in China and had been transplanted to the extreme fringes of civilization (Europe and Islam) before losing vitality in their original home.[f] This myth, an appeal to the Chinese tendency to see perfection in high antiquity, connected Western science with certain ambiguous references in an-

cient historical writing; since it was not intrinsically foreign, it could be taken as more than a curiosity. Mei launched what anthropologists call a "foundation myth" for the institutions (small private groups of masters and disciples) that taught the new astronomy and reorganized themselves around it. There is nothing inherently Chinese about the use of such myths. An analogy that comes to mind is the remarkable European myth that non-European societies could be "discovered," a change of status that authorized their economic despoliation and the systematic destruction of their religious and other customs during the Age of Discovery.

Mei, Wang, and others were aware that, whatever the lost grandeur of archaic times may have been, from about 100 B.C. through the thirteenth century computational astronomy in China had actually continued to grow in power and range within its stylistic limits. Very gradually from the Yüan period (1279–1368), it came to be little practiced outside the Astronomical Bureau, which was dominated by foreign technicians. By 1600 no one was able fully to comprehend the old numerical equations of higher-order, prototrigonometric approximations, applications of the method of finite differences, and other sophisticated techniques. The promise of a renascence seemed to the greatest astronomical figures of the seventeenth century to define the proper field for application of Western knowledge.

**Astronomical Work**. Wang and his contemporaries were motivated by two central problems. The first was how Western knowledge might be used to revive the lost Chinese exact sciences. Traditional knowledge was recorded, and the perennial problems were set, in the easily accessible standard histories of the various dynasties. Each incorporated a variety of technical treatises, which, among other matters, recorded many of the complete systems of ephemerides computation that had been proposed or accepted for official use since about 100 B.C. Wang was familiar with the chief writings of this sort and, although there is no reason to believe that he met any foreign missionary, with the Jesuit treatises of the early 1630's.

The second problem was how to resolve the internal contradictions of European astronomy. Since circumstances had ruled out a closely unified set of treatises, some discrepancies were due to divergences of approach and varying choices of constants, and some to the missionaries' limitations of skill. The most important source of inconsistency was the different cosmological viewpoints

VINCENNES PUBLIC LIBRARY
VINCENNES, INDIANA

through which European writers tried to convey the best knowledge of their time, before and after the limits of contention about the system of the world were drawn by the decree against the teaching of heliocentricism. Matteo Ricci, writing before 1616, was conventionally "Ptolemaic" (that is, he reflected the doctrines of Aristotle and Ptolemy as understood by the Scholastics of his youth). The writers of about 1630 were Tychonists, except for Johann Schreck (1576–1630). Later Jesuit writers never accounted for the shift to Tychonism—nor for the introduction of Copernicanism in the mid-eighteenth century. Chinese could perceive only the lack of conviction and of unanimity. Misleading statements about Copernicus' contributions, contextless references to alternative systems (for instance, a confusing and unexplained allusion by Schreck to the cosmology of Heraclides Ponticus), and additional isolated innovations in Verbiest's later series of writings muddied even more the question of what should be considered the state of the foreign art. The spotty character of publication made it impossible to take the latest as best; in the missionary writings the latest usually presupposed the earlier without criticizing it.

Wang's response belies the occasional assertions of historians that Chinese were incapable of responding creatively to geometrical models, or that a bias against abstraction would have prevented them from taking up Copernican cosmology had it been available. In adapting the missionaries' version of Tycho Brahe's scheme of the cosmos to his own uses, Wang made considerable adaptations and criticized contradictions in its presentation. He noted, for instance, that a secular diminution in the length of the tropical year had been mentioned, but was ignored in a discussion of the precessional constant (which, by implication, should increase). This was not the modern variation in the length of the year, but one of much greater magnitude that was obsolete in Europe by the time Wang wrote.

Wang's *Hsiao-an hsin fa*[10] ("New Method," completed in 1663) was cast in traditional form, with tables that made only the elementary logistic operations necessary for calculating the ephemerides. It provided, for the first time, methods for predicting planetary occultations and solar transits. Some of Wang's techniques were included along with post-Newtonian data in the *Li hsiang k'ao ch'eng*[11] ("Compendium of Observational and Computational Astronomy," printed 1724), part of a great survey of the mathematical arts sponsored by the K'ang-hsi emperor.

Wang's *Wu hsing hsing tu chieh*[12] ("On the Angular Motions of the Five Planets," completed by the autumn of 1673) was a critically overhauled Tychonic model of the planetary motions, substituting eccentrics for major epicycles and opposing the rotational senses of the superior and inferior planets. This work displays a general familiarity with modern trigonometry. Wang's arguments, unlike those of his Chinese predecessors, were clearly concerned with bodies in motion.

The most original idea in "On the Angular Motions" was Wang's proposal that the planetary anomalies be explained by a force radiating from the outermost moving sphere (*tsung tung t'ien*,[13] or *primum mobile*) and attracting each planet to an extent maximal at apogee. Explanation of celestial motions by forces, instead of the assumption in the old kinematics of compounded circles that the celestial motions were eternal, entered the European debate only through Kepler. There had been no such discussion in China, except for a vague statement by Giacomo Rho (1592–1638) that "The motions of [the sun, Mercury, and Venus] are all due to one potential moving force . . . located in the body of the sun." This assertion was not connected with the remainder of Rho's planetary theory, and no extension to the superior planets was hinted at. Wang's force, although it was not universal like Newtonian gravitation, applied to all the planets known to him and was exerted from the periphery rather than from inside the planetary orbits.[g]

Wang's notion of synthesis went deeper than reconciling ancient schemes of calculation with foreign techniques. The power of Western models not only to predict phenomena but also to exhibit their inherent patterns was what attracted many Chinese. Wang sought to establish metaphysical links for further exploration into celestial reality. This motive lay behind his suggestion that the circle be divided into 384 degrees. The traditional division made each degree (*tu*)[14] equal to one tropical day's mean solar travel (so that in Wang's system there would be 365.2422 degrees). He was aware of the convenience offered by the European system of angular division, especially in manufacturing graduated instruments. He chose the number 384 ($3 \times 2^7$) in addition to 360 ($2^3 \times 3^2 \times 5$) because, as the number of lines ($6 \times 64$) in the sixty-four hexagrams of the "Book of Changes," it related astronomical quantities to the fountainhead of conventional speculation about cosmic change and thus uncovered another layer of significance.[h]

Despite his dedication and critical intelligence, it cannot be said that Wang, any more than his con-

VINCENNES PUBLIC LIBRARY
VINCENNES INDIANA

temporaries, succeeded in a mature synthesis of traditional and modern science. They did provide tools and methods as well as a goal. Information from the West was inadequate in many respects, and several generations more were needed to reclaim the traditional corpus of Chinese mathematics and astronomy as part of the astronomer's repertoire.

For many decades students began with the Western writing and went on to study the Chinese technical classics. The latter, as they were successively mastered, increasingly defined the style of research in the exact sciences, even when this research began to be concerned with new problems. By the early nineteenth century, Western mathematics and astronomy were no longer novelties; they had been studied continuously for two hundred years. The basic training in the decades before the Opium Wars (*ca.* 1840) was in the native writings. They served as excellent preparation for up-to-date Western treatises that gradually began to appear as part of a new confrontation—this time a total confrontation—between China and the West.

**General Significance for Chinese Thought.** Wang Hsi-shan's lifetime was a critical epoch in the evolution of Chinese philosophy. What Western historians call neo-Confucianism was, like the earlier trends it built upon, a search for doctrines of education, self-cultivation, and moral life in society. Its successive new departures depended upon reexamination of antiquity to identify and interpret (differently for each age) the authentic core of Confucian teachings. Well before the late Ming period, expanded scope for self-consciousness, increased blurring of social barriers, and the more penetrating influence of Buddhism and Taoism had deepened religious and moral awareness. This trend affected both the Chu Hsi[15] tradition, which explored the phenomenal world (including the mind and experience recorded in books) to grasp the single coherent pattern inherent in all change, and that of Wang Yang-ming,[16] which strongly emphasized enlightenment through self-awareness, particularly of the mind engaged in conscientious social activity.

The great intellectuals of the dynastic transition were, on the whole, Ming loyalists. That is, they were among the minority who did resist, in the main passively and after the transfer of power had taken place. They were convinced that to plumb the failure of their intellectual predecessors would be to uncover the conditions for philosophical and spiritual reinvigoration, and for responsible en-

gagement in the world of affairs. Among the most influential was Wang Hsi-shan's friend Ku Yen-wu, who saw his late Ming predecessors as distracted from moral commitment and public responsibility by sectarianism, by pedantry and triviality in the Chu tradition, and, in the tradition of Wang, by a subjectivity and individualism ignorant of the authoritarian and hierarchic requirements of social order. Above all, in the view of Ku and other Ch'ing survivors, it was the rivalry of schools—a manifestation of blinding selfishness and pride—that corrupted the neo-Confucian teaching, leaving it unable to rise above the political futility that preceded the debacle at the end of the Ming.[i]

The prescription for the ills of thought was to purge postclassical influences that hid the original principles of Confucius and his orthodox followers. A critical method for the examination of texts was the crucial safeguard; the broad study that printing had made feasible revealed to people of Wang's generation how easily the understanding of their predecessors had been led astray. Some now endeavored to recover the earliest—the uncorrupted—versions and interpretations of the classics, and others studied the working out of canonical moral patterns in the events of history. This work was not intended to replace the quest for a living philosophy, to which the fortunes of the empire had given a new poignancy.

By the mid-eighteenth century, narrowly defined scholarly methodology had become an end in itself, narrow in interpretation and intolerant of the urge to generalize. The call for "social utility, concrete practicality, and tangible evidence," which had promised philosophic regeneration a century earlier, outlived the openness to the unexpected that was implied in its original motivation.[j] Classicism flourished, despite the atrophy of metaphysics, because of the cumulative accomplishments it yielded and because it posed no threat to a state which insisted that collective intellectual activity be apolitical.

This final evolution of disciplinary specialization out of a philosophic renaissance is not of further concern here, but how the Ch'ing style of critical neo-Confucian thought began to take shape in Wang Hsi-shan's lifetime bears examination.

It has often been noticed that certain important neo-Confucians of the early Ch'ing era, especially among those close to the Chu tradition, wrote on mathematics and astronomy. That the extent of this scientific interest has been seriously underestimated becomes clear in an unpublished survey of thirty-six people generally considered major neo-

Confucian figures, from the beginning of the Ch'ing period (1644) to Wang Yin-chih[17] (1766–1834). Of the thirty-six, eighteen left a total of seventy-two books on mathematics and astronomy. A large group of these treatises reconstituted early computational techniques, and about the same number were chronological or other mathematical studies of canonical writings before about 200 B.C.[k]

That overlap of intellectual activity is part of a more general pattern that also connects those known only for philosophy with those known only for science. In the mid-seventeenth century the leaders in both fields were people who eschewed politics and public service. This is perhaps not remarkable, since one expects reevaluation and syncretism to begin with talented and ambitious people who, for one reason or another, remain on the margins of the elite. But in addition to obvious consequences of this social overlap, philosophers and scientists shared important convictions.

To sum up the argument so far, certain critical motifs recurred in neo-Confucianism just after the Manchu conquest, pointing the way toward new departures: emphatic rejection of what were seen as decadent and destructive tendencies at the end of the Ming (Ku Yen-wu located them mainly in the Wang Yang-ming school, but other thinkers were more evenhanded in their apportionment of blame); the belief that those tendencies arose partly because of inadequate study and partly because of Buddhist and other heterodox ideas—as well as a variety of misunderstandings and corruptions—that had insinuated themselves into texts and undisciplined scholarly writings; and the conviction that a sound approach to understanding the inherent patterns of cosmic and human activity (li)[18] and the moral imperatives they imply required critical reexamination of classical literature and history.

All of these ideas also motivated Wang Hsi-shan. We are told by his biographer that after he renounced worldly ambition, "He excoriated heterodoxy [this usually refers to Buddhism, sometimes to Christianity as well], attacked 'innate moral consciousness'[19] [the characteristic doctrine of the Wang Yang-ming school], and accepted the orthodox Confucian tradition of the Chu Hsi line[20] as his personal mission." The preface to his "New Method," instead of conventionally affirming the high antiquity of astronomy, began by taking up questions that had been raised about the authenticity of seven calendars that the historians dated prior to the Han period (206 B.C.), and stated flatly, "There is no doubt that they were forgeries of the

Han." Wang emphasized that astronomers of the recent past comprehended less than their predecessors and that the lost meaning of the technical classics had to be rediscovered.

Earlier scientists had argued, with some consistency, that although mathematical astronomy could provide useful knowledge and advance understanding, the subtle texture of the natural order could ultimately be penetrated only by illumination.[1] Wang did not reject this view, but he saw number as a means toward that penetration: "One who seeks rigor must reach it through computation. Numbers are not themselves the inherent pattern [li]; but because the pattern gives rise to number, through number one may reach enlightenment as to the pattern."[m] This conviction was almost certainly influenced by the argument of Matteo Ricci, in his preface to the Chinese translation of Euclid's *Elements* (*Chi-ho yuan pen*, 1607),[21] that geometry is a unique means to knowledge of the inherent pattern, knowledge that does not depend upon individual belief and thus can overcome individual doubts.

These parallels, and others in the writings of Wang's scientific contemporaries, suggest a closer connection than has hitherto been imagined between the scientific revolution of seventeenth-century China and the evolution from philosophy to exact scholarship that took much longer to run its course. In particular, they suggest that Western influence on main currents of early Ch'ing philosophy—on the frontiers of Chinese self-awareness—should not casually be ruled out. Historians have usually ruled it out because they have not studied the scientific literature and because they rely on crude and narrowly defined tests for intellectual influence that ignore the mathematical dimension of human thought.

It is a matter of paramount importance that the first substantial encounter between Chinese traditions and European culture was in mathematical astronomy. Medicine and religion provoked no such response, and confrontations of political ideas were negligible. The style of the response to Western astronomy—how it was assimilated so that it could be understood, how the primacy of traditional values was asserted and the study of the new methods justified in terms of them, how teaching and practice were adapted to existing institutions—set the style of less abstract encounters later, as may be seen in the response to Western military technology in the second half of the nineteenth century. (The broad pattern of response—misconception, ambiguity, interpretation, and piecemeal adaptation—is not utterly unlike that of Americans to Chinese acupuncture in the 1970's.)

This mathematical challenge to values coincided with an even more traumatic challenge, the Manchu invasion. Some shade of ambiguity toward Western science must have come from the Jesuits' prompt tender of services to the Manchus and the immediate official adoption of their astronomical system (although some missionaries accompanied the refugee Ming court south to cover the eventuality of a restoration). It was not, however, characteristic of Chinese to reject what was foreign merely because it was foreign; nationalism had barely been conceived. A willingness to adopt the forms of Chinese culture gave Manchus and Jesuits a right to be where they were—although nothing compelled loyalists to collaborate with either. But Wang Hsi-shan's type of loyalism was only a memory for the following generation, and served as no deterrent to the study of new ideas.

It is merely reasonable to suggest that philosophers were influenced by the early success of astronomers in applying the foreign tools (in eclectic combination with old ones) to the reexamination of classical learning. Reexamination of ancient observations and predictions was an established part of the astronomer's work. Not long after Wang Hsi-shan's lifetime, technical examination of the philosophic classics to fix dates and test authenticity became the explicit end of most astronomical exploration, with the revival of traditional science as an intermediate means that happened to fully occupy many scholars.

Even more important in assessing this channel of European influence is the fact that as time passed, leading neo-Confucian scholars also became mathematicians used to working with Western techniques and concepts. Because these scholars grouped in schools and maintained close relations, even those who never applied European science in their writings were aware of it through discussions with their associates and through reading their monographs.

None of this suggests a simple causal relation between European astronomy as described in the Chinese language in the early seventeenth century and the forms of Chinese thought that became dominant by the middle of the eighteenth. Certainly the relation between astronomy and philosophy was reciprocal as long as philosophy remained vital, despite its moral and social cast and its focus on self-realization. At the beginning the new science offered what were seen as powerful tools toward a reformation of thought. Wang Hsi-shan's belief that number could bring ultimate insight into the universal pattern was pregnant in precisely this way; but the consensus formed in more conventional quarters, and was ultimately barren for a new understanding of nature, society, and man.

Still, the new techniques could never be mere tools. To use them, as so many thinkers did, was to form habits that reinforced long-held convictions about the usefulness of scholarship in exploring reality. Seventeenth-century European science was not, after all, modern science, least of all as it was artificially perpetuated in China for two centuries by the lack of sources alternative to the missionaries' writings. Chinese philosophers, whose sense of man and the cosmos was in part formed by study of canonic books, responded to the universal explanatory character that this foreign science derived from its Scholastic framework much more than to the grip on direct experience of nature that Wang valued.[n] Astronomy, as it was understood and used by neo-Confucian thinkers, converged with philology, gave it added weight, and obviously played a part in tipping the scale.

It would be premature to suggest any particular line of development between the recourse to Western astronomy among philosophers at the beginning of the Ch'ing period and the eventual swamping of earlier philosophical concerns by exact scholarship—exact scholarship of a kind in which mathematical astronomy finally could be perfectly integrated as one specialty among many. The career of Wang Hsi-shan suggests a range of possible patterns that, tested against many other careers, can throw light on the central enigmas which shroud the failure of imperial China.

### NOTES

a. This and the following quotation are from the funerary inscription by Wang Chi in *Sung-ling wen lu*[22] ("Literary Records of Wu-chiang," 1874), 16: 1a–1b.

b. Described in the *Wu-an li suan shu-mu*[23] ("Bibliography of Mei's Writings on Astronomy and Mathematics"; Pai-pu ts'ung-shu chi-ch'eng ed.), 34b–35a. On the relations of Mei and Wang, see the biographical study by Hsi Tse-tsung, "Shih lun Wang Hsi-shan te t'ien-wen kung-tso"[33] (in bibliography). Reliable short biographies of Mei and many other figures mentioned in this article are in Hummel, *Eminent Chinese*.

c. Cited by Hsi Tse-tsung (p. 63) from the MS "Wang Hsiao-an hsien-sheng i-shu pu-pien"[24] ("Supplement to the Posthumous Works of Wang Hsi-shan") in the Peking University Library.

d. Hsi Tse-tsung, *loc. cit.*

e. This point was made by Mikami Yoshio in " 'Chūjin den' ron"[25] ("A Study of the *Ch'ou jen chuan*"), in *Tōyō gakuhō*, **16** (1927), 185–222, 287–333, and was repeated in "Chinese

Mathematics," in *Isis*, **11** (1928), 125. It has been developed considerably by Wang P'ing.

f. Wang Hsi-shan accepted this notion. See his *Tsa chu*[26] ("Miscellaneous Essays"), in *Hsiao-an i shu*,[31] XXXV, 1a–2a, 10b–11a. The best discussion of the Chinese origin theory is in Wang P'ing, *Hsi-fang li-suan-hsueh chih shu-ju*,[36] 77–79, 97–103. I see no reason to doubt that Mei, Wang Hsi-shan, and others sincerely believed it.

g. *Shou shan ko ts'ung-shu*[27] ed., 7b, discussed in Sivin, "Copernicus in China," 74–75.

h. *Hsiao-an hsin fa*[10] (in *Hsiao-an i shu*),[31] 2a.

i. I am grateful for this formulation, and for a number of helpful criticisms, to Lynn Struve. I am also thankful for suggestions by Judy Berman, Dianna Gregory, and Yü Ying-shih.

j. William T. de Bary, "Neo-Confucian Cultivation and the Seventeenth-Century 'Enlightenment,'" in *The Unfolding of Neo-Confucianism*, 193.

k. N. Sivin, "What Can the Study of Chinese Science Contribute to Our Understanding of Neo-Confucianism, and How?" working paper for Planning Conference on Early Ch'ing Thought, Berkeley, Calif., 28–31 Aug. 1975.

l. See *DSB* article on Shen Kua.

m. *Tsa chu*, 4a.

n. Willard J. Peterson, in his perceptive "Fang I-chih: Western Learning and the 'Investigation of Things,'" has shown how Fang[51] (1611–1671) used his knowledge of Western sciences to argue for greater emphasis in philosophy upon accumulating knowledge of "physical objects, technology, and natural phenomena." Because Fang's understanding of the exact sciences was mediocre, he responded more enthusiastically than most of his contemporaries to the Scholastic sciences of the body, the earth, weather, and so on that were then becoming obsolete in the West. His influence on scientific thought was negligible, but Peterson suggests (correctly, I believe) an indirect formative influence on early Ch'ing humanists' taste for "building knowledge item by item." He asserts that the tendencies Fang encouraged were "parallel to the secularization of natural philosophy in seventeenth-century Europe" (p. 401); but they were more closely parallel to the antiquated approach of Fang's sources, products of the Counter-Reformation attempt to overcome secularization. Although Fang was no more reluctant than the European Schoolmen to provide an occasional "experiment" to demonstrate a point, he depended as heavily as they upon hearsay and literature, and as little upon personal experience; in his dream of what would now be called a research institute, the only source of knowledge mentioned was "ancient and modern books" (p. 383). In short, the scientific revolution in seventeenth-century China was in the main a response to outmoded knowledge that gave little attention to, and consistently misrepresented, the significance of developments in the direction of modern science. This thesis is fully documented in Sivin, "Copernicus in China."

| | | |
|---|---|---|
| 1. 王錫闡 | 20. 濂洛洙泗 | 39. 藪内清，中国の天文暦法 |
| 2. 吳江 | 21. 幾何原本 | 40. 吉田光邦 |
| 3. 培真 | 22. 王濟，松陵文録 | 41. 明清時代の科学技術史 |
| 4. 莊 | 23. 勿菴歷算書目 | 42. 徐宗澤，明清間耶穌會士譯著提要 |
| 5. 顧炎武 | 24. 王曉闇先生遺書補編 | 43. 丁福保，周雲青，四部総録算法編 |
| 6. 梅文鼎 | 25. 三上義夫，疇人傳論 | 44. 天文編 |
| 7. 薛鳳祚 | 26. 雜箸 | 45. 近代中算箸述記 |
| 8. 四庫全書 | 27. 守山閣叢書 | 46. 清代文集算學類論文 |
| 9. 西洋新法曆書 | 28. 中西算学叢書 | 47. 年譜 |
| 10. 曉菴新法 | 29. 叢書集成 | 48. 橋本敬造 |
| 11. 曆象考成 | 30. 大統秝法啓蒙 | 49. 梅文鼎の暦算学—康熙年間の天文暦算学 |
| 12. 五星行度解 | 31. 遺書 | 50. 梅文鼎の数学研究 |
| 13. 宗動天 | 32. 木犀軒叢書 | 51. 方以智 |
| 14. 度 | 33. 席澤宗，試論王錫闡的天文工作 | 52. 坂出祥伸，方以智の思想 |
| 15. 朱熹 | 34. 科学史集刊 | 53. 嚴敦杰，伽利略的工作早期在中国的传布 |
| 16. 王陽明 | 35. 疇人傳 | 54. 全漢昇，清末的西學源出中國説 |
| 17. 王引之 | 36. 王萍，西方曆算学之輸入 | 55. 嶺南學報 |
| 18. 理 | 37. 李儼，明清之際西算輸入中國年表 | 56. 毀成 |
| 19. 良知 | 38. 中算史論叢 | |

*BIBLIOGRAPHY*

I. Original Works. Wang Hsi-shan's extant writings are listed in an article by N. Sivin in L. Carrington Goodrich, ed., *Ming Biographical Dictionary* (New York, 1976), 1379–1382. The two most important treatises were *Hsiao-an hsin fa*[10] ("New Methods of Wang Hsi-shan"; completed 1663) and *Wu hsing hsing tu chieh*[12] ("On the Angular Motions of the Five Planets"; completed by the autumn of 1673). Both were first printed in the *Shou shan ko ts'ung-shu*[22] collection (1838) and reprinted in the *Chung-hsi suan-hsueh ts'ung-shu*,[28] 1st ser. (1896) and the *Ts'ung-shu chi ch'eng*[29] collection, 1st ser. (1926). About 1890 the two treatises were combined with *Ta-t'ung li fa ch'i-meng*,[30] an elementary introduction to the Great Concordance system (*Ta-t'ung li*), which had been used throughout the Ming period (1368–1644) for computing the ephemerides, and an assortment of short essays, to form the *Hsiao-an i shu*[31] ("Posthumous Works"), vols. XXXI–XXXV in the *Mu hsi hsuan ts'ung-shu*.[32]

II. SECONDARY LITERATURE. The most thorough study of Wang's life and astronomical work, based on unpublished as well as published sources, is Hsi Tse-tsung, "Shih lun Wang Hsi-shan te t'ien-wen kung-tso"[33] ("An Essay on the Astronomical Work of Wang Hsi-shan"), in *K'o-hsueh-shih chi-k'an*,[34] 6 (1963), 53–65. Its references provide an excellent starting point for further study. The article by Sivin cited above, in a reference book invaluable for the study of Wang's immediate predecessors, is more concerned with biographical and bibliographical matters than is the present essay. The first detailed account of Wang's work, based mainly on excerpts from his writings before they had been printed separately, was in *Ch'ou jen chuan*[35] ("Biographies of Mathematical Astronomers," 1799; Shanghai: Commercial Press, 1935), II, 421–446. This programmatic compendium, which included European as well as Chinese figures, was a major influence on the style of eighteenth-century investigations in the exact sciences.

Although no more than isolated sentences from Wang have been published in translation, N. Sivin has drafted a translation of *Wu hsing hsing tu chieh*[12] for circulation and eventual publication in a source book of Chinese science.

III. EUROPEAN SCIENCE IN SEVENTEENTH-CENTURY CHINA. Little attention has been paid by Western sinologists to the early mathematical encounter of East and West. For instance, Ssu-yu Teng and John K. Fairbank, *China's Response to the West. A Documentary Survey 1839–1923* (Cambridge, Mass., 1954), notes the immediate influence only of "items of practical interest," among which the authors include the calendar. Useful and well-known studies, such as Wolfgang Franke, *China and the West. The Cultural Encounter, 13th to 20th Centuries*, R. A. Wilson, trans. (Oxford, 1967); and Joseph R. Levenson, "The Abortiveness of Empiricism in Early Ch'ing Thought," in *Confucian China and Its Modern Fate* (London–Berkeley, 1958), 3–14, do not reflect knowledge of or curiosity about the technical literature.

The only general history of the Chinese response to European exact sciences is in Wang P'ing, *Hsi-fang li-suan-hsueh chih shu-ju*[36] ("The Introduction of Western Astronomy and Mathematics"), Monographs of the Institute of Modern History, Academia Sinica, 17 (Nankang, Taiwan, 1966), summarized in *Journal of Asian Studies*, 29 (1970), 914–917. This book draws heavily on the biographical articles in *Ch'ou jen chuan* for the seventeenth and eighteenth centuries. A very useful tool for further study of both Jesuit and Chinese

mathematical activities is Li Yen, "Ming-ch'ing chih chi Hsi suan shu-ju Chung-kuo nien-piao"[37] ("A Chronology of the Introduction of Western Mathematics Into China in the Transition Between the Ming and Ch'ing Dynasties"), in *Chung suan shih lun-ts'ung*,[38] vol. III of *Gesammelte Abhandlungen über die Geschichte der chinesischen Mathematik*, rev. ed. (Peking, 1955); 10–68. Jesuit activity has been ably surveyed in Yabuuchi Kiyoshi, *Chūgoku no temmon rekihō*[39] ("Chinese Astronomy"; Tokyo, 1969), 148–174.

There is an important group of studies in Yabuuchi Kiyoshi and Yoshida Mitsukuni,[40] eds., *Min Shin jidai no kaguku gijutsu shi*[41] ("History of Science and Technology in the Ming and Ch'ing Periods"). Research Report. Research Institute of Humanistic Studies, Kyoto University (1970), 1–146. Joseph Needham, in *Science and Civilisation in China*, III (Cambridge, 1959), 437–458, was the first to suggest that the limitations as well as the strengths of the Jesuit missionaries greatly affected the character of the Chinese response. His short and incidental discussion of Wang Hsi-shan (p. 454) includes several errors of fact.

The lives of the Jesuit missionaries and their publications in Chinese have been well-documented by historians of that order. See Henri Bernard, "Les adaptations chinoises d'ouvrages européens. Bibliographie chronologique depuis la venue des Portugais à Canton jusqu'à la Mission française de Pékin, 1514–1688," in *Monumenta serica*, 10 (1945), 1–57, 309–388; Joseph Dehergne, *Répertoire des Jésuites de Chine de 1552 à 1800* (Rome–Paris, 1973); and Louis Pfister, *Notices biographiques et bibliographiques sur les Jésuites de l'ancienne mission de Chine, 1552–1773*, 2 vols. (Shanghai, 1932–1934, completed before Pfister's death in 1891). Dehergne is a comprehensive guide to the extensive literature on missionaries, including archival sources; the last part includes aids to research. See also Henri Cordier, *Essai d'une bibliographie des ouvrages publiés en Chine par les Européens au XVIIe et XVIIIe siècles* (Paris, 1883), based on the collection of the Bibliothèque Nationale. For writings in Chinese, see Hsu Tsung-tse, *Ming Ch'ing chien Ye-su-hui-shih i chu t'i yao*[42] ("Annotated Bibliography of Jesuit Translations and Writings in the Ming and Ch'ing Periods"; Taipei, 1958), with indexes of authors, titles, and subjects.

On European scientific works available to the Jesuits in Peking—and still extant as one of the world's greatest collections of scientific writings of the sixteenth through eighteenth centuries—see H. Verhaeren, *Catalogue of the Pei-t'ang Library*, 3 vols. (Peking, 1944–1948). A list of 251 astronomical books has been excerpted in Henri Bernard-Maitre, "La science européene au tribunal astronomique de Pékin (XVIIe–XIXe siècles)," in *Conférences du Palais de la découverte*, ser. D, 9 (Paris, 1951). See also Boleslaw Szczesniak, "Note on Kepler's *Tabulae Rudolphinae* in the Library of Pei-t'ang in Pekin," in *Isis*, 40 (1949), 344–347.

For studies of Chinese responses, the book of Wang P'ing is especially helpful because of its index, still unusual in Chinese scholarly books. For systematic annotated bibliographies, see Ting Fu-pao and Chou Yun-ch'ing, *Ssu pu tsung lu suan-fa pien*[43] ("General Register of the Quadripartite Library, Section on Mathematics"; Shanghai, 1957) and *Ssu pu tsung lu t'ien-wen pien*[44] ("General Register . . . Section on Astronomy"; Shanghai, 1956), supplemented by Li Yen, "Chin-tai Chung suan chu-shu chi"[45] ("Notes on Books About Chinese Mathematics in Modern Times"), in *Chung suan shih lun-ts'ung*,[38] II (1954), 103–308; and "Ch'ing-tai wen-chi suan-hsüeh lei lun-wen"[46] ("Articles That Can Be Classified as Mathematical in Collected Literary Works of Individuals in the Ch'ing Period"), *ibid.*, V (1955), 76–92.

The first resort for biographies of the most prominent Chinese scientific figures is Arthur W. Hummel, *Eminent Chinese of the Ch'ing Period*, 2 vols. (Washington, D.C., 1943–1944); *Ming Biographical History* (see above) will provide similar information about those who reached maturity before the mid-seventeenth century and about a few later people (such as Wang Hsi-shan) not accorded biographies by Hummel. *Ch'ou jen chuan*[35] is composed mostly of long excerpts from technical writings and does not provide a great deal in the way of biography or overview.

A few topical studies throw light on fundamental issues. The genesis, content, and distribution of major Jesuit scientific writings are described in Pasquale d'Elia, "Presentazione della prima traduzione chinese di Euclide," in *Monumenta serica*, 15 (1956), 161–202, with English summary; and Henri Bernard-Maître, "L'encyclopédie astronomique du Père Schall," *ibid.*, 3 (1938), 35–77, 441–527. Early European writings in Chinese on the qualitative sciences are described in Willard J. Peterson, "Western Natural Philosophy Published in Late Ming China," in *Proceedings of the American Philosophical Society*, 117 (1973), 295–322.

The life, associations, and work of Wang Hsi-shan's contemporary Mei Wen-ting have been treated at length in Li Yen, "Mei Wen-ting nien-p'u"[47] ("A Chronological Biography of Mei Wen-ting"), in *Chung suan shih lun-ts'ung*, III, 544–576; and in Hashimoto Keizō,[48] "Bai Buntei no rekisangaku—Kōki nenkan no temmon rekisangaku"[49] ("The Mathematical Astronomy of Mei Wen-ting—Mathematical Astronomy in the K'ang-hsi Period"), in *Tōhō gakuhō* (Kyoto), 41 (1970), 491–518; and "Bai Buntei no sugaku kenkyū"[50] ("The Mathematical Researches of Mei Wen-ting"), *ibid.*, 44 (1973), 233–279. The thought of Fang I-chih,[51] probably the first Chinese to acquaint himself with the full spectrum of European sciences, has been examined by Sakade Yoshinobu, "Hō Ichi no shisō"[52] ("The Thought of Fang I-chih"), in Yabuuchi Kiyoshi and Yoshida Mitsukuni (see above), 93–134; and by W. J. Peterson, "Fang I-chih: Western Learning and the 'Investigation of Things,'" in W. T. de Bary and the Conference on Seventeenth-Century Chinese Thought, *The Unfolding of Neo-Confucianism*, Studies in Oriental Culture, 10 (New York, 1975), 369–411, an important volume for seventeenth-century thought. Sakade and Peterson should be read together, since Sakade pays comparatively little attention to Fang's treatment of European ideas and techniques; and Peterson, although more concerned with this aspect, is not familiar with the Chinese scientific tradition or with the development of European science.

The introduction of cosmology into China is narrated by Pasquale d'Elia in *Galileo in China, Relations Through the Roman College Between Galileo and the Jesuit Scientist-Missionaries (1610–1640)*, Rufus Suter and Matthew Sciascia, trans. (Cambridge, Mass., 1960), but the emphasis on demonstrating Jesuit accomplishments obscures a number of basic issues. The ambiguities and historic ironies of the Jesuit effort, and the Chinese response after the church's injunction of 1616 limited discussion of the earth's motion, have been examined in detail by N. Sivin in "Copernicus in China," in *Studia Copernicana*, 6 (1973), 63–122, with bibliographical essay, 113–114. A more black-and-white analysis of the same topic, with some important additional information, is Hsi Tse-tsung *et al.*, "Heliocentric Theory in China," in *Scientia sinica*, 16 (1973), 364–376. More limited in scope is Yen Tun-chieh, "Ch'ieh-li-lüeh ti kung-tso tsao-ch'i tsai Chung-kuo ti ch'uan-pu"[53] ("The Early Dissemination of Galileo's Work in China"), in *K'o-hsüeh-shih chi-k'an*,[34] 7 (1964), 8–27. On the notion that Western mathematics originated in China, see Ch'üan Han-sheng, "Ch'ing-mo ti Hsi-hsüeh yuan ch'u Chung-kuo shuo"[54] ("On the Late Ch'ing Theory That Western Science Originated in China"), in *Ling-nan hsüeh pao*,[55] 4 (1935), 57–102; and N. Sivin, "On 'China's Opposition to Western Science During Late Ming and Early Ch'ing,'" in *Isis*, 56 (1965), 201–205. Ch'üan, overlooking the early literature, attributes the Chinese origin theory to Mei Wen-ting's grandson Mei Ku-ch'eng[56] (*ca.* 1681–1763); but his account of the theory's vogue around the turn of the twentieth century deserves attention.

N. SIVIN

**WANKLYN, JAMES ALFRED** (*b.* Ashton-under-Lyne, Lancashire, England, 18 February 1834; *d.* New Malden, Surrey [now part of London], England, 19 July 1906), *organic and analytical chemistry, public health.*

Wanklyn's career followed that of Edward Frankland, who until 1867 did everything possible to further it—but thereafter much to block it. Wanklyn was the son of Thomas Wanklyn and Ann Dakeyne. After education at the Moravian school in Fairfield, Lancashire, from 1843 until 1849, he was apprenticed for seven years to a Manchester doctor. During the last year of his apprenticeship he was allowed to study chemistry at Owens College, Manchester, with Frankland, whose personal assistant he became in 1856. From 1857 to 1859 Wanklyn studied at Heidelberg with Frankland's former teacher Robert Bunsen; and through Frankland's influence he became Lyon Playfair's demonstrator at Edinburgh University in 1859. Wanklyn settled in London in 1863 and until 1870 was professor of chemistry at the financially impoverished London Institution—the Royal Institution's rival in the City of London. In 1886, after various often stormy engagements as public analyst to Buckingham and its county, Peterborough, Shrewsbury, and High Wycombe, and a lectureship in chemistry and physics at St. George's Hospital, London, from 1877 to 1880, he established a private analytical laboratory and consultancy at New Malden, where he died.

Although Wanklyn, according to Liebig, gained a European reputation for his research on organic synthesis, vapor densities, and qualitative analysis, like J. W. L. Thudichum, whom he assisted in 1869, he was ignored and despised by British academic chemists. Blackballed by the Royal Society, he ostentatiously resigned from the Chemical Society in 1871 and, in 1876, from the Society of Public Analysts, of which he had been a founder in 1874. His only honor (engineered by Thudichum and Liebig) was corresponding membership in the Bavarian Academy of Sciences (1869). (Liebig diplomatically awarded Frankland the honor simultaneously.) Wanklyn's faults were excessive haste to publish and a pugnacious nature (he was involved in several lawsuits); but foremost was his tactless and indomitable controversy with Frankland over water analysis—one of the great Victorian scientific debates that had national implications for public health and that led, in Wanklyn's view, to persecution "for the sake of truth."

As a protégé of Frankland's, Wanklyn was until 1867 concerned principally with synthetic organic chemistry. In 1857 he prepared the organometallic compounds sodium ethyl and potassium ethyl, from which, with carbon dioxide, he synthesized propionic acid (1858), thus apparently confirming the structural views of Kolbe and Frankland that carboxylic acids were alkyl-conjugated oxalic acids. For instance,

$$C_4H_5Na + C_2O_4 = C_4H_5C_2O_3 + ONa.$$

sodium   carbon   sodium propionate (C=6)
ethyl     dioxide

At Edinburgh, Wanklyn improved the Will-Varrentrapp method for estimating organic nitrogen as ammonia by adding alkaline potassium permanganate to increase the oxidative effect of soda lime. In 1866 he began collaborating with the ebullient Ernest Theophron Chapman, who, in a short but brilliant career, shared this interest in organic oxidation. At the London Institution, with Miles H. Smith, they devised a new method for detecting the organic impurity, or sewage, content of water (1867). After free ammonia had been boiled off from a water sample, it was oxidized by alkaline potassium permanganate, and the ammonia evolved (which was estimated colorimetrically with Nessler's reagent) was asserted to be a measure of the organic nitrogen content of the water. This "albuminoid ammonia process" was much simpler and faster than the extremely laborious, albeit more accurate, method promulgated by Frankland and H. E. Armstrong (1867), which analyzed evaporated water residues *in vacuo*.

The debates over these two methods had serious consequences for both parties, especially for Wanklyn, who supposed, with some evidence, that Frankland used his government position as an analyst of London's water supplies to promote his own, more complex technique. Wanklyn's method tended to underestimate nitrogen content and therefore to underemphasize possible sewage contamination. Hence samples of water from the same supplies often were reported as more salubrious by Wanklyn than by Frankland, who wished to use his results to ensure government action on the purification of water supplies. If Frankland's attitude was politically and socially profitable, his methods were certainly too complex analytically for ordinary public health analysts, who adopted the Wanklyn method. On the other hand, both the analysts and Frankland were prepared to accept bacteriological evidence for insalubrity; whereas Wanklyn, blinded by prejudice, saw this as another of Frankland's "plots." Nevertheless, despite his jaundiced views, Wanklyn's practical manuals on various analytical subjects proved invaluable in training and setting standards for the professional British public health analyst and medical officer of health.

*BIBLIOGRAPHY*

I. ORIGINAL WORKS. Nearly 150 papers are recorded in the Royal Society *Catalogue of Scientific Papers*, VI, 262–263; VIII, 1192–1195; XI, 746–747; XIX, 465–466; which, however, ignores a large number of interesting letters to *Chemical News and Journal of Physical Science*. In addition there are "On the Physical Peculiarities of Solutions of Gases in Liquids," in *Philosophical Magazine*, 6th ser., **3** (1902), 346–348, 498–500; and his contributions to H. Watts, *A Dictionary of Chemistry*, 7 vols. (London, 1863–1875; 2nd ed., 8 vols., London, 1872–1881). Wanklyn's association with John Gamgee's abortive *Milk Journal and Farmers' Gazette. A Monthly Review of the Dairy* . . . (Jan. 1871–Aug. 1872) should also be noted. Patent literature should also be consulted.

Wanklyn's books, which carried the subtitle . . . *a Practical Treatise on* . . ., were *Water Analysis*, written with E. T. Chapman (London, 1868, 1870, 1874, 1876, 1879, 1884, 1889, 1891, 1896 [10th ed.]; a 9th ed. could not be traced)—the 11th, posthumous ed. lacks Chapman's name and was edited by Wanklyn's assistant, William John Cooper (London, 1907)—and a German trans. (Charlottenburg, 1893), with the 4th (1876) to 8th (1891) eds. containing a polemical historical appendix; *A Manual of Public Health*, Ernest Hart, ed. (London, 1874), written with W. H. Mitchell and W. H. Corfield—Wanklyn claimed responsibility for 303–374 only (see *Chemical News*, **29** [1874], 9); *Milk Analysis* (London, 1874; 2nd ed., 1886); *Tea, Coffee and Cocoa* (London, 1874; reissued 1886); *Bread Analysis* (London, 1881; 2nd ed., 1886), written with W. J. Cooper; *The Gas Engineer's Chemical Manual* (London, 1886; 2nd ed., 1888); *Air Analysis* (London, 1890), written with W. J. Cooper; *Sewage Analysis* (London, 1899; 2nd ed., 1905), written with W. J. Cooper; and *Arsenic* (London, 1901).

The Royal Society has a few of Wanklyn's letters. The archives of the London Institution (1805–1912) are housed at Guildhall Library, London.

II. SECONDARY LITERATURE. The 11th ed. of *Water Analysis* (1907) contains a memoir with photograph by W. J. Cooper, an interesting selection of Wanklyn's testimonials, and an appalling bibliography. See also T. E. James, "J. A. Wanklyn," in *Dictionary of National Biography*, supp. I, vol. III, 587–588. His death was conspicuously ignored by the Chemical Society. The Liebig-Thudichum correspondence on Wanklyn's election to the Bavarian Academy of Sciences is reproduced in David L. Drabkin, *Thudichum, Chemist of the Brain* (Philadelphia, 1958), 244–247. The context and significance of Wanklyn's analytical work can be understood from C. A. Mitchell, *Fifty Years of the Society of Public Analysts* (Cambridge, 1932), esp. 1–13.

W. H. BROCK

**WARBURG, EMIL GABRIEL** (*b*. Altona, near Hamburg, Germany, 9 March 1846; *d*. Grunau, near Bayreuth, Germany, 28 July 1931), *physics*.

Warburg, who came from a wealthy family, grew up in Altona and attended the city's humanistic gymnasium, the Christianeum, where he was almost as interested in languages as in mathematics. His musical education was not neglected, and he became a good pianist.

In 1863, aged seventeen, Warburg began to study science at the University of Heidelberg, which—through the presence of Kirchhoff and Bunsen on its faculty—offered outstanding instruction in physics and chemistry. Warburg was so impressed by Kirchhoff's "magnificent" (*vollendet schöner*) lecture on experimental physics that he decided to change his major from chemistry to physics.

After four semesters at Heidelberg, Warburg transferred to the University of Berlin. He earned his doctorate and qualified as lecturer there, remaining until he received an offer of a professorship. During this period Gustav Magnus attracted many young physicists to his laboratory in Berlin, the only one in Germany besides Franz Neumann's at Königsberg. Warburg soon became friendly with Magnus' assistant, August Kundt; and they remained friends even after Kundt left in 1868 to take up a professorship at the Zurich Polytechnikum.

While at Berlin, Warburg wrote a number of works, most of them on oscillatory problems, including his Latin dissertation, "De systematis corporum vibrantium" (1867). In his *Habilitationsschrift*, "Über den Ausfluss des Quecksilbers aus gläsernen Capillarröhren" (1870), Warburg reported his discovery that no slipping occurs between glass and mercury. He often returned to problems of slipping. Warburg remained a *Privatdozent* for only two years; in 1872 he and Kundt were invited to the newly founded Kaiser Wilhelm University at Strasbourg. Kundt, who brought his assistant Wilhelm Roentgen with him from Würzburg, was named full professor and Warburg was made extraordinary professor.

At Strasbourg, Warburg and Kundt collaborated on two famous studies on the kinetic theory of gases. In 1875 they furnished conclusive experimental confirmation of a consequence that Maxwell had derived from the theory: that the inner friction and the heat conduction of a gas are independent of the pressure, so long as the mean paths of the molecules are negligible with respect to the dimensions of the container. They extended their investigation to very rarefied gases and deduced from the theory the existence of a measurable slipping and of a jump in temperature at the container wall. They also demonstrated the existence of measurable slipping experimentally. Their second prediction, however, was not verified until around the turn of the century, in an experiment carried out at

Warburg's suggestion at Berlin by Marian Smoluchowski and Ernst Gehrcke. In their second joint study (1876) Kundt and Warburg showed that at constant pressure and volume, the specific heats of monatomic gases possess the value 5/3 predicted by the theory.

The explanation of the theoretical relations in these two papers was the work of Warburg, as is evident from a letter mentioned by James Franck. In it Kundt asks Warburg for information on a theoretical point and writes that, since Warburg has developed all the ideas about slipping and has calculated the heat conduction, he ought to help the "thoroughly ordinary experimental physicist" (*ganz gemeinen Experimentalphysiker*) out of a theoretical difficulty. Einstein considered Warburg and Kundt's joint papers of very great significance for the kinetic gas theory. He wrote in 1922:

> This was the first time that a new phenomenon was predicted on the basis of the molecular theory of heat—a phenomenon, moreover, the representation of which on the basis of the theory of continuity of matter was virtually excluded. If the energeticists at the end of the nineteenth century had sufficiently appreciated these arguments, they would have had great difficulty in calling into question the profound validity of the molecular theory.

The collaboration with Kundt ended in 1876, when Warburg obtained a professorship at the University of Freiburg im Breisgau, where he was the sole physicist on the faculty until 1895. At Freiburg he continued his investigation of the kinetic gas theory. It followed from the theory that the friction coefficient is independent of the pressure. He tested this prediction with carbonic acid at high densities and found that the basic notions of the theory were valid. Never losing his interest in this topic, he encouraged his students to work on it and published two comprehensive accounts of it himself. The first, *Über die kinetische Theorie der Gase* (1901), shows that Warburg had mastered the art of good scientific popularization. The second, *Über Wärmeleitung und andere ausgleichende Vorgänge* (1924), is essentially a summary of half a century of research on the subject.

Warburg also undertook research at Freiburg on many other topics. His investigation of elastic aftereffects led him in 1881 to one of his most beautiful results: the experimental discovery and theoretical interpretation of hysteresis in the cyclical magnetization of ferromagnetic materials. Warburg also devoted years of study to electrical conduction in solids, liquids, and gases; and his efforts

yielded many discoveries. For example, he ascertained that conductivity in quartz is 100 times greater in the direction of the axis than in the direction perpendicular to it. Another interesting discovery was the electrolytic migration of magnesium and lithium ions through glass. The drifting of electrolytic impurities toward the electrodes acquired significance for electric purification. Warburg's discovery of the cathode fall enabled him to gain important insights in his study of gas discharges. He recognized the significance of the cathode fall for breakdown voltage and measured this characteristic quantity for many gases.

Warburg's works on gas discharges quickly attracted the attention of other scientists. In his unpublished autobiography Philipp Lenard recounts that Heinrich Hertz considered Warburg a leading expert on electric discharges in rarefied gases. Hertz's opinion, which reached the influential Friedrich Theodor Althoff in the Ministry of Education, through Lenard, undoubtedly contributed to Warburg's being invited to Berlin.

Two events remain to be mentioned from Warburg's period at Freiburg: the dedication of the new physics institute in 1891 and the publication of his *Lehrbuch der Experimentalphysik* (1893). This textbook, precise and tersely written, was not easy to read but nevertheless had great success. At age eighty-three, Warburg prepared the twenty-first and twenty-second editions.

In 1895 Warburg succeeded Kundt as professor of experimental physics at the University of Berlin. He thereby obtained the "most eminent chair of physics in Germany" and became a very close associate of Max Planck. He continued to work on his research projects, enlisting the aid of many of his students. While pursuing studies on gas discharges, from 1897 he undertook others on spark discharges and point discharges and on the resulting ozone formation. According to James Franck, Warburg's research on point discharges constituted the basis for the experiments that J. Franck and Gustav Ludwig Hertz conducted on electron collisions.

Warburg's ten years as director of the Berlin physics institute were the most brilliant of his teaching career. The many students who came there constituted what was called the "Warburg school" of experimental physics. The intensive program of research that he and his students conducted is reflected in the 220 publications that originated in the institute during his tenure. Moreover, Franck calculated that around 1930 approximately one-fifth of the professors of experimental physics at German universities and colleges had studied under Warburg. Among the latter was his son Otto Heinrich (1883–1970), who became director of the Kaiser Wilhelm (now Max Planck) Institute for Cell Physiology in 1930 and received the Nobel Prize for physiology or medicine in 1931.

Warburg's teaching activities included a weekly colloquium for professors and students held in the institute's library. Friedrich Kohlrausch, then president of the Physikalisch-Technische Reichsanstalt, was an active participant. Besides his teaching, Warburg rendered important service to physics through his efforts within professional scientific organizations. He was elected chairman of the Berlin Physical Society in 1897; and in 1899 he led this body into the German Physical Society, heading the latter as well until 1905.

In 1905 Warburg left the University of Berlin to succeed Kohlrausch at the Reichsanstalt. Under Warburg's direction the organization of the institute was streamlined and duplication of effort was eliminated. At the same time, however, several new institutes were created within it, including the radioactivity laboratory (1912), in which Hans Geiger developed his *Spitzenzähler* (or point counter). In addition funds were allotted for visiting researchers, who included Einstein and de Haas when they discovered the gyromagnetic effect named for them (1914–1915).

The pace of Warburg's research did not diminish with his move to the Reichsanstalt. He pursued his investigation of point discharges and concurrently (from 1906) undertook photochemical studies that occupied him until shortly before his death. He was one of the founders of quantitative photochemistry and confirmed the fundamental law of the quantum nature of light absorption formulated by Einstein. Further, assisted by several co-workers, Warburg devoted himself to a task especially suited to the facilities at the Reichsanstalt: making precise measurements designed to test Planck's radiation law.

Following his retirement in 1922, Warburg continued his photochemical studies as an independent researcher. Although more than eighty at this time, he wrote three articles: on silent discharge in gases, spark discharge, and photochemistry. He died a few months after his eighty-fifth birthday.

Until well into old age, Warburg followed advances in physics with great attention and impartiality. In 1913, shortly after the discovery of the Stark effect, he was the first to examine its relationship to the equally new Bohr theory. The experiment he devised, although premature and therefore a failure, reflects his openness and quickness of mind.

Of Warburg's approximately 150 publications, only one is of a polemical nature; even then he did not begin the dispute, and it did not concern any scientific matter. All his other writings display a sober objectivity and critical detachment from his own results.

Unlike his contemporary Wilhelm Roentgen, for example, Warburg never achieved the brilliant success that makes a scientist known far beyond the circle of his colleagues. Nevertheless, he produced a wealth of important results that are now part of basic physical knowledge; and he was able to teach many students the procedures of intensive scientific research.

## BIBLIOGRAPHY

I. ORIGINAL WORKS. Warburg's writings include *Lehrbuch der Experimentalphysik* (Tübingen, 1893; 22nd ed., 1929); *Über die kinetische Theorie der Gase* (Berlin, 1901); *Helmholtz als Physiker* (Karlsruhe, 1922); "Funkenentladung," in H. Geiger and K. Scheel, eds., *Handbuch der Physik*, XIV (Berlin, 1927), 354–390; "Über die stille Entladung bei Gasen," *ibid.*, 149–170; and "Photochemie," *ibid.*, XVIII (1928), 619–657. A list of his works can be compiled from Poggendorff, III, 1415–1416; IV, 1598; V, 1334–1335; and VI, 2806.

II. SECONDARY LITERATURE. See Albert Einstein, "Emil Warburg als Forscher," in *Naturwissenschaften*, 10 (1922), 823–828, with a list of publications to 1921; James Franck, "Emil Warburg zum Gedächtnis," *ibid.*, 19 (1931), 993–997; Philipp Lenard, "Autobiographie" (unpublished); H. Moser, ed., *Forschung und Prüfung. 75 Jahre Physikalisch-technische Bundesanstalt/Reichsanstalt* (Brunswick, 1962), esp. 8–18; C. Müller, "Emil Warburg 80 Jahre," in *Elektrotechnische Zeitschrift*, 47 (1926), 317; J. Stark, ed., *Forschung und Prüfung. 50 Jahre Physikalisch-technische Bundesanstalt/Reichsanstalt* (Leipzig, 1937), esp. 16–19, 60–63; and Eduard Zentgraf, ed., *Aus der Geschichte der Naturwissenschaften an der Universität Freiburg im Breisgau* (Freiburg im Breisgau, 1957), esp. 18–20.

HANS RAMSER

**WARBURG, OTTO HEINRICH** (*b.* Freiburg im Breisgau, Baden, Germany, 8 October 1883; *d.* Berlin-Dahlem, Germany, 1 August 1970), *biochemistry*.

Warburg was the son of Emil Gabriel Warburg and Elizabeth Gaertner. He came with his parents in 1896 to Berlin, where his father had been called to the chair of physics at the University of Berlin. The elder Warburg later became president of the Physikalische Reichsanstalt. The family originated in the beautiful little town of Warburg, about thirty miles west of Göttingen. They first appear in the mid-sixteenth century.

Otto Warburg's mother stemmed from a family of public officials and soldiers; her brother, a general in the army, was killed in World War I. Warburg himself served as an officer in the Prussian Horse Guards on the Russian front and was wounded in action. In the early years of this fighting he carried not only a pistol but a medieval lance. Before the war ended, Albert Einstein wrote a remarkable letter to Warburg persuading him to return to the Kaiser Wilhelm Institute for Biology in Dahlem; he had been made a member in 1913 at the instigation of Emil Fischer, his first mentor ten years earlier.

In Berlin, Warburg grew up in two large official residences, both designed by the wife of Helmholtz. Most of the leading scientists of Germany were frequent guests of his parents during this final period of imperial splendor under Wilhelm II.

Later, at the university, Warburg learned chemistry from Fischer, with whom he worked for three years to obtain his doctorate; medicine in the clinic of Ludolf von Krehl at Heidelberg, to whom he was assistant for three years; thermodynamics from Walther Nernst in Berlin, with whom he worked on oxidation-reduction potentials in living systems; and physics and photochemistry from his father, with whom he worked on the quantum requirement of photosynthesis in 1920 in the Physikalische Reichsanstalt.

Warburg's first scientific work (1903–1906), with Fischer, involved splitting of racemic leucine ethyl ester by pancreatin and resolution of the optically active components. Fischer was a severe master, who instructed Warburg, after he had recrystallized the parent compound first three times, and then five more, "Now go ahead twenty-five times more."

This seemingly harsh training stood Warburg in good stead all his life, during which he invariably distinguished between experimentation made "*Für die Wahrheit*" (for the truth) and that made "*Für das Volk*" (to convince others). Having once satisfied himself as to the truth of a discovery, he always proceeded to repeat his experiments twenty to a hundred times before publishing, which explains why he, like Fischer, produced such a mass of virtually error-free and reproducible results.

Warburg learned early that "convincing others" involved much more than steamroller repetition of experimentation. Because of the great number and magnitude of his discoveries, which rank him as the most accomplished biochemist of all time, no biochemist—or scientist—has met with so much controversy, resistance, and delayed acceptance of his work, often lasting (in his own words) ten, twenty, or even fifty years. The reason for this is given by one of his favorite quotations from Hans Fischer (1881–1945), "All science is all too human"; and from Max Planck in his ninetieth year, "A new scientific truth is often accepted, not as a result of opponents becoming convinced and declaring themselves won over, but rather by the opponents dying off, and the oncoming generation of scientists becoming familiar with the new truth right from the start." He was also fond of Darwin's statement in the "Conclusion" of the *Origin of Species,* ". . . I by no means expect to convince experienced naturalists whose minds are stocked with a multitude of facts all viewed, during a long course of years, from a point of view directly opposite to mine . . . but I look with confidence to the future,—to young and rising naturalists, who will be able to view both sides of the question with impartiality." The significance of these quotations increases, of course, with the magnitude of the discovery, since then there is greater upset of previous conceptions.

Warburg endeavored to advance science mainly through his own experimental work, carried out both personally and by technical assistants whom he trained. He believed that many important discoveries were to be made in the laboratory by very simple but heretofore untried variations in experimental conditions. Thus, he discovered the fermentation of tumor cells when he increased by twentyfold the concentration of bicarbonate in the medium. He discovered iron oxygenase (*Atmungsferment*) by raising the pressure of carbon monoxide from 5 to 95 percent or more. He discovered acyl phosphate when in the oxidation-reduction reaction of fermentation the phosphate concentration was increased twenty times; and the energy cycle and one-quantum reaction of photosynthesis was discovered when the light-dark time intervals measured in manometry were shortened from five minutes to one minute.

Among the forty rooms in Warburg's institute, there was no office, no conference room, and no writing room apart from the general library. He never gave lecture courses to students, never served on committees, and never did administrative work. He selected his staff on the basis of technical ability and talent. He preferred to be regarded as an artisan and, as he frequently asserted, a technician. Nevertheless, he was an artist in everything he did, a commanding speaker in English as well as in German, and a uniquely clear writer in both English and German. Warburg's philosophical outlook is summarized by a statement he made in 1964, ". . . a scientist must have the courage to attack the great unsolved problems of his time, and solutions usually have to be forced by carrying out innumerable experiments without much critical hesitation."

Warburg was first and foremost a pioneer in biochemical methodology and in the creation of new tools of investigation—for example, spectrophotometric methods of identification and analysis of cell constituents and enzymes, manometric methods for the study of cell metabolism, numerous microanalytical methods, and methods for the isolation of cell constituents and crystallization of enzymes.

Following is a chronological listing of his major discoveries and fields of interest during more than sixty-five years of research; each item generally involved five to ten publications. Splitting of racemic leucine ethyl ester by pancreatin (first publication 1904); splitting of racemic leucine into its optically active components by means of formyl derivatives (1905), with Emil Fischer; respiration of sea urchin eggs, red blood cells, and grana (1910–1914); development of biochemical manometry (1918–1920–1968); iron catalyses on surfaces, narcotic action—displacement of substrates from surfaces, cyanide action—chemical reactions with iron (1921–1924); quantum requirements of photosynthesis (1920–1924); tissue slice technique (1923); metabolism of tumors (1923–1925); iron, the oxygen-transferring constituent of the respiration enzyme, "iron oxygenase" or *Atmungsferment* (1924); inhibition of cell respiration by carbon monoxide (1925–1926); action spectrum of iron oxygenase (1927–1932); discovery of the yellow enzymes (1932–1933); first crystallization of a flavin, "luminoflavin" (1932); discovery of nicotinamide as the active group of hydrogen-transferring enzymes (1935); nature of coenzyme action and varying degrees of binding with enzymes (1935); development of the optical methods based upon the ultraviolet absorption band of dihydronicotinamide (1935–1937); mechanism of alcohol formation in nature, dihydronicotinamide + acetaldehyde = nicotinamide + ethyl alcohol (1936); stepwise degradation of phosphorylated hexoses to trioses (1936–1937); discovery of the copper of

phenol oxidases and its action through valence change (1937); isolation and crystallization of flavin adenine dinucleotide (1938); crystallization of the oxidizing fermentation enzyme and mechanism of the oxidation reaction of fermentation, glyceric aldehyde diphosphate + nicotinamide = phosphoglyceric-*acyl phosphate* + dihydro-nicotinamide (1938); crystallization of enolase and chemistry of fluoride inhibition of fermentation (1941); crystallization of muscle zymohexase (1942); *in vitro* Pasteur reaction with hexosediphosphate and yeast zymohexase (1942); crystallization of the reducing fermentation enzyme from tumors and comparison with the homologous crystallized fermentation enzyme from muscle (1943); fermentation enzymes in the blood of tumor-bearing animals (1943); quinone and green grana (1944); heavy metals as active groups of enzymes and hydrogen-transferring enzymes (1946–1947); manometric actinometer (1948); maximum efficiency of photosynthesis (1949); one-quantum reaction and energy cycle in photosynthesis (1950), with Dean Burk; crystallization of the hemin of iron oxygenase (1951); zymohexase and ascites tumor cells (1952); chemical constitution of the hemin of iron oxygenase (1953); oxidation reaction and enzymes in fermentation (1954–1957); measurement of light absorption in *Chlorella* with the Ulbricht integrating sphere (1954); catalytic action of blue-green light in photosynthesis (1954–1956); oxygen capacity of *Chlorella* (1954–1956); carbon dioxide capacity of *Chlorella* (1956); photochemical water decomposition by living *Chlorella* (1955); origin of cancer cells (1956); functional carbon dioxide in *Chlorella* (1956); role of glutamic acid in photosynthesis (1957–1964); D-lactic acid and glycolic acid in *Chlorella* (1957–1964); Hill reactions in photosynthesis (1958–1968); photosynthesis in green leaves (1958–1963); manometric X-ray actinometer and actions of X rays on various cells (1958–1966); phosphorylation in light (1962); effects of low oxygen pressure on cell respiration, growth, and transformation (1960–1965); healing of mouse ascites cancer with glyceric aldehyde (1963); production of cancer metabolism in normal cells grown in tissue culture (1957–1968); red respiratory enzyme in *Chlorella* (1962–1965); photolyte of photosynthesis, a carbon dioxide-chlorophyll complex (1959–1969); facultative anaerobiosis of cancer cells (1962–1965); prime cause and prevention of cancer (1966–1969); chlorophyll catalysis and Einstein's photochemical law in photosynthesis (1966–1969); action of riboflavin and luminoflavin on growing cancer cells

(1967–1968); role of Vitamin B$_1$ (thiamine) on changes of normal to cancer cells and vice versa (1970); changes in chlorophyll spectrum in living *Chlorella* upon splitting and resynthesis of the carbon dioxide photolyte by light (1970).

Had Warburg ceased scientific work after the first four decades of his career, his name would now probably be forgotten. When he left his regiment near the end of World War I, his fellow officers said that he would now "return to feeding sea urchins." Few great scientists have ever matured so late.

Which of Warburg's discoveries involved the greatest originality of conception, execution, and proof? According to Warburg himself it was his discovery in 1924 of *Atmungsferment* (iron oxygenase), for which, after several more years of study and controversy, he was awarded the 1931 Nobel Prize in physiology or medicine.

Warburg became convinced in 1926 that iron oxygenase was a hemin compound, as a result of inhibition studies with carbon monoxide, which Claude Bernard had long before shown to be an inhibitor of hemoglobin. In 1926, while experimenting with yeast cells suspended in phosphate solutions containing glucose, Warburg found that carbon monoxide also inhibits cell respiration. By measuring the inhibitions obtained at different oxygen pressures, he found that the action is dependent upon the ratio of $CO/O_2$ pressures, which indicates that ferrous iron in the enzyme is the point of attack, in contrast to cyanide inhibition of ferric iron long known to occur. But, as Warburg said in his Nobel lecture, "It would never have been possible to reach any certainty of enzyme constitution here, were it not that the carbon monoxide compounds of iron possess in instances the remarkable property of being dissociated by light, as discovered by Mond and Langer in 1891, and, as shown by J. S. Haldane a few years later to alter the equilibrium between hemoglobin, CO, and $O_2$ in favor of $O_2$." Thus, by alternating periods of light and darkness for cells respiring in mixtures of CO and $O_2$, Warburg was able to cause respiration to appear and disappear; in light, carbon monoxide is split from the iron, leaving it free for oxygen activation. In a quantitative examination, Warburg found that Einstein's law of photochemical equivalency was followed, that is, the number of photochemically split Fe—CO groups is equal to the number of light quanta absorbed, independently of wavelength of light. By irradiating with monochromatic light of various wavelengths but of the same intensity, he was able to determine the absorption spectrum of the iron oxygenase–carbon monoxide complex, as judged by the magnitude of respiration increase. This absorption spectrum showed a remarkable similarity to that of CO—hemoglobin, but with some displacement toward the longer wavelengths, yet clearly identifying the iron oxygenase as a hemin compound, in which the iron is bound to nitrogen by two electron pairs and the porphyrins are cyclic compounds formed, as shown by Hans Fischer, by the linkage of four pyrrole rings through methylene bridges. Finally, the absolute absorption spectrum of the enzyme was determined from time-rate measurements of the light action on respiration, in relation to absolute light absorptions at different wavelengths. It became clear that iron oxygenase has an exceptionally strong light absorption, corresponding to an exceedingly minute concentration in the cell, where it is indeed found in the particulate grana (mitochondria) as adumbrated by some of Warburg's studies prior to World War I. In later decades Warburg succeeded in isolating and analyzing further structural details of the iron oxygenase, the prime cellular respiratory enzyme, and showed that it contains somewhat less nitrogen and iron but more carbon than does blood hemin, and also an unusual hydrocarbon chain whose structure was elucidated by Lynen in 1963. Warburg's subsequent work indicated that the heme pigments of both blood and plants (as in chlorophyll) arise in evolution from the iron oxygenase heme.

Warburg worked more or less continuously for the last fifty years of his life on various aspects of photosynthesis. His first major contribution was to demonstrate that photosynthesis can be made to take place, under appropriate conditions, with almost perfect thermodynamic efficiency. In the equation $CO_2 + H_2O$ = sugar equivalent + $O_2$, some 110,000 calories of energy are thermodynamically required per mole of $CO_2$ reduced and $O_2$ produced; and he found that this could be supplied by no more than four mole quanta of red light of 43,000 calories per mole, corresponding to an efficiency of 112,000 ($4 \times 43,000$), or 65 percent. In later years, under even better conditions, three mole quanta were found to suffice, corresponding to an efficiency approaching 100 percent conversion of light energy into chemical energy. Again, this quantum requirement was found to be independent of wavelength of light in the visible spectrum, just as was the action of light on the iron oxygenase–carbon monoxide splitting already described.

In 1950 it was found that the mechanism of light

energy conversion proceeded in steps of one quantum each, as required or predicted by the Einstein law of photochemical equivalence. Indeed, when Warburg told Einstein in 1923 about his "four quantum" requirement measurements, Einstein said, "When you get down to one quantum, come back and tell me about it." Between 1923 and 24 October 1950, Warburg worked on the "quantum riddle"; how can four quanta (or three) seemingly act together simultaneously to reduce one molecule each of $CO_2$ and water to one molecule of $O_2$ (and sugar equivalent)? On the latter date it was found that $XO_2 + 1$ quantum $= X + 1$ $O_2$. $XO_2$ was the substance from which the $O_2$ developed, and at the same time approximately 1 molecule of $CO_2$ disappeared. This occurred over a period of about a minute of illumination and was accompanied and followed by a dark reaction in which the substance $XO_2$ was restored at the expense of two-thirds of the $O_2$ produced in the light reaction. This dark reaction showed up experimentally as a greatly increased rate of respiration ($O_2$ consumption and $CO_2$ production), yielding after three such cycles a net and stable requirement of three quanta for the overall photosynthetic reaction as first written above, and persisting for long periods of time.

It is interesting that the above solution of the quantum riddle was arrived at purely experimentally; no one—not even Einstein—had hypothesized the finally observed quantum mechanism.

Although the experimental solution of the quantum riddle has never been effectively challenged, with respect to the observed one-quantum requirement, nevertheless, the three- or four-quanta requirement for overall photosynthesis, especially during the 1940's and 1950's, was objected to by a host of (but not all) workers who would not or could not adequately reproduce Warburg's experimental conditions. In the late 1950's Warburg proposed to the National Academy of Sciences that a team of selected workers be sent to Dahlem to "see for themselves," but this proposal was not accepted.

Warburg's third great area of endeavor, also on the cancer research, also covered the last fifty years of his life. There were far more scientists and laymen interested in this problem than in cellular respiration and photosynthesis and opposition to many of his findings was much more intense. Beginning in 1922, Warburg discovered the remarkably high production of lactic acid from glucose by cancer cells, both *in vitro* and *in vivo*, as well as aerobically and anaerobically, and, of course, varying in degree over a wide spectrum from cancer to

cancer. In contrast, no growing normal tissue in the animal body produced lactic acid from glucose under aerobic conditions. A few non-growing tissues might, but, as in the case of muscle, usually from glycogen and at rates ordinarily far below that of well-developed malignant tumors.

Accompanying the greatly increased glucose fermentation (glycolysis) by cancer cells was an injured respiration, manifested in a variety of ways—decreased rate, uncoupled rate, low succinate oxidative response, loss of Pasteur effect, etc.

These two major findings led Warburg in the 1950's to the following view of cancer causation:

> Cancer cells originate from normal body cells in two phases. The first phase is the irreversible injuring of respiration . . . followed . . . by a long struggle for existence by the injured cells to maintain their structure, in which part of the cells perish from lack of energy, while another part succeed in replacing the irretrievably lost respiration energy by fermentation energy. Because of the morphological inferiority of fermentation energy, the highly differentiated body cells are converted into undifferentiated cells that grow wildly—the cancer cells. . . . Oxygen gas, the donor of energy in plants and animals, is dethroned in the cancer cells and replaced by an energy yielding reaction of the lowest living forms, namely, a fermentation of glucose.[1]

According to Warburg this is the prime cause of cancer, prime cause being defined as "one that is found in every case of the disease." Thus,

> . . . the prime cause of the plague is the plague bacillus, but secondary causes of the plague are filth, rats, and the fleas that transfer the plague bacillus from rats to man. . . . Cancer, above all other diseases, has countless secondary causes. But, even for cancer, there is only one prime cause. . . . There is no disease whose prime cause is better known.[2]

In his famous 1966 Lindau lecture Warburg recommended, for both prevention and treatment of cancer, dietary additions of large amounts of the active groups of the various respiratory enzymes, these active groups constituting first and foremost iron and certain of the B vitamins. This provoked overnight the most widespread controversy, not only throughout Germany but also the Western world.

No account of Warburg's life and work should fail to mention his close association with Jacob Heiss of Kirn, in southern Germany. Heiss was a person of remarkable character, ability, and shrewdness, who from 1918 until Warburg's death entered into virtually all of his activities. He served as administrator, monitor of all scientific papers, financial adviser, and consultant on all affairs, however small, on a daily—even hourly—basis. They were a unique combination, yet the personal character of each was entirely different. Warburg never married; Heiss was his sole heir.

Throughout his life, Warburg was extremely fond of walking, sailing, dogs, and horses, and kept himself in remarkable physical trim. He rode every morning before going to work, for the better part of an hour, during which time he did much of his sustained thinking. He frequently stated that he was a "slow thinker." To many a question put to him he would reply, "*Man muss es überlegen*" (I must think it over), and the answer would be delivered the next day, after a ride. In his eighty-second year, the day after he received his honorary degree from Oxford, he was standing at the Park Lane end of Rotten Row in London, when he saw a riderless horse charging down the Row. He immediately stepped over the low guardrail in front of the oncoming horse and, with both arms upraised, caught it—to cheers of bystanders. One of them, noting Warburg's bowler hat, remarked, "Those boys from the City have something on us West Enders."

Warburg for decades vacationed in England, for whose inhabitants he had an unbounded admiration, and he was an inveterate reader of the London *Times* and *Manchester Guardian*, as well as of innumerable English authors of all sorts, including Churchill, the Mitfords, and various "aristocrats," of whom he considered himself, with amused emphasis, an example par excellence. The American he most admired was Charles Huggins, winner of the 1966 Nobel Prize for physiology or medicine. The person whom he most enjoyed telling playful stories about was himself.

## NOTES

1. "On the Origin of Cancer Cells," in *Science*, **123** (1956), 312; *The Prime Cause and Prevention of Cancer*, D. Burk, ed., 2nd ed., rev. (Würzburg, 1969), 6.
2. *Ibid.*, 6; 16.

## BIBLIOGRAPHY

Most, although not quite all, of Warburg's original experimental papers to 1961 are, fortunately and conveniently, found in the following books published under his sole authorship: *Ueber den Stoffwechsel der Tumoren* (Berlin, 1926), English trans. by Frank Dickens, *The*

*Metabolism of Tumours* (London–New York, 1930); *Ueber die katalytischen Wirkungen der lebendigen Substanz* (Berlin, 1928); *Schwermetalle als Wirkungsgruppen von Fermenten* (Berlin, 1946); *Wasserstoffuebertragende Fermente* (Berlin, 1948); *Weiterentwicklung der zellphysiologischen Methoden* (Stuttgart–New York, 1962); and *The Prime Cause and Prevention of Cancer*, Dean Burk, trans. (Würzburg, 1969). These collected works contain 200 articles in over 2,000 pages—less than has been written about them by way of reviews, recapitulations, objections, and capitulations.

DEAN BURK

**WARD, SETH** (*b.* Aspenden, Hertfordshire, England, 5 April 1617; *d.* Knightsbridge [now in London], England, 6 January 1689), *astronomy.*

Ward was the second son of John Ward, attorney, and Martha Dalton Ward. He entered Cambridge in 1632, graduated B.A. in 1637, received the M.A. in 1640, and was elected a fellow of his college. He subsequently became mathematical lecturer (1643) before the ascendancy of the Puritans induced him to leave the university. Only in 1649 did he master his scruples sufficiently to subscribe to the Solemn League and Covenant and return to academic life, this time at Oxford, as a replacement for the ousted Savilian professor of astronomy, John Greaves. Although the Puritan "visitors" succeeded, by such means, in securing the allegiance of the universities, there was a strident group of pamphleteers who insisted that reform should go much deeper, to the very heart of the curriculum—the Aristotelian corpus. In 1654 (the year he received the D.D.), Ward published with John Wilkins *Vindiciae academiarum* in defense of the extent to which the universities had responded to the new learning.

In 1660, on the second occasion of being disappointed in his bid for administrative advancement, Ward abandoned his academic career. In two years he accumulated several church livings and rose to bishop, in which post he proved a zealous administrator of church law and property.

Ward is remembered in the history of astronomy for his formulation of an alternative to Kepler's law of areas. Kepler's law of elliptical motion began to find general acceptance with the publication of Boulliau's *Astronomia philolaica* in 1645. In place of the area law, however, Boulliau postulated a complicated motion described by reference to a cone. Ward, in 1653, showed that Boulliau's scheme amounted to assuming uniform angular motion with respect to the empty focus of the ellipse. An idea with a distinguished pedigree (essentially Ptolemy's bisection of the eccentricity), it presented a very attractive alternative to the intractable Kepler equation. During the following generation, it and various modifications of it were widely used in planetary computations.

### BIBLIOGRAPHY

I. ORIGINAL WORKS. Ward's more important writings are *In Ismaelis Bullialdi astronomiae philolaicae fundamenta inquisitio brevis* (Oxford, 1653); *Vindiciae academiarum* (Oxford, 1654), written with John Wilkins; *Astronomia geometrica; ubi methodus proponitur qua primariorum planetarum astronomia sive elliptica sive circularis possit geometrice absolvi* (Oxford, 1656); and *In Thomae Hobbii philosophiam exercitatio epistolica* (Oxford, 1656). He also published a few lesser scientific works and many theological writings.

II. SECONDARY LITERATURE. See Phyllis Allen, "Scientific Studies in the English Universities of the Seventeenth Century," in *Journal of the History of Ideas*, **10** (1949), 219–253; J. L. Russell, "Kepler's Laws of Planetary Motion: 1609–1666," in *British Journal for the History of Science*, **2**, no. 5 (1964), 1–24; and Curtis A. Wilson, "From Kepler's Laws, So-Called, to Universal Gravitation: Empirical Factors," in *Archive for History of Exact Sciences*, **6**, no. 2 (Apr. 1970), 89–170.

VICTOR E. THOREN

**WARGENTIN, PEHR WILHELM** (*b.* Sunne, Jämtland, Sweden, 11 September 1717; *d.* Stockholm, Sweden, 13 December 1783), *astronomy, demography.*

Wargentin seems to have been destined for science from his early years. His father, Wilhelm Wargentin, had devoted much time to scientific studies and had tried to obtain an appointment as professor of physics at the University of Dorpat before he had been called to a parish in northern Sweden. He taught his eager son the wonders of the skies at an early age, and in 1729 they observed a lunar eclipse. Wargentin continued his astronomical observations as a student at the Gymnasium in Härnösand; and after he entered the University of Uppsala in 1735, astronomy soon became his main interest. Initially, the competent observer Olof Hiorter was his teacher; but in 1737 Anders Celsius, professor of astronomy, returned from his travels and took Wargentin's scientific development in hand. At Celsius' suggestion Wargentin began to concentrate upon calculating the orbits of the moons of Jupiter; in 1741 he

completed a work on this subject (*De satellitibus Jovis*), but the important tables were not published until 1746. Wargentin obtained his master's degree in 1743 and remained at the University of Uppsala, where he was appointed assistant professor on the Philosophical Faculty in 1748. In the fall of 1749 he was offered the position of secretary of the Royal Swedish Academy of Sciences and moved to Stockholm to assume his new duties.

Wargentin was active in three fields: astronomy, where Jupiter's moons remained his specialty; population statistics, of which he is considered one of the modern founders; and the Academy of Sciences, which he served until his death.

Founded in 1739, the Academy of Sciences in Stockholm had already acquired stability and respect; but it remained for Wargentin, as its secretary and moving force for a generation, to extend its activities and to bring it into close contact with the international scientific community. Through it Wargentin became a central figure in the scientific flowering of Sweden in the mid-eighteenth century. He edited the Academy's *Transactions*, published the Swedish almanac, for which the Academy had the license, and actively supported Sweden's introduction of the Gregorian calendar in 1753. As the Academy's astronomer he supervised the construction of its astronomical observatory in Stockholm, which was completed in 1753; the necessary instruments were obtained in London. During the international astronomical years, especially at the times of the transits of Venus of 1761 and 1769, Wargentin organized the Swedish effort and saw to it that the results obtained were immediately communicated to foreign astronomers for publication. His immense correspondence with foreign academicians and scholars—over 4,000 letters that he received have been preserved—constitutes an invaluable source for Swedish as well as European history of science.

Wargentin kept a careful journal of his observations from 1749 on. His main interest remained the moons of Jupiter, which he had begun studying in his youth. The first ephemerides of the satellites of Jupiter had been published by Gian Domenico Cassini in 1666. Although better ones were produced by James Pound and James Bradley in England and by Jacques Cassini in France in 1740, the irregularities of the satellites' movements caused great problems and more exact calculations of the orbits were needed. Here Wargentin made a basic contribution. Working in a purely empirical and statistical manner, he collected a great number of trustworthy observations that he interpreted with intuitive certainty. They were first published as "Tabulae pro calculandis eclipsibus satellitum Jovis" in *Acta Regiae societatis scientiarum Upsaliensis pro 1741* (1746).

Wargentin's values were far more accurate than those of his predecessors, but he nevertheless continued his observations and calculations, which he communicated to Lalande, with whom he corresponded regularly. Wargentin's revised tables of the satellites of Jupiter were published by Lalande in his enlarged edition of *Tables astronomiques de M. Halley* (1759); through new equations he had obtained improved calculations for the movements of the third and the fourth satellites. Wargentin continued to publish new contributions to this subject in Swedish and foreign scientific journals and until his last years he was engaged in improving the theory for the third satellite.

Among his contemporaries Wargentin was considered the outstanding expert in his field, and his tables of Jupiter's moons remained authoritative until the improvement of mathematical analysis made possible exact theoretical solutions of the problems. And his empiricism, even when compared with modern theory, must be considered surprisingly reliable.

Outward circumstances led Wargentin to his other lifelong scientific occupation, population statistics. In 1736 it was decreed that the pastors of Sweden should collect yearly reports on births and deaths, and within the Academy of Sciences the idea grew that the collected material should be submitted to statistical analysis. In 1754 the authorities ordered Wargentin to assume this task. The Royal Table Commission, established two years later with Wargentin as the guiding power, was officially assigned to work with the deposited population tables.

In 1754 Wargentin began publishing his results in a series of demographic articles in the *Transactions* of the Academy. He used both the older and the contemporary pioneers in the field of population statistics (Graunt, Petty, J. P. Süssmilch, Deparcieux); but in his later works he surpassed them and showed a sure, methodical touch. In his most important article, "Mortaliteten i Sverige" (1766), he calculated the mortality rate for different groups in the community: men, women, all inhabitants of Stockholm. He also dealt with birth and mortality rates in different months, the population increase of Stockholm, and the total population of the country. Wargentin may well have been the first to compile mortality tables based on exact figures. His results were of practical importance,

especially for life insurance. Richard Price contacted Wargentin and then published the latter's mortality tables in his *Observations on Reversionary Payments* (1783).

Wargentin received many scientific distinctions and in 1783, shortly before his death, became one of the eight foreign members of the Paris Academy. Although not noted for brilliance or innovation, he had a clear and penetrating mind, even when dealing with mundane matters, almost unlimited energy, and a strong moral integrity.

## BIBLIOGRAPHY

I. ORIGINAL WORKS. Wargentin's extensive writings in astronomy, population statistics, and other fields are scattered in many short articles, most of them published in *Kungliga Svenska vetenskapsakademiens handlingar*. His works on the moons of Jupiter are listed by Nordenmark (see below), 224–231. The Royal Swedish Academy of Sciences in Stockholm has his papers, including letters that he received (catalogued by Nordenmark, 425–449).

II. SECONDARY LITERATURE. The basic biography is N. V. E. Nordenmark, *Pehr Wilhelm Wargentin* (Uppsala, 1939), in Swedish. See also Sten Lindroth, in *Kungliga Svenska vetenskapsakademiens historia 1739–1818*, I; pt. 1 (Stockholm, 1967), 48–59, 411–416; and his "Pehr Wilhelm Wargentin," in *Swedish Men of Science* (Stockholm, 1952), 105–112. On the moons of Jupiter, see Bertil Lindblad, "P. W. Wargentins arbeten över Jupitermånarna och modern teori," in *Populär astronomisk tidskrift*, **15** (1934), 9–19. Wargentin as a population statistician has been treated (apart from Nordenmark) by A. R. Cederberg, *Pehr Wargentin als Statistiker* (Helsinki, 1919); and O. Grönlund, *Pehr Wargentin och den svenska befolkningsstatistiken under 1700-talet* (Stockholm, 1946).

STEN LINDROTH

**WARING, EDWARD** (*b.* Shrewsbury, England, *ca.* 1736; *d.* Plealey, near Shrewsbury, 15 August 1798), *mathematics.*

Little is known of Waring's early life. In 1753 he was admitted to Magdalene College, Cambridge, as a sizar, and his mathematical talent immediately attracted attention. He graduated B.A. as senior wrangler in 1757, was elected a fellow of the college, and in 1760 received the M.A. and resigned his fellowship to accept appointment, on the death of John Colson, as sixth Lucasian professor of mathematics. Although his Lucasian professorship was opposed in some quarters because of his age — he was still in his twenties — Waring soon effectively silenced his critics by publishing, in 1762, his *Miscellanea analytica de aequationibus algebraicis et curvarum proprietatibus*, which gave indisputable proof of his ability and at once established him as a mathematician of the first rank. He was elected a fellow of the Royal Society the following year.

The *Miscellanea* was described by Charles Hutton (in *Mathematical and Philosophical Dictionary*, II [1795], 584) as "one of the most abstruse books written in the abstrusest parts of Algebra." It deals largely with the theory of numbers (some of its chapters are "De fluxionibus fluentium inveniendis," "De methodo incrementorum," and "De infinitis seriebus"), a branch of mathematics for which Waring had a special gift. It contains, without proof, the theorem that every integer is the sum of four squares, nine cubes, nineteen biquadrates, "and so on." In 1770 Waring published *Meditationes algebraicae*, a work that was highly praised by Lagrange; in 1772 he brought out *Proprietates algebraicarum curvarum*; and 1776 saw the publication of *Meditationes analyticae*. In addition to these important treatises, he also, during this period, published a number of learned papers in the *Philosophical Transactions of the Royal Society*. His last major work, *Essay on the Principles of Human Knowledge*, published in 1794, is notable for his application of abstract science to philosophy.

As a mathematician, Waring was unfortunate in working at a time in which English mathematics were in a state of decline. This was in part due to the clumsy notation in which Newton had expounded his calculus and to the geometrical exposition that gave the *Principia* a somewhat archaic appearance and persuaded English readers that the great new mathematical tool forged by Newton and Leibniz (which was then being employed with great vigor and skill on the Continent, particularly by the Bernoullis) was, in fact, not really necessary. This melancholy state of affairs persisted for more than a century, despite the efforts of such distinguished mathematicians as Brook Taylor, Colin Maclaurin, and John Wallis, and led Lalande to observe in a "Notice sur la vie de Condorcet" (*Mercure de France*, 20 Jan. 1796, p. 143) that there was not a single first-rate analyst in all England. (Waring, however, stoutly maintained that his *Miscellanea Analytica* disproved Lalande's charge, and cited its commendation by d'Alembert, Lagrange, and Euler.)

Despite the spectacular improvements in notation by which fundamental mathematical operations were expressed on the Continent, Waring, in his own works, used both the *de*ism of Leibniz and the *dot*age of Newton—the two great rival systems—indifferently, and made no notable contribution to the establishment of a permanent notation in any branch of mathematics. His method of writing exponents (as, for example, on page 8 of the 1785 edition of his *Meditationes analyticae*) was clumsy in the extreme, and in general his presentation is unattractive and his books difficult to follow. He suffered from an apparent lack of intellectual order that rendered his mathematical compositions so confused that they are almost impossible to follow in manuscript, while his published works, perhaps because of his extreme myopia, are riddled with typographical errors. His language, at best, was obscure.

Waring received the Copley Medal of the Royal Society in 1784. He was also elected a member of a number of European scientific societies, notably those of Göttingen and Bologna. He served as Lucasian professor until his death; he was also a commissioner of the important Board of Longitude. Nor were his activities exclusively mathematical; simultaneously with his composition of his books he turned to medicine, and received the M.D. from Cambridge in 1770. He does not appear ever to have practiced medicine, but it is believed that he carried out dissections in the privacy of his Cambridge rooms.

## BIBLIOGRAPHY

I. ORIGINAL WORKS. Waring's books include *Miscellanea analytica de aequationibus algebraicis et curvarum proprietatibus* . . . (Cambridge, 1762), his best-known work; *Meditationes algebraicae* (Cambridge, 1770; 3rd ed., 1782); *Proprietates algebraicarum curvarum* (Cambridge, 1772); *Meditationes analyticae* (Cambridge, 1776; 2nd ed., enl., 1785); *On the Principles of Translating Algebraic Quantities Into Probable Relations and Annuities* (Cambridge, 1792); and *Essay on the Principles of Human Knowledge* (Cambridge, 1794).

His papers in the *Philosophical Transactions of the Royal Society* are "Problems," **53** (1763), 294–298; "Some New Properties in Conic Sections," **54** (1764), 193–197; "Two Theorems," **55** (1765), 143–145; "Problems Concerning Interpolations," **69** (1779), 59–67; and "On the General Resolution of Algebraical Equations," *ibid.*, 86–104.

II. SECONDARY LITERATURE. British historians of mathematics have hardly done justice to Waring. *Gentleman's Magazine*, **68**, pt. 2 (1798), 730, 807, contains a brief biography and a list of his principal contributions to mathematics; as does J. A. Venn, *Alumni Cantabrigienses*, pt. 2, IV (Cambridge, 1954), 352. The most exhaustive account of his work is Moritz Cantor, *Vorlesungen über Geschichte der Mathematik*, IV (Leipzig, 1908), 92–95. See also Florian Cajori, *History of Mathematical Notations*, 2 vols. (Chicago, 1928–1929), see indexes and I, 244, which reproduces p. 8 of the 1785 ed. of Waring's *Meditationes analyticae*; and R. T. Gunther, *Early Science in Cambridge* (Oxford, 1937), 60.

J. F. SCOTT

**WARMING, JOHANNES EUGENIUS BÜLOW** (*b.* Mandø, Denmark, 3 November 1841; *d.* Copenhagen, Denmark, 2 April 1924), *botany*.

Warming, professor of botany at the University of Copenhagen from 1886–1911, laid the foundation of a new branch of botany, ecological plant geography, with the publication of his *Plantesamfund* (1895). During the preceding years he had published many papers on various botanical subjects, several of which rank high in the literature of that time. He also had published two excellent textbooks: *Haandbog i den systematiske botanik* (1879) and *Den almindelige botanik* (1880), both of which have since been enlarged, revised, and translated into several languages.

Warming's father was a Lutheran minister on Mandø, one of the north Frisian Islands. From his childhood he loved the west coast of Jutland, with its marshland and dunes, on which he wrote two volumes of *Dansk plantevaekst: Strandvegetationen* (1906) and *Klitterne* (1909); the third volume was *Skovene* (1919). The work is still important for research on the phytoecology of northwestern Europe.

While still a student, Warming became secretary to the Danish zoologist P. W. Lund, who was excavating fossil Bradypodidae at Lagoa Santa, Minas Gerais, Brazil. He spent 1863–1866 in the tropical savannah, carrying out the most detailed and thorough study of a tropical area undertaken at the time. It took twenty-five years for complete presentation of his large collections in "Symbolae ad floram Brasiliae centralis cognoscendandae," printed in *Videnskabelige Meddelelser fra Dansk naturhistorisk Forening i Kjøbenhavn* (1867–1893). Using the "Symbolae" as a basis, Warming published *Lagoa Santa, et bidrag til den biologiske plantegeografi* (1892) with a lengthy summary in French—perhaps his most outstanding work.

After returning from Brazil, Warming studied for a year under Martius, Naegeli, and Ludwig Radlkofer at Munich and, in 1871, under J. L. von Han-

stein at Bonn. The morphological-organogenetic point of view was then the leading principle in botany, and within a few years Warming became one of the most prominent workers in this branch of botany. His main works during this period were *Er koppen hos vortemaelken (Euphorbia) en blomst eller en blomsterstand?* (1871); *De l'ovule* (1878); and his monograph on purple bacteria; *Om nogle ved Danmarks kyster levende bakterier* (1876).

In the 1870's, however, Warming adopted the theory of evolution. From then on, he became an ardent adherent of the Lamarckian view of the causes of evolution, and his research turned from ontogeny to phylogeny. In 1876 he published his first "Smaa biologiske og morphologiske bidrag" in *Botanisk Tidsskrift*, a series of papers that continued into 1878. They give a masterly account of the morphology and flower biology of numerous species, mostly Danish, pointing out their adaptation to the edaphic factors. Having assumed the difficult task of classifying the plants in a morphological-biological system, Warming published the first results in the monograph *Om skudbygning, overvintring og foryngelse* (1884), based on his examination of Scandinavian species. One of his main works, it illustrates both his comprehensive knowledge and his power to present a subject in an easily understood manner.

Warming was the founder of plant ecology. The term "ecology," first used by Haeckel in 1866, was introduced into botany by H. Reiter in 1885; but it was Warming who made ecology a preferred field of activity for many botanists. In *Plantesamfund* (1895) he formulated the program of his research: "To answer the question: Why each species has its own habit and habitat, why the species congregate to form definite communities and why these have a characteristic physiognomy."

The book created an enormous sensation as a new attempt at grouping and characterizing the plant communities—a new phytogeographical term by which Warming meant a group of species forming a physiognomically well-defined unity, such as a meadow. In all essentials the species of a community are subject to the same external conditions arising from the ecological factors. These factors are of fundamental importance to the ecology of the individual plant and the plant community. Considering water to be the most important factor, Warming divided plant communities into four types: hydrophytic, xerophytic, halophytic, and mesophytic.

Warming's ingenious way of elucidating the relation between the living plant and its surroundings opened an entirely new field of problems, and an immense ecological literature appeared during the following years.

BIBLIOGRAPHY

Warming's *Plantesamfund* (Copenhagen, 1895) was trans. into German as *Lehrbuch der ökologischen Pflanzengeographie*, with additions by E. Knoblauch (Berlin, 1896); later eds. (Berlin, 1902, 1918, 1938) had additions by P. Graebner; into Russian (Moscow, 1901); and into English as *Oecology of Plants. An Introduction to the Study of Plant-Communities* (Oxford, 1909). A complete bibliography of 283 titles is in Christensen (see below).

C. F. A. Christensen, *Den danske botanisk historie*, 3 pts. (Copenhagen, 1924–1926), pt. 1(2), 617–665, 776–806; pt. 2, 367–399, written by a pupil of Warming's, gives a detailed account of his life. *Botanisk Tidsskrift*, **39** (1927), 1–56, contains articles on Warming by L. Rosenvinge, C. Christensen, C. Ostenfeld, A. Mentz, C. Flahault, O. Juel, C. Schröter, and A. Tansley.

D. MÜLLER

**WASHBURN, EDWARD WIGHT** (*b.* Beatrice, Nebraska, 10 May 1881; *d.* Washington, D.C., 6 February 1934), *physical chemistry.*

Washburn was the son of William Gilmor Washburn, a lumber and brick merchant, and Flora Ella Wight, both of whom had moved to Nebraska from New England. Having taken all the chemistry courses available at the University of Nebraska (1899–1900) while teaching high school (1899–1901), he entered the Massachusetts Institute of Technology in 1901, obtaining the B.S. in chemistry in 1905 and the Ph.D. in 1908 under Arthur A. Noyes. Later that year he became head of the division of physical chemistry at the University of Illinois. In 1910 he married Sophie de Veer of Boston; they had four children. In 1916 Washburn became chairman of the university's department of ceramic engineering.

In 1920 the International Union of Pure and Applied Chemistry was founded. One of its first projects was to compile the *International Critical Tables of Numerical Data, Physics, Chemistry and Technology*. Washburn was named editor-in-chief in 1922 and moved to Washington. In 1926 he became head of the Division of Chemistry of the National Bureau of Standards.

Washburn was chairman of the Division of Chemistry and Chemical Technology of the National Research Council in 1922–1923, chairman of the International Commission on Physico-Chemical Standards, and a member of the National Academy of Sciences. From 1920 to 1922 he was editor of the *Journal of the American Ceramic Society*.

Washburn's application, as a graduate student, of physicochemical principles to analytical chemistry had led him to the first thermodynamic treatment of buffer solutions and then to the study of indicators. He was the first to make accurate measurements to determine the value of transference numbers—the fraction of an electric current carried by each ion in an electrolyte solution—and he pioneered the study of the hydration of ions.

At the University of Illinois, Washburn developed thermodynamic treatments of a number of colligative properties and apparatus for the precise measurement of electrical conductance and viscosity. Moving to the university's ceramic engineering department, he applied physicochemical principles to the study of ceramics, to glasses at high temperatures, and to the manufacture of optical glass.

At the National Bureau of Standards, Washburn devised greatly improved techniques for the fractionation and isolation of the chemical constituents of petroleum, and he succeeded in obtaining rubber in crystal form. After Harold C. Urey had separated deuterium, the heavy isotope of hydrogen, from ordinary hydrogen,[1] Washburn suggested that the electrolysis of water should yield gaseous hydrogen and oxygen richer in the lighter isotopes, the residual water thereby becoming richer in the heavier isotopes. The first method for producing deuterium oxide in quantity was thus developed.[2] Washburn found evidence of natural isotope fractionation in water from oceans, the Dead Sea, and Salt Lake, in crystalline hydrate deposits, and in willow sap.[3]

NOTES

1. H. C. Urey, F. G. Brickwedde, and G. M. Murphy, "A Hydrogen Isotope of Mass 2," in *Physical Review*, **39** (1932), 164–165.
2. E. W. Washburn and H. C. Urey, "Concentration of the H² Isotope of Hydrogen by the Fractional Electrolysis of Water," in *Proceedings of the National Academy of Sciences of the United States of America*, **18** (1932), 496–498.
3. E. W. Washburn and E. R. Smith, "An Examination of Water From Various Natural Sources for Variations in Isotopic Composition," in *Bureau of Standards Journal of Research*, **12** (1934), 305–311.

*BIBLIOGRAPHY*

I. ORIGINAL WORKS. Washburn's books are *An Introduction to the Principles of Physical Chemistry From the Standpoint of Modern Atomistics and Thermodynamics* (New York, 1915; rev. ed., 1921), French trans. by H. Weiss and W. Albert Noyes, Jr. (Paris, 1922); and *International Critical Tables of Numerical Data, Physics, Chemistry and Technology*, 7 vols. (New York, 1926–1930), of which he was editor-in-chief.

An almost complete bibliography is in the obituary by W. A. Noyes. A detailed bibliography through 1921 appeared in *Bulletin of the American Ceramic Society*, **1**, no. 3 (July 1922), 57–63.

II. SECONDARY LITERATURE. For a detailed biographical memoir, including extensive bibliography, see William Albert Noyes, in *Biographical Memoirs, National Academy of Sciences*, **17** (1937), 67–81. Brief obituaries are T. M. Lowry, in *Nature*, **133** (12 May 1934), 712–713; Lyman J. Briggs, in *Science*, **79** (9 Mar. 1934), 221–222; and an unsigned article in *Bulletin of the American Ceramic Society*, **13**, no. 3 (Mar. 1934), 78.

OTTO THEODOR BENFEY

**WASHINGTON, HENRY STEPHENS** (*b.* Newark, New Jersey, 15 January 1867; *d.* Washington. D.C., 7 January 1934), *geology*.

A distinguished and colorful geologist during the early decades of the twentieth century, Washington pioneered in chemical studies of igneous rocks. He demanded high standards of accuracy in his own analyses and as a result produced the textbook *Manual of Chemical Analysis of Rocks* (1904; 4th ed., 1930), which remained standard for his generation.

A descendant of George Washington, he received the A.B. in 1886, with special honors in natural sciences, and the A.M. in 1888 from Yale College. For the next six years he was involved with the American School of Classical Studies at Athens, participating in archaeological excavations in Attica, Plataea, Argos, and Phillius. This work was influenced by his knowledge of geology in, for example, his determination of the sources of marbles used in Greek sculpture.

In 1891–1892 and 1892–1893 Washington spent the winter semesters at the University of Leipzig, where he received the Ph.D. in 1893 after studying under Zirkel and K. H. Credner. His dissertation was on the volcanoes of the Kula basin in Lydia.

He returned briefly to Yale in 1895 as an instructor in mineralogy. Financially independent, Washington established a private laboratory at Locust, New Jersey, where he initiated the extensive chemical and mineralogical investigations of igneous rocks that he was to pursue for the rest of his life. Economic reverses forced him to undertake consulting work as a mining geologist from 1906 to 1912. In 1912 he became associated with the geophysical laboratory of the Carnegie Institution of Washington, where he remained, except for 1918–1919, when he was the scientific attaché to the American embassy in Rome.

Washington's chemical analyses of igneous rocks transformed into mineral compositions led to the first serious attempt to classify such substances in collaborative efforts with Whitman Cross, J. P. Iddings, and L. V. Pirsson (the CIPW classification). Although their scheme, published as *Professional Papers. United States Geological Survey*, 14, 28, and 99, achieved neither widespread nor lasting acceptance, it did stimulate an interest among earth scientists in the chemical and mineral compositions of rocks and attempts to produce alternative methods of classification.

In 1917 Washington published an enlarged edition of *Chemical Analyses of Igneous Rocks* (the first edition had appeared in 1903), a monumental assemblage of rock assays drawn from the world literature. He sorted them into superior and inferior classes and pointed out the inadequacies of the latter group. The work was of fundamental importance in establishing standards of analysis and became known throughout the world. Washington's other research spanned a wide spectrum of interests in geology, encompassing volcanism, petrography, isostasy, and geochemistry. He was a member of the committee on nomenclature of the Mineralogical Society of America. His linguistic abilities were used to establish the correct etymologies and pronunciations of mineral names.

*BIBLIOGRAPHY*

A bibliography of Washington's works is in *Zeitschrift für Vulkanologie*, **16** (1935), 3–6.

Obituaries include C. N. Fenner, in *Science*, **79** (1934), 47–48; and J. Volney Lewis, in *American Mineralogist*, **20** (1935), 179–184.

EDWARD D. GOLDBERG

**WASSERMANN, AUGUST VON** (*b.* Bamberg, Bavaria, Germany, 21 February 1866; *d.* Berlin, Germany, 15 March 1925), *bacteriology*.

For a detailed account of his life and work, see Supplement.

**WATERSTON, JOHN JAMES** (*b.* Edinburgh, Scotland, 1811; *d.* near Edinburgh, 18 June 1883), *physics, physical chemistry, astronomy.*

During his lifetime Waterston was considered a minor, somewhat eccentric scientist, known chiefly for his investigations of solar radiation; his other publications on astronomy, physical chemistry, and molecular physics attracted little notice. After his death a manuscript on the kinetic theory of gases that he had submitted in 1845 to the Royal Society of London was discovered in the Society's archives. Had this paper been published when it was first presented, an important branch of physics would have been advanced by ten or fifteen years (in the judgment of Lord Rayleigh and other modern commentators) and Waterston would have been generally recognized as one of its leaders. Instead, Waterston's case has become a classic example of the suppression of originality by an established scientific institution.

Waterston's father, George Waterston, was an Edinburgh manufacturer of sealing wax and other stationery requisites. The family was related to Robert Sandeman, the leader in extending the Sandemanian (or Glasite) religious sect to England and America, and to George Sandeman, founder of the London firm of port wine merchants.

George Waterston was greatly interested in literature, science, and music; his family thus grew up in an atmosphere of culture and came into contact with young literary men. John James was the sixth of nine children, all of whom were educated at the Edinburgh High School, then the leading school in Scotland. Following graduation Waterston became a pupil of Messrs. Grainger and Miller, civil engineers, but also attended lectures at the university, where he took an active part in the student literary society. He studied mathematics and physics under Sir John Leslie and was medalist of his year in Leslie's class. He also attended lectures on anatomy, chemistry, and surgery.

Like John Herapath, another early kinetic theorist, Waterston was interested in the problem of explaining gravity without invoking action at a distance. At the age of nineteen, he published a paper in which he discussed the properties of a system of colliding cylindrical particles, arguing that the latter could generate a gravitational force. Some of the ideas developed in this paper were later utilized in his kinetic theory, particularly the idea that

collisions could result in a transfer of energy from the rectilinear to the rotatory mode of motion.

At the age of twenty-one Waterston went to London, where he did drawing and surveying in connection with the rapidly developing British railway system. He became an associate of the Institution of Civil Engineers and contributed a paper to the *Transactions* of that group on a graphical method of estimating the earthwork in embankments and cuttings. In order to have more time free to pursue his scientific interests, he obtained a post in the hydrographers' department of the Admiralty. The head of the department was Captain (afterwards Admiral) Francis Beaufort, who subsequently communicated Waterston s paper on kinetic theory to the Royal Society. On Beaufort's suggestion, and with his backing, Waterston applied in 1839 for the post of naval instructor to the East India Company's cadets at Bombay. He was successful, and found the position satisfactory in that he had sufficient leisure and access to scientific books and journals at the Grant College, Bombay. He taught the theoretical aspects of such subjects as navigation and gunnery.

During his stay in India, Waterston sent home the manuscript of a short book and several scientific papers. The book, an essay on the physiology of the central nervous system, was published anonymously at Edinburgh in 1843. It contains the first expression of Waterston's views on molecules and on the possible application of molecular theory to biology. Some basic principles of the kinetic theory of gases are included, such as "A medium constituted of elastic spherical atoms that are continually impinging against each other with the same velocity, will exert against a vacuum an elastic force that is proportional to the square of this velocity and to this density. . . . The proportion of the whole rectilinear to the whole rotatory momentum is probably constant, and might be found perhaps by calculation." Increase in temperature might correspond to increase of molecular *vis viva.* The distance traveled by a molecule, after hitting one and before encountering another, is inversely related to the density of the medium and to the square of the diameter of the molecules.

These propositions, along with some more fanciful notions, attracted little attention at the time. In December 1845, Waterston presented a more systematic exposition of his theory of gases in a paper entitled "On the Physics of Media That Are Composed of Free and Elastic Molecules in a State of Motion." As a physical justification for his theory he mentioned the wave theory of heat, adopted by analogy with the wave theory of light as a result of the recent experiments by J. D. Forbes and Melloni on radiant heat. He found that "in mixed media the mean square molecular velocity is inversely proportional to the specific weight of the molecules"; this was the first statement of the "equipartition theorem" of statistical mechanics (for translational motion only). Since this conclusion was printed in an abstract of the British Association meeting in 1851, Waterston seems to have established his priority in announcing the theorem even though the rest of his paper was not published until much later (see below). Another original (but quantitatively incorrect) result was that the ratio of the specific heats, at constant pressure and constant volume, for monatomic gases should theoretically be equal to 4/3. (Because of a numerical slip, Waterston failed to obtain the correct value, 5/3.)

Waterston submitted his paper for publication in the *Philosophical Transactions of the Royal Society of London.* At that time the custom of the Society was that a paper submitted by someone not a fellow of the Society could be "read" (officially presented) if it were communicated by a fellow, but it then became the property of the Society and could not be returned to the author even if it was not published. The two referees who examined Waterston's paper recommended that it should not be published. One of them, Baden Powell (professor of geometry at Oxford), said that Waterston's basic principle—that the pressure of a gas is due to impacts of molecules against the sides of the container—was ". . . very difficult to admit, and by no means a satisfactory basis for a mathematical theory." The other referee was the astronomer Sir John William Lubbock, who said, "The paper is nothing but nonsense, unfit even for reading before the Society." These judgments seem rather harsh, not because Waterston's theory was essentially the same as the one successfully proposed in the 1850's by Clausius and Maxwell, but because even by 1845 the physical basis for such a theory—the relation between heat and mechanical energy—was accepted by a substantial portion of the scientific community. Nevertheless, only a brief abstract of Waterston's paper appeared in the *Abstracts of the Papers Printed in the Philosophical Transactions of the Royal Society* in 1846.

Waterston was not able to get his manuscript back, and had failed to keep a copy for himself, so he was unable to publish it elsewhere. He did attempt to draw attention to the paper by privately printing and circulating another abstract of it,

about twelve pages long, and by raising the subject in later papers presented at British Association meetings and in *Philosophical Magazine.* The only immediate response was a critical discussion by W. J. M. Rankine (who preferred a theory of rotating vortices) and an abstract by Helmholtz in *Fortschritte der Physik* that may have had some influence on A. Krönig's revival of the kinetic theory in 1856.

In the paper "On Dynamical Sequences in Kosmos," read at the British Association meeting in 1853, Waterston pointed out that substantial amounts of heat could be generated by the fall of matter into the sun. He thought that the earth might have grown in size over long periods of time by the accretion of such meteoric material, and mentioned other possible astrophysical applications of the theory that heat is equivalent to mechanical energy and may be simply the motion of the elementary parts of bodies. William Thomson adopted a meteoric theory of the sun's heat from this paper, though he later learned that a similar theory had been presented earlier by J. R. Mayer.

In 1857 Waterston resigned his appointment at Bombay and returned to Scotland, apparently having saved enough money to be able to devote his time to scientific work. About this time he published some papers on the experimental measurement of solar radiation, yielding an estimate of about 13 million degrees for the sun's temperature; this figure was frequently quoted in the debate on the sun's temperature during the 1870's. Waterston began experimental work on liquids; and during the next few years he published a series of papers on physical chemistry, mainly in *Philosophical Magazine.* Apparently, he never met any of the scientists who might have recognized the value of his work on the kinetic theory, with the possible exception of Rankine (who spoke at the same session of the British Association meeting at which Waterston presented a paper on gases in 1851).

Among Waterston's chemical papers is one on capillarity and latent heat that reports a calculation of the diameter of a water molecule. The result was 1/214,778,500 inch (approximately $10^{-8}$ cm.). This estimate was published in 1858, seven years before Joseph Loschmidt's determination of molecular sizes from kinetic theory but forty-two years after Thomas Young's estimate, which was somewhat similar to Waterston's.

In 1878 the Royal Astronomical Society rejected two papers by Waterston. A few months later he resigned, having been a member since 1852. This event reinforced his isolation from the scientific world. According to a memoir by his nephew, Waterston "would not attend the meetings of the Royal Society of Edinburgh though some friends sent him billets, and rather avoided the society of scientific men. . . . We could never understand the way in which he talked of the learned societies, but any mention of them generally brought out considerable abuse without any definite reason assigned."[1]

Waterston's paper on the theory of sound, published in *Philosophical Magazine* in 1858, was the ultimate reason for his posthumous recognition by the scientific community. In 1876, S. Tolver Preston wrote to Maxwell about this paper, noting that Waterston had investigated the kinetic theory of gases as early as 1845, although his work had not yet been published.[2] But Maxwell apparently took no interest in this matter; and it was not until 1891, eight years after Waterston's death, that Lord Rayleigh rediscovered the 1858 paper on sound because of his interest in another of Waterston's papers that cited it. The mention of a manuscript lying in the archives of the Royal Society finally reached the right reader, for Rayleigh was secretary of the Royal Society in 1891, and had no difficulty in retrieving this manuscript. The paper was published in the *Philosophical Transactions* for 1892, with an introduction by Rayleigh, according to whom:

> The history of this paper suggests that highly speculative investigations, especially by an unknown author, are best brought before the scientific world through some other channel than a scientific society, which naturally hesitates to admit into its printed records matter of uncertain value. Perhaps one may go further and say that a young author who believes himself capable of great things would usually do well to secure the favourable recognition of the scientific world by work whose scope is limited, and whose value is easily judged, before embarking on greater flights.

*NOTES*

1. R. J. Strutt, *Life of John William Strutt, Third Baron Rayleigh* (London, 1924; augmented ed., Madison, Wis., 1968), 171.
2. I am indebted to Dr. C. W. F. Everitt for informing me of this letter.

*BIBLIOGRAPHY*

I. ORIGINAL WORKS. Most of Waterston's published works are reprinted in *The Collected Scientific Papers of John James Waterston*, edited with a biography by J. S. Haldane (Edinburgh, 1928). This volume omits the following papers: "An Account of an Experiment on the Sun's Actinic Power," in *Monthly Notices of the Royal Astronomical Society*, 17 (1856–1857), 205–206; "On Certain Inductions With Respect to the Heat Engendered by the Possible Fall of a Meteor Into the Sun; and on a Mode of Deducing the Absolute Temperature of the Solar Surface From Thermometric Observation," in *Philosophical Magazine*, 4th ser., 19 (1860), 338–343, and *Monthly Notices of the Royal Astronomical Society*, 20 (1860), 196–202; "Note of an Experiment on Voltaic Conduction," in *Philosophical Magazine*, 4th ser., 31 (1866), 83–84. In addition there are brief reports of his papers presented at British Association meetings in *Athenaeum* (1851), 776; (1852), 980; (1853), 1099–1100. Unpublished materials may be found in the archives of the Royal Society of London.

II. SECONDARY LITERATURE. J. S. Haldane's "Memoir of J. J. Waterston" is printed in the *Papers* (see above); it includes biographical information, portraits, and extensive discussion of Waterston's scientific work and opinions. See also S. G. Brush, "The Development of the Kinetic Theory of Gases. II. Waterston," in *Annals of Science*, 13 (1957), 275–282, and "John James Waterston and the Kinetic Theory of Gases," in *American Scientist*, 49 (1961), 202–214; and E. E. Daub, "Waterston, Rankine, and Clausius on the Kinetic Theory of Gases," in *Isis*, 61 (1970), 105–106.

STEPHEN G. BRUSH

**WATERTON, CHARLES** (*b.* Walton Hall, Yorkshire, England, 3 June 1782; *d.* Walton Hall, 27 May 1865), *natural history.*

Waterton was the twenty-sixth lord of Walton Hall, being the eldest son of Thomas and Ann Bedingfield Waterton. His family staunchly upheld the Roman Catholic faith and consequently had suffered persecution since the Reformation. Waterton was educated at Stonyhurst College, a Jesuit school, and his detestation of all that was Protestant was a formative and decisive factor in his career. As a boy his energy and high spirits, as well as his pursuit of nature, caused the "holy and benevolent" fathers of Stonyhurst to give up the rod and attempt to tame this incorrigible imp by making him, as he wrote, "rat-catcher to the establishment and also fox-taker, foumart-killer, and crossbow-charger at a time when the young rooks were fledged. Moreover I fulfilled the duties of organ-blower and football maker with entire satisfaction to the public" (*Essays*, xxvii).

Thus was formed the eccentric of later years,

whose indomitable courage and love of nature and travel led him to undertake a famous journey in 1812. Starting from Stabroek (now Georgetown, Guyana), where his family owned plantations, Waterton traveled alone up the Demerara and Essequibo rivers and over the Kanuku Mountains as far as the Rio Branco, a tributary of the Rio Negro; this was an incredibly difficult journey, not made easier by Waterton's proneness to accidents and illness caused chiefly by his own eagerness and temerity. His description of this and other journeys in *Wanderings in South America* gave many almost unbelievable stories which upset the orthodox scientists of the time, whom Waterton described as "closet-naturalists"; he included Audubon, James Rennie, and William Swainson in this category. Swainson, who also collected South American birds, described Waterton's "tendency to clothe fact in the garb of fiction," although Waterton was, above all, sincere and truthful, being carried away only by his impetuosity and enthusiasm. Among his many eccentric adventures were his capture of a live caiman (crocodile) by riding on its back (see *Illustrated London News*, 24 August 1844), and his taking of a live ten-foot boa constrictor by the Watertonian expedient of punching it on the nose and hustling it into a bag before it recovered.

In each instance Waterton's object was the scientific one of dissecting the animal and preserving its skin. This led to the formation of his collection of superbly mounted and preserved specimens at Walton Hall. He invented a new and advanced taxidermic technique of removing the whole interior and preserving only the skin and exterior parts with an alcohol solution of mercuric perchloride. The technique is described by Waterton in *Wanderings* (1825 ed., 307). Sir Joseph Banks wrote of his unrivaled skill in preserving birds. His collection, a large part of which may still be seen at Stonyhurst, was greatly enriched on his third visit to Demerara in 1820, when he took 232 birds, two land tortoises, a sloth, five armadillos, an ant bear, and the caiman, but he was justly annoyed when a customs delay caused the loss of his live *Tinamus* eggs, from which he had hoped to breed this little-known quail.

Waterton's original object in his first journey had been to collect "a quantity of the strongest wourali poison" (*ibid.*,1) and he succeeded, giving an early and accurate account of the preparation of the South American arrow poison curare (p. 54). in which he was preceded only by Alexander von Humboldt in 1800. Waterton's descriptions of the blowpipe and darts also were original (p. 58). He tested his curare on animals and correctly deduced that "the quantity of poison must be proportioned to the animal" (p. 69). Back in London, in 1814 Waterton conducted experiments on donkeys with the aid of the veterinarian William Sewell and the surgeon Benjamin Brodie. The most famous related to Wouralia, the ass whose life was preserved by energetic artificial respiration through a tracheostomy after she had received a large dose of curare (p. 81). This is a technique now revived in modern surgery. These experiments served to draw attention to curare, which later was investigated by Claude Bernard and is now in common medical use. Waterton pronounced himself ready at any time to treat cases of hydrophobia with curare but seems usually to have arrived too late. Later the drug was used successfully by others in the treatment of tetanus.

Waterton's fame as an explorer induced Lord Henry Bathurst, then secretary for the colonies, to offer him an important task, the exploration of the then almost unknown island of Madagascar. True to his eccentric nature, Waterton refused, pleading sickness, but probably influenced by religious prejudice, and so was officially ignored for the rest of his life.

Returning to Walton Hall, Waterton began the project of bird protection for which he deserves to be best remembered. It was Waterton—and not Audubon, as is often thought—who set up the first bird sanctuary; he enclosed Walton Park with a three-mile, seven-foot wall at a cost of £10,000. He banned guns and encouraged the birds to return to a natural state. Among his scientific writings, probably the most interesting is his argument with Audubon and Swainson on the manner in which vultures seek out their food (*Essays*, p. 17).

Waterton achieved fame and notoriety in his lifetime both for his journeys and for his literary skill in describing them. Although his style was akin to that of his hero Tristram Shandy, his biographer Norman Moore states that the *Essays* belong to the literary class of Gilbert White and are not inferior in the quality of their observations. The comparison is not without justice; White was among Waterton's favorite reading.

Waterton's contributions to science, ultimately, were small: some increase in knowledge of curare, an original method of taxidermy, and above all the idea of animal and bird conservation. His nature was eccentric, forthright, outspoken, and lovable;

but since he refused to conform, he remained outside the science establishment.

*BIBLIOGRAPHY*

Waterton's books are *Wanderings in South America, the North-West of the United States, and the Antilles, in the years 1812, 1816, 1820 and 1824* (London, 1825), which describes his four journeys and has been republished many times; and *Essays on Natural History Chiefly Ornithology* (London, 1838), which includes an autobiographical note. He wrote many articles for Loudon's *Magazine of Natural History*, some of which appear in the *Essays*.

His admiring but verbose biographer, Richard Hobson, wrote *Charles Waterton, His Home, Habits and Handiwork* (London, 1866), which is the chief source for Waterton's eccentricities. Sir Norman Moore, who had known him intimately, wrote a personal tribute in his article on Waterton for *Dictionary of National Biography*, XX, 906–908. An obituary notice is in *Illustrated London News* (17 June 1865). See also Richard Aldington, *The Strange Life of Charles Waterton* (London, 1949); and K. B. Thomas, *Curare, Its History and Usage* (London, 1964), 34–40.

K. BRYN THOMAS

**WATSON, GEORGE NEVILLE** (*b*. Westward Ho!, Devon, England, 31 January 1886; *d*. Leamington Spa, England, 2 February 1965), *mathematics*.

Watson went up to Cambridge University in 1904 as a major scholar of Trinity College, to which he was intensely devoted throughout his life, and held a fellowship there from 1910 to 1916. After a brief period at University College, London, he went to Birmingham in 1918 as professor of mathematics and remained in this post until his retirement in 1951.

Almost all Watson's work was done in complex variable theory. Within this field he was no narrow specialist, his interests ranging widely over problems arising in the theories of difference and differential equations, number theory, special functions, and asymptotic expansions. As a classical analyst Watson showed great power and an outstanding ability to find rigorous and manageable approximations to complicated mathematical expressions; unlike many pure mathematicians, he was not averse to numerical computation, which he performed on his own Brunsviga machine and in which he found relaxation.

Watson wrote over 150 mathematical papers and three books. The first of these books, a Cambridge tract on complex integration, is now rarely consulted; but the remaining two had, and still have, a wide influence, particularly among applied mathematicians and theoretical physicists. The second, *A Course of Modern Analysis*, was written in collaboration with E. T. Whittaker, who had been one of the younger fellows of Trinity when Watson was an undergraduate. The first edition had appeared in 1902 under Whittaker's sole authorship and Watson offered to share the work of preparing the second, which appeared in 1915 and was a considerably expanded version of the original work. The first part of the book develops the basic principles and techniques of analysis and these are applied in the second part to obtain the properties of the many special functions that occur in applications. "Whittaker and Watson" has appeared in several editions and numerous reprints; Watson never lost his interest in it and, in his retirement, embarked upon a much enlarged version, which was never published.

The first fifty of Watson's mathematical papers are concerned mainly with properties and expansions of special mathematical functions. These investigations culminated in the publication of his monumental and definitive *Treatise on the Theory of Bessel Functions* (1922). A second edition, containing only minimal alterations, appeared in 1944; for by then Watson had lost interest in the subject and, unfortunately for the mathematical public, was not prepared to undertake the continuous revision and expansion that would have kept the book up to date. By 1929, also, he had already embarked on his "Ramanujan period"; and during the next ten years a succession of papers appeared in which he proved and extended numerous results that had been stated in the notebooks of the Indian mathematical genius Srinivasa Ramanujan, who had died in 1920. Watson and B. M. Wilson of Liverpool were invited by the University of Madras to become joint editors of a projected work, of an estimated 600 pages, which would contain proofs of Ramanujan's results.

Both editors made considerable progress, and much of their work was published as original papers. The mass of Ramanujan material was so extensive, however, that the fruit of their combined labors never reached the stage of publication in book form. Wilson died in 1935; and by 1939 Watson's impetus had diminished, possibly because of his increased administrative and teaching commitments following the outbreak of World War II. His work not only had provided proofs of formulas and congruences stated by Ramanujan, but also had considerably extended Ramanujan's work on singular moduli and set his work on mock theta functions on a proper foundation. These investigations were admirably suited to Watson's analytical abilities, since they demanded not only great ingenuity but also enormous industry. Much of this work would now be regarded as being outside the main stream of mathematics; but fashions change! His efforts during this period were not devoted solely to problems arising from Ramanujan's notebooks; his important work on what are now called Watson transforms also dates from this time.

With the exception of his investigations on periodic sigma functions, Watson's papers during the last twenty years of his life are of lesser interest.

## BIBLIOGRAPHY

A complete list of Watson's mathematical writings is in the obituary notice by R. A. Rankin that appeared in *Journal of the London Mathematical Society*, **41** (1966), 551–565, where a more detailed discussion of some of his work is given. See also the obituary notice by J. M. Whittaker in *Biographical Memoirs of Fellows of the Royal Society*, **12** (1966), 521–530, which supplements the latter and includes a photograph.

Watson's unpublished work on the Ramanujan notebooks is in a collection of MSS deposited in the library of Trinity College, Cambridge.

R. A. Rankin

**WATSON, HEWETT COTTRELL** (*b*. Park Hill, Firbeck, Yorkshire, England, 9 May 1804; *d*. Thames Ditton, Surrey, England, 27 July 1881), *phytogeography*, *evolution*, *phrenology*.

Watson was one of ten children born to Holland Watson and Harriett Powell Watson. His father, a magistrate for Cheshire County, planned a military career for his son. While still a youngster, however, Watson crushed his right knee during a game of cricket; he then became destined for the law. It is probable that his limp had a strong influence upon the development of his personality, which was conspicuously hostile.

A small inheritance at the age of twenty-one freed Watson from the necessity of earning a living, and he promptly abandoned his apprenticeship in law in order to collect plants and to study phrenology. The latter interest led him to Edinburgh, where he became intimate with the brothers George and Andrew Combe, and where he studied medicine from 1828 to 1832. Although he won honors as an outstanding student, Watson never took the examinations for a medical degree. There is some evidence that he had a breakdown in either his physical or his mental health.

In 1833 Watson purchased a house at Thames Ditton, near London, where he lived for the rest of his life with a housekeeper. He never married and never held a job, except for one term as a botany instructor in 1837 at the Liverpool School of Medicine. In 1842 William Hooker persuaded him to collect plants for five months in the Azores, which was the only time he ever left Britain.

In his early twenties Watson already had a good knowledge of the geography of British plants, and in 1832 he began publishing both articles on the influence of environmental factors upon the distribution of species and a series of guidebooks to their distribution. This was a promising, though not unusual, start to a career in botany.

At the same time, however, Watson was active in the phrenology movement, and by 1836 phrenology had become his major interest. In that year he published *Statistics of Phrenology, Being a Sketch of the Progress and Present State of That Science in the British Isles*. This book does not contain an application of statistics to phrenological questions; rather, it contains a report on the extent of phrenological activity in Britain. It has been more valuable to historians of phrenology than it was for advancing the movement.

In 1837 Watson purchased the *Phrenological Journal* from the Combes and edited it for three years, hoping to raise the standards of phrenological investigation to the level of a critical science. In this he failed, for two reasons. First, phrenology had developed neither an adequate methodology nor an adequate standard of verification. Merely improving individual phrenological papers was not coming to grips with the fundamental problem. Second, Watson was so blunt and critical in his editorial comments that he succeeded only in arousing the anger of the majority of the journal's readers and contributors. He recognized his failure, concluded that phrenology would never rise to the level of critical science, and in 1840 returned to the study of botany, to which he devoted the remainder of his life.

Watson came to believe in the transformation of species by 1834; and he first defended the idea in a polemical tract, *An Examination of Mr. Scott's Attack Upon Mr. Combe's "Constitution of Man"* (1836). His ideas on the subject were Lamarckian; and although he had aggressively helped to advance phrenological theory, his contributions to evolution were almost devoid of theoretical innovation. Watson agreed with Charles Lyell's judgment that Lamarck had not proved his case, but remained convinced that it could be proved. His subsequent phytogeographical research was motivated in part by a desire to collect evidence that would demonstrate the transformation of species.

Watson published some of his own evidence (1845) in a series of four articles written as a review and a reaction to Robert Chambers' anonymous *Vestiges of the Natural History of Creation* (1844). After revealing the inadequacy of Chambers' knowledge of botany, he went on to present evidence that could stand up to criticism. First, he felt that the paleontological evidence was important; but since this was beyond the scope of his own studies, he did not discuss it. Confining himself to botanical evidence, Watson documented the difficulty of distinguishing the separate species of *Salix*, *Mentha*, *Rosa*, *Rubus*, and *Saxifraga* by citing the divergent estimates of the number of British species of these genera from six manuals on British plants. Other evidence he considered important was the ease with which new varieties could be grown from cultivated species of *Pelargonium*, *Erica*, *Rosa*, *Fuchsia*, *Calceolaria*, *Dahlia*, and the pansy. He then pointed to the prevailing confusion among botanists concerning whether domestic fruits and grains were separate species or only varieties of the same species. Watson's next type of evidence was the existence in nature of "species being tied together (so to speak) by a series of intermediate forms." From his own observations he described clusters from a dozen such genera.

Watson's examples of evolution in action—both from his articles of 1845 and from his *Cybele Britannica*—impressed Charles Darwin, who drew upon them to good advantage in chapter 2 of *The Origin of Species*.

Although he was innovative in many minor ways, Watson's isolation from and contempt for his colleagues may have caused him to fall into a rut in his research. Both his phrenological and phytogeographical investigations were correlational in methodology. He never conducted any extensive experiments. In phytogeography he followed Humboldt's example of constructing numerous correlations between environmental factors and distributional patterns. The results, he hoped, would lead to a new understanding of both phytogeography and evolution.

When he read *The Origin of Species*, Watson realized that Darwin had found what he had unsuc-

cessfully sought—a convincing causal explanation of evolution. He immediately wrote to Darwin, "You are the greatest revolutionist in natural history of this century, if not of all centuries." In his later years, however, he became disturbed by Darwin's inability to explain the origin of variations; and he became less certain of the magnitude of Darwin's achievement.

Watson's own work after 1859 was devoted to increasing the accuracy of knowledge of the distribution of British plants, and he helped make the British flora the best-known in the world. The Botanical Society of the British Isles has acknowledged the importance of his contributions by naming its journal *Watsonia*.

## BIBLIOGRAPHY

I. ORIGINAL WORKS. Watson's articles on phrenology appeared in *Phrenological Journal* (1829–1840) and can be located in the index of each volume. His articles on botany are listed (but neither completely nor entirely accurately) in the Royal Society *Catalogue of Scientific Papers*, VI, 280–281; VII, 1202. There is a list of his botany books in the account by Boulger (see below).

II. SECONDARY LITERATURE. Besides George S. Boulger, in *Dictionary of National Biography*, XX, 918–920, there are two useful biographical sketches of Watson. The first, anonymous but obviously autobiographical, contains the only known portrait of him as a young man; see *Naturalist*, 4 (1839), 264–269. The other is John G. Baker, "In Memory of Hewett Cottrell Watson," in *Journal of Botany, British and Foreign*, 19 (1881), 257–265, with portrait of Watson in old age; reprinted without portrait in Watson's *Topographical Botany*, 2nd ed. (London, 1883). The details of Watson's life and work can, however, be obtained from the more than 300 letters he wrote that are preserved in British libraries. He burned the letters written to him.

There are no detailed discussions of Watson's contributions to science. For indications of Darwin's use of Watson's knowledge, see the dozen letters from Watson in the Darwin MSS, Cambridge University Library, and R. C. Stauffer, ed., *Charles Darwin's Natural Selection, Being the Second Part of His Big Species Book Written From 1856 to 1858* (Cambridge, 1975), see index. For the background of his work in phrenology, see his own *Statistics of Phrenology*; David Armand De Giustino, "Phrenology in Britain, 1815–1855: A Study of George Combe and His Circle" (Ph. D. diss. Univ. of Wisconsin, 1969); and Charles Gibbon, *The Life of George Combe, Author of "The Constitution of Man,"* 2 vols. (London, 1878). There are ample testimonies in the British botanical literature to the importance of Watson's work. One recent discussion is J. E. Dandy, *Watsonian Vice-Counties of Great Britain* (London, 1969).

Frank N. Egerton III

**WATSON, RICHARD** (*b.* Heversham, Westmorland, England, August 1737; *d.* Windermere, Westmorland, England, 9 July 1816), *chemistry.*

A son of Thomas Watson, headmaster of the grammar school at Heversham, Watson in 1754 entered Trinity College, Cambridge, where he distinguished himself in mathematics. In 1760 he became a fellow of the college, a moderator in 1762, and in November 1764 professor of chemistry, although he was completely ignorant of the subject. After fourteen months of intensive study he began to lecture in 1766. The chair was unendowed, but with the help of influential friends Watson obtained an annual royal grant of £100. In 1769 he was admitted to the Royal Society. Watson's main ambition, however, was to become regius professor of divinity; and when the chair became vacant in October 1771, although unqualified, Watson was able "by hard travelling and some adroitness" to obtain the king's mandate for a doctorate of divinity and was thus elected. In 1782 he became bishop of Llandaff. His theological and political writings were extensive; he defended Christianity against the attacks of Edward Gibbon and Thomas Paine. His unorthodox views made him enemies, however: he was attacked as self-seeking—a charge to which his apparent willingness to accept patronage laid him open.

Watson's most original work in chemistry was an investigation of the phenomena of solution. In 1770 he disproved J. T. Eller's assertion, made about 1750, that the volume of water is not increased when a salt is dissolved in it; and in the severe winter of 1771 he found that the times taken by solutions of a given salt to freeze, starting from the instant that pure water began to freeze when exposed to the air, were proportional to the concentrations. Thus he anticipated Blagden's "law."

Watson is best known for his *Chemical Essays,* some of which are still valued for their lucidity—in particular his account of the phlogiston theory, "Of Fire, Sulphur and Phlogiston" (*Essays,* I, 149–180), which has frequently been cited. He also described the now-classic experiment in which hot water in a tightly stoppered flask can be made to boil by pouring cold water over the air space

("Of Degrees of Heat in Which Water Begins to Part With Its Air and in Which It boils," *Essays,* III, 143–169). His "Of the Saltness and Temperature of the Sea" (*Essays,* II, 93–139) is a perceptive contribution to early marine science.

*BIBLIOGRAPHY*

I. Original Works. Watson's chemical works are *Institutionum chemicarum in praelectionibus academicis explicatarum, pars metallurgica* (Cambridge, 1768); *An Essay on the Subjects of Chemistry, and Their General Division* (Cambridge, 1771); and *A Plan of a Course of Chemical Lectures* (Cambridge, 1771). These, together with the papers listed below, are reprinted in *Chemical Essays,* 5 vols. (Cambridge, 1781–1787). There were a number of subsequent eds., published mainly at London, with the same pagination, but the numbering of the eds. is confusing; the last English ed. (London, 1800) is styled "7th edn." Two eds. were published in Dublin—a 1-vol. ("3rd") ed. (1783), containing the essays in vols. I–III, and the complete work in 2 vols. (1791).

Watson's papers are "Experiments and Observations on Various Phoenomena Attending the Solution of Salts," in *Philosophical Transactions of the Royal Society,* **60** (1770), 325–354; "Some Remarks on the Late Cold in February Last," *ibid.,* **61** (1771), 213–220; "Account of an Experiment Made With a Thermometer, Whose Bulb Was Painted Black, and Exposed to the Direct Rays of the Sun," *ibid.,* **63** (1773), 40–41; "Chemical Experiments and Observations on Lead Ore," *ibid.,* **68** (1778), 863–883; "Observations on the Sulphur Wells at Harrogate, Made in July and August 1785," *ibid.,* **76** (1786), 171–188; and "On Orichalcum," in *Memoirs and Proceedings of the Manchester Literary and Philosophical Society,* **2** (1785), 47–67.

II. Secondary Literature. The main biographical source is *Anecdotes of the Life of Richard Watson, Bishop of Landaff; Written by Himself at Different Intervals, & Revised in 1814,* published by his son Richard Watson (London, 1817; 2nd ed., 2 vols., 1818), which contains a number of letters. Watson's character and views were scathingly though anonymously attacked in *A Critical Examination of the Bishop of Landaff's Posthumous Volume . . .* (London, 1818). Accounts of Watson are V. Bartow, "Richard Watson, Eighteenth Century Chemist and Clergyman," in *Journal of Chemical Education,* **15** (1938), 103–111; L. J. M. Coleby, "Richard Watson, Professor of Chemistry in the University of Cambridge, 1764–71," in *Annals of Science,* **9** (1953), 101–123; and J. R. Partington, "Richard Watson (1737–1816)," in *Chemistry and Industry,* **56** (1937), 819–821—see also Partington's *History of Chemistry,* II (London, 1961), 765–767, and his *Text-Book of Inorganic Chemistry* (London, 1921), 103, where he first drew attention to Watson's anticipation of Blagden. A letter from Watson to Lord Rockingham and the reply are reproduced and commented on by W. H. G. Armytage in "Richard Watson and the Marquess of Rockingham; an Unpublished Exchange in 1771," in *Annals of Science*, **14** (1961), 155–156. Some account of Watson's theological writings is given by A. Gordon in *Dictionary of National Biography*, XL (1899), 24–27.

E. L. SCOTT

**WATSON, SERENO** (*b*. East Windsor Hill, Connecticut, 1 December 1826; *d*. Cambridge, Massachusetts, 9 March 1892), *botany*.

Watson was the ninth of the thirteen children of Henry Watson and Julia Reed Watson, both descendants of early Connecticut settlers. Henry Watson was a merchant in the village of East Windsor but moved to the nearby ancestral farm at East Windsor Hill when his father died, shortly after Sereno's birth. The pleasant rural childhood contributed to the boy's love of nature and to his lifelong diffidence.

After preparatory work at East Windsor Hill Academy, Watson attended Yale College, graduating in 1847. He intended to enter medicine and for some years studied under several physicians in New England and New York, and under his brother Louis in Illinois, alternating his studies with various teaching posts. Neither medicine nor teaching appealed to him, so in 1856 he joined another brother in Greensboro, Alabama, where he was secretary of the Planters' Insurance Company until the Civil War began. He left the South to work on the *Journal of Education* in Hartford, Connecticut, from 1861 to 1866 and then attended the Sheffield Scientific School at Yale for a year.

Without definite purpose Watson sailed for California via Panama in 1867. From the Sacramento valley he walked across the Sierra Nevada to volunteer on Clarence King's geological exploration of the fortieth parallel. Among other duties he assisted William Whitman Bailey in botanical collections, since he had enjoyed plant collecting earlier as a minor hobby. Bailey's health was poor; and when he left in March 1868, Watson became the survey's official botanist. He collected extensively in Nevada and Utah. A year later he returned east to study his collections in the herbarium of Daniel C. Eaton at Yale, and in 1870 he removed to Asa Gray's herbarium at Harvard to continue his survey report and botanical studies. In 1874 he became the curator of the Gray Herbarium, and from 1881 to 1884 he was also instructor in phytography at Harvard.

Watson's contributions to botany began with the fifth volume of the fortieth parallel survey (1871), which lists 1,325 plant species and describes and illustrates many of them. This classic was the first account of the distinctive xerophytic and mesophytic vegetation of the Great Basin region. It was also the first example of Watson's painstaking meticulousness in defining the systematics of plants.

In 1873 Watson began compiling the systematic botany of California, started earlier by William H. Brewer, who turned over his material to Watson. This significant work was presented in two volumes in 1876 and 1880. Simultaneously Watson undertook the almost impossible task of indexing all plant species west of the Mississippi River, on which scattered accounts and descriptions had already been published in the accounts of many western explorations. The only completed volume from this undertaking was the very useful one on Polypetalae (1878).

Asa Gray had been revising his classic *Manual of the Botany of Northern United States* before his death in 1888, after which Watson and John M. Coulter completed the work. Most of Watson's other botanical works were published under the title "Contributions to American Botany," in various journals. These, and his separately published works, constitute a fine contribution to plant systematics and relationships.

Watson received an honorary Ph.D. from Iowa College in 1878, and he was elected to the National Academy of Sciences in 1889. He never married and, from lifelong shyness, he never presented his papers in person.

## BIBLIOGRAPHY

I. ORIGINAL WORKS. Watson's most significant works, cited in the text, are *Botany,* vol. V of *United States Geological Exploration of the Fortieth Parallel* (Washington, D.C., 1871); *Botany of California*, 2 vols. (Cambridge, Mass., 1876, 1880) (I, *Polypetalae*, was written with W. H. Brewer); *Bibliographical Index to North American Botany . . . Part I, Polypetalae* (Washington, D.C., 1878); and *Gray's Manual of the Botany of the Northern United States . . .*, 6th ed. (New York–Cincinnati–Chicago, 1889; reissued with corrections, 1890). These and Watson's other publications are listed in the biography by Brewer (see below).

II. SECONDARY LITERATURE. William H. Brewer wrote the only extensive account of Watson's life: *Biographical Memoirs. National Academy of Sciences*, **5** (1903), 267–290 (the year of birth is given incorrectly as

1820). A short account by "M.B." appeared in *Scientific American*, **65** (1892), 233–234.

ELIZABETH NOBLE SHOR

**WATSON, WILLIAM** (*b.* London, England, 3 April 1715; *d.* London, 10 May 1787), *physics, botany, medicine.*

Watson, the son of a cornchandler, obtained a sound basic education at the Merchant Taylors' school before apprenticing himself to an apothecary on 6 April 1731 for a term of eight years.[1] Apothecaries were then enjoying new opportunities and obligations in consequence of having won in 1704, at the expense of their old enemies the physicians, the right to prescribe as well as to compound medicine. An apprentice accordingly had much to learn: botany, chemistry, drug making, and the diagnosis and treatment of common complaints. Watson, "never indolent in the slightest degree" and an "exact economist of his time" (Pulteney, 334), mastered these subjects, especially chemistry and botany, in which he won the annual prize of the Apothecaries Society for skill in identifying plants *in situ* (Pulteney, 297). In June 1738, ten months short of the term of his apprenticeship, he purchased his freedom for two guineas and was sworn into the Apothecaries Society. The same year he married and set up in business for himself.

Through his botanical contacts Watson came to the Royal Society, of which he was to be one of the most productive and influential members. He first attended a meeting on 16 March 1738, as guest of John Martyn, Cambridge professor of botany in absentia, abridger of the *Philosophical Transactions*, and translator of Boerhaave.[2] He was then patronized by Martyn's friend Sir Hans Sloane, who with Martyn, Thomas Birch, and others signed Watson's certificate for admission to the Society, which took place on 9 April 1741. His first communications to the Society dealt either with botany—for instance, an account of the previously undescribed star puffball (*Geaster*), which made him known to Continental authorities (Pulteney, 299)—or with medical oddities encountered in his practice. He continued to write on these matters and, what was more important, to keep his colleagues current with Continental advances in natural history. Among his later botanical papers are studies of the sex of plants, inventories of gardens, and descriptions of useful or poisonous plants. Among his reports those on platinum [7],

on Linnaeus' system, and on Peyssonel's important but neglected demonstration of the animal origin of coral [9], were the most important (Pulteney, 298–309).

Although Watson's natural history papers "do him credit, they would not of themselves have been sufficient to give him celebrity."[3] His reputation came primarily from his studies of electricity, which he began, characteristically, by reproducing and transmitting a discovery made abroad. The discovery, the ignition of warmed spirits by an electric spark, apparently interested Watson as a chemical matter. He successfully extended the operation to all the inflammable liquids he had in stock and showed that they might be fired "repulsively," the spark being drawn across the liquor in an electrified spoon rather than (as was customary) toward the contents of a grounded one [2, 481–487]. These and other small triumphs [3] brought Watson the Copley Medal for 1745 and a public that consumed four editions of his electrical papers [4] before any could be printed in the *Philosophical Transactions*.[4]

Watson's first important discovery, announced in October 1746 [5], was the failure of an expectation authorized by the commonly held effluvial theory of electricity. He anticipated—as did J. N. Allamand, G. M. Bose, and Franklin, all of whom tried the effect independently—that by insulating himself while rubbing a glass tube, he could generate more electricity than if he stood upon the floor and let the effluvia run to ground. Failure suggested to him, as it did to Franklin, that rubbing did not collect electrical matter from the glass, but raised it from the ground; in a word, the tubes and globes acted as "pumps" circulating the electrical "fire." That far Franklin and Watson went independently and together. In extending his system, however, Watson remained within the effluvial frame and did not attain the conception of contrary electrifications. For example, he observed that the usual arrangement, in which the electricity generated by a grounded operator rubbing the globe of an electrical machine runs on to an insulated iron bar, could be inverted by grounding the bar and insulating the operator. But he did not perceive that the bar and the man electrify oppositely, the first positively and second negatively (in Franklin's terminology). Having missed this qualitative difference, Watson developed a crude electrical mechanics that assimilated the effluvia to a subtle, universal, springy "aether." The "pumps" disturb the equilibrium of this ether, which, in straining to regain its balance, brings about electrical attraction and repulsion, much as in the system of the abbé Nollet.

The Leyden jar ruined Watson's theory as it did Nollet's: Neither could account for the opposite electrifications, the condensing action, or the paradoxical role of glass.[5] After an effete try [5, 64], Watson gave up explaining the jar [7, 102] and turned to examining its properties. He found, independently of Le Monnier and Daniel Gralath, that the shock could be increased by arming the bottle with lead[6] or by thinning the glass [5, 31]; that the discharge passed in the most direct way through the conductors forming the external "circuit" [5, 31]; that the discharge occurred in a time too short to measure [6]; and that it might travel great distances through the ground or across water.[7]

Watson's second important electrical discovery was the work of Benjamin Franklin, whose first communication he reviewed before the Royal Society in January 1748 [7, 97–100]. This communication, which introduced the concepts of electrification plus and minus and likened the tube to a pump, may have owed something to Watson's pamphlets of 1745 and 1746 [4, 5]; in any case Watson recommended it as paralleling ideas he himself had recently developed. John Bevis had found that if the operator $A$ and another man $B$ are insulated, $A$ charges whenever $B$ takes a spark from the revolving globe, but never (as Watson had discovered) without $B$'s intervention. $B$ also charges, and $A$ and $B$ can exchange a bigger spark than either can with $C$, who stands on the ground. A similar experiment had taught Franklin to ascribe to $B$ a greater, and to $A$ a less, than ordinary quantity of electrical matter; Watson concluded that $A$ and $B$ had ether at low and high density, respectively, $C$ in all cases being the standard. Although neither quantity of electrical matter nor its density (a rough forerunner of potential) alone sufficed for an exact electrostatics, Franklin's conception, which retained fewer effluvial trappings, was the more progressive. As it developed further from the common view in Franklin's theory of the Leyden jar, Watson regarded it less favorably [8].

With the successful trial of Franklin's theory of lightning at Marly in 1752, Watson ceased to be the innovating leader of English electricians and assumed instead the same roles in electrical studies that he held in botanical ones: promoter, umpire, reviewer, consultant, and minor contributor. He advertised the English confirmation of Marly, joined with Nollet in exposing the strange delusion of the medicated electrical tubes,[8] abstracted foreign literature, advised on the construction of lightning rods,[9] and reported his own competent experiments on discharge *in vacuo* and medical electricity. He became an adherent of Franklin's theory and a friend of its inventor, with whom he shared political views and an interest in technological innovation (Pulteney, 319–323).

Franklin's success was not the only, or perhaps even the chief, cause of Watson's withdrawal from independent electrical studies in the 1750's. As his reputation rose, so did his sights, and the level and intensity of his medical practice. In September 1757 he received or bought an M.D. from the University of Halle;[10] in December he asked to leave the Society of Apothecaries, which generously disfranchised him, for the large fee of £50, early in 1758. No doubt he sought his release to make himself more acceptable to the Royal College of Physicians, which licensed practitioners with foreign degrees but disdained local apothecaries, however qualified. In 1759 he became a licentiate, and three years later he was chosen physician to the Foundling Hospital.[11] The next step, fellowship in the College, came slowly. The College elevated men without an Oxford or Cambridge M.D. only with great reluctance and after long probation. Watson allied himself with "rebel licentiates" led by John Fothergill, who tried to reform the statutes; but only minor concessions were made, and Watson did not attain the fellowship until 1784, and then *speciali gratia*.[12] He subsequently held the office of censor in the College, and received a knighthood in 1786 in connection with his service. As a physician Watson was compassionate, generous, careful, and well-informed (Pulteney, 338). He interested himself chiefly in epidemic children's diseases, which he saw at the Foundling Hospital, and wrote a useful pamphlet comparing methods of inoculating against smallpox [11].[13]

Watson was a leading member of several institutions. His steady service to the Royal Society, of which he became vice-president under the regime of his friend Sir John Pringle, has been mentioned. He acted as a trustee of the British Museum and arranged its botanical garden (Pulteney, 310). He helped support Priestley's experiments. He was a charter member of the Royal Society (dinner) Club, founded in 1743; a regular at the learned social gatherings at the home of one Watson, a grocer in the Strand;[14] and a member of the Society of Collegiate (Licentiate) Physicians and of the Club of Honest Whigs.[15] He was an able, conscientious, clubbable man, "and his exact observance of the duties of social politeness must ever be remembered with pleasure by all those who enjoyed the happiness of his acquaintance" (Pulteney, 338).

## NOTES

1. Society of Apothecaries, Court Minute Books, 8200/6, fol. 61v; Hartog, "Watson," 956; and Pulteney, 296, wrongly begin the apprenticeship in 1730, probably on the strength of Watson's attendance at school (1726–1730), for which see *Register of Merchant Taylors' School*, E. P. Hart, ed., II (London, 1936), 68. Presumably Watson delayed his apprenticeship until just after his sixteenth birthday and then bound himself for eight years rather than for the more usual seven years to satisfy the apothecaries' rule that the apprenticeship should not expire before the candidate reached twenty-four.
2. Royal Society, Journal Book, XVI, 212; G. C. Gorham, *Memoir of John Martyn* . . . (London, 1830).
3. Thomas Thomson, *History of the Royal Society* (London, 1812), 434; see tributes from Musschenbroek and Volta in Pulteney, 313 *n*.
4. Cf. H. Baker to P. Doddridge, 24 Nov. 1747, in Doddridge, *Correspondence and Diary*, J. D. Humphreys, ed., V (London, 1831), 28.
5. J. L. Heilbron, "A propos de l'invention de la bouteille de Leyde," in *Revue d'histoire des sciences*, **19** (1966), 133–142.
6. [5, §28]. Watson had this suggestion from John Bevis (see *Dictionary of National Biography*, II, 451–452).
7. [5, §28]. This was a misapprehension, for in such cases each coating of the jar discharges separately to ground.
8. L. Trenngrove, "Chemistry at the Royal Society . . . II," in *Annals of Science*, **20** (1964), 1–57.
9. [10]. Watson was a member of the committee that advised the government on protecting the powder magazine at Purfleet. See D. W. Singer, "Sir John Pringle and His Circle. I," in *Annals of Science*, **6** (1949), 127–180.
10. Pulteney, 326, which also credits Watson with a degree from Wittenberg; Clark, *History* . . . , 565 makes him a graduate of the medical school of the University of Edinburgh.
11. W. Munk, *The Roll of the Royal College of Physicians of London*, 2nd ed., II (London, 1878), 348–349.
12. Clark, *op. cit.*, 571–572; Fox, *Dr. John Fothergill* . . . , 143–151. See Watson to Fothergill, 16 Sept. 1771, in John Thomson, *Account of the Life, Lectures and Writings of William Cullen*, 2nd ed., I (Edinburgh–London, 1859), 657–660.
13. Charles Creighton, *Epidemics in Britain*, II (Cambridge, 1894), 500–503, 514, 705–706. Watson's papers published in Fothergill's compilation, *Medical Observations and Inquiries*, 6 vols. (London, 1757–1784), are noticed in Pulteney, 331–332. Also see Fox, *op cit.*, 141–142.
14. A. Geikie, *Annals of the Royal Society Club* (London, 1917), 11, 141, 160; Singer, "Sir John Pringle," 160.
15. Clark, *op. cit.*, 565; Fox, *op. cit.*, 317. See V. W. Crane, "The Club of Honest Whigs," in *William and Mary Quarterly*, **23** (1966), 210–233.

## BIBLIOGRAPHY

I. ORIGINAL WORKS. An adequate bibliography of Watson's published work may be pieced together from Pulteney (see below) and from P. H. Maty, *A General Index to the Philosophical Transactions* [vols. 1–70] (London, 1787), 788–791. Neither mentions "An Account of Some of the More Rare English Plants Observed in Leicestershire," in *Philosophical Transactions of the Royal Society*, **49** (1755–1756), 803–866; or Watson's reviews of William Brownrigg's *The Art of Making Common Salt* (1748), *ibid.*, **45** (1748), 351–372, and of J. A. Braun's *De admirando frigore artificiale* (1760), *ibid.*, **52** (1761–1762), 156–172.

Among Watson's important writings are [1] "De planta minus cognita, & hactenus non descripta," *ibid.*, **43** (1744–1745), 234–238; [2] "Experiments and Observations Tending to Illustrate the Nature and Properties of Electricity," *ibid.*, 481–501; [3] "Further Experiments and Observations," *ibid.*, **44** (1746), 41–50; [4] *Experiments and Observations Tending to Illustrate . . .*, a reprinting of the two preceding works, which exists in two versions, one by J. Ilive (London, 1745), and the other, differing by the addition of a preface, by C. Davis (London, 1746); [5] "A Sequel to the Experiments and Observations," in *Philosophical Transactions*, **44** (1747), 704–749, preprinted as a pamphlet (London, 1746); [6] "A Collection of Electrical Experiments," *ibid.*, **45** (1748), 49–92; [7] "Some Further Enquiries . . .," *ibid.*, 93–120; [8] "An Account of Mr. Benjamin Franklin's Treatise," *ibid.*, **47** (1751–1752), 202–210; [9] "An Account of a Manuscript Treatise . . . Intituled *Traité du corail*," *ibid.*, 445–469; [10] "Observations Upon the Effect of Lightning," *ibid.*, **52** (1764), 201–227; and [11] *An Account of a Series of Experiments Instituted With a View of Ascertaining the Most Successful Method of Inoculating the Smallpox* (London, 1768).

MSS of Watson's papers and reviews are preserved at the Royal Society and in the Sloane MSS at the British Museum: see A. H. Church, *The Royal Society: Some Account of the "Letters and Papers" of the Period 1741–1806* (Oxford, 1908), 69; and *A Catalogue of the Manuscripts Preserved in the British Museum*, S. Ayscough, ed. (London, 1782). There are some fifty of Watson's private letters in the British Museum, most among the Hardwicke Papers, for which see British Museum, *Catalogue of Additions to Manuscripts . . . in the Years 1894–1899* (London, 1901). Watson's large scientific correspondence, referred to by Pulteney and Wilson (see below), contained many formal reports intended for publication, the following being those that reached the *Philosophical Transactions*: **46** (1749–1750), 470; **47** (1751–1752), 553, 559; **48** (1753–1754), 153, 579, 786; **49** (1755–1756), 16, 371, 558, 579, 668; **50** (1757–1758), 240, 506; **52** (1761–1762), 40, 302; **58** (1768), 58, 136; **59** (1769), 23, 81, 241; **60** (1770), 233; **61** (1771), 136; **62** (1772), 54, 265, 469; **63** (1773), 1, 79.

There is a portrait of Watson at the Royal Society, reproduced in A. Geikie, *Annals of the Royal Society Club* (London, 1917), opp. 24.

II. SECONDARY LITERATURE. For biographical data see R. Pulteney, *Sketches of the Progress of Botany in England*, II (London, 1790), 295–340, abstracted in H. B. Wilson, *The History of Merchant Taylors' School*, II (London, 1814), *passim*; P. J. Hartog, "Watson, Sir William," in *Dictionary of National Biography*, XX, 956–958; Society of Apothecaries, Court Minute

Books, Guildhall Library MSS, vol. 8200/6, f. 61v, 138v; vol. 8200/7, f. 123v, 125v (information supplied by A. E. J. Hollaender, Keeper of MSS); George Clark, *A History of the Royal College of Physicians*, II (Oxford, 1966), 471, 476–479, 552–573, 586; H. C. Cameron *et al.*, *A History of the Worshipful Society of Apothecaries of London*, I (London, 1963), 78–82, 132–135; and R. H. Fox, *Dr. John Fothergill and His Friends* (London, 1919), 141–151, 215, 317. For Watson's botany see Pulteney. For his electricity see J. Priestley, *The History and Present State of Electricity*, 3rd ed., I (London, 1775), 97–101, 111–118, 130–145, 347–352; I. B. Cohen, *Franklin and Newton* (Philadelphia, 1956), 390–413, 441–452, 501–505; and M. Gliozzi, "Studio comparativo delle teorie elettriche del Nollet, del Watson e del Franklin," in *Archeion*, **15** (1933), 202–215.

J. L. Heilbron

**WATT, JAMES** (*b.* Greenock, Scotland, 19 January 1736; *d.* Heathfield, England, 19 August 1819), *engineering, chemistry.*

Although Watt's achievements as an inventor and an engineer have been fully recognized and universally honored, the dependence of his technical work on contemporary science and his own scientific research have long provoked sharp differences of opinion.

Watt's grandfather and father had both followed technical pursuits: the former, Thomas, as a teacher of surveying and navigation ("professor of the mathematicks") and the latter, James, as a shipwright and maker and supplier of nautical instruments. His mother, Agnes Muirhead (or Muireheid), was descended from a family that had at one time been prominent in Scottish life. Owing to his fragile health Watt's attendance at elementary school was somewhat irregular, but he nonetheless attained some proficiency in geometry (in which he showed great interest), Latin, and Greek. Schooling, however, composed only the lesser part of his education; the more consequential portion he received in his father's shop, where he first gained the knowledge and skills of contemporary craftsmanship—woodworking, metalworking, smithing, instrument making, and model making.

At the age of eighteen, having decided to follow the career of scientific instrument maker, Watt left Greenock and took up residence in nearby Glasgow, which was then becoming a center of commerce and industry. In 1775 he went to London, where he spent a year as an apprentice, rapidly mastering the arts and crafts that entered into the making of navigational and scientific instruments.

He found London both disagreeable and a strain on his health, however, and a year later he returned to Scotland. Watt hoped to establish himself in Glasgow as an instrument maker, but he was prevented from doing so by guild restrictions. It was only through the influence of friends on the faculty of the University of Glasgow that he was able in 1757 to evade the jurisdiction of the corporations of tradesmen through an appointment as "mathematical instrument maker to the university." Watt thus found the setting that fostered much of his technical and scientific work. He soon became acquainted with John Robison (who first directed his attention to the steam engine) and Joseph Black; and it was in 1765, during his association with the university, that he made his first and most important invention, the separate condenser for the Newcomen engine. He patented it in 1769 and developed it commercially, first in partnership with John Roebuck and later with Matthew Boulton.

This initial success was followed over the next quarter-century by a remarkable sequence of additional inventions related to the steam engine—the sun-and-planet gearing system to translate the engine's reciprocating motion into rotary motion without employing the common crank (which was entangled in patent claims); the application to the steam engine of the double-acting principle that was then commonly used in pumps; the "expansive principle" whereby Watt recognized that because of its expansive power, steam need not be admitted into the cylinder during the entire stroke; the "parallel motion" with which he connected a rigid piston rod to the overhead beam without causing the rod to wobble; and the "indicator" for determining the pressure in the cylinder during the cycle. Besides these signal contributions to the technology of the atmospheric steam engine, Watt also originated a perspective drawing machine, a letter-copying process, an indicator liquid for testing acidity, and a steam wheel (which he was unable to perfect) for producing rotary motion directly from steam pressure.

In 1766 Watt closed his shop at the university and opened a land surveying and civil engineering office in Glasgow, where he practiced as a civil engineer until 1774. In the latter year he moved to Birmingham and formed the partnership with Boulton whereby he successfully commercialized his improved steam engine design. During the 1790's he was heavily preoccupied with the litigation through which he preserved his separate condenser patent against a series of challenges. And in 1800 both Watt and Boulton retired, turning their business enterprises over to their sons.

Watt became a fellow of the Royal Society of Edinburgh and of London, and was a member of the Lunar Society of Birmingham. He married Margaret Miller, a cousin, and, after her death in 1773, Ann MacGregor, the daughter of a Glasgow merchant. Of the children born from these marriages only a son, James, outlived the father.

Watt's career as a scientist centered on his interest in chemistry. He performed numerous experiments, was in contact with several of the foremost chemists of the day (including Black, Priestley, and Berthollet), and occasionally ventured into the realm of theory. In 1783 he formed the opinion that water is a compound; but his designation of its components was ambiguous, inasmuch as he described them as "dephlogisticated and inflammable air, or phlogiston," where "phlogiston," as he often used the term, signified various gases. During the nineteenth century a spirited debate arose among the partisans of Watt, Cavendish, and Lavoisier over credit for priority in the discovery of the "composition of water." J. R. Partington, the historian of chemistry, after closely evaluating the conflicting claims has lent his authority to the view that while Watt is entitled to credit for first stating that water is not elementary, it was Lavoisier who clearly specified what its components are.

Watt also did experiments during the 1780's that contributed to the commercial application in Britain of the process, which Berthollet had discovered, of bleaching textiles with chlorine. In this case Watt's role as a chemist must be heavily qualified. Unlike Berthollet, whose chemical research was part of a program of theoretical inquiry and who promptly published his discoveries even when they had commercial possibilities, Watt was more akin to what would presently be described as a chemical engineer. His experiments were designed to render the process effective and economical on a commercial scale. Moreover, Watt's father-in-law, James MacGregor, was in the bleaching business; and Watt hoped that by keeping their improvements secret, they would realize substantial profits. He was openly disappointed that Berthollet was conducting his research "earnestly" and was making "his discoveries on it publick." When Watt proposed to Berthollet that, with MacGregor, they acquire a British patent on the process, Berthollet brushed aside the proposal with the remark, "Quand on aime les sciences on a peu besoin de fortune. . . ." These distinctions between the mo-

tivations and purposes of the engineer and the scientist are of great interest in attempting to reach an understanding of the development of modern science.

Twenty years earlier, during the 1760's, Watt had played a similar role in an attempt to commercialize a process for producing alkali using common salt and lime as ingredients. The "theory," according to Watt's own testimony, was formulated by Black; Watt's contribution consisted of experiments designed to find a commercially feasible procedure. Watt unquestionably displayed considerable knowledge of the chemistry of bleaching, dyeing, and alkali production; but in these fields his contributions were to industrial chemistry, not to chemical theory. They were the chemical equivalents of his mechanical inventions (which likewise followed systematic experiments).

In one additional area of his involvement with chemistry, a misunderstanding continues to confound our appreciation of Watt's career as a scientist. Both Robison and Black advanced the claim that the invention of the separate condenser rested upon Watt's understanding of Black's principle of latent heat. Although Watt denied these assertions and presented a convincing description of the events that led to his invention,[1] some writers have not only repeated the claim but have gone further and asserted that Watt discovered or "rediscovered" the principle itself.[2] In fact, however, Watt only noticed the phenomenon (the apparent loss of heat when water is boiled) that is accounted for by the principle of latent heat. Upon describing his observations to Black, he was told of the principle, which Black had been teaching at the University of Glasgow for several years. Watt's own claim was only that he had "stumbled upon one of the material facts by which that beautiful theory is supported."

If we confine our meaning of science to its theoretical dimensions, we must conclude that Watt's inventions were made for the most part independently of science. But there can be no question that, conversely, theoretical science owes much to his inventions. The steam revolution that Watt's work as an inventor promoted, focused the attention of mathematicians and natural philosophers on problems that prompted important research in the theory of heat and in kinematics. Indeed, his "expansive principle" was embodied in the adiabatic expansion phase of Sadi Carnot's heat cycle.[3] And the parallel motion that Watt substituted for the chain and arch head connection stimulated considerable research in pure kinematics.[4]

If, however, we take a wider view of science, we can find still more meaning in Watt's career. For despite the contrast between his modest achievements as a scientist and his extraordinary originality and inventive power as an engineer, his career displays one of the key developments in the history of science—the entrance by engineers into the world of research. During the eighteenth century the traditional affiliation between engineering and craftsmanship was being revised in favor of a merger of engineering with experimental and theoretical science; and in Watt's work in chemistry, in his associations with chemists and natural philosophers, in his employment at the University of Glasgow, and in his membership in the foremost British scientific societies we have one of the earliest and clearest traces of that emerging pattern.

*NOTES*

1. For a defense of Watt's position, see Donald Fleming, "Latent Heat and the Invention of the Watt Engine," in *Isis*, **43** (1952), 3–5.
2. A. E. Musson and Eric Robinson, *Science and Technology in the Industrial Revolution* (Manchester, 1969), 80. These authors generally claim more for the theoretical content of Watt's work than the present article allows.
3. See Robert Fox, "Watt's Expansive Principle in the Work of Sadi Carnot and Nicolas Clément," in *Notes and Records. Royal Society of London,* **24** (1969–1970), 233–253.
4. See Eugene S. Ferguson, "Kinematics of Mechanisms From the Time of Watt," in *Bulletin of the United States National Museum,* **228**, paper 27 (1962), 185–230.

*BIBLIOGRAPHY*

I. ORIGINAL WORKS. Watt wrote much but published little. His only publication on his inventions is his ed. of John Robison's *Encyclopaedia Britannica* articles on steam and steam engines: *The Articles Steam and Steam-Engines, Written for the Encyclopaedia Britannica, by the Late John Robison, LL.D., F.R.S.L & E.* (Edinburgh, 1818); this material is reproduced in vol. II of the posthumous collection of Robison's articles, *A System of Mechanical Philosophy*, David Brewster, ed., 4 vols. (Edinburgh, 1822). Two letters by Watt setting forth his views on the composition of water were published by the Royal Society: "Thoughts on the Constituent Parts of Water and of Dephlogisticated Air; With an Account of Some Experiments on That Subject. In a Letter From Mr. James Watt, Engineer, to Mr. De Luc, F.R.S.," in *Philosophical Transactions of the Royal Society,* **74** (1784), 329–353; and "Sequel to the Thoughts on the Constituent Parts of Water and Dephlogisticated Air: In a Subsequent Letter From Mr. James Watt, Engineer, to Mr. De Luc, F.R.S.," *ibid.,* 354–357. Watt's biographer, James Patrick Muirhead,

later reprinted these letters with additional material relevant to the composition-of-water controversy: *Correspondence of the Late James Watt on His Discovery of the Theory of the Composition of Water*, James Patrick Muirhead, ed. (London, 1846).

Watt's interest in the application of pneumatic chemistry to medicine resulted in his collaboration with Thomas Beddoes on the following works: *Considerations on the Medicinal Use of Factitious Airs, and on the Manner of Obtaining Them in Large Quantities* (Bristol, 1794; 2nd ed., 1795; 3rd ed., 1796); and *Medical Cases and Speculations; Including Parts IV and V of Considerations on the Medicinal Powers, and the Production of Factitious Airs* (Bristol, 1796)—Watt's contribution to the first of these was also printed separately as *Description of a Pneumatic Apparatus, With Directions for Procuring the Factitious Airs* (Birmingham, 1795). He also published a note on his test for acidity: "On a New Method of Preparing a Test Liquor to Shew the Presence of Acids and Alkalies in Chemical Mixtures," in *Philosophical Transactions of the Royal Society,* **74** (1784), 419–422.

Some of Watt's multitudinous letters and unpublished papers have been reprinted; vol. II of James Patrick Muirhead, *The Origin and Progress of the Mechanical Inventions of James Watt*, 3 vols. (London, 1854), contains a selection of Watt's correspondence; and recently two systematic collections that include much previously unpublished material have appeared: Eric Robinson and A. E. Musson, *James Watt and the Steam Revolution. A Documentary History* (London, 1969); and Eric Robinson and Douglas McKie, eds., *Partners in Science. Letters of James Watt and Joseph Black* (London, 1970). Many of Watt's letters and notes are preserved among the family papers at Doldowlod, Radnorshire.

II. SECONDARY LITERATURE. Writings on Watt's life and work are voluminous, almost all of them on his engineering rather than his science. For his personal life and especially his family background, see George Williamson, *Memorials of the Lineage, Early Life, Education, and Development of the Genius of James Watt* (Edinburgh, 1856). James Patrick Muirhead's 3-vol. work (see above) is the standard nineteenth-century biography; besides the volume of correspondence (II), vol. I contains a narrative of Watt's life and vol. III patent specifications and information. The narrative is recapitulated in Muirhead's *The Life of James Watt* (London, 1858). Among the more recent biographical works the most valuable is H. W. Dickinson and Rhys Jenkins, *James Watt and the Steam Engine. The Memorial Volume Prepared for the Committee of the Watt Centenary Commemoration at Birmingham 1919* (Oxford, 1927); this work contains a narrative biography, descriptions of many of Watt's technical achievements, reproductions of some of his drawings, and an extensive annotated bibliography. The composition-of-water controversy is summarized and the various claims evaluated in J. R. Partington, *A History of Chemistry*, III (London, 1962), 344–362. Partington's *History* is also useful in connection with Watt's other chemical endeavors. An important study of science in the industrial revolution that bears heavily on Watt's career is A. E. Musson and Eric Robinson, *Science and Technology in the Industrial Revolution* (Manchester, 1969).

The following publications are among those that have recently contributed to a fuller understanding of Watt's place in science: Robert E. Schofield, *The Lunar Society of Birmingham* (Oxford, 1963), 60–82, *passim*; D. S. L. Cardwell, *From Watt to Clausius* (Ithaca, N.Y., 1971), 40–55, *passim*; W. A. Smeaton, "Some Comments on James Watt's Published Account of His Work on Steam and Steam Engines," in *Notes and Records. Royal Society of London*, **26** (1971), 35–42; David F. Larder, "An Unpublished Chemical Essay of James Watt," *ibid.*, **25** (1970), 193–210; and Eric Robinson, "James Watt, Engineer and Man of Science," *ibid.*, **24** (1969–1970), 221–232.

HAROLD DORN

**WAYJAN IBN RUSTAM.** See **Al-Qūhī** (or **Al-Kūhī**), **Abū Sahl Wayjan ibn Rustam.**

**AL-WAZZĀN AL-ZAYYĀTĪ AL-GHARNĀTĪ, AL-ḤASAN IBN MUḤAMMAD.** See **Leo the African.**

**WEBER, ERNST HEINRICH** (*b.* Wittenberg, Germany, 24 June 1795; *d.* Leipzig, Germany, 26 January 1878), *anatomy, physiology, psychophysics.*

Weber was the oldest of the three Weber brothers who throughout their lives were closely linked in their scientific activity. Their greatest achievement lay in applying the modern exact methods of mathematical physics to the study of the functioning of various systems of higher animals and man. The leader in this endeavor, Ernst very early drew the attention of the physicist Wilhelm Eduard to the problems of the mechanics of circulation and later influenced the orientation of Eduard Friedrich toward theoretical medicine, helping him to obtain a post at the Leipzig medical school and to remain there as his close collaborator. Eduard was subsequently stimulated and helped by Wilhelm in the study of muscle mechanics.

Their father, Michael Weber, was professor of theology at Wittenberg from 1789 and later—after the fall of the city, a Napoleonic stronghold, in 1814 and the evacuation of the university—at Halle. Ernst, the third of his thirteen children, had been greatly influenced by Ernst Chladni, who of-

ten visited the family and excited the boys' interest in physics as a basis of all natural sciences. Weber attended secondary school in Meissen, where he acquired an excellent knowledge of Latin. In 1811 he began his medical studies at Wittenberg, but the war soon forced him to leave for Leipzig. He received the M.D. in 1815 from the University of Wittenberg, then temporarily evacuated to Schmiedeberg, with a dissertation on comparative anatomy. He could not, however, remain there because the university had no facilities for his anatomical work and its status was uncertain. At Leipzig, Weber became assistant at the medical clinic run by J. C. Clarus, qualified as docent in 1817 with a work on the comparative anatomy of the *nervus sympathicus*, and the following year became extraordinary professor of comparative anatomy. In 1821 he was nominated to the chair of human anatomy, which in 1840 was joined with physiology. In 1865 he gave up physiology and supported the appointment of Carl Ludwig, who established an independent physiological institute that attracted many foreign students. In 1871 Weber retired from the chair of anatomy.

Weber began with research in anatomy and discovered several important structures, some of which still bear his name—for instance, Weber's ossicles, which form a chain of small bones on each side of the air bladder, and the ear atrium of some fishes (the Weberian apparatus). This work marked the beginning of a series of comparative embryological and paleontological studies that led to the discovery of the intermediary stages between the primitive structures of the splanchnocranium and the middle ear auditory ossicles of mammals—a brilliant step in demonstrating the links between isolated facts and continuity in the evolution of structure and function. Weber's injection of the ducts of certain glands showed that their finest branches end blindly in the acini and have no direct communication with the surrounding small blood vessels, as had been supposed despite earlier findings by Malpighi (1686). It proved definitively that the digestive juices are specific products of glands, formed from the material brought by the blood, not just separated from the blood plasma. This finding opened up a new field of physiological and chemical research. Weber's wide experience in both research and teaching enabled him to write a revised edition of C. F. Hildebrandt's *Handbuch der Anatomie*. Its first part, *Allgemeine Anatomie*, entirely rewritten, became a valuable source of information because Weber carefully separated facts from theory and was not satisfied with merely describing structures; rather, he added what was known of their physical properties and chemical composition, as well as an appraisal of their significance. He was convinced that a knowledge of many conditions, not simply anatomical structure, was necessary for understanding the phenomena of life. The disadvantage of Weber's revised edition was that it was completed before the advance brought about by the subsequent development of microscopic research and by the cell theory. He also revised J. C. Rosenmüller's *Handbuch der Anatomie* (1840).

In 1821, assisted by his brother Wilhelm—then only seventeen years old and preparing for his university entrance examination—Weber began a long physical study of the flow and the progress of waves in fluids, particularly in elastic tubes. In their *Wellenlehre* (1825) they formulated the basic laws of hydrodynamics and were the first to apply that branch of physics to the circulation of the blood. Ernst studied—at first with Wilhelm, a precocious genius—the mechanical properties of the arteries, describing them as he would a technical device, the effect of elasticity transforming the pulsatile movement of the blood in the large arteries into a continuous flow into the small ones (1827). He also showed that the pulse is a wave in the arteries caused by the heart action and that its propagation—calculated from the delay of pulsation in a more distant artery—is much faster than the flow of the blood (1834) and that besides dilatation due to the pressure inside an elastic tube, blood vessels also change their diameter under the influence of nerves on the muscle wall (1831). He summarized his findings, the theory of waves in elastic tubes, and the laws of the movement of blood in the vessels in 1850.

Weber also demonstrated the resistance of the capillary bed, the importance of the blood volume, and its influence on the movement and distribution of the blood in the body. His work laid the base for the exact analysis of the movement of fluids in elastic tubes; and although the blood circulation has subsequently been subjected to a thorough research, Weber's work, with some additions but no substantial changes, has remained its foundation.

Another great contribution to the physiology of the blood circulation was the startling discovery by Eduard and Ernst Weber that electrical stimulation of some parts of the brain or of the peripheral end of the vagus nerve slows the action of the heart and can even bring it to a standstill (1845). It was the first instance of nerve action causing inhibition of an autonomic activity, rather than exciting it. It became an important milestone in the evolution of physiology not only for its significance to the circulation but also because its discovery brought to light a hitherto unknown but essential kind of nerve action. The ensuing chain of investigations showed that inhibition is a common phenomenon in the central nervous system and that an adequate balance between excitation and inhibition is indispensable for its normal function.

About 1826 Weber began a long series of remarkable systematic studies of sensory functions, especially of the "lower senses," which had hitherto been one of the most neglected areas of physiology. Physiologists had studied mainly the problems of vision and hearing, which seemed more interesting and promising. In his studies of other physiological problems Weber, a distinguished anatomist, usually followed function in close relation to structure. In this field, however, there was no anatomical basis because the skin, muscle, and visceral receptors were not discovered until later (Meissner, 1852; Krause, 1860). Nonetheless, his physical approach and attempts to determine quantitative relations of the stimulus to its effect, sensation, led to remarkable results despite the very simple methods used in his observations and experiments. An important feature of Weber's examinations and comparisons was the use of the notion of threshold (although this term was not actually used). He was well aware of the significance of its exactly determined values for estimating and comparing the performance of the skin and other sensory organs. A markedly greater ability to distinguish two very slightly different weights when they are lifted from, rather than when placed on, the hand, is explained by a special muscle sense. Examining the sense of touch in great detail, especially the local sense and differential threshold with a compass, Weber determined the characteristics of sensations of pressure and of temperature—positive (warm) and negative (cold)—and stressed the role of adaptation and local differences. Thus he gave sensory physiology a new orientation toward quantitative approach and methods, bringing into prominence both facts (mostly his own findings) and problems. He not only systematically collected facts but also drew rational conclusions about the physiological bases of the observed phenomena. He assumed isolated conduction in nerve fibers and formulated theories of projection and objectification. The division of each nerve fiber into a small circle of nerve endings was the background of local discrimination and of differences in its limen as determined by a compass.

In using his physical considerations as the basis for examining the differential thresholds of skin and muscle sensations, Weber found that two sensations are just noticeably different as long as the ratio between the strengths in each pair of stimuli remains constant. For instance, the smallest appreciable difference between two weights or lengths (usually called "just noticeable difference" or "Weber fraction") is a constant fraction of the weights themselves, approximately 1/30 (a just discriminable increment of intensity).

It was supposed that Weber's law was generally valid, but many discussions and criticisms led to the more moderate view that for most modalities it applies only over a limited range of intensities. Nevertheless, Fechner, assuming that discriminable increments are equal units of sensation, derived the formula

$$S = K \log I + C,$$

where intensity of sensation ($S$) is a linear function of the logarithm of intensity of the stimulus ($I$) and $K$ and $C$ are constants. Fechner's derivation has been criticized mainly because the stimulus—a physical factor—can easily be measured, while sensation—a subjective impression—cannot be expressed in physical terms. Quantitative comparisons became possible, however, when modern electrophysiological methods made it possible to follow the response of single sensory fibers—that is, the frequency of the messages from a single receptor. Over a certain range of intensities, it is indeed a linear function of the logarithm of the stimulus, as has been shown for the muscle spindle by B. H. Mathews and for the *Limulus* eye by H. K. Hartline and C. H. Graham. It cannot be stated whether it is fitting for the response of all forms of sense organs, but it seems that Fechner's equation corresponds to a fundamental feature of sense organ behavior.

Weber was the first to draw the attention of physiologists to the skin as the seat of differentiated sense organs directed toward the external world, like other sensory organs, in contrast with the common sensibility (*Gemeingefühl*) directed toward our own body. His research had many philosophical implications and a great impact on further studies of skin senses and some general problems of sensation by physiologists and psychologists.

He began a very fruitful period in the research on senses and is rightly considered as one of the founders of psychophysics. His work on tactile sensations has become classic.

*BIBLIOGRAPHY*

I. ORIGINAL WORKS. A partial list of Weber's writings was published in *Almanach der K. Akademie der Wissenschaften in Wien*, **2** (1852), 203–211; and, more recently, by P. M. Dawson (see below), 110–113. They include *Anatomia comparata nervi sympathici* (Leipzig, 1817); *De aure et auditu hominis et animalium* (Leipzig, 1820); *Wellenlehre, auf Experimenten begründet* (Leipzig, 1825), written with Eduard Weber; *Zusätze zur Lehre von Bau und Verrichtungen der Geschlechtsorgane* (Leipzig, 1846); "Tastsinn und Gemeingefühl," in R. Wagner, *Handwörterbuch der Physiologie*, III, pt. 2 (Brunswick, 1846, repr. separately 1851), also Ostwalds Klassiker der Exakten Wissenschaften no. 149 (Leipzig, 1905); *Ueber die Anwendung der Wellenlehre auf die Lehre vom Kreislauf des Blutes und insbesondere auf die Pulslehre* (Leipzig, 1850); and "Ueber den Raumsinn und die Empfindungskreise in der Haut und im Auge," in *Berichte über die Verhandlungen der K. Sächsischen Gesellschaft der Wissenschaften*, Math.-phys. Kl. (1852), 85–164, his chief paper on projection and the theory of circles.

Weber's papers were published mainly in *Deutsches Archiv für die Physiologie* and Meckel's *Archiv für Anatomie und Physiologie* (1820–1828), Müller's *Archiv für Anatomie, Physiologie und wissenschaftliche medizin* (1835–1846), and *Berichte über die Verhandlungen der K. Sächsichen Gesellschaft der Wissenschaften zu Leipzig* (1846–1850). Dissertations written under his guidance were collected in *Annotationes anatomicae et physiologicae* (*Programata collecta*), 2 fascs. (Leipzig, 1827–1834, 1836–1848), both reed. (1851) with fasc. 3, containing several of his own important papers.

II. SECONDARY LITERATURE. An appreciation of Weber's scientific achievement is C. Ludwig, *Rede zum Gedächtniss an Ernst Heinrich Weber* (Leipzig, 1878). A fairly detailed account in English is P. M. Dawson, "The Life and Work of Ernest Heinrich Weber," in *Phi Beta Pi Quarterly*, **25** (1928), 86–116. With regard to the importance and impact of his work, papers on Weber are rather scarce. See also Ursula Bueck-Rich, *Ernst Heinrich Weber (1795–1878) und der Anfang einer Physiologie der Hautsinne* (inaug. diss., Zurich, 1970); H. E. Hoff, "The History of Vagal Inhibition," in *Bulletin of the History of Medicine*, **8** (1940), 461–496; P. Hoffmann, "Ernst Heinrich Weber's *Annotationes anatomicae et physiologicae*," in *Medizinische Klinik*, **30** (1934), 1250. There are many references to Weber's works on sensory physiology in E. G. Boring, *A History of Experimental Psychology*, 2nd ed. (New York, 1950);

and *Sensation and Perception in the History of Experimental Psychology* (New York, 1942).

VLADISLAV KRUTA

**WEBER, HEINRICH** (*b.* Heidelberg, Germany, 5 May 1842; *d.* Strasbourg, Germany [now France], 17 May 1913), *mathematics.*

Weber, son of the the historian G. Weber, began the study of mathematics and physics in 1860 at the University of Heidelberg. He then went to Leipzig for a year but subsequently returned to Heidelberg, where he obtained the Ph.D. in 1863. After working at Königsberg under Franz Neumann and F. J. Richelot, he qualified as *Privatdozent* in 1866 at Heidelberg and obtained a post as extraordinary professor there in 1869. He subsequently taught at the Eidgenössische Polytechnikum in Zurich, the University of Königsberg, the Technische Hochschule in Charlottenburg, the universities of Marburg and Göttingen, and, from 1895, at Strasbourg.

Weber was rector of the universities of Königsberg, Marburg, and Strasbourg; member of many German and foreign academies; and recipient of an honorary doctorate from the University of Christiania (now Oslo). He was a cofounder of the Deutsche Mathematiker-Vereinigung and member of the editorial board of *Mathematische Annalen.*

In 1870 Weber married Emilie Dittenberger, daughter of a Weimar court chaplain. Their daughter translated the philosophical writings of Henri Poincaré into German, and their son Rudolf Heinrich became professor of theoretical physics at Rostock. Weber's closest friend was Richard Dedekind, with whom he often collaborated and with whom he edited Riemann's works (1876). Weber's students included Hermann Minkowski and David Hilbert.

An immensely versatile mathematician, Weber focused his research mainly on analysis and its application to mathematical physics and number theory. The direction of his work was decisively influenced by his stay at Königsberg, where Jacobian mathematics still flourished. There he was encouraged by Neumann to investigate physical problems and by Richelot to study algebraic functions. Weber began his research with an examination of the theory of differential equations, which he conducted in Jacobi's manner. Then, building on Carl Neumann's book on Riemann's theory of algebraic functions and on the work of Alfred Clebsch and Paul Gordan on Abelian functions, Weber demonstrated Abel's theorem in its most general form. He also worked on the mathematical treatment of physical problems concerning heat, static and current electricity, the motion of rigid bodies in liquids, and electrolytic displacement. He brought together a portion of this research in *Die partiellen Differentialgleichungen der mathematischen Physik* (1900–1901), a complete reworking and development of a similarly titled book prepared by Karl Hattendorff from Riemann's lectures that had gone through three editions.

Weber investigated important contemporary problems in algebra and number theory, the fields in which he did his most penetrating work. With Dedekind he wrote a fundamental work on algebraic functions that contained a purely arithmetical theory of these functions. One of Weber's outstanding accomplishments was the proof of Kronecker's theorem, which states that the absolute Abelian fields are cyclotomic—that is, they are obtained from the rational numbers through adjunction of roots of unity. In 1891 Weber gave a complete account of the problems of complex multiplication, a topic in which analysis and number theory are inseparably linked. His studies culminated in the two-volume *Lehrbuch der Algebra* (1895–1896), which for decades was indispensable in teaching and research.

Weber was an enthusiastic and inspiring teacher who took great interest in educational questions. In collaboration with Joseph Wellstein and with the assistance of other mathematicians, he edited the *Enzyklopädie der Elementar-Mathematik*, a three-volume work designed for both teachers and students.

*BIBLIOGRAPHY*

Weber's works include "Ueber singuläre Auflösungen partieller Differentialgleichungen erster Ordnung," in *Journal für die reine und angewandte Mathematik*, **66** (1866), 193–236; "Neuer Beweis des Abelschen Theorems," in *Mathematische Annalen*, **8** (1874), 49–53; "Theorie der algebraischen Funktionen einer Veränderlichen," in *Journal für die reine und angewandte Mathematik*, **92** (1882), 181–290, written with R. Dedekind; *Elliptische Funktionen und algebraische Zahlen* (Brunswick, 1891; 2nd ed., 1908, as vol. III of *Lehrbuch der Algebra*); *Lehrbuch der Algebra*, 2 vols. (Brunswick, 1895–1896; 2nd ed., 1898–1899); *Die partiellen Differentialgleichungen der mathematischen Physik*, 2 vols. (Brunswick, 4th ed., 1900–1901: 5th ed., 1910–1912); and *Enzyklopädie der Elementar-Mathematik*, 3 vols. (Leipzig, 1903–1907), written with Joseph Wellstein *et al.*

There is an obituary by A. Voss in *Jahresberichte der*

*Deutschen Mathematiker-Vereinigung*, **23** (1914), 431–444, with portrait.

BRUNO SCHOENEBERG

**WEBER, MAX WILHELM CARL** (*b.* Bonn, Germany, 6 December 1852; *d.* Eerbeek, Netherlands, 7 February 1937), *zoology.*

After attending schools in Oberstein an der Nahe, Neuwied, and Bonn, Weber began the study of medicine at the University of Bonn. His teachers included the zoologists Franz Hermann Troschel and Franz von Leydig (for whom he worked as an assistant) and the anatomist Adolph La Valette St. George. In the winter semester of 1875–1876 Weber studied at Berlin, mainly under the zoologist Eduard von Martens. In 1877 he received the Ph.D. from Bonn for the dissertation "Die Nebenorgane des Auges von einheimischen Lacertiden." Soon afterward he was invited by the anatomist Max Fürbringer to serve as prosector at the anatomy institute of the University of Amsterdam. In 1879 he went to the University of Utrecht as lecturer in anatomy. He was recalled to Amsterdam in 1883 to teach zoology and comparative anatomy.

Weber went on an expedition in the North Atlantic, primarily to study the anatomy of whales. He was aided in this research by his wife, Anna van Bosse, who had studied under Hugo de Vries. Their findings were published in 1886 as the first part of his *Studien über Säugethiere*. In 1888 the couple traveled to the Dutch East Indies, where they visited Sumatra, Java, Celebes, and Flores. On Flores especially, Weber gathered extensive zoological material, as well as ethnographic data. A number of scientists collaborated in publishing descriptions of this material in *Ergebnisse einer Reise nach Niederländisch Ost-Indien* (Leiden, 1890–1907). Weber himself described the freshwater sponges, the trematode genus *Temnocephalus*, and several fish, reptiles, and mammals. With his wife he also investigated the symbiotic algae of the freshwater sponge *Spongilla*. The Webers soon embarked on another voyage, this time to South Africa. Their findings were published in 1897.

The second part of *Studien über Säugethiere* appeared the following year. In 1899 Weber and his wife participated in the Dutch Sibolga expedition, which was sent to examine the marine fauna and flora of Indonesia. Weber himself recorded part of the findings in *The Fishes of the Indo-Australian Archipelago* (Leiden, 1911–1936); the seven-volume work contained descriptions of 131 new species. Weber had acquired an interest in biogeography during his first trip to the Dutch East Indies, and the studies of the Sibolga expedition on freshwater fauna led him to reexamine the well-known differences between the freshwater fauna of Java, Borneo, and Sumatra, on the one hand, and of Celebes, Timor, and Flores, on the other. Weber drew attention to the zoogeographical differences between the northern and southern halves of Celebes and noted the existence of the deepwater zone around the island, the temperature of which differs markedly from that of the rest of the ocean.

During the period of his expeditions and of assessing the material they yielded, Weber also worked on his greatest scientific publication, *Die Säugetiere* (1904), an exposition of both the anatomy and the systematics of the mammals; the second edition is still a standard work.

Weber confined his scientific labors to descriptive zoology. He explicitly defended the old methods of comparative anatomy, although he also recognized the importance of the new experimental areas of biological research.

*BIBLIOGRAPHY*

A list of Weber's more important works follows D'Arcy Wentworth Thompson's biography in *Obituary Notices of Fellows of the Royal Society of London*, **2** (1938), 347–352, with portrait. They include *Studien über Säugethiere*, 2 pts. (Jena, 1886–1898), comprising "Ein Beitrag zur Frage nach dem Ursprung der Cetaceen" and "Über Descensus testiculorum, Anatomische Bemerkungen über Elephas"; the results of Weber's voyage to South Africa, published as "Zur Kenntnis der Süsswasser-Fauna von Südafrika," in *Zoologische Jahrbücher*, **10** (1897), 135–200; *Der indo-australische Archipel und die Geschichte siener Tierwelt* (Jena, 1902); and *Die Säugetiere* (Jena, 1904), which appeared in a 2nd, enl. ed., 2 vols. (Jena, 1927–1928), completed by a section on paleontology by Othenio Abel.

HANS QUERNER

**WEBER, WILHELM EDUARD** (*b.* Wittenberg, Germany, 24 October 1804; *d.* Göttingen, Germany, 23 June 1891), *physics.*

Weber was one of twelve children of Michael Weber, professor of theology at the University of Wittenberg. Of four brothers and a sister who lived to an advanced age, the eldest brother became a minister, while the other brothers turned to science and medicine. Ernst Heinrich, who was almost ten years older than Wilhelm, became a leading anatomist and physiologist, and a professor at Leipzig. Eduard, a year and a half younger than Wilhelm, also became professor of anatomy at Leipzig. The interest of the three brothers in science was undoubtedly awakened by the family friends Christian August Langguth, professor of medicine and natural history, in whose house the Webers lived, and the acoustician E. F. Chladni, a fellow lodger.

Langguth's house was burned during the bombardment of Wittenberg by the Prussians in 1813, and in the following year the Webers settled in Halle. Michael Weber became professor of theology at the University of Halle, with which the University of Wittenberg officially merged in 1817. Here Wilhelm began his first scientific work, in collaboration with Ernst Heinrich. The resulting publication, *Wellenlehre, auf Experimente gegründet* (1825), which contains experimental investigations of water and sound waves, made Wilhelm's name known in scientific circles. Some of the experimental work on waves was done before Wilhelm entered the University of Halle in 1822. There he was most influenced by the physicist J. S. C. Schweigger and perhaps by the mathematician J. F. Pfaff. Weber wrote his doctoral dissertation on the theory of reed organ pipes in 1826 under Schweigger. His *Habilitationsschrift* (1827) treated such systems as coupled oscillators, as did four papers in Poggendorff's *Annalen der Physik und Chemie* (1828, 1829). Weber became lecturer and then assistant professor (1828) at Halle. He traveled to Berlin in September 1828 with Ernst Heinrich to attend the seventh meeting of the Gesellschaft Deutscher Naturforscher und Ärzte, organized by Alexander von Humboldt. He delivered a talk on his work on organ pipes that attracted the notice of Humboldt and Gauss. At this time Humboldt interested Gauss in his work on geomagnetism, and Gauss saw in Weber a worthy co-worker if a position became available for him at Göttingen.

In April 1831 the professorship of physics at Göttingen, vacated upon the death of Tobias Mayer, Jr., was offered to Weber; and six years of collaboration and close friendship with Gauss followed. At the end of 1832 Gauss read his paper "Intensitas vis magneticae terrestris ad mensuram absolutam revocata," written with Weber's assistance. In this paper he introduced absolute units of measurement into magnetism; that is, the measurement of the strength of a magnetic property was reduced to measurements of length, time, and mass, and thus became reproducible anywhere

without the need of a particular precalibrated magnetic instrument. One of the major themes of Weber's later work was to extend this idea to electrical measurements.

Gauss and Weber founded the Göttingen Magnetische Verein to initiate a network of magnetic observatories and to correlate the resulting measurements. This was to be a more sophisticated version of Humboldt's project. In 1833 they set up a battery-operated telegraph line some 9,000 feet long between the physics laboratory and the astronomical observatory, in order to facilitate simultaneous magnetic observations. This was one of the first practical long-range galvanic telegraphs. A year later, induced currents were used in place of the battery. The *Resultate aus den Beobachtungen des Magnetischen Vereins* for the years of its existence (1836–1841), published from 1837 to 1843, contain mostly articles by Gauss and Weber, although in the later volumes observations were published from many stations throughout the world. Weber's major contribution during this period was the development of sensitive magnetometers and other magnetic instruments.

Busy as he was with magnetism at Göttingen, Weber found time to collaborate with his younger brother Eduard on *Mechanik der menschlichen Gehwerkzeuge* (1836). This work on the physiology and physics of human locomotion represented a continuation of the close bond of the three brothers in scientific research, which had begun with the *Wellenlehre*.

With the death of William IV in 1837, Victoria became queen of England and her uncle, Ernst August, acceded to the rule of Hannover and at once revoked the liberal constitution of 1833. Weber was one of seven Göttingen professors who signed a statement of protest. (The others of the "Göttingen Seven" were F. E. Dahlmann, W. E. Albrecht, Jakob and Wilhelm Grimm, G. Gervinus, and G. H. von Ewald.) At the king's order all seven lost their positions; and Dahlmann, Gervinus, and Jakob Grimm were exiled from Hannover. The Seven received much sympathy from all over Germany; in particular, a committee was formed at Leipzig to raise funds to support them. Despite the loss of his position, Weber continued to work for the Magnetische Verein in Göttingen. Gauss and Humboldt attempted to obtain Weber's reinstatement; but the king insisted on a public retraction, which was unacceptable to Weber. Between March and August 1838 he traveled to Berlin; to London, where he spoke with John Herschel about extending the network of magnetic observing stations; and to Paris, becoming acquainted with many of the leading scientists of his time.

After several years in Göttingen without a university position, Weber became professor of physics at the University of Leipzig in 1843, joining his brothers Ernst Heinrich and Eduard. This position had been held by G. T. Fechner, a close friend of the Webers. Because of severe eyestrain induced by his psychophysical experimentation, which led to temporary blindness, Fechner had to relinquish the post, turning afterward to philosophy and psychology. At Leipzig, Weber formulated his law of electrical force, published in the first of his *Elektrodynamische Maassbestimmungen* (1846). Weber and Fechner, who was a staunch atomist, often discussed scientific matters; and the law is adumbrated in a semiquantitative treatment by Fechner in 1846, which refers to Weber's forthcoming work.

The upheavals of 1848 forced a greater liberality upon Ernst August, and in the following year Weber was able to return to his old position at Göttingen. At his request his replacement, J. B. Listing, was retained, thus creating a double professorship in physics. Weber became director of the astronomical observatory and was closely associated with Rudolph Kohlrausch, a friend for some years who had proposed to test Weber's force law directly, using mechanically accelerated charges. As this was not feasible, Weber in 1856 collaborated with Kohlrausch, then at Marburg, to determine the ratio between the electrodynamic and electrostatic units of charge (the former being greater than the presently used electromagnetic unit by the factor $\sqrt{2}$). This measurement was later used by Maxwell as a crucial support for his electromagnetic theory of light. In 1857 Kohlrausch moved from Marburg to Erlangen and began research with Weber on electrical oscillations, but died in the following year. His son, Friedrich, received the doctorate in 1863 at Göttingen with a thesis on elastic relaxation in metal wires, written under Weber's direction, thus extending an investigation Weber had made on nonmetallic fibers. Friedrich later became lecturer at Göttingen and organized the physical laboratory course at Weber's request.

Weber's later years at Göttingen were devoted to work in electrodynamics and the electrical structure of matter. He retired in the 1870's, relinquishing his duties in physics to his assistant, Eduard Riecke. Toward the end of the century, the latter began the development of the electron theory of metals from Weber's ideas, a development soon carried to its completion in classical physics by Paul Drude and H. A. Lorentz.

Weber's closest collaborator in his last years was the Leipzig astrophysicist J. K. F. Zöllner, with whom he worked on electrical conductivity. Zöllner envisaged a physics based solely on the interaction of atoms of the two kinds of electricity, a conception taken up by Weber after Zöllner's death in 1882 and left in manuscript as the last of the *Elektrodynamische Maassbestimmungen*.

The career of Hermann von Helmholtz touched that of Weber at several points, and relations between the men were strained. Results in Helmholtz' memoir on the conservation of energy (1847) were at first taken to imply that Weber's force law violated that principle. By introducing a velocity-dependent potential energy, Weber was able to demonstrate that the criticism was unfounded. But in 1870, while investigating the rival electrical theories then extant, Helmholtz found that Weber's law could lead in certain circumstances to states of motion that appeared to be disallowed physically. Weber and his supporters attempted to refute Helmholtz' arguments; and a rather sterile but sometimes bitter dispute lasted for several years, with Zöllner championing Weber's cause with more ardor than tact. At an international congress on the electrical units held in Paris (1881) Helmholtz, the leader of the German delegation, proposed the name "ampere" for the unit of current, although "weber" enjoyed some use at that time. The term "weber" was officially introduced for the practical unit of magnetic flux in 1935.

Weber died peacefully in his garden at the age of eighty-six. He had received many honors from Germany, France, and England, including the title of *Geheimrat* and the Royal Society's Copley Medal. He was described as being friendly, modest, and unsophisticated. His reputation had suffered in the 1870's when Zöllner introduced the American medium, Henry Slade, into the Leipzig circle of which Fechner and the Webers were the leading lights. Weber enjoyed hiking and did much traveling on foot. He never married, his household being sometimes managed by his sister and, in his later years, by his niece.

*Wellenlehre, auf Experimente gegründet*, which marks the beginning of Wilhelm's scientific career, describes experiments on surface waves in liquids, and on sound and light waves. It is dedicated to Chladni, the family friend who was famed for his experiments on standing waves in plates. The immediate inspiration was the chance observation of standing waves in mercury by Ernst Heinrich. Traveling and standing water waves are described and illustrated in engravings made by the brothers. Using a narrow channel with glass walls, they investigated the dependence of wave velocity on the depth of the water, noted the dispersion of wave packets and the distinction between capillary and gravity waves, and investigated the effect of oil on water and wave interference. The elliptical motion of particles in the water as a wave passes was described. In a historical section they compared their results with contemporary theory, particularly Poisson's. Vortices were treated briefly, without proper comprehension of their peculiarities, an understanding of which did not come until later in the century. The section on sound waves treated the problems connected with resonance in pipes, a field that formed the subject of Wilhelm's next works. Ernst Heinrich also utilized the fruits of this investigation in a later treatise on the circulation of the blood.

Weber's early scientific work—before he was called to Göttingen—centered on acoustics. Several of the earlier papers involve the repetition of experiments of previous investigators. Others develop the discovery in the *Wellenlehre* of the distribution of sound around a tuning fork. His doctoral dissertation (1826) and *Habilitationsschrift* (1827) deal with the acoustic coupling of tongue and air cavity in reed organ pipes. This experimental and theoretical investigation was pursued in papers in *Annalen der Physik und Chemie* (1828–1830). One of the subjects treated was the use of this coupling to maintain constancy of pitch of a pipe under different intensities of blowing, and the possibility that this might provide an improved standard of pitch.

The *Mechanik der menschlichen Gehwerkzeuge* (1836) was a collaborative work by Wilhelm Weber and his younger brother, the anatomist Eduard. It contains an anatomical discussion of the joints used in walking and running, measurements made on living subjects, and a mathematical theory relating the length and duration of a step to anatomical parameters. Drawings were made on the basis of the theory and viewed stroboscopically. Among other results, the work corrected misconceptions about posture and recommended its conclusions to the attention of artists. The introduction suggests the development of a walking machine for traversing rough terrain.

The papers contributed by Weber to *Resultate aus den Beobachtungen des Magnetischen Vereins*

(1836–1841) are concerned partly with the construction of galvanomagnetic instruments, including a beautifully designed portable magnetometer, magnetometers working by electromagnetic induction, and a dynamo. This led him to investigate the dependence of magnetization on temperature and inspired other investigations of unipolar induction and elasticity. Working with the silk fibers used in the magnetometer suspensions, Weber found that aside from the immediate elastic response to a change in load, there was a slow but apparently elastic relaxation (*elastische Nachwirkung*) involving a delayed stretching or shrinking as the stress increased or decreased, respectively. Weber sought to provide a molecular explanation for the phenomenon, and his papers on the subject were published in 1835 and 1841. In the later volumes of the *Resultate*, Weber summarized the results obtained from the various geomagnetic observing stations and helped to create the lithographed maps showing the earth's magnetism. They also contained Weber's first work on extending the idea of absolute units, introduced into magnetism by Gauss, to galvanic measurements.

In the *Resultate* for 1840, Weber defined the absolute electromagnetic unit of current in terms of the deflection of the magnetic needle of a tangent galvanometer. He determined the amount of water decomposed by the flow of a unit of current for one second—that is, by a unit of charge. In the first of the *Elektrodynamische Maassbestimmungen* (1846) he introduced his electrodynamometer, in which a coil is hung by its leads in bifilar suspension in the field of another coil and the current is passed through both. This instrument was used to determine the electrodynamic unit of current, defined in terms of the force between two current elements using Ampère's law, and having a magnitude $\sqrt{2}$ greater than the electromagnetic unit. The response of the electrodynamometer depends on the square of the current and thus is suited for alternating currents. With it Weber measured currents alternating with acoustical frequencies.

In 1846 M. H. von Jacobi circulated an especially prepared copper wire to be used as a resistance standard. Weber was dissatisfied, however, with standards depending on the resistance of a particular object or on the resistivity of a particular substance, and in the *Elektrodynamische Maassbestimmungen* of 1852 he defined an absolute measure for electrical resistance. By use of Ohm's law and the absolute measure of current, the problem is reduced to that of voltage measurement. Weber defined this by the voltage induced in a loop rotating in a given magnetic field. Several practical methods of determining resistance were presented.

In 1855 Weber collaborated with R. Kohlrausch on the measurement of the ratio between the electrodynamic and electrostatic units of charge; their results were published in 1857 as one of the *Elektrodynamische Maassbestimmungen*. A definite small fraction of the charge used was drawn off a large capacitor and measured electrostatically by a Coulomb torsion balance, and the remaining charge was discharged through a ballistic galvanometer. Converting to the ratio between the electromagnetic and electrostatic units, the ratio found was $3.1074 \times 10^8$ meters/second, close to the speed of light; but the researchers took no special notice of this.

Weber's greatest theoretical contributions appear in the *Elektrodynamische Maassbestimmungen*, seven long works published from 1846 to 1878, besides a manuscript published posthumously. In the first of these, Weber introduced his dynamometer to test Ampère's law of force between electric current elements, to a degree of precision exceeding Ampère's, and also to investigate electromagnetic ("Volta") induction. Convinced of the validity of Ampère's law, Weber proceeded to a theoretical derivation of a general fundamental law of electrical action, expressing the force between moving charges. Essential to the derivation were the assumptions of central forces and of currents as consisting of the equal and oppositely directed flow of the two kinds of charge. The law contains the expression

$$F = \frac{e_1 e_2}{r^2}\left[1 - \frac{1}{c^2}\left(\frac{dr}{dt}\right)^2 + \frac{2r}{c^2}\frac{d^2r}{dt^2}\right]$$

where $dr/dt$ is the rate at which the separation $r$ between the charges $e_1$ and $e_2$ increases (or the relative radial velocity), while $d^2r/dt^2$ is the relative radial acceleration, and $c$ is a constant expressing the ratio between the electrodynamic and electrostatic units of charge. On the basis of Maxwell's theory, we know today that $c$ is $\sqrt{2}$ times the speed of light.

The dominant term in the expression is the Coulomb force $e_1e_2/r^2$. The remaining terms modify this attraction or repulsion when the charges are in motion relative to each other. Thus, envisage, as a simple example, two straight, parallel wires carrying identical currents in the same direction, and consider the forces between elements of the two wires that are side by side. Like charges in the two elements have no motion relative to each other and will repel with the Coulomb force. Unlike charges, at the point where they move past each other, are neither approaching nor receding from each other; but the acceleration $d^2r/dt^2$ is positive. This serves to augment the Coulomb attraction between unlike charges in the two wires, which otherwise would simply cancel the repulsion between the like charges. A net attraction between the parallel currents, and hence between the wires, results, in agreement with Ampère's findings.

Suppose, instead, that only one of the wires, $A$, carries a current initially and that the other wire is moved toward it. Consider the forces on the charges contained in an element $B$ of the second wire. Charges in $A$ that are approaching the point $C$ opposite $B$ are associated with higher values of $(dr/dt)^2$ than charges in $A$ that have moved beyond this point, because of the approach of $B$ to $A$. Since the velocity-dependent term always diminishes the effect of the Coulomb force, the positive charge in $A$ approaching $C$ has a diminished repulsion on the positive charge in $B$ and the negative charge in $A$ approaching $C$ from the opposite direction has a diminished attraction—that is, more diminished than the forces excited by charges moving away from $C$. The resultant force on the positive charge in $B$ is opposite to the motion of the current (that is, the positive charge) in $A$. The force on the negative charge in $B$ is of the same magnitude and in the opposite direction. The net effect on the charges in $B$ is to accelerate them in directions opposite to their counterparts in $A$—that is, to induce a current in $B$ opposed to the direction of that in $A$. In fact, Weber's law succeeded in encompassing Ampère's force and the facts of induction, as well as Coulomb's law of electrostatics. Note, however, that if the assumption of the equal and opposite flow of unlike charges in a current is dropped, a constant current would generally exert a force on a static charge, contrary to experience. An abridged version of the paper published two years later also gives a potential function from which the force may be derived.

In the meantime, Helmholtz' memoir on the conservation of energy had appeared, which seemed to disallow velocity-dependent forces. Weber's law depended on the radial components of the relative velocity and acceleration of the charges; but Weber was able to show in 1869, and in greater detail in another of his long papers of 1871, the consistency of his law with energy conservation in a somewhat extended sense. Most decisive for the eventual rejection of Weber's law was its gradual replacement by Maxwell's field theory, particularly with the demonstration of electromagnetic radiation by Hertz in 1888.

From 1848 to 1852 Weber reported his careful quantitative experimental work on the diamagnetism of bismuth. Diamagnetism had been investigated in 1845 by Faraday, who initially interpreted the phenomena in terms of diamagnetic polarity, that is, a reversed magnetic polarity created in the substance when it is introduced into a magnetic field. In 1848 Weber claimed that he had observed induction in a coil caused by the diamagnetism of a piece of bismuth moving in a magnetic field, but at this time he did not distinguish this effect from that of the bulk currents induced in the body of the bismuth. Faraday was unable to observe such an effect attributable to the diamagnetic, rather than to the conducting, property of his samples; and partly as a result, he relinquished his conception of diamagnetic polarity. In research reported in his *Maassbestimmungen* of 1852, however, Weber was able to isolate and demonstrate the existence of the diamagnetic effect. He utilized the effective uniformity of the magnetic field in a long, straight solenoid. A bismuth cylinder moving well inside such a solenoid will not have bulk currents induced in it, but through its motion its diamagnetism will affect surrounding magnetic detectors. In Weber's beautifully designed experiments, such an effect was demonstrated both by the motion of a suspended magnetic needle and by the induction of a current in a surrounding coil.

Weber extended Ampère's theory of magnetism to cover the phenomenon of diamagnetism. In Ampère's theory, ordinary magnetism is accounted for by assuming the existence of permanent molecular electric currents circulating in the molecules of ferromagnetic substances. In an external field these molecules align themselves to give the resulting magnetization. According to Weber, diamagnetism occurs when resistanceless molecular currents are induced in diamagnetic substances. These substances are characterized by molecules that do not contain permanent currents and that have fixed orientation in the substance.

From 1852 Weber attempted to comprehend electrical resistance as a result of the motion of electric fluids or particles. Resistance was presumed to have its cause in the repeated combination and separation of the particles of the two electric fluids, the opposite motions of which composed a current. The existence of permanent Ampèrian currents led Weber to assume that the electric fluids do not interact directly with the material atoms composing the substance, and that in mag-

netic atoms the two kinds of fluid circulate in different, nonintersecting paths about the atoms. At this time he discussed, as a model, a lattice of fixed positive charges about which negative particles rotate in Keplerian ellipses. On application of an electric potential, the negative particles move in widening spirals until they pass over to the region of influence of the neighboring atom, thus migrating along the conductor.

In his article of 1875 and his final, unpublished paper, Weber developed these ideas in an attempt to derive an expression for electrical conductivity in terms of molecular parameters. Success in this was not achieved until the work of Eduard Riecke, Paul Drude, and H. A. Lorentz around the turn of the century; their work introduced the idea of treating the conduction electrons as a gas. Interest in the particulate theory of electricity quickened in the last decades of the century, especially after J. J. Thomson's investigation of cathode rays and Lorentz' interpretation of the Zeeman effect. Nevertheless, Weber's attempts to understand electrical conductivity, as well as thermal conductivity in metals, and thermoelectricity by means of the motion of the electric particles were a very important influence on the later investigations.

In metals, heat presumably was conducted by the jumping of electric particles between the ponderable molecules, those jumping from hotter molecules possessing greater speeds. In insulators, where such a mechanism was ruled out, Weber believed that heat was distributed by radiation through the ether permeating the material (articles of 1862 and 1875). In his doctoral dissertation (1858) Carl Neumann had attempted to explain the magnetic rotation of the plane of polarization of light by assuming an interaction between the Weberian molecular currents and the neighboring ether. Extending these ideas, Weber suggested that the frequency of light emitted by molecules would be the same as the frequency of motion of the electrical particles in the molecular currents. In this connection he developed his planetary model in 1862 and 1871, with charge of one sign fixed to the massive molecule and the oppositely charged electrical particles orbiting around it in accordance with his law of force.

An interesting consequence of Weber's law is that stable, bound orbits exist for two particles of the same sign of charge. Weber speculated that the ether might be composed of particles of like charge bound together, and that the development of the theory of their motion in accord with his law might lead to an understanding of the laws of light and heat radiation. In implementing this view, however, he succeeded no better than Ampère, who had indulged in similar speculations.

Toward the end of his life, Weber developed ideas appearing in Zöllner's *Die Principien einer elektrodynamischen Theorie der Materie* (1876). These included the concept of all matter being compounded of electrically charged particles, held together in various stable configurations by the action of the Weberian law of force. Even gravitation could be subsumed in this unitary picture by adopting in essence the earlier hypotheses of Aepinus and of Mossotti, that the attractive electrostatic forces between unlike charges slightly outbalance the repulsive forces between like charges.

Although he was perhaps most widely known during his life for his law of force, which was discarded with the triumph of Maxwell's field theory, Weber left his more lasting impression on physical theory with his atomistic conception of electric charge and his vision of the role of such charges in determining the electrical, magnetic, and thermal properties of matter.

## BIBLIOGRAPHY

I. ORIGINAL WORKS. Weber's writings are collected in *Wilhelm Webers Werke*, 6 vols. (Berlin, 1892–1894). Many articles are in *Resultate aus den Beobachtungen des Magnetischen Vereins*, Carl Friedrich Gauss and Wilhelm Weber, eds., 6 vols. (Göttingen–Leipzig, 1837–1843).

II. SECONDARY LITERATURE. See Eduard Riecke, *Wilhelm Weber, Rede* (Göttingen, 1892); Heinrich Weber, *Wilhelm Weber, eine Lebensskizze* (Breslau, 1893); and K. H. Wiederkehr, *Wilhelm Eduard Weber, Erforscher der Wellenbewegung und der Elektrizität 1804–1891* (Stuttgart, 1967), vol. xxxii of Grosse Naturforscher, H. Degen, ed. The last contains an extensive bibliography.

A. E. WOODRUFF

**WEBSTER, JOHN** (*b.* Thornton, Craven, England, 3 February 1610; *d.* Clitheroe, England, 18 June 1682), *chemistry, medicine, education.*

Although Webster implied that he studied at Cambridge, there is no record that he was ever a regular student. He also referred to his study of chemistry (*ca.* 1632) under the Hungarian alchemist John Hunyades, who arrived in London sometime after 1623. As with other Renaissance chemists, Webster's interest in chemistry was easily coupled with his concern for religion, and he was ordained a minister sometime after July 1632. Two years later he appears in the records as the curate of Kildwick, in Craven.

Paracelsian chemistry had a special appeal for surgeons, and there is a large iatrochemical literature specifically aimed at the military surgeon. As a Puritan, Webster served both as a surgeon and as a chaplain in the Parliamentary army during the Civil War. By 1648 his opposition to the established church had pushed him into the ranks of the nonconformists; and after the Restoration he was forced to support himself as a "practitioner in Physick and Chirurgery."

It was his concern for those who were preparing for the ministry that led Webster to write the *Academiarum examen*, in which he attacked the English universities. The traditional emphasis on books and disputations, as well as on the "heathen" authors Aristotle and Galen, seemed to him improper for Christians, who should study the glories of the universe (and thus, the Creator) through observation and personal experience. Webster argued against the use of mathematical abstraction in the study of nature, because for him this seemed to emphasize deductive logic. In contrast, the laboratory observations of the chemists offered the proper inductive approach exemplified in the writings of Helmont and Francis Bacon. The *Academiarum examen* is deeply indebted to Robert Fludd's Rosicrucian apology, *Tractatus apologeticus* (1617); and Webster points to Fludd and Bacon as the two authors most to be relied upon in formulating a new philosophy of nature. The most notable reply to Webster's call for educational reform was *Vindiciae academiarum* (1654) of Seth Ward and John Wilkins, in which Webster was taken to task for not having kept abreast of recent changes at the universities that did reflect the new science. He was accused of not having properly understood Bacon and Descartes and also was criticized for his reliance on the chemists. His espousal of Fludd's texts was especially condemned. The conflict between Webster, Ward, and Wilkins clearly points to the sharp division then existing between the chemical philosophers and the early mechanists.

Webster's belief that the aim of true natural magic was to uncover the "secret effects" of nature led him to extend warm support to the foundation of the Royal Society of London; and there is no indication that he was ever disappointed with the course taken by its members. He referred with approval to the society's work in his *Metallogra-*

*phia* (1671), an interesting compendium of current views on the growth and properties of metals. Here again he indicated his debt to Paracelsus, who made chemistry available to all, and to Helmont, whose work seemed to excel that of all his predecessors. The *Metallographia* was reviewed in the *Philosophical Transactions of the Royal Society*, and Daniel George Morhof later praised it as one of the major published works on minerals.

Webster was no less laudatory to the Royal Society in *The Displaying of Supposed Witchcraft*, completed in 1673 but not published until 1677, in which he attacked the views of Meric Casaubon and Joseph Glanvill. The latter, a member of the Royal Society, had written at length on witchcraft, especially in *Philosophical Considerations Touching Witches and Witchcraft* (1666). In his reply Webster countered that "supernatural" effects supposedly caused by witchcraft would eventually be found to have natural causes.

Although not a scientist of major stature, Webster is significant, for his work reflects important themes germane to the period of the scientific revolution. His conflict with Ward and Wilkins underscored the dispute between the chemical philosophers and the mechanists, his treatise on witchcraft did much to shed light on the meaning of magic and the supernatural in this period, and his work on metals and minerals clearly was considered important by his contemporaries on the Continent as well as in England.

## BIBLIOGRAPHY

I. ORIGINAL WORKS. There is a bibliography of Webster's works, including his many sermons, in Bertha Porter's article in the *Dictionary of National Biography*. The most important for the historian of science are *Academiarum examen, or the Examination of Academies* (London, 1654); *Metallographia: or An History of Metals* (London, 1671); and *The Displaying of Supposed Witchcraft* (London, 1677).

*Academiarum examen* has been reprinted, along with the replies of Ward and Wilkins (*Vindiciae academiarum* [Oxford, 1654]) and Thomas Hall (*Histrio-Mastix. A Whip for Webster* [London, 1654]), by Allen G. Debus, in *Science and Education in the Seventeenth Century* (London–New York, 1970).

*Metallographia* is reviewed in *Philosophical Transactions of the Royal Society*, **5**, no. 66 (12 Dec. 1670), 2034–2036. Daniel George Morhof, *Polyhistor, literarius, philosophicus et practicus*, 4th ed., II, pt. 2 (Lübeck, 1747), sec. 4, ch. 29, is devoted mainly to *Metallographia*.

II. SECONDARY LITERATURE. There is a discussion of Webster's work, with special reference to the educational problems raised in *Academiarum examen*, in the introductory essay in Allen G. Debus, *Science and Education in the Seventeenth Century*, 1–65. See also Debus' "The Webster-Ward Debate of 1654: The New Philosophy and the Problem of Educational Reform," in *L'univers à la Renaissance: Microcosme et macrocosme*, Travaux de l'Institut pour l'étude de la renaissance et de l'humanisme, IV (Brussels, 1970), 33–51; and "John Webster and the Educational Dilemma of the Seventeenth Century," in *Actes du XII⁰ Congrès international d'histoire des sciences*, IIIB (Paris, 1970), 15–23. An early, but still useful, discussion of the debate is in Richard F. Jones, *Ancients and Moderns. A Study of the Rise of the Scientific Movement in Seventeenth-Century England* (St. Louis, 1936, 2nd ed., 1961), 101–114.

For references pertinent to education in England and on the Continent, see Debus, *Science and Education in the Seventeenth Century*; but for a further understanding of Webster, see also P. M. Rattansi, "Paracelsus and the Puritan Revolution," in *Ambix*, **11** (1963), 23–32; C. Webster, ed., *Samuel Hartlib and the Advancement of Learning* (Cambridge, 1970), 1–72; and C. Webster, "Science and the Challenge to the Scholastic Curriculum 1640–1660," in *The Changing Curriculum* (London, 1971), 21–35.

ALLEN G. DEBUS

**WEBSTER, THOMAS** (*b.* Orkney Islands, Scotland, 1773; *d.* London, England, 26 December 1844), *geology.*

Webster came to London early in life and trained as an architect. In 1799 he was appointed clerk of the works at the newly founded Royal Institution and built its famous lecture theater. Later, taking up geology as a profession, he became curator, draughtsman, librarian, secretary, and editor to the Geological Society (founded in 1807). Leaving this employment in 1827, he took up public lecturing and in 1841 became the first professor of geology at University College.

Webster's original geological work was entirely concerned with the stratigraphy of the uppermost Jurassic, the Cretaceous, and the Tertiary rocks of southern England. In his chief paper (1814) Webster recorded a highly important piece of research, perhaps the first of its kind (being detailed and thoroughly scientific) on the geology of a British region. He described the characters of the Tertiary strata of southeast England, and particularly those of the Oligocene (later so called) of the Isle of Wight, in which he recognized an alternation of marine and freshwater formations. Webster compared all of these Tertiary strata with those that had been recently described in the Paris Basin by Cuvier and Brongniart. Of even greater importance was his survey of the Isle of Wight (Cretaceous and Tertiary) and "Isle" of Portland (mostly Jurassic and Cretaceous), with the production of one of the first geological maps of any part of Britain and one that was on a larger scale and more accurate than anything previously attempted. The geology of this classic region was almost completely unknown before Webster sketched, in words and picture, the features of its structure (essentially a monocline with vertical limb) in a series of lucid, forceful, and entertaining "letters" (1816). Unfortunately for the progress of geological knowledge, his duties at the Geological Society pressed so heavily upon him that he was prevented from undertaking any further large-scale investigations.

## BIBLIOGRAPHY

I. ORIGINAL WORKS. Webster's autobiography, which was probably written about 1837, is in MS in the library of the Royal Institution, London. Of Webster's ten publications, which are enumerated in Challinor (1964), the following publications are most important: "On the Freshwater Formations of the Isle of Wight, With Some Observations on the Strata Over the Chalk in the Southeast Part of England," in *Transactions of the Geological Society of London*, **2** (1814), 161–254; and "Geological Observations on the Isle of Wight and Adjacent Coast of Dorsetshire in a Series of Letters," in Sir Henry Englefield, *The Picturesque Beauties of the Isle of Wight* (London, 1816), 117–238.

II. SECONDARY LITERATURE. On Webster and his work, see G. S. Boulger, *Dictionary of National Biography*, LX (1899), 126; J. Challinor, "Thomas Webster's Letters on the Geology of the Isle of Wight, 1811–1813," in *Proceedings of the Isle of Wight Natural History and Archaeological Society*, **4** (1949), 108–122; "Some Correspondence of Thomas Webster, Geologist," in *Annals of Science*, **17** (1961), 175–195; **18** (1962), 147–175; **19** (1963), 49–79, 285–297; **20** (1964), 59–80, 143–164; N. Edwards, "Thomas Webster (*circa* 1772–1844)," in *Journal of the Society of Bibliography of Natural History*, **5** (1971), 468–473; E. Forbes, *The Tertiary Fluvio-Marine Formation of the Isle of Wight*, one of the *Memoirs of the Geological Survey of Great Britain* (1856); K. D. C. Vernon, "The Foundation and Early Years of the Royal Institution," in *Proceedings of the Royal Institution of Great Britain*, **39** (1963), 364–402; and H. B. Woodward, *History of the Geological Society of London* (London, 1908), *passim*.

JOHN CHALLINOR

**WEDDERBURN, JOSEPH HENRY MACLAGAN** (*b*. Forfar, Scotland, 26 February 1882; *d*. Princeton, New Jersey, 9 October 1948), *mathematics*.

Wedderburn was the tenth of fourteen children. His father, Alexander Wedderburn, was a physician in a family of ministers (on his father's side) and lawyers (on his mother's side). In 1898 Wedderburn matriculated at the University of Edinburgh; in 1903 he received an M.A. degree with first-class honors in mathematics. No doubt influenced by the work of Frobenius and Schur, he went to Leipzig and Berlin in 1904. During the same year he proceeded to the United States as a Carnegie fellow at the University of Chicago (E. H. Moore and L. E. Dickson were there). From 1905 to 1909 he was lecturer at the University of Edinburgh and assistant to Chrystal. During this time Wedderburn edited the *Proceedings of the Edinburgh Mathematical Society*, and in 1908 was awarded the doctorate of science.

In 1909 Wedderburn became one of the "preceptors" appointed under Woodrow Wilson at Princeton University. At the outbreak of World War I he enlisted in the British Army and fought in France. After the war he returned to Princeton, where he continued to teach until his retirement in 1945. When the mathematics department at Princeton assumed responsibility for publishing the *Annals of Mathematics*, Wedderburn was its editor from 1912 to 1928. Toward the close of the 1920's, he suffered what appears to have been a nervous breakdown. He led an increasingly solitary life and retired from his university post some years before the normal time. Wedderburn published thirty-eight papers and a textbook, *Lectures on Matrices* (1934), which in the last chapter contains an excellent account of his theorems and their background as well as some original contributions to the subject.

Wedderburn's mathematical work includes two famous theorems, which bear his name; both were established in the years 1905–1908. Before Wedderburn began his investigations, the classification of the semisimple algebras was done only if the ground field was the field of real or complex numbers. This did not lead to deeper insight into hypercomplex numbers (linear associative algebra). Wedderburn attacked the problem in a completely general way and introduced new methods and arrived at a complete understanding of the structure of semisimple algebras over any field. He showed that they are a direct sum of simple algebras and finally—in a celebrated paper ("On Hyper-complex Numbers") that was to be the beginning of a new era in the theory—proved that a simple algebra consists of all matrices of a given degree with elements taken from a division algebra.

Wedderburn's second important contribution concerns the investigation of skew fields with a finite number of elements. The commutative case had been investigated before Moore in 1903, and had led to a complete classification of all commutative fields with a given number of fields. Moore showed that for a given number $p^r$ of elements there exists (apart from isomorphisms) only one field, namely the Galois field of degree $r$ and characteristic $k$. Since a noncommutative finite field had never been found, one could suspect that it did not exist. In 1905 Wedderburn showed that every field with a finite number of elements is indeed commutative (under multiplication) and therefore a Galois field. This second theorem ("A Theorem on Finite Algebras") gives at once the complete classification of all semisimple algebras with a finite number of elements. But the theorem also had many other applications in number theory and projective geometry. It gave at once the complete structure of all projective geometries with a finite number of points, and it showed that in all these geometries Pascal's theorem was a consequence of Desargues's theorem. The structure of semisimple groups was now reduced to that of noncommutative fields. Wedderburn's theorem had been the special case of a more general Diophantine property of fields and thus opened an entirely new line of research.

*BIBLIOGRAPHY*

I. ORIGINAL WORKS. Wedderburn's works are "A Theorem on Finite Algebras," in *Transactions of the American Mathematical Society*, **6** (1905), 349–352; "Non-Desarguesian and Non-Pascalian Geometries," *ibid.*, **8** (1907), 379–388, written with O. Veblen; "On Hypercomplex Numbers," in *Proceedings of the London Mathematical Society*, **6**, 2nd ser. (1907–1908), 77–118; "The Automorphic Transformation of a Bilinear Form," in *Annals of Mathematics*, **23**, 2nd ser. (1921–1923), 122–134; "Algebraic Fields," *ibid.*, **24**, 2nd ser. (1922–1923), 237–264; "Algebras Which Do Not Possess a Finite Basis," in *Transactions of the American Mathematical Society*, **26** (1924), 395–426; "A Theorem on Simple Algebras," in *Bulletin of the American Mathematical Society*, **31** (1925), 11–13; "Non-commutative Domains of Integrity," in *Journal für die reine und angewandte Mathematik*, **167** (1931), 129–141; *Lectures on Matrices* (New York, 1934); "Boolean Linear Associative Algebra," in *Annals of Mathematics*, **35**, 2nd ser. (1934), 185–194; and "The Canonical Form of a Matrix," *ibid.*, **39**, 2nd ser. (1938), 178–180.

II. SECONDARY LITERATURE. See E. Artin, "The Influence of J. H. M. Wedderburn on the Development of Modern Algebra," in *Bulletin of the American Mathematical Society*, **56** (1950), 65–72.

HENRY NATHAN

**WEDEL, GEORG WOLFGANG** (*b.* Golssen, Germany, 12 November 1645; *d.* Jena, Germany, 6/7 September 1721), *medicine, chemistry.*

After receiving elementary instruction from his father, Pastor Johann Georg Wedel, Wedel entered the famous school in Schulpforta with a scholarship from the Saxon Elector in 1656. He spent five successful years at Schulpforta and then proceeded to the University of Jena, where he studied philosophy and especially medicine. He also participated in disputations, witnessed dissections, acquired an iatrochemical manuscript, all the while maintaining close relations with Guerner Rolfinck. In 1667 Wedel practiced briefly in Landsberg, toured Silesia, visited Wittenberg and Leipzig, and then returned to Jena, where he qualified for his medical license and started giving lectures. Before the year was out, however, he was called to Gotha as a district physician. While practicing medicine there, he took his M.D. at Jena in 1669.

Three years later, expecting to be appointed to the medical faculty at Jena, Wedel took a brief study tour of Holland. In early 1673, shortly after his return, he assumed the chair of anatomy, surgery, and botany. Then, upon the death of his mentor Rolfinck in the spring, Wedel assumed the chair of theoretical medicine. He held this chair until 1719, when the death of another colleague made it possible for Wedel to rise to the chair of practical medicine and chemistry. Meanwhile, he had received many state honors, including personal ennoblement as count palatine in 1694. He even purchased a country estate. After nearly five decades of teaching and writing, Wedel died as the senior member of Jena's entire faculty.

Wedel stood midway between medieval and modern world views, defending astrology and alchemy and championing iatrochemistry. He was a remarkably prolific author, but it was primarily by teaching at one of Germany's largest universities that he influenced a whole generation of physicians, including Hoffmann and Stahl. (Between 1673 and 1721 the average attendance of the

University of Jena was around 940 students. Roughly five percent of the student body was in medicine. See Franz Eulenburg, "Die Frequenz der deutschen Universitäten von ihrer Gründung bis zur Gegenwart," in *Abhandlungen der Sächsischen Akademie der Wissenschaften*, Philologisch-Historische Klasse, **24**, no. 2 [1904].)

*BIBLIOGRAPHY*

The most complete bibliography of Wedel's publications appears in Johann Heinrich Zedler, ed., *Grosses vollständiges Universal-Lexicon . . .*, LIII (Graz, 1964), 1804–1820. An autobiographical statement written in 1672 is in the Archives of the Deutsche Akademie der Naturforscher, Leopoldina (Halle, German Democratic Republic).

For assessments of his life and work, see Fritz Chemnitius, *Die Chemie in Jena von Rolfinck bis Knorr* (Jena, 1929), 13–53; Ernst Giese and Benno von Hagen, *Geschichte der medizinischen Fakultät der Friedrich-Schiller-Universität Jena* (Jena, 1958), 167–294; and Lynn Thorndike, *A History of Magic and Experimental Science* (New York, 1958), VII, 196, 202; VIII, 146–443.

KARL HUFBAUER

**WEDGWOOD, JOSIAH** (*b.* Burslem, England, 12 July 1730; *d.* Etruria, England, 3 January 1795), *ceramic technology, chemistry.*

Wedgwood was one of the progressive British industrialists of the eighteenth century whose careers touched the world of science. His father, Thomas Wedgwood, was in the pottery business and his mother, Mary Stringer, was the daughter of a dissenting minister. When Wedgwood was nine years old his father died and, as a result, his schooling ended and his employment in the pottery of his brother Thomas began.

Over the next eleven years Wedgwood mastered the skills of the potter; and after several partnerships he founded his own pottery in 1758. His business affairs soon prospered as his tireless experimental efforts resulted in novel and improved products. In the 1770's these efforts culminated in his greatest success, the jasper ware, which achieved exceptionally pleasant chromatic and textural effects, and which is the product generally brought to mind when "Wedgwood" is used as a description of ceramic products. During the 1760's as Wedgwood enlarged his pottery works, he also built a worker's village, which he named Etruria and where he made his home (Etruria Hall). In 1764 he married a distant cousin, Sarah Wedg-

wood, and the line of descendants (which includes the mother and wife of Charles Darwin) has to this day retained an interest in the Wedgwood potteries.

Wedgwood's position in eighteenth-century science rests on a few minor contributions to experimental chemistry, on his active associations with scientists and scientific societies, and on his general interest in experimental research. During the 1780's he contributed three papers on the measurement of high temperature to the *Philosophical Transactions of the Royal Society of London*. Depending on a property of clay that causes it to shrink as it is heated, the pyrometer ("thermometer for strong fire") that Wedgwood described was seen by him as complementary to the mercurial thermometers that were used to measure low temperature. The device enjoyed some use and caught the interest of both Priestley and Lavoisier. Moreover, as an appendix to one of these papers (1783) Wedgwood described the series of experiments he conducted to evaluate Lavoisier's proposal that heat could be measured by determining the quantity of ice that a warm body could melt.

On several occasions Wedgwood supplied experimental apparatus (pyrometers, retorts, crucibles, and tubing) to various scientists (again including Priestley and Lavoisier) and corresponded with them on experimental procedures. In 1783 Wedgwood was elected a fellow of the Royal Society, but his most significant membership was in the Lunar Society of Birmingham, where he was associated with the foremost British chemists of the period. It was indeed the Lunar Society that reflected the changing structure of industry and technology and anticipated the transformation that saw the affiliation between technology and the crafts loosened in favor of a new affiliation between technology and science.

Wedgwood's interest in experimental chemistry also showed itself in his business and personal affairs. Around 1775 he promoted (unsuccessfully) the formation of an experimental "company" to conduct research on the improvement of porcelain, and he both employed a chemist in his pottery and provided instruction in chemistry for his sons.

Differences of opinion have recently sprung up over the significance of Wedgwood's considerable interest in and knowledge of chemistry. That he read deeply and widely in the field and that he corresponded frequently with chemists on matters of research has been amply demonstrated. There are even indications that in a few instances his technical work on ceramics benefited from his knowledge of the experimental results of chemists. But, despite his habitual use of the terminology of contemporary (phlogiston) chemistry, Wedgwood had only the slightest interest in the cognitive structure of the science, and it seems to have contributed nothing to his industrial exploits. The meaning of his career is rather to be found in its clear statement that during the Industrial Revolution technical men were entering the world of research with the Baconian confidence that technology could learn from science.

## BIBLIOGRAPHY

I. ORIGINAL WORKS. The articles that Wedgwood contributed to *Philosophical Transactions of the Royal Society of London* are "An Attempt to Make a Thermometer for Measuring the Higher Degrees of Heat, From a Red Heat Up to the Strongest that Vessels Made of Clay Can Support," **72** (1782), 305–326; "Some Exps. Upon the *Ochra friabilis nigro fusca* of Da Costa Hist. Foss. p. 102; and Called by the Miners of Derbyshire, Black Wadd," **73** (1783), 284–287; "An Attempt to Compare and Connect the Thermometer for Strong Fire, Described in Vol. LXXII of the Philosophical Transactions, With the Common Mercurial Ones," **74** (1784), 358–384; "Additional Observations on Making a Thermometer for Measuring the Higher Degrees of Heat," **76** (1786), 390–408; and "On the Analysis of a Mineral Substance From *New South Wales*," **80** (1790), 306–320.

Many Wedgwood documents are collected in the Wedgwood Museum maintained by Josiah Wedgwood & Sons, Ltd., Barlaston, England. For published collections of Wedgwood's letters, see Ann Finer and George Savage, eds., *The Selected Letters of Josiah Wedgwood* (London, 1965); and Katherine Eufemia Farrer, ed., *Letters of Josiah Wedgwood*, 2 vols. (London, 1903).

II. SECONDARY LITERATURE. The standard biography of Wedgwood is Eliza Meteyard, *The Life of Josiah Wedgwood*, 2 vols. (London, 1865–1866); this work cannot, however, be depended on for an evaluation of Wedgwood's role in science. For an extensive survey of Wedgwood bibliography, see Gisela Heilpern, *Josiah Wedgwood, Eighteenth-Century English Potter: A Bibliography* (Carbondale, Ill., 1967). Wedgwood's association with the Lunar Society is fully discussed in Robert E. Schofield, *The Lunar Society of Birmingham* (London, 1963); see esp. ch. 3 and, for bibliography, p. 455. For a minor dissent from the opinion that Wedgwood was a full member of the Lunar Society, see Eric Robinson, "The Lunar Society: Its Membership and Organization," in *Transactions. Newcomen Society for the Study of the History of Engineering and Technology*, **35** (1964), 153–177.

Many details of Wedgwood's technical work are presented in Robert E. Schofield, "Josiah Wedgwood and the Technology of Glass Manufacturing," in *Technology and Culture*, **3** (1962), 285–297, and in the program of the *Ninth Wedgwood International Seminar: April 23–25, 1964* (New York, 1971), 125–135. Accounts of Wedgwood's role as a chemist are in Eric Robinson, "The Lunar Society and the Improvement of Scientific Instruments: II," in *Annals of Science*, **13** (1957), 1–8; J. A. Chaldecott, "Scientific Activities in Paris in 1791," *ibid.*, **24** (1968), 21–52; and Robert E. Schofield, "Josiah Wedgwood and a Proposed Eighteenth-Century Industrial Research Organization," in *Isis*, **47** (1956), 16–19.

For differing appraisals of the relationship between Wedgwood's chemistry and his technical work, see Robert E. Schofield, "Josiah Wedgwood, Industrial Chemist," in *Chymia*, **5** (1959), 180–192; A. Rupert Hall, "What Did the Industrial Revolution in Britain Owe to Science?", in Neil McKendrick, ed., *Historical Perspectives: Studies in English Thought and Society* (London, 1974), 129–151, esp. 141; Neil McKendrick, "The Role of Science in the Industrial Revolution: A Study of Josiah Wedgwood as a Scientist and Industrial Chemist," in Mikuláš Teich and Robert Young, eds., *Changing Perspectives in the History of Science: Essays in Honour of Joseph Needham* (London, 1973), 274–319; and J. A. Chaldecott, "Josiah Wedgwood (1730–95)—Scientist," in *British Journal for the History of Science*, **8**, no. 28 (1975), 1–16.

HAROLD DORN

**WEGENER, ALFRED LOTHAR** (*b.* Berlin, Germany, 1 November 1880; *d.* Greenland, November 1930), *meteorology, geophysics.*

Wegener was the son of Richard and Anna Wegener; his father, a doctor of theology, was director of an orphanage. Wegener started his schooling at the Kollnisches Gymnasium in Berlin, studied at the universities of Heidelberg and Innsbruck, and presented a thesis on astronomy at Berlin in 1905. He had meanwhile become interested in meteorology and geology, and a desire to learn at first hand about polar air masses led him to join a Danish expedition to northeastern Greenland in 1906–1908. It was the first of four Greenland expeditions in which he participated, and the exploration of that territory remained one of his dominant interests.

From 1908 to 1912 Wegener was a lecturer in meteorology at the Physical Institute in Marburg. His lectures, noted for their vividness, frankness, and open-mindedness, showed an ability and taste for seizing on broad issues in complicated topics as well as considerable distaste for mathematical detail. In 1912–1913, with Captain J. P. Koch of

Denmark Wegener led his second expedition to Greenland; its emphasis was on glaciology and climatology. From 1914 to 1919 he was mainly a junior military officer. After the war he worked at the meteorological experimental station of the German Marine Observatory at Gross Borstel, near Hamburg. A special professorship in meteorology and geophysics was created for Wegener at the University of Graz in 1924. He went to Greenland as a leader of expeditions in 1929–1930 and 1930–1931. In 1930 he was a member of a party that became lost and suffered severe privations. On 1 November of that year, his fiftieth birthday, he left a base in central Greenland for the west coast and was not seen again.

Wegener's fame today rests on his work as an originator of the idea of continental drift. He stated that he first toyed with the idea in 1910, on noting the degree of apparent correspondence between the shapes of the coasts of the Atlantic on its west and east sides, particularly those of South America and Africa. At first Wegener regarded the idea of drifting continents as improbable, but his interest was rekindled in 1911, when he accidentally learned that evidence of paleontological similarities on both sides of the Atlantic was being used to support the theory that a "land bridge" had once connected Brazil with Africa.

At this time many geologists supported the view that various portions of ocean floors had intermittently risen and fallen in the process of progressive solidification and contraction of the earth from a molten state. This view included the notion that land bridges connecting continents would appear and disappear. Moreover, it was found difficult to reconcile Darwin's theory of evolution with the widely acknowledged similarities in former organic life on different continents except through some connection such as land bridges.

After examining in some detail the paleontological and geological evidence of correspondences on the two sides of the Atlantic, Wegener concluded that the similarities were indeed sufficiently close to demand an explanation, and he linked them to his earlier thinking on continental drift. In a lecture at Frankfurt in January 1912, Wegener announced his theory that continents had actually moved thousands of miles apart during geological time, offering it as an alternative to the land bridge theory. Provisional accounts of the theory appeared in two short papers written in the same year.

During a long sick leave from war service (he was wounded twice), Wegener wrote an extended account of his continental drift theory, which appeared as *Die Entstehung der Kontinente und Ozeane* in 1915. This book was his main work on the subject and incorporated the investigations for which he is now noted. (In the book, Wegener referred to "die Verschiebung der Kontinente," which was accurately translated in the English edition of 1924 as "continental displacement." The term "continental drift" was coined later.)

In his detailed elaboration, Wegener postulated that near the end of the Permian period (about 200 million years ago), there existed a single supercontinent, which he called Pangaea. It subsequently split into several pieces that began to move, generally westward and in some cases toward the equator. In broad terms, America moved westward from Eurasia and Africa to form the Atlantic Ocean, with India later drifting away from Africa and Australia moving toward the equator from Antarctica. At the beginning of the Quaternary period (50 million years ago) Greenland started to separate from Norway. Island arcs, for example, the Antilles, Japan, and the Philippines, were envisaged as detached fragments left in the wakes of drifting continents. Mountain formation was associated with compression of the advancing front of a moving continent against the resistance of the ocean floor.

In his effort to supply a mechanical explanation, Wegener set down an argument, based on a meteorological analogy, to the effect that the continents would drift steadily under an "Eötvös force." He held that such a force could cause a floating body on a rotating planet to drift westward. He interpreted evidence on isostasy as indicating that continents are granitelike bodies that can be regarded as floating on a pliable medium. (Isostasy is connected, inter alia, with the notion of mountain "roots" that are somewhat less dense than the surrounding substrata.) Details of Wegener's interpretation were incompatible with the theory of land bridges, leaving, he thought, continental displacement as the plausible explanation for evidence of paleontological similarities between separated continents. Wegener also suggested *Pohlflucht* (flight from the poles) as a possible mechanism.

At first Wegener looked upon his version of continental drift as a working hypothesis that would undergo some modification as new evidence emerged, and he spent much effort in seeking such evidence. His confidence in this theory grew strongly, and the later editions of his book show the evidence he accumulated. His most important new evidence was from his studies of paleoclimatology; as a meteorologist Wegener had become interested in ancient climates and drew inferences bearing on continental drift from his investigations of their varying patterns over geological time.

Wegener also particularly sought to strengthen his case by precise geodetic observations that involved repeated astronomical position-finding methods and measurements of radio time transmissions across oceans over a number of years. His search for geodetic support was one of the main motives for his third and fourth Greenland expeditions: he hoped to establish that Greenland is now drifting westward from Europe. But no significant results emerged.

Wegener was not the first to propose a form of continental drift. The apparent congruence of the western and eastern Atlantic coasts had attracted notice as early as about 1600, and the notion that the Atlantic continents had drifted apart in earlier times had been put forward specifically by A. Snider-Pellegrini in 1858. In 1908 the geologist H. B. Baker had suggested that all the continents had been grouped around Antarctica 200 million years ago, and in 1910 F. B. Taylor had independently proposed a general drift of continents toward the equator. But Wegener went to greater lengths in expounding the theory and in his sustained efforts to establish it, and it is his name that is principally remembered.

From 1919 to 1928 a great international controversy raged over continental drift. Wegener's arguments on mechanism were shown to be untenable, and the paleontological evidence was held to be inconclusive. In 1928, at a historic gathering of fourteen eminent geologists, five supported the notion of continental drift without reservation and two with reservations, while seven opposed it. From then until after World War II, the theory received comparatively little attention. The most noted early variant of the theory was probably du Toit's proposal in 1937 that instead of a single primordial continent Pangaea, there were two, Laurasia in the northern hemisphere and Gondwanaland in the southern.

Wegener's other scientific contributions included work on the dynamics and thermodynamics of the atmosphere, atmospheric refraction and mirages, optical phenomena in clouds, acoustical waves, and the design of geophysical instruments. In his endeavors to test his continental drift theory through geodetic measurements, he designed an efficient balloon theodolite for tracking balloons sent up from ships to great heights.

A principal early objection to Wegener's theory was the failure to find an acceptable mechanism. Some time after his death, the idea of convection currents inside the earth's solid upper mantle was developed and a mechanism based on this idea was suggested. The new proposal envisaged an upper mantle that, although behaving like a solid in response to ordinary stresses, flows like a fluid under stresses that have periods comparable with geological time. According to this theory the flow took the form of convection currents and continents were carried, instead of sliding, on top of a convection cell of the moving mantle material.

The early 1950's saw the development of the new science of paleomagnetism, which indicated that remnant rock magnetism has preferred directions persisting over large areas of individual continents but varying from continent to continent. The directions are, moreover, generally different from the lines of magnetic force existing at the earth's surface today. When continental drift, coupled with polar wandering, was invoked to fit the paleomagnetic evidence, interest in Wegener's work, with the modification that convection currents provide the driving mechanism for continental drift, was strongly revived.

A great quantity of evidence on characteristics of midocean ridges was later brought to bear. These ridges, now known to exist on the floors of all the main oceans, are characterized by some unusual properties, including: abnormally high heat flow from the earth's interior, sequences of magnetic and gravity anomalies, thinning of the sediment cover as a ridge is approached, and interesting sequences in ages of ocean-floor material near ridges, giving rise to the notion of "sea-floor spreading." Many geologists have associated the ridges with the top of rising convection currents, and certain ocean trenches with the locations of descending currents. Other recent evidence has indicated that a layer immediately below continents is much weaker than had previously been supposed.

At the same time, older arguments continue to be maintained and newer arguments to be raised against continental drift. Some distinguished geophysicists assert that the currently proposed mechanism does not stand up to fine analysis. Further questions include the following: Why should the east coastline of South America remain largely undistorted although its postulated westerly drift relative to Africa has involved a sideways global distortion of thousands of miles? How reliable are the assumptions made about the earth's magnetic field? What is the reason for the comparative recency, as compared with the age of the earth, of the envisaged drift? Ad hoc answers to all these questions have been put forward by protagonists of the theory, yet again their answers have been questioned.

The enthusiasms of a considerable number of earth scientists lead them to assert, sometimes with a religious fervor, that continental drift is now established. It can at least be said that, whether large-scale continental drift in the envisaged sense has occurred or not, and whatever the finer detail may turn out to be, it is now widely recognized that movements and distortions of the earth's outer layers over geological time must have been substantial. The theory of continental drift also is stimulating many scientists to gather new observations of much value to ideas on the evolution of the earth.

*BIBLIOGRAPHY*

I. ORIGINAL WORKS. The principal publication for which Wegener is now noted is *Die Entstehung der Kontinente und Ozeane* (Brunswick, 1915; rev. eds., 1920, 1922, and 1929). the 3rd ed. (1922) translated into English, French, Spanish, Swedish, and Russian. A 5th ed., rev. by Kurt Wegener, appeared in 1936. His other publications include *Thermodynamik der Atmosphäre* (Leipzig, 1911); "Die Enstehung der Kontinente und Ozeane," in *Mitteilungen aus Justus Perthes geographischer Anstalt*, **58** (1912), 185–195, 253–256, 305–309; *Die Klimate der geologischen Vorzeit* (Berlin, 1924), written with W. Köppen; "Denkschrift über Inlandeis-Expedition nach Grönland," in *Deutsche Forschung* (Berlin), **42** (1928), 181; and *Mit Motorboot und Schlitten in Grönland* (Leipzig, 1930).

II. SECONDARY LITERATURE. For a full list of Wegener's publications, see H. Benndorf, "Alfred Wegener," in *Beiträge zur Geophysik*, **31** (1931), 337–377. Further details of his life are in Else Wegener, *Alfred Wegener* (Wiesbaden, 1960); J. Georgi, "Memories of Alfred Wegener," in *Continental Drift*, S. K. Runcorn, ed. (London, 1962), 309–324; and K. Wolcken, "Alfred Wegener," in *Meteoros* (1955), 379–382. An important contemporaneous review of Wegener's work on continental drift was published by the American Association of Petrologists in *Theory of Continental Drift; a Symposium on the Origin and Movement of Land Masses, Both Inter-continental and Intra-continental, as Proposed by Alfred Wegener*, E. De Golyer, ed. (London, 1928).

K. E. BULLEN

**WEHNELT, ARTHUR RUDOLPH BERTHOLD** (*b*. Rio de Janeiro, Brazil, 4 April 1871; *d*. Berlin, Germany, 15 February 1944), *physics*.

Wehnelt was the son of Berthold Wehnelt, an engineer and factory owner, who died at an early age, and Louise Muckelberg. He attended the Louisenstädter Gymnasium in Berlin and the Gymnasium in Landsberg an der Warthe (now Gorzów Wielkopolski, Poland), and graduated from secondary school in the spring of 1892. For a year he studied natural science at the Technische Hochschule in Berlin-Charlottenburg, and then from 1893 to 1897 at the University of Berlin. Next he went to the University of Erlangen, where he received the doctorate in the spring of 1898 under Eilhard G. H. Wiedemann. At Erlangen he became successively assistant at the Physics Institute (1900); *Privatdozent* (after obtaining the *venia docendi* in 1901); and extraordinary professor of physics (1904). In 1906 he was called to the University of Berlin as full professor, and in 1926 he was appointed director of its Physics Institute. He remained at the University of Berlin until 1939, becoming professor emeritus about 1938.

In his dissertation Wehnelt investigated the dark space near the cathode in gas-discharge tubes and established that the high resistance of the dark space of the cathode corresponds to that of a dielectric. Pursuing a remark made by Wiedemann and Ebert in 1891, Wehnelt demonstrated that the cross section of the cathode-ray bundle decreases with pressure, or with a decrease in the diameter of the tube placed around the bundle. These are essentially the characteristics of the epoch-making device (now known as the Wehnelt cylinder) that he later developed. In his *Habilitationsschrift* Wehnelt described the processes occurring in the discharge tube, taking into account the entire discharge from the cathode to the anode, and measured the current and voltage to analyze the discharge processes at various points of the tube. In the preface to his essay Wehnelt defended twelve theses, including the propositions that "electrical lighting systems of 220 volts should be avoided wherever possible," and that "the refinement of modern electrical measuring methods has gone too far."

Wehnelt became well known through his discoveries concerning discharge in rarefied gases. In the course of his research he studied cathode rays, canal rays, and Röntgen rays. He was involved in the technical development of the valve tube (the radio tube), Röntgen tubes, and the Braun tube (the oscilloscope); in this manner he made a fundamental contribution to modern electronics.

Three of Wehnelt's discoveries deserve special mention. While investigating certain light and heat phenomena that had earlier been observed at very small electrodes by Davy, Wehnelt recognized in 1899 that current interruptions (up to 2200 $sec^{-1}$) originate in rapid gas explosions at the electrode (for example, the platinum point). One such phenomenon, known as disruptive discharge, was demonstrated with the telephone by F. Richarz in 1892 and was applied to an electrical sweating process by Eugène Lagrange and P. Hoho in 1894. Wehnelt first applied an electrolytic interrupter—based on this phenomenon—to the induction coil, and then to short-exposure X-ray photographs.

In 1903 Wehnelt pointed out that a large potential drop exists between the cathode ray and the wall of the tube, and he used this knowledge to alter the hardness of the X rays, which he regulated with the help of an auxiliary tube placed over the cathode. To measure the hardness itself, he utilized the measurements published by Bénoist in 1902, concerning the comparative absorption of silver and aluminum. Wehnelt improved the measurements by replacing Bénoist's aluminum disk with a continuous aluminum wedge (Wehnelt scale).

In 1903–1904 Wehnelt made his most important discovery, the "oxide cathode." He observed a significant decrease in the cathode fall of glow discharge, occurring in the presence of platinum cathodes that had not been carefully enough cleaned; and then he noticed the same thing in the case of metal compounds, but especially in that of oxides. He found that the phenomenon was caused by an increase (which he estimated as 100 times) in the number of negative ions made available by the cathode metal when treated. A practical use for this insight was found in the production of very high current strengths (at 110 volts and 0.01 Hg pressure it is 3 amperes). More important, the exceptionally low exit potential at the cathode enabled Wehnelt to produce slow electrons, as well as soft canal rays. As a result, he could carry out measurements of velocity and of the ratio of charge to mass of very soft cathode rays. Since he knew how to obtain a good focus for the electron beam and how to make it visible at reduced pressure with the aid of the "Wehnelt cylinder," he was especially successful in this undertaking. Wehnelt saw the theoretical interest of his discovery as possible confirmation of the hypothesis put forth by Kaufmann in 1902 and by Abraham in 1903, that is, that the mass of the electron is a purely electromagnetic quantity.

In subsequent research Wehnelt dealt with the photoelectric effect, secondary emission, mass spectra, thin metal layers, and the thermal conductivity of metals.

## BIBLIOGRAPHY

I. ORIGINAL WORKS. A fairly complete bibliography of Wehnelt's writings is in Poggendorff, IV, 1608–1609; V, 1345; VI, 2829; and VIIa, 887. See especially *Strom- und Spannungsmessungen an Kathoden in Entladungsröhren. Habilitationsschrift zur Erlangung der Venia docendi der hohen philosophischen Fakultät der Friedrich-Alexander-Universität zu Erlangen* (Leipzig, 1901), which contains the 12 interesting theses that Wehnelt defended.

II. SECONDARY LITERATURE. In addition to the titles cited by Poggendorff, the separately printed edition of Wehnelt's Ph.D. (Leipzig, 1908) is reprinted (without the short biographical sketch originally included) in *Annalen der Physik*, **301** (1898), 511–542. Wehnelt's MSS are held at the Staatsbibliothek Preussischer Kulturbesitz in Berlin; a few MSS also can be found at the Universitätsbibliothek in Erlangen.

HANS KANGRO

**WEICHSELBAUM, ANTON** (*b.* Schiltern, Austria, 8 February 1845; *d.* Vienna, Austria, 23 October 1920), *pathology.*

The son of a barrelmaker, Weichselbaum attended the gymnasium in Krems, Austria, from 1855 to 1863 and studied medicine at the Imperial Medical Surgical Military Hospital in Vienna, receiving the M.D. in 1869. He subsequently served as assistant to Rokitansky's student Josef Engel in the medical corps and in 1875 became anatomical demonstrator at the First Imperial and Royal Military Hospital in Vienna; in 1877 he received the *venia legendi* for pathological anatomy at the University of Vienna. In 1882 he was named chief demonstrator at the Rudolf Hospital in Vienna, and in 1885 he became associate professor. From 1893 to 1916 he was director of the Pathological-anatomical Institute of the University of Vienna, and in 1912 he became rector of the university.

Weichselbaum was among the first to recognize the importance of bacteriology for pathological anatomy. This fact is reflected in his discovery of the meningococcus and of the diplococcus *lanceolatus pneumoniae*, which bears his name, as well as in his studies on miliary tuberculosis. Weichselbaum was also extremely receptive to the newly developing science of serology. It was, in fact, while serving as assistant in Weichselbaum's laboratory that Karl Landsteiner discovered interagglutination between serum and blood cells.

Moreover, Weichselbaum was one of the first to stress the importance of "constitutional pathology." In his investigations of the pancreas of patients with diabetes mellitus he very early drew attention to the crucial role of the islets of Langerhans, the organs in which insulin was later discovered.

*BIBLIOGRAPHY*

Weichselbaum's major publications include *Grundriss der pathologischen Histologie* (Leipzig–Vienna, 1892), translated by W. R. Dawson as *The Elements of Pathological Histology* (London, 1895); *Parasitologie* (Jena, 1898); and *Epidemiologie* (Jena, 1899).

On his life and work, see the notice by Siegmund Exner, in *Almanach der Akademie der Wissenschaften in Wien*, **71** (1921), 152–155.

H. CHIARI

**WEIERSTRASS, KARL THEODOR WILHELM** (*b.* Ostenfelde, Westphalia, Germany, 31 October 1815; *d.* Berlin, Germany, 19 February 1897), *mathematics.*

Weierstrass was the first child of Wilhelm Weierstrass, secretary to the mayor of Ostenfelde, and Theodora Vonderforst, who were married five months before his birth. The family name first appeared in Mettmann, a small town between Düsseldorf and Elberfeld; since the sixteenth century they had been artisans and small merchants. Weierstrass' father, an intelligent, educated man with knowledge of the arts and sciences, could have held higher posts than he actually did; little is known about his mother's family. Weierstrass had a brother and two sisters, none of whom ever married. When Weierstrass was eight his father entered the Prussian taxation service; and as a result of his frequent transfers, young Karl attended several primary schools. In 1829, at the age of fourteen, he was accepted at the Catholic Gymnasium in Paderborn, where his father was assistant and subsequently treasurer at the main customs office.

A distinguished student at the Gymnasium, Weierstrass received several prizes before graduating. Unlike many mathematicians, he had no musical talent; nor did he ever acquire an interest in the theater, painting, or sculpture. He did, however, value lyric poetry and occasionally wrote verses

himself. In 1828, a year after his mother's death, Weierstrass' father remarried. At the age of fifteen Weierstrass reportedly worked as a bookkeeper for a merchant's wife—both to utilize his abilities and to ease the strain of his family's financial situation. A reader of Crelle's *Journal für die reine und angewandte Mathematik* while in his teens, he also gave his brother Peter mathematical coaching that does not seem to have proved helpful: Weierstrass' proofs were generally "knocking," his brother later admitted.

After leaving the Gymnasium in 1834, Weierstrass complied with his father's wish that he study public finance and administration, and entered the University of Bonn. The course of studies that he pursued was planned to permit him to obtain a background in law, administration, and economics—the requisites for those seeking higher administrative posts in Prussia. The study of mathematics or related areas was his first choice, however; and the conflict between duty and inclination led to physical and mental strain. He tried, in vain, to overcome his problems by participating in carefree student life, but he soon came to shun lectures and to restrict himself to studying mathematics on his own, beginning with the *Mécanique céleste* of Laplace. Weierstrass was fortunate in having an understanding adviser in astronomy, mathematics, and physics, Dietrich von Münchow. However, Münchow was of the old school and, because he gave only elementary lectures, was remote from the advances of modern mathematics.

Around this time Weierstrass read Jacobi's *Fundamenta nova theoriae functionum ellipticarum* (1829); the work proved difficult for him, based, as it was, on prior knowledge of Legendre's *Traité des fonctions elliptiques*, published shortly beforehand. A transcript of Christof Gudermann's lecture on modular functions rendered the theory of elliptic variables understandable to him and inspired him to initiate his own research. In a letter to Sophus Lie of 10 April 1882, Weierstrass explained his definitive decision to study mathematics:

For me this letter [from Abel to Legendre], when I became aware of it in Crelle's *Journal* [**6** (1830), 73–80] during my student years, was of the utmost importance. The immediate derivation of the form of representation of the function given by Abel and designated by him by $\lambda(x)$, from the differential equation defining this function, was the first mathematical task I set myself; and its fortunate solution made me determined to devote myself wholly to mathematics; I made this decision in my seventh semester [winter semester 1837–1838], although originally I undertook the study of public finance and administration [*N. H. Abel, Mémorial* (1902), 108].

After eight semesters Weierstrass left the university without taking the examination. Although his father was greatly disappointed, a family friend, president of the court of justice of Paderborn, persuaded him to send Weierstrass to the Theological and Philosophical Academy at Münster, where he would be able to take the teacher's examination after a short time. Weierstrass enrolled on 22 May 1839. Helped and encouraged by Gudermann— Weierstrass was the only university student at his lectures on elliptic functions, he left Münster that autumn to prepare for the state examination.

In January 1840 Weierstrass' father assumed the more remunerative post of director of the saltworks and the family moved to Westernkotten, near Lippstadt. Two months later Weierstrass registered for the examination, and at the beginning of May he received the philological, pedagogical, and mathematical problems for the written examination. The first mathematical problem was one that Weierstrass himself had requested, the representation of elliptic functions. Following Abel, for whose work he had always had the highest regard, Weierstrass presented in his examination an important advance in the new theory of elliptic functions, and this work contains important starting points for his subsequent investigations. Gudermann recognized the significance of his accomplishment and wrote in his evaluation that Weierstrass was "of equal rank with the discoverers who were crowned with glory." The school superintendent was somewhat more restrained. When Weierstrass later read Gudermann's complete critique, he admitted that had he learned of it earlier, he would have published the work immediately and most certainly would have obtained a university chair sooner. He considered it especially fine of Gudermann to have praised him so highly, even though his work contained sharp criticism of Gudermann's method. It is of interest that one of the other mathematical problems that Weierstrass was assigned, on elementary geometry, gave him much difficulty, at least according to his brother's account.

After having passed the oral examinations in April 1841, Weierstrass taught for a one-year probationary period at the Gymnasium in Münster, before transferring to the Catholic secondary school in Deutsch-Krone, West Prussia (1842–1848), and then to the Catholic Gymnasium in Braunsberg, East Prussia (1848–1855). In addition to mathematics and physics, he taught German, botany, geography, history, gymnastics, and even calligraphy. (Reminiscent of this is his peculiar $\mathscr{P}$ of the Weierstrassian $p$-function.) In recalling the misery of these years, Weierstrass remarked that he had neither a colleague for mathematical discussions nor access to a mathematical library, and that the exchange of scientific letters was a luxury that he could not afford. The "unending dreariness and boredom" would have been unbearable for him without hard work, and his every free minute was devoted to mathematics.

Fortunately he found an understanding senior colleague in Ferdinand Schultz, director of the Braunsberg Institute. Weierstrass was in Deutsch-Krone during the Revolution of 1848. Dirichlet had stated that a mathematician could only be a democrat, and Weierstrass' beliefs were not contrary to this belief. Commissioned to oversee the belletristic section of the local newspaper, he approved reprinting the freedom songs of Georg Herwegh—under the eyes of the censor.

Although not involved in nationalistic struggles, Weierstrass was no stranger to national feelings. He aspired to neither title nor decorations and was reluctant to exchange the simple title of professor for the more pretentious one of privy councillor. His religious views were moderate and tolerant, and he eschewed political as well as religious bigots. Reared a Catholic, he paid homage in a public speech as rector to the cultural significance of the Reformation. In his philosophical outlook he was a frank adherent of Kant and an opponent of Fichte and Schelling.

Weierstrass' first publications on Abelian functions, which appeared in the Braunsberg school prospectus (1848–1849), went unnoticed; but the following work, "Zur Theorie der Abelschen Functionen" (Crelle's *Journal*, **47** [1854], 289–306), elicited enormous interest and marked a decisive turning point in his life. In this memoir he demonstrated the solution to the problem of inversion of the hyperelliptic integrals, which he accomplished by representing Abelian functions as the quotients of constantly converging power series. Many of his results were only hinted at in this work, for since 1850 he had suffered painful attacks of vertigo, which lasted up to an hour and subsided only after a tormenting attack of vomiting. These attacks, which contemporaries called brain spasms, recurred for about twelve years and made it impossible for him to work. Although the 1854 paper was merely a preliminary statement,

Liouville called it "one of those works that marks an epoch in science." On 31 March 1854 the University of Königsberg awarded Weierstrass an honorary doctorate. He was promoted to senior lecturer at Braunsberg and in the fall of 1855 was granted a year's leave to continue his studies. Firmly determined not to return to the school, he applied in August 1855 for the post of Kummer's successor at the University of Breslau—an unusual mode of procedure. (Kummer had been called to Berlin to succeed Dirichlet, who had assumed Gauss's chair at Göttingen.) Weierstrass did not receive the appointment at Breslau.

In the famous "Theorie der Abelschen Functionen" (Crelle's *Journal*, **52** [1856], 285–380), which contains an excerpt from the previously mentioned examination work, Weierstrass proved what previously he had only hinted. According to Hilbert, he had realized one of the greatest achievements of analysis, the solution of the Jacobian inversion problem for hyperelliptic integrals. There was talk of appointment to a post in Austria, but before formal discussions could take place Weierstrass accepted on 14 June 1856 an appointment as professor at the Industry Institute in Berlin, a forerunner of the Technische Hochschule. While he did not have to return to the Gymnasium in Braunsberg, his hopes for appointment to the University of Berlin had not been realized. In September 1856, while attending a conference of natural scientists in Vienna, Weierstrass was offered a special professorship at any Austrian university of his choice. He was still undecided a month later, when he was invited to the University of Berlin as associate professor. He accepted. On 19 November 1856 he became a member of the Berlin Academy. It was not until July 1864 that he was able to leave the Industry Institute and assume a chair at the university.

Having spent the most productive years of his life teaching elementary classes, far from the centers of scientific activity, Weierstrass had found time for his own research only at the expense of his health. Heavy demands were again made on him at Berlin, and on 16 December 1861 he suffered a complete collapse; he did not return to scientific work until the winter semester of 1862–1863. Henceforth he always lectured while seated, consigning the related work at the blackboard to an advanced student. The "brain spasms" were replaced by recurrent attacks of bronchitis and phlebitis, which afflicted him until his death at the age of eighty-one. Nevertheless, he became a recognized master, primarily through his lectures.

He delayed publication of his results not—as has often been charged—because of a "basic aversion to printer's ink" but, rather, because his critical sense invariably compelled him to base any analysis on a firm foundation, starting from a fresh approach and continually revising and expanding.

It was only gradually that Weierstrass acquired the masterly skill in lecturing extolled by his later students. Initially his lectures were seldom clear, orderly, or understandable. His ideas simply streamed forth. Yet his reputation for lecturing on new theories attracted students from around the world, and eventually some 250 students attended his classes. Since no one else offered the same subject matter, graduate students as well as university lecturers were attracted to Berlin. Moreover, he was generous in suggesting topics for dissertations and continuing investigations.

One of Weierstrass' first lectures at Berlin was on the application of Fourier series and integrals to problems of mathematical physics. But the lack of rigor that he detected in all available works on the subject, as well as the fruitlessness of his own efforts to surmount this deficiency, frustrated him to the degree that he decided not to present this course again. It was not until 1885 that he took up the representation of single-valued functions of a real variable by means of trigonometric series, stressing that "he had considered the needs of mathematical physics." Here again are manifest his proverbial striving for the characteristic "Weierstrassian rigor" that virtually compelled him to carry his investigations to an ever higher degree of maturity and completion. His position concerning the applications of his research was clarified in his inaugural speech at the Berlin Academy on 9 July 1857, in which he stated that mathematics occupies an especially high place because only through its aid can a truly satisfying understanding of natural phenomena be obtained. To some degree his outlook approached that of Gauss, who believed that mathematics should be the friend of practice, but never its slave.

Over the years Weierstrass developed a great lecture cycle: "Introduction to the Theory of Analytic Functions"; "Theory of Elliptic Functions," sometimes beginning with the differential calculus, at other times starting with the theory of functions, the point of departure being the algebraic addition theorem; "Application of Elliptic Functions to Problems in Geometry and Mechanics"; "Theory of Abelian Functions"; "Application of Abelian Functions to the Solution of Selected Geometric Problems"; and "Calculus of Variations." Within this cycle Weierstrass erected the entire structure of his mathematics, using as building blocks only that which he himself had proven.

During seven semesters (1864–1873) Weierstrass also lectured on synthetic geometry, thereby honoring his promise to Jakob Steiner before the latter's death in 1863. Steiner's discussions, which Weierstrass had read in Crelle's *Journal* as a student, had especially stimulated his interest; and he was one of the few people in Berlin with whom the old crank had remained on good terms. These lectures were given only out of a sense of obligation, however—not from any interest in the subject; for Weierstrass considered geometric demonstrations to be in very poor taste. If, as has been alleged, he sometimes permitted himself to clarify a point by using a diagram, it was carefully erased.

In addition to lecturing, Weierstrass introduced the first seminar devoted exclusively to mathematics in Germany, a joint undertaking with Kummer at the University of Berlin in 1861. Here again he developed many fruitful concepts that were frequently used by his students as subjects for papers. In his inaugural lecture as rector of the University of Berlin, Weierstrass called for lecturers to "designate the boundaries that had not yet been crossed by science . . . from which positions further advances would then be made possible." The lecturer should neither deny his students "a deeper insight into the progress of his own investigations, nor should he remain silent about his own errors and disappointments."

Weierstrass' students included Heinrich Bruns, Georg Frobenius, Georg Hettner, Ludwig Kiepert, Wilhelm Killing, Johannes Knoblauch, Ernst Kötter, Reinhold von Lilienthal, Hans von Mangoldt, Felix Müller, Eugen Netto, Friedrich Schottky, Ludwig Stickelberger, and Wilhelm Ludwig Thomé. Auditors or participants in the seminar included Paul Bachmann, Oskar Bolza, Friedrich Engel, Leopold Gegenbauer, August Gutzmer, Lothar Heffter, Kurt Hensel, Otto Hölder, Adolf Hurwitz, Felix Klein, Adolf Kneser, Leo Koenigsberger, Fritz Kötter, Mathias Lerch, Sophus Lie, Jacob Lüroth, Franz Mertens, Hermann Minkowski, Gösta Mittag-Leffler, Hermann Amandus Schwarz, and Otto Stolz. The philosopher Edmund Husserl—insofar as he was a mathematician—was also a student of Weierstrass.

Weierstrass was not without his detractors: Felix Klein, for instance, remarked that he and Lie had merely fought for their own points of view in the seminars. Most of Weierstrass' students, however, accepted his theories as an unassailable standard. Doubts were not permitted to arise, and checking was hardly possible since Weierstrass cited very few other sources and arranged his methodical structure so that he was obliged to refer only to himself. Independent opinions, such as Klein's, were the exception.

Weierstrass' criticism of Riemann's basic concept of the theory of functions, namely the application and use of the principle of Dirichlet, resulted in the fact that until the twentieth century his approach to the theory of functions, starting with the power series, was preferred to Riemann's, which originated with complex differentiation. Weierstrass formulated his credo in a letter to his student H. A. Schwarz (3 October 1875):

> The more I ponder the principles of function theory—and I do so incessantly—the more I am convinced that it must be founded on simple algebraic truths and that one is therefore on the wrong path if, instead of building on simple and fundamental algebraic propositions, one has recourse to the "transcendental" (to put it briefly), no matter how impressive at first glance, for example, seem the reflections by means of which Riemann discovered so many of the most important properties of algebraic functions. It is self-evident that any and all paths must be open to a researcher during the actual course of his investigations; what is at issue here is merely the question of a systematic theoretical foundation.

Although Weierstrass enjoyed considerable authority at Berlin, he occasionally encountered substantial resistance from his colleagues; and such criticism hurt him deeply. In the late 1870's his relations with his close friend Leopold Kronecker cooled considerably when Kronecker imparted to Weierstrass his antipathy for the work of Georg Cantor. Weierstrass had been one of the first to recognize the value of Cantor's accomplishments and had in fact stimulated his work on the concept of countability. Kronecker, by contrast, proclaimed that he had set himself the task "of investigating the error of every conclusion used in the so-called present method of analysis." Weierstrass' reaction to Kronecker's attack may well have been excessive; but in 1885 he decided to leave Germany and go to Switzerland, believing that everything for which he had worked was near collapse. Determined to prevent such a catastrophe, he resolved to remain in Berlin after all. The choice of his successor and publication of his works were problems still to be resolved—and his successor would have to be endorsed by Kronecker. Kronecker's death in 1891 cleared the path for the appointment of Hermann Amandus Schwarz.

But the publication of Weierstrass' writings was another matter. He was satisfied with neither the circulating transcripts of his lectures nor with the textbooks that followed his concepts and that he had, to some degree, authorized; and his major ideas and methodology remained unpublished. In 1887, having already edited the works of Steiner and Jacobi, Weierstrass decided to publish his own mathematical lifework, assured of the help of the younger mathematicians of his school. He lived to see only the first two volumes appear in print (1894, 1895). According to his wishes, volume IV was given preferential treatment, and it appeared in 1902. The altered title, "Lectures on the Theory of Abelian Transcendentals"—they had always been called the theory of Abelian functions—more accurately reflects the scope of his lectures. Volume III was published the following year. Twelve years elapsed before the appearance of volume V ("Lectures on Elliptic Functions") and volume VI ("Selected Problems of Geometry and Mechanics to be Solved With the Aid of the Theory of Elliptic Functions"), and another dozen years before volume VII ("Lectures on the Calculus of Variations"). All of Weierstrass' efforts to ensure the publication soon after his death of a complete edition of his works were fruitless: volumes VIII–X, intended to contain works on hyperelliptic functions, a second edition of his lectures on elliptic functions, and the theory of functions, remain unpublished.

In 1870, at the age of fifty-five, Weierstrass met the twenty-year-old Russian Sonya Kovalevsky, who had come to Berlin from Heidelberg, where she had taken her first semester under Leo Koenigsberger. Unable to secure her admission to the university, Weierstrass taught her privately; and his role in both her scientific and personal affairs far transcended the usual teacher-student relationship. In her he found a "refreshingly enthusiastic participant" in all his thoughts, and much that he had suspected or fumbled for became clear in his conversations with her. In a letter to her of 20 August 1873, Weierstrass wrote of their having "dreamed and been enraptured of so many riddles that remain for us to solve, on finite and infinite spaces, on the stability of the world system, and on all the other major problems of the mathematics and the physics of the future." It seemed to him as though she had "been close . . . throughout [his] entire life . . . and never have I found anyone who could bring me such understanding of the highest aims of science and such joyful accord with

my intentions and basic principles as you!" Through his intercession she received the doctorate *in absentia* at Göttingen in 1874.

Yet their friendship did not remain untroubled. Her links with socialist circles, her literary career as author of novels, and her advocacy of the emancipation of women strongly biased the judgment of her contemporaries, and resulted in defamation of the friendship. On the other hand, many of his letters to her were unanswered. At one juncture she remained silent for three years. He was instrumental in her obtaining an appointment as lecturer in mathematics at Stockholm in 1883 and a life professorship in mathematics in 1889. The misinterpretation of their relationship and her early death in 1891 brought him additional physical suffering. During his last three years he was confined to a wheelchair, immobile and dependent. He died of pneumonia.

In his inaugural speech to the Berlin Academy, Weierstrass characterized his scientific activity as having centered on the search for "those values of a wholly new type of which analysis had not yet had an example, their actual representation, and the elucidation of their properties." One of his earliest attempts at solving this problem was a treatise (1841) on the representation of an analytic function exhibiting an absolute value that lies between two given boundaries. It contained the Cauchy integral proposition and the Laurent proposition. It was published only fifty-three years later, however, when it became clear that Weierstrass at the age of twenty-six had already had at his disposal the principles of his theory of functions, to the development of which he subsequently devoted his lifework. Yet his contribution to reestablishing the theory of analytic functions ultimately served only to achieve his final aim: the erection of a general theory of Abelian integrals (all integrals over algebraic functions) and the consideration of their converse functions, the Abelian functions.

What Weierstrass considered to be his main scientific task is now held to be less important than his accomplishments in the foundation of his theory. The special functions which he investigated, and the theory of which he lucidly elaborated or transformed, now elicit less interest than his criticism, rigor, generally valid concepts, and the procedures and propositions of the theory of functions. Weierstrass' name remains linked to his preliminary proposition, approximation propositions, double series proposition, proposition of products, and fundamental proposition—as well as the Casorati-Weierstrass proposition. Hundreds of mathematicians were influenced by his uncompromising development of a systematic foundation and his pursuit of a fixed plan after appropriate preparation of detail; and they in turn instilled in their students Weierstrass' concepts of the necessity of clarity and truth, and his belief that the highest aim of science is to achieve general results. Admired by Poincaré for his "unity of thought," Weierstrass was the most important nineteenth-century German mathematician after Gauss and Riemann.

## BIBLIOGRAPHY

I. ORIGINAL WORKS. Weierstrass' writings were published as *Mathematische Werke*, 7 vols. (Berlin, 1894–1927). His papers are listed in Poggendorff, II, 1282; III, 1424; IV, 1610; V, 1345; and VI, 2831.

The following letters have been published: to Paul du Bois-Reymond, G. Mittag-Leffler, ed., in *Acta mathematica*, **39** (1923), 199–225; to Leo Koenigsberger, G. Mittag-Leffler, ed., *ibid.*, 226–239; to Lazarus Fuchs, M. Wentscher and L. Schlesinger, ed., *ibid.*, 246–256. Excerpts of Weierstrass' correspondence with Sonya Kovalevsky were included by Mittag-Leffler in his discussion, "Une page de la vie de Weierstrass," in *Compte rendu du deuxième Congrès international des mathématiciens* (Paris, 1902), 131–153; and in "Zur Biographie von Weierstrass," in *Acta mathematica*, **35** (1912), 29–65, which also includes Weierstrass' letters to Mittag-Leffler. His letters to Kovalevsky were also used by Mittag-Leffler in "Weierstrass et Sonja Kowalewsky," *ibid.*, **39** (1923), 133–198; by P. Y. Polubarinova-Kochina, in "K biografii S. V. Kovalevskoy" ("Toward a Biography . . ."), in *Istoriko-matematicheskie issledovaniya*, **7** (1954), 666–712; and by K.-R. Biermann, "Karl Weierstrass," in *Journal für die reine und angewandte Mathematik*, **223** (1966), 191–220, which presents a survey of the known archives and their places of deposition. The Weierstrass letters to Kovalevsky have been published completely in P. Y. Polubarinova-Kochina, *Pisma Karla Weierstrassa K Sof'e Kovalevskoj 1871–1891* (Moscow, 1973).

Propositions for academic elections of Weierstrass are in K.-R. Biermann, "Vorschläge zur Wahl von Mathematikern in die Berliner Akademie," in *Abhandlungen der Deutschen Akademie der Wissenschaften zu Berlin*, Kl. für Mathematik, Physik und Technik (1960), no. 3, 25–34, *passim*. Weierstrass' analysis is discussed in Pierre Duac, "Éléments d'analyse de Karl Weierstrass," in *Archive for History of Exact Sciences*, nos. 1–2, **10** (1973), 41–176.

II. SECONDARY LITERATURE. See Henri Poincaré, "L'oeuvre mathématique de Weierstrass," in *Acta mathematica*, **22** (1899), 1–18; and G. Mittag-Leffler, "Die ersten 40 Jahre des Lebens von Weierstrass," *ibid.*, **39** (1923), 1–57. A number of Weierstrass' students and auditors have published reminiscences of him; see the bibliography to Biermann's memoir (cited above), in *Journal für die reine und angewandte Mathematik*, **223** (1966), 219–220. See also *Festschrift zur Gedächtnisfeier für Karl Weierstrass*, H. Behnke and K. Kopfermann, eds. (Cologne–Opladen, 1966); and especially Heinrich Behnke, "Karl Weierstrass und seine Schule," 13–40; as well as K.-R. Biermann, "Die Berufung von Weierstrass nach Berlin," 41–52. See also the following articles by Biermann: "Dirichlet über Weierstrass," in *Praxis der Mathematik*, **7** (1965), 309–312; "K. Weierstrass und A. v. Humboldt," in *Monatsberichte der Deutschen Akademie der Wissenschaften zu Berlin*, **8** (1966), 33–37; "Karl Weierstrass in seinen wissenschaftlichen Grundsätzen," in *Sudhoffs Archiv*, **50** (1966), 305–309; and the book by Biermann, *Die mathematik und ihre Dozenten an der Berliner Universität 1810–1920* (Berlin, 1973).

KURT-R. BIERMANN

**WEIGEL, CHRISTIAN EHRENFRIED** (*b.* Stralsund, Germany, 24 May 1748; *d.* Greifswald, Germany, 8 August 1831), *chemistry.*

After receiving instruction from his father, Dr. Bernhard Nicolaus Weigel (inventor of Weigel's medicinal drops) and attending a private school in Stralsund, young Weigel entered the University of Greifswald in 1764. He studied medicine and the natural sciences there for five years, then proceeded to the University of Göttingen, where for the next two years he worked closely with the botanist J. A. Murray, the chemist R. A. Vogel, and the technologist J. Beckmann. Weigel also visited the Harz mining district to collect minerals and to observe metallurgical techniques. In 1771 he took his M.D. at Göttingen with a chemical-mineralogical dissertation.

Weigel then returned to Stralsund, where he practiced medicine and continued his chemical research in his father's laboratory. In 1772 he became an adjunct lecturer and supervisor of the botanical garden at the University of Greifswald; and two years later he was appointed to a new chair of chemistry and pharmacy in the medical faculty of the university. Besides holding this post for the rest of his life, he continued to run the botanical garden until 1781, served on the medical board for Pomerania and Rügen from 1780 to 1806, and directed the chemical institute of the university from 1796 until his death. In 1806 he was ennobled by Emperor Francis II.

Weigel did almost all of his important work during the 1770's and 1780's. In his dissertation he argued at length for J. F. Meyer's pinguic acid theory and published the first diagram of a counter-current condenser. Weigel's two-volume *Grundriss der reinen und angewandten Chemie* (1777) was one of the first German chemistry texts to be directed beyond a medical audience to readers of all classes. In it he first dealt with pure chemistry and then with applications of chemistry in natural philosophy, natural history, medicine, and especially in agriculture, mining, and manufacturing. Weigel also did much to keep German chemists abreast of foreign developments with his translations of works by Wallerius (1776–1780); Guyton de Morveau, Maret, and Durande (1777–1778); H. T. Scheffer (1779); G. v. Engeström (1782); and Lavoisier (1783–1785).

*BIBLIOGRAPHY*

The most complete list of Weigel's publications is in Fritz Ferchl, ed., *Chemisch-Pharmazeutisches Bio- und Bibliographikon* (Mittenwald, 1937), 571–572.

On Weigel's life and work, see *Neuer Nekrolog der Deutschen*, **9** (1831), 699–705; O. Anselmino, "Nachrichten von früherer Lehrern der Chemie an der Universität Greifswald," in *Mitteilungen des Naturwissenschaftlichen Vereins für Neu-Vorpommern und Rugen in Greifswald*, **38** (1906), 117–130; G. A. Fester, "Zur Geschichte des Gegenstromkühlers," in *Sudhoffs Archiv für Geschichte der Medizin und der Naturwissenschaften*, **45** (1961), 341–350; J. R. Partington, *A History of Chemistry*, III (London, 1962), 148, 175, 372, 521, 594–595, 609; and Johannes Valentin, "Die Entwicklung der pharmazeutischen Chemie an der Ernst Moritz Arndt-Universität in Greifswald," in *Festschrift zur 500-Jahrfeier der Universität Greifswald*, II (Greifswald, 1956), 472–475.

KARL HUFBAUER

**WEIGEL, VALENTIN** (*b.* Naundorf [near Dresden], Saxony, Germany, 1533; *d.* Zschopau, Saxony, Germany, 10 June 1588), *mysticism, philosophy of nature.*

Weigel occupies an important position in the history of religion and philosophy between Luther and the seventeenth century. He belongs with the mystics who reacted against Lutheran orthodoxy and the rigid institutionalization of the church, advocating instead that all men are created with innate resources that make faith and knowledge independent of the priesthood and even of the spoken or written word. These are merely aids to the awakening of preexisting inward knowledge. Sin being the consequence of contrary will, rebirth and

salvation can occur only when the abandonment of will creates a state of total passivity and submission in the act of union with God. This is the state of *Gelassenheit*, which played an important role in the thought of such early German mystics as Master Eckhart and Johann Tauler, who, with the so-called *Theologia Germanica*, are the chief spiritual fathers of sixteenth-century German mysticism. The early Luther was close to this tradition, which also deeply influenced Thomas Müntzer, Sebastian Franck, and Caspar Schwenckfeld. A generation younger than these figures, Weigel knew and used their work as well as the older sources, in addition to the German mystics including Plotinus, Proclus, Hermes Trismegistus, Dionysius the Areopagite, Johannes Scottus Eriugena, Boethius, and the Neoplatonists of his own century. The special mark of Weigel's thought is the combination of this mystical spiritualism with Paracelsian naturalism, chiefly in his later writings. Weigel founds his theory of knowledge on the doctrine of harmony between the macrocosm and the microcosm; it is by virtue of this harmony that man is capable of knowledge. To know oneself is therefore the beginning of wisdom and faith. Cosmology and anthropology are complementary sources of insight.

The son of poor Catholic parents, Weigel owed his early education to a local patron who secured free schooling for him at the recently established ducal school of St. Afra in Meissen, which Weigel attended from 1549 to 1554. He spent the next ten years at the University of Leipzig, where he gained the B.A. in 1558 and the M.A. the following year. During this time he was among a small number of students who were not only supported by the elector Augustus I (1526–1586), but also given special attention at the university. In addition to theology, Weigel's studies included philosophy, mathematics, natural science, and medicine. He took part in the usual academic disputations and also taught at the university, but in 1564 he transferred to Wittenberg, where he also taught. It is not known why he made the transfer. This long academic career gave Weigel philosophic training and dialectical skill beyond the normal accomplishments of Lutheran pastors. In 1565 he married Katherina Poch, the daughter of a local pastor. In addition to a daughter, they had two sons who grew up to practice medicine. In 1567 the elector appointed him pastor of Zschopau, where he remained until his death, loved and respected by his parishioners for his dedicated work among them.

The years of Weigel's pastorate coincided with a period of growing Lutheran orthodoxy and tightening church discipline. This movement found expression in the Formula of Concord (1577), which enjoined commitment to articles that no spiritual reformer could accept, such as the doctrine of justification and the scriptural principle of the necessity of the outward word. Weigel subscribed to the formula. The ecclesiastical visitors found no grounds to suspect him of unorthodoxy, except on one occasion, in 1572, when he quickly and successfully cleared himself in a written defense that was dedicated to his bishop. In this skillful piece, Weigel relied on both the ideas of the *Theologia Germanica* (first put into print by the young Luther in 1518) and of Luther, thus retaining as much as possible for his own theological position without giving cause for further suspicion.

Underneath this calm official surface, however, Weigel was leading a double life. From 1570 until his last years he wrote a number of works advancing a religious philosophy that constituted a total rejection of the ruling orthodoxy. The large number of still surviving manuscripts indicate that these writings were copied and circulated, perhaps chiefly on the initiative of Weigel's deacon and successor at Zschopau, Benedikt Biedermann, who a dozen years after Weigel's death was disciplined by the church for spreading heretical doctrines. Weigel's writings finally found their way into print between 1609 and 1618, when at least a dozen of his works appeared at Halle and Magdeburg. As a consequence, the authorities took stronger action against Weigelian doctrine, but it was now too late. It seems clear that Boehme during these very years came under the influence of Weigel, whom he resembles in a number of ways, although most clearly in the heavy dependence on Paracelsus. Weigel's thought also had affinity with Rosicrucianism, which during these same years was taking shape in people's imaginations owing to Andreae's mystifications. Weigel's name meant so much that at least a dozen items were falsely published under his name in 1618 alone, a few of them written by other well-known mystics. In consequence Weigel's thought was diffused into a debased form of philosophy, which for the rest of the century was mentioned along with other forms of enthusiasm. Weigel was well known and respected among English Quakers, and like the mystical Protestant tradition in general, his thought was taken up by the Pietists.

It is Weigel's basic doctrine that all men are born with the means of knowing all that pertains to their spiritual welfare. The divine or inward light is infused by God and the Holy Ghost. In conformity with the macrocosm-microcosm doctrine, the light of nature reveals all things pertaining to God's creation, while the light of grace ensures supernatural knowledge. The inward word is the term he commonly uses to refer both to the innate capacity for knowledge and to the innate knowledge itself. The objects of cognition seen by the eye only awaken what is already in the mind; but these objects are necessary just as the kernel of wheat will not grow and bear fruit without being planted in the soil. It is clear that this radical subjectivist doctrine entails a thorough rejection of all outward authority and forms: church, priesthood, sacraments, confession, ceremonies, outward speech or scripture, books, and universities. Even the historical Christ has no meaning; faith and religion do not depend on the revelation of religious events in time and space. With the mystics of his own and the next century, Weigel shared the doctrine that the only true church is invisible as well as the commitment to toleration in all matters. The first three chapters of Genesis constitute an epitome of the scriptural story of creation, fall, and redemption written for this secular life; but in the future world of perfection, there will again be no need of languages, art, and knowledge, just as Adam in his angelic state had no need of them. In that future state, nature as we know it will cease to exist. For the time being, however, we must continue to make the effort to learn by seeking to let the outward world awaken our innate knowledge; the chief obstacle is the false teaching of the pseudotheologians. Weigel's epistemology and cosmology are chiefly set forth in the following works: *Gnothi seauton, nosce teipsum, erkenne dich selbst; Vom Ort der Welt;* and *Der güldene Griff, alle Dinge ohne Irrthum zu erkennen, vielen hochgelehrten unbekannt, und doch allen Menschen nothwendig.*

## BIBLIOGRAPHY

I. ORIGINAL WORKS. The canon of Weigel's writings is the subject of Winfried Zeller's *Die Schriften Valentin Weigels: Eine literarkritische Untersuchung* (Berlin, 1940), which is *Historische Studien*, no. 370. In addition to the printed items attributed to Weigel, Zeller lists no less than 130 MSS, of which more than a dozen are judged genuine; a few of these have been printed only recently. The early printings are very rare, but since 1962 Will-Erich Peuckert and W. Zeller have edited the *Sämtliche Werke*, eventually to contain all the genuine works. The following have appeared: *Vom Ort der Welt*, W.-E. Peuckert, ed. (1962); *Von der Vergebung der Sünden oder vom Schlüssel der Kirchen*, W. Zeller, ed.

(1964); *Zwei nützliche Tractate* and *Kurzer Bericht und Anleitung zur Deutschen Theologie*, W. Zeller, ed. (1966); *Dialogus de Christianismo*, Alfred Ehrentreich, ed. (1967); *Ein Büchlein vom wahren seligmachen Glauben*, W. Zeller, ed. (1969)—this last item is Weigel's defense of 1572.

Two of Weigel's works appeared in English trans. during the 17th century: *Of the Life of Christ* (London, 1648) and *Astrologie Theologized* (London, 1649); the latter is presumably a translation of *Gnothi seauton*, pt. II. John Locke's friend, the Quaker Benjamin Furly, with whom Locke stayed while in exile in Rotterdam, left a translation of "A Brief Instruction of the Way and Manner to Know all Things . . . Written by Valentyn Weigelius, in Hyhdutch and New Englished by a Lover of Truth, Benj. Furly 1664" (see W. Zeller, *Schriften*, p. 77).

II. SECONDARY LITERATURE. Three early works have rich bibliographies and important information about the ways in which Weigel and his thought have been judged. There is a long chapter "Vom Weigelianismo," in Ehregott Daniel Colberg's critique of all forms of enthusiasm, *Das Platonisch-Hermetisches Christenthum, begreiffend die historische Erzehlung vom Ursprung und vielerley Secten der heutigen fanatischen Theologie, unterm Namen der Paracelsisten, Weigeliander, Rosencreutzer, Quäker, Böhemisten, Wiedertäuffer, Bourignisten, Labadisten, und Quietisten* (Frankfurt–Leipzig, 1690), 205–264. A very well-informed and sympathetic treatment will be found in Gottfried Arnold, *Unpartheyische Kirchen- und Ketzer-Historie*, 2 vols. in 4 pts. (Frankfurt, 1699–1700), pt. 2, 615–640. *Zedler's Grosses Universal-Lexicon aller Wissenschaften und Künste*, **54** (1747), has two articles (with full bibliographies) that are critical of Weigel's heretical doctrines: "Weigel," cols. 293–304; and "Weigeliander," cols. 304–326.

For a brief bibliography of the secondary literature, see W. Zeller, *Schriften*, pp. 86–87. There is a useful survey of the primary literature, also indicating the subject and argument of each work, in Ludolf Pertz, "Beiträge zur Geschichte der mystischen und ascetischen Literatur. I. Weigels Leben und Schriften," in *Zeitschrift für die historische Theologie* (1857), pp. 3–94; and "II. Weigels Theologie," *ibid.* (1859), pp. 49–123. There is no recent work that compares in scope to that of these two items: Julius Otto Opel, *Valentin Weigel: Ein Beitrag zur Literatur- und Culturgeschichte im 17. Jahrhundert* (Leipzig, 1864); and August Israel, *Valentin Weigels Leben und Schriften* (Zschopau, 1888). For a penetrating and critical review of Israel, see G. Kawerau, in *Theologische Literaturzeitung*, **13** (1888), cols. 594–598.

The author's Lutheran orientation deepens the interest of Hans Maier, "Der mystische Spiritualismus Valentin Weigels," in *Beiträge zur Förderung christlicher Theologie*, **29**, no. 4 (1926), 389–495. Since several of Weigel's works are not readily available, Heinz Längin, "Grundlinien der Erkenntnislehre Valentin Weigels," in *Archiv für Geschichte der Philosophie*, **41** (1932), 434–478, is useful not merely for its cogent analyses but also owing to its extensive quotations. See also Winfried Zeller, "Meister Eckhart bei Valentin Weigel. Eine Untersuchung zur Frage der Bedeutung Meister Eckharts für die mystische Renaissance des sechzehnten Jahrhunderts," in *Zeitschrift für Kirchengeschichte*, **57** (1938), 309–355; and Alexandre Koyré, "Un mystique protestant: Valentin Weigel," in *Mystiques, spirituels, alchimistes du XVIe siècle allemand* (Paris, 1955), which is in *Cahiers des Annales*, no. 10, pp. 81–116; originally published in 1930 soon after the same author's monograph on Boehme, this essay has all the virtues of Koyré's insight and clarity, but it should be noted that Koyré accepts *Studium universale* in the Weigel canon, contrary to later and, it would seem, well-founded judgment. Fritz Lieb, *Valentin Weigels Kommentar zur Schöpfungsgeschichte und das Schriftum seines Schülers Benedikt Biedermann* (Zurich, 1962), argues that Biedermann is the author of the pseudo-Weigelian works and that they were written while he was Weigel's deacon, that is, concurrently with Weigel's own works. Lieb also argues that Weigel was the author of the Genesis commentary, "Viererley Auslegung über das erste Capittel Mosis, von der Schöpfung aller Dinge" (see W. Zeller, *Schriften*, pp. 66–67); he shows that it was published early in the 18th century, and that it was translated into Russian during the reign of Catherine II owing to the popularity of Weigel and other mystics in masonic circles. For an important aspect of the relationship between Paracelsus and Weigel, see Kurt Goldammer, "Friedensidee und Toleranzgedanke bei Paracelsus und den Spiritualisten. Franck und Weigel," in *Archiv für Reformationsgeschichte*, **47** (1956), 180–211. Ernst Wilhelm Kämmerer, *Das Leib-Seele-Geist-Problem bei Paracelsus und einigen Autoren des 17. Jahrhunderts* (Wiesbaden, 1971), deals with a Paracelsian doctrine that Weigel took over (esp. pp. 70–76). Two useful recent books place Weigel in the larger context of his century: Siegfried Wollgast, *Der Deutsche Pantheismus im 16. Jahrhundert. Sebastian Franck und seine Wirkungen auf die Entwicklung der pantheistischen Philosophie in Deutschland* (Berlin, 1972), esp. pp. 267–286, and Steven E. Ozment, *Mysticism and Dissent. Religious Ideology and Social Protest in the Sixteenth Century* (New Haven, 1973), pp. 203–245. Weigel's role in Quaker thought is treated in Rufus M. Jones, *Spiritual Reformers in the Sixteenth and Seventeenth Centuries* (New York, 1914), chiefly in the chapter devoted to "Valentine Weigel and Nature Mysticism," pp. 133–150.

HANS AARSLEFF

**WEIGERT, CARL** (*b.* Munsterberg, Silesia [now Poland], 19 March 1845; *d.* Frankfurt am Main, Germany, 4 August 1904), *pathology, histology, neurology.*

Weigert was born in the same district in Silesia as his cousin Paul Ehrlich, his junior by nine years. The problem of the selective action of dyes on biological materials (microchemical reactions), which led Ehrlich to develop chemotherapy, led Weigert to make revolutionary advances in histological techniques. These advances made it possible for researchers to gain fundamental insights into the fine structure of the central nervous system. Weigert is thus closely associated with brain and spinal cord research and with neurology and psychiatry.

After attending the Gymnasium in Breslau, Weigert studied medicine at the University of Breslau. His teachers included Ferdinand Cohn and Rudolf Heidenhain. Weigert continued his studies in Berlin, where he worked as Virchow's amanuensis. In 1866 he received his medical degree from the University of Berlin for a dissertation, "De nervorum laesionibus telorum ictu effectis." Two years later Weigert became an assistant of Waldeyer-Hartz, professor of pathology at Breslau, who undoubtedly strengthened Weigert's interest in morphology. In 1871 Weigert became clinical assistant to Hermann Lebert, and in 1874 assistant to Julius Cohnheim, under whom he qualified for teaching pathology in 1875. Three years later he followed Cohnheim to the University of Leipzig, where in 1879 he was named extraordinary professor of pathology. For a long time Weigert lectured in place of Cohnheim, who had fallen ill. Cohnheim died in 1884, and when the faculty did not nominate him even as a possible successor, Weigert resigned from his post the following year. He decided to take up medical practice, but he was dissuaded by an offer to become director of the pathological-anatomical institute of the Senckenberg Foundation in Frankfurt. He held this post until his death at age fifty-nine from a coronary embolism. Curiously, he himself had made a major contribution to knowledge of this disease. Weigert never married.

Weigert's most notable personal characteristic was his excessive modesty. He was plagued by doubts about the value of his work and was never satisfied with what he had accomplished. Yet, he was indisputably successful in teaching advanced science students, both in the classroom and in the laboratory. His friend Ludwig Edinger wrote:

> What attracted the many students from all over the world and what persuaded them to persevere in the small, poorly equipped rooms of the Frankfurt institute, which were in no way comparable to the proud university institutes, was the intimate relationship that existed between teacher and students. The door between his work room and the laboratory always stood open. . . . A basic characteristic of his manner of working was never to stick too closely to details. Rather, he always sought to grasp pathological processes as biological processes. . . . Weigert possessed an excellent philosophical training, and philosophical thinking governed his entire way of working. He disciplined himself to renounce any attempt to penetrate what could not be known and was made uneasy by metaphysical speculation. . . . He always viewed the many facts he discovered as mere building stones. In his leisure he amused himself with mathematics.

According to the pathologist O. Lubarsch, Weigert was

> . . . inwardly happy, a truly distinguished and good man, who viewed the weaknesses of those around him with the deep sense of humor of the philosopher and who reacted only mildly against those who wished to harm him. Nothing human was foreign to him, and after a day of hard work he sought relaxation in literature and society, amusing everyone with his warm-hearted humor and his witty conversation. His contact with Scandinavian students prompted him to learn their languages.

With his first major work on the eruption of smallpox on the skin (1874), Weigert opened a new area of research in pathological anatomy—the demonstration of the primary damage of cells and tissues by external influences. First he had to develop the histological techniques necessary to detect this process. With the aid of the improved microtome Weigert dissected pathological tissue into complete serial sections and devised a technique that enabled him to differentiate tissues sharply under the microscope. By 1871 he was able, by staining, to demonstrate the presence of bacteria in tissue sections. This advance was of the greatest importance for the subsequent work of Robert Koch. According to Ehrlich, Weigert's monograph of 1874–1875 already contained "the points of view that guided his work for the rest of his life." In this monograph he began to develop the theory of the "coagulation necrosis" (the term is due to Cohnheim) and to illustrate the reparative (bioplastic) processes of the supporting tissue. Before Roux he had developed also the concept that the cells of the organism are in equilibrium among themselves. Cells cannot disappear without the neighboring cells attempting to take over their place. If elements of the parenchyma disappear, then they are generally replaced by elements of the connective tissue group. Such substitute growth is at first excessive, but gradually a new equilibrium is established. Weigert later applied his theory of the secondary, reparative processes to the substitute growth of neuroglia following atrophy of the nervous parenchyma.

Weigert's experiments on the staining of fibrin (1887) were also important for general pathology, since they exercised a lasting influence on the study of inflammation and on the theory of thrombosis. Weigert's method for staining elastic fibers was also important (although published in 1898, the preliminary work on it began in 1884). In addition, Weigert conducted studies on the genesis of acute general miliarial tuberculosis (affecting the veins and thoracic duct). The studies are remarkable for pointing out its spread from a tubercular source, before the agent of the disease was even known.

Weigert's most important work was in the field of neurohistology. After long preliminary investigation, he presented in 1884 the definitive method of staining medullary sheaths (myelin sheaths). This method enabled scientists to establish a reliable anatomy of the central nervous system. The number of works in this field multiplied within a few years of Weigert's announcement. The research on comparative anatomy of the brain owes its existence to myelin staining; previously, the path of scarcely a single pathway in a lower vertebrate brain had really been established with certainty. Starting about 1886 the new results, which eliminated much speculation, found their way into the textbooks. Recalling this pioneering time, Edinger wrote (1906):

In the first years [of research] fetal brains, which contain only a few medullary sheaths and therefore provide particularly clear views, were a rich source of important facts. Myelin staining finally allowed us, in the middle of the 1880's, to determine, for example, how the afferent nerves reach the brain. Their termination in the nuclei of the dorsal columns was known. From there, as has now been established, a crossed pathway leads to the thalamus. At that time, [however,] people proposed all kinds of uncertain paths leading from those nuclei through the olive into the cerebellum. One of the first works, begun in Weigert's presence, was Lissauer's study of the dorsal roots and the spinal cord, which is still absolutely valid. He and Weigert discovered in the first months that in the disease tabes dorsalis the dorsal (Clarke) columns degenerate.

Weigert sought to find evidence of the selective behavior of the supporting tissue of the nervous system in order to establish the system's pathological histology. This effort led to his successful demonstration in 1887 of the existence of the neuroglia. (His findings were not published until 1890.) He found, again, that the atrophy of the parenchyma is the primary process and results in the growth of the neuroglia as a secondary process. In this area, too, Weigert's work has influenced neurohistological research up to the present, although his notion of the existence of neuroglia fibers "emancipated" from the cell and differentiable by staining did not remain unchallenged.

*BIBLIOGRAPHY*

I. ORIGINAL WORKS. A chronological list of Weigert's works is in R. Rieder (see below). See also J. Springer, ed., *Gesammelte Abhandlungen von Carl Weigert*, II (Berlin, 1906), which has biographical contributions by R. Rieder, K. Edinger, and P. Ehrlich.

Weigert's works include "Über Bacterien in der Pockenhaut," in *Zentralblatt für die medizinischen Wissenschaften*, 8 (1871), 609–611; *Anatomische Beiträge zur Lehre von den Pocken*, written with Max Cohn, 2 vols.: I. *Die Pockeneffloreszenz der äusseren Haut* (Breslau, 1874), II. *Über pockenähnliche Gebilde in parenchymatösen Organen und deren Beziehung zu Bakterienkolonien* (Breslau, 1875); "Bismarckbraun als Färbemittel," in *Archiv für mikroskopische Anatomie und Entwicklungsmechanik*, 15 (1878), 258–260; *Die Brightsche Nierenerkrankung vom pathologisch-anatomischen Standpunkte*, which is Sammlung klinischer Vorträge No. 162/63 (Leipzig, 1879); "Über Entzündung (Inflammatio, Phlogosis)," in *Eulenburgs Real-Encyclopädie der gesamten Heilkunde* (2nd ed., rev. and enl.), VI (1886), 325–358 (Weigert's contribution was replaced by a corresponding article by Ernst Ziegler in the 3rd ed. [1895]); "Zur Technik der mikroskopischen Bakterienuntersuchungen," in *Virchows Archiv für pathologische Anatomie und Physiologie und für klinische Medizin*, 84 (1881), 275–315; "Über eine neue Untersuchungsmethode des Centralnervensystems," in *Zentralblatt für die medizinischen Wissenschaften*, 20 (1882), 753–757, 772–774; "Thrombose," in *Eulenburgs Real-Encyclopädie der gesamten Heilkunde*, 19 (1889), 638–648, also replaced by Ziegler in 1900; "Über Schnittserien von Celloidinpräparaten des Centralnervensystems," in *Zentralblatt wissenschaftliche Mikroskopie*, 2 (1885), 490–495; "Über eine neue Methode zur Färbung von Fibrin und von Microorganismen," in *Fortschritte der Medizin*, 5 (1887), 228–232; "Zur pathologischen Histologie des Neurogliafasergerüstes," in *Zentralblatt für allgemeine Pathologie und pathologische Anatomie*, 1 (1890), 729–737; "Beiträge zur Kenntnis der normalen menschlichen Neuroglia," in *Abhandlungen der Senckenbergischen Naturforschenden Gesellschaft*, 19 (1895), fasc. 11;

"Die histologische Technik des Centralnervensystems II.2. Die Markscheidenfärbung," in *Ergebnisse der Anatomie und Entwicklungsgeschichte*, **6** (1897), 1–25; "Über eine Methode zur Färbung elastischer Fasern," in *Zentralblatt für allgemeine Pathologie und pathologische Anatomie*, **9** (1898), 289–292; and "Fibrinfärbung," "Markscheiden der Nervenfasern," "Neurogliafärbung," in Paul Ehrlich, Rudolf Krause, Max Mosse, Heinrich Rosin, Carl Weigert, eds., *Enzyklopädie der mikroskopischen Technik*, 2nd ed. (Berlin–Vienna, 1910), I, 457–460; II, 231–238; 298–311.

II. SECONDARY LITERATURE. On Weigert and his work, see L. Edinger, "Carl Weigerts Verdienste um die Neurologie," in R. Rieder (see below), pp. 133–137: P. Ehrlich, "Weigerts Verdienste um die histologische Wissenschaft," *ibid.*, pp. 138–141; G. Herxheimer, "Carl Weigert," in *Zentralblatt für allgemeine Pathologie und pathologische Anatomie*, **15** (1904), 657–662; W. Krücke, "Carl Weigert (1845–1904)," in W. Scholtz, *50 Jahre Neuropathologie in Deutschland* (Stuttgart, 1961), 5–19; W. Krücke and H. Spatz, "Aus den Erinnerungen von Ludwig Edinger," in Ludwig-Edinger-Gedenkschrift (*Schrifter der Wissenschaftlichen Gesellschaft an der Johann Wolfgang Goethe-Universität Frankfurt am Main*, 1st ser. (Wiesbaden, 1959), 19–23; L. Lichtheim, "Karl Weigert," in *Deutsche Zeitschrift für Nervenheilkunde*, **27** (1904), 340–350.

See also O. Lubarsch, "Karl Weigert," in *Deutsche medizinische Wochenschrift*, **30** (1904), 1318–1319; H. Morrison, "Carl Weigert," in *Annals of Medical History*, **6** (1924), 163–177; R. Rieder, *Carl Weigert und seine Bedeutung für die medizinische Wissenschaft unserer Zeit, eine biographische Skizze* (Berlin, 1906); A. Strümpell, "Zur Erinnerung an Carl Weigert," in *Deutsche medizinische Wochenschrift*, **31** (1905), 230–232; and I. H. Talbott, "Carl Weigert (1845–1904)," in *A Biographical History of Medicine* (New York, 1970), 837–840.

G. RUDOLPH

**WEINBERG, WILHELM** (*b*. Stuttgart, Germany, 25 December 1862; *d*. Tübingen, Germany, 27 November 1937), *human genetics, medical statistics.*

Weinberg was the son of Julius Weinberg, a Stuttgart merchant, and Maria Magdalena Humbert. Weinberg's father was Jewish, and his mother was Protestant; both of his parents died early. Weinberg belonged to the Protestant faith as did his wife, Bertha Wachenbrönner, whom he married in 1896. They had four sons and one daughter. Weinberg studied medicine at the universities of Tübingen and Munich and obtained his M.D. in 1886. After clinical experience in Berlin, Vienna, and Frankfurt, he established himself in Stuttgart

as a general practitioner and obstetrician (1889). For forty-two years he had a large private practice and also acted in public capacities as physician to the poor and to the socially insured. He attended more than 3,500 births, including more than 120 twin births.

Weinberg's discoveries center around four areas: multiple births, population genetics, and ascertainment and medical statistics. His first important paper was the eighty-five-page "Beiträge zur Physiologie und Pathologie der Mehrlingsgeburten beim Menschen" (1901). In the article he established the difference method, which enabled him to derive the proportion of monozygotic and dizygotic twin births from statistical data on the sex combinations of otherwise undifferentiated twin births. He proceeded to discover differences between mono- and dizygotic twins in a variety of traits, including an inheritance of a twinning tendency for dizygotic but not for monozygotic twins.

When Weinberg became aware of Mendelism he asked himself "how different laws of inheritance would influence the composition of the relatives of given individuals." Answers were provided in four extraordinary papers: "Über den Nachweis der Vererbung beim Menschen" (1908), "Über Vererbungsgesetze beim Menschen I and II" (1908–1909), and "Weitere Beiträge zur Theorie der Vererbung" (1910). Weinberg discovered the equilibrium law of monohybrid populations and the varied processes of attainment of equilibria in polyhybrid populations. He had become a founder of population genetics. The equilibrium law was also discovered slightly later by G. H. Hardy. It is now known as the Hardy-Weinberg law. In his studies of population genetics Weinberg's derivations of the correlations between relatives expected under Mendelian heredity took into account both genetic and environmental factors. Indeed, he was the first to partition the total variance of phenotypes into genetic and environmental portions (1909, 1910).

Weinberg recognized early that different types of ascertainment may bias greatly the results of statistical inquiries. In "Über Methode und Fehlerquellen der Untersuchung auf Mendelsche Zahlen beim Menschen" (1912) he furnished methods of correction for various types of ascertainment. One such device is the sib method, in which correct proportions for traits are obtained by finding the ratio of affected to nonaffected traits among the sibs of the affected. Other methods also described by Weinberg are the proband and a priori methods.

Weinberg made detailed studies of mortality statistics and the statistics and genetics of specific diseases. He was the first to construct morbidity tables modeled after the long-known mortality tables.

Weinberg had no personal collaborators or students, although a few contemporary investigators were strongly influenced by him. Only in Weinberg's later years did a new generation again begin to explore the areas in which he had achieved so much.

## BIBLIOGRAPHY

I. ORIGINAL WORKS. A bibliography of Weinberg's numerous publications, most of which are journal articles, has been compiled by Eva R. Sherwood; it is on deposit in the biology library of the University of California at Berkeley and has been reprinted in Jh. Ver. Naturkde. Württemberg 118/119 (1964), 61–67.

II. SECONDARY LITERATURE. An obituary (probably written by E. Rüdin) is in *Archiv fur Rassen- und Gesellschaftsbiologie einschliessend Rassen- und Gesellschaftshygiene*, **31** (1937), 54.

See also K. Freudenberg, "Wilhelm Weinberg zum 70. Geburtstage," in *Klinische Wochenschrift*, **12** (1933), 46–47; E. Hübler, "Zum 100. Geburtstag von Wilhelm Weinberg," Jh. Ver. vaterl. Naturkde. Württemberg 118/119 Jahrgang (1964), 57–67; F. J. Kallmann, "Wilhelm Weinberg, M.D.," in *Journal of Nervous and Mental Diseases*, **87** (1938), 263–264; H. Luxenburger, "Wilhelm Weinberg," in *Allgemeine Zeitschrift für Psychiatrie*, **107–109** (1938), 378–381; Curt Stern, "Wilhelm Weinberg, 1862–1937," in *Genetics*, **47** (1962), 1–5; and "Wilhelm Weinberg. Zur hundertjährigen Wiederkehr seines Geburtsjahres," in *Zeitschrift menschliche Vererbungs und Konstitutionslehre*, **36** (1962), 374–382.

CURT STERN

**WEINGARTEN, JULIUS** (*b*. Berlin, Germany, 2 March 1836; *d*. Freiburg im Breisgau, Germany, 16 June 1910), *mathematics*.

The son of a weaver who had emigrated from Poland, Weingarten graduated from the Berlin municipal trade school in 1852 and then studied mathematics and physics at the University of Berlin and chemistry at the Berlin Gewerbeinstitut. Between 1858 and 1864 he was an assistant teacher at various schools in Berlin. After receiving the Ph.D. from the University of Halle in 1864, Weingarten taught at the Bauakademie in Berlin, where he was promoted to the rank of professor in 1871. His next position was at the newly founded Technische Hochschule in Berlin. In 1902, for reasons of health, he moved to Freiburg im Breisgau, where he taught as honorary professor until 1908.

Weingarten was inspired by Dirichlet's lectures to study potential theory and later in his career he occasionally published papers on theoretical physics. It was, however, in pure mathematics, particularly in differential geometry, that he made his greatest contribution. Lack of money obliged Weingarten to accept unsatisfactory teaching positions for many years. It was not until he came to Freiburg that, at an advanced age, he found a suitable academic post.

In 1857 the University of Berlin awarded Weingarten a prize for a work on the lines of curvature of a surface, and in 1864 he received the doctorate for the same work. In the meantime he had written other major papers on the theory of surfaces (1861, 1863). This was the most important subject in differential geometry in the nineteenth century, and one of its main problems was that of stating all the surfaces isometric to a given surface. The only class of such surfaces known before Weingarten consisted of the developable surfaces isometric to the plane. These included the cones.

Weingarten was the first to go beyond this stage. For example, he gave the class of surfaces isometric to a given surface of revolution. He had the important insight of introducing those surfaces for which there exists a definite functional relationship between their principal curvatures (1863). These are now called W-surfaces in his honor. Weingarten showed that the one nappe of the central surface of a W-surface is isometric to a surface of revolution and, conversely, that all surfaces isometric to surfaces of revolution can also be obtained in this manner. The W-surfaces are best conceived by considering their spherical image and, operating from this point of view, Weingarten also described various classes of surfaces that are isomorphic to each other. Later he cited classes of this kind in which there are no surfaces of revolution (1884).

In 1886 and 1887 Weingarten studied the infinitesimal deformation of surfaces. Jean-Gaston Darboux, the leading differential geometer of the nineteenth century and author of the four-volume *Leçons sur la théorie générale des surfaces . . .*, stated that Weingarten's achievements were worthy of Gauss. Darboux's work inspired Weingarten to undertake further research, which appeared in a long paper that was awarded a prize by the Paris Academy of Sciences in 1894 and was published in *Acta mathematica* in 1897. In this paper Weingarten reduced the problem of determining all the surfaces isometric to a given surface $F$ to that of determining all solutions of a certain partial differential equation of the Monge-Ampère type.

### BIBLIOGRAPHY

Weingarten's writings include "Über die Oberflächen, für welche einer der beiden Hauptkrümmungsmesser eine Funktion des anderen ist," in *Journal für die reine und angewandte Mathematik*, **62** (1863), 160–173; "Über die Theorie der aufeinander abwickelbaren Oberflächen," in *Festschrift der Königlichen Technischen Hochschule zu Berlin* (Berlin, 1884), 1–43; "Über die Deformation einer biegsamen unausdehnbaren Fläche," in *Journal für die reine und angewandte Mathematik,* **100** (1887), 296–310; "Sur la déformation des surfaces," in *Acta mathematica*, **20** (1897), 159–200; and "Mémoire sur la déformation des surfaces," in *Mémoires présentés par divers savants*, 2nd ser., **32** (1902), 1–46.

An obituary is Stanislaus Jolles, "Julius Weingarten," in *Sitzungsberichte der Berliner mathematischen Gesellschaft*, **10** (1911), 8–11.

WERNER BURAU

**WEISBACH, JULIUS LUDWIG** (*b.* Mittelschmiedeberg, near Annaberg, Germany, 10 August 1806; *d.* Freiberg, Germany, 24 February 1871), *hydraulics.*

The eighth of nine children born to Christian Gottlieb Weisbach, a mine foreman, and Christina Rebekka Stephan, Weisbach received his early education at the lyceum in Annaberg and the Bergschule in Freiberg. In 1822 borrowed funds enabled him to enter the Bergakademie, where Mohs advised him to go on to Göttingen. After two years at the latter university, he followed Mohs in 1829 to the Technical University and University of Vienna, where he studied mathematics, physics, and mechanics. Weisbach spent six months of the following year traveling on foot through Hungary, the Tirol, Bavaria, and Bohemia. From 1831 to 1835 he gradually assumed responsibility for all instruction in mathematics at the Freiberg Gymnasium and, from 1832, that at the Bergakademie as well, despite a low salary and little recognition. In 1832 he married Marie Winkler; their son, Albin, later became professor of mineralogy at the Bergakademie.

The first of Weisbach's numerous publications, *Bergmaschinenmechanik*, appeared in 1835, and the following year he was promoted to full professor of mathematics, mine machinery, and surveying. A trip to the Paris Industrial Exposition in 1839 increased Weisbach's interest in hydraulics and led to his first papers in this field. At the same time he contributed greatly to the development of mine surveying methods, introducing the theodolite in place of compass and protractor. Apparently an indefatigable worker, he assumed responsibility for courses in descriptive geometry, crystallography, and optics, as well as general mechanics.

In 1854 Weisbach was offered a position at the Zurich Polytechnikum (to open in 1855); he chose to remain at Freiberg and the following year assumed the further task of teaching machine design. Also in 1855 he attended the Paris World Exposition, receiving and correcting proof for a new edition of his *Mechanik* en route. During his professional career Weisbach published fourteen books and fifty-nine papers on mathematics, mechanics, and surveying, but primarily on hydraulics. An able experimenter, he presented most of his results in *Experimental-Hydraulik* (Freiberg, 1855); they are also summarized in the hydraulics section of his *Lehrbuch der Ingenieur- und Maschinenmechanik* (Brunswick). The two- (and eventually three- ) volume work went through five editions between 1845 and 1901 and was translated into English and other languages. Some of his hydraulic data and formulas are still in use.

From 1850 Weisbach received a series of professional honors, including an honorary doctorate from the University of Leipzig in 1859 and the first honorary membership granted by the Verein Deutscher Ingenieure in 1860. He was a corresponding member of the St. Petersburg Academy of Sciences, the Royal Swedish Academy of Sciences, and the Accademia dei Lincei.

### BIBLIOGRAPHY

See H. Undeutsch, *Zum Gedächtnis an Oberbergrat Professor Dr. h. c. Julius Ludwig Weisbach anlässlich seiner hundertjährigen Geburtstagsfeier* (Freiberg, 1906); *Julius Weisbach, Gedenkschrift zu seinem 150. Geburtstag*, Freiberger Forschungsheft Kultur und Technik, 16 (Berlin, 1956), with a complete list of published books and papers; and H. Rouse and S. Ince, *History of Hydraulics* (New York, 1963).

HUNTER ROUSE

**WEISMANN, AUGUST FRIEDRICH LEOPOLD** (*b.* Frankfurt am Main, Germany, 17 January 1834; *d.* Freiburg im Breisgau, Germany, 5 November 1914), *zoology.*

Weismann's most influential contribution to biological thought was his theory of the continuity of the germ plasm, an explanation of heredity and development. He maintained that the germ plasm, the substance of heredity, was transmitted from generation to generation, distinguishing it from the somatoplasm; he also was foremost in his day in denying that acquired characters were inherited. Keeping abreast of current researches on the cell and the growing understanding of the role of the nucleus and the chromosomes in inheritance, Weismann modified and developed the theory of germinal continuity. Cytology repeatedly confirmed phenomena the existence of which he had presumed from theoretical considerations. He was a strong defender of Darwin's theory of evolution and a leader among Neo-Darwinists arguing for the sufficiency of natural selection.

Weismann was the son of Johann Konrad August Weismann, a classics professor at the Gymnasium in Frankfurt, and Elise Eleanore Lübbren, a talented musician and painter, who understood her son's love of nature. At an early age Weismann gathered butterflies and beetles, bred caterpillars, and assembled an impressive herbarium of the plants in the vicinity of Frankfurt; his pleasure in his butterfly collections and in music was lifelong. He attended the Gymnasium at Frankfurt, and then—despite his preference for physics, chemistry, and botany, and his hopes perhaps to become a chemist—he began the study of medicine at the University of Göttingen; Friedrich Wöhler, a family friend, advised that Weismann take up medicine first, and his father thought he ought to have a practical means of earning a living. Among his professors at Göttingen were Wöhler, Siebold, Lotze, and Henle, who was an especially stimulating teacher to Weismann and one who was wary of the speculation that characterized *Naturphilosophie*. In 1856 Weismann received his medical degree with a dissertation on the formation of hippuric acid in the organism. When he looked back at his education, he felt that detailed research had been emphasized, with little attempt to interrelate the facts and subject matter of the various disciplines, or to deal with broader problems. He was therefore particularly sensitive to the impact of Darwin's *Origin of Species*, which he first read at one sitting in 1861. Thereafter he was a proponent of Darwin's theory of evolution by means of natural selection, and like Fritz Müller and Ernst Haeckel, through his addresses and writings, as well as his lectures to his classes, he was able to draw the theory of descent to the attention of the public.

After graduation Weismann continued his researches, first while he served as an assistant in a clinical hospital in Rostock, then as private assistant to Schulze. A paper on hippuric acid won him a prize at Rostock, as did a chemical investigation of the salt content of the water of the Baltic Sea. He visited Vienna, and late in 1858 he took his examinations and entered the practice of medicine in his native Frankfurt. Medicine did not take up all of Weismann's time, for he now turned to histological investigations stemming from his association with Henle at Göttingen and studied the minute structure of the muscle fibers of the heart. During the summer of 1859 he was a field doctor in Italy but soon returned to zoology, visiting the Jardin des Plantes in Paris, and hearing Geoffroy Saint-Hilaire lecture. Early in 1861 he spent two months at the University of Giessen under Leuckart, who, even during this brief period, exerted a strong influence upon Weismann. It was Leuckart who interested the young physician in developmental studies of insects, the Diptera in particular.

Weismann again practiced medicine for a short while in Frankfurt. Then he served from 1861 to 1863 as the private physician of the Archduke Stephan of Austria at Schaumburg Castle, and meanwhile studied insect development and metamorphosis and pursued researches in his spare time. Then Weismann gave his full attention to zoology. Strongly attracted to the beauty of Freiburg, he habilitated at its university in 1863 and taught comparative anatomy and zoology as a *Privatdozent*. Weismann was appointed extraordinary professor in 1866 and full professor in 1874. The first to hold the chair in zoology, he spent the rest of his career at the University of Freiburg. In 1864 his eyesight became seriously affected, but he continued his work. From 1862 to 1866 six memoirs on insects and another memoir on heart muscle appeared, even when he himself could not use the microscope. Weismann was helped immeasurably by his wife, Marie Dorothea Gruber of Genoa, whom he had met during his 1859 stay in Italy. She read to him and aided in countless ways over the years. They had six children and the family shared many interests; music was a part of their life, and their son became a musician and composer.

It was ten years before Weismann could again use his eyes to make his own observations with the microscope, although a sojourn in Italy from 1869 to 1871, during which his family accompanied him, proved beneficial to his eyesight. Throughout this period and afterward, he was well informed, however, and his lectures continued, although perhaps he was forced more to theorize and to delegate certain researches to others. From insects and their embryology he turned to the small crustaceans, daphnids and ostracods; and with the improvement of his eyesight a series of publications appeared. He then took up the examination of the Hydrozoa and followed the origin of the sexual cells through generations of Hydromedusae. The culmination of this work was *Die Entstehung der Sexualzellen bei den Hydromedusen* (Jena, 1883), and his conclusions, as he traced the fate of the primitive germ cells and those after them, were strong evidence to Weismann that there was a continuity of the germ plasm. When in 1884 his eyesight was again severely limited, his students and other assistants shared his work, his wife helped him, and the research continued under his guidance. Weismann approached his theoretical determinations from an evolutionary standpoint, but he correlated his theories with cytological investigations, and was always alert to the interpretations and arguments of his colleagues. He was not rigid, but, heeding the growing knowledge of the cell, was willing to develop and change his ideas.

In the intervening years Weismann had given the Darwinian theory of evolution his full support, and he called his inaugural lecture, in "justification" of Darwin's ideas, *Über die Berechtigung der Darwin'schen Theorie* (Leipzig, 1868), a "kind of confession of faith." When the trouble with his eyesight restricted his work, Weismann gave Darwin's theory more of his attention, and in his *Studien zur Descendenztheorie* (Leipzig, 1875–1876)—with a preface by Darwin himself in the English translation (London, 1882)—Weismann treated the seasonal dimorphism of butterflies and questions of evolution and heredity. Although he remained one of the foremost defenders of the Darwinian theory of evolution through natural selection, Weismann—a strict selectionist, more so indeed than Darwin—proceeded to construct his own theory of heredity rather than accept Darwin's hypothesis of pangenesis.

Weismann had come to an early conclusion that the "direction of development," the same as that of the parent, was transferred by means of the protoplasm of the sperm and of the egg cell (1868). Studying the Diptera, he found that the sexual glands had originally been derived from pole cells that were formed by segmentation of the egg. But most crucial to him was the evidence of the Hydromedusae for a continuity of the germ plasm.

Through evolutionary considerations and in probing the question as to whether acquired characters could be inherited, Weismann came to develop his theory of the germ plasm. He decided that acquired characters could not be inherited, for to become inheritable, changes would have to affect the germ plasm itself. Weismann was not the first to conceive of a continuity of the substance of heredity. Galton had outlined it (1872); and Gustav Jäger had actually written of a "continuity of the germ-protoplasm" in 1875, although this was at the time unknown to Weismann. Moritz Nussbaum and August A. Rauber later claimed to have originated the theory; still, it is Weismann with whom the theory of the continuity of the germ plasm is associated, for he first developed it into a coherent explanation of inheritance and brought it into agreement with the new understanding of the cell. While the phenomena of the cell, and specifically of the chromosomes, were being followed in the laboratory, he modified his theory, and in later years it was a presupposition of his views on the sources of variation in evolution.

In 1881 Weismann gave a lecture ("The Duration of Life") before the Deutsche Naturforscher Gesammlung. In the lecture he contrasted the "immortality" of one-celled organisms, which reproduce by division to form two organisms of the same age—this potential immortality was, of course, abrogated by accidents and other vicissitudes—with the division of labor that natural selection had brought about in the more complex forms of life. In the latter forms there was an early separation of the elements that were to form the "immortal" reproductive cells from the elements that were to form the body cells that perished in each succeeding generation. In "On Heredity" (1883) Weismann still conceived of the germ cells as containing configurations of molecules that led to the reproductive cells, as well as other configurations for the somatic cells. The germ cells contained the *Anlagen*—the concept of *Anlagen* was current then, and to Weismann, these were hereditary tendencies or predispositions for certain characters to develop. The *Anlagen* were not affected by the outer conditions that affected the organism, but they were subject to natural selection. Weismann was still dealing with heredity in terms of the entire cell.

In the following years Weismann's concept of the germ plasm changed, and he developed his theory further. He borrowed the term "idioplasm" from the botanist Naegeli, who in 1884 described a continuity of the idioplasm, the protoplasm concerned with inheritance (as distinguished from the rest of the protoplasm) and thereby accounted also for variation. The idioplasm that Naegeli described had a structure of parallel rows of "micelles," which sometimes branched, and formed a network that coursed through the body; cell structure bore little importance in his theory. Since he did not subscribe to the structure Naegeli claimed for the idioplasm, Weismann continued to develop his own concept, but kept in mind the cytological researches then under way.

Following the independent observations (1873) of cell division—and Schneider's illustrations of the stages of division—the previous decade had brought many new discoveries dealing with the cell in division. In 1875 Oscar Hertwig had seen the apparent fusion of the nuclei during fertilization; and in 1879 Walther Flemming had clearly shown that the threads seen in the nucleus split longitudinally, and had pointed to the possible significance of this segmentation. Wilhelm Roux's conclusions influenced Weismann especially; Roux remarked how complicated the process of mitosis was: It seemed to be the means of accomplishing more than a division of the quantity of the substance of the nucleus between the two resulting daughter cells; the mechanism could divide the qualities equally between the new cells that were formed in division. Roux went on to propose that after the first equal segmentation there might possibly be unequal divisions in which the quantity might be the same in each cell, but the distribution of the qualities unequal.

In 1884 several scientists including Weismann independently came to attribute the main role in heredity to the nucleus (as Haeckel had proposed for theoretical reasons in 1866). After studying plant cells and following the reproduction of angiosperms, Strasburger arrived at this conclusion. Shortly thereafter Hertwig published a paper on his researches (Weismann had reached similar views before he read it). Koelliker decided also that the nucleus was involved in inheritance, although he later criticized other tenets of Weismann's theory.

In the essay "The Continuity of the Germ-Plasm" (1885) Weismann reflected upon his new views, for he now located the germ plasm more precisely within the nucleus, and he took up other questions as well. He still had some reservations as to whether the idioplasm was definitely to be identified with the portions of the nuclear filaments that took up chromatin stain, although he had decided that the nucleus indeed contained the idio-

plasm of Naegeli. Weismann made his stand on the germ plasm clear: Germ cells did not necessarily lead directly to other germ cells, for germ plasm might be transmitted through a series of cells—its particles remaining discrete—before reproductive cells were again formed.

Weismann was already attempting to find the significance of the process of meiosis that his colleague Edouard Van Beneden had been investigating. He was dissatisfied with the interpretations of Van Beneden, Minot, and Balfour of the apparent casting-out from the egg of some of the hereditary material, for he did not agree that the egg cell was hermaphroditic, shedding the male element preparatory to fertilization. Weismann struggled to solve the problem. At first he maintained that in the maturation of the egg the formation of the polar bodies separated the germ plasm from a "histogenic" plasm in the nucleus, and that this resulted in a necessary preponderance of germ plasm in the reproductive cell. But by 1887 he had decided instead that this was a means of preventing the indefinite increase of ancestral plasms, which each fertilization would otherwise double.

Weismann believed that sexual reproduction led to variation, through the ever-new combinations of *Anlagen*. In the essay "On the Number of Polar Bodies" (1887) he reported on the researches he had undertaken, aided by his pupil and collaborator C. Ishikawa (who later became professor of zoology at Tokyo), when his sight was again severely affected. Although Weismann had for some time assumed that the hereditary qualities were linearly arranged along the "nuclear loops," as he described the chromosomes, and that differentiation occurred by means of qualitative divisions, such as Roux had proposed, he inferred—on theoretical grounds—that there must be a reduction division. He described the mounting complexity of the ancestral plasms, and it was his theory that there were two kinds of division: an equal division or *Aequations-theilung*, whereby the nuclear threads in splitting longitudinally divided the germ plasms equally; and a "reduction division," *Reduktions-theilung*, with half of the loops simply distributed to each of the daughter nuclei. Not only did Weismann theorize that reduction division takes place, but he suggested also that a similar process to that in the maturation of the ovum would occur during spermatogenesis; this was confirmed by cytological investigation.

Meanwhile, Weismann's interest in the problem of the possibility of the inheritance of acquired characters persisted, and he experimented to determine whether environmentally produced changes were inherited. He followed the results of mutilations, cutting off the tails of hundreds of mice, but without any apparent hereditary effects.

Weismann was aware of the attention the thread-like structures in the nucleus—first called chromosomes in 1888 by Waldeyer—were receiving. They were frequently described as rods or loops and seemed to be present in characteristic numbers in certain organisms and tissues. Rabl remarked that the chromosomes must persist throughout the various changes during cell division (1885), and in 1887 he advanced the concept of chromosomal individuality, which was basic to chromosome theory, and which Boveri brought to clearer development and a more definitive statement in the course of his cytological studies. In 1889 de Vries outlined his theory of "intracellular pangenesis" and his concept of the "pangen," an invisibly small vital unit concerned in heredity; this affected Weismann's thinking on the germ plasm, although they disagreed on important points (such as the necessity of a reduction division).

Comparable to de Vries's pangenes were Weismann's "biophors," as he developed his theory of the germ plasm. The biophors, however, did not mix freely as did the hereditary factors that de Vries described. Weismann then postulated the existence of larger, although still submicroscopic units, the "determinants." Weismann proceeded to describe the progression of units that were the "bearers of heredity." In accordance with the appearance of the visible chromosome, there were next the "ids," made up of determinants (the ancestral plasms of his germ plasm theory and linked together in definite groupings). The ids were the disks or microsomes that had been observed beneath the microscope and were linearly arranged on the chromosomes, in Weismann's terms, the "idants." Weismann thought that each id carried the entirety of the ancestral plasms that the individual inherited. Weismann gave his theory with his views of the significance of the laboratory investigations of the cell and of contemporary hypotheses, in *Das Keimplasma. Eine Theorie der Vererbung* (Jena, 1892; English translation, *The Germ-Plasm* [London, 1893]). The theory of the continuity of the germ plasm was now more completely developed and formulated in terms of the cell theory, although necessarily in his own interpretation, for phenomena that were being observed remained to be more clearly understood.

Through these units Weismann also explained the process of differentiation during embryogeny. He continued to maintain the existence of the eternal germ plasm and the mortal somatoplasm, but, in addition, described a sort of breakdown of the complexes of the hereditary units by which specific determinants eventually direct development in the cells concerned. This was predicated on Weismann's belief, based on Roux's opinions years before, that both equal and unequal divisions were possible. But Weismann later made some minor compromises in his theory when eventually he allowed that some changes might occur in the germ plasm itself, although he continued to think in terms of variation, natural selection, and a struggle for existence that took place on various levels.

Weismann's theories elicited praise from some of his contemporaries, criticism from others. Whatever his interpretation of the actual mechanism of the processes he described (the reduction division, for example, which drew much further research and dispute in the 1890's), Weismann brought important questions to active discussion and was especially influential through his stress on chromosome theory and his repudiation of the inheritance of acquired characters. No doubt, too, many of the disagreements in his day were due to the different materials and life histories that were investigated by botanists and zoologists. There seemed to be too many difficulties and exceptions for broad theories to explain them in a way that was completely acceptable. To Oscar Hertwig, for example, Weismann's theory smacked of preformation, and questions of the importance of the relationship between the individual and the environment in determining the direction of development arose.

Early in his career, in advocating the Darwinian theory in Germany, Weismann had joined its most famous popularizers, Müller and Haeckel; but each of the three overstepped the bounds of Darwin's own propositions. According to Darwin's theory, evolution results from the natural selection of heritable, favorable variations that are always occurring by chance. New varieties grow up, and, in time, species are formed by this means. But even Darwin did not rule out some effect of external conditions and use and disuse; in his later years he granted a greater role to these factors than he had in the *Origin of Species* in 1859.

Even as natural selection drew wide attention, naturalists who applied it to specific instances in their experiences and investigations found difficulties and came to various conclusions. Opinions divided on the way in which evolution actually takes place, and differed as to the sources of variation and their relative importance: on whether external changes and acquired characters play a part in inherited variation; and on the role of slow, cumulative change as opposed to saltatory changes. Even if natural selection were accepted, it was difficult to explain the degeneration and loss of organs, and to account for continuing changes below the level at which natural selection could be expected to act at all.

Weismann, who was the most notable of the Neo-Darwinists, claimed that natural selection alone could provide for the formation of varieties and, in time, species, although the Neo-Lamarckians found support in Darwin's own admitted doubts as to the degree to which natural selection alone acted. In addition, there were other variations of the Lamarckian or Darwinian positions, and some naturalists departed from both.

In 1893 and 1894 the *Contemporary Review* carried Weismann's controversy with Herbert Spencer. Weismann contended that natural selection acting on innate variation was the sole factor in establishing varieties and species, and that acquired characters were not transmitted, and therefore were not a source of evolutionary change; Spencer took a Lamarckian view. Weismann's own experiments supported his arguments, and he could point also to the general lack of proof for such inheritance. He became widely known for the stand he took; indeed, it was cited in his day as one of his great contributions to biology.

In his 1894 Romanes lecture, "The Effect of External Influences Upon Development," Weismann dealt with the difficulties of explaining by means of the "all sufficient principle" of natural selection not only the progressive development of some variations, but degenerative changes and the disappearance of useless organs. He maintained that heritable peculiarities occurred among the biophors and cells, and that the peculiarities were actually variations in the primary cell constituents and might be acted upon by natural selection.

Weismann believed that natural selection was adequate even beyond Darwin's hopes—in the light of further researches—but he found it necessary to fortify the theory with some additional, although subsidiary, explanations. Indeed, Weismann was forced to support his arguments for natural selection, first with his theory of "panmixia," then with his further theory of "germinal selection." He thereby extended what he had come to refer to as the "Darwin-Wallace principle of natural selection"; but both panmixia and germinal selection were also based upon Weismann's own theory of the germ plasm, for he took for granted the theory of idants, ids, determinants, and the smallest units, biophors.

In defending the Darwinian theory, dealing with apparent difficulties or omissions, Weismann "extended" it and expressed his concepts in new terms. He had maintained that sexual reproduction, or to use his term, "amphimixis," was the source of variation; but he also found that he had to explain the disappearance of organs. Arguing that external influences could act only in a selective way on changes that had already occurred in the germ plasm, he ascribed regressive changes to variations that occurred in the primary constituents. But the problem remained. To account for the degeneration and ultimate disappearance of organs or parts, Weismann modified the Darwinian concept of natural selection with his own theory of "panmixia." Resisting Lamarckism, and trying to broaden the usefulness of the theory of natural selection, Weismann now inferred that natural selection not only brings about the development of the part but must actively cause it to be retained. Unless selection continued, the organ that lost its usefulness or specialized importance and became disused would tend to diminish and, in time, to disappear.

But how to explain its complete disappearance? To Weismann, panmixia was still not satisfactory, and his views changed as he looked next to what he called "germinal selection" as a further auxiliary to the selection theory. He went quite beyond Darwin's original account of the way in which natral selection acts and sought the selection process even in the germ plasm itself. Weismann came to see selection as taking place on many levels and in terms of his own later description of the hereditary units. There were fluctuations in nourishment and in conditions of life even among the biophors and determinants, and natural selection determined their chances to reach development and expression in the individual. Thus Weismann had come to conceive of a struggle of parts within the germ plasm. This enabled him to continue to deny that there was a direct effect upon heredity through external conditions, and to insist that, although external causes might eventually lead to variations, this would be through selection acting on the variations that occurred in the internal and innate hereditary tendencies and within the germ plasm itself. Nevertheless, it was quite a change of view for Weismann to admit that internal causes could intensify variational tendencies; and that these were "simply accumulated by natural selection in an ever-growing majority of ids in a germ-plasm through the selection of individuals" (*The Evolution Theory*, II, 332). It was almost impossible at the time for Weismann to separate his considerations of evolution and heredity. De Vries's mutation theory made it necessary for Weismann to define variation more completely in terms of natural selection, and he concluded that no lines could be drawn between variation and mutation, and that ultimately the difference was a matter of the number of similarly varying ids.

For decades Weismann drew a constant stream of students to his laboratory, and they returned to foreign countries with descriptions of his laboratory, reporting him as a teacher of impressive stature. Many students had been drawn to him through hearing of his views; one of his prominent pupils recalled his desire to go to study under Weismann and to hear his theories after having been well-schooled by the opposition. At the University of Freiburg, Weismann saw the Zoological Institute, of which he was the director, installed in a new building with the expansion of the facilities.

Weismann's wife died in 1886, and his second marriage at the age of sixty to Willemina Tesse of Holland lasted but six years. His five surviving children, often with him during summers at his home at Lake Constance, became his greatest comfort. One of his daughters, Hedwig, married the English zoologist W. Newton Parker, who translated *Das Keimplasma* (with Harriet Rönnfeldt). After retiring in 1912 as professor emeritus, Weismann gave his attention to the third edition of his *Vorträge über Descendenztheorie* (1913), which provides an overview of his ideas in an era in which cytology had developed as a science, Mendel's work had become known, and questions of evolution and heredity had been the subject of research and controversy. Following the outbreak of World War I, Weismann was ill and deeply unhappy, with members of his family on both sides during the conflict.

Weismann belonged to the Bavarian Academy of Sciences and was a corresponding member of the Academy at Vienna. He was a foreign member of the Linnean Society and the Royal Society of London, and of the American Philosophical Society.

Weismann traveled throughout Europe, and once to Constantinople. He was often in Italy and on the Riviera, and his work on the Hydromedusae was largely the result of a stay at the Naples zoological station during the winter of 1881–1882.

Weismann took three trips to England but he never met Darwin, although they corresponded.

In Germany the government designated Weismann *Wirklicher Geheimer Rat*, and the king of Bavaria bestowed the Grand Cross of the *Zähringer Löwensorden*. The University of Freiburg gave him the Ph.D. *honoris causa* in 1879. The University of Oxford made him doctor of common law, and the University of Utrecht made him doctor of botany. He received wide recognition when biologists from many countries honored him at the celebration of his seventieth birthday and a bust was given to the Zoological Institute at Freiburg, while the *Zoologische Jahrbücher* marked the anniversary with a *Festschrift*.

Weismann's influence was well summarized in the citations he received in London in 1908. Accompanying the medal awarded him by the Linnean Society at the Darwin-Wallace celebration (which his duties at Freiburg unfortunately prevented his attending) was the following:

> Professor Weismann has played a brilliant part in the development of Darwinian theory, and is indeed the protagonist of that theory in its purest form, retaining all that was the peculiar property of Darwin and Wallace and eliminating the traces of Lamarckism which still survived. . . . his profound knowledge of cytology enabled him to base his theory of heredity on a firmer foundation of fact than had been possible in the case of previous speculations.

The following citation was given him with the award of the Darwin Medal at the anniversary meeting of the Royal Society: "The fact remains that he has done more than any other man to focus attention on the mechanism of inheritance."

## BIBLIOGRAPHY

I. ORIGINAL WORKS. Weismann's writings are comprehensively listed in the biography by Gaupp (see below), pp. 290–297. His collected essays are in Edward B. Poulton, Selmar Schönland, and Arthur E. Shipley, trans., *Essays Upon Heredity and Kindred Biological Problems* (Oxford, 1889); and in a two-volume 2nd ed. (Oxford, 1891–1892). For the continued development of his theory of the germ plasm, see *Das Keimplasma* or its translation, noted above. See also *Vorträge über Descendenztheorie* (Jena, 1902, 1904, 1913), trans. by J. Arthur Thomson and Margaret R. Thomson as *The Evolution Theory*, 2 vols. (London, 1904), which provides some account of Weismann's changes in thinking over the years. A short autobiography is Herbert Ernest

Cushman, trans., "Autobiography of Professor Weismann," in *Lamp* (new series of *Book Buyer*), n.s. **26** (1903), 21–26. For a further personal glimpse of Weismann, see his correspondence with Haeckel in Georg Uschmann and Bernhard Hassenstein, "Der Briefwechsel zwischen Ernst Haeckel und August Weismann," in Manfred Gersch, ed., *Kleine Festgabe aus Anlass der hundertjährigen Wiederkehr der Gründung des Zoologischen Institutes der Friedrich-Schiller-Universität Jena im Jahre 1865 durch Ernst Haeckel* (Jena, 1965), 7–68.

II. SECONDARY LITERATURE. The major biography of Weismann is Ernst Gaupp, *August Weismann, sein Leben und sein Werk* (Jena, 1917). Among the articles on his life and work are Edward G. Conklin, "August Weismann," in *Proceedings of the American Philosophical Society*, **54** (1915), iii–xii, and in *Science*, n.s. **41** (1915), 917–923; F. Doflein, "August Weismann," in *Münchener medizinische Wochenschrift*, **61** (1914), 2308–2310; and V. Haecker, "August Weismann," in *Deutsches Biographisches Jahrbuch*, 1914–1916, I (Berlin, 1925), 97–103. See also R. v. Hanstein, "August Weismann," in *Naturwissenschaftliche Wochenschrift*, n.s. **14** (1915), 113–120, 129–136; and the obituary by R. Hertwig, in the *Jahrbuch der bayerischen Akademie der Wissenschaften* (1915), 118–127; Prof. and Mrs. W. N. Parker, "August Friedrich Leopold Weismann," in *Proceedings of the Linnean Society of London*, 129th session (1914–1915), 33–37; and for the recollections of one of Weismann's students, Alexander Petrunkevitch, "August Weismann, Personal Reminiscences," in *Journal of the History of Medicine and Allied Sciences*, **18** (1963), 20–35. Further accounts of his life include E. B. Poulton, "Prof. August Weismann," in *Nature*, **94** (1914), 342–343, and "August Friedrich Leopold Weismann," in *Proceedings of the Royal Society*, ser. B, **89** (1916), xxvii–xxxiv; and H. E. Ziegler, "August Weismann," in *Neue Rundschau*, **26** (1915), 117–124.

Because Weismann's work drew so much attention and controversy, a list of discussions of his views and contributions is necessarily incomplete; contemporary assessments include George John Romanes, *An Examination of Weismannism* (Chicago, 1893); Vernon L. Kellogg, *Darwinism To-Day* (New York–London, 1908), 45–46, 77–78, and *passim*, for Weismann's position as a Neo-Darwinist and his colleagues' stands, and his theories of panmixia and germinal selection; and Yves Delage and Marie Goldsmith, *The Theories of Evolution*, André Tridon, trans. (New York, 1913), 134–162. A later résumé of the course of Weismann's work and of his theories is W. Schleip, "August Weismann's Bedeutung für die Entwicklung der Zoologie und allgemeinen Biologie," in *Naturwissenschaften*, **22** (1934), 33–41. A more recent evaluation of Weismann's work in the context of the growing understanding of cytological phenomena, and his views and those of his contemporaries, is William Coleman, "Cell, Nucleus, and Inheritance: An Historical Study," in *Proceedings of the American Philosophical Society*, **109** (1965), 126, 149–154. The origins and the development by Weismann of the germ plasm theory, and its implications for him, are discussed in Frederick B. Churchill, "August Weismann and a Break From Tradition," in *Journal of the History of Biology*, **1** (1968), 91–112. For Weismann's theory of the germ plasm against the background of theories of heredity from Darwin's pangenesis, see Gloria Robinson, *A Prelude to Genetics* (Lawrence, Kans., 1976). For an analysis and discussion of Weismann's views on the problem of the reduction division, see Frederick B. Churchill, "Hertwig, Weismann, and the Meaning of Reduction Division Circa 1890," in *Isis*, **61** (1970), 429–457.

GLORIA ROBINSON

**WEISS, CHRISTIAN SAMUEL** (*b*. Leipzig, Germany, 26 February 1780; *d*. Eger, Hungary, 1 October 1856), *crystallography, mineralogy.*

Weiss's grandfather and father were archdeacons of Nicolai Church. At the age of twelve he began a classical education at the liberal Evangelische Gnadenschule at Hirschberg (now Jelenia Gora, Poland), under the philologist C. L. Bauer. In 1796 he returned to Leipzig to study medicine at the university; but after receiving his baccalaureate degree he switched to chemistry and physics, in which he was awarded the doctorate in 1800, and was then admitted to the faculty. Before teaching, Weiss spent two years in the chemical laboratory of Martin Klaproth (and Valentin Rose the younger) at Berlin, then a center for quantitative mineral analysis. Here he also became acquainted with Dietrich Karsten, curator of the royal mineral collection, and the eminent geologist Leopold von Buch. At their urging he went to the Freiberg Bergakademie for a year with A. G. Werner.

In 1805–1806 Weiss toured areas of geological interest in Austria, Switzerland, and France, spending some months in Paris with René-Just Haüy, André Brochant de Villiers, and Claude Berthollet. From 1803 he taught chemistry, physics, and mineralogy at Leipzig, and in 1808 he was appointed professor of physics. At about that time the University of Berlin was being organized under Wilhelm von Humboldt's leadership with the intention to make it the major center of philosophy and science in Germany by assembling the most eminent faculty. At Buch's instigation Weiss was appointed to the professorship of mineralogy and Klaproth to one in chemistry. Classes at the new university began in 1810, and Weiss occupied the chair of mineralogy until his death. After Dietrich Karsten's death in 1810, Weiss also became curator of the mineralogical museum and was instrumental in getting the government to purchase Buch's priceless collections for the museum in 1853. He served as rector of the university in 1832–1833.

Weiss's ability as a teacher was attested to by generations of students, several of whom made major contributions in science: Gustav Rose, Karl Rammelsberg, Friedrich Quenstedt, Adolph de Kupffer, and particularly Franz Neumann.

In addition to his major contributions to crystallography, Weiss published a number of papers in geology; and with Alexander von Humboldt and Buch he helped lay Werner's neptunist theories to rest.

While he was still a young man, Weiss's many contacts put him at the very center of the quickly developing science of crystallography. At Karsten's suggestion, he early embarked on a translation of Haüy's *Traité de minéralogie*, to which he added lengthy supplements on the process of crystallization. His intimate acquaintance with Werner's very practical view on mineralogy was an effective antidote to Haüy's imaginative but often unsubstantiated speculations. He had high regard for both men, but he did not show either of them the uncritical devotion that each asked of his followers.

Weiss's interpretations of the geometry of crystals were first indicated in his inaugural dissertation for the professorship at Leipzig (1809). They were developed in a long series of papers published in the *Abhandlungen der Königlichen Akademie der Wissenschaften in Berlin* (he was elected a member of the academy in 1815) and in publications of the Gesellschaft Naturforschender Freunde in Berlin. He never published his own textbook of crystallography, although those of Quenstedt (Tübingen, 1840; 1855; 1873) are perhaps derived from his work. His contributions to crystallography were early shaped around the directional aspect of crystals, which he regarded in an abstract, theoretical way as the expression of processes of growth. Haüy's theories of crystallography, then preeminent, interpreted crystals in terms of cleavage-shaped "molecules," which had to be combined in various steps to explain the varieties of crystal forms. By 1815 Weiss had developed the idea of crystallographic axes, which were at once a direction of growth and a basis of classification. In this most important contribution Weiss distinguished crystal systems by the way in

## TABLE I
### CLASSIFICATION OF CRYSTALS

| Weiss[1] | Modern |
|---|---|
| Three dimensions perpendicular | |
| All dimensions equal: | |
| Sphäroëdrisches | Cubic |
| Homosphäroëdrisches | Holohedral (hexoctahedral class) |
| Hemisphäroëdrisches | Hemihedral |
| Tetraëdrisches | Hextetrahedral class |
| Pentagon-dodekaëdrisches | Didodecahedral class |
| Two dimensions equal and one different: | |
| Viergliedrige | Tetragonal |
| Three dimensions different: | |
| Zwei-und-zwei-gliedrige | Orthorhombic |
| Zwei-und-ein-gliedrige | Monoclinic |
| Ein-und-ein-gliedrige | Triclinic |
| Three equal dimensions perpendicular to one other dimension | |
| Sechsgliedrige | Hexagonal |
| Drei-und-drei gliedrige | Trigonal |

which faces were related to such axes: first by whether they resulted in axial intercepts of equal length, and second by whether all or only a fraction of a set of related faces (modern "form") were developed by crystals of a given mineral species.

In the second of these criteria Weiss incidentally provided the first recognition of hemihedrism[2]— that is, a crystal class or point group that displays lower symmetry with a fraction of the faces, while retaining the same basic symmetry or crystal system. It should be clear, however, that while Weiss and others before him implicitly recognized the main rotational axes of symmetry, as well as mirror planes of symmetry, the classification was essentially metrical; and the complete symmetrical classification of crystals into both the seven crystal systems and Hessel's thirty-two crystal classes or point groups (1830) was not completed until 1849 by Auguste Bravais. As shown in the table, we can read into Weiss's listing the crystal systems that are now the primary classification of crystals; but two fundamental faults of Weiss's crystallography continued to be a source of confusion and debate for the next decade or so. First, Weiss insisted on choosing crystallographic axes at right angles, describing as hemihedrisms of the orthorhombic system the crystals now recognized as separate monoclinic and triclinic systems. Second, the axial lengths, while recognized as being unequal in each system except the cubic, were nevertheless thought to have ratios related by square roots of integers.

These two assertions were made plausible by the marked pseudosymmetries of many minerals of low symmetry, such as feldspar. But they were soon disproved by the accurate measurements of interfacial angles made by Kupffer and others using William Wollaston's optical goniometer, by Neumann's demonstration of the variation of angles with temperature, and by Eilhard Mitscherlich's demonstration of the variation of angles in a series of solid solutions. Much of this work had been done at the University of Berlin in Weiss's laboratory and that of his colleague Gustav Rose. But throughout his life Weiss insisted on perpendicular "rational" axes, while increasingly precise measurements pushed him to justify his position with calculations such as an axial ratio for gypsum[3]

$$of\ a:b:c = \frac{1}{\sqrt{3^2 + 1^2}} : 1 : \frac{1}{\sqrt{3^2 + 2^2 + 1^2}}.$$

Weiss's philosophical emphasis on important directions in crystals resulted not only in the crystallographic axes and crystal systems but also, even earlier, in the concept of the zone. Although originally conceived as a direction of prominent crystal growth, the term soon was formally defined as the collection of crystal faces parallel to a single line, the zonal direction. The zone concept enabled Weiss to propose replacing Haüy's symbolism for crystal faces with parameters that described the face direction in terms of its intercepts in units of his crystallographic axes. The Weiss symbols were widely used, and eventually they were replaced by the reciprocal symbols known today as Miller (although earlier used by Carl Naumann) indices. Weiss's last important contribution (1820) was the development of algebraic relations among the parameters (e.g., Weiss or Miller indices) of the faces that constitute a zone—Weiss's zone law—which remains a powerful tool in crystallographic calculations. Its application was greatly simplified by Franz Neumann, using projections, in his *Beiträge zur Kristallonomie* (Berlin–Posen, 1823).

From his earliest years Weiss's development as a scientist was strongly influenced by contemporary philosophers, and notably by the theories of nature of Immanuel Kant, Friedrich Schelling, and Johann Fichte—much to the dismay of his clerical father. Weiss was a keen observer but constitutionally disinclined to any experimental work, preferring to base his developments on abstract concepts of mathematical order—to the extent that where experiment was in disagreement, he chose to believe the more orderly theory. It is perhaps ironic that his student Franz Neumann went on to form at Königsberg the most important school of experimental physics (including crystal physics) of the nineteenth century. But Weiss's contributions—crystallographic axes, crystal systems, the zone law, and the concept of hemihedrism—constructed a formal edifice in which much of nineteenth-century crystallography found a compatible home and a place to grow.

*NOTES*

1. "Uebersichtliche Darstellung . . . der Kristallisations-systeme," table, 336 f. Friedrich Mohs independently worked out an analogous arrangement of crystal systems (but correctly, with inclined axes for the monoclinic and triclinic systems), published in his *Grundriss der Mineralogie*, 2 vols. (Dresden, 1822–1824). David Brewster had already seen the MS of William Haidinger's English trans. of this work— *Treatise on Mineralogy*, 3 vols. (Edinburgh, 1825)—and immediately applied the crystal systems to the interpretation of his observations on double refraction of crystals. A polemical debate on priority ensued in the *Edinburgh Philosophical Journal*, 8 (1823), 103–110 (Weiss) and 275–290 (Mohs). It is an interesting commentary on scientific communications of the day that although Weiss's paper was read at the Berlin Academy of Sciences on 14 Dec. 1815, the *Abhandlungen* for that year was not printed until 1818; and at the end of 1822 a copy was still not in the library of the Bergakademie at Freiberg.
2. Weiss soon recognized other hemihedrisms in the tetragonal and hexagonal systems—see his paper in *Edinburgh Philosophical Journal*, 8 (1823), 103–110.
3. "Über das Gypssystem," in *Abhandlungen der Königlichen Akademie der Wissenschaften in Berlin* (1834), 623–647.

*BIBLIOGRAPHY*

I. Original Works. Most of Weiss's scientific writings are listed in the Royal Society *Catalogue of Scientific Publications*, IV, 308–310. The most important books are *De indagando formarum crystallinarum charactere geometrico principali* (Leipzig, 1809), trans. into French with commentary by André Brochant de Villiers in *Journal des mines*, 29 (1811), 349–391, 401–444; and *De charactere geometrico principali formarum crys-*

*tallinarum octaedricarum pyramidibus rectis basirectangula oblonga commentatio* (Leipzig, 1809).

Articles include "Uebersichtliche Darstellung der verschiedenen natürlichen Abteilung der Krystallisations-systeme," in *Abhandlungen der Königlichen Akademie der Wissenschaften in Berlin* (1814–1815), 289–344; "Ueber ein verbesserte Methode für die Bezeichnung der verschiedenen Flächen eines Krystallisations-systeme, nebst Bemerkungen über den Zustand von Polarisirung der Seiten in der Linien der krystallinischer Struktur," *ibid.* (1816–1817), 286–314; and "Ueber mehrere neobeobachtete Krystallflachen des Feldspathes und die Theorie seines Krystallsystems im Allgemeinen," *ibid.* (1820–1821), 145–184.

His translation of Haüy is of primary importance for the original commentaries by Weiss: R. J. Haüy, *Lehrbuch der Mineralogie*, 4 vols., trans. by K. J. B. Karsten and C. S. Weiss (Paris–Leipzig, 1804–1810).

Some of Weiss's teaching materials are preserved at the Deutsche Staatsbibliothek, Berlin, D.D.R.; see Peter Schmidt, "Zur Geschichte der Geologie, Mineralogie und Paläontologie," in *Veroffentlichungen der Bibliothek der Bergakademie Freiberg*, no. 40 (1970), items 675, 807. A large collection of Weiss's letters to his oldest brother, Benjamin, are at the University of Marburg; they were used by both Groth and Fischer in preparing their discussions of Weiss.

II. SECONDARY LITERATURE. Biographical notices of Weiss are by K. F. P. von Martius, in *Akademische Denkreden . . . von Martius* (Leipzig, 1866), 327–344; and in Martin Websky *et al., Gedenkworte am Tage der Feier des hundertjahrigen Geburtstages von Christian Samuel Weiss den 3 März 1880* (n.p., n.d.). A contemporary evaluation of Weiss's crystallography is in Franz von Kobell, *Geschichte der Mineralogie von 1650–1860* (Munich, 1864), 202–214. The most useful and modern critical discussions of Weiss's scientific contributions are Paul Groth, *Entwicklungsgeschichte der mineralogischen Wissenschaften* (Berlin, 1926; repr. Wiesbaden, 1970), 59–76; and Emil Fischer, "Christian Samuel Weiss und seine Bedeutung für die Entwicklung der Krystallographie," in *Wissenschaftliche Zeitschrift der Humboldt-Universität zu Berlin*, Math.-naturwiss. ser., **11** (1962), 249–255. See also Fischer's "Christian Samuel Weiss und die zeitgenössische Philosophie (Fichte, Schelling)," in *Forschungen und Fortschritte*, **37** (1963), 141–143. A more general evaluation of Weiss's influence in the development of crystallography is J. G. Burke, *Origins of the Science of Crystals* (Berkeley, 1966), 147–164.

The founding of the University of Berlin, in which Weiss had a part, is described by Rudolf Virchow in "The Founding of the Berlin University and the Transition From the Philosophic to the Scientific Age," in *Annual Report of the Board of Regents of the Smithsonian Institution* (1894), pt. 1, 681–695.

WILLIAM T. HOLSER

**WEISS, EDMUND** (*b.* Freiwaldau, Austrian Silesia [now Jesenik, Czechoslovakia], 26 August 1837; *d.* Vienna, Austria, 21 June 1917), *astronomy.*

Weiss, son of Joseph Weiss, a physician, and twin of the botanist Gustav Adolph Weiss, received his earliest education in England (1843–1847). After his father's death, he attended the secondary school at Troppau, Austrian Silesia. In 1855 he entered the University of Vienna, where he studied astronomy, mathematics, and physics, receiving the doctorate in 1860. He was hired as assistant astronomer at the university observatory in 1858 and became an associate astronomer in 1862. In addition to participating in both astronomical and geodetical observations, Weiss became a lecturer in mathematics in 1861 and associate professor in 1869.

When, in 1872, Littrow's idea of building a great modern observatory on the hills of Währing, a suburb of Vienna, approached realization, Weiss was sent to visit new observatories and optical factories in England and the United States. This experience enabled him to contribute substantially to the definitive plans of the new institute. He became full professor of astronomy in 1875 and, eight months after Littrow's death, succeeded him as director of the observatory (1878). He was also president of the Austrian Commission for Geodesy and a member of the Imperial Academy of Sciences.

Weiss organized and participated in expeditions to observe several solar eclipses, the 1874 transit of Venus, and the Leonid meteor showers in 1899. His main contributions to astronomy concern the determination of the orbits of comets, of minor planets, and of meteor showers. In opposition to Schiaparelli's opinion that comets might have been formed by accretion in meteor showers, Weiss proposed in 1868 the now generally accepted view that the latter are products of gradual destruction of comets by tidal forces.

*BIBLIOGRAPHY*

I. ORIGINAL WORKS. Weiss's books include *Bilder-Atlas der Sternenwelt* (Esslingen, 1892); *Über Kometen mit besonderer Beziehung auf den Halley'schen* (Vienna, 1909); and *Katalogisierung von Argelanders Zonen vom 45. bis 80. Grade nördlicher Deklination* (Vienna, 1919).

Weiss's most important papers were published by the Kaiserliche Akademie der Wissenschaften zu Wien, math. naturwiss. Kl., in its *Denkschriften* and *Sitzungsberichte*, 2nd ser. (here abbreviated, respectively, as *Ak.D.* and *Ak.SB.*): "Bahnbestimmung von (66) Maja," in *Ak.SB.*, **51** (1865), 77–96; "Berechnung der Sonnenfinsternisse der Jahre 1867–1870," *ibid.*, **54** (1866), 796–810, and **56** (1867), 429–454; "Bericht über die Beobachtungen während der ringförmigen Sonnenfinsternis 1867 in Dalmatien," *ibid.*, **55** (1867), 905–944; "Beiträge zur Kenntnis der Sternschnuppen," *ibid.*, **57** (1868), 281–342, and **62** (1870), 277–344; "Beobachtungen während der totalen Sonnenfinsternis 1868 in Aden, etc.," *ibid.*, **58** (1868), 697–720, 882–894; **60** (1869), 326–340; **62** (1870), 873–1016; "Sprungweise Änderungen in einzelnen Reductionselementen eines Instruments," *ibid.*, **64** (1871), 77–104; "Bestimmung der Längendifferenz Wien–Wiener Neustadt durch Chronometer-Übertragung," *ibid.*, **65** (1872), 97–119; "Die praktische Astronomie in Amerika," in *Vierteljahrschrift der Astronomischen Gesellschaft*, **8** (1873), 296–321; "Beobachtung des Venusdurchganges 1874 in Jassy," in *Ak.SB.*, **71** (1875), 185–203; "Bahn der Cometen 1843 I und 1880 a," *ibid.*, **82** (1880), 95–114; "Differentialquotient der wahren Anomalie und des Radiusvectors nach der Excentricität in stark excentrischen Bahnen," *ibid.*, **83** (1881), 466–478; and "Entwicklungen zum Langrange'schen Reversions-Theorem und Anwendung auf die Lösung der Kepler'schen Gleichung," in *Ak.D.*, **49** (1885), 133–170.

Further articles by Weiss are "Der Binomialreihe verwandte Reihengruppen," in *Ak.SB.*, **91** (1885), 587–596; "Bestimmung von *M* bei Olbers' Methode der Berechnung einer Cometenbahn mit besonderer Berücksichtigung auf den Ausnahmefall," *ibid.*, **92** (1885), 1456–1477; "Berechnung der Präzession etc.," in *Ak.D.*, **53** (1887), 53–80; "Berechnung einer Cometenbahn mit Berücksichtigung von Gliedern höherer Ordnung," in *Ak.SB.*, **100** (1891), 1132–1150; "Systematische Differenzen südlicher Sternkataloge," *ibid.*, **101** (1892), 1269–1406; "Bestimmung der Bahn eines Himmelskörpers aus drei Beobachtungen," in *Ak.D.*, **60** (1893), 345–394; "Höhenberechnung der Sternschnuppen," *ibid.*, **77** (1905), 255–356; "Beiträge zur Kenntnis der atmosphärischen Elektrizität, in *Ak.SB.*, **115** (1906), 1285–1320; "Sichtbarkeitsverhältnisse des Kometen 1905 IV," *ibid.*, **116** (1907), 3–16; "Berechnung einer Ellipse aus zwei Radien und dem eingeschlossenen Winkel," *ibid.*, 345–366; and "Untersuchungen über die Bahn der Kometen 1907 II und 1742," in *Ak.D.*, **84** (1909), 1–14.

Collections of observations of shooting stars were presented by Weiss in *Annalen der Universitäts sternwarte in Wien*, 3rd ser., **20** (1870), 1–114; **23** (1873), 1–113; and **27** (1877), 1–133; Many records of observations, and other minor notes, are in *Astronomische Nachrichten*, **48** (1848)–**176** (1907).

His works are listed in Poggendorff, II, 1290; III, 1429; IV, 1615–1616, 1716; V, 1350–1351.

II. SECONDARY LITERATURE. Joseph von Hepperger wrote three obituaries: in *Astronomische Nachrichten*, **204** (1917), 431; in *Almanach der Akademie der Wissenschaften in Wien*, **68** (1918), 243–248; and *Viertel-*

*jahrschrift der Astronomischen Gesellschaft*, **53** (1918), 6–14.

KONRADIN FERRARI D'OCCHIEPPO

**WEISS, PIERRE** (*b.* Mulhouse, France, 25 March 1865; *d.* Lyons, France, 24 October 1940), *magnetism.*

Weiss's fame derives from the success of his phenomenological theory of ferromagnetism, which he conceived and developed on the basis of a large body of experimental results, many of them obtained by himself or his students. The theory is founded on the hypothesis of a molecular field proportional to the magnetization and acting on the orientation of each atomic moment like a magnetic field of very high intensity. With his theory he was able to account for the known characteristic properties of ferromagnetic bodies (notably the abrupt disappearance of ferromagnetism above a temperature known as the Curie point) and to discover the properties of spontaneous magnetization and magnetocaloric phenomena. Modern quantum theories of ferromagnetism have substantiated Weiss's molecular field hypothesis as a first approximation. According to these theories, the molecular field results from exchange forces of electric origin between the electrons, which bear the atomic magnetic moments.

Weiss came from a petit bourgeois Alsatian family. His father, who owned a haberdashery in Mulhouse, remained there when Alsace was annexed by the German Empire following the Franco-Prussian War. After attending secondary school in Mulhouse, Weiss went to the Zurich Polytechnikum. At his majority he chose French citizenship. In 1887 he graduated, first in his class, from the Polytechnikum with a degree in mechanical engineering. Wishing to undertake basic research, he attended the Lycée St. Louis in Paris to prepare for the competitive entrance examination for the École Normale Supérieure. Admitted in 1888, he was *agrégé* in physical science in 1893 and remained at the school as an assistant (*préparateur*) until 1895. During this period he became friendly with a number of fellow students who later became famous: the mathematicians Élie Cartan, Émile Borel, and Henri Lebesgue and the physicists Aimé Cotton, Jean Perrin, and Paul Langevin.

In 1895 Weiss was named *maître de conférences* at the University of Rennes and, in 1899, at the University of Lyons. In the meantime he had defended his doctoral dissertation, "Recherches sur l'aimantation de la magnétite cristallisée et de quelques alliages de fer et d'antimoine" (1896). In 1902 he returned as professor to the Zurich Polytechnikum, where, in addition to teaching, he directed the physics laboratory until 1918. His stay there was interrupted for two years, at the beginning of World War I, when he worked in Paris for the Office of Inventions, helping to create an acoustical method for locating enemy gun emplacements (Cotton-Weiss method). At Zurich, where his colleagues included Einstein, also a professor at the Polytechnikum, and Peter Debye, professor at the University of Zurich, Weiss gradually developed a great laboratory for magnetic research. He endowed it with a remarkable array of equipment and, above all, trained or attracted many distinguished physicists.

In 1919, following the return of Alsace to France, Weiss went to his native province to create and direct a major physics institute at the University of Strasbourg. Under his guidance, and with the aid of several associates drawn from among the best of his former staff, the laboratory soon surpassed even that of Zurich as a center of magnetic research. Among his numerous students during this period, the most outstanding was Louis Néel. While supervising the many projects undertaken at the institute, Weiss continued to do personal research, even after his retirement in 1936. He was elected to the Paris Academy in 1926.

With the evacuation of Strasbourg at the beginning of World War II, Weiss fled to Lyons, where his best friend, Jean Perrin, also had taken refuge. He died of cancer in October 1940.

In 1898 Weiss married Jane Rancès, whose mother was of English origin. Before her death in 1919, they had had one child, Nicole, who in 1936 married Henri Cartan, son of Élie Cartan and one of the leading mathematicians of his generation. In 1922 Weiss married Marthe Klein, who taught physics in a Paris *lycée*.

Weiss was thin and rather tall. Distinguished-looking and extremely courteous, he wore a pince-nez and wing collar that gave him an air of elegance. His hair and large moustache became completely white when he was still quite young.

Weiss's scientific works, which deal almost exclusively with magnetism, are characterized by great unity. From the time he was an engineering student, Weiss was interested in the complex phenomena of ferromagnetism, and it was to them that he devoted his initial research. He was influenced in this choice by the theoretical studies of Alfred

Ewing and Pierre Curie's "Les propriétés magnétiques des corps à diverses températures" (1895). At first he investigated magnetite and pyrrhotite, hoping that their large natural ferromagnetic monocrystals would enable him to discover the fundamental laws of magnetization. In the case of magnetite (1894–1896), he discovered only that it does not behave as an isotropic medium, even though it is crystallized in the cubic system.

The difficult study of pyrrhotite, the crystals of which are hexagonal prisms, proved much more rewarding (1896–1905). First he discovered that whatever the strength and direction of the magnetic field, the resulting magnetization remains, to a very good approximation, directed in the plane perpendicular to the axis of the crystalline prism. He then found that in this plane there is a direction of easy magnetization, in which saturation is reached in fields of twenty or thirty oersteds, and, perpendicularly, a direction of difficult magnetization, in which saturation has the same value but is reached only in fields exceeding 10,000 oersteds. Finally, he showed that the magnetization produced by an arbitrary field can be determined by vectorially subtracting from this field a "structural field" directed along the axis of difficult magnetization and proportional to the component of the magnetization along that axis. The resulting field assumes the direction of the magnetization, and its strength is linked to that of the magnetization by a relation that is independent of that direction.

In 1905 Paul Langevin published a theory of the paramagnetism of dilute substances. In Langevin's view, one may neglect the interactions between the magnetic moments $\mu$ that are assumed to be borne by each molecule of such substances. In the case of weak fields, the theory led to the Curie law, which states that the magnetization is proportional to the magnetic field $H$ and to the reciprocal of the absolute temperature $T$. For very strong fields, or at very low temperatures, however, the law predicts that the magnetization $I$ will tend toward a limit $I_0$. According to the theory, this saturation corresponds to the situation in which all the molecular moments are oriented in the direction of the field, despite the thermal agitation tending to vary their directions. Using classical statistical mechanics, Langevin obtained a formula giving the magnetization as a function of the ratio $H/T$:

(1) $\quad I = I_0 f\left(\dfrac{\mu H}{kT}\right)$, where $f(a) = \coth a - 1/a$.

In order to develop Langevin's ideas, Weiss broadened the concept of structural fields proportional to the magnetization, which he had previously introduced to account for the magnetic anisotropism of pyrrhotite. Langevin's theory led Weiss to conclude that the characteristic properties of the ferromagnetic metals, of which the microcrystalline structure is macroscopically isotropic, result from a global action of the magnetically polarized milieu on each elementary magnetic moment. This orienting action was to be considered equal to that of a magnetic field $H_m$, called molecular field, proportional to the magnetization ($H_m = NI$). According to Weiss, in the presence of an external field $H$ producing a magnetization $I$, each atomic moment would be subjected to the total field $H + H_m$; and the mean orientation of these moments, which creates the magnetization $I$, should be given by Langevin's formula, if $H$ is replaced by $H + H_m = H + NI$. The result is

$$(2) \qquad I = I_0 f\left(\frac{\mu H}{kT} + \frac{\mu N}{kT}I\right).$$

This is the fundamental formula of ferromagnetism in the theory based on the hypothesis of the molecular field. It remains valid when the Langevin function $f$ is replaced by functions arising from the application of quantum statistical mechanics to those moments $M$ that can assume only quantized orientations with respect to this field.

The first consequence of Weiss's formula is that when the temperature $T$ is lower than a certain temperature $\Theta$, a zero magnetization is unstable in the presence of a zero field. In such a case the result will be the appearance of a spontaneous magnetization $I_s$ determined by the implicit relation

$$(3) \qquad I_s = I_0 f\left(\frac{\mu N}{kT}I_s\right).$$

This spontaneous magnetization, equal to $I_0$ at very low temperatures, at first decreases slowly as the temperature rises, then very rapidly, and finally disappears altogether at the instant that the temperature reaches the critical level of $\Theta = \alpha\,\mu N I_0 / k$ ($\alpha$ being the slope, at the origin, of the curve representing the function $f$; accordingly, it will be $\frac{1}{3}$ for the Langevin function, or 1 for the quantum function $f(a) = \mathrm{th}a$, relative to the magnetic moment associated with the electron spin $\frac{1}{2}$).

The predicted spontaneous magnetization, however, generally is not apparent: most ferromagnetic metals have a zero magnetization in a zero field. The explanation must be that the variously oriented spontaneous magnetizations cancel each other in very small domains (known as Weiss domains, the existence of which was demonstrated much

later). A very strong exterior field is required to render parallel the spontaneous magnetizations of such domains. Further, the saturated macroscopic magnetization at a given temperature differs very little from the spontaneous magnetization, so that the latter quantity can be determined from the former. When the temperature is higher than the temperature $\Theta$, which is that of the Curie point, the spontaneous magnetization is zero. In this case the exterior field $H$ induces a very small magnetization, which according to the general formula (2) assumes the value

$$(4) \qquad I = I_0 \alpha \frac{\mu H}{k(T - \Theta)} = C\frac{H}{T - \Theta}.$$

The material under examination should then behave like a paramagnetic substance, with a magnetic susceptibility proportional to the reciprocal of the excess of the temperature over that of the Curie point. This relation, known as the Curie-Weiss law, is very well established by experiment. It can even be applied to many more or less concentrated paramagnetic substances with very low Curie temperatures, which are often negative (negative molecular field).

Applying the principles of thermodynamics to ferromagnetic substances, Weiss showed in 1908 that the existence of the spontaneous magnetization should add to the ordinary specific heat a magnetic specific heat proportional to the derivative with respect to the temperature of the square of this spontaneous magnetization. This quantity, therefore, should be zero at absolute zero and increase with the temperature, at first slowly and then more and more quickly up to the Curie point, where it should suddenly vanish. Measurements made on nickel gave quantitative confirmation of this prediction and highlighted, in particular, the discontinuity of the specific heat at the Curie point. In 1918 Weiss also discovered the magnetocaloric effects and showed how thermodynamics can be used to calculate the temperature variation of a magnetic substance placed in a field the intensity of which is altered adiabatically.

The absolute saturation $I_0$ of the magnetization, deduced from the limit toward which the experimental saturation tends at very low temperatures, yields in a very direct manner the value of the atomic moments $\mu$. Measurements on iron and nickel gave values for their atomic moments the ratio of which was almost exactly that of the whole numbers five and three. This finding led Weiss to postulate in 1911 that the moments of the various magnetic atoms are whole multiples of an elementary moment that he called the magneton. Many other measurements of other ferromagnetic substances — and, through the intermediary of Langevin's theory, of paramagnetic substances — seemed to verify this hypothesis. Several of his contemporaries immediately suggested that his result might well be explained as a quantum effect due to a restriction on the orbital energy of electrons. But Weiss's experimental magneton was found to be approximately equal to one-fifth of the Bohr magneton, which was deduced several years later from the quantification of the electron orbits. Subsequent research in quantum mechanics, however, has provided no grounds for thinking that all atomic moments are whole multiples of the Bohr magneton or of one-fifth of this quantity. It appears that the integral values found by Weiss arose, in general, from an insufficiently founded interpretation of indirect and difficult measurements.

## BIBLIOGRAPHY

Weiss's major book is *Le magnétisme* (Paris, 1926), written with G. Foëx.

His earlier articles include "Recherches sur l'aimantation de la magnétite cristallisée et de quelques alliages de fer et d'antimoine," in *Éclairage électrique*, 7 (1896), 487–508, and 8 (1896), 56–68, 105–110, 248–254, his dissertation; "Aimantation de la magnétite cristallisée," in *Journal de physique*, 3rd ser., 5 (1896), 435–453; "Un nouvel électro-aimant de laboratoire donnant un champ de 30.000 unités," in *Éclairage électrique*, 15 (1898), 481–487; "Sur l'aimantation plane de la pyrrhotine," in *Journal de Physique*, 3rd ser., 8 (1899), 542–544; "Un nouveau système d'ampèremètres et de voltmètres indépendants de leur aimant permanent," in *Comptes rendus . . . de l'Académie des sciences*, 132 (1901), 957; "Un nouveau fréquence-mètre," in *Archives des sciences physiques et naturelles*, 18 (1904), 241; "Le travail d'aimantation des cristaux," in *Journal de physique*, 4th ser., 3 (1904), 194–202; "Propriétés magnétiques de la pyrrhotine," *ibid.*, 4 (1905), 469–508, 829–846; "Variation thermique de l'aimantation de la pyrrhotine," *ibid.*, 847–873, written with J. Kunz; "La variation du ferromagnétisme avec la température," in *Comptes rendus . . . de l'Académie des sciences*, 143 (1906), 1136; and "Sur la théorie des propriétés magnétiques du fer au delà du point de transformation," *ibid.*, 144 (1906), 25.

Additional articles are "L'hypothèse du champ moléculaire et la propriété ferromagnétique," in *Journal de physique*, 4th ser., 6 (1907), 661–690; "Sur la biréfringence des liquides organiques," in *Comptes rendus . . . de l'Académie des sciences*, 145 (1907), 870, written with A. Cotton and H. Mouton; "L'intensité d'aimantation à saturation du fer et du nickel," *ibid.*, 1155; "Électro-aimant de grande puissance," in *Journal de physique*, 4th ser., 6 (1907), 353–368; "Mesure du phénomène de Zeeman pour les trois raies bleues du zinc," *ibid.*, 429–445, written with A. Cotton; "Hystérèse dans les champs tournants," *ibid.*, 4th ser., 7 (1908), 5–27, written with V. Planer; "Chaleur spécifique et champ moleculaire des substances ferromagnétiques," *ibid.*, 249–264, written with P. N. Beck; "Sur le rapport de la charge à la masse des électrons," in *Comptes rendus . . . de l'Académie des sciences*, 147 (1908), 968, written with A. Cotton; "Mesure de l'intensité d'aimantation à saturation en valeur absolue," in *Journal de physique*, 4th ser., 9 (1910), 373–397; and "Recherches sur l'aimantation aux très basses températures," *ibid.*, 555–584, written with H. Kamerlingh Onnes.

Also see "Sur l'aimantation du nickel, du cobalt et des alliages nickel-cobalt," in *Comptes rendus . . . de l'Académie des sciences*, 153 (1911), 941, written with O. Bloch; "Étude de l'aimantation des corps ferromagnétiques au-dessus du point de Curie," in *Journal de physique*, 5th ser., 1 (1911), 274–287, 744–753, 805–814, written with G. Foëx; "Sur la rationalité des rapports des moments magnétiques moléculaires et le magnéton," *ibid.*, 900–912, 965–988; "Sur l'aimantation de l'eau et de l'oxygène," in *Comptes rendus . . . de l'Académie des sciences*, 155 (1912), 1234, written with A. Piccard; "Magnetic Properties of Alloys," in *Transactions of the Faraday Society*, 8 (1912), 149–156; "L'aimantation des cristaux et le champ moléculaire," in *Comptes rendus . . . de l'Académie des sciences*, 156 (1913), 1836–1837; "Sur les champs magnétiques obtenus avec un électro-aimant muni de pièces polaires en ferrocobalt," *ibid.*, 1970–1972; "Le spectrographe à prismes de l'École polytechnique de Zurich," in *Archives des sciences physiques et naturelles*, 35 (1913), 5, written with R. Fortrat; and "Sur la nature du champ moléculaire," in *Annales de physique*, 9th ser., 1 (1914), 134–162.

Weiss's later papers include "Ferromagnétisme et équation des fluides," in *Journal de physique*, 5th ser., 7 (1917), 129–144; "Calorimétrie des substances ferromagnétiques," in *Archives des sciences physiques et naturelles*, 42 (1917), 378, and 43 (1917), 22, 113, 199, written with A. Piccard and A. Carrard; "Le phénomène magnétocalorique," in *Journal de physique*, 5th ser., 7 (1917), 103–109, written with A. Piccard; "Sur un nouveau phénomène magnétocalorique," in *Comptes rendus . . . de l'Académie des sciences*, 166 (1918), 352, written with A. Piccard; "Sur les coefficients d'aimantation de l'oxygène, de l'oxyde azotique et la théorie du magnéton," in *Comptes rendus . . . de l'Académie des sciences*, 167 (1918), 484–487, written with E. Bauer and A. Piccard; "Sur le moment atomique de l'oxygène," in *Journal de physique*, 6th ser., 4 (1923), 153–157; "Les moments atomiques," *ibid.*, 5 (1924), 129–152; "Aimantation et phénomène magnétocalorique du nickel," in *Annales de physique*, 10th ser., 5 (1926), 153–213; "Sur les moments atomiques," in *Comptes rendus . . . de l'Académie des sciences*, 187 (1928), 744, written with G. Foëx; "La saturation absolue des ferromagné-tiques et les lois d'approche en fonction du champ et de la température," in *Annales de physique*, 10th ser., **12** (1929), 279–374, written with R. Forrer; and "La con-stante du champ moléculaire. Équation d'état magné-tique et calorimétrique," in *Journal de physique*, 7th ser., **1** (1930), 163–175.

Some of his papers appeared in works issued by the Solvay Council: "Les actions mutuelles des molécules aimantées," in *Atomes et électrons* (Paris, 1923), 158–163; "Équation d'état des ferromagnétiques," in *Le magnétisme* (Paris, 1932), 281–323; "L'anomalie de volume des ferromagnétiques," ibid., 325–345; and "Les phénomènes gyromagnétiques," ibid., 3.7–379.

On his life and work, see Albert Perrier, "In memo-riam (Pierre Weiss)," in *Actes de la Société helvétique des sciences naturelles*, **121** (1941), 422–433, with bibli-ography; and G. Foëx, "L'oeuvre scientifique de Pierre Weiss," in *Annales de physique*, 11th ser., **20** (1945), 111–130.

FRANCIS PERRIN

**WEIZMANN, CHAIM** (*b.* Motol, White Russia, 27 November 1874; *d.* Rehovot, Israel, 9 November 1952), *organic chemistry*, *biochemistry*.

"Chemistry is my private occupation. It is this activity in which I rest from my social tasks." Thus did Chaim Weizmann describe the contra-puntal relationship between his lifelong career as a scientist and his leadership of the Zionist move-ment. In his disciplined mind these two vocations, representing reason and faith, were made harmoni-ous. The intellectual and physical power that sci-ence conveys was to help free the Jews for their return to Palestine and was to form a vital, integral part of a revived, modern Jewish culture.

After early religious and secular schooling with-in the segregated Jewish community of rural Rus-sia, Weizmann, at the age of twelve, entered the Gymnasium at Pinsk and was there exposed to gen-tile ways and Western European thought. Al-though his grades were uniformly high, chemistry was his favorite subject. With parental encourage-ment he set out to gain advanced knowledge in that field at the technical institutes of Darmstadt (1893–1894) and Berlin (1895–1898), where Lie-bermann and his students (among them Bistrzycki) were investigating polycyclical aromatic com-pounds of particular interest to dye manufacturers. When Bistrzycki went to the University of Fri-bourg, Switzerland, Weizmann followed. Soon af-terward (1899), Weizmann wrote the dissertation "I. Elektrolytische Reduktion von 1-Nitroanthra-chinon. II. Ueber die Kondensation von Phenan-threnchinon U. 1-Nitroanthrachinon mit einigen Phenolen" and was awarded the Ph.D. *summa cum laude*. He subsequently joined Karl Graebe at the University of Geneva as *Privatdozent*. Exten-sive research on the naphthacene quinones led to patents that Weizmann sold profitably to French and German dye companies. Meanwhile he was rising to leadership in the world Zionist movement.

Weizmann's decision to move to Manchester in 1904 was prompted by numerous considerations, including greater professional opportunity and a premonition that England could do the most for establishing a Jewish national homeland in Pales-tine. At Manchester, Weizmann enrolled as a stu-dent at the university. The following year, the head of the chemistry department, William H. Perkin, Jr., appointed him research fellow, and in 1907 senior lecturer, in biochemistry. Weizmann se-cured additional income by serving as consultant for local industry and selling new patents. At this time he also married Vera Chatzmann, a physician.

The university's exceptional scientific faculty stimulated Weizmann in this, the most scientifical-ly productive period of his life. Effective teaching attracted students who did research under his direction. The quest for alizarin-type dyes contin-ued along previous lines: the polyhydroxylation of naphthacene quinone, for example, yielded colors of moderate utility. About 1909 Weizmann added biochemical investigations to his research, seeking to synthesize various naturally occurring peptides; he later studied the photochemical behavior of amino acids, proteins, and ketones. He also began investigating fermentation reactions, searching for a strain of bacteria that would convert carbo-hydrates into isoamyl alcohol—a precursor, via isoprene, of synthetic rubber. Instead, in 1912, he found the strain *Clostridium acetobutylicum*, which broke starches down into one part ethanol, three parts acetone, and six parts butanol. During World War I, when great quantities of acetone were needed to plasticize the propellant cordite, Weizmann successfully engineered its massive production in Great Britain for the Admiralty and Ministry of Munitions. Plants were also built in India, Canada, and the United States; their pro-duction continued after the war, butanol then being the preferred product for use in auto lacquers. Weizmann, in effect, opened the microbiological road to the production of industrial chemicals.

Meanwhile, in 1917, Weizmann secured from Lord Balfour a declaration of British help in estab-lishing a national homeland for the Jews, the sub-sequent realization of which took so much of

Weizmann's time that he stopped all scientific activity except for promoting the growth of Hebrew University in Jerusalem and his founding of the Daniel Sieff (later Weizmann) Institute of Science in Rehovot (1934), both of which soon became notable centers of scientific learning.

In 1934 Weizmann simultaneously resumed his research at Rehovot and London, adding significantly to lines of investigation begun before 1918, particularly those that were relevant to Palestine's economy: the commercial synthesis of organic compounds from agricultural products or petroleum. Of considerable technical significance was his discovery of several reaction mechanisms by which petroleum fractions could be reduced, by cracking to ethylene and diene fragments, and then recombined into polynuclear aromatics of the type he had used earlier in his dye researches. Previously such dye intermediates could be obtained only from coal tar.

Practical, rather than fundamental, scientific considerations motivated Weizmann's research. Apart from some interest late in his career in reaction mechanisms, his work is generally devoid of theoretical content. With his elevation in 1948 to the presidency of Israel, his career as a Zionist came to a climax and his career as a creative scientist came to an end.

*BIBLIOGRAPHY*

I. ORIGINAL WORKS. A nearly complete list of Weizmann's 100 or so patents and of his 102 scientific publications can be obtained from the Weizmann Archives, Rehovot, Israel. Abstracts of most of his articles are in *Chemisches Zentralblatt* or *Chemical Abstracts*. The Weizmann Archives hold the great bulk of his papers and continue to expand their collection. The documents are written in English, French, German, Hebrew, Russian, and Yiddish. The nonscientific *Letters and Papers of Chaim Weizmann* are currently being edited in a proposed 25 vols.; vols. I–VII, covering correspondence, 1885–1917, appeared in Hebrew and English eds., the latter published by Oxford University Press (London, 1968–1975). Weizmann's scientific correspondence is being edited for publication under the supervision of Ernst D. Bergmann, of Hebrew University, Jerusalem, and David Lavie of the Weizmann Institute. Weizmann's autobiography, *Trial and Error* (New York, 1949), was written between 1940 and 1948. Less than 5 percent of its 482 pages are devoted to his scientific career.

II. SECONDARY LITERATURE. *Chaim Weizmann, a Biography by Several Hands*, Meyer W. Weisgal and Joel Carmichael, eds. (London, 1962), contains Selman A. Waksman's, "Weizmann as a Bacteriologist." By far the best review of Weizmann's contributions to science is E. D. Bergmann's obituary notice in *Journal of the Chemical Society* (1953), 2840–2844.

JOHN J. BEER

**WELCH, WILLIAM HENRY** (*b*. Norfolk, Connecticut, 8 April 1850; *d*. Baltimore, Maryland, 30 April 1934), *pathology, bacteriology, public health, medical education.*

Welch was born into a family of physicians who for two generations had practiced medicine in Connecticut. His mother died when he was six months old, and he and his slightly older sister, Emma, were raised with the help of their paternal grandmother. The elder William Welch, a busy family practitioner, was a kind but somewhat distant father. The son prepared for college at a boarding school in Winchester Center and entered Yale in 1866, at the age of sixteen. By the time he graduated in 1870, third in his class, Welch had become interested in the classics and hoped for a position as tutor in Greek.

Not successful in obtaining a post at Yale, Welch accepted a teaching job at an academy in Norwich, New York, for 1870–1871. He then returned home to apprentice himself to his father, thereby beginning medical studies. In the fall of 1871, a very brief exposure to the medical lectures at the College of Physicians and Surgeons in New York City convinced him of the need for science courses. Welch therefore returned to New Haven to spend the academic year 1871–1872 at the Sheffield Scientific School of Yale University, where he concentrated on chemistry. Resuming medical studies at the College of Physicians and Surgeons in the fall of 1872, Welch found little more than a series of didactic lectures. He therefore eagerly accepted a prosectorship in anatomy in 1873, so that at least he could learn by firsthand investigation. Welch's dissertation on goiter was awarded a prize; and several months prior to receiving the M.D. in 1875, he began duty as an intern at Bellevue Hospital, where he had an excellent opportunity to observe and study a large variety of patients. Under the direction of Francis Delafield, Welch soon developed a keen interest in pathology. He also was greatly stimulated by two teachers who had emigrated from Europe, E. C. Seguin and Abraham Jacobi. Welch followed their advice to make a European study tour beginning in the spring of 1876.

During this sojourn of two years Welch visited

and studied at the major medical centers of Strasbourg, Leipzig, Breslau, and Vienna. Two of his research endeavors had special influence in shaping his career. With the physiologist Carl Ludwig at Leipzig, Welch learned to handle living tissue. He investigated the nerve distribution in the auricular septum of the frog heart and visualized the nerve network that later was fully described by Louis Ranvier. At Breslau, under Julius Cohnheim's direction, Welch studied the pathogenesis of pulmonary edema, showing, contrary to Cohnheim's presuppositions, that the condition is primarily mechanical in origin. With the publication of his findings in *Virchows Archiv* in 1878, Welch was launched in the scientific, laboratory-based study of pathology that Virchow, Cohnheim, and other German physicians were developing so fruitfully. For Welch there was no turning back, and he rejected a career in country practice with his father.

Returning to New York in 1878, Welch set out to bring the laboratory tradition in pathology to American medical students. His own school, the College of Physicians and Surgeons, was willing to let him teach a summer course but offered inadequate facilities and no salary. Bellevue Hospital and its medical school, on the other hand, offered to renovate three small rooms and to supply very modest equipment. Here Welch inaugurated the first teaching pathology laboratory in the United States. The student response was heartening but the financial returns meager. To support himself Welch performed autopsies and examined specimens for his medical colleagues, held a popular private class for medical students, wrote a section of the sixth edition (1886) of Austin Flint's *Principles and Practice of Medicine*, and saw a few private patients. It is therefore not surprising that in six years he failed to complete a single piece of pathological research. It was this frustration, as well as the dream of bringing a real science of pathology to America, that had intrigued Welch about the new Johns Hopkins University. From 1876, if not before, Welch had hoped that he might be offered a chair in the proposed medical school faculty. When the offer was made in 1884, Welch accepted the professorship of pathology.

Prior to moving to Baltimore, Welch took an additional year of study in Europe, concentrating on the rapidly emerging field of bacteriology, a subject he had entirely bypassed six years earlier. Study with Carl Flügge, Robert Koch, and Max von Pettenkofer gave Welch the groundwork he needed to bring another aspect of the study of disease to America. When Welch arrived in Baltimore at the end of 1885 to assume his duties at Johns Hopkins, no hospital or medical school existed. It fell to Welch, with John Shaw Billings; Daniel Coit Gilman, president of the university; and H. Newell Martin, the professor of biology, to recruit the rest of the medical faculty. Welch moved into Martin's laboratory and, with the assistance of William T. Councilman, began a series of pathological and bacteriological studies on thrombosis, embolism, hog cholera, diphtheria, and a number of other projects. In contrast with New York, Welch now had both able assistants and adequate laboratory facilities, which enabled him to bring a number of projects to a successful conclusion. The most renowned discovery coming from Welch's laboratory (opened in 1886) was the correct identification of the gas gangrene bacillus. In 1892, with the help of G. H. F. Nuttall, Welch published his findings regarding the isolation of *Clostridium perfringens*.

With the opening of the Johns Hopkins Hospital in 1889, William Osler, Howard A. Kelly, and William Halsted began residency programs patterned on the German system of postgraduate medical training. This was doubtless one of the most important contributions of the hospital to American medicine. Although not involved directly in clinical training, Welch played a key role in setting the climate for these developments. When the medical school, after overcoming financial difficulties, finally opened in 1893, Welch became its first dean, a post he held until 1898. The students were taken to the wards and were given clinical responsibility. The outstanding basic science chairmen, Franklin P. Mall in anatomy and John J. Abel in pharmacology, had been recruited by Welch. With him, they and the clinical chairmen were instrumental in making basic science and laboratory work, as well as study of patients on the wards, the norm for medical education in America. As much as any individual, Welch made the Johns Hopkins Hospital a new kind of hospital in America, one devoted to science as much as to charity.

It fell to Welch and a handful of colleagues who also had been in the European bacteriological laboratories to alert the American medical profession to the practical applications of the germ theory of disease in relation to medicine and public health. His address to the Medical and Chirurgical Faculty of Maryland in 1887, "Modes of Infection," stressed what he had learned in such cities as Munich. Cholera and typhoid, he pointed out, were caused by specific microorganisms, not a vague miasma. The bacteria could be found in the open sewers still prevalent in Baltimore; and Welch subsequently worked to improve the city's health conditions, serving for many years on the Maryland State Department of Health.

In the spring of 1888 Welch was asked to deliver the Cartwright lectures in New York City. His speech, "On the General Pathology of Fever," presented one of several general reviews for which he became well known. In later years he wrote similar essays on the immune mechanism, thrombosis, and wound infections. Although this work was not derived primarily from his own research, Welch here evidenced his great gift for expression and for cogent summary.

His general summations of current scientific work, his editorship of the *Journal of Experimental Medicine* (1896–1906), and the numerous scientific and civic organizations to which he belonged, more than his own scientific investigations, increasingly made Welch one of the most influential spokesmen for American medicine. Many sought his counsel and he served in some key policy-making positions. He headed the Board of Scientific Directors of the Rockefeller Institute and served as a trustee from 1910 until 1933. At the same time Welch was a member of the board of the Carnegie Institution of Washington. He also served, for shorter periods of time, on the boards or councils of the Milbank Memorial Fund, the Rockefeller Sanitary Commission, and the International Health Board of the Rockefeller Foundation. In 1910 he was president of the American Medical Association and, from 1913 to 1916, president of the National Academy of Sciences.

Long active in the public health movement in America, Welch agreed in 1916 to leave his chair at the school of medicine to become dean of the new School of Hygiene and Public Health at Johns Hopkins. This was the first full-scale school of its kind, although Harvard and M.I.T. had begun a joint effort a few years earlier to train health officers. Welch continued as dean until 1925, when the trustees persuaded him to take the newly established chair in medical history.

Welch's eightieth birthday was celebrated by friends, students, and colleagues. In Washington, President Herbert Hoover called him "our greatest statesman in the field of public health." Welch himself, with characteristic modesty, agreed to accept the accolades only insofar as "I stand here to represent an army of teachers, investigators, pupils, associates, and colleagues, whose work and contributions during this period have advanced the science and art of medicine and public health to the eminent position which they now hold in this country."

## BIBLIOGRAPHY

I. ORIGINAL WORKS. A bibliography of Welch's publications was prepared by Walter C. Burket, *Bibliography of William Henry Welch* (Baltimore, 1917); Burket also edited the collected *Papers and Addresses by William Henry Welch*, 3 vols. (Baltimore, 1920). Those few items that appeared after 1920 are listed in the bibliography appended to Simon Flexner's memoir (see below).

The Welch MSS, consisting of many file boxes of letters, diaries, and clippings, indexed and arranged by Simon Flexner and James T. Flexner, are deposited in the William H. Welch Medical Library of Johns Hopkins University, Baltimore.

II. SECONDARY LITERATURE. The most thorough biography is Simon Flexner and James T. Flexner, *William Henry Welch and the Heroic Age of American Medicine* (New York, 1941; repr. 1966). A shorter and more interpretive study is Donald Fleming, *William Henry Welch and the Rise of American Medicine* (Boston, 1954). Two collections of articles are *The Eightieth Birthday of William Henry Welch* (New York, 1930) and a series describing Welch's influence on pathology, public health, medical history, and medical education in a special supp. to *Bulletin of the Johns Hopkins Hospital*, **87**, no. 2, pt. 2 (1950), 1–54.

See also the following listed chronologically: Fielding H. Garrison, "In Memoriam: William Henry Welch (1850–1934)," in *Scientific Monthly*, **38** (1934), 579–582; Harvey Cushing, "The Doctors Welch of Norfolk," in *Connecticut State Medical Journal*, **5** (1941), 557–560; Simon Flexner, "Biographical Memoir of William Henry Welch 1850–1934," in *Biographical Memoirs. National Academy of Sciences*, **22** (1943), 215–231; Owsei Temkin, "The European Background of the Young Dr. Welch," in *Bulletin of the History of Medicine*, **24** (1950), 308–318; Barnett Cohen, "Comments on the Relation of Dr. Welch to the Rise of Microbiology in America," *ibid.*, 319–324; and Carl J. Salomonsen, "Reminiscences of the Summer Semester, 1877, at Breslau," C. L. Temkin, trans., *ibid.*, 333–351.

On Welch's role in the development of the medical institutions of Johns Hopkins University, see Alan M. Chesney, *The Johns Hopkins Hospital and the Johns Hopkins University School of Medicine; a Chronicle*, 3 vols. (Baltimore, 1943–1963); Richard H. Shryock, *The Unique Influence of the Johns Hopkins University on American Medicine* (Copenhagen, 1953); and Thomas B. Turner, *Heritage of Excellence, the Johns Hopkins Medical Institutions, 1914–1917* (Baltimore, 1974).

GERT H. BRIEGER

**WELDON, WALTER FRANK RAPHAEL** (*b*. London, England, 15 March 1860; *d*. Oxford, England, 13 April 1906), *biometrics*.

One of the founders of biometrics, Weldon was born into a wealthy London family (his father was an industrialist and a Swedenborgian) and was initially educated by private tutors and at fashionable boarding schools. In 1876 he entered University College, London, and began to study zoology under E. Ray Lankester. Two years later he moved to St. John's College, Cambridge, where he continued his study of zoology under Francis Balfour; he graduated in 1881 with a first-class degree in the natural sciences tripos.

At this point Weldon seemed on his way to becoming an orthodox zoologist. He spent some time at the Naples zoological station (1881), was demonstrator for W. T. Sedgwick at Cambridge (1882), completed a dissertation on invertebrate morphology and embryology (1883), and became a fellow of St. John's and a university lecturer in invertebrate morphology (1884). Weldon's style of life was perfectly suited to his profession; he spent two terms of each year in Cambridge, and from June to January he and his wife (whom he had married in 1883) traveled and did research at various marine laboratories. In 1883 he became associated with the laboratory of the Marine Biological Association at Plymouth, and in 1890 he succeeded Lankester as professor at University College.

The move to University College signaled a profound transformation in Weldon's interests. After reading Francis Galton's *Natural Inheritance* (1889), he became convinced that statistical studies of variation would contribute more toward solving the problems of Darwinism than the embryological work in which he had been engaged.

Between 1890 and 1892 Weldon published two papers that were classics of their kind, on variation in the shrimp *Crangon vulgaris*. In the first he demonstrated that body measurements for large populations of shrimp (carapace length, for example) are normally distributed; this was the first normal distribution observed in a wild population subject to the influence of natural selection. The second paper presented the first correlation coefficients derived for a wild population; Weldon demonstrated that in the shrimp pairs of organ lengths are highly correlated in individuals of the same species. Weldon hoped that these correlations would yield quantitative definitions of species and races, replacing the older descriptive definitions, which were based upon a single type specimen. In

1893, in studies of the crab *Carcina moenas*, Weldon found an asymmetrical distribution for frontal breadth. He thus concluded that he was actually measuring two different races of crab that inhabited the same environment but were physically distinguishable.

In 1891 Weldon began to learn probability theory and sought the help of his colleague Karl Pearson. Pearson soon became enthusiastic about the prospect of solving the problems of evolution statistically; he and Weldon began a collaboration that lasted until Weldon's death. One of the first fruits of their combined effort was the formation in 1893 of the Royal Society Evolution Committee (with Galton as chairman), dedicated to large-scale studies of variation.

Weldon's most significant contribution to biometrics was his study of differential death rates in crabs (1894), which was sponsored by the Evolution Committee. He reasoned that if natural selection works by killing "unfit" individuals before they can breed, it should be possible to correlate death rates in youthful populations with physical characteristics. To test this assumption he raised 7,000 young female crabs in jars filled with polluted water from their natural environment, assiduously measured several characteristics of each crab at different times during its growth, and discovered that individuals with greater than normal frontal breadths were more likely to die before reaching reproductive age. From these results Weldon concluded that natural selection can operate on small, apparently insignificant variations and that there is no need to postulate large jumps or discontinuous variations (as had been suggested by Galton in 1889 and by Bateson in 1894) in order to understand how evolution progresses. Weldon knew that his results were tentative, since the experimental procedure was quite faulty; but he was not prepared for the storm of protest that broke about his head. Naturalists were not ready to admit that regression lines and correlation coefficients were relevant in what had been, until then, a purely descriptive science.

The controversy between the advocates of continuous variation and the proponents of discontinuity grew increasingly acrimonious, and eventually the biometricians resigned from the Evolution Committee and founded a journal, *Biometrika* (1901), in which to publish and to propagandize for their new science. After the rediscovery of Mendel's work and the founding of *Biometrika*, two separate schools of genetics developed in England:

the Mendelians, who believed in discontinuous variation and devoted themselves to breeding studies; and the biometricians (including Weldon and Pearson), who believed in continuous variation and devoted themselves to statistical study of variation. In 1900 Weldon moved to Oxford, where he became Linacre professor; but the distance between Weldon and Pearson did not dampen their collaboration. Weldon undertook studies of moths (unpublished), snails, thoroughbred horses, poppies, mice, and men in an effort to find clear-cut cases of evolutionarily significant continuous variation; but none of these studies was as fruitful, either methodologically or substantively, as his earlier work on shrimp and crabs. Perhaps because of his frustration, Weldon worked at a pace and with an intensity that worried his friends. His debate with the Mendelians became even more acrimonious; and a stream of critical articles flowed from his pen, to be published in *Biometrika*. In the midst of an Easter holiday devoted to biometric research Weldon collapsed and died. Many of his colleagues considered his death particularly tragic for having come when he seemed to be entering a very promising phase of his career.

*BIBLIOGRAPHY*

Weldon's most significant biometric papers are "The Variations Occurring in Certain Decapod Crustacea. I. *Crangon vulgaris*," in *Proceedings of the Royal Society*, **47** (1890), 445–453; "On Certain Correlated Variations in *Crangon vulgaris*," ibid., **51** (1892), 2–21; "On Certain Correlated Variations in *Carcina moenas*," ibid., **54** (1893), 318–329; and "Attempt to Measure the Death-Rate due to the Selective Destruction of *Carcina moenas* With Respect to a Particular Dimension," ibid., **57** (1895), 360–379.

For an understanding of his theoretical dispute with the Mendelians see "Remarks on Variation in Animals and Plants," in *Proceedings of the Royal Society*, **57** (1895), 379–382; "Mendel's Laws of Alternative Inheritance in Peas," in *Biometrika*, **1** (1901–1902), 228–254; "Professor de Vries on the Origin of Species," ibid., 365–374; and "On the Ambiguity of Mendel's Categories," ibid., **2** (1902), 44–55.

The best source for information about Weldon is Karl Pearson, "Walter Frank Raphael Weldon," in *Biometrika*, **5** (1906), 1–50.

RUTH SCHWARTZ COWAN

**WELLS, HARRY GIDEON** (*b*. Fair Haven [now New Haven], Connecticut, 21 July 1875; *d*. Chicago, Illinois, 26 April 1943), *pathology*.

A distinguished teacher and investigator in chemical and general pathology, Wells was the son of Romanta Wells, a pharmacist. He graduated in 1895, from the Sheffield Scientific School of Yale University, where he was particularly influenced by the biochemist Lafayette B. Mendel. He received the M.D. from Rush Medical College in Chicago in 1898, became assistant there to the pathologist Ludvig Hektoen, and in 1901 entered the department of pathology of the University of Chicago, of which Hektoen was titular chief. Wells was given a free hand in developing the department and was promoted through the ranks to full professor in 1913 and head of the department in 1932. In 1904–1905 he spent a fruitful year with Emil Fischer in Berlin.

Wells was a gifted teacher and a productive investigator, with a genius for succinct compilation of significant literature in his fields of interest. His widely diversified research led to his general acceptance as the country's chief authority on chemical aspects of pathology and immunology, and *Chemical Pathology* (1907) went through five editions.

Like other pathologists Wells found a wealth of important subjects for research in his frequent postmortem examinations. His practice of engaging in personal research on problems about which he felt his knowledge was inadequate led him to studies on fat necrosis, resulting in a clear understanding of this condition; of tissue autolysis, and especially its relation to histological change in the cell nucleus in disease processes; of enzyme changes involved in cell autolysis; of pathological calcification (still recognized as among the country's best studies); of fatty degeneration of the liver, in which his findings are basic to modern knowledge; and unusually productive investigations, in cooperation with Thomas B. Osborne, of the chemical composition of proteins as determined by immunological methods. With Maude Slye and other associates he carried out a long series of investigations of cancer, including its hereditary aspects, that now forms part of the background of this extensive field of medical research.

After 1911, concomitantly with his professorship, Wells was director of medical research at the Sprague Memorial Institute, a medical organization affiliated with the University of Chicago. During and after World War I he was Red Cross commissioner to Rumania, with heavy responsibilities for relief work in the Balkans.

In 1902 Wells married Bertha Robbins; their only son, Gideon R. Wells, became a practicing physician.

*BIBLIOGRAPHY*

I. ORIGINAL WORKS. Wells's writings include *Chemical Pathology* (Philadelphia, 1907; 5th ed., 1925); *The Chemistry of Tuberculosis* (Baltimore, 1923; 2nd ed., 1932), written with L. M. DeWitt and E. R. Long; and *The Chemical Aspects of Immunity* (New York, 1925; 2nd ed., 1929).

II. SECONDARY LITERATURE. See P. R. Cannon, "H. Gideon Wells, M.D., Ph.D., 1875–1943," in *Archives of Pathology*, **36** (1943), 331–334; and E. R. Long, "Biographical Memoir of Harry Gideon Wells, 1875–1943," in *Biographical Memoirs. National Academy of Sciences*, **26** (1950), 233–263.

ESMOND R. LONG

**WELLS, WILLIAM CHARLES** (*b.* Charleston, South Carolina, 24 May 1757; *d.* London, England, 18 September 1817), *meteorology, physiology, medicine, natural philosophy.*

Wells was the son of Robert Wells, a printer, and Mary Wells, Scots recently settled in America. At the age of eleven he was sent to Dumfries, Scotland, for schooling; and in 1770 he entered the University of Edinburgh. From 1771 to 1774 he was apprenticed to Alexander Garden, a Charleston physician with an international reputation in botany. He subsequently studied medicine at Edinburgh (1775–1778) and then went to St. Bartholomew's Hospital, London. Wells wrote his thesis, "De frigore," at Leiden and received the M.D. from the University of Edinburgh on 24 July 1780. After practicing at Charleston and at St. Augustine, Florida (1781–1784), he returned to London. He was licensed by the Royal College of Physicians in 1788 and was physician at St. Thomas' Hospital from 1795 until his death. Wells's practice was small, his life austere, and his circle of friends small but distinguished. He suffered from heart failure after 1812 and wrote a memoir on his life in what he correctly thought was his last year. It was published in 1818, together with a collection of his most important works and a violent criticism of the Royal College of Physicians.

Wells's essay "Single Vision With Two Eyes" (1792) led to his becoming a fellow of the Royal Society (1793). In 1795 he published a confirmation of Galvani's report (1791) that muscular contraction could be evoked by weak electrical currents. During the next two decades he wrote on the color of blood, conducted further studies on vision and optics, and provided accurate descriptions of rheumatic heart disease, of proteinuria, hematuria, and edema due to scarlet fever, and similar cases not due to scarlatina. The studies of albuminuria, promptly translated into French and published at Geneva in 1814, prepared the way for the definitive observations of Richard Bright (1827).

Wells's most important contribution was his meticulous study of the formation of dew and the correct interpretation of his data. He proved that dew is neither invisible rain, falling from heaven, nor "sweat" from plants, but is due to condensation from air in contact with objects that have been cooled by radiating their heat into the cloudless night sky. He showed that a dark substance, charcoal, accumulated more dew than pale material, such as chalk, and that poor conductors of heat, such as plants, were covered with more dew than good conductors, such as metal objects. He also noted that windless nights favored dew formation, because they allowed the air to remain in contact with the cooled objects long enough to deposit its moisture. Although criticized by such eminent men as Thomas Young, the "Essay on Dew" (1814) led to Wells's being awarded the Royal Society's Rumford Medal. This complete and original theory was not generally accepted until its confirmation and extension by John Aitken in 1885.

Charles Darwin considered Wells to have been the first to state the theory of evolution by natural selection of those best fitted to survive in a given environment. His "Observations on the Causes of the Differences in Colour and Form Between the White and Negro Races of Men" was appended to a case report of a white woman with patchy brown discoloration of the skin. He noted how man improves domestic beasts by selection and drew an analogy to the way in which nature effects a similar development of varieties of men best suited to various climates.

Because he pioneered in the study of disease and of the physiology of vision, as well as in natural science, Wells has been claimed as an early American scientist. He was born and remained a loyal British subject, and chose to study, work, and practice at Edinburgh and London. Nevertheless, most articles dealing with his life and work have been written by American physicians, and the New York Academy of Medicine files his publications in its collection of rare Americana.

*BIBLIOGRAPHY*

I. ORIGINAL WORKS. At Wells's request the works he considered most important were republished in one volume with an autobiographical memoir as *Two Essays:*

*Upon Single Vision With Two Eyes. On Dew . . .* (London, 1818) (the other titles follow). Most of his papers on medical topics, heart and kidney disease, and so on are in *Transactions of the Society for Improvement of Medical and Chirurgical Knowledge,* **2** (1808) and **3** (1812).

II. SECONDARY LITERATURE. Wells's life is reviewed in *Dictionary of National Biography* and by E. Bartlett, in *Western Journal of Medicine and Surgery,* 3rd ser., **5** (1850), 22–44; W. Dock, in *California and Western Medicine,* **31** (1929), 340–341; and F. S. Pleadwell, in *Annals of Medical History,* n.s. **6** (1934), 128–142.

WILLIAM DOCK

**WENDELIN (VENDELINUS), GOTTFRIED** (*b.* Herck-la-Ville (or Herk), Belgium, 6 June 1580; *d.* Ghent, Belgium, 1667), *astronomy, meteorology, natural science, humanism, law.*

In the laudatory style of the period, Wendelin was called the Ptolemy of his age. He studied first in his native place and then at Tournai and at Louvain, where at the age of seventeen he observed a lunar eclipse. He subsequently spent time in Nuremberg, Marseilles, Rome, and Digne, before returning to Liège and Herck. He was ordained priest at Brussels and became a curate and a canon of Condé and Tournai, where he was an official of the cathedral. Like many deeply Catholic scientists, he was more attracted by the physical sciences and mathematics than by the biological sciences.

A convinced Copernican, Wendelin upheld his views with a courage that is the more impressive when it is recalled that both Descartes and Galileo were obliged to have their works (respectively, *Discours de la méthode* [1637] and *Discorsi* [1638]) printed in Protestant Holland. The Protestant presses of Leiden had become vital organs in the dissemination of new ideas. Wendelin's audacity appears all the greater in the light of the misfortunes experienced even much later, in 1691, by Martin-Étienne van Velden, a professor at the University of Louvain. A century and a half after Copernicus (1543) and four years after Newton (1687), the rector of the university formally ordered the arrest of van Velden for having attempted to make a student say that one cannot doubt the Copernican system regarding the movement of the planets around the sun.[1]

Wendelin was apparently the first to propose a law of the variation of the obliquity of the ecliptic. According to Bigourdan, Wendelin also observed the influence of temperature on the period of the oscillations of a pendulum, noting that the oscillations are more numerous in winter than in summer. He also recognized—as Galileo had not—that an increase in amplitude increases the period of the oscillations.

Wendelin corresponded with Mersenne, Gassendi, whom he taught astronomy, and Constantijn Huygens.[2] They were all younger than Wendelin. In a letter to Plempius, Descartes solicited Wendelin's opinion of his *Géométrie.*[3] In a letter to Colvius, Descartes wrote: "I'auois aussi desia vu la lampe de Vendelinus [*G. W. Luminarcani . . . Lampas*]; mais elle ne m'a point esclairé."[4] Finally, in a letter to Constantijn Huygens, Descartes praised Wendelin for his *Pluvia purpurea,* calling him "homme sçauant aux Mathematiques, et de tres-bon esprit."[5]

While Wendelin does not appear in the first four volumes of *The Correspondence of Isaac Newton,* he does figure among the seventy-one authors cited in the *Principia* (1687). There he has the honor of being mentioned in the company of Ptolemy, Huygens, Copernicus, Street, Tycho Brahe, and Kepler (book III, proposition 4, theorem 4).

*NOTES*

1. See J. Pelseneer, in *Biographie nationale publiée par l'Académie royale de Belgique,* XXVI (1936–1938), cols. 562–567.
2. *Correspondance du P. Marin Mersenne,* C. de Waard, R. Pintard, and B. Rochot, eds. (Paris, 1932–    ); see the indexes to vols. 2–6, 8–10, and 12.
3. See letter of 3 October 1637, in *Oeuvres de Descartes,* C. Adam and P. Tannery, eds., I (Paris, 1897), 411.
4. Letter of 5 September 1643, in *Oeuvres de Descartes, Supplément, Index général* (1913), 16.
5. Letter of 5 October 1646, in *Oeuvres de Descartes,* IV, 516.

*BIBLIOGRAPHY*

I. ORIGINAL WORKS. Wendelin's works are *Loxias seu de obliquitate solis diatriba . . .* (Antwerp, 1626); *De diluvio liber primus* (Antwerp, 1629); *Id . . . secundus* (incomplete); *Aries seu aurei velleris encomium* (ca. 1632); *De tetracty Pythagorae dissertatio epistolica* (1637); *G. W. Luminarcani . . . Lampas* (Brussels, 1644); *Eclipses lunares ab anno 1573 ad 1643 observatae* (Antwerp, 1644); *Pluvia purpurea Bruxellensis* (Paris, 1647); *Leges salicae illustratae* (Antwerp, 1649); *Luminarcani, Teratologia cometica . . .* (1652); *De causis naturalibus pluviae purpureae Bruxellensis . . .* (London, 1655); *Epistola didactica de calcedonio lapide . . .* (ca. 1655); and *Arcanorum caelestium Sphinx et Oedipus . . .* (Tournai, 1658).

II. SECONDARY LITERATURE. On Wendelin and his

work, see the notice by Lucien Godeaux, in *Biographie nationale publiée par l'Académie royale de Belgique*, XXVII (1938), cols. 180–184, with a bibliography.

JEAN PELSENEER

**WENT, FRIEDRICH AUGUST FERDINAND CHRISTIAN** (*b.* Amsterdam, Netherlands, 18 June 1863; *d.* Wassenaar, near The Hague, Netherlands, 24 July 1935), *botany.*

Went studied at the University of Amsterdam under Hugo de Vries. As director of a sugarcane experimental station in Kagok, Java (1891–1896), he worked on cane diseases and on the physiology of sugarcane. He established that the first product of photosynthesis is sucrose and determined the sugar concentrations in leaves and stalk during the lifetime of the cane, thereby providing the basis for a method of determining the maturity of cane in the field that is still used. This early experience resulted in a lifelong interest in and promotion of research in tropical agriculture.

Twice during his tenure as professor of botany and director of the botanical laboratory and gardens at the University of Utrecht (1896–1934), the laboratory was rebuilt and enlarged, making it one of the most modern of botanical institutions and a model for many other laboratories.

Went's personal research became increasingly limited because of very heavy teaching duties, but his work (1901) on enzyme formation in the fungus *Monilia* (now named *Neurospora*) was the forerunner of very fruitful work on the biochemistry of *Neurospora*. In later years he became interested in the anatomy and embryology of Podostemonaceae, a family of flowering plants found only in rapids and waterfalls, on which he published extensively (1908–1929).

Went exerted his greatest influence on the development of botany in the first half of the twentieth century through the research of his graduate students. The "Utrecht school" became known for work in many areas of plant physiology, especially temperature responses, tropisms, and auxins. When F. F. Blackman published his important paper on physiological processes and limiting factors (1905), the experimental basis for his theory was meager. Some of the most significant support for Blackman's theory of limiting factors was supplied by Went's students during the next twenty-five years.

The second major contribution of the Utrecht school was work on tropisms, spearheaded by Blaauw's thesis on phototropism. This work for the first time placed tropisms—the responses of plants to environmental factors such as light and gravity—on a quantitative basis, and it became clear that responses to light were explainable strictly as photochemical reactions. An extension of this work explained phototropic responses as differential growth reactions to differential light intensities.

This reduction of phototropism to differential growth initiated the third major research contribution of the Utrecht school, the work on auxins. Went and his colleague Fritz Kögl were the most effective advocates of introducing the concept of plant growth hormones into European biological circles, and the eight theses on auxin published at Utrecht between 1927 and 1934 formed the basis for modern ideas about plant hormones.

Went, especially as president of the Royal Netherlands Academy of Sciences (Amsterdam), contributed immeasurably to improved international understanding among scientists.

*BIBLIOGRAPHY*

Went's works, published mainly in the *Verhandelingen* of the Royal Netherlands Academy of Sciences, include *De jongste toestanden der vacuolen* (Amsterdam, 1886), his doctoral diss.; and *Untersuchungen über Podostemaceen*, 3 pts. (Amsterdam 1910–1926); he also collaborated on vol. II of the German ed. of S. P. Kostychev, *Lehrbuch der Pflanzenphysiologie* (Berlin, 1931). For a list of his writings, see Royal Netherlands Academy of Sciences (Afd. natuurkunde), *Naamregister van de Verhandelingen en Bijdragen*, I (Amsterdam, 1943), 65; and II (1944), 148–149.

There is an obituary by J. van der Hoeve, in *Verslagen van de gewone vergadering der Afdeeling natuurkunde, K. Akademie van Wetenschappen*, **44** (1935), 90–95.

F. W. WENT

**WEPFER, JOHANN-JAKOB** (*b.* Schaffhausen, Switzerland, 23 December 1620; *d.* Schaffhausen, 26 January 1695), *medicine, physiology, toxicology.*

Wepfer graduated from the secondary school in Schaffhausen. Among his teachers was Johannes Fabritius of the Palatinate, who taught him natural history and instilled in him a passion for observing the living world. In 1637 Wepfer left Schaffhausen for Strasbourg and then went to Padua, where he studied at the Faculty of Medicine and Pharmacy. In 1647 he received the doctorate in medicine at

Basel and became municipal physician of Schaff-hausen, where he remained as physician and scientist. Although Wepfer never occupied a faculty chair—Schaffhausen had no university—he had numerous students, J. C. Payer and J. C. Brunner among them, from throughout Europe. He also became the private physician of several German princes, as well as a famous consultant.

In 1647 Wepfer presented two dissertations, *Disputatio medica inauguralis de palpitatione cordis* and *Oratio de thermarum potu*. In 1648, when he became municipal physician of Schaffhausen, he was given the right to perform autopsies and made extremely complex observations, using a novel method that was not taken up again until the nineteenth century. He first followed the evolution of an illness, carefully noting all its symptoms. He completed his investigations upon cadavers. Wepfer later sought to confirm his hypotheses by performing experiments on animals, which he described in reports published mainly in the *Miscellanea curiosa* issued by the Leopoldina.

Wepfer's major research centered on the brain and, being a skilled experimentalist, he devised new techniques. For instance, he was the first to color cervical vessels through injecting dye. The essentials of his anatomical observations concerning the nervous system are presented in *Historia anatomica de puella sine cerebro nata* (1665). In his classic work, reprinted many times, *Observationes anatomicae ex cadaveribus eorum, quos sustulit apoplexia, cum exercitatione de eius loco affecto* (Schaffhausen, 1658), he collected a large number of original observations based on comparative anatomy of human cadavers. In it he was the first to report that apoplexy involved hemorrhage from blood vessels.

It was in toxicological analysis, however, that Wepfer made his greatest contributions. He systematically studied poisons, with particular attention to the toxic substances synthesized by certain umbellifers, especially the poison and water hemlocks. He was the first to analyze the pharmacological effects of coniine, an alkaloid of hemlock that was not isolated until much later; and his classic description of hemlock poisoning was often cited as the standard. He also experimented upon animals and found an efficacious remedy: the administration of strong emetics. At the same time he noted that coniine, in minute doses, could be useful as an antineuralgic and antispasmodic. He also discovered its remarkable analgesic effect and was the first to use it in minor surgery. One of his publications was *Cicutae aquaticae historia et noxae*

*commentario illustrata* (Basel, 1679). His numerous discoveries about poisons and their uses made Wepfer an undoubted pioneer in toxicology. He also studied the characteristics of mercury poisoning and was the first to indicate the dangers for workers with this metal who fail to take the proper precautions. This study led him to publish articles on occupational diseases.

After Wepfer's death his heirs, B. and G. M. Wepfer, published some of his writings as *Observationes medico-practicae de affectibus capitis internis et externis* (Schaffhausen, 1727). As a scholarly physician Wepfer made a tremendous contribution to medical treatment and research through his resolute opposition to the influence of dogmatic and traditionalist scientists who stressed ancient texts rather than actual facts.

*BIBLIOGRAPHY*

Wepfer's works are cited in the text.
Secondary literature includes H. Buess, *Recherches, découvertes et inventions de médecins suisses*, R. Kaech, trans. (Basel, 1946), 25–26; and H. Fischer, *J. Jakob Wepfer* (Zurich, 1931); and *Briefe J. J. Wepfer an seinem Sohn Johann Conrad* (Leipzig, 1943).

P. E. PILET

**WERNER, ABRAHAM GOTTLOB** (*b.* Wehrau, Upper Lusatia [now Osiecznica, Poland], 25 September 1749; *d.* Dresden, Germany, 30 June 1817), *geology, mineralogy*.

Werner was the only son of Abraham David Werner and Regina Holstein Werner. He had one older sister, Sophia. His family had a long history of association with various ironworks, and his father was inspector of the Duke of Solm's ironworks in Wehrau and Lorenzdorf. The family was well off financially. According to his own "Biographical Notes," Werner received his first formal education from his father, who encouraged his early interest in mineralogy. He also studied with a private tutor before entering the Waisenschule at Bunzlau (now Boleslawiec, Poland) at the age of nine. He remained at the Waisenschule until 1764, when his mother died and his father took him out of the school and made him a *Hüttenschreiber*[1] in the ironworks. After five years of this work, in 1769, Werner was enrolled in the recently founded Bergakademie Freiberg and began studies intended to prepare him for the administration of the Duke of Solm's ironworks.

However, in Freiberg, he was induced to enter

the Saxon mining service; and since no one could expect to achieve an advanced position in the service without a degree in jurisprudence, Werner left the Bergakademie after two years to enter the University of Leipzig, where he studied for three years. During his first two years at the university, he devoted himself mainly to the necessary courses in law, but he became increasingly interested in the study of languages and what is now called historical linguistics, and his interest in mineralogy persisted, until he abandoned the study of law altogether, leaving the university in 1774 without a degree.

In 1773, however, he had written his first book, *Von den äusserlichen Kennzeichen der Fossilien*, which was published in 1774. On the strength of its immediate success, his friend and former teacher K. E. Pabst von Ohain suggested to the Board of the Bergakademie that he be offered a position as teacher of mining and curator of the mineral collection there. Werner accepted the offer, joining the faculty in 1775, and remained at the school for the rest of his life. During his forty-two years there, largely because of his fame as a mineralogist and his skill as a teacher, the little mining academy became one of the most famous schools in the world. And in turn Werner came to be acknowledged as the foremost geologist of his day. He moved in a brilliant circle of friends and was received at the Saxon court. Among his many illustrious students, he counted not only such noted geologists and mineralogists as Leopold von Buch, Alexander von Humboldt, Jean d'Aubuisson de Voisins, Robert Jameson, and Friedrich Mohs, but also such romantic philosophers and writers as Gotthilf Heinrich von Schubert, Henrik Steffens, and Friedrich von Hardenberg (Novalis).

During his lifetime Werner was elected to twenty-two scientific societies, including the Geological Society of London, the Institut National and the Institut Impérial of France, the Imperial Society of Physics and Medicine of Moscow, the Royal Prussian Academy of Sciences, the Royal Stockholm Academy of Sciences, and the Wernerian Society of Edinburgh. During his last years he suffered increasingly from ill health, going frequently to take the waters at various health resorts. He never married, and the will that he dictated shortly before his death bequeathed most of his estate to the Bergakademie Freiberg, which had been such an important part of his life and work.

Although Werner is best known for his contribution to the founding of geology as a science, he first achieved recognition as a mineralogist. He considered mineralogy to be the basis for all study of the earth, dividing it into five branches, of which geognosy (historical geology) was one and oryctognosy (descriptive mineralogy) another. And during all the years in which his theories on geognosy were arousing so much interest and controversy, he continued to work on his mineral system, the final version of which appeared after his death in 1817. His first important mineralogical work, however, *Von den äusserlichen Kennzeichen der Fossilien*, was not a mineral system but a classification of external characteristics of minerals, designed to aid the worker or the student in the field. In it Werner gave an unprecedented number of external characteristics with definitions, usually accompanied by homely examples which could be understood by both the layman and the natural philosopher. He also attempted to establish some standards of quantification and thus to clear away the vagueness in the terminology then in use. As chemistry and crystallography developed, mineralogists came to rely more on chemical analysis and less on external characteristics, but *Von den äusserlichen Kennzeichen der Fossilien*, published when Werner was twenty-five years old, continued to be an important work into the nineteenth century. Thomas Weaver's translation into English was published in Dublin in 1805, and a revised translation by Charles Moxon appeared in 1849.

Werner remained convinced of the importance of external characteristics, not only in the identification of minerals but also in the study of their composition. He reasoned that since the appearance of a mineral changes when its chemical composition is changed, there should be a correlation between chemical composition and external characteristics. On the other hand, he recognized that external characteristics cannot form the basis of a mineral system. He wrote: "One can indeed recognize in the external character of minerals the differences of their composition, provided both are previously determined, but the correlation between these two features cannot be discovered in them."[2] He was convinced that ultimately mineral systems must be based on chemical composition, and to that end he kept abreast of developments in chemistry and helped to bring about the building of a chemical laboratory at the Bergakademie and the engagement of W. A. Lampadius as teacher of chemistry. He himself analyzed minerals in his laboratory and stayed in close contact with M. H. Klaproth, who has been called the founder of quantitative mineral analysis.

In his later years, however, Werner took the position that chemistry was still not sufficiently developed for mineralogy to rely upon it completely. In his own system he retained the four traditional classes—earths, salts, combustibles, and metals—and he began to give priority to geological rather than chemical considerations. A good example is his classification of the diamond among the earths rather than the combustibles, even though he was well aware that the diamond is a carbon. He wrote:

> The diamond, . . ., is by nature, according to its exterior, characterized wholly as an earthy mineral, as a stone. Its geognostic occurrence also speaks for its place among the earths, because the diamond, as far as is known, occurs only with and among stones, and not among combustible minerals, among which it has recently been classed. All uses which are made of it are as a stone. And finally, its identification is not aided in any way by placing it, in lectures and mineral collections, among earth pitch, the three coal species, graphite, and so forth; but it is helpful to place it with the far more similar zircon and the other gems. Let the mineralogical chemist regard this stone as one of the coals and place it among them; but he should permit the oryctognost to act according to the purpose he has in mind in placing the diamond in an oryctognostic system.[3]

Werner considered crystallography to be only a branch of mineralogy, which, although important to the study of mineralogy, is unsuitable as a basis for a mineral system and of limited practical value. However, he did study crystallography himself. He emphasized its importance in his lectures, and urged his students to study it. He was well acquainted with the work of Romé de l'Isle and Haüy, being especially interested in the study of primary crystal forms, especially with what Haüy came to call laws of decrement (décroissement). In his own system he incorporated crystal form as an external characteristic.

In spite of his abiding interest in the practical aspects of mineralogy, Werner was not merely a practical mineralogist. Throughout his scientific life, he was concerned with the philosophical aspects of classification in general and of mineral classification in particular. His fullest exposition of his ideas on this subject was published without his permission in 1816 under the title "Werner's oryctognostische Classifikationslehre." In a manuscript of this treatise, Werner wrote that the work represented more than forty years of reflection and research.

The article is especially concerned with the various classificatory categories which Werner understood and the three fundamental tasks of the classification of minerals: *Gattierung, Gradierung,* and *Reihung*—that is, the determination of species, which he considered to be the cornerstone of a mineral system; the establishment of categories more general and less general than species; and the establishment, wherever possible, of kinships among the members of a particular classificatory category. Werner believed that there are only two possible kinds of kinship among minerals. One leads to a complete transition, or *Übergang*, in which "the crystallization suite of one species is so closely related to that of another that both are able to cross over completely into the other."[4] In the other, which he called *Aneinanderstossen* ("coming in touch with one another"), the minerals are related to one another interruptedly, making a complete transition impossible.

Werner's mineral system, complete as it stood at the time, was published three times, once in 1789, once in 1816, and again in 1817. In addition, parts of it appeared incorporated in other works. In 1780 Werner's partial translation of Axel Cronstedt's *Försök til Mineralogie* was published. Werner believed that, at the time, Cronstedt's work was the best available on the subject. He translated only the portion dealing with earths and stones, however, correcting errors, adding information on the constitution of minerals, and making extensive additions concerning external characteristics. His comments and additions so enlarged Cronstedt's work that his translation became a textbook of mineralogy in its own right and was widely used as a teaching aid and reference work.

In 1791–1793 Werner's two-volume catalog of Pabst von Ohain's mineral collection appeared. In this work Werner not only incorporated his mineral system but also put into practice his ideas of what should constitute a complete mineral cabinet, a subject which he had discussed in a 1778 article, "Von den verschiedenerley Mineraliensammlungen, aus denen ein vollständiges Mineralienkabinet bestehen soll." In the article Werner emphasized that a mineral collection should be more than a systematic arrangement of minerals: it should further the understanding of the entire mineral kingdom. He therefore cataloged Pabst von Ohain's collection in five separate collections according to external characteristics, the natural order of minerals in a mineral system, the historical development of the earth's crust, the places of origin of minerals, and the uses of minerals. Von Ohain's collection was ultimately sold to the government of Portugal and shipped to Brazil, where it was used in the teaching of geology and mineralogy in Rio de Janeiro. And the catalog, which was widely used in Europe, was one of the important avenues through which Werner's influence on mineralogy and geology was spread.

None of the complete editions of Werner's system was prepared by Werner himself. The 1789 version was prepared under his supervision by his student C. A. S. Hoffman and was published with Werner's permission. It was also Hoffman who, along with another student, A. W. Köhler, revised the system in 1812 (this is the version which was published in 1816). The 1817 edition, which was published posthumously by order of the Saxon government, was prepared from Werner's notes by his students J. C. Freiesleben, August Breithaupt, and Köhler.

It is interesting to look at the 1789 and the 1817 versions together, for they show not only the changes in Werner's system but also the progress that mineralogy had made in the intervening years. The most striking difference between them is that the earlier work covers only 183 species, whereas the later one covers 317. Of these 317, Werner had independently discovered eight and had given names to numerous others. The names of the eight minerals that he discovered, as well as twenty-six other names which he employed, are still used today to designate the same minerals to which Werner applied them.[5]

Werner's scientific life spanned a time of unusual interest in mineralogy, an interest not confined to scientists but fostered to a large extent by romantic conceptions on the one hand and utilitarian considerations on the other. The store of mineralogical knowledge was rapidly increasing; and advances in chemistry, crystallography, and geology were opening new paths for the study of mineralogy. Through his own research Werner added to the knowledge of mineralogy and helped to systematize that knowledge. Through his teaching and writing he contributed greatly to the dissemination of knowledge. Conservative and cautious, he was always hesitant to add a "new" mineral to his system until he was certain that it was really a mineral and really new; and, although he was willing to employ new methods, he was always reluctant to abandon old ones which he felt had proved their worth. Thus, Werner was a steadying influence at a time of great and varied activity. His work represents the culmination of a long development in mineralogy and the beginning of a new mineralogy, of which he was fully conscious.

Although many earlier writers had speculated on the origin of the earth's crust, Werner is rightly called the father of historical geology, for he was the first to work out a complete, universally applicable geological system. It was he who, more than any other, made geology into a science and an academic discipline. According to William Brande, ". . . to him belongs the principal merit of pointing up the order of succession which the various natural families of rocks are generally found to present, and of having himself developed that order to a considerable extent, with a degree of accuracy which before his time was unobtainable. . . ."[6]

Werner's interest in historical geology stemmed partly from his interest in mineralogy and partly from his interest in mining. But it also reflected his interest in history, for he believed that natural history is an important branch of the history of man, and he felt that the earth's crust is a more reliable source of history than written histories. His system was based on the principle of geological succession, as Brande indicates, and all his geological work was consistent with this historical principle as he saw it.

Werner was well versed in the mineralogical and geological literature of his day, being familiar with the writings of the leading exponents of both fire and water as the major agent in the creation of the earth's crust. A list of writers on geology that he prepared includes among others Steno, Lehmann, Ferber, Hamilton, Füchsel, Saussure, Buffon, and Moro. His own ideas were undoubtedly influenced in one way or another by what he had read and, in fact, his theories bear a rather striking resemblance to those of Steno, with whose work he was apparently familiar.[7] But whatever the background of his theories, Werner thought, on the basis of the geological knowledge of his day, that they were firmly supported by the evidence—a fact which goes far to explain the popularity of his system. Unlike Steno, Lehmann, Moro, and many other earlier and even contemporary writers on geology, he felt no need to fit his theories into the biblical story of creation. There is no indication in his writings, published or unpublished, that any of the floods which are an important part of his theory was the biblical flood. His early religious background was Pietist, at the university he was accused of being an atheist, and in general his attitudes reflected the deism of the eighteenth century. Thus, although his theories, being basically neptunistic, were more acceptable to the defenders of the biblical account of creation than those of the vulcanists, he himself was in no way engaged in the religious aspects of the controversy.

The two basic postulates of the Wernerian theory were that the earth was once enveloped by a universal ocean and that all the important rocks that make up the crust of the earth were either precipitates or sediments from that ocean. Werner placed the rocks in four (later five) classes according to the period in which they were formed, believing that characteristics of the rocks were the result of the depth, content, and conditions of the universal ocean at the time when they were formed. His classification was basically historical. As he himself put it,

> I had to be guided completely in the classificatory presentation or tabulation of these masses by the discoverable time sequence of the particular formations if I wanted to remain true to my plan to sketch through this classification a foundation for a complete canvass of the universal formation of these masses.[8]

Although he did not conceive of the immensity of geological time on the same scale as present-day scientists do, he did write of a time "when the waters, perhaps 1,000,000 years ago, completely covered our earth . . ."; and in his lectures he spoke of the history of the earth "in contrast to which written history is only a point in time."[9] In order to discover the time sequence of rock formation, he used various means, such as compositional and textural features and, especially, the structure of rocks and stratigraphic relations, which he considered the most important clues to the understanding of the history of the earth's crust. His theory included two unexplained general risings of the universal ocean as well as some local floods; but he believed that, in general, the waters had receded very slowly but steadily. The four periods of formation and their corresponding classes of rocks were the primitive, the floetz, the volcanic, and the alluvial.

At the beginning of the primitive period, according to Werner's theory, the universal ocean was very deep and calm; and the first rocks were chemical precipitates which adhered to an originally uneven surface, granite being the first rock formed. Gradually the waters became less calm, so that later rocks of the primitive period are not as crystalline as the older ones; and toward the end of the period there was a general rising of the waters, followed by a comparatively rapid recession, which explains the position of some of the later primitive rocks relative to the older ones. No life existed during the primitive period, and thus the primitive rocks are entirely free of fossils.

The floetz period was characterized by storms in the then low-standing ocean and by the development of life in great abundance, the storms destroying much of the newly developed life as well as some of the older rocks. Once again there was a general inundation, with the waters this time reaching a greater height than ever before. It is with these variations from stormy to calm to stormy and the general inundation that Werner explains the relative position of the floetz rocks and their often broken stratification.

The volcanic and alluvial periods are almost contemporaneous and both extend into the present (as does the floetz period). The volcanic and alluvial rocks, however, are not deposits from the universal ocean but the result of local conditions.

Werner added the transition period and the class of transition rocks to his system after the discovery that some rocks which he had previously classified as primitive contain fossils. According to his explanation, the relatively low-standing waters toward the end of the primitive period were calm at first, but gradually they became increasingly stormy, destroying some of the previously formed rocks as well as some living organisms, which had just begun to develop. Some of the rocks formed from these stormy waters are chemical precipitates and some mechanical depositions.

Thus the Wernerian system in its final form included five periods of formation: primitive, transition, floetz, volcanic, and alluvial. The rocks of the first three periods, which constitute most of the earth's crust, were precipitates or deposits from the universal ocean, those of the two later periods the result of local conditions.

Since Werner believed that the contents of the universal ocean had varied from time to time and from place to place, his theory could account for variations from the general principle that the rocks had been laid down by the universal ocean in layers one above the other. For instance, if the essential contents had at some time been missing from some part of the ocean, an entire formation might be missing from the corresponding area of the earth's crust. Also, there is nothing in the theory to preclude the formation of similar rocks at different times. Thus, it is only in an idealization of the system that the rocks of the earth's crust can be envisioned as enveloping the earth in layers much like the layers of an onion. In fact, the theory was flexible enough that, with the addition of factors such as differential settling and the subsequent effects of erosion, cave-ins, etc., it could explain virtually all the phenomena which were observable in Werner's time. Through his personal magnetism and skill as a teacher, Werner was able to inspire a host of eager students and admirers to go out to attempt that complete canvass of the earth's crust which he had hoped that his system would make possible.

Werner's geological theories were first included in his teaching in the introduction to the course on mining, which he had taught since his arrival at the Bergakademie. By the academic year 1778–1779 he had recognized that he could not cover this theoretical part of the course as thoroughly as he wished in one year and at the same time give sufficient practical instruction. He therefore announced that he would offer the theoretical introduction as a separate course entitled "Lehre von den Gebirgen." Although this was the course which eventually attracted students from all over Europe and from the Americas, bringing fame to the Bergakademie and spreading Werner's theories, it did not attract many students at first; and it was not until the academic year 1786–1787 that it began to be offered yearly. In the meantime, Werner had written his "Kurze Klassifikation und Beschreibung der verschiedenen Gebirgsarten," which was published in the 1786 volume of *Abhandlungen der Böhmischen Gesellschaft der Wissenschaften* and subsequently in at least two pamphlet editions.

Short though it is, the "Kurze Klassifikation" is important to the history of geology for a number of reasons. Although it contains no discussion of Werner's theories, it exemplifies them; and it is the only printed presentation of those theories to come from Werner's own hand. The principle of geologic succession is implicit in it. The rocks are classified according to the period of formation, and virtually all are assumed to be of aqueous origin. The "Kurze Klassifikation" was the first work to separate rock classification from the classification of minerals, and thus it did much to establish petrography as an independent branch of the geological sciences. It gave clear definitions of rocks, many of which had not previously been generally agreed upon. And it inspired the research of many geologists, including many who did not accept Werner's theories, well into the nineteenth century. But the "Kurze Klassifikation" is also important in another way. In a note on the section dealing with volcanic rocks, Werner asserted for the first time that all basalt is of aqueous origin, thus precipitating the great basalt controversy.

Until the end of the eighteenth century, it was generally agreed that granite is of aqueous origin; and many other rocks now considered to be mag-

matic played only a minor role in discussions of the origin of volcanoes. Therefore, for a long time, the whole question of the relative importance of fire and water as agents in the creation of the earth's crust revolved about the origin of basalt, since basalt is so abundant and so widely distributed. There had long been differences of opinion on the matter; but at the time when Werner entered the debate, the weight of opinion seemed to favor igneous origin. Werner's assertion received a great deal of publicity, however; and the debate was resumed with a fervor not shown before, as a host of geologists rushed into the field to seek evidence for one theory or the other.

As early as 1776 Werner had maintained that not all basalt is volcanic in origin. He had previously felt that the theory of the volcanic origin of basalt was "paradoxical," and an examination of the basalt mountain at Stolpen in Saxony had convinced him that that formation at least was of aqueous origin. Further investigations had strengthened his convictions, so that by the time of the publication of the "Kurze Klassifikation" he apparently felt prepared to defend his position. In the spring of 1787, he examined the basalt deposit at Scheibenberg, in the Erzgebirge, where he found layers of sand, clay, and wacke below basalt. He took this as indisputable evidence of the correctness of his assumption and subsequently wrote an article explaining his discovery. This article appeared in the *Intelligenzblatt* of the *Allgemeine Litteraturzeitung* of Jena in the autumn of 1788. In the meantime, the *Magazin für die Naturkunde Helvetiens* had offered a prize for the best essay in answer to the question "What is basalt?" Two of Werner's students entered the competition: J. C. W. Voigt, who advocated the volcanic origin of basalt, and J. F. W. Widenmann, who defended aqueous origin. With the appearance of Werner's article, Voigt wrote a letter to the *Intelligenzblatt* "correcting" Werner; Werner replied with some heat. Subsequently Werner wrote seven more short articles on the subject, all but one of which appeared in *Bergmännisches Journal* in the spring of 1789.[10] In September of the same year the *Magazin für die Naturkunde Helvetiens* published both Voigt's and Widenmann's essays in the same issue that carried Werner's article on the origin of volcanoes.[11] Widenmann won the prize; but neither essay settled the controversy, and the matter continued to be debated and investigated with keen interest for many years. Werner, however, took no further part in it except to explain in his *Neue Theorie von der Entstehung der Gänge* (1791) that basalt veins, like others, are the result of settling from above.

At the time, neither side had any means of proving conclusively that it was right. Petrography alone could not provide sufficient proof; microscopic methods were not then available; and chemical analysis, which showed great constitutional uniformity among basalts but great diversity among lavas, was hardly convincing. Werner's theory was better substantiated by evidence and reasoning than those of his opponents, at least until the 1790's. And it is to his credit as a teacher and investigator that his own students, trained in his methods of research, who had originally gone out to prove him right, were in many instances in the forefront of the investigations that ultimately proved him wrong.

Werner could never bring himself to place basalt among the volcanic rocks. He shifted it from the primitive to the floetz period; but to go further would have been to remove one of the cornerstones of his system, something that few scientists have ever been willing to do.

As a result of his interest in mineralogy and his long association with mining and smelting, Werner was of course interested in ores and ore deposits. But in order to remain faithful to his idea of a universally applicable geological system into which all observable phenomena would fit, he had to work out a theory of the origin of ore deposits which would be consistent with his general theory of the origin of the earth's crust. The result of his work in this area was the *Neue Theorie von der Entstehung der Gänge*, published in 1791.

In this work Werner defined veins as "particular mineral depositories of tabular shape, which in general traverse the strata of rocks . . . and are filled with mineral masses differing more or less from the rocks in which they occur."[12] He distinguished between veins and ore beds, giving an explanation which is in principle historical: minerals which occur in veins are very diverse and give every indication that they were formed during different periods than the surrounding rocks, whereas those in ore beds have the same direction as the strata among which they are found, indicating that they are of contemporaneous origin. He also gave a historical definition of the concept of a vein formation: "I designate all veins of one and the same origin as a vein formation . . . whether they are close together in one region or widely separated from one another in distant countries. . . ."[13]

Werner built his theory of the formation of veins on two major premises. The first of these is that "all true veins are really rents which (of necessity) were originally open and were only later filled from above."[14] He supported this premise on the basis of the structure of veins, comparisons of the structure of veins with that of the country rock, the structure of druses in veins, fragments of country rock in veins, analogy with existing rents, and the laws of mechanics. He explained the formation of rents as a result of diagenetic settling—compaction of the originally wet rock masses and the simultaneous loss of the support of the high-standing waters as these receded—shrinkage, and earthquakes. He thought that on the basis of his first premise the relative age and order of succession of veins, metals, ores, and vein minerals could be determined; and he formulated three criteria for determining the relative age of veins and vein stuff: (1) a vein is always newer than another which it traverses; (2) the materials in the center of a vein are newer than those near its walls, and those that are in its upper parts are newer than those in its lower parts; (3) a mineral which occurs above others in a specimen is newer than the others, and one that appears to be grown into others is older than they.

The second premise is that "the same depositions from water that formed the beds and strata of rock masses, and among these produced many ore-bearing ones, also formed the vein stuff; this took place during the time when the solution which contained such substances was standing above the already existing rents, which were wholly or partly open."[15] Werner pointed out that the materials in veins are structurally different from the same materials in beds and strata. In veins they are usually coarser and better crystallized because in veins they were not so much affected by the activities of the waters, and thus the deposition of materials in veins could proceed much more calmly than the depositions in beds and strata. On the basis of the structure of the vein stuff and the pattern of association of certain minerals, metals, and ores in veins, he tried to establish their relative ages and the sequence of their formation. Thus, he considered tin to be one of the oldest metal formations, since it occurs in granite, and bog iron-ore to be the newest, since it occurs in the alluvial lowland formations.

Neither of Werner's major premises was new, and his theory met with opposition even in his own day and was later discarded. However, many of its elements were of lasting value. Werner formulated basic questions about the origin and history of veins and their contents, established criteria for determining the relative age of veins and vein materials, and presented a comparative study of the structure of veins and rock masses. His student Breithaupt was probably the first to stimulate widespread research on the paragenesis of minerals, but it was Werner who set up the problem and gave impetus to a search for a solution. Perhaps the most important contribution of *Von der Entstehung der Gänge*, however, was that it made the study of vein formation an integral part of historical geology.

After the appearance of the second volume of his catalog of Pabst von Ohain's mineral cabinet in 1793, Werner published little on geology. In 1794, he published a fifty-page article, "Über den Trapp der Schweden," and a lecture which he had given before the Gesellschaft für Mineralogie zu Dresden was published after his death under the title "Allgemeine Betrachtungen über den festen Erdkörper." This work, however, was nothing but the introduction to his course on geognosy. A collection of works on mining and ferrous metallurgy, for which Werner had written three articles and coauthored another, appeared in 1811; however, all the articles had been written much earlier, before 1785.

In his later years, Werner devoted himself to his teaching and his duties as Councillor of Mines. He was always surrounded by students and received numerous visitors. The manuscripts that he left to the Bergakademie are extensive; but during the last twenty years of his life, his contributions to geology were made known largely by word of mouth. Yet he remained a towering figure in his field. Probably no other geologist has ever been so extensively eulogized by followers and opponents alike as he was during the two decades following his death.

## NOTES

1. A *Hüttenschreiber* was something of a combination bookkeeper, secretary, assayer, and payroll clerk.
2. *Äusserliche Kennzeichen*, 26–27.
3. S. G. Frisch, *Lebensbeschreibung . . . Werners*, 62–63.
4. Werner MSS.
5. Guntan and Rösler. *Werner Gedenkschrift*, 56–57.
6. W. T. Brande, *Outlines of Geology*, 20.
7. Two copies of Steno's *Prodromus*, one the 1763 ed., are among the books that Werner left to the Bergakademie library.
8. Unpublished reply to a review of the "Kurze Klassifikation," Werner MSS.
9. Geognosy, Werner MSS.
10. Of the six articles published in the *Bergmännische Journal* (1789), four were letters annotated by Werner, in which other geologists gave examples supporting his position. The seventh article, "Von den Butzen-Wacken zu Joachimsthal," was published in Crell's *Chemische Annalen*, **1** (1789).

11. Werner admitted that the concept of volcanoes resulting from the inflammation of coal beds was old, but he maintained that his elaboration of this concept and the proofs that he offered to support it were new.
12. Werner, *Neue Theorie von der Entstehung der Gänge*, 2–3.
13. *Ibid.*, 5–6.
14. *Ibid.*, 51–52.
15. *Ibid.*, 52.

## BIBLIOGRAPHY

I. ORIGINAL WORKS. Werner's writings include *Von den äusserlichen Kennzeichen der Fossilien* (Leipzig, 1774), English trans. by Thomas Weaver (Dublin, 1805), rev. trans. by Charles Moxon (London, 1849); "Von den verschiedernerley Mineraliensammlungen, aus denen ein vollständiges Mineralienkabinet bestehen soll . . .," in *Sammlungen zur Physik und Naturgeschichte von einigen Liebhabern dieser Wissenschaften*, **1** (1778), 387–420; *Axel Kronstedts Versuch einer Mineralogie. Aufs neue aus dem schwedischen übersetzt und nächst verschiedenen Anmerkungen vorzüglich mit aeussern Beschreibungen der Fossilein vermehrt von Abraham Gottlob Werner*, **2**, pt. 1 (Leipzig, 1780); "Kurze Klassifikation und Beschreibung der verschiedenen Gebirgsarten," in *Abhandlungen der Böhmischen Gesellschaft der Wissenschaften*, **2** (1786), 272–297; "Bekanntmachung einer am Scheibenberger Hügel über die Entstehung des Basaltes gemachten Entdeckung," in *Allgemeine Litteraturzeitung, Intelligenzblatt* (1788), no. 57, 484–485; "Antwort auf Herrn Bergsekretär Voigts im *Intelligenzblatte* der allgemeinen Litteraturzeitung . . . eingerückte sogennante Berichtigung meiner . . . neuen Entdeckung," *ibid.* (1789), no. 23, 179–184; "Mineralsystem des Herrn Inspektor Werners mit dessen Erlaubnis herausgegeben von C. A. S. Hoffman," in *Bergmännisches Journal*, **1** (1789), 369–398; and "Versuch einer Erklärung der Entstehung der Vulkanen durch die Entzündung mächtiger Steinkohlenschichten, als ein Beytrag zu der Naturgeschichte des Basalts," in *Magazin für die Naturkunde Helvetiens*, **4** (1789), 239–254.

Further works are *Neue Theorie von der Entstehung der Gänge, mit Anwendung auf den Bergbau besonders den freibergischen* (Freiberg, 1791); *Ausführliches und systematisches Verzeichnis des Mineralienkabinets des Herrn Karl Eugen Pabst von Ohain*, 2 vols. (Freiberg, 1791–1793); *Kleine Sammlung Berg- und Hüttenmännischer Schriften* (Leipzig, 1811); "Mineral-System des Herrn Bergrath Werner vom Jahre 1812," in *Neues Bergmännisches Journal*, **4** (1816), 204–231; "Werners oryctognostische Classifikationslehre," in *Hesperus* (1816), 345–349, 377–381, 414–416, 428–430; *Abraham Gottlob Werners letztes Mineral-System. Aus dessen Nachlass auf oberbergamtliche Anordnung herausgegeben und mit Erläuterungen versehen* (Freyberg, 1817); and "Allgemeine Betrachtungen über den festen Erdkörper," in *Auswahl aus den Schriften der unter Werners Mitwirkung gestifteten Gesellschaft für Mineralogie zu Dresden*, **1** (1818), 39–57.

A complete collection of Werner MSS is in the archives and library of the Bergakademie Freiberg. These have now been cataloged. Photostatic copies of some of these MSS are in the History of Science Collections of the University of Oklahoma, in the library of Oklahoma State University, and in the author's private collection. The catalog of the Bergakademie Freiberg collection has been published: Karl-Fritz Zillman, *Bestandsübersicht des handschriftlichen wissenschaftlichen Werner-Nachlasses*, publication no. 24 of the Library of the Bergakademie Freiberg (Freiberg, 1967).

II. SECONDARY LITERATURE. See *Abraham Gottlob Werner Gedenkschrift aus Anlasz der Wiederkehr seines Todestages nach 150 Jahren am 30. Juni 1967* (Leipzig, 1967), which contains the most extensive published bibliography on Werner; Richard Beck, "Abraham Gottlob Werner. Eine kritische Würdigung des Begründers der modernen Geologie. Zu seinem hundertjährigen Todestage," in *Jahrbuch für das Berg- und Hüttenwesen im Königreich Sachsen* (1917), A3–A50; J. P. van Berghem-Berthout and J. H. Struve, *Principes de minéralogie, ou exposition succincte des caractères extérieurs des fosiles, d'après les leçons du Professeur Werner, augmentés d'additions manuscrites fournies par cet auteur* (Paris, 1795); Heinrich Bingel, *Abraham Gottlob Werner und seine Theorie der Gebirgsbildung* (Marburg, 1934); Karl August Blöde, "Kurzer Nekrolog Abraham Gottlob Werners," in *Auswahl aus den Schriften der unter Werners Mitwirkung gestifteten Gesellschaft für Mineralogie zu Dresden*, **2** (1819), 252–304; William Thomas Brande, *Outlines of Geology* (London, 1829); Leopold von Buch, *Leopold von Buch's Gesammelte Schriften*, J. Ewald, J. Roth, and H. Eck, eds.. 4 vols. (Berlin, 1867–1885); Albert Carozzi, trans., *On the External Characters of Minerals*, by A. G. Werner (Urbana, Ill., 1962); and Jean François d'Aubuisson de Voisins, *Traité de géognosie, ou exposé des connaissances actuelles sur la constitution physique et minérale du globe terrestre*, 2 vols. (Strasbourg, 1819; 2nd ed., Paris, 1828–1835).

See also Walther Fischer, "Abraham Gottlob Werner," in *Mitteilungen des Roland*, nos. 4–5 (July–Oct. 1936), 54–60; and *Mineralogie in Sachsen von Agricola bis Werner. Die ältere Geschichte des Staatlichen Museums für Mineralogie und Geologie zu Dresden (1560–1820)*, (Dresden, 1939); Samuel Gottlob Frisch, *Lebensbeschreibung Abraham Gottlob Werners* (Leipzig, 1825); C. A. S. Hoffman and August Breithaupt, *Handbuch der Mineralogie*, 8 vols. (Freiberg, 1811–1817); and Traugott L. Hasse, *Denkschrift zur Erinnerung an die Verdienste des in Dresden am 30. Juni 1817 verstorbenen K. S. Bergrath's Werner und an die Fortschritte bei der Bergakademie zu Freiberg nebst einer übersichtlichen Nebeneinanderstellung der Mineralsysteme Werners und seiner Nachfolger bei dieser Akademie . . .* (Dresden, 1848).

Further works are Robert Jameson, *System of Mineralogy, Comprehending Oryctognosy, Geognosy, Mineralogical Chemistry, Mineralogical Geography, and Oeconomical Mineralogy*, 3 vols. (Edinburgh, 1804–1808); John Murray, *A Comparative View of the Huttonian and Neptunian Systems of Geology: In Answer to the Illustrations of the Huttonian Theory of the Earth, by Professor Playfair* (Edinburgh, 1802); Alexander M. Ospovat, "Abraham Gottlob Werner's Influence on American Geology," in *Proceedings of the Oklahoma Academy of Science*, **40** (1960), 98–103; "Abraham Gottlob Werner and His Influence on Mineralogy and Geology" (doctoral diss., Univ. of Oklahoma, 1960), available from University Microfilms, Inc., Ann Arbor, Mich.; "Abraham Gottlob Werners Gedanken über Wissenschaft und Bildung," in *Neue Hütte*, **12** (1967), 308–313; and trans. of Abraham Gottlob Werner, *Short Classification and Description of the Various Rocks*, with intro. and notes (New York, 1971); Franz Reichetzer, *Anleitung zur Geognosie insbesondere zur Gebirgskunde. Nach Werner für die K. K. Berg-Akademie* (Vienna, 1812); Franz Ambrosius Reusz, *Lehrbuch der Mineralogie nach des Herrn O. B. R. Karsten mineralogischen Tabellen*, 4 pts. in 8 vols. (Leipzig, 1801–1806); and Otfried Wagenbreth, "Abraham Gottlob Werner und der Höhepunkt des Neptunistenstreits um 1790," in *Freiberger Forschungsheft*, ser. D, **11** (1955), 183–241.

ALEXANDER OSPOVAT

**WERNER, ALFRED** (*b*. Mulhouse, France, 12 December 1866; *d*. Zurich, Switzerland, 15 November 1919), *chemistry*.

**Life and Work.** The founder of coordination chemistry, Werner was the fourth and last child of Jean-Adam Werner, an ironworker, and his second wife, Salomé Jeanette Tesché. Although the family decided to remain in Mulhouse after Alsace was annexed to the German Empire in 1871, they continued to speak French at home and their sympathies remained entirely with France. The spirit of rebellion and resistance to authority, so much a part of Werner's childhood, may well have contributed to the revolutionary and iconoclastic character of the theory with which his name is associated. Despite his great reverence for German science—most of his articles appeared in German journals—Werner's political and cultural ties were to France.

His mother had been converted from Protestantism to Catholicism, and at the age of six Werner was enrolled at the Catholic École Libre des Frères (Bruderschule), where the dominant traits of his personality—a remarkable self-confidence and a stubborn independence that made it impossible for him to submit blindly to authority—became evident. The religious teachings of the brothers apparently had little effect on him, for in later life his interest in religion was minimal. From 1878 to 1885 Werner attended the École Professionelle (Höhere Gewerbeschule), a technical school where he studied chemistry. During this time he built his own laboratory in the barn behind his house.

Even at this early stage Werner was preoccupied with classification, systematization, and isomeric relationships. His earliest known scientific work, "Contribution de l'acide urique, des séries de la théobromine, caféine, et leurs derivés," a holograph manuscript that he submitted in September 1885 to Emilio Noelting, director of the Mulhouse Chemie-Schule, was banal in style and unsound in its chemical thinking; but its broad scope and daring attempts at systematization foreshadowed the intellectual heights that Werner attained only a few years later. During 1885–1886 Werner served his year of compulsory military duty in the German army at Karlsruhe, where he audited courses in organic chemistry at the Technische Hochschule. He then entered the Polytechnikum in Zurich, where he studied under Arthur Hantzsch, Georg Lunge, Heinrich Goldschmidt, and Emil Constam.

Werner was a typical nonquantitative genius. At the Polytechnikum he failed his courses in mathematics, and throughout his career his contributions were essentially of a qualitative nature; even his celebrated conductivity studies with Arturo Miolati were only semiquantitative. His failure in descriptive geometry, however, is surprising inasmuch as his coordination theory represents an inspired and ingenious application of geometry to chemistry.

On 3 August 1889 Werner was awarded a degree in technical chemistry. During 1889 and 1890 he served as an unsalaried assistant in Lunge's chemical-technical laboratory while carrying out research under Hantzsch for which he received the doctorate on 13 October 1890.

In three short but eventful years (1890–1893) Werner produced his three most important theoretical papers. His doctoral dissertation, "Über räumliche Anordnung der Atome in stickstoffhaltigen Molekülen," was his first publication and remains his most popular and important work in organic chemistry. By extending the Le Bel and van't Hoff concept of the tetrahedral carbon atom (1874) to the nitrogen atom, Werner and Hantzsch simultaneously explained a great number of puzzling cases of geometrically isomeric trivalent nitrogen derivatives (oximes, azo compounds, hydroxamic acids) and for the first time placed the stereochemistry of nitrogen on a firm theoretical basis. Despite attacks by Victor Meyer, Karl von

Auwers, Eugen Bamberger, and others that extended several decades into the twentieth century, the Werner-Hantzsch theory has withstood the test of time. Today, with only slight modification, it takes its rightful place beside the Le Bel–van't Hoff concept of the tetrahedral carbon atom as one of the cornerstones of stereochemistry.

Werner spent the next two years working on his *Habilitationsschrift*, "Beiträge zur Theorie der Affinität und Valenz," in which he chose to attack the supreme patriarch of structural organic chemistry, August Kekulé. In this work Werner attempted to replace Kekulé's concept of rigidly directed valences with his own more flexible approach, in which he viewed affinity as a variously divisible, attractive force emanating from the center of an atom and acting equally in all directions. By the use of this new concept and without assuming directed valences, Werner was able to derive the accepted van't Hoff configurational formulas. Although this important paper contains the seeds that later flowered in the primary valence (*Hauptvalenz*) and secondary valence (*Nebenvalenz*) of the coordination theory, it deals exclusively with organic compounds. Unfortunately, it was published in a rather obscure journal of limited circulation, where it elicited little notice until brought to the attention of the scientific world in 1904 by a discussion of its concepts in Werner's first textbook.

During the winter semester of 1891–1892 Werner worked on thermochemical problems with Marcellin Berthelot at the Collège de France. Except for the publication of an admittedly minor work on a basic nitrate of calcium and the incorporation of thermochemical data into Werner's later lecture notes, this *Wanderjahr* had little effect on him. The acceptance of Werner's *Habilitationsschrift* by the Swiss authorities early in 1892 permitted him to return to Zurich as a *Privatdozent* at the Polytechnikum. He did not remain there long, for in the fall of 1893 he became associate professor as successor to Viktor Merz at the University of Zurich, where he remained for a quarter-century. In 1894 Werner married Emma Wilhelmine Giesker, a resident of Zurich, and became a Swiss citizen. The following year he was promoted to full professor. His appointment at the University of Zurich originally came about largely because of the almost overnight fame that he had received as a result of the publication of his most important theoretical paper, "Beitrag zur Konstitution anorganischer Verbindungen" (1893), in which he had proposed the basic postulates of his epochal and controversial coordination theory.

The circumstances surrounding the creation of the coordination theory provide a classic example of the "flash of genius" that ranks with Kekulé's dreams of the self-linking of carbon atoms (1858) and of the benzene ring (1865). At the time (late 1892 or early 1893) Werner was a comparatively unknown twenty-six-year-old *Privatdozent* whose primary interest was organic chemistry and whose knowledge of inorganic chemistry was extremely limited. Yet one morning he awoke at two with the solution to the riddle of "molecular compounds," which had come to him like a flash of lightning. He arose from his bed and wrote so quickly and steadily that by five that afternoon he had finished his most important paper.

For the next decade Werner's attention was divided between organic and inorganic chemistry. He had originally been called to the University of Zurich to teach organic chemistry, and it was not until the winter semester of 1902–1903 that he was finally assigned the main lecture course in inorganic chemistry, which he continued to teach along with organic chemistry throughout his career. Although he became increasingly preoccupied with coordination chemistry, more than one-quarter of his publications deal with such organic topics as oximes; hydroxamic and hydroximic acids; phenanthrenes; carboxonium and carbothionium salts; hydroxylamines; azo, azoxy, hydrazo, and nitro compounds; dyestuffs; and the Walden inversion.

Nevertheless, Werner's fame is securely grounded in inorganic chemistry. He began with a study of metal-ammines, hydrates, and double salts; but his ideas soon encompassed almost the whole of systematic inorganic chemistry and even found application in organic chemistry. He was the first to show that stereochemistry is a general phenomenon and is not limited to carbon compounds, and his views of valence and chemical bonding stimulated subsequent research on these fundamental topics.

The coordination theory, with its concepts of coordination number, primary and secondary valence, addition and intercalation compounds, and octahedral, square planar, and tetrahedral configurations, not only provided a logical explanation for known "molecular compounds" but also predicted series of unknown compounds, the eventual discovery of which lent further weight to Werner's controversial ideas. Werner recognized and named many types of inorganic isomerism: coordination, polymerization, ionization, hydrate, salt, coordination position, and valence isomerism. He also postulated explanations for polynuclear complexes, hydrated metal ions, hydrolysis, and acids and bases.

The average chemist probably has become familiar with Werner's views more through his books than through his journal articles. His first, *Lehrbuch der Stereochemie* (1904), never achieved the popularity of his second, *Neuere Anschauungen auf dem Gebiete der anorganischen Chemie* (1905), which went through five editions. As Werner's fame grew and the value of his views became recognized, he received a number of offers from Continental universities, all of which he declined. Honorary memberships and degrees were extended by many European and American universities and scientific societies. In 1913 he became the first Swiss to be awarded the Nobel Prize in chemistry, "in recognition of his work on the linkage of atoms in molecules, by which he has thrown fresh light on old problems and opened new fields of research, particularly in inorganic chemistry." Soon afterward he began to show the signs of a chronic degenerative disease (arteriosclerosis of the brain, aggravated by excessive drinking) that progressively destroyed his physical health and mental faculties. On 15 October 1919 he was forced to resign from his laboratory and teaching duties. Exactly one month later he died after prolonged suffering.

Today, when the practical and theoretical significance of coordination compounds is unquestioned, it is clear that the foundations of modern structural inorganic chemistry were erected by Werner, who has justly been called the inorganic Kekulé.

**Coordination Theory.** Although Werner was awarded the Nobel Prize in 1913 specifically for his monumental work on coordination compounds, the implications and applications of his research extend far beyond the confines of inorganic chemistry. In fact, they have been of inestimable value in biochemistry and in analytical, organic, and physical chemistry, as well as in such related sciences as mineralogy and crystallography. Even before Werner began his extensive series of experimental researches on "molecular compounds," an almost unprecedented tour de force requiring a quarter of a century, he was vitally concerned with one of the most basic problems of chemistry—the nature of affinity and valence. "Molecular compounds" provided him with a challenging and exciting means to explore this question.

It may come as a surprise that the Kekulé valence theory, so flexible and fruitful in organic chemistry, proved to be a virtual straitjacket when applied to inorganic chemistry. Yet, by his own admission, Kekulé's concept of constant valence proved "embarrassing to the chemist." Instead of abandoning this obviously untenable belief, however, he compounded the error by invoking a still more unsatisfactory concept, that of "molecular compounds," in order to maintain it.

An example or two will suffice to illustrate Kekulé's concept of "molecular compounds." Since he regarded the valences of nitrogen and phosphorus as invariably three, Kekulé was forced to consider ammonium chloride and phosphorus pentachloride as "molecular compounds" with the formulas $NH_3 \cdot HCl$ and $PCl_3 \cdot Cl_2$, respectively. At most, Kekulé's artificial division of compounds into "molecular" and "valence" compounds on the basis of their amenability or nonamenability to the doctrine of constant valence had some limited value as a formal classification, but it in no way explained the nature or operation of the forces involved in the formation of "molecular compounds" by the combination of "valence compounds."

Whereas Kekulé disposed of metal-ammines by banishing them to the limbo of "molecular compounds," other chemists developed highly elaborate theories in order to explain the constitution and properties of these intriguing substances. Probably the most successful and widely accepted of such theories was the one proposed in 1869 by Christian Wilhelm Blomstrand, professor of chemistry at the University of Lund. This "chain theory" was subsequently modified during the 1880's

and 1890's by the chemist destined to become Werner's principal scientific adversary, Sophus Mads Jørgensen, professor of chemistry at the University of Copenhagen.

Under the predominant influence of organic chemistry during the latter half of the nineteenth century, Blomstrand suggested that ammonia molecules could link together as $-NH_3-$ chains in a manner analogous to $-CH_2-$ chains in hydrocarbons. Provision was also made for the observed differences in reactivities of various atoms and groups in metal-ammines. For example, halogen atoms that could not be precipitated immediately by silver nitrate were regarded as bonded directly to the metal atom, while those that could be precipitated were considered to be bonded through the ammonia chains. Despite the theory's admitted limitations, a considerable amount of empirical data could be correlated by its use.

In his revolutionary theory, which marked an abrupt break with the classical theories of valence and structure, Werner postulated two types of valence—primary or ionizable (*Hauptvalenz*) and secondary or nonionizable (*Nebenvalenz*). According to the theory, every metal in a particular oxidation state (primary valence) has a definite coordination number—that is, a fixed number of secondary valences that must be satisfied. Whereas primary valences can be satisfied only by anions, secondary valences can be satisfied not only by

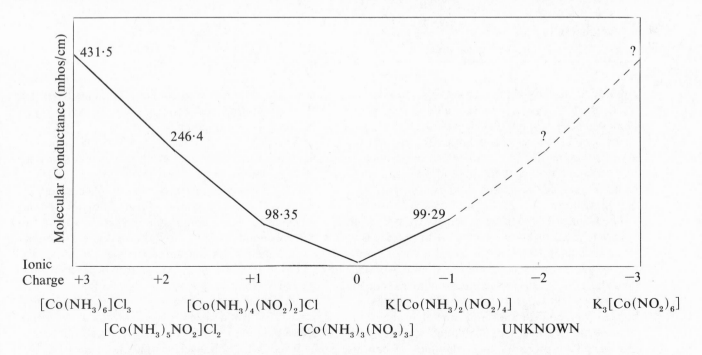

FIGURE 1.   Conductivities of cobalt(III) coordination compounds (Werner and Miolati, 1894).

## TABLE I

| Class of Compound | BLOMSTRAND-JØRGENSEN | | WERNER | |
|---|---|---|---|---|
| | Formula | No. of Ions | Formula | No. of Ions |
| Hexammines $MA_6$ | $Co{\overset{NH_3-NO_2}{\underset{NH_3-NH_3-NH_3-NH_3-NO_2}{-NH_3-NO_2}}}$ | 4 | $[Co(NH_3)_6](NO_2)_3$ | 4 |
| | $\downarrow -NH_3$ | | $\downarrow -NH_3$ | |
| Pentammines $MA_5B$ | $Co{\overset{NO_2}{\underset{NH_3-NH_3-NH_3-NH_3-NO_2}{-NH_3-NO_2}}}$ | 3 | $[Co(NH_3)_5NO_2](NO_2)_2$ | 3 |
| | $\downarrow -NH_3$ | | $\downarrow -NH_3$ | |
| Tetrammines $MA_4B_2$ | $Co{\overset{NO_2}{\underset{NH_3-NH_3-NH_3-NH_3-NO_2}{-NO_2}}}$ | 2 | $[Co(NH_3)_4(NO_2)_2]NO_2$ | 2 |
| | $\downarrow -NH_3$ | | $\downarrow -NH_3$ | |
| Triammines $MA_3B_3$ | $Co{\overset{NO_2}{\underset{NH_3-NH_3-NH_3-NO_2}{-NO_2}}}$ | 2 | $[Co(NH_3)_3(NO_2)_3]$ | 0 |
| | | | $\downarrow -NH_3$ | |
| Diammines $MA_2B_4$ | Unaccountable | – | $K[Co(NH_3)_2(NO_2)_4]$ | 2 |
| | | | $\downarrow -NH_3$ | |
| Monoammines $MAB_5$ | Unaccountable | – | Unknown for Cobalt | (3) |
| | | | $\downarrow -NH_3$ | |
| Double Salts $MB_6$ | Unaccountable | – | $K_3[Co(NO_2)_6]$ | 4 |

anions but also by neutral molecules such as ammonia, water, organic amines, sulfides, and phosphines. These secondary valences are directed in space around the central metal ion (octahedral for coordination number 6, square planar or tetrahedral for coordination number 4); and the aggregate forms a "complex," which should exist as a discrete unit in solution.

The acknowledged test of a scientific theory is its ability to explain known facts and to predict new ones. In examining the success of Werner's coordination theory in meeting these criteria, we shall consider two aspects of the metal-ammines: constitution (how the constituent atoms and groups are bonded) and configuration (the spatial arrangement of these atoms and groups). Although we shall confine ourselves primarily to compounds of coordination number 6 [cobalt (III)], we should bear in mind that Werner used similar arguments to prove the constitution and configuration for compounds of coordination number 4.

Werner's first published experimental work in support of his coordination theory was a study of conductivities, carried out during 1893–1896 in collaboration with Arturo Miolati. According to the new theory, the charge of a complex ion should be equal to the algebraic sum of the charges of the central metal ion and of the coordinated groups. Consequently, as neutral molecules of ammonia (A) in a metal-ammine ($MA_6$) are successively replaced by anions (B), the number of ions in the resulting compounds should progressively decrease until a nonelectrolyte is formed and then should increase as the complex becomes anionic.

Friedrich Kohlrausch's principle of the additivity of equivalent conductivities of salts (1879) pro-

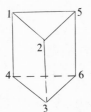

Trigonal Prismatic

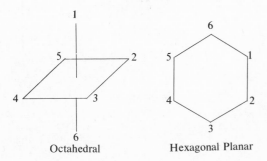

Octahedral          Hexagonal Planar

FIGURE 2. Configurational possibilities for coordination number 6.

vided Werner and Miolati with a convenient method for determining the number of ions in various complexes. After having established the ranges of conductivities to be expected for salts of various types, they were able to demonstrate the complete agreement in magnitude, variation, and pattern between their experimentally measured conductivities (Figure 1) and those predicted according to the coordination theory. Their results were also concordant with the number of precipitable halogen atoms. The constitutions and predicted numbers of ions according to the two theories are contrasted in Table I.

For compounds of the first three classes, the electrolytic character predicted by the two theories is in complete agreement, and conductivity data do not permit a choice between the two. For triammines, however, the ionic character differs radically according to the two theories; and the conductivities of these compounds became an important

and bitterly contested issue. For some nonelectrolytes, unfortunately, Werner and Miolati's conductivity values were not always zero because of aquation reactions:

$$[Co(NH_3)_3Cl_3]^0 + H_2O \rightleftarrows$$
$$[Co(NH_3)_3(H_2O)Cl_2]^+ + Cl^-.$$

Jørgensen immediately seized upon such "discrepancies" in an attempt to discredit their results. But in its explanation of anionic complexes and its demonstration of the existence of a continuous transition series (*Übergangsreihe*) between metal-ammines ($MA_6$) and double salts ($MB_6$), the Werner theory succeeded in an area in which the Blomstrand-Jørgensen theory could not pretend to compete.

The technique of "isomer counting" as a means of proving configuration admittedly did not originate with Werner. The idea of an octahedral configuration and its geometric consequences with respect to the number of isomers expected had been considered as early as 1875 by van't Hoff, and the general method probably is most familiar through Wilhelm Körner's work of 1874 on disubstituted and trisubstituted benzene derivatives. Yet the technique of comparing the number and type of isomers actually prepared with the number and type theoretically predicted for various configurations probably reached the height of its development with Werner's work. By this method he was able not only to discredit completely the rival Blomstrand-Jørgensen chain theory but also to demonstrate unequivocally that trivalent cobalt possesses an octahedral configuration rather than another possible symmetrical arrangement, such as hexagonal planar or trigonal prismatic. The method is summarized in Figure 2 and Table II.

In most cases the number and type of isomers prepared corresponded to the expectations for the octahedral arrangement, but there were a few exceptions; and Werner required more than twenty

TABLE II. Predicted Number of Isomers

| Compound Type | Octahedral | Hexagonal Planar | Trigonal Prismatic* |
|---|---|---|---|
| $MA_6$ | One | One | One |
| $MA_5B$ | One | One | One |
| $MA_4B_2$ | Two (1,2; 1,6) | Three (1,2; 1,3; 1,4) | Three (1,2; 1,3; 1,4) |
| $MA_3B_3$ | Two (1,2,3; 1,2,6) | Three (1,2,3; 1,2,4; 1,3,5) | Three (1,2,3; 1,2,5; 1,2,6) |
| $M(\overline{AA})_3$ | Two *Optical* Isomers | One | Two *Geometrical* Isomers |

*Coordination compounds with this configuration have recently been synthesized.

Praseo

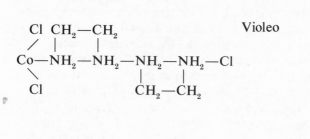

Jørgensen

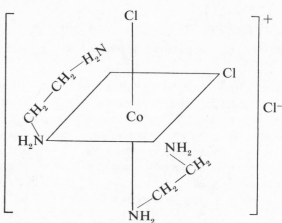

Werner

Violeo

FIGURE 3.   Jørgensen and Werner's formulas for praseo and violeo ethylenediamine isomers.

years to accumulate a definitive proof for his structural ideas. For example, the best known case of geometrical (cis-trans) isomerism was observed (by Jørgensen) not among simple tetrammines $MA_4B_2$ but among salts $M(\overline{AA})_2B_2$, in which the four ammonia molecules have been replaced by two molecules of the bidentate (chelate) organic base, ethylenediamine (en); that is, among the so-called praseo (green) and violeo (violet) series of formula $CoCl_3 \cdot 2en$. Jørgensen regarded the difference in color as due to structural isomerism connected with the linking of the two ethylenediamine molecules, whereas Werner regarded the compounds as stereoisomers, compounds composed of the same atoms and bonds but differing in the orientation of these atoms and bonds in space (Figure 3).

If this type of isomerism were merely a geometrical consequence of the octahedral structure, as Werner maintained, it should also be observed among simple tetrammines $MA_4B_2$, which do not contain ethylenediamine. Yet for compounds $[Co(NH_3)_4Cl_2]$ X, only one series (praseo) was known. Jørgensen, a confirmed empiricist, quite correctly criticized Werner's theory on the ground that it implied the existence of unknown compounds. It was not until 1907 that Werner succeeded in synthesizing the unstable, highly crucial violeo tetrammines, cis-$[Co(NH_3)_4Cl_2]$ X, which were a necessary consequence of his theory but not of Jørgensen's (Figure 4). His Danish opponent immediately conceded defeat.

Even though the discovery of the long-sought violeo salts convinced Jørgensen that his own views could not be correct, Werner's success in preparing two—and only two—isomers for compounds of types $MA_4B_2$ and $MA_3B_3$ was not sufficient for conclusive proof of his octahedral configuration. Despite such "negative" evidence, it could still be argued logically that failure to isolate a third isomer did not necessarily prove its non-

270

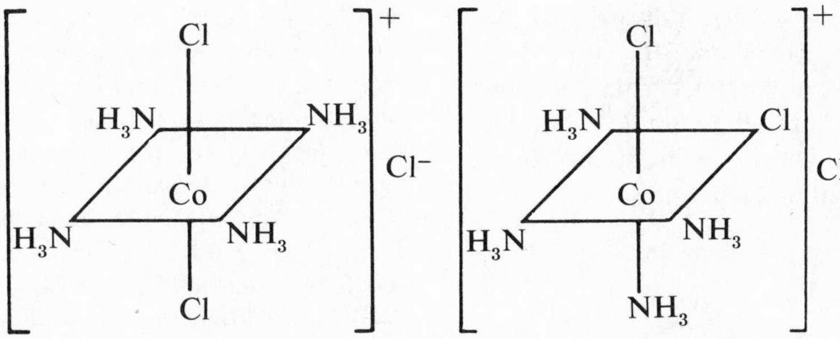

Praseo (trans; 1, 6)
Gibbs and Genth (1857)

Violeo (cis; 1, 2)
Werner (1907)

FIGURE 4.  Ammonia praseo and violeo isomers.

existence. A more "positive" type of proof was necessary.

As early as 1899, Werner recognized that the resolution into optical isomers of certain types of coordination compounds containing chelate groups, which can span only cis positions, could provide the "positive" proof that he needed. After many unsuccessful attempts, in 1911 he succeeded. His resolution, with his American student Victor King (1886–1958), of cis-chloroammine-bis(ethylenediamine)cobalt(III) salts by means of the resolving agent silver d-α-bromocamphor-π-sulfonate was sufficient to prove conclusively the octahedral configuration for cobalt(III) (Figure 5). Yet because of the prevalent view that optical activity was almost always connected with carbon atoms, a number of Werner's contemporaries argued that the optical activity of these and the many other mononuclear and polynuclear coordination compounds subsequently resolved by him was somehow due to the organic chelate groups present, even though these symmetrical ligands were all optically inactive. Any vestige of doubt was finally dispelled by Werner's resolution in 1914 of completely carbon-free coordination compounds—the tris[tetrammine-μ-dihydroxocobalt(III)]cobalt(III) salts,

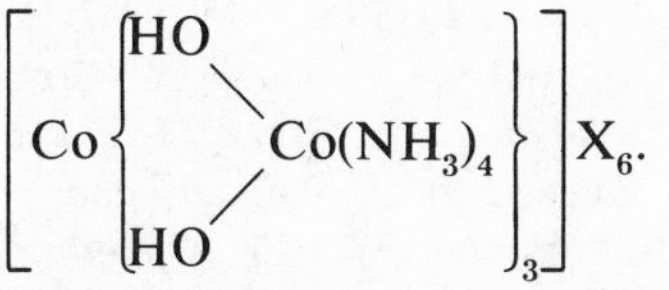

$$\left[ Co \left\{ \begin{matrix} HO \\ \\ HO \end{matrix} Co(NH_3)_4 \right\}_3 \right] X_6.$$

These salts are compounds of the $M(\overline{AA})_3$ type, in which $\overline{AA}$ is the inorganic bidentate ligand

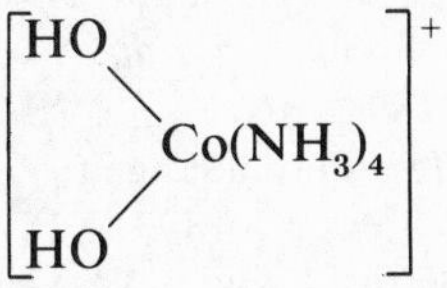

$$\left[ \begin{matrix} HO \\ \\ HO \end{matrix} Co(NH_3)_4 \right]^+$$

At the beginning of his career Werner had destroyed the monopoly of the carbon atom on geometrical isomerism. In his doctoral dissertation he had explained the isomerism of oximes as due to the tetrahedral configuration of the nitrogen atom. Now, at the peak of his career, he had likewise forced the tetrahedron to relinquish its claim to a monopoly on optical isomerism. One of the major goals of his lifework, the demonstration that stereochemistry is a general phenomenon not limited to carbon compounds and that no fundamental difference exists between organic and inorganic compounds, had been attained.

Finally, we must note that the validity of Wer-

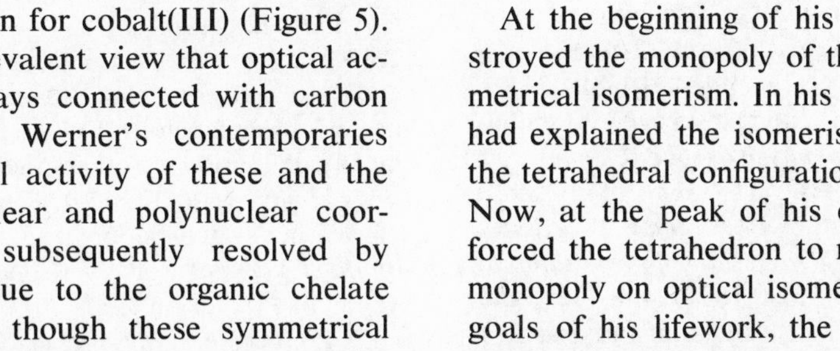

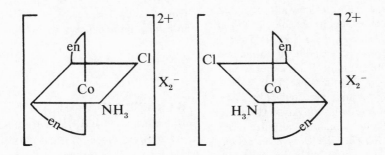

FIGURE 5.  Optical antipodes of cis-[Coen₂NH₃Cl]X₂.

ner's structural views was amply confirmed by X-ray diffraction studies. Yet, despite the advent of more direct modern techniques, his classical configurational determinations by simple indirect methods remain a monument to his intuitive vision, experimental skill, and inflexible tenacity.

## BIBLIOGRAPHY

I. ORIGINAL WORKS. Werner's writings include "Über räumliche Anordnung der Atome in stickstoffhaltigen Molekülen," in *Berichte der Deutschen chemischen Gesellschaft,* **23** (1890), 11–30, English trans. in G. B. Kauffman, "Foundation of Nitrogen Stereochemistry: Alfred Werner's Inaugural Dissertation," in *Journal of Chemical Education,* **43** (1966), 155–165; "Beiträge zur Theorie der Affinität und Valenz," in *Vierteljahrsschrift der Naturforschenden Gesellschaft in Zürich,* **36** (1891), 129–169, discussed in G. B. Kauffman, "Alfred Werner's Habilitationsschrift," in *Chymia,* **12** (1967), 183–187, English trans. in G. B. Kauffman, "Contributions to the Theory of Affinity and Valence," *ibid.,* 189–216; "Sur un nitrate basique de calcium," in *Annales de chimie et de physique,* **27** (1892), 6th ser., 570–574, also in *Comptes rendus . . . de l'Académie des sciences,* **115** (1892), 169–171; "Beitrag zur Konstitution anorganischer Verbindungen," in *Zeitschrift für anorganische Chemie,* **3** (1893), 267–330, repr. as Ostwald's Klassiker der Exakten Wissenschaften no. 212 (Leipzig, 1924), English trans. in G. B. Kauffman, *Classics in Coordination Chemistry,* Part I, *The Selected Papers of Alfred Werner* (New York, 1968), 5–88; "Beiträge zur Konstitution anorganischer Verbindungen. I," in *Zeitschrift für physikalische Chemie,* **12** (1893), 35–55, "Beiträge . . . II," *ibid.,* **14** (1894), 506–521, and "Beiträge . . . III," *ibid.,* **21** (1896), 225–238—Italian trans. in *Gazzetta chimica italiana,* 2nd ser., **23** (1893), 140–165, **24** (1894), 408–427, and **27** (1896), 299–316, and English trans. of the first two papers in G. B. Kauffman, *Classics in Coordination Chemistry,* Part I (New York, 1968), 89–139; "Beitrag zur Konstitution anorganischer Verbindungen. XVII. Über Oxalatodiäthylendiaminkobaltisalze $(Co_{en_2}^{C_2O_4})x$," in *Zeitschrift für anorganische Chemie,* **21** (1899), 145–158; *Lehrbuch der Stereochemie* (Jena, 1904)—Werner's views on structural organic chemistry may also be found in an extremely rare monograph by E. Bloch, *Alfred Werners Theorie des Kohlenstoffatoms und die Stereochemie der karbocyklischen Verbindungen* (Vienna–Leipzig, 1903); *Neuere Anschauungen auf dem Gebiete der anorganischen Chemie* (Brunswick, 1905, 1909, 1913, 1920, 1923), 2nd ed. trans. into English by E. P. Hedley as *New Ideas on Inorganic Chemistry* (London, 1911); "Über 1.2-Dichloro-tetrammin-kobaltisalze (Ammoniakvioleosalze)," in *Berichte der Deutschen chemischen Gesellschaft,* **40** (1907), 4817–4825, English trans. in G. B. Kauffman, *Classics in Coordination Chemistry,* Part I (New York, 1968), 141–154; "Zur Kenntnis des asymmetrischen Kobaltatoms. I," in *Berichte der Deutschen chemischen Gesellschaft,* **44** (1911), 1887–1898, English trans. in G. B. Kauffman, *Classics in Coordination Chemistry,* Part I (New York, 1968), 155–173; "Zur Kenntnis des asymmetrischen Kobaltatoms. XII. Über optische Aktivität bei kohlenstofffreien Verbindungen," in *Berichte der Deutschen chemischen Gesellschaft,* **47** (1914), 3087–3094, English trans. in G. B. Kauffman, *Classics in Coordination Chemistry,* Part I (New York, 1968), 175–184; and "Über die Konstitution und Konfiguration von Verbindungen höherer Ordnung," in *Les prix Nobel en 1913* (Stockholm, 1914), trans. into English as "On the Constitution and Configuration of Compounds of Higher Order," in *Nobel Lectures in Chemistry, 1901–1921* (Amsterdam, 1966), 256–269.

II. SECONDARY LITERATURE. A full-length biography by G. B. Kauffman, *Alfred Werner—Founder of Coordination Chemistry* (Berlin–Heidelberg–New York, 1966), deals primarily with Werner's life and career but also includes brief discussions of his work. G. B. Kauffman, *Classics in Coordination Chemistry,* Part I, *The Selected Papers of Alfred Werner* (New York, 1968), presents English translations of Werner's six most important papers together with critical commentary and biographical details. For other papers on various aspects of Werner and his work by G. B. Kauffman, see *Journal of Chemical Education,* **36** (1959), 521–527, and **43** (1966), 155–165, 677–679; *Chemistry,* **39** (1966), no. 12, 14–18; *Education in Chemistry,* **4** (1967), 11–18; *Chymia,* **12** (1967), 183–187, 189–216, 217–219, 221–232; *Naturwissenschaften,* **54** (1967), 573–576; and *Werner Centennial,* Advances in Chemistry series, no. 62 (Washington, D.C., 1967), 41–69. Articles, mostly obituaries, by others include P. Karrer, in *Helvetica chimica acta,* **3** (1920), 196–224, with bibliography of Werner's publications; G. T. Morgan, in *Journal of the Chemical Society* (London), **117** (1920), 1639–1648; P. Pfeiffer, in *Zeitschrift für angewandte Chemie und Zentralblatt für technische Chemie,* **33** (1920), 37–39; and in *Journal of Chemical Education,* **5** (1928), 1090–1098; and J. Lifschitz, in *Zeitschrift für Elektrochemie und angewandte physikalische Chemie,* **26** (1920), 514–529.

The figures and tables in this article are reprinted, by permission, from G. B. Kauffman, "Alfred Werner's Coordination Theory—A Brief Historical Introduction," in *Education in Chemistry,* **4** (1967), 11–18.

GEORGE B. KAUFFMAN

**WERNER, JOHANN(ES)** (*b.* Nuremberg, Germany, 14 February 1468; *d.* Nuremberg, May [?] 1522), *astronomy, mathematics, geography.*

While still a student in Nuremberg, Werner was drawn to the exact sciences and later said that he was intended for the study of mathematics from his early childhood. He enrolled at the University of Ingolstadt on 21 September 1484; and in 1490 he was appointed chaplain in Herzogenaurach. While studying in Rome (1493–1497) Werner was ordained a priest and met Italian scholars. By then his knowledge of mathematics, astronomy, and geography had increased; and he was allowed to inspect scientific manuscripts. He owned a Menelaus manuscript and was acquainted with unpublished works by Jābir ibn Aflaḥ (Geber) and Theodosius. Werner probably acquired his excellent knowledge of Greek in Italy. After his return to Nuremberg he celebrated his first mass in the church of St. Sebald on 29 April 1498. Probably in response to the requests of Empress Bianca Maria, in 1503 he was appointed priest at Wöhrd, just outside Nuremberg. In 1508 he was serving at St. Johannis Church in Nuremberg, where he remained until his death (between 12 March and 11 June 1522).

Werner was reputed to have been "very diligent" in carrying out all official responsibilities. Since his pastoral duties were rather limited, he devoted much of his time to scientific study. His works brought him recognition from such Nuremberg scholars as Willibald Pirkheimer (1470–1530), Sebald Schreyer (1446–1520), and Cardinal Matthäus Lang (1468–1540). He was friendly with Bernhard Walther (ca. 1430–1504) and the choirmaster Lorenz Beheim (1457[?]–1521) from Bamberg, as well as Albrecht Dürer, who occasionally asked his advice on mathematical problems. Werner enjoyed an excellent reputation even among scholars from Vienna: in 1514 the mathematician and imperial historiographer Johannes Stabius arranged the publication of a collection of writings on geography that included works by Werner. The humanist Konrad Celtis, whom Werner regarded as his "most beloved teacher," tried in 1503 to have Werner transferred to Vienna. Emperor Maximilian I appointed him chaplain at his court.

Not all of Werner's numerous works were published during his lifetime. Some remain unprinted, and others have been lost. Besides the 1514 collection containing Werner's and other authors' writings on geography, a collection of mathematical and astronomical works was published at Nuremberg in 1522. A handwritten remark in the Munich copy of the latter work leads us to believe that Werner died while the work was being printed. His meteorological treatise appeared after his death, and his works on spherical trigonometry and me-

teoroscopes were not published until 1907 and 1913, respectively.

**Astronomy.** In a sense Werner can be regarded as a student of Regiomontanus, for he had access to the latter's writings. Although a skilled maker of astronomical instruments, he showed less talent in theoretical work. The Germanisches Nationalmuseum in Nuremberg possesses a gold-plated brass astrolabe from 1516, probably made by Werner (see Zinner, pl. 25, 4). The clock on the south side of the parish church in Herzogenaurach and the two sundials in the choir of the church at Rosstal may be by Werner. He improved the Jacob's staff that had been used by Regiomontanus to measure interstellar distances, and he described it in the 1514 collection ("In eundem primum librum . . . Ptholomaei . . .," ch. 4, annotations 3–5).

Werner also invented an instrument that he called a "meteoroscope" to solve problems in spherical astronomy. It consists of a metal disk divided into quadrants with a pointer attached. Like the saphea, the first and fourth quadrants contain a stereographic projection of the circles of latitude and longitude, while the second and third quadrants have two different types of sine divisions. The device, which is only known from the description in "De meteoroscopiis," was built not for observational purposes but to replace as many mathematical tables as possible. Even here Werner proved to be a student of Regiomontanus, although his meteoroscope had nothing in common with the device of the same name built by his famous predecessor: Regiomontanus' instrument, the directions for use of which were published by Werner, is an armillary sphere. Werner's treatises on sundials and on astronomical and geographical problems that can be solved by methods of spherical trigonometry have been lost.

A manuscript dated 1521 concerning the making of a device designed to determine the latitudes of planets and one containing tables for the five planets are among Werner's unpublished works, as is a letter to Sebald Schreyer about the comet of 1500. Several horoscopes give evidence of Werner's work in astrology. They were cast for Ursula Gundelfinger, Erasmus Topler, Willibald Pirkheimer, Christoph Scheurl, and Sebald Schreyer.

Werner had less success with his treatises on the movement of the eighth sphere, which constitute the last section of the collection of works published in 1522. He maintains that the so-called precession of the stars would be an irregular movement, thus showing that he was a disciple of the Arab trepidation theory. In a letter to the canon of

Cracow cathedral, Bernhard Wapowski, Copernicus attacked the treatise vigorously; and Tycho Brahe criticized it by accusing Werner of having failed to observe accurately enough the three stars that Werner took as the basis of the movement of the eighth sphere.

**Mathematics.** Werner's mathematical works are in spherical trigonometry and the theory of conic sections. His principal work on spherical triangles was printed in 1907 from the copy in Codex Vaticanus Reginensis Latinus 1259 (fols. lr–184r). A second copy of the autograph that contains figures was later discovered by Ernst Zinner (Landesbibliothek Weimar, no. f 324, fols. 1–103). Rheticus intended to publish the two writings, but only the letter of dedication to Ferdinand I of Bohemia and Hungary appeared (Cracow, 1557). The work, in four parts, which was written between 1505 and 1513, was not revised for publication by Werner. A fifth part for which he collected material has been lost. Although the treatise is incomplete, Werner's work was the best of its kind at the time, and its presentation surpassed that in Regiomontanus' books on triangles. In comparison with Regiomontanus' treatise, Werner's work is notable for its methodical presentation and practical applicability.

The various types of triangles are systematically described in part I. The following parts, which probably were written earlier, contain a theory of triangular calculation suitable for practical purposes. The basic formulas of spherical trigonometry and instructions for the solution of right spherical triangles are given in part II, and parts III and IV concern the calculation of oblique-angled triangles. In part IV Werner uses formulas that correspond to the cosine formula. Thus in proposition 5 he does not use the cosine formula as it is known today,

$$\cos b = \cos a \cos c + \sin a \sin c \cos B$$

(angle $B$ is sought; $a$, $b$, $c$ are the sides), but writes

$$\frac{\frac{1}{2}(\sin[90° - a + c] - \sin[90° - c - a])}{\sin(90° - b) - \sin(90° - c - a)} = \frac{r}{\sin \text{vers}(180° - B)}.$$

This means that Werner implicitly used the formula

$$2 \sin a \sin c = \cos(a - c) - \cos(a + c),$$

whereby he could replace multiplication and division with addition and subtraction. This method, which later became known as prosthaphaeresis,

was first used by Werner, but mathematicians soon realized that it simplified calculation. Perhaps through Rheticus, Tycho Brahe learned of this procedure, which was used until the introduction of logarithms.

The treatise containing twenty-two theorems on conic sections was intended as an introduction to his work on duplication of the cube. For that reason Werner dealt only with the parabola and hyperbola but not with the ellipse. In a manner similar to the methods of Apollonius, Werner produced a cone by passing through the points of the circumference straight lines that also pass through a point not in the plane of the circle. In contrast to the ancients he did not consider the parabola and the hyperbola to be defined as plane curves but regarded them in connection with the cone by which they were formed. He proved the theorems on conic sections through geometrical observations on the cone.

Werner's report on duplication of the cube contained nothing new, being only a revision of the eleven solutions to this problem found in classical antiquity; they were known to Werner from the translation of the commentary by Eutocius on Archimedes prepared by Giorgio Valla. Werner added twelve supplementary notes to his treatise. The first ten dealt with the transformation of parallelepipeds and cylinders. In the eleventh note Werner proved that the sun's rays fall on the earth in parallel, and in the twelfth he showed that the rays are gathered in one point on a parabolic mirror.

The third writing in the collection of works dated 1522 also contained an Archimedean problem already treated by Eutocius, in which a sphere is to be cut by a plane so that the volumes of the two spherical sections are in a given proportion to each other (*De sphaera et cylindro* II, 4). Werner added his own solution, in which a parabola and hyperbola intersect each other, to those of Dionysodorus and Diocles.

Some mathematical works by Werner have been lost, including one on arithmetic, a work that apparently was influenced by Euclid's *Data*, and a translation of Euclid's *Elements* into German that Werner completed at the request of Pirkheimer and Sebald Beheim for the sum of 100 taler.

**Geography and Meteorology.** The collection dated 1514 contains Werner's works on mathematical geography. In the commentary on the first book of Ptolemy's *Geography*, Werner explains the basic concepts of spherical geography and then turns to the measurement of degrees on the sphere. When determining the declination of the sun, he refers to the tables compiled by Georg von Peuerbach and Domenico Maria. Werner's method is interesting in that it determines simultaneously the longitude and the latitude of a place (ch. 3, annotation 8): For the first time it was possible for two sites the locations of which are being sought to be found by a combined series of observations. Since for the determination of latitude it is necessary merely to observe the upper and lower culmination of a circumpolar star, but not the position of the sun, quite a few sources of errors were removed. The fourth chapter deals with the determination of the difference in longitude of two places, which can be obtained by simultaneous observation of a lunar eclipse. Another method is based on the determination of the distance of a zodiac star from the moon as seen from two places (ch. 4, annotation 8). This method of calculating the distances to the moon requires only the determination of the angular distances, which can be carried out by means of the Jacob's staff, and the precise knowledge of the true and mean motions of the moon. This method soon replaced the older ones and was then used as the principal method for determining longitude in nautical astronomy.

The methods used by Werner enabled him to improve or to explain certain details of the ancient geographers, especially those of Marinus. Werner's remarks in chapters 7–10 refer to Marinus' determination of places, which he proves to be often incorrect, or to the sea voyages mentioned and explained by Marinus. Werner demonstrated a knowledge of the existence and direction of the trade winds and explained their origin. In addition, he tried to present a theoretical proof of approximate formulas for the determination of distances that were used in navigation.

Werner's contributions to cartography are based on his criticism of Marinus; they can be found at the end of the commentary on Ptolemy and in the "Libellus quatuor terrarum orbis . . . ." The remarks on chapter 24 of the *Geography* lead us to believe that Werner understood the two projections used by Ptolemy (simple conic projection and modified spherical projection) and developed them. The treatise on four other projections of the terrestrial globe, which is dedicated to Pirkheimer, contains more new ideas. In it Werner outlines the principles of stereographic projection and emphasizes that any point on the surface of the sphere can be chosen as the center of projection. In addition, Werner develops three cordiform map projections that resemble one another; the second gives an equal-area projection of the sphere. The idea of an equivalent projection occurred earlier in the works of Bernard Sylvanus, but Werner and Johannes Stabius were the first to work it out mathematically. Later, Oronce Fine, Peter Apian, and Gerardus Mercator adopted the cordiform projection. It is not known whether Werner designed a map of the world.

Werner's work in geography gained widespread recognition. Peter Apian, in particular, was a student of Werner's in theoretical cartography. The treatises contained in the collection dated 1514 were included almost unchanged in Apian's *Introductio geographica* (1533); Apian even used the proof sheets from the beginning of "In eundem primum librum . . . argumenta" to the end of "Joannis de Regiomonte epistola . . . de compositione et usu cuiusdam meteoroscopii," and admits in several places in his writings how much he had learned from Werner.

In meteorology Werner paved the way for a scientific interpretation. Meteorology and astrology were connected, but he nevertheless attempted to explain this science rationally. A short text on weather forecasting is still available in the manuscript "Regula aurea . . . ." The "guidelines that explain the principles and observations of the changes in the atmosphere," published in 1546 by Johann Schöner, contain meteorological notes for 1513–1520. The weather observations are based mainly on stellar constellations, and hence the course of the moon is of less importance. Although Werner did not collect the data systematically, as Tycho Brahe did, he attempted to incorporate meteorology into physics and to take into consideration the geographical situation of the observational site. Thus he can be regarded as a pioneer of modern meteorology and weather forecasting.

**Other Works.** The manuscript Codex Guelf. 17.6 Aug. 4° (Herzog-August Bibliothek, Wolfenbüttel) is an autograph in which words occasionally are crossed out and numerous addenda appear in the margin. The treatise gives an annal-like presentation of important events that occurred in Nuremberg between 1506 and 1521, most of which were political. On folios 41v and 70v two astronomical drawings that refer to Nuremberg are incorporated into the text.

*BIBLIOGRAPHY*

I. ORIGINAL WORKS. Writings published during Werner's lifetime were a collection on geography, *In hoc opere haec continentur . . . .* (Nuremberg, 1514), which contained as well as "Nova translatio primi libri geographiae Cl. Ptolomaei," "In eundem primum librum geographiae Cl. Ptolomaei argumenta, paraphrases, quibus idem liber per sententias ac summatim explicatur, et annotationes," "Libellus de quatuor terrarum orbis in plano figurationibus ab eodem I.V. novissime compertis et enarratis," "Ex fine septimi libri eiusdem geographiae Cl. Ptolomaei super plana terrarum orbis descriptione a priscis instituta geographis," "De his quae geographiae debent adesse Georgii Amirucii Constantinopolitani opusculum," "In idem Georgii Amirucii opusculum appendices," and "Ioannis de Regiomonte epistola ad reverendissimum patrem et dominum Bessarionem de compositione et usu cuiusdam meteoroscopii"—all re-edited by Peter Apian in his *Introductio geographica in doctissimas in Verneri annotationes* (Ingolstadt, 1533); and works on mathematics and astronomy, *In hoc opere haec continentur . . .* (Nuremberg, 1522), which contains "Libellus super vigintiduobus elementis conicis," "Commentarius seu paraphrastica enarratio in undecim modos conficiendi eius problematis quod cubi duplicatio dicitur," "Commentatio in Dionysodori problema, quo data sphaera plano sub data secatur ratione," "Alius modus idem problema conficiendi ab eodem I.V. novissime compertus demonstratusque," "De motu octavae sphaerae tractatus duo," and "Summaria enarratio theoricae motus octavae sphaerae."

Published after Werner's death were *Canones sicut brevissimi, ita etiam doctissimi, complectentes praecepta et observationes de mutatione aurae clarissimi mathematici Ioannis Verneri,* J. Schöner, ed. (Nuremberg, 1546); *Ioannis Verneri de triangulis sphaericis libri quatuor,* A. A. Björnbo, ed., XXIV. pt. 1, of the series Abhandlungen zur Geschichte der Mathematischen Wissenschaften mit Einschluss Ihrer Anwendungen (Leipzig, 1907); and *Ioannis Verneri de meteoroscopiis libri sex,* Joseph Würschmidt, ed., XXIV, pt. 2, of the same series (Leipzig, 1913). Some of Werner's letters are published in H. Rupprich, ed., *Der Briefwechsel des Konrad Celtis* (Munich, 1934).

The following writings remain in MS: "Tabulae latitudinum Saturni, Jovis, Martis, Veneris et Mercurii" (1521), Codex Oxoniensis Digby 132, fols. 1r–28v; "Compositiones et usus organorum latitudinum lunae et quinque planetarum" (1521), *ibid.,* fols. 29r–64r; "Judicium de cometa anni 1500 ad Sebaldum Clamosum alias Schreyer civem Nurembergensem" (1500), Vienna, Codex Vind. lat. 4756, fols. 143r–146v; two horoscopes, *ibid.,* 5002, fols. 104r–111v; "Regula aurea de aeris dispositione diiudicanda singulis diebus," *ibid.,* 5212, fols. 5v–6v; astrological writings, *ibid.,* 10534, fols. 248v, 260r; horoscopes (1498), *ibid.,* 10650, fols. 42r–87r; horoscope (1513), Munich, Clm 27083, fols. 1r–8v; horoscope, Paris, BN Reg. 7417; and "Historicus diarius inde ab anno 1506–1521 Johannis Verneri presbiteri Bambergensis diocesis et vicarii seu rectoris cappelle beatorum Johannis baptiste et Johannis evangeliste Norinbergensis," Wolfenbüttel, Codex Guelf. 17.6 Aug. 4°.

Lost works written before 1514 are "Liber de multimodis tam in astronomia quam in geographia problematis, quae ope arteque horum quinque librorum (Libri quinque de triangulis) absolvuntur"; "Opusculum de nonnullis scioteris, quibus linea meridiana, sublimitas axis mundani et hora diei sub omni climate per umbram solis simul examinantur"; "Tractatus resolutorius, qui prope pedissequus existit libris *Datorum* Euclidis"; and "Libellus arithmeticus, qui complectitur quaedam commenta numeralia." Also lost is a translation of Euclid's *Elements* into German.

II. SECONDARY LITERATURE. On Werner's life, see Johann Gabriel Doppelmayr, *Historische Nachricht von den Nürnbergischen Mathematicis und Künstlern* (Nuremberg, 1730), 31–35; Siegmund Günther, in *Allgemeine deutsche Biographie,* XLII (Leipzig, 1897), 56–58; Abraham Gotthilf Kästner, *Geschichte der Mathematik seit der Wiederherstellung der Wissenschaften bis ans Ende des 18. Jahrhunderts,* II (Göttingen, 1797; repr. Hildesheim–New York, 1970), 52–64; Hans Kressel, "Hans Werner. Der gelehrte Pfarrherr von St. Johannis. Der Freund und wissenschaftliche Lehrmeister Albrecht Dürers," in *Mitteilungen des Vereins für Geschichte der Stadt Nürnberg,* **52** (1963–1964), 287–304; Karl Schottenloher, "Der Mathematiker und Astronom Johann Werner aus Nürnberg. 1466 [*sic*]–1522," in *Festgabe an Hermann Grauert* (Freiburg im Breisgau, 1910), 147–155; and Ernst Zinner, "Die fränkische Sternkunde im 11. bis 16. Jahrhundert," in *Bericht der Naturforschenden Gesellschaft in Bamberg,* **27** (1934), 111–113. A biography of Werner is being prepared by Kurt Pilz as part of his work *600 Jahre Astronomie in Nürnberg.*

Werner's achievements in astronomy are discussed in Ernst Zinner, *Verzeichnis der astronomischen Handschriften des deutschen Kulturgebietes* (Munich, 1925), nos. 11641–11650; and *Deutsche und niederländische astronomische Instrumente des 11.–18. Jahrhunderts* (2nd ed., Munich, 1967), 148, 151 f., 208 f., 584.

Copernicus' criticism of Werner is presented in Maximilian Curtze, "Der Brief des Coppernicus an den Domherrn Wapowski zu Krakau über das Buch des Johannes Werner De motu octavae sphaerae," in *Mittheilungen des Coppernicus-Vereins für Wissenschaft und Kunst, Thorn,* no. 1 (1878), 18–33; Siegmund Günther, "Der Wapowski-Brief des Coppernicus und Werners Tractat über die Praecession," *ibid.,* no. 2 (1880), 1–11; and *Three Copernican Treatises,* translated with intro. and notes by Edward Rosen (2nd ed., New York, 1959), 7–9, 91–106.

Brahe's criticism of Werner appears in *Tychonis Brahe opera omnia,* J. L. E. Dreyer, ed., VII (Copenhagen, 1924), 295, ll. 23–42.

Werner's achievements in mathematics are treated in Moritz Cantor, *Vorlesungen über Geschichte der Mathematik,* II, *Vom Jahre 1200 bis zum Jahre 1668* (2nd ed., Leipzig, 1900; repr. New York–Stuttgart, 1965), 452–459; C. J. Gerhardt, *Geschichte der Mathematik in Deutschland,* which is vol. XVII of Geschichte der

Wissenschaften in Deutschland (Munich, 1877; repr. New York–London, 1965), 23–25; and Johannes Tropfke, *Geschichte der Elementar-Mathematik in systematischer Darstellung*, 2nd ed., V (Berlin–Leipzig, 1923), 62, 107–110.

On the history of the text of Werner's trigonometry, see A. A. Björnbo, *Ioannis Verneri*, 140–175; E. Zinner, *Deutsche . . . Instrumente . . .*, 358; and Karl Heinz Burmeister, *Georg Joachim Rhetikus 1514–1574. Eine Bio-Bibliographie* (Wiesbaden, 1967), I, 78, 134, 159 f., 181 f., and II, 78.

Werner's achievements in geography and meteorology are discussed in Siegmund Günther, *Studien zur Geschichte der mathematischen und physikalischen Geographie* (Halle, 1878), 273–332.

MENSO FOLKERTS

**WERNICKE, CARL** (*b.* Tarnowitz [now Tarnowskie Gory], Upper Silesia, Germany [now Poland], 15 May 1848; *d.* Dörrberg im Geratal, Germany, 15 June 1905), *neuropsychiatry, neuroanatomy.*

After receiving a medical degree from the University of Breslau in 1870, Wernicke worked there under Heinrich Neumann, qualifying in psychiatry in 1875. During this period he spent six months in Vienna with Theodor Meynert and from 1876 to 1878 was Karl Westphal's assistant in the psychiatric and neurologic clinic at the Charité Hospital in Berlin. He then established a private neuropsychiatric practice in Berlin until 1885, when he became associate professor of neurology and psychiatry at Breslau. He obtained the chair at Breslau in 1890 and in 1904 went to Halle as full professor. He died a year later from injuries received in a bicycling accident.

Wernicke and his teachers Meynert and Westphal were part of the prominent tradition of nineteenth-century German neuropsychiatry stemming from Wilhelm Griesinger. These neuropsychiatrists made no distinction between diseases of the "mind" and diseases of the "brain." As Griesinger had announced, "Mental diseases are affections of the brain." Accordingly, Wernicke called his first major work, *Der aphasische Symptomencomplex* (1874), a "psychological study on an anatomical basis." In that monograph he developed his concept of cerebral localization, fully described sensory aphasia (Wernicke's aphasia) for the first time, and located the lesion causing this condition in the posterior portion of the first left temporal convolution. Wernicke's work also helped to establish firmly the notion of right and left cerebral dominance.

Between 1881 and 1883 Wernicke published his three-volume *Lehrbuch der Gehirnkrankheiten*. This comprehensive survey included a number of original anatomical, pathological, and clinical observations, such as the subsequently confirmed postulation of the symptoms resulting from occlusion of the posterior inferior cerebellar artery. Wernicke also first described (II, 229–242) a condition he called acute hemorrhagic superior polioencephalitis. Since renamed Wernicke's encephalopathy, the syndrome is manifested by particular disturbances of consciousness and gait and paralysis of the eye muscles. Wernicke's encephalopathy is frequently seen in chronic alcoholics, but it is also observed in other pathologic states. His original description was in a case of sulfuric acid ingestion.

In his later work Wernicke remained concerned both with brain anatomy and pathology and with clinical neuropsychiatry. With four collaborators he published the three-part *Atlas des Gehirns* between 1897 and 1903. His clinical studies are contained principally in *Grundriss der Psychiatrie in klinischen Vorlesungen* (1894; 2nd ed., 1906) and in *Krankenvorstellungen aus der psychiatrischen Klinik in Breslau* (1899–1900). Wernicke also continued to write on aphasia; his last summary of this "symptom complex" appeared in 1903 in the multivolume system of medicine edited by Ernst von Leyden and Felix Klemperer, *Die deutsche Klinik am Eingange des 20. Jahrhunderts.*

Wernicke excelled in careful neuropsychiatric description of patients, but he contended that psychiatry was not sufficiently developed to demarcate specific psychiatric syndromes. This attitude brought him into conflict with Emil Kraepelin, the great psychiatric nosologist of the period.

*BIBLIOGRAPHY*

I. ORIGINAL WORKS. Most of Wernicke's major publications are mentioned in the text. Others include "Das Urwindungssystem des menschlichen Gehirns," in *Archiv für Psychiatrie*, **6** (1876), 298–326; "Ueber das Bewusstsein," in *Allgemeine Zeitschrift für Psychiatrie*, **35** (1879), 420–431; and "Die neueren Arbeiten über Aphasie," in *Fortschritte der Medizin*, **3** (1885), 824–830, and **4** (1886), 371–377, 463–482. Many of Wernicke's collected papers on neuropathology were published as *Gesammelte Aufsätze und kritische Referate zur Pathologie des Nervensystems* (Berlin, 1893).

Wernicke's 1903 summary of aphasia was translated into English in A. Church, ed., *Diseases of the Nervous System* (New York–London, 1908), 265–324.

II. SECONDARY LITERATURE. The best general treatment of Wernicke is the article by Karl Kleist in Kurt

Kolle, ed., *Grosse Nervenärzte*, II (Stuttgart, 1959), 106–128. There are also short biographical essays by Kurt Goldstein in Webb Haymaker, ed., *Founders of Neurology* (Springfield, Ill., 1953), 406–409; and by H. Liepmann in Theodor Kirchhoff, ed., *Deutsche Irrenärzte*, II (Berlin, 1924). Other articles on Wernicke include H. Liepmann, "Über Wernickes Einfluss auf die klinische Psychiatrie," in *Monatschrifte für Psychiatrie und Neurologie*, **30** (1911), 1–37; P. Schröder, "Die Lehren Wernickes in ihrer Bedeutung für die heutige Psychiatrie," in *Zeitschrift für die gesamte Neurologie und Psychiatrie*, **165** (1939), 38–47; and O. M. Marx, "Nineteenth-Century Medical Psychology. Theoretical Problems in the Work of Griesinger, Meynert, and Wernicke," in *Isis*, **61** (1970), 355–370.

There is a good concise treatment of nineteenth-century German neuropsychiatry in Erwin H. Ackerknecht, *A Short History of Psychiatry* (2nd ed., New York, 1968), 60–71; and several references to Wernicke's work in Lawrence C. McHenry, Jr., *Garrison's History of Neurology* (Springfield, Ill., 1969), 358–361.

WILLIAM F. BYNUM

**WERTHEIM, ERNST** (*b.* Graz, Austria, 21 February 1864; *d.* Vienna, Austria, 15 February 1920), *gynecology.*

Son of the professor of chemistry at the University of Graz, Wertheim studied medicine there and received his medical degree on 29 February 1888, before becoming an assistant in the department of general and experimental pathology. Under the supervision of Rudolf Klemensiewicz he learned the bacteriological and histological techniques that later enabled him to conduct his fundamental research on gonorrhea in the female genital tract. The first result of his work at Graz, however, was a paper on fowl cholera.

Wertheim left Graz on 30 April 1889 and studied until mid-November under Otto Kahler at Vienna's Second University Clinic. In the same year he became interested in gynecology, the field to which he was to devote a lifetime of research. At the time both of Vienna's women's clinics possessed excellent facilities for specialized postgraduate training in obstetrics and gynecology, where pupils studied for two years at state expense. Upon leaving Kahler, Wertheim entered the institute attached to the Second Vienna Women's Clinic, which was headed by Rudolf Chrobak, and remained there as a student until 30 September 1890. He then moved to Prague as assistant to Friedrich Schauta at the university's women's clinic, returning to Vienna in 1891 when Schauta was appointed head of the First Vienna Women's Clinic.

In his years as an assistant, Wertheim focused his research on gonorrhea in the female genital tract. His training in experimental and bacteriological methods allowed him to give a unique, definitive explanation of the then much-disputed path of the gonorrheal infection. In 1890 he demonstrated the existence of gonococci in tissue of the Fallopian tubes; previously they had been detected only in smear samples. More important, in a series of papers containing the results of bacteriological and histological studies and of experiments on animals, Wertheim showed that the gonococcus affects not only the cylindrical epithelium—as Ernst Bumm maintained in his widely accepted theory (1895)—but also the squamous epithelium (the peritoneum). Through these papers, especially in "Die aszendierende Gonorrhoe beim Weibe. Bakteriologische und klinische Studien zur Biologie des *Gonococcus neisser*" (*Archiv für Gynäkologie*, **42** [1892], 1–86), Wertheim placed his theory of ascending gonorrhea in the female on a firm foundation.

Wertheim gained world fame for systematically developing—to the point where it became standard practice—a radical abdominal operation for cervical cancer. In 1897 he was named chief surgeon of the gynecological service (Bettina Pavilion) of the Elisabeth Hospital and thereby obtained his own operating facilities. By then he had long realized that the customary method of vaginal extirpation was highly unsatisfactory because of its bad aftereffects. (The abdominal method had been abandoned because of its mortality rate of 72 percent.) Consequently, elaborating the work of his predecessors Emil Ries, Theodor Rumpf, and J. G. Clark, Wertheim decided to place the operation for cervical cancer on a modern surgical basis. No longer satisfied with the extirpation of the diseased organ, he sought to remove as much as possible of the organ's surroundings, the perimetrium, along with the neighboring lymph glands. He recognized, as had Julius Massari in 1878, that the greatest possible attention must be directed to protecting the ureters during their exposure and preparation.

On 16 November 1898 Wertheim performed his first radical abdominal operation based on these principles. For his first twenty-nine operations he reported a mortality rate of 38 percent (*Archiv für Gynäkologie*, **61** [1900], 627–668). Tirelessly working to improve his surgical technique, he succeeded in reducing the mortality rate to 10 percent. This assured universal acclaim for his radical abdominal surgery. He gave a full account of his success in *Die erweiterte abdominale Operation bei Carcinoma colli uteri (auf Grund von 500 Fällen)* (Berlin–Vienna, 1911).

In 1910 Wertheim was appointed director of the First University Women's Clinic in Vienna. Firmly determined to replace unsatisfactory surgical procedures with improved ones, he returned his attention to the treatment of uterine prolapse. He had already made a contribution in this area in 1899 with his interposition method, which involved covering the uterus with vaginal lobes. He then developed a version of the operation that is known as suspension and superposition; his richly illustrated book on it appeared a year before his death as *Die operative Behandlung des Prolapses mittelst Interposition und Suspension des Uterus* (Berlin, 1919). Wertheim was as difficult in his personal relations as he was brilliant in his research. Held in great esteem by his colleagues, he was a corresponding or honorary member of many foreign learned societies. At Vienna he created a distinguished school of gynecological surgeons; and his work was carried on there, as well as in Prague and Berlin, by his most outstanding students, Wilhelm Weibel and Georg August Wagner.

*BIBLIOGRAPHY*

Many of Wertheim's works are mentioned in the text. See also the bibliography in the obituary by Weibel (below).

Secondary literature includes J. Artner and A. Schaller, *Die Wertheimsche Radikaloperation. Anfänge, Fortschritte, Ergebnisse. 1898–1968* (Vienna, 1968); R. Elert, "Zum Gedenkjahr des doppelten Jubiläums der abdominellen Radikaloperation des Gebärmutterkrebses. W. A. Freund (1878)–Wertheim (1898)," in *Klinische Medizin*, **4** (1949), 249–262, very detailed; F. Kermauner, in *Wiener klinische Wochenschrift*, **33** (1920), 183–185; W. Latzko, in *Wiener medizinische Wochenschrift*, **70** (1920), 545–549; E. Lesky, "Die Wiener geburtshilflich-gynäkologische Schule," in *Deutsche medizinische Wochenschrift*, **87** (1962), 2096–2102; and *Die Wiener medizinische Schule im 19. Jahrhundert* (Graz–Cologne, 1965); E. Navratil, "Die Entwicklung der Operationsmethoden zur Entfernung der karzinomatösen Gebärmutter," in *Wiener klinische Wochenschrift*, **60** (1948), 233–238; G. Reiffenstuhl, *ibid.*, **82** (1970), 554–559; W. Weibel, in *Monatsschrift für Geburtshülfe und Gynäkologie*, **61** (1920), 271–279, with bibliography, in *Archiv für Gynäkologie* (Berlin), **113** (1920), v–xvi; in *Zentralblatt für Gynäkologie*, **44** (1920), 281–285; and "25 Jahre 'Wertheimscher' Carcinomoperation," in *Archiv für Gynäkologie* (Berlin), **135** (1929), 1–57; P. Werner and J. Sederl, *Die Wertheimsche Radikaloperation bei Carcinoma colli uteri* (Vienna–Innsbruck, 1952); and T. Antoine, "Letter From Austria," in *Obstetrical and Gynecological Survey*, **24** (1969), 1129–1137.

ERNA LESKY

**WESSEL, CASPAR** (*b.* Vestby, near Dröbak, Norway, 8 June 1745; *d.* Copenhagen, Denmark, 25 March 1818), *surveying, mathematics.*

Although he was born when Norway was part of Denmark and spent most of his life in Denmark, Wessel is regarded as a Norwegian. (Niels Nielsen, in his *Matematiken i Danmark, 1528–1800* [Copenhagen–Christiania, 1912], gives his birthplace as Jonsrud in Akershus.) His father, Jonas Wessel, was a vicar in the parish of which his grandfather was the pastor; his mother was Maria Schumacher.

After attending the Christiania Cathedral School in Oslo from 1757 to 1763, Wessel spent a year at the University of Copenhagen. In 1764 he began work on the cartography of Denmark, as an assistant with the Danish Survey Commission operating under the Royal Danish Academy of Sciences. He passed the university examination in Roman law in 1778 and became survey superintendent in 1798. He continued as a surveyor and cartographer even after his retirement in 1805, working on special projects until rheumatism forced him to stop in 1812. He was frequently in financial difficulty; but since he would accept no remuneration for special maps of Schleswig and Holstein requested by the French government, the Royal Danish Academy awarded him a silver medal and a set of its *Mémoires* and maps. He was made a knight of Danebrog in 1815.

Wessel's fame as a mathematician is based entirely on one paper, written in Danish and published in the *Mémoires* of the Royal Danish Academy, that established his priority in publication of the geometric representation of complex numbers. John Wallis had given a geometric representation of the complex roots of quadratic equations in 1685; Gauss had had the idea as early as 1799 but did not explicitly publish it until 1831. Robert Argand's independent publication in 1806 must be credited as the source of this concept in modern mathematics because Wessel's work remained essentially unknown until 1895, when its significance was pointed out by Christian Juel. Despite its lack of influence upon the development of mathematics, Wessel's publication was remarkable in many ways: he was not a professional mathematician; Norway and Denmark were not mathematically productive or stimulating at that time; he was not a member of the Royal Danish Academy (he had been helped and encouraged by J. N. Tetens, councillor of state and president of the science section of the Academy); and yet his exposition was, in some respects, superior to and more modern in spirit than Argand's.

The title of Wessel's treatise calls it an "attempt" to give an analytic representation of both distance and direction that could be used to solve plane and spherical polygons. The connection of this goal with Wessel's work as a surveyor and cartographer is obvious. The statement of the problem also suggests that Wessel should be credited with an early formulation of vector addition. In fact, Michael J. Crowe, in *A History of Vector Analysis* (University of Notre Dame Press, 1967), defines the first period in that history as that of a search for hypercomplex numbers to be used in space analysis and dates it from the time of Wessel, whom he calls the first to add vectors in three-dimensional space. Wessel's first step was to note that two segments of the same line, whether of the same or opposite sense, are added by placing the initial point of one at the terminus of the other and defining the sum to be the segment extending from the initial point of the first to the terminal point of the second. He immediately defined the sum of two nonparallel segments in the same way and extended this definition to apply to any number of segments.

For multiplication of line segments, Wessel drew his motivation from the fact that, in arithmetic, a product of two factors has the same ratio to one factor as the other factor has to 1. Assuming that the product and the two factors are in the same plane and have the same initial point as the unit segment, he reasoned that the product vector should differ in direction from one factor by the same amount by which the other factor differed from unity. Wessel then designated two oppositely directed unit segments having the same origin by $+1$ and $-1$, and assigned to them the direction angles $0°$ and $180°$. To unit segments perpendicular to these he assigned the symbols $+\epsilon$ and $-\epsilon$ and the angles $90°$ and either $270°$ or $-90°$. Wessel immediately pointed out that multiplication of these numbers corresponded to addition of their angles and gave a table in which $(+\epsilon) \cdot (+\epsilon) = -1$. He then noted that this means that $\epsilon = \sqrt{-1}$, and that these operations do not contradict the ordinary rules of algebra. From this and his definition of addition of vectors, Wessel next wrote $\cos v + \epsilon \sin v$ as the algebraic formula for a unit segment and then derived the algebraic formula $(a + \epsilon b) \cdot (c + \epsilon d) = ac - bd + \epsilon(ad + bc)$ for the product of any two segments from the formula for the product of two unit segments derived from the equation $(\cos v + \epsilon \sin v)(\cos u + \epsilon \sin u) = \cos(u + v) + \epsilon \sin (u + v)$, using trigonometric identities.

Thus Wessel's development proceeded rather directly from a geometric problem, through geometric-intuitive reasoning, to an algebraic formula. Argand began with algebraic quantities and sought a geometric representation for them.

Wessel was more modern than Argand in his recognition of the arbitrary nature of the definitions of operations that Argand initially attempted to justify by intuitive arguments. Wessel also sought to extend his definition of multiplication to lines in space. T. N. Thiele's view that Wessel should be credited with anticipating Hamilton's formulation of quaternion multiplication, however, seems to exaggerate the extent of his work, which Wessel himself recognized as incomplete.

Wessel used in his development trigonometric identities that Argand derived by means of his definitions of operations on complex numbers. Argand presented a greater variety of applications of his work, including a proof of the fundamental theorem of algebra and of Ptolemy's theorem. Wessel worked at his original problem of applying algebra to the solution of plane and spherical polygons, after expanding his discussion to include formulas for division, powers, and roots of complex numbers.

Wessel's initial formulation was remarkably clear, direct, concise, and modern. It is regrettable that it was not appreciated for nearly a century and hence did not have the influence it merited.

## BIBLIOGRAPHY

I. ORIGINAL WORKS. Wessel's paper "Om directionens analytiske betegning, et forsøg, anvendt fornemmelig til plane og sphaeriske polygoners opløsning," read to the Royal Danish Academy of Sciences on 10 Mar. 1797, was printed in 1798 by J. R. Thiele and was incorporated in *Nye samling af det Kongelige Danske Videnskabernes Selskabs Skrifter*, 2nd ser., **5** (1799), 496–518. Almost a century later the Academy published a French trans., *Essai sur la représentation analytique de la direction, par Caspar Wessel* (Copenhagen, 1897), with prefaces by H. Valentiner and T. N. Thiele.

In the meantime, Sophus Lie published a reproduction in *Archiv for mathematik og naturvidenskab*, **18** (1896). The English trans. by Martin A. Nordgaard of portions of the original paper first appeared in D. E. Smith, ed., *A Source Book in Mathematics* (New York, 1929), 55–66, repr. in H. O. Midonick, ed., *The Treasury of Mathematics* (New York, 1965), 805–814.

II. SECONDARY LITERATURE. The most complete discussions are Viggo Brun, *Regnekunsten i det gamle Norge* (Oslo, 1962), 92–111, with English summary on 120–122; and "Caspar Wessel et l'introduction géométrique des nombres complexes," in *Revue d'histoire des sciences et de leurs applications*, **12** (Jan.-Mar. 1959), 19–24; and Webster Woodruff Beman, "A Chapter in the History of Mathematics," in *Proceedings of the American Association for the Advancement of Science*, **46** (1897), 33–50, which includes a survey of the development of the concept of a complex number with especial emphasis on graphical representation, particularly the work of Wessel—French trans. in *Enseignement mathématique*, **1** (1899), 162–184.

Much information on Wessel's cartographic and surveying activity is in Otto Harms, "Die amtliche Topographie in Oldenburg und ihre kartographischen Ergebnisse," in *Oldenburger Jahrbuch*, **60**, pt. 1 (1961), 1–38.

PHILLIP S. JONES

**WEYL, HERMANN** (*b.* Elmshorn, near Hamburg, Germany, 9 November 1885; *d.* Zurich, Switzerland, 8 December 1955), *mathematics, mathematical physics.*

Weyl attended the Gymnasium at Altona and, on the recommendation of the headmaster of his Gymnasium, who was a cousin of Hilbert, decided at the age of eighteen to enter the University of Göttingen. Except for one year at Munich he remained at Göttingen, as a student and later as *Privatdozent*, until 1913, when he became professor at the University of Zurich. After Klein's retirement in 1913, Weyl declined an offer to be his successor at Göttingen but accepted a second offer in 1930, after Hilbert had retired. In 1933 he decided he could no longer remain in Nazi Germany and accepted a position at the Institute for Advanced Study at Princeton, where he worked until his retirement in 1951. In the last years of his life he divided his time between Zurich and Princeton.

Weyl undoubtedly was the most gifted of Hilbert's students. Hilbert's thought dominated the first part of his mathematical career; and although later he sharply diverged from his master, particularly on questions related to foundations of mathematics, Weyl always shared his convictions that the value of abstract theories lies in their success in solving classical problems and that the proper way to approach a question is through a deep analysis of the concepts it involves rather than by blind computations.

Weyl arrived at Göttingen during the period when Hilbert was creating the spectral theory of self-adjoint operators, and spectral theory and harmonic analysis were central in his mathematical research throughout his life. Very soon, however, he considerably broadened the range of his interests, including areas of mathematics into which Hilbert had never penetrated, such as the theory of Lie groups and the analytic theory of numbers, thereby becoming one of the most universal mathematicians of his generation. He also had an important role in the development of mathematical physics, the field to which his most famous books, *Raum, Zeit und Materie* (1918), on the theory of relativity, and *Gruppentheorie und Quantenmechanik* (1928), are devoted.

Weyl's first important work in spectral theory was his *Habilitationsschrift* (1910), on singular boundary conditions for second-order linear differential equations. The classical Sturm-Liouville problem consists in determining solutions of a self-adjoint differential equation

$$(1) \qquad (py')' - (q - \lambda)y = 0$$

in a compact interval $0 \leq x \leq l$, with $p(x) > 0$ and $q$ real in that interval, the solutions being subject to boundary conditions

$$(2) \qquad y'(0) - wy(0) = 0$$

$$(3) \qquad y'(l) - hy(l) = 0$$

with real numbers $w, h$; it is known that nontrivial solutions exist only when $\lambda$ takes one of an increasing sequence $(\lambda_n)$ of real numbers $\geq 0$ and tending to $+\infty$ (the spectrum of the equation). Weyl investigated the case in which $l = +\infty$; his idea was to give arbitrary complex values to $\lambda$. Then, for given real $h$, there is a unique solution satisfying (2) and (3), provided $w$ is taken as a complex number $w(\lambda, h)$. When $h$ takes all real values, the points $w(\lambda, h)$ are on a circle $C_l(\lambda)$ in the complex plane. Weyl also showed that when $l$ tends to $+\infty$, the circles $C_l(\lambda)$ (for fixed $\lambda$) form a nested family that has a circle or a point as a limit. The distinction between the two cases is independent of the choice of $\lambda$, for in the "limit circle" case all solutions of (1) are square-integrable on $[0, +\infty]$, whereas in the "limit point" case only one solution (up to a constant factor) has that property. This was actually the first example of the general theory of defects of an unbounded Hermitian operator, which was created later by von Neumann. Weyl also showed how the classical Fourier series development of a function in a series of multiples of the eigenfunctions of the Sturm-Liouville problem was replaced, when $l - +\infty$, by an expression similar to the Fourier integral (the spectrum then being generally a nondiscrete subset of **R**); he thus anticipated the later developments of the Carleman integral operators and their applications to differential linear equations of arbitrary order and to elliptic linear partial differential equations.

In 1911 Weyl inaugurated another important chapter of spectral theory, the asymptotic study of the eigenvalues of a self-adjoint compact operator $U$ in Hilbert space $H$, with special attention to applications to the theory of elasticity. For this purpose he introduced the "maximinimal" method for the direct computation of the $n$th eigenvalue $\lambda_n$ of $U$ (former methods gave the value of $\lambda_n$ only after those of $\lambda_1, \lambda_2, \cdots, \lambda_{n-1}$ had been determined). One considers an arbitrary linear subspace $F$ of codimension $n - 1$ in $H$ and the largest value of the scalar product $(U \cdot x \mid x)$ when $x$ takes all values on the intersection of $F$ and the unit sphere $\|x\| = 1$ of $H$; $\lambda_n$ is the smallest of these largest values when $F$ is allowed to run through all subspaces of codimension 1. This method has a very intuitive geometric interpretation in the theory of quadrics when $H$ is finite-dimensional; it was used with great efficiency in many problems of functional analysis by Weyl himself and later by Richard Courant, who did much to popularize it and greatly extend its range of applications.

Weyl published the famous paper on equidistribution modulo 1, one of the highlights of his career, in 1916. A sequence $(x_n)$ of real numbers is equidistributed modulo 1 if for any interval $[\alpha, \beta]$ contained in $[0,1]$, the number $\nu(\alpha, \beta; n)$ of elements $x_k$ such that $k \leqslant n$ and $x_k = N_k + y_k$, with $\alpha \leqslant y_k \leqslant \beta$ and $N_k$ a (positive or negative) integer, is such that $\nu(\alpha, \beta; n)/n$ tends to the length $\beta - \alpha$ of the interval when $n$ tends to $+\infty$. Led to such questions by his previous work on the Gibbs phenomenon for series of spherical harmonics, Weyl approached the problem by a completely new—and amazingly simple—method. For any sequence $(y_n)$ of real numbers, write $M((y_n))$ the limit (when it exists) of the arithmetic mean $(y_1 + \cdots + y_n)/n$ when $n$ tends to $+\infty$; then to say that $(x_n)$ is equidistributed means that $M((f(x_n))) = \int_0^1 f(t)dt$ for any function of period 1 coinciding on $[0,1]$ with the characteristic function of any interval $[\alpha, \beta]$. Weyl's familiarity with harmonic analysis enabled him to conclude (1) that this property was equivalent to the existence of $M((f(x_n)))$ for all Riemann integrable functions of period 1 and (2) that it was enough to check the existence of that limit for the particular functions $\exp(2\pi i k x)$ for any integer $k \in Z$. This simple criterion immediately yields the equidistribution of the sequence $(n\alpha)$ for irrational $\alpha$ (proved independently a little earlier by Weyl, Bohl, and Wacław Sierpiński by purely arithmetic methods), as well as a quantitative form of the Kronecker theorems on simultaneous Diophantine approximations.

Weyl's most profound result was the proof of the equidistribution of the sequence $(P(n))$, where $P$ is a polynomial of arbitrary degree, the leading coefficient of which is irrational; this amounts to showing that

$$s_N = \sum_{n=0}^{N} \exp(2\pi i P(n)) = o(N)$$

for $N$ tending to $+\infty$. To give an idea of Weyl's ingenious proof, consider the case when $P(n) = \alpha n^2 + \beta n$ with irrational $\alpha$. One writes

$$|s_N|^2 = s_N \bar{s}_N = \sum_{m,n=0}^{N} \exp(2\pi i (\alpha(m^2 - n^2) + \beta(m - n)))$$

$$= \sum_{r=-N}^{N} \sigma_r \cdot \exp(2\pi i (\alpha r^2 + \beta r)),$$

where $\sigma_r = \sum_{n \in I_r} \exp(2\pi i \alpha r n)$, $I_r$ being the interval intersection of $[0,N]$ and $[-r, N - r]$ in **Z**. This yields $|s_N|^2 \leqslant \sum_{r=-N}^{N} |\sigma_r|$. One has two majorations, $|\sigma_r| \leqslant N + 1$ and $|\sigma_r| \leqslant 1/\sin(2\pi\alpha r)$. For a given $\epsilon \in [0, \frac{1}{2}]$, the number of integers $r \in [-N, N]$ such that $2\alpha r$ is congruent to a number in the interval $[-\epsilon, \epsilon]$ has the form $4\pi\epsilon N + o(N)$ by equidistribution; hence it is $\leqslant 5\epsilon N$ for large $N$. Applying to these integers $r$ the first majoration, and the second to the others, one obtains

$$|s_N|^2 \leqslant 5\epsilon N(N + 1) + (2N + 1)/\sin(\pi\epsilon) \leqslant 6\epsilon N^2$$

for large $N$, thus proving the theorem. The extension of that idea to polynomials of higher degree $d$ is not done by induction on $d$, but by a more elaborate device using the equidistribution of a multilinear function of $d$ variables. Weyl's results, through the improvements made later by I. M. Vinogradov and his school, have remained fundamental tools in the application of the Hardy-Littlewood method in the additive theory of numbers.

Weyl's versatility is illustrated in a particularly

striking way by the fact that immediately after these original advances in number theory (which he obtained in 1914), he spent more than ten years as a geometer—a geometer in the most modern sense of the word, uniting in his methods topology, algebra, analysis, and geometry in a display of dazzling virtuosity and uncommon depth reminiscent of Riemann. His familiarity with geometry and topology had been acquired a few years earlier when, as a young *Privatdozent* at Göttingen, he had given a course on Riemann's theory of functions; but instead of following his predecessors in their constant appeal to "intuition" for the definition and properties of Riemann surfaces, he set out to give to their theory the same kind of axiomatic and rigorous treatment that Hilbert had given to Euclidean geometry. Using Hilbert's idea of defining neighborhoods by a system of axioms, and influenced by Brouwer's clever application of Poincaré's simplicial methods (which had just been published), he gave the first rigorous definition of a complex manifold of dimension 1 and a thorough treatment (without any appeal to intuition) of all questions regarding orientation, homology, and fundamental groups of these manifolds. *Die Idee der Riemannschen Fläche* (1913) immediately became a classic and inspired all later developments of the theory of differential and complex manifolds.

The first geometric problem that Weyl attempted to solve (1915) was directly inspired by Hilbert's previous work on the rigidity of convex surfaces. Hilbert had shown how the "mixed volumes" considered by Minkowski could be expressed in terms of a second-order elliptic differential linear operator $L_H$ attached to the "Stützfunktion" $H$ of a given convex body; Blaschke had observed that this operator was the one that intervened in the theory of infinitesimal deformation of surfaces, and this knowledge had enabled Hilbert to deduce from his results that such infinitesimal deformations for a convex body could only be Euclidean isometries. Weyl attempted to prove that not only infinitesimal deformations, but finite deformations of a convex surface as well, were necessarily Euclidean isometries. His very original idea, directly inspired by his work on two-dimensional "abstract" Riemannian manifolds, was to prove simultaneously this uniqueness property and an existence statement, namely that any two-dimensional Riemannian compact manifold with everywhere positive curvature was uniquely (up to isometries) imbeddable in Euclidean three-dimensional space. The bold method he proposed for the proof was to proceed by

continuity, starting from the fact that (by another result of Hilbert's) the problem of existence and uniqueness was already solved for the $ds^2$ of the sphere, and using a family of $ds^2$ depending continuously on a real parameter linking the given $ds^2$ to that of the sphere and having all positive curvature. This led him to a "functional differential equation" that he did not completely solve, but later work by L. Nirenberg showed that a complete proof of the theorem could be obtained along these lines.

Interrupted in this work by mobilization into the German army, Weyl did not resume it when he was allowed to return to civilian life in 1916. At Zurich he had worked with Einstein for one year, and he became keenly interested in the general theory of relativity, which had just been published; with his characteristic enthusiasm he devoted most of the next five years to exploring the mathematical framework of the theory. In these investigations Weyl introduced the concept of what is now called a linear connection, linked not to the Lorentz group of orthogonal transformations of a quadratic form of signature (1, 3) but to the enlarged group of similitudes (reproducing the quadratic form only up to a factor); he even thought for a time that this would give him a "unitary theory" encompassing both gravitation and electromagnetism. Although these hopes did not materialize, Weyl's ideas undoubtedly were the source from which E. Cartan, a few years later, developed his general theory of connections (under the name of "generalized spaces").

Weyl's use of tensor calculus in his work on relativity led him to reexamine the basic methods of that calculus and, more generally, of classical invariant theory that had been its forerunner but had fallen into near oblivion after Hilbert's work of 1890. On the other hand, his semiphilosophical, semimathematical ideas on the general concept of "space" in connection with Einstein's theory had directed his investigations to generalizations of Helmholtz's problem of characterizing Euclidean geometry by properties of "free mobility." From these two directions Weyl was brought into contact with the theory of linear representations of Lie groups; his papers on the subject (1925–1927) certainly represent his masterpiece and must be counted among the most influential ones in twentieth-century mathematics.

In the early 1900's Frobenius, I. Schur, and A. Young had completely determined the irreducible rational linear representations of the general linear group GL($n$,C) of complex matrices of order $n$; it was easy to deduce from Schur's results that all rational linear representations of the special linear group $SL(n,\mathbf{C})$ (matrices of determinant 1) were completely reducible—that is, direct sums of irreducible representations. Independently, E. Cartan in 1913 had described all irreducible linear representations of the simple complex Lie algebras without paying much attention to the exact relation between these representations and the corresponding ones for the simple groups, beyond exhibiting examples of group representations for each type of Lie algebra representations. Furthermore, Cartan apparently had assumed without proof that any (finite-dimensional) linear representation of a semisimple Lie algebra is completely reducible.

Weyl inaugurated a new approach by deliberately focusing his attention on global groups, the Lie algebras being reduced to the status of technical devices. In 1897 Hurwitz had shown how one may form invariants for the orthogonal or unitary group by substituting, for the usual averaging process on finite groups, integration on the (compact) group with respect to an invariant measure. He also had observed that this yields invariants not only of the special unitary group $SU(n)$ but also of the special linear group $SL(n,\mathbf{C})$ (the first example of what Weyl later called the "unitarian trick"). Using Hurwitz's method, I. Schur in 1924 had proved the complete reducibility of all continuous linear representations of $SU(n)$ by showing the existence, on any representation space of that group, of a Hermitian scalar product invariant under the action of $SU(n)$; by using the "unitarian trick" he also was able to prove the complete reducibility of the continuous linear representations of $SL(n,\mathbf{C})$ and to obtain orthogonality relations for the characters of $SU(n)$, generalizing the well-known Frobenius relations for the characters of a finite group. These relations led to the explicit determination of the characters of $SL(n,\mathbf{C})$, which Schur had obtained in 1905 by purely algebraic methods.

Starting from these results, Weyl first made the connection between the methods of Schur and those of E. Cartan for the representations of the Lie algebra of $SL(n,\mathbf{C})$ by pointing out for the first time that the one-to-one correspondence between both types of representations was due to the fact that $SU(n)$ is simply connected. He next extended the same method to the orthogonal and symplectic complex groups, observing, apparently for the first time, the existence of the two-sheeted covering group of the orthogonal group (the "spin" group, for which Cartan had only obtained the linear rep-

resentations by spinors). Finally, Weyl turned to the global theory of all semisimple complex groups. First he showed that the "unitarian trick" had a validity that was not limited to the classical groups by proving that every semisimple complex Lie algebra $\mathfrak{g}$ could be considered as obtained by complexification from a well-determined real Lie algebra $\mathfrak{g}_u$, which was the Lie algebra of a compact group $G_u$; E. Cartan had obtained that result through a case-by-case examination of all simple complex Lie groups, whereas Weyl obtained a general proof by using the properties of the roots of the semisimple algebra. This established a one-to-one correspondence between linear representations of $\mathfrak{g}$ and linear representations of $\mathfrak{g}_u$; but to apply Hurwitz's method, one had to have a compact Lie group having $\mathfrak{g}_u$ as Lie algebra and being simply connected. This is not necessarily the case for the group $G_u$, and to surmount that difficulty, one had to prove that the universal covering group $G_u^*$ of $G_u$ is also compact; the a priori proof that such is the case is one of the deepest and most original parts of Weyl's paper. It is linked to a remarkable geometric interpretation of the roots of the Lie algebra $\mathfrak{g}_u$ relative to a maximal commutative subalgebra $\mathfrak{t}$, which is the Lie algebra of a maximal torus $T$ of $G_u$. Each root vanishes on a hyperplane of $\mathfrak{t}$, and the connected components of the complement of the union of these hyperplanes in the vector space $\mathfrak{t}$ are polyhedrons that are now called Weyl chambers; each of these chambers has as boundary a number of "walls" equal to the dimension of $\mathfrak{t}$.

Using this description (and some intuitive considerations of topological dimension that he did not bother to make rigorous), Weyl showed simultaneously that the fundamental group of $G_u$ was finite (hence $G_u^*$ was compact) and that for $G_u$ the maximal torus $T$ played a role similar to that of the group of diagonal matrices in $SU(n)$: every element of $G_u$ is a conjugate of an element of $T$. Furthermore, he proved that the Weyl chambers are permuted in a simply transitive way by the finite group generated by the reflections with respect to their walls (now called the Weyl group of $\mathfrak{g}$ or of $G_u$); this proof gave him not only a new method of recovering Cartan's "dominant weights" but also the explicit determination of the character of a representation as a function of its dominant weight.

In this determination Weyl had to use the orthogonality relations of the characters of $G_u$ (obtained through an extension of Schur's method) and a property that would replace Frobenius' fundamental theorem in the theory of linear representations of finite groups: that all irreducible representations are obtained by "decomposing" the regular representation. Weyl conceived the extraordinarily bold idea (for the time) of obtaining all irreducible representations of a semisimple group by "decomposing" an infinite-dimensional linear representation of $G_u$. To replace the group algebra introduced by Frobenius, he considered the continuous complex-valued functions on $G_u$ and took as "product" of two such functions $f,g$ what we now call the convolution $f*g$, defined by $(f*g)(t) = \int f(st^{-1})g(t)dt$, integration being relative to an invariant measure. To each continuous function $f$ the operator $R(f)$: $g \rightarrow f*g$ is then associated; the "decomposition" is obtained by considering the space of continuous functions on $G_u$ as a pre-Hilbert space and by showing that for suitable $f$ (those of the form $h*h$, where $h(t) = \overline{h(t^{-1})}$), $R(f)$ is Hermitian and compact, so that the classical Schmidt-Riesz theory of compact operators can be applied. It should be noted that in this substitute for the group algebra formed by the continuous functions on $G_u$, there is no unit element if $G_u$ is not trivial (in contrast with what happens for finite groups); again it was Weyl who saw the way out of this difficulty by using the "regularizing" property of the convolution to introduce "approximate units" — that is, sequences $(u_n)$ of functions that are such that the convolutions $u_n*f$ tend to $f$ for every continuous function $f$.

Very few of Weyl's 150 published books and papers — even those chiefly of an expository character — lack an original idea or a fresh viewpoint. The influence of his works and of his teaching was considerable: he proved by his example that an "abstract" approach to mathematics is perfectly compatible with "hard" analysis and, in fact, can be one of the most powerful tools when properly applied.

Weyl had a lifelong interest in philosophy and metaphysics, and his mathematical activity was seldom free from philosophical undertones or afterthoughts. At the height of the controversy over the foundations of mathematics, between the formalist school of Hilbert and the intuitionist school of Brouwer, he actively fought on Brouwer's side; and if he never observed too scrupulously the taboos of the intuitionists, he was careful in his papers never to use the axiom of choice. Fortunately, he dealt with theories in which he could do so with impunity.

BIBLIOGRAPHY

Weyl's writings were brought together in his *Gesammelte Abhandlungen*, K. Chandrasekharan, ed., 4 vols. (Berlin – Heidelberg – New York, 1968). See also *Selecta Hermann Weyl* (Basel – Stuttgart, 1956).

J. DIEUDONNÉ

**WHARTON, GEORGE** (*b*. Strickland, near Kendal, Westmorland, England, 4 April 1617; *d*. London, England, 12 August 1681), *astronomy*.

To his contemporaries George Wharton was renowned as a mathematician and almanac calculator whose main interests lay in the astrological possibilities of astronomy. Although he was not a systematic student of natural science, his beliefs and approach to nature probably placed him closer to the mainstream ideas of the educated gentleman of his time than to many of the followers of the "New Philosophy."

Wharton has been alternatively described as the son of a gentleman of good estate and as the son of a blacksmith who was brought up by a genteel relative. In any case his childhood was comfortable, and in 1633 he went to Oxford. How long he remained there is not known; but he became acquainted with the Durham astronomer William Milbourne, who "addicted" him to astronomy.

With the outbreak of the Civil War in 1642, Wharton raised a troop of horse for the king; but it was wiped out at Stow-on-the Wold, Gloucestershire, in 1645. He then joined the Royalist artillery at Oxford, where he met Elias Ashmole, and remained in the city until it fell to the Parliamentarian army in 1646.

Almanac calculation required little scientific originality but, rather, routine astronomical computation to determine information regarding the calendar, eclipses, and astrology. In 1641, when Wharton began to issue his almanacs, books were beyond the means of most of the population; and the threepenny almanacs were among the few pieces of secular literature to pass through the hands of most people. The influence of these almanacs came not from their astronomical content but from the astrological interpretations drawn therefrom. Wharton's fiercely Royalist interpretation of celestial phenomena was directed to embarrass the parliamentary side. This purpose soon brought him into a vitriolic pamphlet battle with its two leading astrologers, William Lilly and John Booker. The conflict illustrates the widely differing interpretations that astrologers could place on the same phenomenon, depending upon their viewpoint. During the Civil War astrology was a serious business that influenced the morale of armies.

Wharton's world view was that of the astrologer. He showed great deference to Ptolemy and Aristotle; and although respectful toward Copernicus, he apparently considered the earth to be immovable in space. Although not explicit on the subject of the earth's motion, he probably subscribed to the Tychonic world scheme. Wharton saw the cosmos as possessing both physical and metaphysical dimensions that operated through the macrocosm and microcosm. This balancing of qualities runs through all his ideas: just as a planet had two qualities, natural (physical) and astrological, so man's personality had natural and supernatural aspects that operated within a hierarchically conceived universe in which the moral and physical orders ran parallel. They also help explain Wharton's political ideas, for he saw the king as appointed by God within this hierarchy; and rebellion against him would lead not merely to social, but also to philosophical and cosmic, anarchy.

After 1648 Wharton's writings resulted in his being arrested several times by the now triumphant Parliamentarian party. Each time he escaped from prison but was sentenced to death upon his capture in 1650. Fortunately, however, the charitable William Lilly, who had no wish to see his rival hanged, succeeded in securing his pardon.

During the Interregnum, Wharton lived in obscurity although still pursuing his studies and collaborating with his friend, the Oxford antiquarian, Elias Ashmole. Problems of the calendar were an abiding interest; and some of his surviving manuscript material, in the Bodleian Library, discusses the errors in the Julian calendar and their suggested corrections. Elsewhere, Wharton relates his formula for determining the astrological influence of an eclipse. At the Restoration his loyalty was rewarded; and in 1677 he was created a baronet.

Wharton seems to have shown little interest in the scientific movement that developed in the 1660's. He never joined the Royal Society, nor did he have any concern for the new experimental philosophy, in which emphasis tended to be upon other criteria than the astrological. He did, however, on one occasion visit the Royal Greenwich Observatory.

BIBLIOGRAPHY

I. Original Works. Wharton's principal works were collected by John Gadbury and published as *The Works*

*of That Late Most Excellent Philosopher and Astronomer Sir George Wharton* (London, 1683). The Bodleian Library, Oxford, has a few of Wharton's surviving astrological and other MSS in Ashmole 242. Some of Wharton's correspondence with Ashmole is reproduced in C. H. Josten, *Elias Ashmole*, 5 vols. (Oxford, 1966). This work also includes Ashmole's diaries, which record his acquaintance with Wharton from the 1640's on.

II. Secondary Literature. Edward Shereburne includes a short life of Wharton in his "Catalogue of Astronomers," in the *Appendix* to his *The Sphere of Marcus Manilus* (London, 1675). A full bibliography of Wharton's works is reproduced in the life of Wharton in Anthony Wood's *Athenae Oxoniensis* II (London, 1691), 509–510.

Allan Chapman

**WHARTON, THOMAS** (*b*. Winston-on-Tees, Durham, England, 31 August 1614; *d*. London, England, 15 November 1673), *anatomy, endocrinology.*

The son of John Wharton and Elizabeth Hodson, Wharton studied at Pembroke College, Cambridge, from 1637 to 1642. He subsequently moved to Trinity College, Oxford; spent three years in further study at Bolton, Lancashire; and graduated M.D. at Oxford on 7 May 1647. Thereafter he had a medical practice in London, where he was elected a fellow of the Royal College of Physicians on 23 December 1650. Wharton served as one of its censors six times between 1658 and 1673 and gave the Goulstonian lectures in January 1654. In 1656 he published, at his own expense, his Latin treatise *Adenographia*, "a description of the glands of the entire body," which he dedicated to the College of Physicians. Wharton was appointed physician to St. Thomas's Hospital on 20 November 1657 and practiced in the City through the epidemic of bubonic plague in 1665.

*Adenographia* gave the first thorough account of the glands of the human body, which Wharton classified as excretory, reductive, and nutrient. He differentiated the viscera from the glands and explained their relationship, describing the spleen and pancreas. He discussed in turn the abdominal and thoracic glands, those of the head, and the reproductive glands, concluding with a section on pathology. His approach was physiological, like Harvey's; but his explanations were often teleological—he suggested, for instance, that one function of the thyroid was "to fill the neck and make it shapely."

Wharton discovered the duct of the submaxillary salivary gland and the jelly of the umbilical cord, both of which are named for him; he also provided the first adequate account of the thyroid and gave it that name. He explained the role of saliva in mastication and digestion but considered that the function of certain glands, such as the adrenals and the thyroid, was to restore to the veins certain humors that were not useful to the nerves. In discussing the reproductive glands Wharton corroborated Harvey's account of the placenta and gave a clear description of the mucoid jelly of the umbilical cord, which keeps it supple and conveys and cushions the fetal vessels. He noted that this jelly does not extend beyond the umbilicus.

Much of Wharton's research was performed on animals: he mentions dissection of calves, and Izaak Walton published his description of an anglerfish (*Lophius*). He also acknowledged the opportunities for human dissection afforded him by the physicians in charge of the hospitals. Most of the glands had been mentioned in general treatises on anatomy, and the lacteals were much discussed at the time when Wharton wrote; but *Adenographia* was the first comprehensive survey. The widely acclaimed book was reprinted six times in Europe. Boerhaave wrote that Wharton "was not a great thinker, but uniquely trustworthy with his scalpel." Although special aspects of glandular anatomy were further explored by some of Wharton's younger contemporaries, the glands were little studied for nearly 200 years.

Wharton's sympathies in the Civil War were republican. In the preface to *Adenographia* he thanked Cromwell's physician, John French, and his surgeon, Thomas Trapham, for their help in his research. He also named Francis Glisson "for shared experiments," George Ent "for advice and help," and his senior hospital colleagues Francis Prujean and Edward Emily. Wharton was also friendly with the mathematician William Oughtred, and he helped Elias Ashmole to compile the catalog of John Tradescant's museum. He was not connected with Gresham College, disliking its "new brood of virtuosi" who founded the Royal Society.

On 25 June 1653 Wharton married Jane Asbridge, who died in 1669. Their son, Thomas II, became a clergyman; but their grandson George and great-grandson Thomas III, George's nephew, were prominent London physicians.

## BIBLIOGRAPHY

I. ORIGINAL WORKS. *Adenographia: Sive glandularum totius corporis descriptio* (London, 1656; repr. Am-

sterdam, 1659; Nijmegen, 1664; Wesel, 1671; Leiden, 1679; Geneva, 1685; Düsseldorf, 1730) contains descriptions of "Wharton's duct" on 128–137 and of "Wharton's jelly" on 243–244. The Royal College of Physicians, London, owns Wharton's "letter book," which contains autograph copies of letters written in English in the last months of his life (Mar.–Oct. 1673). It also has almanacs for 1663–1666, in which Wharton had written miscellaneous notes, including a few prescriptions, case histories, and copies of letters.

II. SECONDARY LITERATURE. Izaak Walton, *The Compleat Angler* (1653), ch. 19, describes Wharton as "a man of great learning and experience and of equal freedom to communicate it." Thomas Bartholin, *Spicilegia bina ex vasis lymphaticis* (Amsterdam, 1661), pt. 2, ch. 5, praises Wharton's discoveries and "incomparable accuracy." Girolamo Barbato, discoverer of blood serum, mentions Wharton's work several times in his *Dissertatio . . . de sanguine et eius sero* (Paris, 1667). Hermann Boerhaave praises *Adenographia* in his *Method of Studying Physick* (London, 1719), 228. Elias Ashmole, *Autobiographical and Historical Notes*, C. H. Josten, ed., 5 vols. (Oxford, 1966), contains numerous personal references from Ashmole's MSS in the Bodleian Library.

H. D. Rolleston, *The Endocrine Glands With an Historical Review* (Oxford, 1936), discusses Wharton's accounts of the thyroid (p. 142) and the adrenals (p. 317); H. Speert, "The Jelly of the Umbilical Cord," in *Obstetrics and Gynecology*, **8**, no. 3 (1956), 380–382, translates and comments on Wharton's description; K. F. Russell, *British Anatomy* (Melbourne, 1963), nos. 854–859, records the editions of *Adenographia*. Biographies are J. F. Payne, "On Some Old Physicians of St. Thomas's Hospital," in *St. Thomas's Hospital Reports*, n.s. **26** (1897), 8–15, with portrait; and Bertha Porter, in *Dictionary of National Biography*, with references to sources and earlier studies.

WILLIAM LeFANU

**WHATELY, RICHARD** (*b.* London, England, 1 February 1787; *d.* Dublin, Ireland, 1 October 1863), *logic.*

Whately's father, Joseph Whately, was a minister and a lecturer at Gresham College. Shortly before his death in 1797, he placed his son in a private school at Bristol. Whately then went to Oriel College, Oxford, where he studied under Edward Copleston. He received the B.A. in 1808 and was elected fellow of Oriel in 1811. In his first well-known work, the pamphlet *Historic Doubts Relative to Napoleon Buonaparte* (1819), Whately offered a reductio ad absurdum disproof of Hume's challenge to the belief in miracles, arguing that if Hume was right in claiming that one should never believe in a miracle, then, for the same reasons, one also should not believe that Napoleon ever existed.

After marrying in 1821, Whately left Oxford to serve as a minister in Suffolk but returned to Oxford in 1825 to serve as principal of St. Alban Hall. He contributed two famous articles to the *Encyclopedia Metropolitana*, one on logic and the other on rhetoric. Both were reprinted as books: *The Elements of Logic* (1826) and *The Elements of Rhetoric* (1828). He was appointed Drummond professor of political economy in 1829 but resigned in 1831 in order to accept an appointment as archbishop of Dublin, after which he was primarily involved in local politics. His major academic efforts, until the time of his death, consisted in editing the writings of Francis Bacon, Copleston, and Paley.

Whately made no significant technical contributions to logic. His importance is due, instead, to his having been the first English logician to correct a mistaken conception of the nature and function of logic that had dominated English thought since the time of Locke and had led to the sterility of that discipline in England for over 150 years. Whately's work laid the philosophical foundations for the revolutionary developments in logic (notably Boole's algebra of logic) that took place in England during the nineteenth century.

The sterility of eighteenth-century English logic is reflected in two of the most popular texts of that period, Isaac Watts's *Logick, or the Right Use of Reason* (1725) and William Duncan's *Elements of Logick* (1748), neither of which emphasized the formal analysis of the conditions for the validity of reasoning. Duncan's book barely presented any of the traditional formal analysis; and Watts, while including some of it, always prefaced it with the apology that it had little significance. In place of the traditional formal analysis Duncan substituted a description of Locke's views on psychology and epistemology; Watts, who had little interest in theoretical issues, discussed the ways in which men abuse their intellectual faculties and offered practical advice.

Watts and Duncan, following Locke, rejected the traditional formal analysis of reasoning apparently because they felt that it was not helpful in guiding man in the proper use of his intellectual faculties. Since they believed that this sort of practical guidance was the proper role of logic, they concluded that logic must be radically reformed by deemphasizing the traditional formal analysis and by replacing it with the material found in their books.

Maintaining that this mistaken conception of logic had been responsible for its decline, Whately devoted most of *The Elements of Logic* to refuting objections to the traditional formal analysis. According to Whately, logic is concerned with an analysis of the forms of all valid reasoning, that is, with providing forms to which all valid arguments can be reduced. If a formal analysis provides these forms, then it has succeeded in fulfilling the proper role of logic. It would then be totally irrelevant to object to it on the grounds that it does not provide practical rules for the process of reasoning.

This Lockean tradition of logic as a guide for reason was not the only obstacle to traditional formal analysis in eighteenth-century Britain; Thomas Reid and other Scottish philosophers of common sense had also raised a set of objections. Taking their point of departure from Francis Bacon, they argued that deductive reasoning, of the type formally analyzed by the traditional logicians, was of little importance in the acquisition of knowledge, which increases only by observations and experimentation. This point was reinforced by Dugald Stewart's acute observation, long before John Stuart Mill, that deductive arguments are in some sense circular and cannot yield new knowledge because the premises of a valid deductive argument presuppose the truth of its conclusion. If the deductive mode of reasoning that had been formally analyzed by the traditional analysis was of such little value, these philosophers argued, then it would seem to follow that its formal analysis also had little worth.

Whately realized that any defense of logic as the formal analysis of the conditions for the validity of deductive reasoning would have to contain a reply to this set of criticisms, and he began his reply by granting Stewart's point that there is a perfectly good sense in which we learn nothing new in a deductive argument. He claimed, however, that it is nevertheless true that deductive reasoning plays an important role in our cognitive activities. Its purpose is to enable us to discover previously unnoticed consequences of propositions the truth of which we have already established. Since deductive reasoning does play this important role, a formal analysis of the conditions for its validity obviously is of great significance.

For Whately, the much more serious objection to the traditional formal analysis was that it did not present a formal analysis of the conditions for the legitimacy of inductive reasoning. His response to this was twofold. He began by claiming that any inductive inference is really a deductive one: its first premise is a summary of the evidence that certain objects of a given type have a given property, and the second premise is a claim of the form "The property had by the examined individuals is had by all members of that type." Therefore, the conditions for the legitimacy of inductive inferences are given by any adequate account of the conditions for the validity of deductive inferences. Whately admitted, however, that there is a special mode of inference by which we establish the second premise, a mode of which the conditions for legitimate use are not analyzed by an analysis of deductive reasoning. He felt, however, that there could be no formal analysis of these conditions and that the question of the legitimacy of such an inference would have to be decided on independent grounds in each case.

Not all of Whately's responses to the eighteenth-century critiques of logic as a formal analysis of deductive reasoning are valid, and his final remarks about induction are particularly dubious. Most of his writings, however, are quite sound and—more important from the historical point of view—seemed quite valid to his contemporaries. The re-evaluation of formal deductive logic stimulated by Whately's works resulted in tremendous progress in deductive logic in England during the nineteenth century, culminating in the formulation of the algebra of logic.

*BIBLIOGRAPHY*

I. ORIGINAL WORKS. The only writings by Whately that are still of interest are *Historic Doubts Relative to Napoleon Buonaparte* (London, 1819); *The Elements of Logic* (London, 1826); and *The Elements of Rhetoric* (London, 1828).

II. SECONDARY LITERATURE. The main works are B. A. Brody, *The Rise of the Algebra of Logic* (Ann Arbor, Mich., 1967); M. Prior, "Richard Whately," in P. Edwards, ed., *Encyclopedia of Philosophy*, VIII (New York, 1967), 287–288; and E. J. Whately, *Life and Correspondence of Richard Whately, D.D.*, 2 vols. (London, 1866).

B. A. BRODY

**WHEATSTONE, CHARLES** (*b.* Gloucester, England, 6 February 1802; *d.* Paris, France, 19 October 1875), *physics.*

Wheatstone was an experimenter and pioneering inventor in acoustics, optics, electricity, and telegraphy. He came from a family of musical instrument makers and dealers, a background that was relevant for much of his early acoustical research. He did not have any formal scientific education. In 1816 he was apprenticed to an uncle in the music business in London. Although Wheatstone became directly involved in the music business in 1823, he worked mainly on practical musical inventions (he patented the concertina in 1829) and on experimental studies of acoustic vibrations. His early work in acoustics became known (some of his papers were translated into French and German), and he was appointed professor of experimental physics at King's College, London, in 1834. He gave some lectures on sound, but most of his work consisted of research in electricity and in optics. Many of his results were communicated by Faraday. In 1836 he became a fellow of the Royal Society, he was knighted in 1868, and in 1873 he was made a foreign associate of the Paris Academy of Sciences. He received many other scientific honors.

Wheatstone's interest in acoustics was basically inspired by his desire to understand properties of a tone, such as timbre, in terms of vibration.[1] During the fifteen years that he worked on acoustics, he investigated the mechanical transmission of sound, visible demonstrations of vibrations, and properties of the vibrating air column (the Wheatstone family was involved in the making of flutes). When he was nineteen, he publicly exhibited an "enchanted lyre" that was activated by the vibrations from a remote piano transmitted to it along a wire. In Wheatstone's kaleidophone (1827) the free end of a vibrating rod was illuminated to provide a visual display of vibration. Because of persistence of vision, one saw intricate curves characteristic of the vibrational modes. Wheatstone was interested in Chladni's sand pattern technique for displaying the vibrational modes of a plate, and in 1833 he tried to use the sand patterns of a square plate to demonstrate the superposition of vibrational modes. In 1832 Wheatstone demonstrated that in the case of a standing wave in an open pipe, the motions at the ends are in opposite directions.[2] He used a pipe bent into a circle so that its ends were on either side of a vibrating square plate; when the ends faced the same region of the plate there was no resonance, but when they faced different regions (which moved in opposite directions), the resonance was strong.

In electricity one of Wheatstone's earliest and most important works (1834) was the measurement of the velocity of an electrical discharge through a wire. Wheatstone had the idea of studying very rapid motions by reflection from a rotating mirror. After trying unsuccessfully to "draw out" the spark produced by an electric discharge, he used the rotating mirror technique to observe the intervals between sparks produced by a single discharge across three spark gaps, located side by side and connected to each other by quarter-mile lengths of copper wire. From the displacement of the middle spark relative to the other two, he estimated the velocity of electricity to be over 250,000 mi./sec. (1.3 times the velocity of light[3]). In 1838 Arago suggested that Wheatstone's rotating mirror technique be used to compare the velocities of light in air and in water—an experiment performed by Foucault and Fizeau in 1850. The technique was also used by Lissajous from 1855, to study acoustic vibrations.

In 1843 Wheatstone published an experimental verification of Ohm's law, helping to make the law (already well known in Germany) more familiar in England. In connection with the verification he developed new ways of measuring resistances and currents. In particular, he invented the rheostat and popularized the Wheatstone bridge, originally invented by Samuel Christie.

In the early years of his acoustic experiments Wheatstone had speculated on the possibilities of conducting sound (including speech) over long distances,[4] and his experiments with the electric telegraph date from the early 1830's. In 1837 he and W. F. Cooke obtained their first patent for a telegraph, the "five needle" instrument, in which each letter was indicated directly by the deflections of two (magnetic) needles. Wheatstone subsequently did considerable work to develop the telegraph into a practical device. His letter-showing dial telegraph and his automatic transmitting and receiving system were particularly important. Wheatstone also worked on submarine telegraphy, performing the first experiments in 1844.

Beginning with his work on the kaleidophone, Wheatstone maintained an interest in vision and optics throughout his career. As the inventor of the stereoscope, later developed by Brewster, Wheatstone found himself—to his own surprise—the first since Leonardo da Vinci to discuss depth perception in terms of the different image received by each eye. He associated the spectrum of the light of a discharge with the metals that constituted the electrodes,[5] and in 1848 he invented the polar clock, which determines the position of the sun from the angle of polarization of sunlight.

Wheatstone also did work on audition, vowel sounds, electrical recording devices, and the dynamo. He was interested in cryptography, deciphering certain historic manuscripts and inventing a cryptograph instrument.[6]

### NOTES

1. Wheatstone indicated this in his first published paper, "New Experiments on Sound" (1823). Wheatstone, *Scientific Papers*, 6.
2. *Report of the British Association for the Advancement of Science*, **2** (1832), 558.
3. The estimate was high, probably because the wire was looped back and forth, not straight. Edmund Whittaker, *A History of the Theories of Aether and Electricity*, I (New York, 1960), 228.
4. "On the Transmission of Musical Sounds." Wheatstone. *Scientific Papers*, 62–63.
5. *Report of the British Association for the Advancement of Science*, **5** (1835), pt. 2, 11–12.
6. David Kahn, *The Codebreakers* (New York, 1967), 196–198.

### BIBLIOGRAPHY

I. ORIGINAL WORKS. Wheatstone's papers include "Description of the Kaleidophone, or Phonic Kaleidoscope," in *Quarterly Journal of Science, Literature and the Arts*, n.s. **1** (1827), 344–351; "On the Transmission of Musical Sounds Through Solid Linear Conductors, and on Their Subsequent Reciprocation," in *Journal of the Royal Institution*, **2** (1831), 223–238; "On the Figures Obtained by Strewing Sand on Vibrating Surfaces, Commonly Called 'Acoustic Figures,'" in *Philosophical Transactions of the Royal Society*, **123** (1833), 593–634; "An Account of Some Experiments to Measure the Velocity of Electricity and the Duration of Electric Light," *ibid.*, **124** (1834), 583–591; "Contribution to the Physiology of Vision: Part 1. On Some Remarkable and Hitherto Unobserved Phenomena of Binocular Vision," *ibid.*, **128** (1838), 371–394; and "An Account of Several New Instruments and Processes for Determining the Constants of a Voltaic Circuit," *ibid.*, **133** (1843), 303–328.

Most of Wheatstone's published papers are listed in Royal Society *Catalogue of Scientific Papers*, VI, 343–344, and VIII, 1227–1228. Almost all of them are in *The Scientific Papers of Sir Charles Wheatstone* (London, 1879), published by the Physical Society of London.

II. SECONDARY LITERATURE. There are essays on Wheatstone in *Minutes of Proceedings of the Institution of Civil Engineers*, **47** (1876–1877), pt. 1, 283–291; *Proceedings of the Royal Society*, **24** (1875–1876), xvi–xxvii; *Nature*, **13** (1875–1876), 501–503; and *Proceedings of the American Academy of Arts and Sciences*, **81** (1951–1952), 92–96, which contains references to other works on Wheatstone.

Some of Wheatstone's work in musical acoustics is discussed in W. G. Adams, "On the Musical Inventions and Discoveries of the Late Sir Charles Wheatstone," in *Proceedings of the Musical Association*, **2** (1875–1876), 85–93. An account of Wheatstone's verification of Ohm's law is H. J. J. Winter, "The Significance of the Bakerian Lecture of 1843," in *London, Edinburgh, and Dublin Philosophical Magazine and Journal of Science*, 7th ser., **34** (1943), 700–711.

SIGALIA DOSTROVSKY

**WHEELER, WILLIAM MORTON** (*b.* Milwaukee, Wisconsin, 19 March 1865; *d.* Cambridge, Massachusetts, 19 April 1937), *entomology.*

Because of his misbehavior in public school, Wheeler's parents, Julius Morton and Caroline Anderson Wheeler, sent him to the Engelmann German Academy in Milwaukee, which was noted for its severe discipline. He continued at the attached German-American Normal College, where he haunted the small museum until he knew every specimen. He graduated in 1884. A chance visit by H. A. Ward, of Ward's Natural Science Establishment in Rochester, New York, with specimens for the museum led to an offer to Wheeler to work for Ward in 1884. In the year Wheeler worked at the establishment he began his lifelong friendship with Carl Akeley.

In 1885 Wheeler returned to Milwaukee to teach German and physiology in the Milwaukee High School, of which George W. Peckham was principal. The biology courses of the school were unusually advanced for the day, and Peckham's own principal interest was arachnids and social insects. When E. P. Allis founded the Lake Laboratory not far from the Milwaukee High School, Wheeler met the inspiring C. O. Whitman. From William Patten, also at the Lake Laboratory, Wheeler acquired an interest in the embryology of insects and began work on a detailed study of the development of the cockroach. From 1887 to 1890 Wheeler was custodian of the Milwaukee Public Museum and absorbed embryology on his own. In 1890 he accepted a fellowship at Clark University in Worcester, Massachusetts, to study under Whitman. After receiving his Ph.D. in 1892, Wheeler studied for a year in Europe and then followed Whitman to the University of Chicago as instructor in embryology; he advanced to assistant professor in 1897.

Until this time Wheeler had emphasized embryology and morphology but also had shown considerable interest in insects; he had published on all of these fields. When he became professor of zoology at the University of Texas in 1899, he concentrated on entomology, although he always retained a strong interest in broad aspects of biology. In 1903 he became curator of invertebrate zoology at the American Museum of Natural History in New York City, where in addition to his research he designed the spectacular Hall of the Biology of Invertebrates. The appeal of an academic life drew him to his final position: professor of economic entomology at the Bussey Institution of Harvard University, at Forest Hills, Massachusetts. He preferred the title professor of entomology, to which he had it changed in 1926, and he retired in 1934. As dean of the faculty from 1915 to 1929, Wheeler led the Bussey Institution to a position of excellence in biological research. In 1931 he moved with the institution to its new quarters in the biological laboratories in Cambridge. Wheeler was president of the Entomological Society of America in 1908, and in addition was a member of many academies and the recipient of several honorary degrees.

In his early career Wheeler joined the trend of biology to morphology and embryonic development, beginning with his classic report on the cockroach (1889) and continuing with his brief entry in 1893 into marine biology at Naples, where he studied Myzostoma. About the turn of the twentieth century he began to concentrate on ants, and went on to become the foremost expert on ants in particular and social insects in general. "Ants interest me" was his simple explanation. As ecology became specialized, Wheeler contributed to it in his analyses of the structure within ant colonies and the relationships of the colonies to their environment; but he did not consider himself an ecologist. His own change of title at Bussey showed his preference for research for its own sake. He was not a participant in the many projects to control insects in agriculture. With single-minded attention to his research, Wheeler devoted himself to the collection, classification, structure, distribution, habits, and social life of ants. His collected specimens are chiefly at the American Museum of Natural History and the Museum of Comparative Zoology (Harvard).

Outside his immediate research Wheeler wrote also on broader aspects of biology. He considered the animal society essentially an organism from which development could evolve. A firm believer in organic evolution, he nevertheless insisted that Lamarckism had never been disproved, thus incurring the wrath of Neo-Darwinists. He extended his knowledge of social insects to discussions of man as a social animal. Fascinating in conversation and facile in writing, Wheeler attracted good students and co-workers and inspired many of the next generation of entomologists.

## BIBLIOGRAPHY

I. ORIGINAL WORKS. Wheeler's complete list of almost 500 publications is in Parker's memoir (see below). Although some of the publications are reviews and other descriptive articles are short, the total list is an impressive record. A summary of his studies appeared as *Ants: Their Structure, Development and Behavior*, Columbia University Biological Series, IX (New York, 1910). In addition to many taxonomic papers, Wheeler's most valuable books are: *Social Life Among the Insects* (New York, 1923); *The Social Insects, Their Origin and Evolution* (New York, 1928); *Emergent Evolution and the Development of Societies* (New York, 1928); and *Foibles of Insects and Men* (New York, 1928).

II. SECONDARY LITERATURE. A fine memorial to Wheeler was written by George Howard Parker, in *Biographical Memoirs. National Academy of Sciences*, **19** (1938), 201–241, which includes his youth, accomplishments, and a complete bibliography. Some autobiographical material is in Wheeler's paper, "Carl Akeley's Early Work and Environment," in *Natural History*, **27** (1927), 133–141, part of which is included in Parker. Wheeler's place in entomology is summarized in E. O. Essig, *A History of Entomology* (New York, 1931; repr., 1965); and in Herbert Osborn, *Fragments of Entomological History*, pt. 1 (Columbus, Ohio, 1937), pt. 2 (1946).

ELIZABETH NOBLE SHOR

**WHEWELL, WILLIAM** (*b*. Lancaster, England, 24 May 1794; *d*. Cambridge, England, 6 March 1866), *history and philosophy of science, physical astronomy, science education.*

Whewell was the eldest son of a master carpenter, who hoped his son would follow him in his trade. Early displays of intellectual ability convinced the father, however, to send him to the grammar school at Heversham, in Westmorland. In 1812 Whewell began a lifelong career at Trinity College, Cambridge, where he received a classical literary education and what he soon recognized as outdated training in mathematics and science. After election as fellow of the college in 1817, Whewell took his M.A. degree in 1819 and his D.D. degree in 1844. He was ordained deacon around 1825 and then priest (1826) in the Church of England. In 1841 Whewell was appointed master of Trinity, a post he held until his death. He was named vice-chancellor of the University of Cambridge in 1842 and again in 1855. In 1841 he married Cordelia Marshall, who died in 1855; three years later he married Lady Evering Affleck.

Tall and massively built, Whewell enjoyed good health throughout his life. Friends and foes alike admired his intelligence and breadth of scholarship, his capacity for profound affection, and his generosity. Whewell was self-consciously awkward in dealing with others, however, and he cannot be said to have been a generally popular figure at Cambridge. There can be no doubt about his quick-tempered resentment of criticism, his autocratic and often arbitrary exercise of academic power, and his jealous defense of his own position. Nevertheless, he was widely recognized as one of the central figures in Victorian science. He was a member or honorary member of at least twenty-five British and foreign scientific societies, including the Royal Society, the Royal Astronomical Society, the Royal Irish Academy, and the Royal Society of Edinburgh.

The range of Whewell's scholarly and scientific interests was immense. He composed sermons, English hexameter verses, translations of German literary works, and essays on architecture, theology, philosophy, political economy, and university education. He translated Plato's dialogues into English.

In response to the need for more accurate instruments for use in meteorology Whewell invented a self-registering anemometer that measured the direction, velocity, and temporal duration of the velocity of the wind. Anemometers in use at the time measured direction and pressure of the wind, but did not permit charting of the total movement of the air as did Whewell's device. Whewell's instrument failed to show accurate results in measuring slow movements of the air. The technical problem was solved by the Reverend T. R. Robinson in 1846 by modifying Whewell's instrument by the introduction of the now-familiar windmill with hemispherical cups.

Whewell was especially adept in coining new scientific terms. In correspondence with Michael Faraday he contributed "ion," "anode," and "cathode," among others. To geology he contributed "Eocene," "Miocene," and "Pliocene," and he introduced the terms "physicist" and "scientist."

Apart from his teaching, Whewell's major work in the decade beginning with 1819 was in science education, architecture, experimental physics, and mineralogy. As a member of a group of reformers in which John Herschel, Charles Babbage, and

George Peacock were prominent, Whewell contributed to the attempt to bring the mathematical methods of the French analysts into Cambridge scientific education. In textbooks on mechanics and dynamics, he introduced the calculus for solving problems, while insisting that analysis is no substitute for experimental physics. The reformers were successful; as a college tutor in the 1820's, and later as a major figure in guiding educational changes at Cambridge, Whewell contributed to the development of British physics and to the centrality of Cambridge in that development. In architecture Whewell attempted to refute the contention that the pointed arch is the defining property of Gothic style, arguing that in the history of German architecture the flying buttress, not the pointed arch, completed the transition from Romanesque to high Gothic.

In 1826 and 1828 Whewell and Airy made unsuccessful attempts to measure the density of the earth at a copper mine in Cornwall. Of greater importance was Whewell's work in mineralogy. In a paper read before the Royal Society in 1824, Whewell, according to Herbert Deas, "laid the foundations of mathematical crystallography." His system for calculating the angles of planes of crystals assumed that crystals are aggregates of small rhomboids that can be thought to shrink below the level of possible measurement, thus suggesting that crystals are latticelike. In 1825 Whewell visited Mohs in Germany. In 1828, the year in which Whewell became professor of mineralogy, he published a revision of Mohs's system of mineralogical classification.

Between 1833 and 1850 Whewell published fourteen memoirs on the tides. Before the 1830's little reliable observation of the tides had been undertaken; and the two leading theories, the Newton-Bernoulli equilibrium theory and the Laplace dynamical theory, were largely untested. The British Admiralty and the British Association initiated work on the tides that soon became international in scale. Whewell, with the help of John Lubbock, received and interpreted observations from all over the world; their work earned them the Royal Medal. Whewell's investigation of the tides began with an attempt to apply Thomas Young's idea of cotidal lines to the world's oceans. Had the idea applied, it would have allowed plotting the movements of tidal waves through all the oceans on the basis of initial observations of simultaneous high tides at different places. Whewell abandoned the idea in its general application, however, although the application of the idea did ob-

tain some results for small, confined bodies of water and for shorelines.

Whewell stressed the "diurnal inequality" of the tides ("that which makes the tide of the morning and evening of the same day at the same place, differ both in height and time of high water, according to a law depending on the time of the year"). He showed large variations in this effect in accordance with local circumstances and thought the inequality to be more basic than other features of the tides. From the failure of the idea of cotidal lines and the empirical prominence of the daily inequality, Whewell concluded that no theory of physical astronomy could account for tidal phenomena in a general way. Instead, the variety and multiplicity of the data suggested that detailed study of each individual shoreline was required. Given this conclusion, it is not surprising that Whewell's work did not contribute directly to theory of the tides. Consistent with the principles of his own philosophy of science, however, he could regard himself as having fathered the science of the tides. He thought that the beginning of a science involved the laborious collection and organization of data; full theoretical generality, if any, would come later.

From the late 1830's until his death, Whewell worked mainly in the history and philosophy of science. His three-volume *History of the Inductive Sciences* appeared in 1837; in 1838 he was appointed professor of moral philosophy; and the first edition of his two-volume *The Philosophy of the Inductive Sciences, Founded Upon Their History* was published in 1840. Both the *History* and the *Philosophy* were ambitious works, and together they constitute Whewell's major scholarly achievement. The *History* had no rivals in its day and remains, despite unevenness, one of the important surveys of science from the Greeks to the nineteenth century. Whewell appreciated the importance of Greek science, especially astronomy, but showed typical disregard for the contributions of medieval scientists. His assessment of the importance of contributions of such major figures as Galileo and Descartes suffers from a heavy intrusion of religious and philosophical biases. But his treatment of Newton and other modern mathematical scientists is fair and sometimes brilliant, and is based throughout upon detailed considerations of texts. Whewell's *Philosophy* stimulated major philosophical exchanges between its author and Sir John Herschel, Augustus De Morgan, Henry L. Mansel, and John Stuart Mill. Alongside Mill's *System of Logic* and Herschel's *Preliminary Dis-*

*course on the Study of Natural Philosophy*, the work ranks as one of the masterpieces of Victorian philosophy of science.

Whewell's effort in these works was unique in his attempt to derive a philosophy of science from the general features of the historical development of empirical science. The importance of this attempt has not been fully appreciated. Whewell thought that the history of science displayed a progressive movement from less to more general theories, from imperfectly understood facts to basic sciences built upon a priori foundations that he called "Fundamental Ideas." All science was theoretical in that no body of data comes to us self-organized; even collection of data involves the imposition of a guiding interpretive idea. Major advances in science occur in what Whewell called an "Inductive Epoch," a period in which the basic ideas of a science are well understood by one or more scientists, and in which the generality and explanatory power of a science are seen to be much more illuminating than those of rival theories. Each such "Epoch" had a "Prelude," a period in which older theories experienced difficulties and new ideas were seen to be required, and a "Sequel," a period in which the new theory was applied and refined.

Largely ignoring the British tradition of empiricist philosophy and methodology, Whewell erected a philosophy of science upon his understanding of history that derived partly from Kant and Plato, and partly from an anachronistic theological position. Like his British predecessors, he thought that induction was the basic method of science. He understood induction not as a form of inference from particulars to generalizations, but as a conceptual act of coming to see that a group of data can best be understood and organized (his term was "colligated") under a certain idea. Furthermore, induction was demonstrative in that it yields necessary truths, propositions the logical opposites of which cannot be clearly conceived. The zenith of the inductive process was reached when a "consilience of inductions" took place—when sets of data previously considered disjoint came to be seen as derivable from the same, much richer theory. Although Whewell thought that the paradigm form of a scientific theory was deductive, he departed from the orthodox hypothetico-deductivist view of science by claiming that tests of the acceptability of given theories are extraevidential, based on considerations of simplicity and consilience. He made some attempt to justify the necessity of the conclusions that induction yields by arguing for the identity of facts and theories, and for the theological view that we know the world the way it is because that is the way God made it.

In physical astronomy Whewell's work on the tides ranks second only to that of Newton. Also of great importance was his lifelong effort to modernize and improve science education at Cambridge. The achievement in history and philosophy of science probably is less significant, although recent revival of interest in Whewell has centered mainly upon his insights in philosophy of science and methodology. Interest is growing in the interrelations of history and philosophy of science; and so long as this interest continues to be fruitful, it will be well worthwhile considering what Whewell had to say on the nature of scientific discovery, inductive methodology, and the characteristics of scientific progress.

## BIBLIOGRAPHY

I. Original Works. Whewell's papers are in the Wren Library, Trinity College, Cambridge. A catalog of these papers is available (to libraries) from the Royal Commission on Historical Manuscripts, Quality House, Quality Court, Chancery Lane, London WC2A 1 HP. Unfortunately no complete bibliography of his works exists, although fairly complete ones in history and philosophy of science are available. The projected 10-vol. collection of facsimiles, *The Historical and Philosophical Works of William Whewell*, G. Buchdahl and L. L. Laudan, eds. (London, 1967–   ), will help make his works in those areas more easily available. A selection of Whewell's central works in methodology appears in *William Whewell's Theory of Scientific Method*, Robert E. Butts, ed. (Pittsburgh, 1968).

Whewell's major writings in science include *An Elementary Treatise on Mechanics* (Cambridge, 1819); *A Treatise on Dynamics* (Cambridge, 1823); "A General Method of Calculating the Angles Made by Any Planes of Crystals, and the Laws According to Which They Are Formed," in *Philosophical Transactions of the Royal Society*, **115** (1825), 87–130; *An Essay on Mineralogical Classification and Nomenclature; With Tables of the Orders and Species of Minerals* (Cambridge, 1828); *Architectural Notes on German Churches, With Remarks on the Origin of Gothic Architecture* (Cambridge, 1830); *Analytical Statics* (Cambridge, 1833); "Essay Towards a First Approximation to a Map of Cotidal Lines," in *Philosophical Transactions of the Royal Society*, **123** (1833), 147–236; "On the Results of an Extensive System of Tide Observations Made on the Coasts of Europe and America in June 1835," *ibid.*, **126** (1836), 289–341; "On the Diurnal Inequality Wave Along the Coasts of Europe," *ibid.*, **127** (1837), 227–244; *The Mechanical Euclid* (Cambridge, 1837);

and "On the Results of Continued Tide Observations at Several Places on the British Coasts," in *Philosophical Transactions of the Royal Society*, **140** (1850), 227–233.

Major writings in history and philosophy of science include "On the Nature of the Truth of the Laws of Motion," in *Transactions of the Cambridge Philosophical Society*, **5** (1834), 149–172; *History of the Inductive Sciences*, 3 vols. (London, 1837); *The Philosophy of the Inductive Sciences, Founded Upon Their History*, 2 vols. (London, 1840), the 3rd ed. of which appeared as 3 separate vols.: *The History of Scientific Ideas*, 2 pts. (London, 1858), *Novum organon renovatum* (London, 1858), and *On the Philosophy of Discovery* (London, 1860).

II. SECONDARY LITERATURE. There is very little informed and up-to-date commentary on Whewell's scientific achievements; in recent years his philosophy of science has begun to receive the attention it deserves. There are two biographies: Mrs. Stair Douglas, *Life and Selections From the Correspondence of William Whewell* (London, 1881), on his personal, including university, life; and Isaac Todhunter, *William Whewell* (London, 1876), which surveys his scientific and scholarly work. Both works contain large collections of letters; Todhunter is the best source of bibliography. Of considerable interest are Robert Robson, "William Whewell, F.R.S. (1794–1866), I. Academic Life," and Walter F. Cannon, "II. Contributions to Science and Learning," in *Notes and Records. Royal Society of London*, **19**, no. 2 (Dec. 1964), 168–191. Cannon's paper is the first attempt at a general assessment of Whewell's scientific achievements. Robert Willis, *Remarks on the Architecture of the Middle Ages, Especially of Italy* (Cambridge, 1835), extends and improves upon Whewell's work in architecture. George Airy, "Tides and Waves," in *Encyclopaedia metropolitana*, V (London, 1845), secs. VII and VIII, esp. arts. 496 and 571, praises Whewell's work on the tides, especially his methods of graphical representation of results of observations. Airy preferred the Laplace theory, however, and argued against Whewell's continuing reliance upon the Bernoulli equilibrium theory. Herbert Deas, "Crystallography and Crystallographers in Early 19th-Century England," in *Centaurus*, **6** (1959), 129–148, presents a sympathetic evaluation of Whewell's work in that area.

Whewell's philosophy attracted no disciples; and except for various references to his work in the writings of C. S. Peirce, his system received no serious study until the early 1930's. There are two book-length studies: Robert Blanché, *Le rationalisme de Whewell* (Paris, 1935); and Siivestro Marcucci, *L' "idealismo" scientifico di William Whewell* (Pisa, 1963). British and American studies of Whewell's philosophy in the context of contemporary problems in philosophy of science have taken the form of monographs and papers on specific problems. A potentially quite productive exchange of views on Whewell's concept of consilience of inductions exemplifies the richness and novelty of his insights in methodology. Among the relevant papers are Robert E. Butts, "Whewell's Logic of Induction," in Ronald Giere and Richard Westfall, eds., *Foundations of Scientific Method: The Nineteenth Century* (Bloomington, Ind., 1973), 53–85; Mary Hesse, "Consilience of Inductions," in Imre Lakatos, ed., *The Problem of Inductive Logic* (Amsterdam, 1968), 232–247; and Larry Laudan, "William Whewell on the Consilience of Inductions," in *Monist*, **55**, no. 3 (1971), 368–391.

ROBERT E. BUTTS

**WHISTON, WILLIAM** (*b.* Norton, Leicester, England, 9 December 1667; *d.* Lyndon, Rutland, England, 22 August 1752), *mathematics, cosmogony, theology.*

Whiston's father, Josiah Whiston, who was also his first teacher, was a pastor. Whiston studied mathematics at Cambridge, where he earned the master's degree in 1693. He was then, successively, tutor to the nephew of John Tillotson; chaplain of the bishop of Norwich; and rector of Lowestoft and Kessingland, Suffolk. Isaac Newton, who liked and admired Whiston, engaged him as his assistant lecturer in mathematics at Cambridge and in 1701 arranged for Whiston to succeed him as Lucasian professor. But the two men became estranged because of a difference of opinion concerning the interpretation of Biblical chronology. Whiston published several theological works in which he defended heterodox opinions and supported Arianism against the dogma of the Trinity. In 1710 he was deprived of his chair and driven from the university. Newton did nothing at all to help him, even though he himself was secretly anti-Trinitarian.

Whiston moved to London, where he led a bohemian life, while continuing to occupy himself with literature and theology. He often had no money, but he nevertheless frequented the court and high society. He wrote many theological and scientific works in this period, and fell into mystic and prophetic trances. At the age of eighty he became an Anabaptist. He retired to the home of his daughter in Lyndon, where he died in 1752.

Whiston's scientific writings include several mathematical treatises, notably a Latin edition of Euclid (Cambridge, 1703), and *Praelectiones astronomicae* (1707). His most important work is *A New Theory of the Earth, From Its Original to the Consummation of All Things. Wherein the Creation of the World in Six Days, the Universal Deluge, and the General Conflagration, as Laid Down in the Holy Scriptures, Are Shewn to be Perfectly Agreeable to Reason and Philosophy* (London,

1696), which went through six editions, an indication of considerable success. It was dedicated to Newton, and its goal was to redo, with the aid of Newtonian cosmology, what Burnet had done with the aid of Descartes in *Telluris theoria sacra* (London, 1681). Whiston prefaced his book by a long dissertation entitled "A Discourse Concerning the Nature, Stile, and Extent of the Mosaick History of the Creation." In its ninety-four separately numbered pages he set forth the principles of a very free interpretation of *Genesis*. In particular, like Burnet, he contended that the Mosaic account (except for the general introduction consisting of the first verse: "In the beginning God created the heaven and the earth") concerns only the earth, and not even the entire solar system. Again like Burnet, Whiston thought that Moses, whose audience consisted of illiterate Jews, was not able to give a scientific account of the formation of the earth.

Seeking to give his arguments a geometric rigor, Whiston presented the theory itself in four books entitled *Lemmata*, *Hypotheses*, *Phaenomena*, and *Solutions*. According to the theory, the earth was originally a comet, revolving around the sun in a very eccentric orbit. This is the situation commonly described by the term "chaos." Then one day God decided to make the earth a planet, and the chaos vanished; this is the transformation recounted in Genesis. From this time and until the Flood, the earth revolved around the sun in a perfectly circular orbit; the axis of its poles was perpendicular to the plane of the ecliptic, and there were no seasons and no daily rotation. The Flood, which put an end to this state of affairs, was produced by a comet guided by God. The head of the comet, by its attraction or by its impact, broke the surface layer of the earth, causing the waters of the "great abyss" to overflow; the vapors of the tail of the comet condensed to form torrential rains. The oblique impact of the comet displaced the axis of the poles, transformed the circular orbit into an ellipse, and imparted to the earth its rotational movement. Like Woodward, Whiston thought that the layers of sedimentary rocks and the marine fossils discovered on the continents resulted from this flood. Whiston's exposition of his system lacks clarity, and he sometimes contradicted himself.

Like Newton, but less cautiously, Whiston pictured God as intervening in nature, not only to create matter and endow it with gravitation, but also to direct the course of the history of the earth. Whiston's view was that God intervenes both directly (for example, in the creation of man) and through the intermediary of physical agents (such as a comet). Whiston explicitly stated that these two modes ultimately amount to the same thing. The ideas expressed on this point in *A New Theory of the Earth* were taken up again and made more precise in *Astronomical Principles of Religion Natural and Reveal'd*, which Whiston published in London in 1717. His thinking was similar to that of Richard Bentley and Samuel Clarke but displayed less precision and clarity. Whiston also attempted to justify his hypotheses by an interesting theory of scientific knowledge, derived from Newton but also showing the deep influence of Burnet and Cartesianism.

Whiston was more than simply a representative of an age and of a group of scientists who sought to reconcile science and Revelation. As in the case of Burnet, from whom he took a great deal, his writings were much disputed but also widely read, throughout the entire eighteenth century, and not just in England. For example, Buffon, who summarized Whiston's theory in order to ridicule it, borrowed more from him than he was willing to admit and thus unconsciously promoted the spread of his ideas. It may be said that all the cosmogonies based on the impact of celestial bodies, including that of Jeans, owed something, directly or indirectly, to Whiston's inventions.

*BIBLIOGRAPHY*

On Whiston and his work, see Paolo Casini, *L'universo-macchina. Origini della filosofia newtoniana* (Bari, 1969); Hélène Metzger, *Attraction universelle et religion naturelle chez quelques commentateurs anglais de Newton* (Paris, 1938); and Victor Monod, *Dieu dans l'univers* (Paris, 1933).

JACQUES ROGER

**WHITE, CHARLES** (*b*. Manchester, England, 4 October 1728; *d*. Sale, Cheshire, England, 20 February 1813), *obstetrics, surgery.*

White received his early education in Manchester and was apprenticed in medicine to his father, Thomas White. He subsequently studied in London, where he was greatly influenced by John and William Hunter, and in Edinburgh. He then joined his father in practice and soon achieved a reputation in surgery and obstetrics. White helped to found the Manchester Infirmary (1752) and served as its chief surgeon until 1790. He took a leading part in establishing the Lying-in Charity Hospital

(1790), now known as St. Mary's Hospital, and served on its staff. He was also a founder of the Manchester Literary and Philosophical Society (1781). On 18 February 1762 White was elected a fellow of the Royal Society and a member of the Corporation (now the Royal College) of Surgeons of London. The first to lecture on anatomy in Manchester, he eventually became the most eminent surgeon in the north of England. In 1803 an eye infection affected his vision; and in 1811 he retired to Sale, where he died completely blind.

White possessed great stamina, an acute and agile mind, and a forceful character tinged with arrogance. His contributions to surgery were extensive, and he introduced conservative techniques. Stimulated by John Hunter, he studied gradation in animals and plants and in 1799 published a suggestive treatise on evolution, unknown to Darwin, in which he rejected the idea that acquired characteristics could become hereditary. For the study of skulls upon which this work is based, White has been called the founder of anthropometry. His main fame, however, derives from his work in obstetrics. Alexander Gordon (1795), Oliver Wendell Holmes (1843), and Ignaz Semmelweis (1847) are correctly given credit for discovering the infectious nature of puerperal fever. Nevertheless, White, although unaware of its causative agent, recognized some of the associated etiological factors and instituted prophylaxis and therapy accordingly. He was the first to insist on absolute cleanliness during delivery and was thus a pioneer in aseptic midwifery. Together with his astute account of puerperal fever (1773), his recognition of "white leg" (1784), and his enlightened approach to obstetrics in general, it brought him widespread recognition.

## BIBLIOGRAPHY

I. ORIGINAL WORKS. White's main works were *A Treatise on the Management of Pregnant and Lying-in Women* . . . (London, 1773, 1777, 1784, 1791), repr. in J. George Adami, *Charles White of Manchester (1728–1813), and the Arrest of Puerperal Fever* (London, 1922), also in French (Paris, 1774), American (Worcester, Mass., 1793), and German eds. (Leipzig, 1775); and *An Inquiry Into the Nature and Cause of That Swelling in One or Both of the Lower Extremities Which Sometimes Happens to Lying-in Women*, 2 vols. (Warrington, 1784–London, 1801).

A list of his surgical writings is in J. E. Dezeimeris, *Dictionnaire historique de la médecine*, IV (Paris, 1839), 402–403. He also published *An Account of the Regular Gradation in Man, and in Different Animals and Vegetables and From the Former to the Latter* (London, 1799); and three papers of less importance in *Philosophical Transactions of the Royal Society*, **51** (1760) and **59** (1769).

II. SECONDARY LITERATURE. Adami (see above), with portrait, makes unwarranted claims for White, as do Charles J. Cullingworth, *Charles White, F.R.S., a Great Provincial Surgeon and Obstetrician of the 18th Century* (London, 1904), and *Lancet* (1903), **2**, 1071–1076. Edward A. Schumann, "Charles White and His Contribution to the Knowledge of Puerperal Sepsis," in *Medical Life*, **36** (1929), 257–270, gives a more balanced judgment of his work. See also E. M. Brockbank, *Sketches of the Lives and Work of the Honorary Staff of the Manchester Infirmary* (Manchester, 1904), 28–65, with a list of local biographical sources; *Dictionary of National Biography*, xxi, 33–34; and H. Thoms, *Classical Contributions to Obstetrics and Gynecology* (Springfield, Ill., 1935), 170–178, with extracts from his book of 1773.

EDWIN CLARKE

**WHITE, CHARLES DAVID** (*b.* near Palmyra, New York, 1 July 1862; *d.* Washington, D.C., 7 February 1935), *geology*.

A childhood spent on the farm of his parents, Asa Kendrick and Elvira Foster White, instilled in White a love of botany and the outdoors. He prepared for college at nearby Marion Collegiate Institute, where its principal, Daniel Van Cruyningham, a former hired hand on the White farm, strengthened his interest in botany. After teaching in rural schools for two years, David—as he came to be known—won a scholarship to Cornell University (B.S., 1886); and attracted by the courses of Henry Shaler Williams, he turned to paleobotany. Williams recommended him for his ability in drawing fossil plants to Lester F. Ward of the U.S. Geological Survey, and in 1886 White began his forty-nine-year research and administrative career with that organization.

From 1910 to 1912 White was head of the Section of Eastern Coalfields and then served as chief geologist for ten years. In 1922 he returned to his own research but gave considerable time to advisory committee appointments for the National Academy of Sciences, the National Research Council, and professional societies. He was also curator of paleobotany at the U.S. National Museum from 1903 to 1935.

In addition to his many memberships (some honorary) in professional societies, White received numerous awards: D.Sc. from the University of Rochester (1924), the University of Cincinnati

(1924), and Williams College (1925); the Walcott Medal and the Mary Clark Thompson Medal of the National Academy of Sciences, of which he became a member in 1912; the Penrose Medal of the Society of Economic Geologists; and the Boverton Redwood Medal of the Institute of Petroleum Technologists of London. He served as president of the Paleontological Society, the Washington Academy of Sciences, the Geological Society of Washington, and the Geological Society of America.

White's work on fossil plants began with a restudy of the Lacoe collection of Carboniferous specimens, followed by fieldwork on Paleozoic plants in the Appalachian trough and elsewhere. By 1896 he was convincingly able to correlate stratigraphy on the basis of paleobotany and to persuade doubting geologists of the vast extent of the Pennsylvanian Pottsville formation. Turning to the origin of peats and coals and then to the new field of petroleum, he soon established himself as the foremost authority on carbonaceous deposits. Coal and oil, he said in 1908, were the products of sedimentary deposits of organic materials, changed into carbon by chemical and physical action over a long period of time and varied by the original composition, the length of time, and fluctuations in pressure and temperature. The plants forming them grew under uniform humid tropical conditions, and coals formed directly from these in place. One of the first strong advocates of the theory that carbonaceous sediments are progressively of higher grade with increasing metamorphism, White presented contoured maps of Appalachian regions that showed the increases in coal hardness as the intensity of deformation increased (1909). This theory proved to be of considerable economic value in the search for coal.

In 1915 White presented his most valuable contribution, the carbon-ratio theory: As the percentage of fixed carbon in coals increases with higher temperature and pressure, the accompanying oils became increasingly lighter (that is, of higher grade) until, above 70 percent fixed carbon, only gas or neither oil nor gas is found. Ignored by the profession until Myron L. Fuller revived it ten years later, this theory, despite known exceptions, has saved considerable useless drilling. White enlarged upon it in 1935 and revised the "dead line" to 60 percent fixed carbon.

Deeply involved in petroleum research through his Geological Survey position, White led a drive to estimate the nation's oil reserves, especially because of World War I commitments. He pioneered in the investigation of oil shales for future use, instigated studies of temperature records in deep bore holes and mines, and was the first to apply gravimetry to finding anticlinal structure (Damon Mound, Texas). Through the National Research Council he founded a program of basic research on petroleum.

In addition to his many publications on Paleozoic flora, White also dealt with climates of that era and concluded that the extensive Pennsylvanian Pottsville represented its most luxuriant vegetation. He postulated that diastrophism, in creating geographic alterations, is the major cause of climatic change. In his final years he began studies of the Precambrian lime-secreting algae of the Grand Canyon and Glacier National Park.

## BIBLIOGRAPHY

I. ORIGINAL WORKS. White's 200 publications deal most significantly with coal and petroleum geology. The comprehensive "The Origin of Coal," *Bulletin of the United States Bureau of Mines,* **38** (1913), was written with Reinhardt Thiessen. The carbon-ratio theory was first expounded in "Some Relations in Origin Between Coal and Petroleum," in *Journal of the Washington Academy of Sciences,* **5** (1915), 189–212; and was amplified, just prior to White's death, in "Metamorphism of Organic Sediments and Derived Oils," in *Bulletin of the American Association of Petroleum Geologists,* **19,** no. 5 (1935), 589–617. His mature views on coals and oils were effectively stated in "The Carbonaceous Sediments," in W. H. Twenhofel, ed., *Treatise on Sedimentation* (Baltimore, 1926; 1932), 351–430.

White produced a number of early papers on paleobotany, of which the monumental "Fossil Flora of the Lower Coal Measures of Missouri," *U.S. Geological Survey Monograph,* no. 37 (1899), is an outstanding example. A long-intended monograph on the Pottsville flora was never completed, but the MS of "Fossil Flora of the Wedington Sandstone Member of the Fayetteville Shale" was published posthumously as *U.S. Geological Survey Professional Paper* no. 186-B (1937).

His studies of plants led White to theories of climate changes, mainly of the Paleozoic, as in "Permo-Carboniferous Climatic Changes in South America," in *Journal of Geology,* **15** (1907), 615–633; and in his significant "Permian of Western America From the Paleobotanical Standpoint," in *Proceedings of the Pan-Pacific Science Congress, 1923,* II (Melbourne, 1924), 1050–1077. His discussion of diastrophism as the major cause of climatic change appeared in "Upper Paleozoic Climate as Indicated by Fossil Plants," in *Scientific Monthly,* **20,** no. 5 (1925), 465–473; and is elaborated in his paper on more recent changes, "Geologic Factors Affecting and Possibly Controlling Pleistocene Ice Sheet Development in North America," in *Journal of the Washington Academy of Sciences,* **16,** no. 3 (1926), 69–72, an abstract.

Further papers on these and his other varied interests, including the estimates of petroleum reserves, are listed in the bibliographies cited below.

II. SECONDARY LITERATURE. White dropped the name of Charles in 1886 and thus is commonly found in indexes as David White. Charles Schuchert summarized his early life and contributions to geology in *Biographical Memoirs. National Academy of Sciences*, **17** (1935–1937), 187–221, with bibliography; see also W. C. Mendenhall, "Memorial of David White," in *Proceedings. Geological Society of America* for 1936 (1937), 271–292, with bibliography. Hugh D. Miser, "David White," in *Bulletin of the American Association of Petroleum Geologists*, **19,** no. 6 (1935), 925–932, covers especially White's work in petroleum geology.

ELIZABETH NOBLE SHOR

**WHITE, GILBERT** (*b.* Selborne, Hampshire, England, 18 July 1720; *d.* Selborne, 26 June 1793), *zoology, botany, horticulture.*

Edmund Gosse, the distinguished poet and critic, wrote, "The literature of the 18th century has left us no model of innocence, delicacy and alert natural piety more perfect than was the spirit of Gilbert White of Selborne . . . a man who has done more than any other to reconcile science with literature."

White was the eldest son of John White and Anne Holt, daughter of a wealthy clergyman from Streatham, south London. After preliminary schooling in Farnham and then at Basingstoke, he entered Oriel College, Oxford, where he received the B.A. in 1743. White then spent another year at Oxford prior to his election as fellow, finally taking the master's degree in October 1746. He received deacon's orders the following year and became curate at Swarraton, the parish of his uncle, the Reverend Charles White. Three years later White was ordained a priest by the bishop of Hereford, but, not being ambitious for a clerical career nor anxious to move far from Selborne, where his parents had made the family home, he refused all preferments offered him except that at Moreton Pinkney, Northamptonshire, a living belonging to and offered by his own college at Oxford. It provided him with a steady income but did not require him to reside within its boundaries, as it was administered by the curate from the next parish. This situation left White free to accept the curacy at Selborne or of a nearby parish whenever one was vacant, thus permitting his continued stay at the family home, "The Wakes"—a large house in the center of Selborne village (later bequeathed to him through his uncle)—and to indulge his pursuit of the study of natural history.

It was in his study at "The Wakes" that White entered in diary form daily notes on natural phenomena observed in the garden and during walks that took him into the countryside near Selborne or into adjacent parishes. Much of this material was shared in letters to his many correspondents, in particular with the zoologist Thomas Pennant and with the Honorable Daines Barrington, a well-to-do barrister and keen amateur naturalist. Despite repeated requests by Pennant and others, diffidence prevented White from being persuaded to edit his letters and have them issued in book form until four years before his death, when a selection of a lifetime of observations was published as *The Natural History and Antiquities of Selborne.* The work not only has become a classic of the English literature of the eighteenth century but also has inspired many a tyro in the study of natural history. It has been published in about 200 English editions and reprints and been translated into several foreign languages.

The *Natural History* makes abundantly clear how intense was White's interest in bird life. Unlike many contemporary ornithologists, who confined themselves to studying avian anatomy or to describing plumage, White made detailed notes on bird habits and habitats. He was the first to recognize the difference between the three British *Phylloscopi* (leaf warblers), previously considered as a single species first described by Linnaeus. The plumage is almost identical, but White pointed out that their songs are quite different. He also devoted much time to studying the habits of the nightjar; the parasitical egg-laying of the cuckoo in another species' nest; and whether swallows migrated or hibernated in Britain. Satisfactory explanations of the life styles of both cuckoo and swallow were not put forward until long after White's day. He conjectured that the domestic pigeon stemmed from the blue rock pigeon and not, as had been thought, from either the wood pigeon or the stock dove. This hypothesis was later elaborated by Charles Darwin as part of his marshaling of evidence bearing on his theory of evolution.

White also was the first to recognize Britain's smallest mammal—the harvest mouse—and he added the noctule bat to the British list, although it had earlier been described by Daubenton on the Continent. In the reptilian kingdom White's observations on a pet tortoise named Timothy are best known, although he drew attention to the fact that the blindworm could not be a snake because it produced viviparous young. He also noted many aspects of insect biology, his observations on the habits of the field, house, and mole crickets being his most significant contribution to entomology.

White recorded many species of wild flowers found around Selborne and kept phenological notes each year on their times of flowering and seeding. He was also a keen gardener, as is evident from his manuscript "Garden Kalender" and his "Naturalist's Journal," some entries from which were finally incorporated in the *Natural History*. He also noted various aspects of local agriculture, folk life, weather lore, and even archaeology and astronomy. In fact, few facets of natural phenomena observable around Selborne escaped White's attention, although wider issues affecting the country as a whole drew no comment from him. White was not unaware of the suffering brought about by wars and the industrial revolution, especially among the poor, for after his death many local inhabitants vouched for his manifold kindness and understanding. It was perhaps, rather, that he felt that in the study of natural history he could give of his best; and thus his environment at Selborne became increasingly the center of his world.

Why, then, has a single published volume written by a country cleric developed in generations of its readers so much happiness from studying natural history or engendered within them an undeniable love for the countryside? The answer has best been crystallized in the words of another zoologist, L. C. Miall, written in 1901 but nevertheless still true. Of White he wrote:

> . . . his personal knowledge of nature was great not in relation to knowledge accumulated in books but in comparison with the direct experience of most other naturalists of any age. Here is the one great difference between him and the imitators who have hoped to succeed by mere picturesque writing. White is interesting because nature is interesting; his descriptions are founded upon natural fact, exactly observed and sagaciously interpreted. Very few of his observations . . . need correction more than a hundred years after his death.

White died a bachelor at the age of seventy-two. He willed that his grave in St. Mary's churchyard, Selborne, should not be elaborate. In keeping with his wishes and his unpretentious nature, its plain headstone bears the simple inscription "G. W. June 26, 1793."

*BIBLIOGRAPHY*

I. ORIGINAL WORKS. White's fame stems from his one book, *The Natural History and Antiquities of Selborne* (London, 1789; facs. repr., Menston, 1970). Many eds. of this work have appeared, some with footnotes that have enhanced the original text, or with copious illustrations. Others have included further material extracted from White's MSS or have given details of his life. The three best are those by Thomas Bell, 2 vols. (London, 1877); R. Bowdler Sharpe, 2 vols. (London–Philadelphia, 1900); and Grant Allen (London–New York, 1900). All eds. published up to 1930 have been collated by E. A. Martin in his *Bibliography of Gilbert White* (London, 1934; repr. Folkestone–London, 1970).

Of White's other MS material, his "Garden Kalender" was published in vol. II of R. Bowdler Sharpe's ed. (see above); the "Calender of Flora, 1766" was published in facs. by the Selborne Society, edited with notes by W. M. Webb (London, 1911); and a further selection from White's "Naturalist's Journal" was edited by W. Johnson and published as *Gilbert White's Journals* (London, 1931; repr. Newton Abbot, Devon, 1970).

II. SECONDARY LITERATURE. Rashleigh Holt White, *The Life and Letters of Gilbert White*, 2 vols. (London, 1901), should be consulted by those who wish to know more of his correspondence and MSS. Two other texts of value are Rev. Walter Sidney Scott, *White of Selborne* (London, 1950); and W. Johnson, *Gilbert White: Pioneer, Poet and Stylist* (London, 1928). C. S. Emden, *Gilbert White in His Village* (London, 1956), and Anthony Rye, *Gilbert White and His Selborne* (London, 1970), both accounts of his life and times, may also be useful.

ERIC W. GROVES

**WHITE, ISRAEL CHARLES** (*b*. Monongalia County, Virginia [now West Virginia], 1 November 1848; *d*. Baltimore, Maryland, 25 November 1927), *geology.*

The son of Michael White, a progressive farmer, Israel received his early education in private schools. In 1867 he entered what is now West Virginia University, where he studied under John J. Stevenson, who later became an eminent geologist. White graduated in 1872 with highest honors, received the A.M. three years later, and in 1919 was awarded an honorary LL.D. Shortly after his twenty-ninth birthday he became head of the department of geology at West Virginia University. In 1880 Arkansas Industrial University (now the University of Arkansas) awarded him the Ph.D., and in 1921 he received the D.Sc. from the University of Pittsburgh.

White worked on the Second Geological Survey of Pennsylvania and on the U.S. Geological Survey, making a general survey of the coalfields of Pennsylvania, West Virginia, and Ohio that formed the basis for all subsequent detailed study of bituminous coals of the Appalachian region. As an authority on coal he was selected by the government of Brazil to survey and prepare a report on the coals of that country. He advocated and secured the establishment in 1897 of the West Virginia Geological and Economic Survey and headed it for thirty years as state geologist.

White's most notable accomplishment was the practical application of the anticlinal theory of oil and natural gas accumulation. In this theory, which he promulgated in 1885, he demonstrated the important part played by specific gravities of the fluids in the separation of oil and gas into commercial pools in conjunction with anticlinal and domal types of geologic structures. While others had arrived at the same conclusion independently, credit must be given to White for the successful application of the theory and for convincing the industry of its importance.

*BIBLIOGRAPHY*

I. ORIGINAL WORKS. White wrote over 170 publications. His most important books and papers are "The Geology of Natural Gas," in *Science*, **5** (1885), 521–552, in which he promulgated his anticlinal theory; "Stratigraphy of the Bituminous Coal Field of Pennsylvania, Ohio, and West Virginia," *Bulletin of the United States Geological Survey*, no. **65** (1891); "The Mannington Oil Field, West Virginia, and the History of Its Development," in *Bulletin of the Geological Society of America*, **3** (1892), 187–216; *Report on the Coal Measures and Associated Rocks of South Brazil*, I (Rio de Janeiro, 1908), in English and Portuguese; "Petroleum Fields of Northeastern Mexico Between the Tamesi and Tuxpan Rivers," in *Bulletin of the Geological Society of America*, **24** (1913), 253–274, 706; and "The Anticlinal Theory," in *Report of Proceedings. American Mining Congress*, **19** (1917), 550–556.

II. SECONDARY LITERATURE. See Lloyd L. Brown, "The Life of Dr. Israel Charles White" (M.A. thesis, Univ. of West Virginia, 1936); Herman L. Fairchild, "Memoirs of Israel C. White," in *Bulletin of the Geological Society of America*, **39** (1928), 126–145; and Ray V. Hennen, "Israel C. White, Memorial," in *Bulletin of the American Association of Petroleum Geologists*, **12** (1928), 339–351.

PAUL H. PRICE

**WHITE, THOMAS** (*b*. Runwell, Essex, England, 1593; *d*. London, England, 6 July 1676), *natural philosophy*, *theology*.

Very little is known of White's early life. His father, Richard White, married Mary Plowden, daughter of the Catholic lawyer Edmund Plowden. White was sent to the Continent for a carefully supervised Catholic education. He studied first at the English College at St.-Omer; but by the fall of 1609 he had become a member of St. Albans College at Valladolid, where he spent three years before transferring to the English college at Seville. White went to Louvain in 1614 and completed his last years of study for the priesthood at Douai; he was ordained at Arras on 25 March 1617 with the name of Blacklow. In later years he wrote under the names Blacklow, Blacloe, Vitus, Albius, and Anglus.

White became a teacher of philosophy at Douai in 1617; and the following year, after receiving his baccalaureate degree, he began to teach theology. He studied canon law at Paris in 1624–1625 and in the spring of 1626 was sent to Rome as a representative of the secular clergy of England, a duty he fulfilled until 1630. From 1631 to 1633 White was president and professor of theology at the English College of Lisbon. In May 1633 he returned to England; in the following year he was involved in the internal controversies of the English Catholics and became a candidate for the English bishopric. While in England he became a close friend of Sir Kenelm Digby. Through the late 1640's, White lived in Paris. The last two decades of his life were those of White's greatest scholarly productivity and his most sustained involvement in intellectual controversy. In 1662 he returned to England from Douai, where he had taught since about 1650, and remained there until his death. The movement embodying his theological positions, "Blackloism," maintained his ecclesiastical opinions for several decades after his death.

Although he was remarkably productive in philosophy and science, White's ideas were not acceptable to the papacy. On 17 November 1661 the Holy Office condemned eight of his books explicitly (and implicitly all of his other writings, both past and future). Theologically his thought was similar to Jansenism, for in his writings he continually condemns the Jesuits and skeptics. A devoted follower of Aristotle, White viewed the skepticism of the late sixteenth century as the principal hindrance to scientific advancement. His scientific treatises contain modifications and revisions of

Aristotle's thought; his *De mundo* of 1642, for instance, was an analysis and amplification of Aristotelian cosmology. In his *Institutionum peripateticarum* (1646) White presented the most detailed description of his philosophical and scientific approach to the study of nature. His view of nature was qualitative, and he sought spiritual demonstrability in the physical world. In 1657 and 1658 he published *Euclides physicus* and *Euclides metaphysicus*, in which he examined and amplified Aristotle's theory of causation.

White used science as a weapon with which to confront skeptics and as a tool for compounding the certitude of faith. His scientific thought was subordinate to his desire to render theology scientifically verifiable.

## BIBLIOGRAPHY

I. ORIGINAL WORKS. White's principal scientific works are *De mundo dialogi tres* . . . (Paris, 1642); *Institutionum peripateticarum* (Lyons, 1646), also in English trans. (London, 1656); *Sonus buccinae sive tres tractatus* . . . (Paris, 1654); *Euclides physicus sive de principiis naturae* (London, 1657); *Euclides metaphysicus sive De principiis sapientiae* (London, 1658); *Exercitatio geometrica* (London, 1658); *Scirri sive scepticis & scepticorum a jure disputationis* (London, 1663); and *An Exclusion of Scepticks From All Title to Dispute* (London, 1665).

II. SECONDARY LITERATURE. The most detailed study of White is Robert I. Bradley, "Blacklo: An Essay in Counter-Reform" (Ph.D. diss., Columbia Univ., 1963). For an examination of White's activities as an English recusant, see Robert I. Bradley, "Blacklo and the Counter-Reformation: An Inquiry Into the Strange Death of Catholic England," in Charles H. Carter, ed., *From the Renaissance to the Counter Reformation* (New York, 1965), 348–370. There are biographical notices in *Dictionary of National Biography* and in various Catholic encyclopedias.

PHILLIP DRENNON THOMAS

**WHITEHEAD, ALFRED NORTH** (*b.* Ramsgate, Kent, England, 15 February 1861; *d.* Cambridge, Massachusetts, 30 December 1947), *mathematics, mathematical logic, theoretical physics, philosophy.*

Education, religion, and local government were the traditional interests of the family into which Whitehead was born, the son of a southern English schoolteacher turned Anglican clergyman. As a child Whitehead developed a strong sense of the enduring presence of the past, surrounded as he was by relics of England's history. The school to which he was sent in 1875, Sherborne in Dorset, traced its origin to the eighth century. At Sherborne, Whitehead excelled in mathematics, grew to love the poetry of Wordsworth and Shelley, and in his last year acted as head of the school and captain of games. In the autumn of 1880 he entered Trinity College, Cambridge. Although during his whole undergraduate study all his courses were on pure or applied mathematics, he nevertheless developed a considerable knowledge of history, literature, and philosophy. His residence at Cambridge, first as scholar, then as fellow, and finally as senior lecturer in mathematics, lasted from 1880 to 1910. During the latter part of this period he used to give political speeches in the locality; these favored the Liberal party and often entailed his being struck by rotten eggs and oranges. In 1890 he married Evelyn Willoughby Wade, whose sense of beauty and adventure fundamentally influenced Whitehead's philosophical thought. Three children were born to them between 1891 and 1898: Thomas North, Jessie Marie, and Eric Alfred, who was killed in action with the Royal Flying Corps in 1918.

In 1910 Whitehead moved to London, where he held a variety of posts at University College and was professor at the Imperial College of Science and Technology. During this period, while active in assisting to frame new educational programs, he turned his reflective efforts toward formulating a philosophy of science to replace the prevailing materialistic mechanism, which in his view was unable to account for the revolutionary developments taking place in science.

In 1924, at the age of sixty-three, Whitehead became a professor of philosophy at Harvard University. There his previous years of reflection issued in a rapid succession of philosophical works of first importance, principally *Process and Reality: An Essay in Cosmology* (1929). He retired from active teaching only in June 1937, at the age of seventy-six. Whitehead died in his second Cambridge ten years later, still a British subject, but with a great affection for America. He had enjoyed the rare distinction of election to fellowships both in the Royal Society and in the British Academy. In 1945 he was also awarded the British Order of Merit.

Whitehead's life and work thus fall naturally into three periods which, although distinct, manifest a unity of development in his thought. At Cambridge University his writings dealt with mathematics and logic, although his thought already displayed those more general interests that would lead him to philosophy. In his second, or London, period, Whitehead devoted himself to rethinking the conceptual and experiential foundations of the physical sciences. He was stimulated in this work by participating in the discussions of the London Aristotelian Society. The writings of his third, or Harvard, period were distinctly philosophical, commencing with *Science and the Modern World* (1925), and culminating in *Process and Reality* (1929) and *Adventures of Ideas* (1933). These three works contain the essentials of his metaphysical thinking. Noteworthy among his several other books are *The Aims of Education* (1929) and *Religion in the Making* (1926), in which he combines a sensitivity to religious experience with a criticism of traditional religious concepts.

Although Whitehead's intellectual importance lies mainly in philosophy itself, he did significant work in mathematics, mathematical logic, theoretical physics, and philosophy of science.

**Mathematics and Mathematical Logic.** Whitehead's mathematical work falls into three general areas, the first two of which belong to his residence at Cambridge University, the third to his London period. The first area, algebra and geometry, contains his writings in pure mathematics, chief among which is his first book, *A Treatise on Universal Algebra* (1898). Other examples are papers on "The Geodesic Geometry of Surfaces in Non-Euclidean Space" (1898) and "Sets of Operations in Relation to Groups of Finite Order" (1899). The second area consists in work that would today be termed logic and foundations. It includes work on axiomatics (projective and descriptive geometry), cardinal numbers, and algebra of symbolic logic; it culminates in the three-volume *Principia Mathematica*, written with Bertrand Russell. The third area—less relevant from a mathematical point of view—contains the mathematical work that overlaps other fields of Whitehead's scientific activity, mainly his physics and his philosophy of mathematics. His paper "On Mathematical Concepts of the Material World" (1906) is typical of the former; his *Introduction to Mathematics* (1911) lies in the border area between mathematics and the philosophy of mathematics.

*Algebra and Geometry.* Whitehead's first book, *A Treatise on Universal Algebra*, seems at first glance entirely mathematical. Only in view of his subsequent development are several of his introductory remarks seen to have a philosophical import. This lengthy book, begun in 1891 and published in 1898, formed part of that nineteenth-century pioneering development sometimes referred to

as the "liberation of algebra" (from restriction to quantities). Although the movement was not exclusively British, there was more than half a century of British tradition on the subject (George Peacock, Augustus De Morgan, and William Rowan Hamilton), to which Whitehead's mathematical work belonged.

Whitehead acknowledged that the ideas in the *Universal Algebra* were largely based on the work of Hermann Grassmann, Hamilton, and Boole. He even stated that his whole subsequent work on mathematical logic was derived from these sources, all of which are classical examples of structures that do not involve quantities.

After an initial discussion of general principles and of Boolean algebra, the *Universal Algebra* is devoted to applications of Grassmann's calculus of extension, which can be regarded as a generalization of Hamilton's quaternions and an extension of arithmetic. Major parts of the modern theory of matrices and determinants, of vector and tensor calculus, and of geometrical algebra are implied in the calculus of extension. Whitehead's elaboration of Grassmann's work consists mainly in applications to Euclidean and non-Euclidean geometry.

Although the *Universal Algebra* displayed great mathematical skill and erudition, it does not seem to have challenged mathematicians or to have contributed in a direct way to further development of the topics involved. It was never reprinted during Whitehead's lifetime. It is plausible to think that, by the time the mathematical world became aware of the many valuable items of the work, these had been incorporated elsewhere in more accessible contexts and more modern frameworks.

*Logic and Foundations.* Confining itself to the algebras of Boole and Grassmann, the *Universal Algebra* never became what it was intended to be, a comparative study of algebras as symbolic structures. Whitehead planned to make such a comparison in a second volume along with studies of quaternions, matrices, and the general theory of linear algebras. Between 1898 and 1903 he worked on this second volume. It never appeared, and neither did the second volume of Bertrand Russell's *Principles of Mathematics* (1903). The two authors discovered that their projected second volumes "were practically on identical topics," and decided to cooperate in a joint work. In doing so their vision expanded, and it was eight or nine years before their monumental *Principia Mathematica* appeared.

The *Principia Mathematica* consists of three volumes which appeared successively in 1910,

1912, and 1913. A fourth volume, on the logical foundations of geometry, was to have been written by Whitehead alone but was never completed. The *Principia* was mainly inspired by the writings of Gottlob Frege, Georg Cantor, and Giuseppe Peano. At the heart of the treatment of mathematical logic in the *Principia* lies an exposition of sentential logic so well done that it has hardly been improved upon since. Only one axiom (Axiom 5, the "associative principle") was later (1926) proved redundant by Paul Bernays. The development of predicate logic uses Russell's theory of types, as expounded in an introductory chapter in the first volume. The link with set theory is made by considering as a set all the objects satisfying some propositional function. Different types, or levels, of propositional functions yield different types, or levels, of sets, so that the paradoxes in the construction of a set theory are avoided. Subsequently several parts of classical mathematics are reconstructed within the system.

Although the thesis about the reduction of mathematics to logic is Russell's, as is the theory of types, Russell himself stressed that the book was truly a collaboration and that neither he nor Whitehead could have written it alone.[1] The second edition (1925), however, was entirely under Russell's supervision, and the new introduction and appendices were his, albeit with Whitehead's tacit approval.

Taken as a whole, the *Principia* fills a double role. First, it constitutes a formidable effort to prove, or at least make plausible, the philosophical thesis best described by Russell in his preface to *The Principles of Mathematics*: "That all pure mathematics deals exclusively with concepts definable in terms of a very small number of fundamental logical concepts, and that all its propositions are deducible from a very small number of fundamental logical principles." This thesis is commonly expressed by the assertion that logic furnishes a basis for all mathematics. Some time later this assertion induced the so-called logicist thesis, or logicism, developed by Wittgenstein—the belief that both logic and mathematics consist entirely of tautologies. There is no evidence that Whitehead ever agreed with this; on the contrary, his later philosophical work indicates a belief in ontological referents for mathematical expressions. The thesis that logic furnishes a basis for all mathematics was first maintained by Frege but later (1931) refuted by Kurt Gödel, who showed that any system containing arithmetic, including that of the *Principia*, is essentially incomplete.

The second role of the *Principia* is the enrichment of mathematics with an impressive system, based on a thoroughly developed mathematical logic and a set theory free of paradoxes, by which a substantial part of the body of mathematical knowledge becomes organized. The *Principia* is considered to be not only a historical masterpiece of mathematical architecture, but also of contemporary value insofar as it contains subtheories that are still very useful.

*Other Mathematical Work.* At about the time Whitehead was occupied with the axiomatization of geometric systems, he turned his attention to the mathematical investigation of various possible ways of conceiving the nature of the material world. His paper "On Mathematical Concepts of the Material World" (1906) is just such an effort to create a mathematical although qualitative model of the material world. This effort differs from applied mathematics insofar as it does not apply known mathematics to situations and processes outside mathematics but creates the mathematics *ad hoc* to suit the purpose; yet it resembles applied mathematics insofar as it applies logical-mathematical tools already available. The paper conceives the material world in terms of a set of relations, and of entities that form the "fields" of these relations. The axiomatic mathematical system is not meant to serve as a cosmology but solely to exhibit concepts not inconsistent with some, if not all, of the limited number of propositions believed to be true concerning sense perceptions. Yet the system does have a cosmological character insofar as it tries to comprehend the entire material world. Unlike theoretical physics the paper is entirely devoid of quantitative references. It is thus an interesting attempt to apply logical-mathematical concepts to ontological ones, and is an early indication of Whitehead's dissatisfaction with the Newtonian conception of space and time. In a qualitative way the paper deals with field theory and can be regarded as a forerunner of later work in physics.

The delightful little book *An Introduction to Mathematics* (1911) is another early example of Whitehead's drifting away from the fields of pure mathematics and logic, this time more in the direction of philosophy of mathematics. The book contains a fair amount of solid although mainly fundamental and elementary mathematics, lucidly set out and explained. The object of the book, however, "is not to teach mathematics, but to enable students from the very beginning of their course to know what the science is about, and why it is necessarily the foundation of exact thought as applied to natural phenomena" (p. 2). In it Whitehead stresses the three notions of variable, form, and generality.

**Theoretical Physics.** Whitehead's contributions to relativity, gravitation, and "unified field" theory grew out of his preoccupations with the principles underlying our knowledge of nature. These philosophical considerations are presented chiefly in *An Enquiry Concerning the Principles of Natural Knowledge* (1919), *The Concept of Nature* (1920), and *The Principle of Relativity* (1922). A. S. Eddington, in his own book *The Nature of the Physical World* (Cambridge, 1929), comments: "Although this book may in most respects seem diametrically opposed to Dr. Whitehead's widely read philosophy of Nature, I think it would be truer to regard him as an ally who from the opposite side of the mountain is tunnelling to meet his less philosophically minded colleagues" (pp. 249–250).

In a chapter on motion in the *Principles of Natural Knowledge*, Whitehead derives the Lorentz transformation equations, now so familiar in Einstein's special theory of relativity. Whitehead's derivation, however, was based on his principle of kinematic symmetry,[2] and was carried through without reference to the concept of light signals. Consequently the velocity $c$ in the equations is not necessarily that of light, although it so happens that in our "cosmic epoch," $c$ is most clearly realized in nature as the velocity of light. There are three types of kinematics, which Whitehead termed "hyperbolic," "elliptic," or "parabolic," according to whether $c^2$ is positive, negative, or infinite. Whitehead pointed out that the hyperbolic type of kinematics corresponds to the Larmor-Lorentz-Einstein theory of electromagnetic relativity and that the parabolic type reduces to the ordinary Newtonian relativity (Galilean transformation). He rejected the elliptic type as inapplicable to nature.

In *The Principle of Relativity* Whitehead challenged the conceptual foundations of both the special and general theories of Einstein by offering "an alternative rendering of the theory of relativity" (page v). One of Whitehead's fundamental hypotheses was that space-time must possess a uniform structure everywhere and at all times—a conclusion that Whitehead drew from a consideration of the character of our knowledge in general and of our knowledge of nature in particular. He argued that Einstein's view that space-time may exhibit a local curvature fails to provide an adequate theory of measurement:

Einstein, in my opinion, leaves the whole antecedent theory of measurement in confusion when it is confronted with the actual conditions of our perceptual knowledge. . . . Measurement on his theory lacks systematic uniformity and requires a knowledge of the actual contingent field before it is possible.[3]

Whitehead proposed an action-at-a-distance theory rather than a field theory. He relieved the physicist of the task of having to solve a set of nonlinear partial differential equations. J. L. Synge, who ignored any consideration of the philosophical foundations of the theory, has clearly presented the mathematical formulas of Whitehead's gravitational theory in modern notation.[4]

Using Synge's notation, the world lines of test particles and light rays in Whitehead's theory may be conveniently discussed by the Euler-Lagrange equations:

$$\frac{d}{d\lambda}\frac{\partial L}{\partial \dot{x}_p} - \frac{\partial L}{\partial x_p} = 0, \tag{1}$$

where $2L = -1$ for test particles; $2L = 0$ for light rays; and $\dot{x}_p = \dfrac{dx_p}{d\lambda}$. The Lagrangian $L$ is defined:

$$L = \frac{1}{2}g_{mn}\dot{x}_m\dot{x}_n, \tag{2}$$

where $g_{mn}$ is a symmetrical tensor defined by

$$g_{mn} = \delta_{mn} + \frac{2mG}{c^2 w^3}y_m y_n. \tag{3}$$

In equation (3) $\delta_{mn}$ is the Kronecker delta; $G$ is the gravitational constant; $c$ is a fundamental velocity; and $m$ is the mass of a particle with a world line given by $x'_n = x'_n(s')$, where $s'$ is the Minkowskian arc length such that $ds'^2 = -dx'_n dx'_n$; $y_m = x_m - x'_m$; and $w = -y_n\dfrac{dx'_n}{ds'}$. The parameter $\lambda$ in equation (1) is such that $d\lambda = (-g_{mn}dx_m dx_n)^{\frac{1}{2}}$. Latin suffixes have the range 1, 2, 3, 4. Thus Whitehead's theory of gravitation is described in terms of Minkowskian space-time with $x_4 = ict$ (where $i = \sqrt{-1}$ and $c$ is the speed of light in a vacuum).[5] The basic physical laws of the Whitehead theory are invariant with respect to Lorentz transformations but not necessarily with respect to general coordinate transformations. Whitehead invoked neither the principle of equivalence nor the principle of covariance.

Clifford M. Will has challenged the viability of Whitehead's theory by arguing that it predicts "an anisotropy in the Newtonian gravitational constant $G$, as measured locally by means of Cavendish experiments."[6] Using Synge's notation, Will calculated Whitehead's prediction of twelve-hour sidereal-time earth tides, which are produced by the galaxy, and found Whitehead's prediction in disagreement with the experimentally measured value of these geotidal effects. In Whitehead's theory the anisotropy in $G$ is a result of the uniform structure of space-time demanded by the theory.

In order to understand the relation of the anisotropy to uniformity we must recognize that in Whitehead's theory gravitational forces are propagated along the geodesics of the uniform structure of space-time, while electromagnetic waves are deflected by the contingencies of the universe.[7] This restriction in the propagation of gravity produces the variation in the gravitational constant. While Whitehead's mathematical formulas imply this restriction, it is not demanded by his philosophy of nature. For Whitehead, gravitational forces share in the contingency of nature, and may therefore be affected, as electromagnetic waves are, by the contingencies of the universe.

In addition to the consideration of gravitation, in chapter 5 of *The Principle of Relativity* Whitehead extends his equations of motion to describe the motion of a particle in a combined gravitational and electromagnetic field. As Rayner points out,[8] this is not a "true" unified field theory since it does not interpret gravitational and electromagnetic phenomena in terms of a single primitive origin.

It is possible to demonstrate, as did Eddington[9] and Synge,[10] that the predictions of Whitehead's theory and those of Einstein's general theory of relativity are equivalent with respect to the four tests of relativity: the deflection of a light ray, the red shift, the advance in the perihelion of a satellite, and radar time delay. The equivalence of the two theories with respect to these tests rests in the remarkable fact that both theories, when solved for a static, spherically symmetrical gravitational field, produce the Schwarzschild solution of the field equations.

In accordance with his usual practice, Whitehead assembled *Relativity* from lectures that he delivered at the Imperial College, the Royal Society of Edinburgh, and Bryn Mawr College. He did not publish in the journals of physical science nor enter into active discourse with members of the scientific community. His gravitational theory is not referred to in the formal treatments of relativity given by such authors as Bergmann, Einstein, and Pauli. The mathematical physicists who studied and extended Whitehead's physical theories in the 1950's had difficulty understanding his esoteric language and his philosophical ideas.

While the two ends of Eddington's tunnel have not yet been joined under the mountain, considerable progress has been made by the careful exposition of Whitehead's philosophy of science by Robert M. Palter.[11]

In 1961 C. Brans and R. H. Dicke developed a modified relativistic theory of gravitation apparently compatible with Mach's principle.[12] It is significant that the Einstein, Whitehead, and Brans-Dicke theories represent distinct conceptual formulations, the predictions of which with regard to observational tests are all so close that it is not yet possible on this basis to make a choice among them. New experiments of high precision on the possible Machian time variation of $G$ and on the precession of the spin axis of a gyroscope,[13] as well as theoretical considerations such as the "parametrized post-Newtonian" (PPN) formalism,[14] may be decisive. At present the Einstein theory is regarded as the most influential and elegant; the Brans-Dicke theory has perhaps the most attractive cosmological consequences;[15] and the Whitehead theory, although clearly the simplest, suffers from its obscurity.

**Philosophy of Science.** Whitehead once remarked that what worried him was "the muddle geometry had got into" in relation to the physical world.[16] Particularly in view of Einstein's theory of relativity, it was unclear what relation geometrical space had to experience. It was therefore necessary to find a basis in physical experience for the scientific concepts of space and time. These are, Whitehead thought, "the first outcome of the simplest generalisations from experience, and . . . not to be looked for at the tail end of a welter of differential equations."[17] The supposed divorce of abstract scientific concepts from actual experience had resulted in a "bifurcation of nature," a splitting into two disparate natures, of which one was a merely apparent world of sense experience, the other a conjectured, causal world perpetually behind a veil. Aside from extrinsic quantitative relations, the elements of this latter world were presumed to be intrinsically self-contained and unrelated to one another. Somehow this conjectured, monadically disjunctive nature, although itself beyond experience, was supposed to account causally for the unified nature of experience. Whitehead rejected this view as incoherent and as an unsatisfactory foundation for the sciences. According to Whitehead, "we must reject the distinction between nature as it really is and experiences of it which are purely psychological. Our experiences of the apparent world are nature itself."[18]

In his middle writings Whitehead examined how space and time are rooted in experience, and in general laid the foundations of a natural philosophy that would be the necessary presupposition of a reorganized speculative physics. He investigated the coherence of "Nature," understood as the object of perceptual knowledge; and he deliberately, although perhaps unsuccessfully, distinguished nature as thus known from the synthesis of knower and known, which falls within the ambit of metaphysical analysis.

Two special characteristics of Whitehead's analysis are of particular importance: his identification of noninstantaneous events as the basic elements of perceived nature, and the intrinsically relational constitution of these events (as displayed in his doctrine of "significance"). Space and time (or space-time) are then shown to be derivative from the fundamental process by which events are interrelated, rather than a matrix within which events are independently situated. This view contrasts sharply with the prevalent notion that nature consists in an instantaneous collection of independent bodies situated in space-time. Such a view, Whitehead thought, cannot account for the perception of the continuity of existence, nor can it represent the ultimate scientific fact, since change inevitably imports the past and the future into the immediate fact falsely supposed to be embodied in a durationless present instant.

Whitehead's philosophy of nature attempts to balance the view of nature-in-process with a theory of elements ingredient within nature ("objects"), which do not themselves share in nature's passage. Whitehead's boyhood sense of permanences in nature thus emerged both in his mathematical realism and in his philosophic recognition of unchanging characters perpetually being interwoven within the process of nature.

*Method of Extensive Abstraction.* "Extensive abstraction" is the term Whitehead gave to his method for tracing the roots within experience of the abstract notions of space and time, and of their elements.

In this theory it is experienced events, not physical bodies, that are related; their fundamental relation lies in their overlapping, or "extending over," one another. Later Whitehead recognized that this relation is itself derivative from something more fundamental.[19] The notions of "part," "whole," and "continuity" arise naturally from this relation of extending-over. These properties lead to defining an "abstractive set" as "any set of events that possesses the two properties, (i) of any two

members of the set one contains the other as a part, and (ii) there is no event which is a common part of every member of the set."[20] Such a set of events must be infinite toward the small end, so that there is no least event in the set. Corresponding to the abstractive set of events there is an abstractive set of the intrinsic characters of the events. The latter set converges to an exactly defined locational character. For instance, the locational character of an abstractive set of concentric circles or squares converges to a nondimensional but located point. In analogous fashion, an abstractive set of rectangles, all of which have a common length but variable widths, defines a line segment. With the full development of this technique Whitehead was able to define serial times, and, in terms of them, space. He concluded that all order in space is merely the expression of order in time. "Position in space is merely the expression of diversity of relations to alternative time-systems."[21]

In general Whitehead held that there are two basic aspects in nature. One is its passage or creative advance; the other its character as extended—that is, that its events extend over one another, thus giving nature its continuity. These two facts are the qualities from which time and space originate as abstractions.

The purpose of the method of extensive abstraction is to show the connection of the abstract with the concrete. Whitehead showed, for instance, how the abstract notion of a point of instantaneous space is naturally related to the experience of events in nature, which have the immediately given property of extension. Whitehead's procedure, however, is easily subject to misunderstanding. Most Whitehead scholars agree that Whitehead was trying neither to deduce a geometry from sense experience, nor to give a psychological description of the genesis of geometric concepts. Rather, he was using a mathematical model to clarify relations appearing in perception. Another misinterpretation would be to assume that Whitehead took as the immediate data for sense awareness some kind of Humean sensa instead of events themselves.

In his notes to the second edition of the *Principles of Natural Knowledge* Whitehead suggested certain improvements in his procedure. The final outcome of extensive abstraction is found in part 4 of *Process and Reality*, "The Theory of Extension," in which Whitehead defines points, lines, volumes, and surfaces without presupposing any particular theory of parallelism, and defines a straight line without any reference to measurement.

*Uniformity of Spatiotemporal Relations.* In the Preface to *The Principle of Relativity* Whitehead states:

> As the result of a consideration of the character of our knowledge in general, and of our knowledge of nature in particular, . . . I deduce that our experience requires and exhibits a basis of uniformity, and that in the case of nature this basis exhibits itself as the uniformity of spatio-temporal relations. This conclusion entirely cuts away the casual heterogeneity of these relations which is the essential of Einstein's later theory.

The mathematical consequences of this conclusion for Whitehead's theory of relativity have already been noted. It remains to indicate summarily the reasons that persuaded Whitehead to adopt this view.

Consonance with the general character of direct experience was one of the gauges by which Whitehead judged any physical theory, for he was intent on discovering the underlying structures of nature as observed. Further, he maintained the traditional division between geometry and physics: it is the role of geometry to reflect the relatedness of events; that of physics to describe the contingency of appearance. He also claimed that it is events, not material bodies, that are the terms of the concrete relations of nature. But since for Whitehead these relations were essentially constitutive of events, it might seem that no event can be known apart from knowledge of all those other events to which it is related. Thus, nothing can be known until everything is known—an impossible requirement for knowledge.

Whitehead met this objection by distinguishing between essential and contingent relations of events. One can know that an event or factor is related to others without knowing their precise character. But since in our knowledge no event discloses the particular individuals constituting the aggregate of events to which it is related, even contingently, this relatedness must embody an intrinsic uniformity apart from particular relationships to particular individuals. This intrinsic and necessary uniformity of the relatedness of events is precisely the uniformity of their spatiotemporal structure.

Whitehead provided an illustration of this in a discussion of equality.[22] Equality presupposes measurement, and measurement presupposes matching (not vice versa). It must follow that "measurement presupposes a structure yielding definite stretches which, in some sense inherent in the structure, match each other."[23] This inherent matching is spatiotemporal uniformity.

It is well known that in his later philosophy Whitehead came to hold—contrary to his earlier belief—that nature is not continuous in fact, but "incurably atomic." Continuity was recognized to belong to potentiality, not to actuality.[24] It has even been claimed that this later revision removes the basic difference between Einstein and Whitehead, so that the Whitehead of *Process and Reality* offers only an alternative interpretation of Einstein's theory of relativity, not an alternative theory.[25] This claim, however, has not found wide support.

Despite some recent interest in it, Whitehead's theory of relativity has been mainly ignored and otherwise not well understood. *The Principle of Relativity* has long been out of print, and it is impossible now to say whether it has a scientific future.

*NOTES*

1. Bertrand Russell, "Whitehead and Principia Mathematica," *Mind*, n.s. **57** (1948), 137–138.
2. For a discussion and derivation, see C. B. Rayner, "Foundations and Applications of Whitehead's Theory of Relativity," University of London thesis, 1953; "The Application of the Whitehead Theory of Relativity to Non-static, Spherically Symmetrical Systems," in *Proceedings of the Royal Society of London*, **222A** (1954), 509–526.
3. *The Principle of Relativity*, p. 83.
4. J. L. Synge, in *Proceedings of the Royal Society of London*, **211A** (1952), 303–319.
5. Whitehead's requirement that space-time be homogeneous is not violated by a space-time of constant curvature. This extension of Whitehead's theory has been carried out by G. Temple, "A Generalisation of Professor Whitehead's Theory of Relativity," in *Proceedings of the Physical Society of London*, **36** (1923), 176–193; and by C. B. Rayner, "Whitehead's Law of Gravitation in a Space-Time of Constant Curvature," in *Proceedings of the Physical Society of London*, **68B** (1955), 944–950.
6. Clifford M. Will, "Relativistic Gravity in the Solar System . . .," p. 141.
7. Misner, Thorne, and Wheeler, *Gravitation*, p. 430. Whitehead's theory is termed a "two metric" theory of gravitation. The first metric defines the uniform structure of space-time; the second, the physically contingent universe.
8. Rayner, "Foundations and Applications . . .," p. 23.
9. Sir A. S. Eddington, "A Comparison of Whitehead's and Einstein's Formulae," p. 192.
10. J. L. Synge, *The Relativity Theory of A. N. Whitehead* (1951). In ch. 13 of *The Principle of Relativity* Whitehead obtains a red shift that disagrees with Einstein's by a factor of 7/6. This is in disagreement with the terrestrial Mössbauer experiments (see R. V. Pound and G. A. Rebka, Jr., "Apparent Weight of Photons," *Physical Review Letters*, 4 [1960], 337–341). Synge observes, however, that the discrepancy lies in Whitehead's use of a classical rather than a quantum mechanical model of an atom and is not due to Whitehead's gravitational theory. See also C. B.

Rayner, "The Effects of Rotation of the Central Body on Its Planetary Orbits, After the Whitehead Theory of Gravitation," in *Proceedings of the Royal Society of London*, **232A** (1955), 135–148.

11. Robert M. Palter, *Whitehead's Philosophy of Science*.

12. C. Brans and R. H. Dicke, in *Physical Review*, **124** (1961), 925–935.

13. L. I. Schiff, "Experimental Tests of Theories of Relativity," in *Physics Today*, **14**, no. 11 (November 1961), 42–48.

14. C. M. Will, *op. cit.*

15. R. H. Dicke, "Implications for Cosmology of Stellar and Galactic Evolution Rates," in *Review of Modern Physics*, **34** (1962), 110–122.

16. Lowe, *Understanding Whitehead*, p. 193.

17. *Principles of Natural Knowledge*, p. vi.

18. *The Principle of Relativity*, p. 62.

19. *Principles of Natural Knowledge*, p. 202.

20. *The Concept of Nature*, p. 79; *Principles of Natural Knowledge*, p. 104.

21. *The Principle of Relativity*, p. 8.

22. *Ibid.*, ch. 3.

23. *Ibid.*, p. 59.

24. Leclerc, "Whitehead and the Problem of Extension."

25. Seaman, "Whitehead and Relativity."

## BIBLIOGRAPHY

I. ORIGINAL WORKS. A chronological list of all Whitehead's writings may be found in P. A. Schilpp (see below). The following works are of most scientific importance: *A Treatise on Universal Algebra, With Applications* (Cambridge, 1898); "On Mathematical Concepts of the Material World," in *Philosophical Transactions of the Royal Society of London*, **205A** (1906), 465–525, also available in the Northrop and Gross anthology (see below): *Principia Mathematica*, 3 vols. (Cambridge, 1910–1913), written with Bertrand Russell; *An Introduction to Mathematics* (London, 1911); "Space, Time, and Relativity," in *Proceedings of the Aristotelian Society*, n.s. **16** (1915–1916), 104–129, also available in the Johnson anthology (see below); *An Enquiry Concerning the Principles of Natural Knowledge* (Cambridge, 1919); *The Concept of Nature* (Cambridge, 1920); *The Principle of Relativity, With Applications to Physical Science* (Cambridge, 1922), which is out-of-print but may be obtained from University Microfilms, Ann Arbor, Mich.; also, pt. 1, "General Principles," is reprinted in the Northrop and Gross anthology; *Science and the Modern World* (New York, 1925); *Process and Reality: An Essay in Cosmology* (New York; 1929), which is of scientific interest chiefly insofar as it gives Whitehead's final version of his theory of extensive abstraction; and *Essays in Science and Philosophy* (New York, 1947), a collection of earlier essays.

Two useful anthologies of Whitehead's writings are F. S. C. Northrop and Mason W. Gross, eds., *Alfred North Whitehead: An Anthology* (New York, 1961); and A. H. Johnson, ed., *Alfred North Whitehead: The Interpretation of Science, Selected Essays* (Indianapolis, 1961).

II. SECONDARY LITERATURE. Paul Arthur Schilpp, ed., *The Philosophy of Alfred North Whitehead*, Library of Living Philosophers Series (New York, 1951), contains Whitehead's "Autobiographical Notes," a complete chronological list of Whitehead's writings, and essays pertinent to Whitehead's science by Lowe, Quine, and Northrop. Victor Lowe, *Understanding Whitehead* (Baltimore, 1962), is a valuable tool, especially pt. 2, "The Development of Whitehead's Philosophy," which is an enlargement of Lowe's essay in the Schilpp volume. Robert M. Palter, *Whitehead's Philosophy of Science* (Chicago, 1960), is a perceptive mathematical exposition of Whitehead's views on extension and on relativity. In 1971 appeared *Process Studies* (published at the School of Theology at Claremont, California), a journal devoting itself to exploring the thought of Whitehead and his intellectual associates. The fourth issue of vol. 1 (Winter 1971) contains a bibliography of secondary literature on Whitehead, to be periodically updated.

The following are cited as examples of the influence of Whitehead's thought on scientists or philosophers of science. In *Experience and Conceptual Activity* (Cambridge, Mass., 1965), J. M. Burgers, a physicist of some distinction, presents for scientists a case for a Whiteheadian rather than a physicalistic world view. Also, a strong Whiteheadian perspective dominates Milič Čapek, *The Philosophical Impact of Contemporary Physics* (New York, 1961).

Whitehead's later metaphysics, although consistent with and developed out of his reflections on science, forms another story altogether. For a more general introduction to his thought and to the literature, see the article on Whitehead in Paul Edwards, ed., *The Encyclopedia of Philosophy*, VIII (New York–London, 1967), 290–296.

On Whitehead's mathematics and logic, see Granville C. Henry, Jr., "Whitehead's Philosophical Response to the New Mathematics," in *Southern Journal of Philosophy*, **7** (1969–1970), 341–349; George L. Kline, ed., *Alfred North Whitehead: Essays on His Philosophy*, pt. 2 (Englewood Cliffs, N.J., 1963); J. J. C. Smart, "Whitehead and Russell's Theory of Types," in *Analysis*, **10** (1949–1950), 93–96, which is critical of the theory of types; Martin Shearn, "Whitehead and Russell's Theory of Types: A Reply," *ibid.*, **11** (1950–1951), 45–48.

On Whitehead's theoretical physics, see Sir A. S. Eddington, "A Comparison of Whitehead's and Einstein's Formulae," in *Nature*, **113** (1924), 192; Charles W. Misner, Kip S. Thorne, John Archibald Wheeler, *Gravitation* (San Francisco, 1973); C. B. Rayner, "Foundations and Applications of Whitehead's Theory of Relativity" (Ph.D. thesis, University of London, 1953); A. Schild, "Gravitational Theories of the Whitehead Type and the Principle of Equivalence," in *Proceedings of the International School of Physics*, "Enrico Fermi," course 20 (Italian Physical Society and Academic Press, 1963), 69–115; Francis Seaman, "Discussion: In Defense of

Duhem," in *Philosophy of Science*, **32** (1965), 287–294, which argues that Whitehead's physical theory in *Process and Reality* illustrates the assumption of geometric, without physical, continuity; J. L. Synge, *The Relativity Theory of Alfred North Whitehead* (College Park, Md., 1951); Clifford M. Will, "Relativistic Gravity in the Solar System, II: Anisotropy in the Newtonian Gravitational Constant," in *Astrophysical Journal*, **169** (1971), 141–155; and "Gravitation Theory," in *Scientific American*, **231**, no. 5 (1974), 24–33, which compares competing theories.

On Whitehead's philosophy of science, see Ann P. Lowry, "Whitehead and the Nature of Mathematical Truth," in *Process Studies*, **1** (1971), 114–123; Thomas N. Hart, S. J., "Whitehead's Critique of Scientific Materialism," in *New Scholasticism*, **43** (1969), 229–251; Nathaniel Lawrence, "Whitehead's Method of Extensive Abstraction," in *Philosophy of Science*, **17** (1950), 142–163; Adolf Grünbaum, "Whitehead's Method of Extensive Abstraction," in *British Journal for the Philosophy of Science*, **4** (1953), 215–226, which attacks the validity of Whitehead's method (see Lowe's reply in *Understanding Whitehead*, pp. 79–80); Caroline Whitbeck, "Simultaneity and Distance," in *Journal of Philosophy*, **66** (1969), 329–340; Wolfe Mays, "Whitehead and the Philosophy of Time," in *Studium generale*, **23** (1970), 509–524; Robert R. Llewellyn, "Whitehead and Newton on Space and Time Structure," in *Process Studies*, **3** (1973), 239–258; Ivor Leclerc, "Whitehead and the Problem of Extension," in *Journal of Philosophy*, **58** (1961), 559–565; Robert M. Palter, "Philosophic Principles and Scientific Theory," in *Philosophy of Science*, **23** (1956), 111–135, compares the theories of Einstein and Whitehead.

See also Francis Seaman, "Whitehead and Relativity," in *Philosophy of Science*, **22** (1955), 222–226; A. P. Ushenco, "A Note on Whitehead and Relativity," in *Journal of Philosophy*, **47** (1950), 100–102; Dean R. Fowler, "Whitehead's Theory of Relativity," in *Process Studies*, **5** (1975), which treats the philosophical foundations of Whitehead's theory of relativity; and Richard J. Blackwell, "Whitehead and the Problem of Simultaneity," in *Modern Schoolman*, **41** (1963–1964), 62–72. The extent to which applications of Whitehead's philosophical scheme agree with modern quantum theory has been discussed by Abner Shimony, "Quantum Physics and the Philosophy of Whitehead," in *Boston Studies in the Philosophy of Science*, II (New York, 1965), 307–330; and by J. M. Burgers, "Comments on Shimony's Paper," *ibid.*, pp. 331–342. Henry J. Folse, Jr., "The Copenhagen Interpretation of Quantum Theory and Whitehead's Philosophy of Organism," in *Tulane Studies in Philosophy*, **23** (1974), 32–47, challenges Shimony's conclusions.

WILLIAM A. BARKER
KAREL L. DE BOUVÈRE, S.C.J.
JAMES W. FELT, S.J.
DEAN R. FOWLER

**WHITEHEAD, JOHN HENRY CONSTANTINE** (*b.* Madras, India, 11 November 1904; *d.* Princeton, New Jersey, 8 May 1960), *mathematics*.

Whitehead is perhaps best remembered for his idea of developing the theory of homotopy equivalence by the strictly combinatorial method of allowed transformations. He built up an important school of topology at Oxford.

Whitehead was the son of the Right Reverend Henry Whitehead, from 1899 to 1922 bishop of Madras, and of Isobel Duncan of Calne, Wiltshire. She had been one of the first undergraduates to study mathematics at Lady Margaret Hall, Oxford. Bishop Whitehead was the brother of the mathematician Alfred North Whitehead.

Sent to England before he was two, Whitehead saw little of his parents until his father's retirement to England in 1922. He was educated at Eton and Balliol College, Oxford. His Balliol tutor was J. W. Nicholson, who had studied under A. N. Whitehead. Whitehead boxed for the university, was a good cricketer, and an even better poker player. After graduating in mathematics he joined a firm of stockbrokers, but in 1928 he returned to Oxford to do further mathematical work. There he met Oswald Veblen, on leave from Princeton University, and it was arranged that Whitehead should visit Princeton on a Commonwealth fellowship. He was there from 1929 to 1932, when, having taken a Ph.D., he returned to Oxford and a fellowship at Balliol. In 1934 Whitehead married Barbara Shiela Carew Smyth, a concert pianist. They had two sons.

From 1941 to 1945 Whitehead worked at the Admiralty and Foreign Office. He was elected a fellow of the Royal Society in 1944, and Waynflete professor of pure mathematics and fellow of Magdalen College, Oxford, in 1947. He was president of the London Mathematical Society from 1953 to 1955. He died of a heart attack during a visit to Princeton.

On Whitehead's first visit to Princeton he took up the studies that were to occupy the remainder of his life. There he collaborated with S. Lefschetz on a proof that all analytic manifolds can be triangulated (*Mathematical Works*, II, no. 15 [1933]; see bibliography for details of the edition). He offered a proof (*ibid.*, no. 16 [1934]; corrected in no. 18 [1935]) of the Poincaré hypothesis that a simply connected 3-manifold, compact and without boundary, is a topological 3-sphere. Although Whitehead soon found his proof to have been erroneous, work on it committed him to topology. One memorable early discovery was of a counterexample for open 3-manifolds (*ibid.*, no. 20 [1935]). Before turning to topology, Whitehead had made an important study of the geometry of paths. A monograph on the foundations of differential geometry, written with Veblen, contains the first precise definition, through axioms, of a differential manifold (*Mathematical Works*, I, no. 7 [1932]). This definition was much more precise than the concept of a global differential manifold offered, for example, by Robert König (1919) and E. Cartan (1928). In another work written with Veblen (*ibid.*, no. 6 [1931]) the independence of the axioms is proved.

Under the influence of Marston Morse, Whitehead studied differential geometry in the large, and his paper "On the Covering of a Complete Space by the Geodesics Through a Point" (*Mathematical Works*, I, no. 17 [1935]) marks a turning point in this subject. Assuming an analytic manifold with a Finsler metric, he discussed the relationship between different concepts of completeness in the manifold. He also made a detailed investigation of the properties of the locus of characteristic points of a given point. Other notable work in differential geometry includes his new and elegant proof of a theorem first stated by E. E. Levi and of an important analogue (*ibid.*, no. 22 [1936], and no. 36 [1941]).

After 1941 Whitehead was mainly concerned with topology. He had never lost his early interest in the subject, and J. W. Milnor describes his "Simplicial Spaces, Nuclei and *M*-Groups" (*Mathematical Works*, II, no. 28 [1939]) as the paper that will probably be remembered as his most significant work. Milnor discusses this and related work at length (*Mathematical Works*, I, xxv–xxxiii). The 1939 paper was a brilliant extension of the strictly combinatorial type of topology developed by J. W. Alexander and M. H. A. Newman between 1925 and 1932. (Whitehead had met Newman on his first visit to Princeton.) The contents of the paper were characterized by Whitehead's idea of using the strictly combinatorial method of allowed transformations to solve problems in the theory of homotopy equivalence.

Whitehead's interests gradually shifted toward algebraic topology as a result of his search for invariants to characterize the homotopy type of complexes, and for methods of computing their homotopy groups. Newman explains how Whitehead's discovery of certain mistakes he had made in a paper written in 1941 persuaded him to avoid a free "geometrical" style of composition. Whitehead therefore undertook a complete restatement of his earlier work on homotopy, in a way expertly

outlined by Newman. In the last three years of Whitehead's life there was a revival of geometrical topology, which led him to offer, jointly with A. Shapiro, a proof of Dehn's lemma much simpler than the one given in 1957 by C. D. Papakyriako-poulos (*Mathematical Works*, IV, no. 84 [1958]). Here, and in his elaboration of methods laid down by B. Mazur (1958) and Morton Brown (1960), there is ample evidence that Whitehead died at the height of his mathematical powers.

*BIBLIOGRAPHY*

I. ORIGINAL WORKS. Ninety papers, some of them lengthy memoirs, are collected in *Mathematical Works of J. H. C. Whitehead*, I. M. James, ed., 4 vols. (Oxford, 1962). References in text are to this collection, the numbers corresponding to the list of Whitehead's publications in I, ix–xiii, and the original year of publication being added in brackets. The papers are classified as follows: vol. I, differential geometry; vol. II, complexes and manifolds; vol. III, homotopy theory; vol. IV, algebraic and classical topology. Whitehead collaborated with Oswald Veblen on *The Foundations of Differential Geometry* (Cambridge, 1932), included in *Mathematical Works*, I. His Oxford lectures on Riemannian geometry and linear algebras, which were separately duplicated and circulated by the Mathematical Institute, Oxford, in 1959, are not included in the collected edition.

II. SECONDARY LITERATURE. Vol. I of the *Mathematical Works* is prefaced by a biographical note by M. H. A. Newman and Barbara Whitehead, and by a mathematical appreciation by John W. Milnor. Two other valuable surveys of Whitehead's work are M. H. A. Newman's obituary notice in *Biographical Memoirs of Fellows of the Royal Society*, 7 (1961), 349–363; and P. J. Hilton, "Memorial Tribute to J. H. C. Whitehead," in *L'enseignement mathématique*, 2nd ser., 7 (1961), 107–124.

J. D. NORTH

**WHITEHURST, JOHN** (*b.* Congleton, Cheshire, England, 10 April 1713; *d.* London, England, 18 February 1788), *geology.*

Whitehurst was a practical natural philosopher in many fields but was particularly celebrated as a clockmaker. In pure science he is important chiefly as a geological pioneer who did work in Derbyshire that was published in a well-known book (of which the first part is entirely speculative) in 1778. He established for the first time the succession of the Carboniferous strata: limestone, Millstone grit (named by him), and coal measures.

Whitehurst formulated the general proposition of

VINCENNES PUBLIC LIBRARY
VINCENNES, INDIANA

a worldwide orderly superposition of strata, each with its characteristic lithology and fossils. Although the proposition was somewhat vaguely imagined, he here hit on the most significant of all geological generalizations. He investigated the origin of the Derbyshire "toadstones," associated with the limestones, and in so doing examined by implication the origin of all rocks of a like kind. Whitehurst found the rock to be so similar to specimens of recent lavas he had seen that he had no hesitation in assigning to it a volcanic origin, although it was situated in a region—indeed, in a country—that showed not the slightest sign of any recent volcanic activity. He was among the first to recognize the true nature and origin of this great class of rocks, the basalts, and thus to establish the fact of volcanism in past geological times.

Whitehurst went further, however, and realized the possibility of igneous intrusion and recorded an instance of contact thermal metamorphism. In the second edition (1786) of his book he described the basaltic rocks of the Giant's Causeway, on the north coast of Ireland, recognizing their volcanic origin and making a reasonable suggestion as to how they might have been erupted in that region.

## BIBLIOGRAPHY

I. ORIGINAL WORKS. Whitehurst's chief writings are *An Inquiry Into the Original State and Formation of the Earth, to Which Is Added an Appendix Containing Some General Observations on the Strata in Derbyshire* (London, 1778; 2nd ed., enl., 1786; repr. as 3rd ed., 1792) and *An Attempt Towards Obtaining Invariable Measures of Length, Capacity, and Weight, From the Mensuration of Time* (London, 1787). His writings are collected in *The Works of John Whitehurst, F.R.S., With Memoirs of His Life and Writings*, C. Hutton, ed. (London, 1792).

II. SECONDARY LITERATURE. See E. I. Carlyle, in *Dictionary of National Biography*; J. Challinor, "From Whitehurst's Inquiry to Farey's Derbyshire: A Chapter in the History of British Geology," in *Transactions and Annual Report. North Staffordshire Field Club*, **81** (1947), 52–88, esp. 53–65; and "The Early Progress of British Geology—II," in *Annals of Science*, **10** (1954), 1–19, see 13–16; T. D. Ford, "Biographical Notes on Derbyshire Authors: John Whitehurst, F.R.S. 1713–1788," in *Bulletin of the Peak District Mines Historical Society*, **5** (1974), 362–369; and W. D. White, "Derbyshire Clockmakers Before 1850; The Whitehurst Family," supp. to *Derbyshire Miscellany*, **1** (1958).

JOHN CHALLINOR

**WHITFIELD, ROBERT PARR** (*b*. Willowvale, near New Hartford, New York, 27 May 1828; *d*. Troy, New York, 6 April 1910), *invertebrate paleontology, stratigraphy.*

Whitfield was a second-generation American, son of William Fenton Whitfield, an immigrant English maker of mill spindles, and Margaret Parr. His only formal instruction, which he received principally at a Stockport Sunday school and its library during six years spent with his parents in England, ended when the family returned to New York in 1841. He then worked for seven years in his father's trade. In 1847 he married Mary Henry of Utica; of their four children, three survived him. At twenty Whitfield was employed by a Utica "philosophical" instruments firm, where he developed his considerable mechanical skills and drafting ability, serving as manager after 1849.

Participation in the Utica Society of Naturalists and collecting local fossils brought Whitfield to the attention of James Hall, whose assistant he became in 1856, succeeding Fielding Meek in 1858. In 1870 he was appointed principal assistant curator of the New York State Museum. At Albany, Whitfield undertook official field studies in New York and western states. More significantly, he drew thousands of superb illustrations and made preliminary analyses of fossil brachiopods, crinoids, and graptolites for the *Palaeontology of New York* and for the various state surveys of which Hall was either head or contract paleontologist. Much of Whitfield's best work was produced during his twenty-year association with Hall. It included studies of Paleozoic bivalve mollusks, internal structures of fossil brachiopods, the Paleozoic-Mesozoic paleontology of Nevada and Utah for Clarence King's Fortieth Parallel Survey, and descriptions of the Black Hills fossils from the Newton-Jenney survey of 1875.

Although he wrote nine papers with Hall during this interval, like his sometime fellow assistants Meek, Charles White, and William Gabb, Whitfield received less credit in authorship than was his due.[1] From 1872 to 1875 he also lectured informally at Rensselaer Polytechnic Institute, fulfilling Hall's nominal commitment;[2] he served as professor of geology there in 1876–1878, after Hall's retirement.

Early in 1877 Whitfield became the first curator of the newly organized American Museum of Natural History, with initial charge of geology. Its holdings had just been expanded by the purchase of an immense collection of invertebrate fossils from Hall. Whitfield's long-continued task of curation led to a protracted, lively correspondence with Hall as to exactly what percentage of the collection had been merely loaned or sold outright.[3] Whitfield remained at the Museum, with varying curatorial titles and additional responsibilities, until his retirement in December 1909. He was chiefly responsible for the establishment of the Museum's *Bulletin* in 1881, to which he contributed its first five articles. He subsequently wrote numerous descriptions and comparisons of an array of fossil invertebrates, faunas, and their stratigraphic relations. Some were brief, as were many works of late nineteenth-century American paleontologists who often dealt with biotas new to science.

Whitfield's systematic paleontology included investigations of sponges, brachiopods, mollusks, trilobites, scorpions, crustaceans, and crinoids from diverse locales and periods. Some studies involved new or continued contracts from the state surveys of Minnesota, Wisconsin, Indiana, Ohio, and New Jersey. Of his three quarto investigations of Cretaceous and Miocene invertebrates in New Jersey, which were significant contributions to the paleontology of the Atlantic coast, two were published by both the New Jersey and the U.S. Geological Surveys. Whitfield's published discussions of species variability and transmutation reflect the American neo-Lamarckian emphasis on environmental modifying influences and inheritance of acquired characters.

## NOTES

1. A controversy over coauthorship of an unsigned preliminary paper on New York Devonian bivalves, inevitably inferred to be by Hall, embittered Whitfield during his last years at Albany. See G. Arthur Cooper, "Concerning the Authorship of the Preliminary Notice of the Lamellibranch Shells of the Upper Helderberg, Hamilton and Chemung Groups, etc., Part 2," in *Journal of the Washington Academy of Sciences*, **21**, no. 18 (1931), 459–467.
2. Complaints in the student yearbook, *Transit*, and Rensselaer archival records suggest the position was essentially a sinecure for Hall. "WH-TF---D *alias* TRILOBITE. First differential coefficient of James H-ll, a function of the Ecozoic fossils . . ." appears in the April 1874 *Transit*. Whitfield is credited with formal service in 1877–1878 by Palmer C. Ricketts, *History of the Rensselaer Polytechnic Institute, 1824–1914* (New York–London, 1914), 228. Ricketts, then president of the Institute, as an undergraduate had coedited "the boisterously critical *Transit* of 1874." Samuel Rezneck, *Education for a Technological Society. A Sesquicentennial History of Rensselaer Polytechnic Institute* (Troy, N.Y., 1968), 176, 181.
3. Whitfield sold his own personal collection, including more than 100 type specimens, to the University of California at Berkeley in 1886; see Joseph H. Peck, Jr., and Herdis B.

McFarland, "Whitfield Collection Types at the University of California," in *Journal of Paleontology*, **28**, no. 3 (1954), 297–309, pl. 29.

*BIBLIOGRAPHY*

I. ORIGINAL WORKS. The James Hall Papers (KW 13835) in the Manuscripts and History Department, New York State Library, Albany, contain Whitfield's letters to Hall written between 1856 and 1893. Record Unit 33 and the uncatalogued collection of the Geology Department in the American Museum of Natural History Archives form the principal depository of Whitfield's correspondence during the 1896–1910 portion of his curatorship. John James Stevenson's letter to Fielding Bradford Meek of 10 October 1875 discusses Whitfield's search for a new position, as do Whitfield's letters to Meek, Fielding B. Meek Papers, Record Unit 7062, Smithsonian Institution Archives.

In addition to the bibliographies in the memorials by Gratacap and Clarke, 97 of Whitfield's 110 listed publications are cited in John M. Nickles, "Geologic Literature on North America 1785–1918," in *U.S. Geological Survey Bulletin* no. 746, pt. I (1923), 1103–1106. Three additional papers published before 1890 are among those noted in Nelson H. Darton, "Catalogue and Index of Contributions to North American Geology," *ibid.*, no. 127 (1896), 1010–1011.

II. SECONDARY LITERATURE. Articles on Whitfield are John M. Clarke, "Biographical Memoir of Robert Parr Whitfield," in *Bulletin of the Geological Society of America*, **22** (1911), 22–32, with bibliography by Louis Hussakof; Louis P. Gratacap, "Professor Robert Parr Whitfield," in *American Journal of Science*, 4th ser., **29** (1910), 565–566; and "Biographical Memoir of Robert Parr Whitfield," in *Annals of the New York Academy of Sciences*, **20** (1911), 385–398, with bibliography by Louis Hussakof; Edmund O. Hovey, "Robert Parr Whitfield," in *American Museum Journal*, **10** (1910), 119–121; Henry B. Nason, ed., *Biographical Record of the Officers and Graduates of the Rensselaer Polytechnic Institute, 1824–1886* (Troy, N.Y., 1887), 158–161; Chester A. Reeds, "Robert Parr Whitfield," in *Dictionary of American Biography*, XX (1936), 134–135; and the unsigned "Robert Parr Whitfield," in *National Cyclopaedia of American Biography*, V (1907), 92–93.

CLIFFORD M. NELSON

**WHITMAN, CHARLES OTIS** (*b.* North Woodstock, Maine, 14 December 1842; *d.* Chicago, Illinois, 6 December 1910), *zoology.*

Whitman grew up on a farm, where at an early age he became interested in natural history, particularly pigeons. He was exceptionally skilled as a self-taught taxidermist and built up quite a museum in his father's house. By tutoring and teaching in private schools he earned enough to enter Bowdoin College in 1865, receiving the B.A. in 1868. From 1868 to 1872 he was principal of Westford Academy in Massachusetts, and in 1872–1874 he taught at English High School in Boston. The latter post was of crucial importance for his career because it was in Boston that Whitman came under the influence of Louis Agassiz. As a result he was a participant in the first course in marine biology on Penikese Island, conducted by Agassiz in June and July 1873.

In 1875 Whitman went to Europe, first to Dohrn in Naples and then to Leuckart in Leipzig, where he learned the modern methods of microscopy and embryology. His Ph.D. dissertation (he received the degree in 1878) was on the embryology of *Clepsine* (*Glossiphonia*). In 1879 he went for two years to the Imperial University of Tokyo, as professor of zoology. Since eight of his students later became well-known zoologists, four of them holding major chairs, he has rightly been called the father of zoology in Japan. From November 1881 to May 1882, Whitman was again at the Zoological Station in Naples, working on the embryology, life history, and classification of the dicyemids, publishing a standard reference work on these mesozoans in 1883. One of the most productive periods in his life was the period 1882–1886, when he was assistant in zoology at the Museum of Comparative Zoology at Harvard, under Alexander Agassiz. From 1886 to 1889 Whitman served as director of the Allis Lake Laboratory at Milwaukee, Wisconsin, where he founded the *Journal of Morphology*, the first periodical in America devoted to zoology and anatomy. It served as a model for other publications founded in later years.

In 1889 Whitman accepted the chair of zoology at the newly founded Clark University in Worcester, Massachusetts, where he stayed until 1892. In that year he and most of his colleagues in the science departments moved to the newly established University of Chicago.

Whitman played a leading role in the founding of the Marine Biological Laboratory at Woods Hole in 1888 and served as its first director (1893–1908), developing the policies that have made this institution such a signal success. He resigned because his research on the heredity and behavior of pigeons was seriously impeded by his spending every summer at Woods Hole.

Being extremely unselfish, a person of complete integrity, and dedicated to science, Whitman played an important role as an organizer and first director of new institutions, and as the founder and first editor of new journals. Many of them are still flourishing, such as the Woods Hole Marine Biological Laboratory, the American Society of Zoologists (founded in 1890 as the American Morphological Society), *Journal of Morphology*, and *Biological Bulletin*.

Whitman's research was of unusual breadth. For instance, he became interested in leeches as material for embryological research; but he soon turned to the study of their anatomy and taxonomy, and finally of behavior, all of these interests resulting in publications. He found abundant evidence that the development of the leech egg was completely predetermined but—of course—not preformed in a homunculus-type way. He fought the extreme cell-lineage ("mosaic") interpretation, stressing the contribution to development made by the interaction of cells. Whitman's exceptionally careful work and perceptive interpretation had a profound impact on the embryology of his period. His discovery of the sensilla, segmental sense organs in the leeches, greatly facilitated the study of leech morphology and taxonomy.

When, after 1900, the great split occurred between evolutionists who ascribed evolutionary change to the pressure of a few major mutations and those who ascribed it to selection, Whitman was emphatically on the side of selection. He found numerous (now known to be polygenic) characters in his pigeon crosses that did not mendelize in the simple manner claimed by de Vries and Bateson. For more than ten years he bred pigeons, hybridizing 200 domestic varieties and 40 wild species. The results of his crosses are recorded in two posthumously published volumes (1919). Seeing the similarity of variation in related species and the unmistakable trends of evolutionary change from the most primitive to the most advanced species, Whitman developed a theory of orthogenetic evolution. At first held to be totally erroneous, it is now considered far less of a failure since it has been realized that the potential for variation in a phyletic line is very narrowly prescribed by the existing genotype. Whitman's emphasis was ahead of its time. Some of his studies dealt with the analysis of sexual dimorphism and led to Oscar Riddle's endocrinological research.

Whitman was one of the pioneers of ethology. His paper "Animal Behavior" (1898) contains many well-chosen examples of innate (nonlearned) behavior. In his later work he analyzed particularly the relation between innate and learned behavior and the ability of animals to adjust their behavior to new experiences. His posthumous "The Behavior of Pigeons" (1919) is an extraordinarily detailed analysis. In particular, courtship and breeding behaviors of some forty species are compared. With Oskar Heinroth's pioneering work on ducks (1911), it was the first extensive study in comparative ethology.

*BIBLIOGRAPHY*

I. ORIGINAL WORKS. A full bibliography of Whitman's contributions (67 titles) is given by Lillie (see below). The more important ones are "The Embryology of *Clepsine*," in *Quarterly Journal of Microscopical Science*, **18** (1878), 215–315; "A Contribution to the Embryology, Life History and Classification of the Dicyemids," in *Mitteilungen aus der Zoologischen Station zu Neapel*, **4** (1883), 1–89; "A Contribution to the History of the Germ Layers in *Clepsine*," in *Journal of Morphology*, **1** (1887), 105–182; "A Series of Lectures on Bonnet and the History of Epigenesis and Preformation," in *Biological Lectures. Marine Biological Laboratory, Woods Hole, Mass.* (1894), 205–272; "Animal Behavior," *ibid.* (1898), 285–338; and the posthumous works edited by Oscar Riddle (vols. I and II) and Harvey A. Carr (vol. III): "Orthogenetic Evolution in Pigeons," *Publications. Carnegie Institution of Washington*, no. 257 (1919), vol. I; "Inheritance, Fertility, and the Dominance of Sex and Color in Hybrids of Wild Species of Pigeons," *ibid.*, vol. II; and "The Behavior of Pigeons," *ibid.*, vol. III.

II. SECONDARY LITERATURE. Information on Whitman's life and work is in C. B. Davenport, "The Personality, Heredity and Work of Charles Otis Whitman," in *American Naturalist*, **51** (1917), 5–30; F. R. Lillie, "Charles Otis Whitman," in C. O. Whitman memorial volume, *Journal of Morphology*, **22** (1911), xv–lxxvii; and E. S. Morse, in *Biographical Memoirs. National Academy of Sciences*, **7** (1912), 269–288.

ERNST MAYR

**WHITNEY, JOSIAH DWIGHT** (*b.* Northampton, Massachusetts, 23 November 1819; *d.* Lake Sunapee, New Hampshire, 19 August 1896), *geology.*

Whitney was the oldest of the eight children of Josiah Dwight Whitney and Sarah Williston. His father, whose ancestors had come to Massachusetts in 1635, was a prosperous banker; his mother, the daughter of a minister, was a teacher. His parents placed a strong emphasis on education, and Whitney attended the Round Hill School founded at Northampton by George Bancroft and Joseph Green Cogswell, then Phillips Academy at Andover, Massachusetts, before entering Yale College in 1836. While at Yale he attended Benjamin Silliman's lectures on chemistry and Denison Olmsted's course on astronomy, which awakened his interest in science. Upon graduation in 1839, Whitney worked for a time on Charles T. Jackson's geological survey of New Hampshire, but it was a lecture on geology given in Boston by Sir Charles Lyell that determined him to be a scientist, and in May 1842 he left for Europe for advanced training. During the next five years he studied with Élie de Beaumont at the Paris École des Mines, with Karl F. Rammelsberg and Heinrich Rose in Berlin, and with Justus von Liebig in Giessen.

In May 1847 Whitney returned to the United States as a fully trained professional geologist, and was immediately employed by Jackson as an assistant in the latter's geological survey of Michigan. He remained with the survey for two years, then established himself as a mining consultant with an office first in Brookline, then in Cambridge, Massachusetts. He incorporated the experience that he gained into his *The Metallic Wealth of the United States*, published in 1854. This work was a milestone in the literature of ore deposits, and remained a standard text for two decades; one of the first systematic texts in the field, it stimulated serious research on mineral ores and helped to establish mining geology as a scientific discipline. The book enhanced Whitney's national reputation, and he was soon appointed professor of chemistry at the University of Iowa; during the same years, 1855 to 1858, he also served as a member of the Iowa state geological survey (under James Hall), the Illinois survey (under Amos H. Worthen), and (again with Hall) the Wisconsin survey. His work in Illinois dealt largely with zinc and lead deposits, while in Wisconsin he was primarily concerned with lead deposits alone.

Whitney was thus well suited to assume, in 1860, the directorship of the new California geological survey, which he served, intermittently, over the next fourteen years. He also participated in founding the California Academy of Sciences, the University of California, and Yosemite National Park. A number of the young scientists that he trained—including William H. Brewer, James G. Cooper, William M. Gabb, and Clarence King—later became famous, and one of the methods developed by Whitney's group for topographical mapping by triangulation was widely adopted.

In 1865 Whitney was granted a leave of absence from the California survey in order to assume an appointment as Sturgis-Hooper professor at Harvard College, where he was also to be responsible for establishing a school of mines. The school (which was later merged with the Lawrence Scientific School) opened in 1868, the same year in which the California geological survey was suspended after the state legislature refused to pass an appropriation for its continuation. Although Whitney remained as director of the nominal survey until 1874, only three volumes of its findings were published by the state; the Harvard Museum of Comparative Zoology aided him in publishing, in 1880, the important *The Auriferous Gravels of the Sierra Nevada of California*, and he himself brought out a volume of general geological observations in 1882.

Whitney returned to Cambridge permanently in 1875, and was reappointed to the Sturgis-Hooper professorship. He continued to teach at Harvard for the rest of his life, although his gruffness in the classroom and his cool, even unfriendly. personality limited his effectiveness as a teacher. His last major work, *Climatic Changes in Later Geological Times*, published in 1882, drew largely upon the researches he had conducted in the West.

Whitney was, perhaps, not so prominent a leader of American science as some of his contemporaries, and received fewer honors. He became a member of the American Philosophical Society and the National Academy of Sciences in 1865, and was later one of the few American foreign members of the Geological Society of London. Mt. Whitney, the highest point in the contiguous United States, is named in his honor. Whitney died at his summer retreat in New Hampshire; his wife, Louisa Goddard Howe, whom he had married in 1854, and his only child, a daughter, had both predeceased him in 1882.

## BIBLIOGRAPHY

I. ORIGINAL WORKS. Whitney's scientific publications include *Report of a Geological Survey of the Upper Missouri Lead Region* (Albany, 1862); *Earthquakes, Volcanoes, and Mountain Building* (Cambridge, Mass., 1871); *Geology and Geological Surveys* (Cambridge, Mass., 1875); *The Auriferous Gravels of the Sierra Nevada of California* (Cambridge, Mass., 1880); *The Climatic Changes of Later Geological Times; a Discussion Based on Observations Made in the Cordilleras of North America* (Cambridge, Mass., 1882); and *The Azoic System and its Proposed Subdivisions* (Cambridge, Mass., 1884), a contribution to classification.

The Whitney Family Manuscripts Collection at Yale University has nearly one thousand letters between Josiah Dwight Whitney and his brother William Dwight Whitney. The Josiah Dwight Whitney MSS at the Bancroft Library of the University of California contain more than six hundred letters to his close associate William H. Brewer, dealing with both scientific and personal matters. The William H. Brewer manuscripts at Yale University relate to Whitney's California years, as does a published account, *Up and Down California in 1860–1864: the Journal of William H. Brewer*, Francis P. Farquhar, ed. (New Haven, 1930).

II. SECONDARY LITERATURE. The fullest account is the somewhat uncritical Edwin T. Brewster, *Life and Letters of Josiah Dwight Whitney* (Boston, 1909). See also William H. Goetzman, *Exploration and Empire: the Explorer and the Scientist in the Winning of the American West* (New York, 1966), a fine survey of Whitney's activities in the West; George P. Merrill, *The First One Hundred Years of American Geology* (Washington, 1924); and Gerald T. White, *Scientists in Conflict: the Beginnings of the Oil Industry in California* (San Marino, 1968), which deals with the controversy between Whitney and Benjamin Silliman, Jr., over oil in California, and is unduly critical of Whitney. Gerald D. Nash, "The Conflict Between Pure and Applied Science in Nineteenth Century Public Policy: the California State Geological Survey, 1860–1874," in *Isis*, **64** (1963), 217–228, summarizes Whitney's career as director of the California Geological Survey.

GERALD D. NASH

**WHITTAKER, EDMUND TAYLOR** (*b.* Birkdale, Lancashire, England, 24 October 1873; *d.* Edinburgh, Scotland, 24 March 1956), *mathematics, physics, philosophy.*

Whittaker was educated at Manchester Grammar School and Trinity College, Cambridge. He was bracketed second wrangler in the mathematical tripos of 1895, was elected a fellow of Trinity College the following year, and was first Smith's prizeman in 1897. In 1905 he was elected a fellow of the Royal Society, and was awarded the Sylvester and Copley medals of the society in 1931 and 1954 respectively. In 1906 he became astronomer royal for Ireland and from 1912 until his retirement in 1946 was professor of mathematics at the University of Edinburgh. From 1939 to 1944 Whittaker was president of the Royal Society of Edinburgh, and was an honorary member of several learned societies. In 1935 Pope Pius XI conferred on him the cross *pro ecclesia et pontifice* and a year later appointed him to the Pontifical Academy of Sciences. In 1945 Whittaker was knighted and in 1949 became an honorary fellow of Trinity College, Cambridge.

In 1901 Whittaker married Mary Boyd, daughter of the Reverend Thomas Boyd of Cambridge; they had three sons and two daughters. The second son, J. M. Whittaker, became a mathematician and was vice-chancellor of the University of Sheffield. Whittaker's elder daughter married the mathematician E. T. Copson.

Whittaker's deepest interest was in fundamental mathematical physics, and consequently much of his earlier work was concerned with the theory of differential equations. Perhaps his most significant paper in this field was the one published in 1902 in which he obtained the most general solution of Laplace's equation in three dimensions, which is analytic about the origin, in the form

$$\int_0^{2\pi} f(x \cos x + y \sin \alpha + iz, \alpha)\, d\alpha$$

and the corresponding solution of the wave equation in the form

$$\int_0^{\pi}\int_0^{2\pi} f(x \sin \alpha \cos \beta + y \sin \alpha \sin \beta + z \cos \alpha + ct,$$
$$\alpha, \beta)\, d\alpha d\beta.$$

The discovery of the general integral representation of any harmonic function brought a new unity into potential theory; the integral representations of Legendre and Bessel functions, for example, were immediate consequences. Moreover, entirely new fields of research in the theory of Mathieu and Lamé functions were opened up. Whittaker also made a detailed study of the differential equation obtained from the hypergeometric equation by a confluence of two singularities, and he introduced the functions $W_{k,m}(z)$, which now bear his name. Another lifelong interest of Whittaker's was the theory of automorphic functions and the standard English book on the subject by L. R. Ford owes much to Whittaker. He also wrote a few papers on special problems in algebra and on numerical analysis.

Whittaker had an intense interest in the theory of relativity and from 1921 onward wrote ten papers on the subject. In one of the papers he gave a definition of spatial distance in curved space-time, which is both mathematically elegant and practical. In other papers he extended well-known formulas in electromagnetism to general relativity, gave a relativistic formulation of Gauss's theorem, and dealt with the relation between tensor calculus and spinor calculus.

Whittaker will long be read, since his textbooks on several diverse branches of mathematics have become classics. *Modern Analysis* (1902) was the first book in English to present the theory of functions of a complex variable at a level suitable for undergraduate and beginning graduate students. Forsyth's *Theory of Functions* had appeared in 1893, but its contents had not penetrated to the general body of mathematicians. *Modern Analysis* was extensively revised and enlarged in 1915 in collaboration with G. N. Watson, whose name was then added to the title page. Whittaker's *Analytical Dynamics*, which was published in 1904, was the first book to give a systematic account in English of the superbly beautiful theory that springs from Hamilton's equations; and it was of fundamental importance in the development of the quantum theory. Then, in 1910 there appeared *The History of the Theories of Aether and Electricity*. In 1951 a revised version of the book was published and constituted the first volume of a new treatise with the same title; it deals with the history up to the end of the nineteenth century. The second volume, which appeared in 1953, describes the developments made between 1900 and 1926 and is concerned mainly with relativity and quantum theory. The two volumes together form Whittaker's *magnum opus*. A contemplated third volume dealing with later theories was never completed.

Notwithstanding the excellence of *Aether and Electricity*, the chapter in the second volume dealing with the special theory of relativity has been criticized for the emphasis it places on the work of Lorentz and Poincaré, and for the consequent impression it gives that the work of Einstein was of minor importance. The consensus is that Whittaker made an error of judgment. As early as 1899 Poincaré had thought it possible that there might not be such a thing as absolute space, and in 1904 he had discussed without mathematics the possibility of a new mechanics in which mass would depend on velocity and in which the velocity of light would be an upper limit to all physically possible velocities. Also, Lorentz had derived the transformation that now bears his name before Einstein published his paper in 1905, but Lorentz interpreted it in terms of absolute space and time, concepts that, according to Born, he was still clinging to a few years before his death in 1928. Likewise, Poincaré seemed to regard the Lorentz transformation (which he discussed in a mathematically impressive paper in 1906) as physically important only because Maxwell's equations are invariant under it. It was Einstein (who had doubts about the ultimate validity of Maxwell's equations) who derived the transformation law from more fundamental physical principles.

Soon after his arrival at the University of Edinburgh, Whittaker instituted a mathematical laboratory and lectured on numerical analysis. His book *The Calculus of Observations*, written with G. Robinson, grew out of these lectures and was published in 1924. At that time very little of its content was to be found in any other book in English.

Although Whittaker expended a tremendous effort on advanced study and research, he regarded his undergraduate teaching as of paramount importance and, in addition to lecturing to the honors classes, he lectured once a week to the first-year class on the history and development of mathematics. He was an outstanding lecturer and by his dignified bearing, his great command of language, his eloquent delivery, and his obvious mastery of his subject, he made a tremendous impression upon young students. They knew at once that they were in the presence of a scholar and teacher of the first rank and in all his prelections they saw at work a mind of astonishing accuracy and force, ranging at will over the whole field of ancient and modern mathematics and presenting with insight and great persuasive power the profundities there disclosed.

Whittaker was a deeply religious man all through his life and, after having belonged to several branches of the Protestant faith—including the Church of Scotland, of which he was an elder—he was received into the Roman Catholic Church in 1930. After retiring from his chair at Edinburgh, Whittaker spent much of his time studying the philosophical aspects of modern physics and the repercussions that recent developments might have on theology. He expounded his views in *The Beginning and End of the World* (1942), *Space and Spirit* (1947), *From Euclid to Eddington* (1949), and in a large number of papers. He wrote from an orthodox Roman Catholic point of view with great emphasis on natural theology and the work of Thomas Aquinas. He deplored that in modern life "the sense of creatureliness and dependence has passed away, and God is left out of account." He was undoubtedly one of the few men of his time who could speak with authority on both physics and theology.

## BIBLIOGRAPHY

An extensive account of Whittaker's life and work is in the Whittaker Memorial Number of *Proceedings of the Edinburgh Mathematical Society*, **11**, pt. 1 (1958), 1–70, which includes a general biographical notice and articles by five contributors on different aspects of Whittaker's work. See also biographical notices by G. F. J. Temple, in *Biographical Memoirs of Fellows of the Royal Society*, **2** (1956), 299–325; and by W. H. McCrea, in *Journal of the London Mathematical Society*, **32** (1957), 234–256.

The question concerning the origin of the special theory of relativity is discussed by G. Holton, in *American Journal of Physics*, **28** (1960), 627–636; and M. Born, *The Born-Einstein Letters* (New York, 1971), 197–199.

DANIEL MARTIN

**WHYTLAW-GRAY, ROBERT** (*b.* London, England, 14 June 1877; *d.* Welwyn Garden City, Hertfordshire, England, 21 January 1958), *physical chemistry.*

Whytlaw-Gray designed and utilized precision techniques for weighing both aerosols and gases, notably radon. The second son of a prosperous Australian businessman, he was educated at Glasgow. From 1896 to 1903 he studied and conducted research under Ramsay and Morris W. Travers at University College, London, beginning a lifelong career in the exact manipulation of gases. In 1903 Gray went to Bonn to continue his redetermination of Stas's atomic weight of nitrogen; he obtained a value of 14.01 (O = 16), compared with the then current standard of 14.04 and with the more recent standard of 14.008. After obtaining the Ph.D. in 1906, he returned to University College, becoming assistant professor in 1908. In 1911 he incorporated the matronymic Whytlaw to his name, possibly to distinguish himself from a colleague, J. A. Gray.

From 1906 to 1914 Gray measured the physical constants of gases in order to determine their atomic weights. Collaborating with Ramsay in the 1910–1911 classic determinations of the density of niton (now called radon), Gray used a modified Steele-Grant microbalance to weigh the minute quantity available—less than 0.10 cubic mm. The new gravity balance, announced in 1909, was constructed of fused quartz having a counterpoised sealed quartz bulb containing a known quantity of air. Balance was effected by varying the external pressure within the case. Absolute weight as a function of buoyancy could be determined by the original instrument with an accuracy of $10^{-7}$ gram, the instrument being about 100 times more sensitive than the Nernst microbalance. In 1910 their experiments yielded an average atomic weight of 220 for radon; they modified this value to 223 on the basis of their 1911 results. By this means they had well estimated the correct order of magnitude.

On the theoretical side, following the then accepted atomic weight for radium of 226.5, Ramsay and Gray in 1910 suggested on genetic considerations the atomic weight of 222.5 for radon. Using the microbalance again the following year, they redetermined the atomic weight of radium to be 226.36, confirming the results of Curie, and derived thereby an independent check on their proposed atomic weight of 222.4 for radon. It was the value they expected (given their value for radium) if radon and helium were the only products of the disintegration of radium. However, after the official adoption in 1916 of 226.0 for radium, based, rather, upon the 1912 results of Hönigschmid, the value 222.0 was eventually assigned to radon.

From 1915 to 1922 Gray was science master at Eton. In 1917 he began a twenty-year series of confidential investigations concerning toxic and other smokes for the War Office. Gray further improved the design of the microbalance and used an ultramicroscope to count the number of smoke particles, determine their sizes, and study their lifetimes. He modified Smoluchowski's theory concerning the rate of coagulation of homogeneous sols so that it would apply rigorously to gaseous systems. He was also interested in the structure of the coagulating particles and examined the effects of electrification and photophoresis.

In October 1923 Gray succeeded Arthur Smithells at Leeds. While continuing government-supported research on aerosols, he resumed some of his investigations on the compressibilities and densities of simple gases. From 1939 to 1945 Gray led a government inquiry into defense against possible chemical warfare, in addition to serving on the International Committee on Atomic Weights. He retired pro forma in 1942, remaining in office until 1945 and at Leeds until 1950. He continued to improve the microbalance and extended his research to include complex organic gases and vapors. After a brief rest at Coventry, Gray, at seventy-five, resumed his research and consultation at Imperial Chemical Industries in Welwyn Garden City.

## BIBLIOGRAPHY

I. ORIGINAL WORKS. An almost complete list of Gray's nearly 100 papers and reports is part of the notice by E. G. Cox and J. Hume, in *Biographical Memoirs of Fellows of the Royal Society*, 4 (1958), 327–339. The best-known papers are the joint communications with Ramsay concerning the dramatic series of density determinations of radon: "La densité de l'émanation du radium," in *Comptes rendus . . . de l'Académie des sciences*, 151 (1910), 126–128; and "The Density of Ni-

ton ('Radium Emanation') and the Disintegration Theory," in *Proceedings of the Royal Society*, 84A (1911), 536–550. His work on aerosols is summarized in *Smoke: A Study of Aerial Disperse Systems* (London, 1932), written with H. S. Patterson.

II. SECONDARY LITERATURE. F. Challenger, who presented Gray for a degree *honoris causa* at Leeds in 1950, wrote a note in *Nature*, 181 (1958), 527; and R. S. Bradley wrote a detailed obituary notice in *Proceedings of the Chemical Society* (Jan. 1959), 18–20. There is also a brief, unsigned notice in *Chemistry and Industry* (1958), 134.

The original microbalance is described in B. D. Steele and K. Grant, "Sensitive Micro-Balances and a New Method of Weighing Minute Quantities," in *Proceedings of the Royal Society*, 82A (1909), 580–594; and W. A. Tilden and S. Glasstone, *Chemical Discovery and Invention* (London, 1936), 58–61. The designation "radon" was first suggested by C. Schmidt, in "Periodisches System und Genesis der Elemente," in *Zeitschrift für anorganische und allgemeine Chemie*, 103 (1918), 79–118. The value 235 for the atomic weight of radon was suggested by P. B. Perkins, in "A Determination of the Molecular Weight of Radium Emanation. . . ," in *American Journal of Science*, 4th ser., 25 (1908), 461–473, on the basis of diffusion evidence.

For a discussion of the nitrogen problem as it appeared at the time, see I. Freund, *The Study of Chemical Composition* (Cambridge, 1904; repr. New York, 1968), 313–316. A contemporary consideration of Gray's work on radon is in A. T. Cameron, *Radiochemistry* (London, 1910), *passim*; and W. Ramsay, *The Gases of the Atmosphere*, 4th ed. (London, 1915), 283–291. S. C. Lind, in "The Atomic Weight of Radium Emanation (Niton)," *Science*, 43 (1916), 464–465, argued on genetic considerations that radon should be assigned the atomic weight of 222.0 once 226.0 had been established for radium.

A general treatment of Gray's early work is included in the account by his brother-in-law, M. W. Travers, *A Life of Sir William Ramsay, K.C.B., F.R.S.* (London, 1956), *passim*.

THADDEUS J. TRENN

**WHYTT, ROBERT** (*b.* Edinburgh, Scotland, 6 September 1714; *d.* Edinburgh, 15 April 1766), *medicine, neurophysiology.*

Remarkably rational in an age in which reaction of a muscle to artificial nerve stimulus was considered magical, Robert Whytt (pronounced "White") was a practitioner of physic, teacher of medicine, and the foremost neurologist of his time. The first to demonstrate reflex action in the spinal cord, he also localized the site of a single reflex (Whytt's reflex), wrote the first important treatise on neurology after Thomas Willis, and gave the first clear description of tuberculous meningitis in children.

The second son of Robert Whytt, an advocate of Bennochy, and Jean Murray, of Woodend, Perthshire, Whytt was born six months after his father died; and his mother died when he was six years old. When he was fourteen, he succeeded to the family estate when his older brother died. After education in the public school at Kirkcaldy, in Fife, he went to St. Andrews University, where he received a degree in arts in 1730. For the next four years he studied medicine at the newly organized medical faculty of Edinburgh, which included Alexander Monro (Primus), Andrew St. Clair (Sinclair), John Rutherford, John Innes, and Andrew Plummer.

In 1734 Whytt went to London, where he studied under William Cheselden and walked the wards of the hospitals; from there he traveled to Paris and the wards of the Charité and Hôtel Dieu, also attending lectures and private dissections by Jacques Benigne Winslow, who condensed and simplified the study of anatomy. Finally, following Edinburgh tradition, he studied under the aged Hermann Boerhaave at Leiden, where he also had the advantages of anatomical instruction under Bernhard Siegfried Albinus. On his way home in 1736, Whytt tarried three days at Rheims to acquire the M.D. from the university after separate Latin examinations "for a considerable space," in anatomy, physiology, and the diagnosis and treatment of various diseases. After his return to Scotland, St. Andrews also awarded him an M.D. on 3 June 1737. Not quite three weeks later (21 June 1737) he became licentiate of the Royal College of Physicians of Edinburgh and set up practice as a physician. He was admitted a fellow of the College on 27 November 1737.

About this time Mrs. Joanna Stephens was stirring up public excitement with her well-publicized sovereign remedy for urinary bladder stones; and after enriching herself for several years, she offered to sell the secret of her nostrum for £5,000. Since it was enthusiastically endorsed by *Gentleman's Magazine*, a popular journal of the period, such highly regarded persons as Horace Walpole, dukes, earls, bishops, and even doctors of medicine offered to contribute to a fund to buy the secret; but not enough money was forthcoming. Parliament then appointed a commission that included such experts as Stephen Hales, William Cheselden, Caesar Hawkins, and other highly respected scientists; and upon their recommendation the government paid the sum asked in order that this medicine might be sold cheaply to the poor.

It was then revealed that the secret consisted of calcined egg and snail shells, with "alicant" soap. This finding induced Whytt to carry out elaborate experiments with limewater and soap, from which he concluded that this mixture had considerable power of disintegrating calculi *in vitro*; he thereupon tested courses of injections into the bladders of patients at the Royal Infirmary of Edinburgh suffering from the stone. His results were first published as "Essay on the Virtues of Lime-Water and Soap in the Cure of the Stone" (1743). This was followed by subsequent reports for nearly a score of years. An important result of this work on alkalies in the treatment of urinary calculi was that it led Joseph Black, then at Glasgow, to do his historic series of experiments on the chemistry of magnesia alba, quicklime, and other alkaline substances in search of a better solvent for stones. In 1754, in the course of that work, Black discovered the first known gas, "fixed air" (carbon dioxide). Soap was recommended as a lithontriptic, especially when dissolved in limewater, well into the latter half of the nineteenth century.

The rebellion of 1745 produced great confusion throughout Scotland, but by the winter of 1746–1747 affairs settled down and the medical faculty at Edinburgh was reorganized. Innes had died, and Whytt was elected to succeed him as professor of the institutes of medicine; and on 26 August 1747 he was elected professor of the practice of medicine, taking over the duties of John Rutherford, who thereafter devoted himself entirely to clinical lectures at the Royal Infirmary. Andrew Sinclair, in failing health, seems to have ceased lecturing entirely, Whytt having officiated for him at the university for some time before this; and Andrew Plummer, another member of the original medical faculty, devoted himself to teaching only chemistry. Whytt was associated with Alexander Monro and William Cullen at the Royal Infirmary, where he gave clinical lectures in 1760 and where he treated many of the patients upon whose clinical records he based much of his speculations and publications.

During his teaching career from 1747 to 1766, Whytt attracted throngs of students to his lecture theater. A practicing physician, he taught physiology in the modern spirit, lecturing in English instead of the customary Latin. One of the first doctors in Scotland to do research in the modern sense, he demonstrated his experiments to his classes and spent considerable time in experimental work on animals. Like his predecessors, Whytt at first used Boerhaave's *Institutiones medicae*, which dealt with physiology, as his textbook; but in 1762 he switched to *Institutiones pathologiae medicinalis* by Boerhaave's disciple Hieronymus David Gaubius (originally published in 1750), which was less limited in its approach.

In 1751 Whytt published *The Vital and Other Involuntary Motions of Animals*, a classic in neurophysiology, which attracted wide attention. After numerous vivisections he concluded that the capacity for muscle movement is preserved for some time after death. He referred to decapitated frogs and other animals moving in a coordinated manner—with some degree of intelligence, as it were— and concluded that the brain cannot be the only center of neurological activity. In 1649 Descartes had explained reflex action as exemplified in blinking of the eyelids on the sudden approach of an object; Robert Boyle had shown that a viper wriggles when pricked even several days after decapitation; and Stephen Hales had shown that destruction of the spinal cord prevents reflex action. The animistic system of Georg Ernst Stahl, based upon the premise that the soul is the *principium vitae*, was not abandoned until Albrecht von Haller convinced the scientific world with his arguments, backed by experimental demonstrations, concerning sensibility and irritability of parts of the human body in 1752. Whytt, however, was not yet able to divert his thinking of the soul as the basis of life and vitality so that he ascribed involuntary movement to the effect of a stimulus acting upon an unconscious "sentient principle." "By the sentient principle," he explained, "I understand the mind or soul in man, and that principle in brutes which resembles it."

Haller called Whytt a "semi-animist," but Whytt was actually opposed to the views of Stahl, Paracelsus, and others that there was a conscious soul in each living thing to direct its vitality and movement. Stahl and his followers looked upon the spinal cord as a simple conductor of nerve impulses; Whytt, however, demonstrated conclusively that centers for involuntary action could be located in "the brain of the spinal marrow." For the first time in the history of physiology, he presented a clear description of what Marshall Hall a century later called "reflex action." Whytt gave admirable accounts of various kinds of reflexes, even of what is now known as the "stretch reflex." He hypothesized the continuity of nerve fibers from the brain and the identity of separate nerve fibrils. Johann August Unzer, who first differentiated between voluntary and involuntary movements and who had experimented upon beheaded people in 1746, denied the intervention of any soul in reflex actions; and Haller, busily engaged in similar physiological pursuits, praised Whytt's book while criticizing it severely in a review published by the Royal Society of Sciences of Göttingen.

In 1753 in the *Commentaries* of this society Haller published his "De partibus corporis humani sensibilibus et irritabilibus," in which he laid down the principle that only certain parts of the body possess sensibility and contended that "irritability," or power of muscle contraction, was an innate property (*vis insita*) of muscle fibers independent of nervous influence and having no connection with sensation or stimulus. Haller had much greater practical experience than Whytt; but Whytt was a more brilliant philosopher, given to freer speculation and gifted with shrewd logic and extraordinary insight, so that his ideas served as the starting points for later physiologists.

Whytt subsequently published *Physiological Essays* (1755), consisting of "An Inquiry Into the Causes Which Promote the Circulation of the Fluids in the Very Small Vessels of Animals" and "Observations on the Sensibility and Irritability of the Parts of Men and Other Animals: Occasioned by M. de Haller's Late Treatise on These Subjects." The first essay concerned the peristaltic action of peripheral blood vessels, which assists the pumping action of the heart, a theory opposed by Haller and not generally accepted until capillary contractility was clearly demonstrated more than a century later. In the second essay Whytt contended that all muscle action was governed by nervous control. Admittedly uncertain about the minute structure of nerves, he nevertheless asserted that sensation, motion, and other functions are brought about through nervous connections between all parts of the body. This was long before Charles Bell (1811) and François Magendie (1822) proved the separate existence of sensory and motor nerve paths.

The dispute between Whytt and Haller attracted much attention on the Continent. By showing that lasting dilatation of the pupil could be due to compression of the optic thalamus, he was the first to localize a reflex (Whytt's reflex). He likewise showed that only a portion of the spinal cord suffices for reflex action. In addition he made the first attempts since Galen to localize the seat of reflex action.

*Observations on . . . Nervous, Hypochondriac or Hysteric Disorders* (1764) reveals great clinical acumen and provides vivid accounts of a wide range of neurological and psychiatric patients whom Whytt attended at the Royal Infirmary. He declared that disorders variously called flatulent, spasmodic, hypochondriac, hysteric, and, more recently, nervous, had become the wastebasket diagnosis for those conditions about which physicians were ignorant; and therefore he set out "to wipe off this reproach" and to throw some light on these ailments. He resorted to his previous work to explain the nature of these diseases, emphasizing the "sentient and sympathetic power of the nerves," and described instances of referred pain—anticipating, by his explanations of the causes, modern demonstrations of the reasons for them. Whytt clarified Thomas Willis' term "nervous," already in use for over 100 years, and explained such physical phenomena as blushing, lacrimation, and sweating, brought on by emotion or passion, as owing to some change made in the brain or nerves by the mind or sentient principle. This work added significant contributions to scientific medicine.

Through his *Observations on the Dropsy in the Brain*, published posthumously in 1768 by his son, Whytt achieved lasting remembrance in the history of pediatrics for the first clear description of tuberculous meningitis. It is a masterpiece of clinical observation, the finest first description of a disease to appear until then. Brief and lucid, the monograph is based upon about a dozen cases in which everything of clinical value that could be detected without modern laboratory apparatus is recorded. Monro's foramen, connecting the lateral and third ventricles of the brain, was first observed greatly dilated in one of the cases here described, which Monro (Secundus) and Whytt saw in 1764 during a consultation. Allusions to tuberculous meningitis before Whytt, usually included under a general heading of "phrenitis," generally went unnoticed. Whytt's description is a pediatric milestone that gave great impetus to the study of meningitis.

*The Works of Dr. Whytt* (1768) included papers on a range of subjects which indicate Whytt's versatility. These included "The Difference Between Respiration and Motion of the Heart, in Sleeping and Waking Persons," "Cure of Fractured *tendo achilles*," "Use of Bark in Dysenteries," "Hoarseness After Measles," and "Anomalous and True Gout."

In 1752, upon the recommendation of his friend and former classmate Sir John Pringle, Whytt was elected a fellow of the Royal Society of London. He was appointed physician to the king in Scotland in 1761 and, two years later, was elected president of the Royal College of Physicians of Edinburgh. His first wife was Helen Robertson, the sister of James Robertson, governor of New York. The two children of his first marriage died in infancy. Whytt's interest in colonial America was also enhanced by correspondence with Alexander Garden, Lionel Chalmers, John Moultrie, and John Lining, all living in Charleston, South Carolina, and all of Scottish extraction. His second wife, Louisa Balfour of Pilrig, Midlothian, whom he married in 1743, bore him fourteen children, of whom six survived.

Whytt was not of a robust constitution. He became ill in 1765 and died the next year of symptoms suggestive of diabetes. His grave, in Old Greyfriars Church, is marked by a handsome monument. When Whytt died, William Cullen vacated the chair of chemistry at Edinburgh in favor of Joseph Black, in order to succeed Whytt as professor of the theory of medicine.

### BIBLIOGRAPHY

I. Original Works. "Essay on the Virtues of Lime-Water and Soap in the Cure of the Stone," in *Observations and Essays in Medicine by a Society in Edinburgh*, **2**, pt. 2 (1743), followed by "An Essay Towards the Discovery of a Safe Method for Dissolving the Stone," in *Medical Essays and Observations Revised and Published by a Society in Edinburgh*, **5** (1744), 667–750, and **5**, pt. 2 (1747), 156–242, was a long tract attempting to develop a rational form of treatment for urinary calculus. *Essay on the Virtues of Lime-Water in the Cure of the Stone; With an Appendix, Containing the Case of The Right Honourable Horatio Walpole, Written by Himself* (Edinburgh, 1752; 2nd ed., 1755; 3rd ed., Edinburgh, 1761; Dublin, 1762), contains in the 3rd ed. a further account of the Walpole case, as well as that of the bishop of Llandaff; there was also a French trans. of the 2nd ed. by M. A. Roux (Paris, 1757).

*Essays and Observations, Physical and Literary, Read Before the Philosophical Society in Edinburgh*, **1** (1754), contains "Of the Difference Between Respiration and the Motion of the Heart, in Sleeping and Waking Persons" (436–446); "On the Various Strengths of Different Lime-Waters" (372–385); and "Of the Anthelmintic Virtues of the Root of the Indian Pink, Being Part of a Letter From Dr. John Lining, Physician at Charlestown, South Carolina, to Dr. Robert Whytt" (386–389). The same journal, **2** (1756), includes "Description of the Matrix or Ovary of the *Buccinum ampullatum*" (8–10), concerning the hermit crab in its shell; and "Some Experiments Made With Opium on Living and Dying Animals" (280–316).

These *Essays and Observations Physical and Literary* were republished in 3 vols. (Edinburgh, 1770–1771). Vol. I contains Whytt's essay on the strengh of different kinds of limewater, read to the Philosophical Society in Edinburgh in 1751 (240); the article by John Lining on Indian pink, addressed to Whytt (436); and the difference in respiration and pulse in people asleep and awake (492). Vol. II includes "The Description of a New Plant by Alexander Garden, Physician at Charleston in South Carolina," which described to Whytt the gardenia found in 1753 and in 1754 "about a mile from the Town of New York, in New England" (1–7); the opium experiments on animals (307–346); and "A Description of the American Yellow Fever in a Letter From Dr. John Lining, Physician at Charlestown in South Carolina, to Dr. Robert Whytt," dated 14 Dec. 1753 and read to the Society on 7 Mar. 1754 (404–432). In vol. III are a critique read to the Philosophical Society by Alexander Monro in 1761 concerning Whytt's opinions regarding the effects of opium on the nervous system of animals (299); "Use of the Bark in Dysenteries, and a Hoarseness After the Measles," read in Jan. 1761 (366–379); and observations (on *arthritis anomala*, or imperfect gout), in reference to a similar article on this subject by another author (466–470).

Other works are *An Essay on the Vital and Other Involuntary Motions of Animals* (Edinburgh, 1751; 2nd ed., 1763); and *Physiological Essays* (Edinburgh, 1755; repr. 1757; 2nd ed., 1759; repr. 1761; 1763; 3rd ed. 1766). The National Library of Medicine, Bethesda, Md., has a MS copy of Whytt's clinical lectures, transcribed by one of his students at Edinburgh in 1761.

*Observations on the Nature, Causes and Cure of Those Diseases Which are Commonly Called Nervous, Hypochondriac or Hysteric* (Edinburgh, 1764) is the first important English work on neurology. The 2nd ed., corrected, with the author's name spelled "Whyte" (Edinburgh, 1765), was entitled *Observations on the Nature, Causes and Cure of Those Disorders Which Have Been Commonly Called Nervous, Hypochondriac or Hysteric* and includes "Remarks on the Sympathy of the Nerves." The 3rd ed. is dated 1767, in which year a French trans. also appeared at Paris (2nd French ed., 1777); there also are a German ed. (Leipzig, 1766) and a Swedish ed. (Stockholm, 1786). Whytt's last separately and posthumously printed work was *Observations on the Dropsy in the Brain; to Which Are Added His Other Treatises Never Hitherto Published by Themselves* (Edinburgh, 1768).

A collected ed., *Works of Robert Whytt* (Edinburgh, 1768), also was issued by his son, who was assisted in collecting and editing the material by Sir John Pringle; a letter to Pringle dated 10 Nov. 1758, entitled "Account of an Epidemic Distemper at Edinburgh and Several Other Parts in the South of Scotland in the Autumn of 1758," is on 747–752. The collected *Works* was also translated into German as *Saemmtliche zur Practischen Arzneykunst Gehoerige Schriften* (Leipzig, 1771). It in-

cludes the research on limewater and soap in the cure of the stone, 1–238; "Nervous, Hypochondriac or Hysteric Disorders," 239–616; "Cure of a Paralysis by Electricity," 619–623; vesicatories in pulmonary congestion, 623–637 (addressed to the Royal Society in Feb. 1758 and published in the *Philosophical Transactions*, **50**, pt. 2 [1758], 569–578); the epidemic distemper of 1758, 637–646, read by Pringle to the Medical Society of London on 12 Feb. 1759; a work on the uses of the corrosive sublimate of quicksilver in the cure of phagadenic ulcers (in a letter to Pringle, 10 Jan. 1757, read 16 Feb. 1759 and published in *Medical Inquiries and Observations*, **2** [1762]) and additional case reports, 646–662; and "Observations on the Dropsy in the Brain," 662–696. The *Collected Works Relating to Theoretical Medicine* were translated by Johann Ephraim Lietzau as *Sämmtliche zur theoretischen Arzneikunst gehoerige Schriften* (Berlin–Stralsund, 1790) and included "Vital and Involuntary Motions in Animals," "Circulation of Fluids in the Small Vessels," "Sensibility and Irritability," and "Experiments With Opium on Living and Dying Animals."

II. SECONDARY LITERATURE. See Rachel Mary Barclay, *The Life and Work of Robert Whytt, M.D.* (Edinburgh, 1922), M.D. diss.; Alexander Bower, *History of the University of Edinburgh*, II (Edinburgh, 1817), 345, 355; Charles W. Burr, "Robert Whytt," in *Medical Life*, **36** (1929), 109; John D. Comrie, "An Eighteenth Century Neurologist," in *Edinburgh Medical Journal*, n.s. **32** (1925), 755; and *History of Scottish Medicine*, 2nd ed., I (London, 1932), 306; *Documents and Dates of Modern Discoveries in the Nervous System* (London, 1839), 112, 152, 162, 203, which reprints excerpts from Whytt's writings; Roger K. French, *Robert Whytt, the Soul, and Medicine*, Publications of the Wellcome Institute, Historical Monograph ser., no. 17 (London, 1969); John F. Fulton, *Muscular Contraction and the Reflex Control of Movement* (Baltimore, 1926), 32; and *History of Physiology* (London, 1931), 43, 90; Fielding H. Garrison, *History of Medicine*, 4th ed. (Philadelphia, 1929), 326; and Alexander Grant, *Story of the University of Edinburgh*, II (London–Edinburgh, 1884), 401.

See also Heinz Hürzeler, *Robert Whytt (1716–1766) und seine physiologischen Schriften* (Zurich, 1973); Max Neuburger, *Die historische Entwicklung der experimentellen Gehirn- und Rückenmark-Physiologie* (Stuttgart, 1897), 122, 174–192; John Ruräh, *Pediatrics of the Past* (New York, 1925), 401; William Seller, "Memoir of the Life and Writings of Robert Whytt," in *Transactions of the Royal Society of Edinburgh*, **23** (1861–1862), 99–131; George Frederic Still, *History of Paediatrics*, repr. ed. (New York, 1965), 443; G. Stronach, in *Dictionary of National Biography*; John Thomson, *Life of William Cullen*, I (Edinburgh, 1859), 241–258, which presents an extensive evaluation of Whytt; Ilza Veith, *Hysteria: The History of a Disease* (Chicago–London, 1965), 159; and Joseph I. Waring, *History of Medicine in South Carolina 1670–1825*

(Charleston, 1964), 57 and *passim*, which discusses Whytt's relationships with physicians in Charleston and includes excerpts from John Lining's account of yellow fever.

SAMUEL X. RADBILL

**WICKERSHEIMER, ERNEST** (*b*. Bar-le-Duc, France, 12 July 1880; *d*. Strasbourg, France, 6 August 1965), *history of medicine.*

Wickersheimer's father, of Alsatian origin, was a military physician who had studied at the Strasbourg Faculty of Medicine and at the École du Service de Santé Militaire. Wickersheimer himself studied medicine at Paris, becoming *externe des hôpitaux* in 1899. Quickly drawn to the history of medicine, he defended a doctoral dissertation in this field, *La médecine et les médecins en France à l'époque de la Renaissance* (1905), which established his reputation. (It was cited as early as 1915 in the second edition of J. L. Pagel's *Einführung in die Geschichte der Medizin*.) This early work contained the outline of the research that occupied more than sixty years of a highly productive life in science.

Wickersheimer's dissertation oriented him toward both aspects of his career, for he became a librarian as well as a historian. In 1906 he began his training at the library of the Paris Faculty of Medicine, and the following year he spent six months at the University of Jena. At about the same time he studied under Karl Sudhoff at Leipzig. Wickersheimer furthered his training by working as a librarian at the Sorbonne in 1909, and in 1910 he was named librarian of the Académie de Médecine. Also in 1910 he made his first trip to the United States, where he established contacts with American libraries and formed close relationships with American colleagues. During World War I he served as a military physician.

From 1920 to 1950 Wickersheimer was administrator of the Bibliothèque Universitaire et Régionale de Strasbourg, which became the Bibliothèque Nationale et Universitaire in 1926. He reorganized it in 1919, upon the return of Alsace to France, and in 1945, after World War II. In the latter year the medical division of the library was in a particularly poor state, having been almost totally destroyed in a fire.

Despite his very heavy responsibilities, in 1920 Wickersheimer again took up his historical research. In 1936 he published *Dictionnaire biographique des médecins en France au Moyen-Âge,* an authoritative book on which he continued to work throughout his life. An impressive bibliography of 230 items (which is incomplete, since it stops in 1961), published on the occasion of his scientific jubilee, shows the abundance and variety of the subjects Wickersheimer treated: medicine in the Middle Ages and in the Renaissance, notably at the school of Salerno; medicine in society; medical schools; the teaching of surgery; medical doctrines; hospitals; and therapy—in brief, almost all aspects of the profession. He also made an inventory of the Latin books of the High Middle Ages in French libraries. A distinguished local historian as well, he studied various details relating to the hospitals of Strasbourg.

Wickersheimer received many honors. Elected an officer of the Legion of Honor in 1948, he had earlier received the Croix de Guerre 1914–1918 and was also an officer of public instruction and commander of the Order of Carlos Finlay (Republic of Cuba, 1928). He was awarded the silver medal of the Paris Faculty of Medicine for his dissertation in 1905 and was granted an honorary M.D. by the Johann Wolfgang Goethe University at Frankfurt am Main on 12 July 1960. Posthumously he was awarded a prize by the Académie de Médecine for the body of his work on the history of medicine (see *Bulletin de l'Académie de médecine,* **149** [1965], 784).

A secretary or member of numerous French and foreign learned societies, Wickersheimer served as perpetual secretary of the Académie Internationale d'Histoire des Sciences and honorary president of the Académie Internationale d'Histoire de la Médecine and of the Société Française d'Histoire de la Médecine.

*BIBLIOGRAPHY*

I. ORIGINAL WORKS. Very extensive, but not complete, bibliographies of Wickersheimer's writings are in "Jubilé scientifique du Dr. Wickersheimer," in *Histoire de la médecine,* spec. no. 1960 (1961), 102–109; and in M. T. d'Alverny, "Travaux du Dr. E. Wickersheimer," in E. Wickersheimer, *Les manuscrits latins de médecine du haut Moyen-Âge dans les bibliothèques de France* (Paris, 1966), 236–248.

II. SECONDARY LITERATURE. See M. T. d'Alverny, "L'oeuvre scientifique du Dr. E. Wickersheimer," in *Humanisme actif, mélanges d'art et de littérature offerts à Julien Cain,* II (Paris, 1968), 299–307; "Jubilé scientifique du Dr. Wickersheimer" (see above), 89–109; and M. Klein, "Le Dr. E. Wickersheimer," in *Clio medica,* **1** (1966), 351–356.

Many French and foreign journals published obituaries of Wickersheimer. The Bibliothèque Nationale et

Universitaire of Strasbourg has, in its Alsatian division, numerous documents written by or pertaining to Wickersheimer.

MARC KLEIN

**WIDMAN** (or **WEIDEMAN** or **WIDEMAN**), **JOHANNES** (*b*. Eger, Bohemia [now Czechoslovakia], *ca*. 1462; *d*. Leipzig, Germany, after 1498), *mathematics*.

The little known about Widman's life is based on the records of the University of Leipzig. He was entered in the matriculation register in 1480 as "Iohannes Weideman de Egra."[1] He received the bachelor's degree in 1482 and the master's degree in 1485.[2] He then lectured on the fundamentals of arithmetic, on computation on lines, and on algebra, as can be seen from the announcements for and invitations to his courses.[3] Widman's algebra lecture of 1486, the first given in Germany, is preserved in a student's notebook.[4] In this lecture he discussed the twenty-four types of equations generally treated by the Cossists and illustrated them with many problems. He employed the Cossist signs for the powers of the unknowns, as well as symbols for plus, minus, and the root.[5] As Widman explicitly stated elsewhere,[6] he considered computation with irrational numbers and polynomials (*De additis et diminutis*) to be part of the subject matter of algebra. He also treated fractions and proportions in order to prepare his students for the study of algebra.

The work for which Widman is best known, *Behend und hüpsch Rechnung uff allen Kauffmanschafften*, appeared in 1489. After the Trent *Algorismus* (1475) and the Bamberg arithmetic books (1482, 1483), it was the first printed arithmetic book in German; and it far surpassed its predecessors in the scope and number of its examples.[7] It also was notable for containing the first appearance in print of the plus and minus signs. Widman dedicated the book to Sigismund Altmann of Schmidtmühlen, who also enrolled at Leipzig in 1480.[8] There are no direct reports of Widman's activities after 1489; his brief mathematical works that were printed later appeared anonymously and without date of publication. Yet, according to Conrad Wimpina, Widman was still working on mathematical topics in 1498.

Widman's knowledge of arithmetic was based on the *Algorismus Ratisbonensis* and the Bamberg arithmetic book of 1483, as can be seen by comparing the problems treated in these works with those in his own. His arithmetic book of 1489 went through several editions until 1526,[9] when it was superseded by those of Köbel, Adam Ries, and others.

Widman learned algebra primarily from a volume of manuscripts he owned (now known as Codex Dresdensis C 80)[10] that later came into the possession of Georg Sturtz of Erfurt, who about 1523 placed it at the disposition of Ries. A compilation of all that was then known about arithmetic and algebra, the volume contained, in particular, a German algebra of 1471 and one in Latin.[11] The Latin algebra, in the margins of which Widman entered further examples of the twenty-four types of equations, was the basis of his algebra lecture of 1486.[12] The lecture also is partially preserved in another Dresden manuscript (C 80^m) and in manuscripts from Munich and Vienna.[13] This manuscript (C 80) was also the source of Widman's writings that were printed at Leipzig about 1495.[14] Ries borrowed problems for his *Coss* from Widman's algebra, but he was not aware of the author's identity.[15] Following the appearance of printed works on algebra by Grammateus, Rudolff, and Stifel at the beginning of the sixteenth century, Widman's writings fell into neglect.

### NOTES

1. See G. Erler, *Die Matrikel der Universität Leipzig*, I, 323. Widman was a member of the Natio Bavarorum.
2. *Ibid.*, II, 228, 289. Master Widman was allowed to live outside the dormitory (*petivit dimissionem burse et obtinuit*).
3. See W. Kaunzner, "Über Johannes Widmann von Eger," 1 f., 45; and E. Wappler, "Zur Geschichte der deutschen Algebra im 15. Jahrhundert," 9 f.; and "Beitrag zur Geschichte der Mathematik," 149, 167.
4. The fee for the lecture was 42 groschen (2 florins). See Kaunzner, *op. cit.*, 45.
5. On the root symbol see Wappler, "Zur Geschichte der deutschen Algebra im 15. Jahrhundert," 13. On the earliest use of the minus sign see Kaunzner, "Deutsche Mathematiker des 15. und 16. Jahrhunderts und ihre Symbolik," 22 f.
6. In Codex Lipsiensis 1470, fol. 432. On this point see Kaunzner, "Über Johannes Widmann von Eger," 41, 92 f.
7. Widman did not use line reckoning; he did, however, present a thorough treatment of proportions using the traditional terminology.
8. He was *Dr. utriusque juris* and rector in 1504.
9. See D. E. Smith, *Rara arithmetica*, 36 f.
10. Widman knew the Regensburg algebra of 1461, and he took certain problems from it (*Regula dele cose super quartum capitulum*). On this point see M. Curtze, in *Abhandlungen zur Geschichte der Mathematik*, 7 (1895), 72; and Wappler, "Zur Geschichte der deutschen Algebra," 540.
11. A description of Codex Dresdensis C 80 is in Kaunzner, "Über Johannes Widmann von Eger," 27–39.
12. See Codex Lipsiensis 1470, fols. 479–493. On this point see Kaunzner, "Über . . . Widmann . . . ," 45.

13. See Kaunzner, "Deutsche Mathematiker des 15. und 16. Jahrhunderts und ihre Symbolik," 21.
14. Wappler, "Beitrag zur Geschichte der Mathematik," 167, proposes 1490 as the year of publication. All six treatises have the same format, the same type, and the same size pages and length of lines. They all appeared anonymously, without date and, with one exception (Leipzig), without city. Wimpina (b. 1460; enrolled at Leipzig in 1479) enumerated all these works except *Regula falsi*; at the time he made his list the works were commercially available.
15. They are problems that Widman had entered in the margins of Codex Dresdensis C 80. See Wappler, "Zur Geschichte der deutschen Algebra," 541 ff.

## BIBLIOGRAPHY

I. ORIGINAL WORKS. Widman's *Behend und hüpsch Rechnung uff allen Kauffmanschafften* appeared at Leipzig in 1489. The rest of his works, published anonymously and without city or date, are *Algorithmus integrorum cum probis annexis*; *Algorithmus linealis*; *Algorithmus minutiarum phisicarum; Algorithmus minutiarum vulgarium; Regula falsi apud philozophantes augmenti et decrementi appellata;* and *Tractatus proportionum plusquam aureus.* On these latter works, see Klebs (below), 35, 36, 281, 324; Wimpina (below), 50; and Wappler, "Beitrag zur Geschichte der Mathematik" (below).

II. SECONDARY LITERATURE. See M. Cantor, *Vorlesungen zur Geschichte der Mathematik*, 2nd ed., II (Leipzig; 1913), 228 ff.; M. W. Drobisch, *De Ioanni Widmanni Egeriani compendio arithmeticae mercatorum* (Leipzig; 1840); G. Erler, *Die Matrikel der Universität Leipzig*, 3 vols. (Leipzig, 1895–1902), I, 323; II, 228, 289; W. Kaunzner, "Über Johannes Widmann von Eger. Ein Beitrag zur Geschichte der Rechenkunst im ausgehenden Mittelalter," *Veröffentlichungen des Forschungsinstituts des Deutschen Museums für die Geschichte der Naturwissenschaften und der Technik*, ser. C., no. 4 (1968); and "Deutsche Mathematiker des 15. und 16. Jahrhunderts und ihre Symbolik," *ibid.*, ser. A, no. 90 (1971); A. C. Klebs, "Incunabula scientifica et medica," in *Osiris*, **4** (1938), 1–359; D. E. Smith, *Rara arithmetica* (Boston–London, 1908), 36, 40, 44; E. Wappler, "Zur Geschichte der deutschen Algebra im 15. Jahrhundert," in *Programm Gymnasium Zwickau* (1887), 1–32; "Beitrag zur Geschichte der Mathematik," in *Abhandlungen zur Geschichte der Mathematik*, **5** (1890), 147–169; and "Zur Geschichte der deutschen Algebra," *ibid.*, **9** (1899), 537–554; and C. Wimpina, *Scriptorum insignium, qui in celeberrimis praesertim Lipsiensi, Wittenbergensi, Francofurdiana ad Viadrum academiis, a fundatione ipsarum usque ad annum Christi MDXV floruerunt centuria, quondam ab J. J. Madero Hannoverano edita, ex mspto autographo emendata, completa, annotationibusque brevibus ornata*, J. F. T. Merzdorf, ed. (Leipzig, 1839), 50 f.

KURT VOGEL

**WIDMANNSTÄTTEN** (or **WIDMANSTETTER**), **ALOYS JOSEPH BECK EDLER VON** (b. Graz, Austria, 13 July 1754; d. Vienna, Austria, 10 June 1849), *mineralogy.*

Widmannstätten succeeded his father, Johann Andreas, in the printing trade in 1764. From 1650 the family had enjoyed the exclusive privilege of printing for the province of Steiermark. In 1784, however, they were deprived of this monopoly as a consequence of the introduction of the freedom of the press. Widmannstätten then lost interest in his concern, leased it, and sold it in 1807 to his chief competitor in Graz. He nevertheless maintained an active role in the technical arts, and was often consulted because of his experience. In 1807 Widmannstätten became a director of Emperor Francis I's private technology collection in Vienna. He made several journeys (some on government order) to Germany, France (1815), England (1816), and Italy. For these activities Widmannstätten became a member of the Société d'Encouragement pour l'Industrie Nationale, and in 1817 he was granted a pension.

The "Widmannstätten figures" named after him were discovered by Widmannstätten in 1808 in an iron meteorite from Zagreb. By etching polished sawing planes with diluted nitric acid, he showed a regular pattern of slightly affected intersecting bands, between narrow frames, and angular fields, which were deepened by the acid. The pattern of bands, which is repeated on a small scale by the interstices, corresponds to the traces of octahedral planes in the etched section. Chemically the frames are enriched in nickel. The rugged interstices, having a higher iron content than the bands, constitute fine lamellar aggregates of nickel-poor and nickel-rich phases. Widmannstätten later distinguished these patterns in meteorites from Mexico (1810), Elbogen (now Loket, Czechoslovakia; 1812), and Lénarto (1815).

In 1813 Widmannstätten decided to make direct imprints of such etched surfaces with printer's ink and to publish them. But it was not until 1820 that Carl von Schreibers, at whose institute Widmannstätten made his investigations, published the prints.

## BIBLIOGRAPHY

Widmannstätten published no writings.
Biographies are J. K. Hofrichter, "Alois Beck von Widmannstätten," in *Mittheilungen des historischen Ve-*

*reins für Steiermark*, **2** (1851), 144–150; and C. Wurzbach, in *Biografisches Lexicon für Oesterreich*, LV (Vienna, 1887), 258–261.

Descriptions of Widmannstätten figures are in W. Haidinger, "Bemerkungen über die zuweilen im geschmeidigen Eisen entstandene krystallinische Structur, verglichen mit jener des Meteoreisens," in *Sitzungsberichte der Wiener Akademie der Wissenschaften*, math.-naturwiss. Cl., **15** (1855), 354–361; C. von Schreibers, *Beyträge zur Geschichte und Kenntniss meteorischer Stein- und Metall-Massen* (Vienna, 1820), 70–73, with one print of Widmannstätten figures; R. Vogel, "Physikalisch-Chemisches über Meteoreisen," in C. A. Doelter, *Handbuch der Mineralchemie*, III, pt. 2, C. Doelter and H. Leitmeier, eds. (Dresden–Leipzig, 1926), 566–567.

JOYCE WEVERS

**WIECHERT, EMIL** (*b.* Tilsit, Germany, 26 December 1861; *d.* Göttingen, Germany, 19 March 1928), *physics, geophysics.*

Wiechert was the only son of Johann Christian Wiechert, a merchant who died when his son was very young. His mother devoted herself to providing for Wiechert's education and moved with him to Königsberg. Wiechert never left her until she died in 1927, although he married the daughter of a Göttingen lawyer named Ziebart in 1908.

Wiechert graduated in physics from Königsberg University in 1889 and became a lecturer in physics there in 1890. During the following seven years he carried out research on the atomic structure of electricity and matter. In 1897 he was appointed to the University of Göttingen and became the founder of one of the world's most famous schools of geophysics. From 1897 to 1914 some of the most far-reaching results concerning the internal structure of the earth emerged from the work of Wiechert and his pupils, who included B. Gutenberg, K. Zöppritz, L. Geiger, and G. Angenheister.

When Wiechert took up his appointment at Göttingen, seismology was beginning to develop as a quantitative science. In 1892 John Milne had produced the first seismograph capable of providing global coverage of ground motions resulting from large earthquakes. Following a study trip to Italy in 1899 Wiechert decided that he could greatly improve the seismographs then in use, and by 1900 he had produced his famous inverted-pendulum seismograph and had worked out its theory. This instrument was radically different in design from all previous seismographs and consisted essentially of a heavy mass (up to several tons in some versions) that can oscillate about a pivot be-

low it, the mass being held near the equilibrium position by the pressure of thin springs at the top. The records which were made on smoked paper were outstandingly clear and gave a far closer representation of the ground motion than any previous seismographs had done. Wiechert's first seismograph recorded horizontal components of the motion, but he later designed instruments to measure vertical components as well. Wiechert seismographs are still used in some of the world's observatories and continue to supply valuable information.

The Göttingen school of geophysics produced much important work under Wiechert's leadership including the early tables prepared by Zöppritz that gave the travel times of earthquake waves through the interior of the earth, and Gutenberg's calculation giving the value of 2,900 kilometers for the depth of the earth's core. Wiechert himself had contributed to the mathematical theory underlying these calculations and, with Gustav Herglotz, he evolved the basic mathematical process whereby the velocities of seismic waves deep in the interior of the earth can be derived from the travel-time tables. Wiechert had, moreover, been one of the first to suggest the presence of a dense core in the earth and had produced the first theoretical model of the planet that allowed for it.

Wiechert played an important part in the world organization of seismology as one of a small group responsible for founding the International Association of Seismology in 1905, an organization that still flourishes. He also set up geophysical observational centers in the German colonies before World War I, a network that contributed vitally to the early development of seismology.

In addition to his work on seismology, Wiechert contributed to other branches of geophysics, particularly atmospheric electricity. Under his direction various methods were developed for measuring potential gradients and conductivity in the atmosphere.

When World War I came, Wiechert turned his attention to the transmission of sound waves through the atmosphere, applying his knowledge of earthquake theory to observations of sound waves with a view to determining features of the stratification of the atmosphere. He also began investigating the fine structure of the crust of the earth, using specially designed portable seismographs to record waves from artificial explosions. In this research he was one of the pioneers of geophysical prospecting by seismic methods.

Wiechert carried out his work with indefatigable energy and tenacity despite extreme deafness in his later years and the shadow of a serious illness, to which he succumbed at the age of sixty-six.

*BIBLIOGRAPHY*

Wiechert's most important publications are "Theorie der automatischen Seismographen," in *Abhandlungen der K. Gesellschaft der Wissenschaften zu Göttingen*, Math.-phys. Kl., n.s. **2**, no. 1 (1903), 1; "Über Erdbebenwellen I, II," in *Nachrichten von der Gesellschaft der Wissenschaften zu Göttingen*, Math.-phys. Kl. (1907), 415–549, written with K. Zöppritz; "Our Present Knowledge of the Earth," in *Report of the Board of Regents of the Smithsonian Institution* (1908), 431–449; and "Bestimmung des Weges der Erdbebenwellen im Erdinneren," in *Physikalische Zeitschrift*, **11** (1910), 294–311, written with L. Geiger.

An account of Wiechert's life and scientific work is in "Zum Gedenken Emil Wiecherts anlässlich der 100. Wiederkehr seines Geburtstages," in *Veröffentlichungen des Institutes für Bodendynamik und Erdbebenforschung in Jena*, no. 72 (1962), 5–21, which includes a full list of Wiechert's publications.

K. E. Bullen

**WIED, MAXIMILIAN ZU** (*b.* Neuwied, Germany, 23 September 1782; *d.* Neuwied, 3 February 1867), *natural history, ethnology.*

Alexander Philip Maximilian, prince of Wied-Neuwied, was the eighth child and second son of Prince Friedrich Karl, the ruler of a small principality near Koblenz in Rhenish Prussia. His mother encouraged his interest in natural history when he was a youth, and in later years he became a student of Johann Friedrich Blumenbach, from whom derived Wied's interest in studying man as an object of natural history.

Wied had planned to visit America in 1803, but the political and military confusion of the Napoleonic era prevented the trip. He served with the Prussian army at the battle of Jena, during which he was captured by the French. He was exchanged and returned to Neuwied. Resuming military service, he rose to the rank of major general and was with the allied army when it entered Paris in 1814.

As soon as possible after the cessation of hostilities, Wied retired from active military service and began to pursue the study of natural history. With the United States in the process of recovering from the War of 1812, he postponed his trip there and sailed instead for South America. His two-year journey along the coast of Brazil enabled him to observe the primitive Indian tribes of the Brazilian forests and to record the manners and life styles of the Purí, Botocudos, Patachos, and Camacans. In his journals Wied noted the distinctive native flora and fauna of the region between Rio de Janiero and Bahía. After returning to Germany, he arranged his collections and prepared his notes for publication: *Reise nach Brasilien in den Jahren 1815 bis 1817* (1820–1821). This work, soon translated into Dutch, French, and English, established his reputation as a naturalist.

In 1832 Wied sailed for the United States, intending to compare the Indians of South America with those of North America and to journey as far west as the Rocky Mountains in order to examine the flora, fauna, and aboriginal peoples of the trans-Mississippi area. He was accompanied on this trip by the young Swiss artist Karl Bodmer, who had been hired by Wied to illustrate his scientific journals. After spending some time in Boston, New York, and Philadelphia, Wied crossed the Appalachian Mountains and wintered at New Harmony, Indiana, where he met Thomas Say, Charles Alexandre Lesueur, and William and Robert Dale Owen.

In the spring of 1833, Wied received the support of the American Fur Company and was allowed to travel up the Missouri River on their steamers. At Fort McKenzie, below the great falls of the Missouri, he began his investigation of Indian life, collecting data about Indian languages; he later published vocabularies for the Arikaras, Assiniboine, Blackfoot, Cheyenne, Crow, Mandan, and Sioux tribes. Besides studying Indian life, Wied collected plant and animal specimens. With the approach of winter, he returned to Fort Clark on the Missouri, where he remained until the spring of 1834, making an intensive study of the Mandans. Wied's studies of the Indians of the upper Missouri are characterized by a sincere attempt to portray them not as savages but as civilized individuals with acquired skills and mores ideally suited for life in a wilderness. His detailed ethnographical description of these tribes assumes additional importance when it is noted that the smallpox epidemic of 1837–1838 destroyed several of these tribes and substantially reduced the populations of others.

Wied returned to Europe in the summer of 1834. Although many of the animal and plant specimens that he had laboriously collected were lost in a river accident, he published a meticulously edited and handsomely illustrated account of his travels in the American West in his *Reise in das innere Nord-America in den Jahren 1832 bis 1834.*

The rest of Wied's life was devoted to cataloging and studying the specimens he had collected on his trips to North and South America. His primary contribution to science was his detailed ethnographical descriptions of the native tribes of Brazil and the upper Missouri, for he sensitively recorded a way of life that was soon to disappear. His zoological collections were purchased by the American Museum of Natural History. In the field Wied was a skilled observer who carefully recorded the dimensions and habitat of the flora and fauna he collected. Nevertheless, his ethnographical observations are the more valuable aspect of his work.

*BIBLIOGRAPHY*

I. ORIGINAL WORKS. Wied's account of his trip to Brazil is in *Reise nach Brasilien in den Jahren 1815 bis 1817,* 2 vols. (Frankfurt, 1820–1821), and *Beiträge zur Naturgeschichte von Brasiliens,* 4 vols. in 6 (Weimar, 1825–1833). His account of his American tour, with beautiful plates by Karl Bodmer, is in *Reise in das innere Nord-America in den Jahren 1832 bis 1834,* 2 vols. and atlas (Koblenz, 1839–1841). An English trans. of this work was published in Reuben Gold Thwaites' *Early Western Travels 1748–1846,* XXII–XXV (Cleveland, 1906). Wied's scientific papers are listed in Royal Society *Catalogue of Scientific Papers,* VI, 357–358, and VIII, 1235. The Joslyn Art Museum in Omaha, Nebraska, has a collection of Wied papers that includes MS diaries, correspondence, a scientific journal, and the originals of many of Bodmer's paintings.

II. SECONDARY LITERATURE. There is no definitive study of Wied's life and work. For general surveys of his life, see Vernon Bailey, "Maximilian's Travels in the Interior of North America, 1832 to 1834," in *Natural History,* **23,** no. 4 (July–Aug. 1923), 337–343; the very popular account in Bernard DeVoto, *Across the Wide Missouri* (New York, 1947), 133–146; and Joseph Röder, "The Prince and the Painter," in *Natural History,* **64,** no. 6 (June 1955), 326–329. For a more detailed account consult Philipp Wirtgen, *Zum Andenken an Prinz Maximilian zu Wied, sein Leben und wissenschaftliche Thätigkeit* (Neuwied–Leipzig, 1867); and *Allgemeine deutsche Biographie,* XXIII (1886), 559–564.

PHILLIP DRENNON THOMAS

**WIEDEMANN, GUSTAV HEINRICH** (*b.* Berlin, Germany, 2 October 1826; *d.* Leipzig, Germany, 23 March 1899), *physics, physical chemistry.*

Wiedemann was one of the outstanding members of the group of physicists trained in Berlin by H. G. Magnus. He held the first professorship of physical chemistry created in Germany (at Leipzig); and he became famous through his works on electromagnetism, especially his textbook on the theory of electricity, and through his long editorship of *Annalen der Physik und Chemie,* known as *Wiedemanns Annalen.*

Wiedemann came from a merchant family. His father died when the boy was two and his mother when he was fifteen, and subsequently he lived with his grandparents. From 1838 to 1844 he studied at the Köllnische Realgymnasium in Berlin. At that time the school's director was the physicist E. F. August, and its teachers included Louis Seebeck. Wiedemann also received much encouragement and help in his studies from an uncle in Berlin, the mechanic C. A. Gruel.

From 1844 to 1847 Wiedemann studied natural sciences at the University of Berlin. His professors included the mathematicians Dirichlet and Joachimsthal; the chemists Heinrich Rose, F. L. Sonnenschein, and E. Mitscherlich; and the physicists Magnus and Dove. Magnus allowed students to use his private laboratory; and it was there that Wiedemann met Helmholtz, who became a lifelong friend. Since Magnus, in conscious rejection of the nineteenth-century *Naturphilosophie,* concerned himself exclusively with experimental physics and neglected all theoretical questions, Helmholtz and Wiedemann decided to work through Poisson's work on the theory of elasticity. In 1847 Wiedemann received the doctorate from Berlin for a dissertation on the urea derivative biuret. In 1850 he qualified as a lecturer with a work on the turning of the polarization plane of light discovered by Faraday. He lectured at the university on selected topics in theoretical physics.

In 1851 Wiedemann married Mitscherlich's daughter Clara; they had a daughter and two sons: Eilhard, who became a physicist and historian of science, and Alfred, who became an Egyptologist. In 1854 Wiedemann was appointed professor of physics at the University of Basel, where he worked closely with the chemist C. F. Schönbein. He returned to Germany in 1863 to accept a post at the Polytechnische Schule in Brunswick. In 1866 he moved to the Polytechnische Schule in Karlsruhe, where, in addition to his duties as professor of physics, he organized meteorological observations for the state of Baden. His works on physical chemistry brought him an offer from Leipzig in 1871 to occupy Germany's first chair of physical chemistry. Upon the retirement of Wilhelm Hankel in 1887, Wiedemann succeeded him as professor of physics at Leipzig, and Wilhelm Ostwald was given the chair of physical chemistry.

In 1877, following Poggendorff's death, Wiedemann became editor of the *Annalen der Physik und Chemie*, a position he held for the rest of his life. During his editorship the *Annalen* became one of the most distinguished German physics periodicals. He was able to increase its usefulness by publishing the *Beiblätter zu den Annalen der Physik*, of which his son Eilhard became editor.

At Berlin, Wiedemann devoted his first studies to electrical conductivity on the surfaces of various metals, to the rotation of the plane of polarization of light under the influence of electric current, and to the thermal conductivity of metals. In 1853, collaborating with Rudolph Franz, he discovered the physical law named for them. It states that at a constant, not very low temperature $T$, the electrical conductivity $\kappa$ of metals is approximately proportional to their thermal conductivity $\lambda$; that is,

$$\frac{\lambda}{\kappa} = \text{constant } T.$$

At Basel, Wiedemann continued the studies he had begun at Berlin on endosmosis, in which he established the dependence of the osmotic pressure on the current intensity and composition of the solutions. He also performed experiments on torsion and on the magnetization of steel and iron, and examined the influence of temperature on both phenomena. In later years he returned to the problem of the relations between magnetic and mechanical phenomena. This research also constituted the preliminary steps toward Wiedemann's greatest work, *Die Lehre vom Galvanismus* (1861–1863), a systematic presentation of everything known about the subject. This textbook was quickly recognized as the standard work on galvanism and was widely read.

At Brunswick, Wiedemann discovered the additive law for the magnetism of chemical compounds. He also investigated the vapor pressures of salts containing water of crystallization and demonstrated that they depend solely on temperature. At Karlsruhe he worked with R. Rühlmann on an exhaustive study of the processes involved in gas discharge and thereby became a pioneer in that field as well.

Pursuing his early research on magnetism while at Leipzig, Wiedemann posited the existence of "magnetic molecules." His new, reliable determinations of the unit of electrical resistance, the ohm, won the admiration of his colleagues. In making these measurements Wiedemann used the large induction coil designed by Wilhelm Weber. In addition he improved the existing techniques for measuring temperature and devised a new galvanometer that bears his name.

Through both his teaching and his research, Wiedemann made important contributions to physics and chemistry, especially in electromagnetism. In addition, as an editor and as an organizer, he possessed a virtually universal knowledge of physical science and performed many valuable services for his fellow physicists.

## BIBLIOGRAPHY

I. Original Works. A bibliography of Wiedemann's numerous scientific papers is in Poggendorff, II, 1319; III, 1441; IV, 1631; and A. von Harnack, *Geschichte der Königlichen Preussischen Akademie der Wissenschaften zu Berlin*, III (Berlin, 1900), 288 (Wiedemann's academic writings only).

His papers include his dissertation, "De nova quodam corpore ex urea producto" (Berlin, 1847); "Ueber die Wärmeleitungsfähigkeit der Metalle," in *Annalen der Physik und Chemie*, 89 (1853), 457–531, written with R. Franz; "Ueber den Einfluss der Temperaturänderungen auf den Magnetismus des Eisens und Stahls," *ibid.*, 122 (1864), 346–358; "Magnetische Untersuchungen über den Magnetismus der Salze der magnetischen Metalle," *ibid.*, 126 (1865), 1–38; "Ueber den Magnetismus der chemischen Verbindungen," *ibid.*, 135 (1868), 177–237; "Ueber den Durchgang der Elektricität durch Gase," *ibid.*, 145 (1872), 235–259, 364–399; and 158 (1876), 71–87, 252–287, written with R. Rühlmann; "Ueber die Dissociation der gelösten Eisenoxydsalze," *ibid.*, n.s. 5 (1878), 45–83; "Ueber die Torsion," *ibid.*, 6 (1876), 71–87, 252–287, written with Rühlmann; "Ueber die Dissociation der gelösten Eisenoxydsalze," 452–461; and 37 (1889), 610–628; and "Ueber die Bestimmung des Ohm," *ibid.*, 42 (1891), 227–256, 425–449, first published as *Abhandlungen der Preussischen Akademie der Wissenschaften*, phys. Kl. (1884), no. 3.

His book is *Die Lehre vom Galvanismus und Elektromagnetismus nebst technischen Anwendungen*, 2 vols. (Brunswick, 1861–1863; 2nd ed., 1872–1873; 3rd ed., *Die Lehre von der Elektricität*, 4 vols., 1882–1885; 4th ed., 1893–1898).

II. Secondary Literature. See H. von Helmholtz, "Gustav Wiedemann beim Beginn des 50. Bandes seiner *Annalen der Physik und Chemie* gewidmet," in *Annalen der Physik*, n.s. 50 (1893), iii–xi; F. Kohlrausch, "Gustav Wiedemann," in *Verhandlungen der Deutschen physikalischen Gesellschaft*, 1 (1899), 155–167; W. Ostwald, "Zur Erinnerung an Gustav Wiedemann," in *Berichte der Kgl. Sächsischen Gesellschaft der Wissenschaften*, math.-phys. Kl., 51 (1899), lxxvii–lxxxiii; M. Planck, "Gustav Wiedemann, dem Herausgeber der Annalen zum Fünfzigjährigen Doctorjubiläum gewidmet," in *Annalen der Physik und Chemie*, n.s. 63 (1897), vii–xi; and H. Reiger, "Wiedemann, Gustav Heinrich," in *Allgemeine deutsche Biographie*, LV (1910), 67–70.

HANS-GÜNTHER KÖRBER

**WIEDERSHEIM, ROBERT** (*b.* Nürtingen, Baden-Württemberg, Germany, 21 April 1848; *d.* Lindau im Bodensee, Germany, 23 July 1923), *comparative anatomy, embryology.*

Wiedersheim was greatly influenced by his father, who practiced general medicine and was also a naturalist and collector of zoological specimens; his mother, Berta Otto Wiedersheim, died after his birth. At the age of fifteen Wiedersheim devoted most of his time to the microscopic study of the freshwater hydra *fusca* and *viridis*. Consequently his final school report in classical languages was a minor disaster. Although he wanted to study zoology, at the insistence of his father he began medical studies in October 1868 at the University of Tübingen, where he was a pupil of Leydig. In 1871 Wiedersheim transferred to the University of Würzburg to study under A. Koelliker and C. Hasse; the latter proposed to Wiedersheim a thesis on the structure of the stomach of birds, which was completed in 1872.

Wiedersheim finished his medical studies at the University of Freiburg, and became a university demonstrator and lecturer at Würzburg, where he worked under Koelliker until 1876. At Würzburg he established himself as an excellent teacher of systematic and comparative anatomy. At the same time he also published papers on comparative vertebrate anatomy. At the end of 1876 Wiedersheim was appointed associate professor of anatomy at Freiburg, and, in 1883, full professor and director of the Institute of Anatomy and Comparative Anatomy. During his early years at Freiburg, Wiedersheim began the work that led to his world-famous textbook on comparative anatomy *Vergleichende Anatomie der Wirbeltiere*—based on the comparison of vertebrates, and their embryologic and phylogenetic development. English editions of *Comparative Vertebrate Anatomy* by E. N. Parker appeared in 1886 and 1897. In 1907 a rewritten and revised third edition was published. Wiedersheim's fame as a morphologist rests on his book, and numerous students from Europe and the United States were thus attracted to the Institute.

When Wiedersheim retired at the age of seventy, he had firmly established the teaching of comparative anatomy. The respect and affection that his pupils and colleagues had for him is evident in the special issue of the *Zeitschrift für Morphologie*

*und Anthropologie* (1924) published in honor of his seventy-fifth birthday. Wiedersheim was survived by his wife, Tilla Gruber, and one son.

*BIBLIOGRAPHY*

I. ORIGINAL WORKS. Wiedersheim's works include "Die feineren Strukturverhältnisse der Drüsen im Muskelmagen der Vögel," in *Archiv für mikroskopische Anatomie und Entwicklungsmechanik*, **8** (1872), 435–452; "Beiträge zur Kenntnis der württemberg. Höhlenfauna," in *Verhandlungen der Würzburger physikalische medizinische Gesellschaft*, **4** (1873), 207–222; "Über den Mädelhofener Schädelfund in Unterfranken," in *Archiv für Anthropologie*, **8** (1874), 225–238; "Salamandrina perspicillata und Geotriton fuscus. Versuch einer vergleichenden Anatomie der Salamandrinen," in *Annali del Museo civico di storia naturale Giacomo Doria*, **7** (1875), 5–206; "Bemerkungen zur Anatomie des Euproctus Rusconii," *ibid.*, 545–568; "Zur Anatomie und Physiologie des Phyllodactylus europaeus mit besonderer Berücksichtigung des Aquaeductus vestibuli der Ascalaboten im allgemeinen," in *Morphologisches Jahrbuch*, **1** (1876), 495–534; "Die Kopfdrüsen der geschwänzten Amphibien und die Glandula intermaxillaris der Anuren," in *Zeitschrift für wissenschaftliche Zoologie*, **27** (1876), 1–50; "Die ältesten Formen des Carpus mit Tarsus der heutigen Amphibien," in *Morphologisches Jahrbuch*, **2** (1876), 421–434; "Über Neubildung von Kiemen bei Siren Lacertina," *ibid.*, **3** (1877), 630–631; "Zur Fortpflanzungsgeschichte des Proteus anguineus," *ibid.*, 632; "Das Kopfskelett der Urodelen," *ibid.*, 352–448; "Labyrinthodon Rütimeyeri," in *Abhandlungen der Schweizerischen paläontologischen Gesellschaft*, **5** (1878), 1–56; "Ein neuer Saurus aus der Trias," *ibid.*, **6** (1879), 75–124; "Die spinalartigen Hirnnerven von Ammocoetes und Petromyzon Planeri," in *Zoologischer Anzeiger*, **3** (1880), 446–449; "Über den sogenannten Tentakel der Gymnophionen," *ibid.*, 493–496; "Über den Tarsus der Saurier," *ibid.* (1880), 496; *Morphologische Studien* (1880); "Über die Vermehrung des Os centrale im Carpus und Tarsus des Axolotl," in *Morphologisches Jahrbuch*, **6** (1880), 581–583; "Zur Histologie der Dipnöer-Schuppen," in *Archiv für mikroskopische Anatomie und Entwicklungsmechanik*, **18** (1880), 122–129; "Zur Anatomie des Amblystoma Weismanni," in *Zeitschrift für wissenschaftliche Zoologie*, **32** (1880), 214–236; "Vomero-Nasal (Jacobson's) Organ," in *Comparative Anatomy of Vertebrates*, **3** (1907), 271–273; and "Über das Becken der Fische," in *Morphologisches Jahrbuch*, **1** (1881), 326–327.

II. SECONDARY LITERATURE. See "Robert Wiedersheim, Festschrift zu seinem 75. Geburtstag von seinen Schülern und Freunden," in *Zeitschrift für Morphologie und Anthropologie*, **24** (1924).

PAUL GLEES

**WIEGLEB, JOHANN CHRISTIAN** (*b.* Langensalza, Germany, 21 December 1732; *d.* Langensalza, 16 January 1800), *pharmacy, chemistry.*

From the end of the seventeenth century, apothecaries played an increasingly active role in scientific research, especially in chemistry. The expansion of the number of medicines through the addition of chemical preparations, begun by Paracelsus, was at first supported by physicians. Later this development stimulated apothecaries to undertake investigations of their own, however, many of which went far beyond the confines of their professional interests. Wiegleb was one of the most important figures among this steadily growing group.

His father, a lawyer, died while Wiegleb was still young; and his mother remarried—again a lawyer—in order to provide a good upbringing for her children. While still at school Wiegleb was an assistant to his stepfather, and thus acquired considerable skill in the use of language and knowledge of legal matters.

Wiegleb was related to several local apothecaries and, by observing them at work, he became interested in entering the profession. Although his family would have preferred him to become a theologian, they allowed him to make his own decision. In 1748, at age sixteen, Wiegleb began his apprenticeship at the Marienapotheke, in Dresden. Unfortunately, the proprietor took virtually no interest in his training, leaving this matter to his assistants, who were far from equal to the task. As a result Wiegleb learned only manual skills. He therefore had to study on his own; and in order to master the relevant technical writings, most of which were in Latin, Wiegleb had to better his scanty knowledge of the language. This he did with great enthusiasm, practicing on the scholarly books he found in the shop, although many of them were outdated. In the beginning he was especially drawn to alchemical writings, which for a time he considered to be the summit of human knowledge.

Wiegleb's apprenticeship lasted six years; but since no successor could be found for him, he remained in Dresden for another six months. The next year he was an assistant to an apothecary in Quedlinburg but, receiving no more instruction there than in his previous position, he returned to Langensalza. The owner of the apothecary shop there had just died; and Wiegleb, now aged twenty-six, was offered the opportunity to manage it for the man's widow. But, wishing to be fully independent, he declined the offer and, with money inherited from his parents, built his own pharmacy. The new building, which was finished in 1759, contained a splendid shop and a model laboratory.

During this period Wiegleb became friendly with Ernst Baldinger, a physician practicing in Langensalza who was very interested in scientific research and who later held professorships at Jena and Marburg. The two men conducted chemistry experiments together, and in the course of their work Baldinger acquainted Wiegleb with the latest developments in chemistry. In 1767 Wiegleb published his first book, which contained a number of brief writings. This was followed by a work on fermentation. He then investigated the alkaline salts found in plants and confirmed Marggraf's discovery of this type of substance. In a number of papers Wiegleb displayed an excellent knowledge of analytic procedures. For instance, he repeated with remarkable exactness the analyses of Torbern Bergman and corrected a considerable number of the latter's errors.

In 1775 Wiegleb published a German translation of R. A. Vogel's *Institutiones chemiae,* a work he greatly admired. It probably was while preparing the book for publication that Wiegleb decided to create an institute for training pharmacists, and he founded such a school in 1779. There the students, after attending lectures, were expected to participate in laboratory experiments and to do independent work. They had the use of an extensive library and could obtain instruction in languages. Later critics believed that the teaching was more suited to training chemists than to providing a general knowledge of all branches of pharmacy, but this view seems exaggerated. In the approximately twenty years of its existence, the school trained about fifty students, including J. F. A. Göttling (later a professor of chemistry at Jena), Klaproth, Hermbstädt, and the botanist Willdenow—which suggests that the curriculum was, in fact, broadly based.

Wiegleb's reputation extended far beyond northern Germany: scientists from throughout Europe visited him. Besides purely scientific questions, he was much concerned with improving technology. Whenever he could, he supported such crafts as dyeing and brewing. Wiegleb even studied the economic problems of Langensalza, and he was elected both a member of the city council and municipal treasurer.

Very little is known about Wiegleb's family. He had nine children, four of whom survived him. Two of the children were deaf and dumb. The last years of his life were difficult, for in 1789 an accident with fulminate of mercury almost blinded him. In addition, he sold his apothecary shop but lost most of the purchase price.

Wiegleb's critical attitude in assessing scientific questions earned him high esteem in learned circles. After several years of work he published *Historisch-kritische Untersuchung der Alchemie* (1777), which went through a second edition. In this work he stated:

> The best accounts from the period when the name alchemy is encountered, . . . are examined, and it is thereby demonstrated that they are, taken together, incapable of confirming the reality of alchemy. Then, the strongest proof is adduced to show that the entire imaginary art of alchemy is impossible according to all known, certain natural laws of human art; thus [it is shown] that it has never truly been practiced by anyone.

Wiegleb carefully examined famous reports of the transformation of metals and pointed out their deficiencies; in a short time his work became widely known. His motto was "To doubt is the beginning of knowledge," so it is all the more astonishing that Wiegleb was a convinced proponent of Stahl's phlogiston theory throughout his life. He believed that phlogiston was a "subtle but destructible" substance that never can be produced in the pure state. Somewhat later he conjectured that phlogiston is a kind of hydrogen. Even after the triumph of Lavoisier's ideas, Wiegleb did not abandon the phlogiston theory. For a long time he contended that phlogiston possessed a negative weight. In the ensuing debates he argued objectively with his opponents and even adopted several of their experimental findings—for instance, he considered the two hypothetical "substances" light and phlogiston to be identical. On the whole, however, he clung to Stahl's theory.

After his book on alchemy, Wiegleb published a great many works. In 1779 he reported that oxalic acid is a separate compound. He also devised an improved method of preparing Glauber's salt and took special pains to work out new and improved mineral analyses. Wiegleb was interested in the history of chemistry and wrote a two-volume work on the subject, as well as a history of gunpowder.

Except for an educational trip to almost all the countries of Europe, Wiegleb never left his native city. Nevertheless, at his death he was one of Germany's best-known men of learning.

*BIBLIOGRAPHY*

I. Original Works. Wiegleb's writings include *Kleine chymische Abhandlungen von dem grossen Nutzen der Erkenntniss des acidi pinguis bey der Erklärung vieler chymische Erscheinungen* (Langensalza, 1770), which contains "Entstehung des Glases," "Grüne Flamme borhalt. Alkohols," and "Über die rote Farbe des Zinnobers"; *Vertheidigung der Mayerischen Lehre vom acido pingui gegen verschieden dawider gemachte Einwendungen* (Altenburg, 1770); *Chymische Versuche über die alkalischen Salze* (Berlin, 1774); *Fortgesetzte kleine chymische Abhandlungen* (Langensalza, 1770), which contains "Farbe des Quecksilberoxydes" and "Zerlegung des Salmiaks durch Eisen"; *Rudolf Aug. Vogels Institutiones chemiae als Lehrsätze der Chemie* (Weimar, 1775; 2nd ed., 1785); *Neuer Begriff von der Gährung und den ihr unterwürfigen Körpern* (Weimar, 1776); *Geschichte der Alchimie: Historische-kritische Untersuchung der Alchimie oder der eingebildeten Goldmacherkunst, von ihrem Ursprunge als Fortgang . . .* (Weimar, 1777; 2nd ed., 1793); *Revision der Grundlehren von der chemischen Verwandtschaft der Körper* (Erfurt, 1777); "Untersuchungen der Waffen der Bronzezeit," in *Acta Academiae Electonum Moguntiaca scientiarum utilis* (Erfurt, 1777); and *Die natürliche Magie* (Berlin, 1779; 1782–1786), completed by G. E. Rosenthal (1805).

Further works are "Über Oxalsäure," in *Chemisches Journal*, **2** (1779); *Handbuch der Allgemeine Chemie* (Berlin, 1781; 2nd ed., 1787; 3rd ed., 1796), also translated into English by C. R. Hopson as *General System of Chemistry Theoretical and Practical, Digested and Arranged With a Particular View to Its Applications. . .* (London, 1789); *P. v. Musschenbroeks Elementa Chemiae als Anfangsgründe der Chemie* (Berlin, 1782); *Onomatologia curiosa artificiosa et magica oder natürliches Zauberlexikon* (Nuremberg, 1784); *Unterhaltende Naturwunder* (Erfurt, 1788), written with F. Kroll; "Über Phlogiston," in *Chemische Annalen*, **2** (1791); *Geschichte des Wachstums und der Erfindungen in der Chemie in der ältesten und mittleren Zeit, aus dem Lateinischen Werk Bergmans mit Zusätzen* (Berlin, 1792); *Deutsches Apothekerbuch*, 2 vols. (Gotha, 1793; 4th ed., 1804), written with J. C. T. Schlegel; "Herstellung der Soda aus Kochsalz mit Hilfe von Vitriol," in *Chemische Annalen* (1793); "Chemische Nomenclatur," *ibid.*, **2** (1796); and "Verkalken des Bleies," *ibid.*, **1** (1797).

Wiegleb also published many essays in booklet form for analytic chemists. In addition, he translated works by Boerhaave and Demachy, and edited writings by G. A. Hoffmann, Dorothea Erxleben, and others.

II. Secondary Literature. See H. Gutbier, *Beiträge zur Geschichte der Apotheken in Langensalza* (Langensalza, 1929); and R. Möller, "Ein Apotheker und Chemiker der Aufklärung," in *Pharmazie* (Berlin), **20** (1965), 230–239.

Gunther Kerstein

WIELAND, HEINRICH OTTO (*b*. Pforzheim, Germany, 4 June 1877; *d*. Starnberg, Germany, 5 August 1957), *organic chemistry*.

Wieland was the son of Theodor Wieland, a pharmaceutical chemist. He studied chemistry at the University of Munich in 1896, the University of Berlin in 1897, and at the Technische Hochschule at Stuttgart in 1898. The following year he returned to Munich and in 1901 received the Ph.D. for his research in organic chemistry under the direction of Johannes Thiele. In 1904 Wieland was appointed *Privatdozent* at the University of Munich and in 1913 received a senior lectureship in organic chemistry. He remained at Munich until 1917, during which time he devoted his research chiefly to the chemistry of organic nitrogen compounds.

Wieland's earliest work concerned the mechanism of addition of the oxides of nitrogen to olefins and the mechanism of the nitration of aromatic hydrocarbons. He was able to isolate the intermediate nitro compounds and show the similarity between the two classes of reactions. At this time Wieland also undertook a study of fulminic acid, and in a review published in 1909 he summarized his investigations of its polymerization and its step-by-step synthesis from ethanol and nitric acid.

Wieland's most significant work during his early career was the chemistry of the hydrazines, a project that led him to the discovery of the first known nitrogen free radicals. In 1911 Wieland prepared tetraphenylhydrazine from the oxidation of diphenylamine. He showed that when heated in toluene, tetraphenylhydrazine dissociates into two diphenylnitrogen free radicals, characterized by the green color that they impart to the solution. Wieland then undertook an extensive study of the effect of ring substituents on the production of radicals from substituted tetraphenylhydrazines.

In 1917 Wieland accepted a position at the Technische Hochschule in Munich, but during 1917–1918 was given a leave of absence to take part in chemical warfare research under the direction of Fritz Haber at the Kaiser-Wilhelm Institute in Berlin-Dahlem. After the war Wieland returned to the Technische Hochschule in Munich, where he remained until 1921, when he accepted a position at the University of Freiburg. In 1924 Willstätter resigned his post as director of the famous Baeyer laboratory at the University of Munich and recommended Wieland to be his successor. Wieland returned to Munich in 1925 and directed the Baeyer laboratory for twenty-five years until his

appointment as emeritus professor in 1950. During this time he became more interested in the structural determination of natural products. He had already shown considerable interest in biochemistry, for in 1912 he first proposed his theory of biological oxidation. In his subsequent studies on the mechanisms of oxidation reactions published in over fifty papers from 1912 to 1943, Wieland was able to demonstrate that many biological oxidation reactions proceed through dehydrogenation. While director of the Baeyer laboratory Wieland and his students worked on the isolation and structural determination of many natural products, including morphine alkaloids, lobeline alkaloids, strychnine alkaloids, pterins that he first isolated from butterfly pigments, mushroom poisons, and cardioactive toad poisons.

Wieland's best-known work, however, concerned the structure of bile acids, for which he received the 1927 Nobel Prize in chemistry. Wieland's research on this subject began in 1912, and for twenty years he and his collaborators sought to gain insight into the complicated structure of cholic acid and other bile acids related to cholesterol, through oxidation of specific portions of the molecule. Gradually information was assembled from such studies performed by Wieland's research group and also those carried out by other chemists, especially Windaus, who received the 1928 Nobel Prize for his work on the constructions of sterols. The following structures were generally accepted for cholic acid and cholesterol when Wieland and Windaus presented their Nobel lectures on 12 December 1928. Only two carbon atoms (numbered 15 and 16) remained to be assigned with certainty, and they were provisionally placed on carbon atom number 10, as shown.

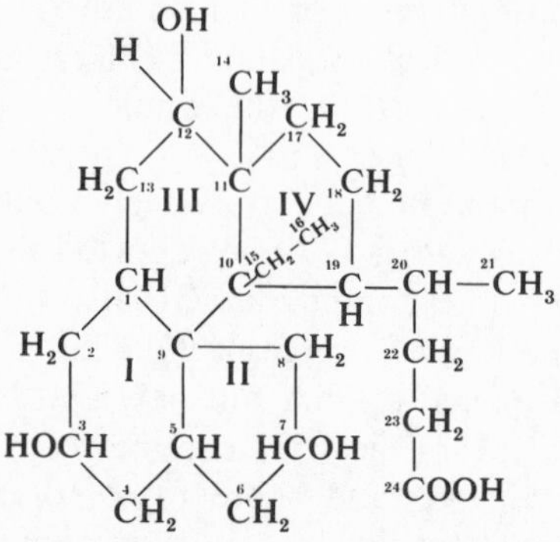

FIGURE 1. Cholic acid (Wieland, 1928)

During the next four years Wieland and his co-workers at Munich tried to establish the location of

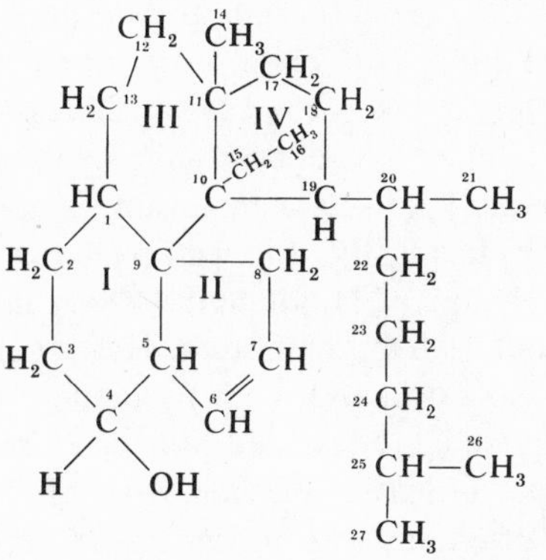

FIGURE 2. Cholesterol (Windaus, 1928)

these two carbon atoms, yet they met with little success. In 1932 new evidence of the molecular size of steroids, gained from X-ray crystallographic analysis, cast doubt on the basic structure. By reconsidering the data collected over the previous twenty years, Wieland and the British chemists O. Rosenheim and H. King independently arrived at the presently accepted structure of cholic acid.

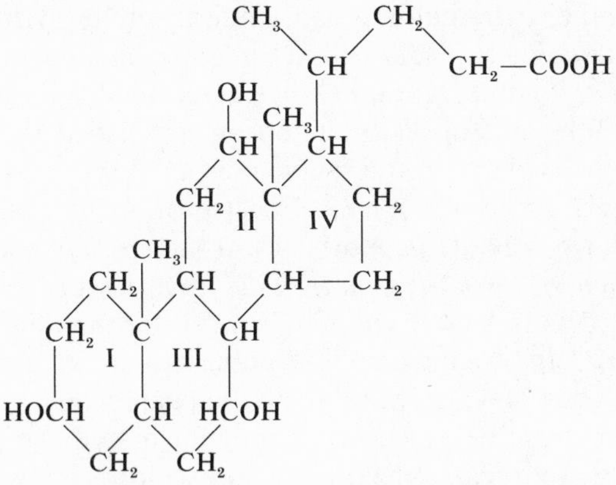

FIGURE 3. Cholic acid (Wieland, 1932)

Wieland's research continued until his retirement in 1950. He served as editor of the *Annalen der Chemie* for over twenty years and received the Otto Hahn Prize in 1955.

*BIBLIOGRAPHY*

I. ORIGINAL WORKS. Wieland published over 350 papers and several books, which are listed in Poggendorff, V, 1366–1367; VI, 2876–2877; VII, 985–987. Some of his most important publications are "Die Knallsäure," in *Sammlung chemischer und chemisch-technischer Vorträge,* **14** (1909), 385–461; *Die Hydrazine* (Stuttgart, 1913); "Die Chemie der Gallensäuren," in *Zeitschrift für angewandte Chemie und Zentralblatt für technische Chemie,* **42** (1929), 421–424; "Recent Researches on Biological Oxidation," in *Journal of the Chemical Society* (1931), 1055–1064; *On the Mechanism of Oxidation* (New Haven, Conn., 1932); and "Die Konstitution der Gallensäuren," in *Berichte der Deutschen chemischen Gesellschaft,* **67** (1934), 27–39.

II. SECONDARY LITERATURE. An autobiographical sketch appeared in *Nachrichten aus Chemie und Technik* (1955), 222–223. A useful summary of his work as a tribute on his 65th birthday was given by Elisabeth Dane, "Die Arbeiten H. Wieland auf dem Gebiet der Steroide," in *Die Naturwissenschaften,* **30** (1942), 333–342; Wilhelm Franke, "H. Wielands Arbeiten zum Mechanismus der biologischen Oxydation," *ibid.,* 342–351; Friedrich Klages, "Die Stickstoffarbeiten von H. Wieland," *ibid.,* 351–359; and Clemens Schöpf, "Die Arbeiten Heinrich Wielands über stickstoffhaltige Naturstoffe (Alkaloide und Pterine)," *ibid.,* 359–373.

Other accounts include Rolf Huisigen, "The Wieland Memorial Lecture," in *Proceedings of the Chemical Society* (1958), 210–219; Gulbrand Lunde, "The 1927 and 1928 Nobel Chemistry Prize Winners, Wieland and Windaus," in *Journal of Chemical Education,* **7** (1930), 1763–1771; and Adolph Windaus, "The Chemistry of the Sterols, Bile Acids, and Other Cyclic Constituents of Natural Fats and Oils," in *Annual Review of Biochemistry,* **1** (1932), 109–134.

DANIEL P. JONES

**WIELAND** (or **GUILANDINUS**), **MELCHIOR** (*b.* Königsberg, Germany [now Kaliningrad, R.S.F.S.R.], *ca.* 1520; *d.* Padua, Italy, 8 January 1589), *botany.*

Very little is known about this remarkable scholar, polemicist, able botanist, and traveler. His name probably was Wieland—it certainly was latinized as Guilandinus. He began his studies at the University of Königsberg and continued them in Rome. He traveled as far as Sicily, supporting himself by selling medicinal herbs. He journeyed through many parts of Asia, Palestine, and Egypt with financial support and letters of recommendation from Senator Marino Cavalli, one of the reformers of the Padua Studium. Wieland's return to Italy was not without danger: after being captured by Algerian pirates and being shipwrecked he landed at Genoa, then went to Venice. On 20 September 1561, because of his fame as a scholar, he was asked to succeed Anguillara as director of the botanical garden at Padua. He was equally successful in his university career and was reappointed several times to the chair of "lecture and demonstration of medicinal herbs," which combined botany and pharmacognosy. Wieland, who is buried in the cloister of the Basilica of Saint Anthony in Padua, left his library to the Venetian Republic (it is now in the library of San Marco) and most of his possessions to Benedetto Zorzi.

A scholar of vast knowledge, Wieland was an outstanding director of the Padua botanical garden, into which he introduced many rare plants and a machine for irrigation (1575). He left no writings of particular value. His scientific observations are contained in *epistolae*, letters on botany that include descriptions of now-forgotten and little-known plants.

In keeping with his reputation as a polemicist, Wieland aroused violent enmities, such as that of Mattioli, and formed friendships equally strong, such as that with Falloppio.

BIBLIOGRAPHY

A. von Haller, *Bibliotheca botanica*, I (Zurich, 1771), 320–321; J. J. Mangetus, *Bibliotheca scriptorum medicorum, veterum et recentiorum*, I, pt. 2 (Geneva, 1781), 539; R. de Visiani, *L'Orto botanico di Padova* (Padua, 1842), 9–12; and G. B. de Toni, "Melchiorre Guilandino," in A. Mieli, ed., *Gli scienziati italiani,* I (Rome, 1933), 73–76.

LORIS PREMUDA

**WIELEITNER, HEINRICH** (*b.* Wasserburg am Inn, Germany, 31 October 1874; *d.* Munich, Germany, 27 December 1931), *mathematics, history of mathematics.*

Wieleitner received his higher education at the Catholic seminaries at Scheyern and Freising but subsequently decided to study mathematics (rather than classical languages and theology) at the University of Munich. Since his parents lived in simple circumstances, C. L. F. Lindemann proposed that Wieleitner be allotted the Lamont stipend for Catholic students of mathematics in 1895. This enabled the gifted young man to complete his studies in 1897 with excellent marks. Three years later he obtained the doctorate with a dissertation on third-order surfaces with oval points, a subject suggested to him by Lindemann.

Meanwhile, Wieleitner had become a high school teacher, his first appointment being at the Gymnasium at Speyer. In 1909 he was made *Gymnasialprofessor* at Pirmasens; in 1915 he returned to Speyer as headmaster of the *Realschule*; in 1920 he moved to Augsburg, and in 1926 he

was promoted to *Oberstudiendirektor* at the Neue Realgymnasium in Munich, a post he held until his death. Parallel to his career as an educator, Wieleitner established a reputation as a geometer and – increasingly so – as a historian of mathematics. Probably during the International Congresses of Mathematicians at Heidelberg (1904) and Rome (1908), he met Italian geometers. He translated an article by Gino Loria and, with E. Ciani, contributed to the revised German edition of *Pascals Repertorium der höheren Mathematik.*[1] In 1905 his *Theorie der ebenen algebraischen Kurven höherer Ordnung* had been published, and in 1908 it was supplemented by *Spezielle ebene Kurven.* In 1914 and 1918 the two volumes of Wieleitner's *Algebraische Kurven* followed. Wieleitner's books were noted for their simple, straightforward presentation and the author's great didactic skill, which made ample use of geometric intuition and insight.

Although always interested in the history of mathematics, Wieleitner would most probably not have become involved in the field had Alexander von Braunmühl not died in 1908. With Siegmund Günther, Braunmühl had undertaken to write a *Geschichte der Mathematik* in two volumes. Günther's volume (antiquity to Descartes)[2] appeared in 1908, but his partner left an unfinished manuscript. Wieleitner was persuaded to step in. Thoroughly going through G. Eneström's many critical remarks about Cantor's *Vorlesungen über Geschichte der Mathematik,*[3] he revised and completed part I of Braunmühl's work (arithmetic, algebra, analysis), which was published in 1911; part II (geometry, trigonometry) appeared in 1921. Apart from being based on a detailed study of primary sources, Wieleitner's presentation always stressed the notion of development and progress of mathematics. Giving only minor attention to individual biographies, the author brought the leading ideas to the fore, and wrote a history of mathematical ideas. He followed the same general concept in his *Geschichte der Mathematik,* published in two small volumes in the Sammlung Göschen in 1922–1923.

Shortly after moving to Munich in 1928, Wieleitner, at Sommerfeld's suggestion, was made *Privatdozent,* and in 1930 honorary professor, at the university. Since 1919 he had been corresponding member of the Deutsche Akademie der Naturforscher Leopoldina, and in 1929 he was elected member of the Académie Internationale d'Histoire des Sciences.

Wieleitner published about 150 books and articles and more than 2,500 book reviews. Many of his papers and books—in geometry and the history of mathematics—were addressed to teachers and students of mathematics. In inexpensive source booklets he presented carefully chosen excerpts from mathematical classics for classroom use. His work in the history of mathematics was continued in the same spirit and with the same close connection to mathematical education by Kurt Vogel and J. E. Hofmann.

## NOTES

1. *Pascals Repertorium der höheren Mathematik*, 2nd, completely rev. German ed., E. Salkowski and H. E. Timerding, eds., II, pt. 1, *Grundlagen und ebene Geometrie* (Leipzig – Berlin, 1910).
2. Siegmund Günther, *Geschichte der Mathematik*, I, *Von den ältesten Zeiten bis Cartesius* (Leipzig, 1908).
3. Moritz Cantor, *Vorlesungen über Geschichte der Mathematik*, 4 vols. (I: Leipzig, 1880; 2nd ed., 1894; 3rd ed., 1907; II: 1892; 2nd ed., 1899 – 1900; III: 1894 – 1898; 2nd ed., 1900 – 1901; IV: 1908).

## BIBLIOGRAPHY

I. ORIGINAL WORKS. Wieleitner's most important books are *Theorie der ebenen algebraischen Kurven höherer Ordnung* (Leipzig, 1905), Sammlung Schubert no. 43; *Spezielle ebene Kurven* (Leipzig, 1908), Sammlung Schubert no. 56; *Geschichte der Mathematik*, II, *Von Cartesius bis zur Wende des 18. Jahrhunderts*, 2 vols. (Leipzig, 1911 – 1921), Sammlung Schubert nos. 63, 64; *Algebraische Kurven*, 2 vols. (Berlin – Leipzig, 1914 – 1918; I: 2nd ed., 1919; 3rd ed., 1930; II: 2nd ed., 1919), Sammlung Göschen nos. 435, 436; *Geschichte der Mathematik*, 2 vols. (Berlin – Leipzig, 1922 – 1923), Sammlung Göschen nos. 226, 875; *Die Geburt der modernen Mathematik*, 2 vols. (Karlsruhe, 1924 – 1925); and *Mathematische Quellenbücher*, 4 vols. (Berlin, 1927 – 1929). A combined Russian trans. of the 2 vols. of *Geschichte der Mathematik*, II (Sammlung Schubert nos. 63, 64) and of *Geschichte der Mathematik*, II (Sammlung Göschen no. 875), 53 – 147, was edited under the title *Istoria matematiki ot Dekarta do serednii XIX stoletia* by A. P. Youschkevitch (Moscow, 1966).

II. SECONDARY LITERATURE. The most extensive obituaries (including bibliographies and a portrait) are J. E. Hofmann, in *Jahresbericht der Deutschen Mathematiker-vereinigung*, **42** (1933), 199 – 223, with portrait; and J. Ruska, in *Isis*, **18** (1932), 150 – 165.

CHRISTOPH J. SCRIBA

**WIEN, WILHELM CARL WERNER OTTO FRITZ FRANZ** (*b.* Gaffken, near Fischhausen, East Prussia [now Primorsk, R.S.F.S.R.], 13 January 1864; *d.* Munich, Germany, 30 August 1928), *theoretical and experimental physics, philosophy of science.*

**Life.** Wien was the only child of Carl Wien, a farmer with land in Gaffken, and Caroline Gertz,[1] both of whose families were descended from ancestors in Mecklenburg. When Wilhelm was two, they left Gaffken, which was no longer capable of supporting them, and moved to a smaller farm, Drachenstein, in the district of Rastenburg, East Prussia, where Wien spent his youth.[2] He frequently rode through the fields with his father, who was confined to a wagon because of a spinal ailment, and thus Wien early learned about agriculture—in which his mother assumed the bulk of the family's responsibilities.

Wien was especially close to his mother, whose excellent knowledge of history and literature stimulated his interest in those subjects. An introvert, like his father, he made no friends during his early childhood. He learned to ride, swim, and skate; and, as was then customary, a woman was engaged to give him private lessons in French, which he spoke before he was able to write his native language. In 1875 Wien's parents sent him to the Gymnasium in Rastenburg; but he had little inclination for study, preferring to wander through the fields. Furthermore, his preparation, especially in mathematics, was deficient; and in 1880 he was taken out of this municipal school, which was considered by Wien to be democratic, and sent home to learn agriculture. He compensated for his lack of academic instruction through private tutoring (in mathematics he had an outstanding teacher in Switalski) and then entered the Altstädtisches Gymnasium in Königsberg, from which he graduated in 1882, in less time than was usual.

Encouraged mainly by his mother, Wien enrolled at the University of Göttingen in the summer of 1882 to study mathematics and natural sciences. He was not, however, very much taken with what he learned in his mathematics course. Also, being of an independent spirit, he found the lavish life in the student societies distasteful and left the university after only one semester to travel through the Rhineland and Thüringen. Wien returned home with the intention of becoming a farmer but was soon discontented with the training required. He therefore resumed his studies, this time in mathematics and physics at the University of Berlin. In the winter of 1883 – 1884, after two semesters, he entered Hermann von Helmholtz' laboratory, where he "really came into contact with physics for the first time." During the summer semester of 1884 Wien learned "a great deal" studying under

G. H. Quincke at Heidelberg, then resumed his training under Helmholtz in Berlin. In his second semester as a physics student Wien was given the subject of his doctoral dissertation, the diffraction of light when it strikes a grating. After two more semesters, in 1886, he was awarded the doctorate, although he did not receive a good grade on his final examination.

In the summer of 1886 Wien went to Drachenstein to help his parents reconstruct some buildings that had been destroyed in a fire. Once again he began to consider becoming a farmer. August Kundt, who in 1888 became Helmholtz' successor at the University of Berlin, and Helmholtz himself, who at the same time had been appointed the first president of the newly founded Physikalisch-Technische Reichsanstalt (PTR), reinforced Wien's doubts about physics, maintaining that as an only son he should take over his parents' property; if he wished, he could always pursue scientific research as a hobby. Fate soon decided the issue for Wien, who did not feel capable either of buying a horse or of communicating with farm workers: in 1890 drought forced his parents to sell the farm. Wien thereupon became an assistant to Helmholtz at the PTR in Charlottenburg and his parents moved to Berlin-Westend. Wien, moreover, felt a period of his life come to an end, because his mother fell seriously ill, his father died suddenly the following year, and Bismarck was dismissed by the Emperor.

Even during the time he spent on the farm, Wien continued to study theoretical physics, arbitrarily selecting the problems he would investigate. At the Reichsanstalt, which in 1890 became the center of his professional activities, he conducted an unsuccessful series of experiments, employing platinum foil, that sought to establish a new unit of light. In this dual concern with theory and experiment lay the seed of Wien's development into the rare physicist who possesses equally good knowledge of both areas. Wien in 1892 received the *venia legendi* at the University of Berlin with a work on the localization of energy. From 1894 to 1897, at the suggestion of Helmholtz, he also considered problems of hydrodynamics: specifically, the theory of sea waves and of cyclones.

Wien's independence enabled him to make his own choice of problems for study and soon bore fruit. In 1893 he demonstrated, in a highly original manner, the constancy of the products $\lambda \cdot \theta$, given a shift of the wavelength $\lambda$ and the corresponding change in temperature $\theta$. In fact, his findings refuted Helmholtz' initial view that the radiation could no longer be treated in exclusively thermodynamic terms. Wien also published, in 1896, the theoretical derivation of a law of the energy distribution of the radiation, which differs only slightly from the currently accepted Planck law.[3]

In collaboration with his friend Ludwig Holborn, Wien executed a series of high- and low-temperature measurements from which he derived considerable satisfaction. Nevertheless, he was happy to receive an offer in 1896 from the Technische Hochschule of Aachen because Friedrich Kohlrausch, who had succeeded Helmholtz as head of the PTR, had drawn up a rigid plan of research that ran counter to Wien's need for freedom. Soon after reaching Aachen, in its gay society, Wien met Luise Mehler; they were married in 1898 and had four children: Gerda, Waltraut, Karl, and Hildegard. In Aachen he continued research begun in Berlin, on Röntgen and cathode radiation, using the apparatus left by his predecessor, Philipp Lenard. The investigation of vacuum radiation of this kind was to constitute the principal area of Wien's research.

In 1899 Wien accepted a post as full professor at the University of Giessen but left after only six months to take up a similar position at the University of Würzburg, where he spent the next twenty years—the most eventful of his scientific career. His experiments, conducted with the aid of the rapidly improving methods of high-vacuum technology, encouraged him to turn his attention to a study of the decay periods of excited atoms (and ions), a topic that occupied the final years of his career.

Wien visited Norway, Spain, Italy, England (1904), Greece (1912), and the Baltic region (1918), in the latter of which he gave several lectures. In 1911 he was awarded the Nobel Prize in physics "pour des découvertes concernant les lois de la radiation de la chaleur"; in his acceptance speech he voiced serious doubts about Planck's radiation theory.[4] In the spring of 1913 he went to Columbia University to deliver six lectures on recent problems of theoretical physics and also visited Harvard and Yale universities. In addition Wien went to Washington to see Arthur Day (Kohlrausch's son-in-law), whose high-temperature measurements—with those of Wien and Holborn—had furnished the data used to confirm the energy distribution law of Wien and later Planck. While at Würzburg, Wien did not confine his attention exclusively to physics. He also studied the subjects to which his mother had introduced him—history and especially foreign literature—as well as the fine arts.

World War I affected Wien deeply, but the struggle against the "Bolsheviks, incited by literary figures (*Literaten*)" in Germany during 1918 and 1919 had an even greater impact. In 1920 he assumed his last post, at the University of Munich, where he had a new physics institute built and served as rector from 1925 to 1926. Whereas in the 1890's Wien had chosen problems arbitrarily according to their appeal to him, he took pains at Munich to select the topics first before trying them together with his students. Although satisfied with his scientific achievements, he took a gloomy view of Germany's situation in the 1920's, marked by "war tribute and socialism."[5]

**Scientific Work.** In his first scientific publication, when he was twenty-one, Wien demonstrated that when very bright light (whether white or colored) strikes a single metallic edge (grids failed), it is bent far into the geometric shadow of the intercepting screen. He also found that the diffracted light is polarized parallel to the edge. Further, comparison of the color formation in this type of diffraction with the absorption of the diffracting material yielded the complementary color (dissertation, Berlin, 1886). Wien perceived that the difficulties of explaining the phenomenon on the basis of the previous theories lay in their failure to take into account the oscillation of the molecules of the diffracting edge. Turning to optics, in 1888 Wien demonstrated experimentally, using the bolometer, that the dependence of the transmission of a metal on the conductance does not follow—at least in the case of silver—from Maxwell's theory of light and that the latter required further work.

Following his move to the Reichsanstalt in 1890, Wien made temperature measurements and with Holborn developed a thermoelectric temperature scale, in the form of a function of the third power of the temperature, from the "electromotive force" of the thermocouples (1892). He also extended his earlier exploration of the "flux of light" to a study of the energy of thermal radiation.[6] In 1890 and in his habilitation essay of 1892 Wien linked, very generally, J. H. Poynting's "energy flux" of electric currents with the concept of the entropy of radiation. Further, by analogy with the continuous change in position of matter in motion, he also established the motion of the energy of electrodynamic radiation, pursuing the question raised by Hertz of whether this energy can be localized at all during movement. A year later, using theoretical considerations, Wien found a characteristic of electrodynamic radiation, the displacement $\theta \cdot \lambda = \theta_0 \cdot \lambda_0$—for any wavelength $\lambda$ at the same position on the $x$-axis—of any two temperature curves characterized by the different temperatures $\theta$ and $\theta_0$;[7] he also formulated in words the constancy of the products. In this derivation Wien started from Boltzmann's finding (1884) that the expression for the electrodynamic radiation pressure could be equated with an expression for the thermodynamic radiation pressure. From this equality Boltzmann had formulated a proof of Stefan's law, which Wien completed by considering the wavelength with the aid of Doppler's principle. At the same time, as a subsidiary result, Wien determined that the individual values $\phi$ of the energy of two temperature curves are related as the ratio of the fifth power of their temperatures:

$$\phi = \phi_0 \frac{\theta^5}{\theta_0^5}.$$

On the basis of Wien's findings, Paschen in 1896 derived the temperature independence of the expression

$$(I_{\lambda\max}, T) : (I_\lambda, T) = f\left(\frac{\lambda}{\lambda_{\max}}\right).$$

Wien then discovered other characteristics of the still unknown Kirchhoff energy distribution function $F(\lambda, T)$. The first was that the radiation energy disappears as wavelengths increase even within the region of finite lengths (1893); the second, that two curves for different temperatures do not intersect and that, beyond the energy maximum, they decrease no more rapidly than in proportion to $\lambda^{-5}$ (1894). Both phenomena occur because of the inviolability of the second law of thermodynamics.

Starting from these regularities and others (on the whole six),[8] Wien used theoretical considerations to achieve his energy distribution law, which he published in June 1896:

$$\phi_\lambda = C\lambda^{-5} \exp\left(\frac{c}{\lambda\theta}\right),$$

where $\phi_\lambda$ is the energy at a given small interval of the abscissa and $\theta$ is the temperature. Paschen had previously communicated to Wien his experimentally derived formulation

$$\phi_\lambda = C\lambda^{-\alpha} \exp\left(\frac{c}{\lambda\theta}\right), \text{ with } \alpha = 5.67.$$

Wien replied that he had already derived his law but that, on theoretical grounds, $\alpha$ must equal 5. To support his derivation, Wien referred to W. A. Michelson's "ansatz" (1887) that the radiation function should be handled in accordance with Maxwell's statistical treatment of the velocities $v$. Starting from Maxwell's distribution law for the number $u_v$ of atoms with velocity $v$,

$$u_v = \frac{4N}{\sqrt{\pi}} \alpha^3 \exp\left(\frac{-v^2}{\alpha^2}\right) v^2 \, dv,$$

Wien replaced the velocity independent factor $\frac{4N}{\sqrt{\pi}} \alpha^3$ with an initially unknown function $F(\lambda)$ for $v^2$ on the assumption that the wavelength of radiation from molecules with velocity $v$ is a function only of $v^2$. By integration and application of Stefan's law, Wien found $F(\lambda)$ to be $\lambda^{-5}$, a result that depended also on setting Maxwell's mean energy $\alpha^2$ proportional to temperature. The exponent was found by the displacement law in such a manner that $v^2 = f(\lambda)$ and $\alpha^2 \propto \theta$. Thus, in Wien's treatment, the fragment $v^2 \exp\left(\frac{-v^2}{\alpha^2}\right)$ of Maxwell's distribution becomes

$$F(\lambda) \exp\left(\frac{-f[\lambda]}{\theta}\right).$$

In this derivation Wien relinquished the assumption he had held since 1890 of the existence of a pure vacuum radiation, replacing it with the "hypothesis" that such radiation enters an empty space from a gas outside that space. This device, which he adopted in order to use Maxwell's gas statistics, was as much a concrete illustration and guide as was Planck's hypothesis of concrete Hertzian resonators. In 1900, and again later, physicists attacked Wien for this new interpretation of the quantities of the Maxwell distribution and, in general, for the reintroduction of gas—instead of his earlier mere cavity radiation. Nevertheless, Wien's treatment of the theory proved to be a masterstroke in the application of his well-founded suppositions of 1893–1894.

In 1897 Wien found confirmation that cathode rays were particles and of their very high velocity (about one-third the velocity of light); and in the following year he determined that they are negatively charged. Around the same time, with the help of combined electric and magnetic deflection, he also discovered the corpuscular nature, the positive charge, and the velocity (about $3.6 \times 10^7$ centimeters per second) of the positive rays. This new aspect of Wien's research, inspired by Lorentz' views on the electrostatic origin of gravitation, reached a logical conclusion in Wien's "Über die Möglichkeit einer elektromagnetischen Begründung der Mechanik" (1900). This publication constitutes the high point in the discussion of the change in size arising from the high velocity of the electrons and records the strong doubts concerning the constancy of mass.

While at Würzburg, Wien also continued his experiments with vacuum tubes. In 1905 he determined the lower boundary of the mass of the "positive electron" (called "Kanalstrahlen") as being that of the hydrogen ion. As early as 1908, following Stark's discovery of the Doppler displacement of radiation from these "electrons," Wien examined the mechanism by which they emit light; he pursued these experiments, involving the measurement of the decay time, for the rest of his life. Believing this decay to be much smaller than was supposed, Wien in 1919 devised a way of observing it in the vacuum tube that did not involve collisions: separating the space in which the positive rays are produced from the space in which they are observed. (Unlike cathode rays, they do not penetrate metal foils.) Wien allowed the positive rays to enter through a narrow slit in the vacuum tube, which he had emptied by means of the diffusion air pump recently invented by W. Gaede. (Wien used ten of these pumps.) The production space was maintained at an arbitrary, constant pressure through the gas flow method (*Durchströmungsmethode*) developed in vacuum processing. This separation technique later gained importance in the construction of elementary particle accelerators. Wien calculated the decay constant $2a$ for the decrease $\exp(-2at)$ of the light intensity of the luminous particle as being approximately $5 \times 10^7$ $s^{-1}$, which was in good agreement with the known value of the beam velocity. In 1922 Wien successfully applied his technique to the separation of arc lines (light from uncharged atoms) from spark lines (light from ions the charge of which could be shown by electrostatic deflection).

In this connection Wien in 1916 demonstrated the existence—which accords with the relativity principle—of a phenomenon that is the inverse of the Stark effect (that is, of the line splitting of a stationary light source in an electric field), experimentally showing the corresponding splitting in the case of a moving light source in a magnetic field. Also in the realm of radiation physics, Wien in 1907 sought to ascertain the lengths of Röntgen waves by measuring the impulse width. His assumption was that these waves arise through the slowing of electrons in the electromagnetic field. In the same year, working with quantum theoretical assumptions, on which the photoelectric effect was based recently, he obtained the good value $\lambda = 6.75 \times 10^{-9}$ cm, five years before Max von Laue, and suggested that Röntgen wavelengths could be measured by means of crystal lattice.

In theoretical physics Wien won recognition for his conceptual experiments.[9] In his view, "such imagined processes . . . ought to correspond to realization with an unlimited degree of approximation" (1893). In 1911 Wien wrote: "Thought experiments" are devised "because for practical reasons it is often impossible to carry them out, and yet they lead to reliable results." He maintained, however, that to posit these imagined "processes . . . the lawlike manner in which they take place . . . must be fully known," although he granted that it is permissible to "idealize."

In *Ziele und Methoden der theoretischen Physik* (1914), Wien distinguished mathematical from theoretical physics.[10] The former, he held, should furnish the mathematical tools—just as mathematics establishes exact relationships between numerical quantities. The latter should seek to determine quantitative laws, for which it must develop hypotheses; it can, however, attain only approximate exactness. Wien held that the laws of nature are simpler than is generally supposed by scientists, who see the infinite variety of their intricate effects. Only quantitative verification through comparison with observed data can protect the theoretician—who generally does not feel bound by experiments—from the many unsuitable ideas he generates. This quantitatively controlled interaction between theory and experiment excludes a possible carelessness in the use of mathematical expressions.

## NOTES

1. For these biographical data the author is indebted to Wien's daughter, Waltraut Wien, of Munich.
2. Wien was stimulated to record this review of his career by a letter of 17 Aug. 1927 from an unidentified American living in Denver, who solicited Wien's response to use for pedagogical purposes. See *Aus dem Leben und Wirken eines Physikers*, 1–50.
3. Wien's laws were assimilated so quickly into physics that when Wien went to England in 1904, people expected to see an older man instead of a "young" man of forty years of age.
4. In 1915 Wien again expressed reservations concerning Planck's quanta; see "Theorie der Wärmestrahlung," 217–220.
5. In 1927 Wien believed he could observe "the encroaching

Americanization of all of life that is now taking place in Europe"; see *Aus dem Leben und Wirken eines Physikers*, 74: letter to E. Schrödinger, 1 May 1927.
6. For details of this and of the following contributions by Wien to the study of thermal radiation, see H. Kangro, *Vorgeschichte des Planckschen Strahlungsgesetzes, passim*.
7. The term "displacement law" (*Verschiebungsgesetz*) was coined by Otto Lummer and Ernst Pringsheim in 1899.
8. See H. Kangro, *Vorgeschichte des Planckschen Strahlungsgesetzes*, ch. 3; 4.2; and 5.3.
9. For more on this topic, see H. Kangro, *Vorgeschichte des Planckschen Strahlungsgesetzes, passim*.
10. Wien equated theoretical physics with the English "natural philosophy": see *Aus der Welt der Wissenschaft*, 170. Similarly, Helmholtz and G. T. Wertheim gave the title *Handbuch der theoretischen Physik* to the German translation of William Thomson and P. G. Tait's *Natural Philosophy*.

## BIBLIOGRAPHY

I. Original Works. Karl Wien, ed., *Aus dem Leben und Wirken eines Physikers* (Leipzig, 1930), includes a nearly complete bibliography of his writings; "Ein Rückblick," pp. 1–50, was written about 1927 and contains a mine of information given by Wien himself; a selection of Wien's correspondence with his mother, wife, Professor Oseen (possibly Carl Wilhelm Oseen), G. Mie, A. Sperl, W. Ostwald, Beggerow, and E. Schrödinger is on 51–76. See also Poggendorff, IV, 1633; V, 1368–1369; and VI, 2879.

The first Memoir of the student W. Wien is "Über den Einfluss der ponderablen Theile auf das gebeugte Licht," in *Sitzungsberichte der Königlich Preussischen Akademie der Wissenschaften zu Berlin*, II (1885), 817–819; and "Über die Energievertheilung im Emissionsspectrum eines schwarzen Körpers," in *Annalen der Physik*, 294 (June 1896), 662–669, also in English trans. as "On the Division of Energy in the Emission-Spectrum of a Black Body," in *Philosophical Magazine*, 5th ser., 43 (1897), 214–220. Wien's views on heat radiation are summarized in "Theorie der Strahlung," in *Encyklopädie der Mathematischen Wissenschaften mit Einschluss ihrer Anwendungen*, V: *Physik* (Leipzig, 1909), pt. 3, 182–357, and in "Theorie der Wärmestrahlung," in *Kultur der Gegenwart*, pt. 3, sec. 3, vol. 1 (Berlin, 1915), 217–220.

Wien's early memoirs include "Über die Messung hoher Temperaturen," in *Zeitschrift für Instrumentenkunde*, 12 (1892), 257–266, 296–307; also in *Annalen der Physik*, 283 (1892), 107–134; and 292 (1895), 360–396, both written with Ludwig Holborn; and "Über die Messung tiefer Temperaturen," *ibid.*, 295 (1896), 213–228, also in *Sitzungsberichte der Königlich Preussischen Akademie der Wissenschaften zu Berlin* (1896), 673–677, both written with Holborn.

Subsequent writings are "Untersuchungen über die elektrische Entladung in verdünnten Gasen," in *Annalen der Physik*, 301 (1898), 440–452; "Zur Theorie der Strahlung schwarzer Körper. Kritisches," *ibid.*, 308 (1900), 530–539, dated 12 Oct. 1900—cf. Planck's response, *ibid.*, 764–766, and Wien's answer, "Zur Theorie der Strahlung; Bemerkungen zur Kritik des Herrn Planck," *ibid.*, **309** (1901), 422–424, dated 29 Dec. 1900; "Über die Möglichkeit einer elektromagnetischen Begründung der Mechanik," in *Archives néerlandaises des sciences exactes et naturelles*, 2nd ser., **5** (1900), 96–107; also in *Annalen der Physik*, **310** (1901), 501–513; and "Die Temperatur und Entropie der Strahlung," in *Physikalische Zeitschrift*, **2** (1901), 111 (as *Vorträge und Diskussionen von der 72. Naturforscherversammlung zu Aachen*); which includes remarks on the discussions thereon held at the 72nd Conference of the Gesellschaft Deutscher Naturforscher at Aachen, 20 Oct. 1900.

Later works are "Über die Natur der positiven Elektronen," in *Annalen der Physik*, **314** (1902), 660–664; "Über eine Berechnung der Wellenlänge der Röntgenstrahlen aus dem Planckschen Energie-Element," in *Nachrichten von der Königlichen Gesellschaft der Wissenschaften zu Göttingen*, Math.-naturwiss. Klasse, (1907), 598–601; and "Über die Berechnung der Impulsbreite der Röntgenstrahlen aus ihrer Energie," in *Annalen der Physik*, **327** (1907), 793–797.

Like Planck, Wien gave six lectures in the United States on theoretical physics; they were published as *Vorlesungen über neuere Probleme der Theoretischen Physik, gehalten an der Columbia-Universität in New York im April 1913* (Leipzig–Berlin, 1913); they were followed by *Ziele und Methoden der theoretischen Physik* (Würzburg, 1914), (=Festrede zur Feier des 332, jährigen Bestehens der Julius-Maximilian-Universität in Würzburg am 11. März 1914), also in *Jahrbuch der Radioaktivität und Elektronik*, **12** (1915), 241–259.

On Wien's last main field of research, see "Über Messungen der Leuchtdauer der Atome und die Dämpfung der Spektrallinien," in *Annalen der Physik*, **365** (1919), 597–637; and II, **371** (1921), 229–236; and "Über eine Methode zur Trennung der Bogen- und Funkenlinien der Emissionsspektra," *ibid.*, **374** (1922), 325–334.

Wien's general lectures and papers are included in *Aus der Welt der Wissenschaft* (Leipzig, 1921).

Wien's curricula vitae are the MS "Vita," composed probably in the early 1890's, at the Staatsbibliothek Preussischer Kulturbesitz, Berlin-Dahlem; and "Vita," only printed in his original dissertation on *Untersuchungen über die bei der Beugung des Lichtes auftretenden Absorptionserscheinungen. Inaugural-Dissertation zur Erlangung der Doctorwürde . . . nebst beigefügten Thesen öffentlich zu verteidigen am 3. Februar 1886* (Berlin, n.d. [1886]).

On Wien's MSS, see T. S. Kuhn *et al.*, eds., *Sources for the History of Quantum Physics* (Philadelphia, 1967), 97a. The American Philosophical Society, Philadelphia, has some of Wien's letters to Planck; and nearly 150 letters from Planck to Wien are at the Staatsbibliothek Preussischer Kulturbesitz. The Deutsches Museum, Munich, recently acquired various other papers of Wien.

II. SECONDARY LITERATURE. There is a nearly complete bibliography in Poggendorff, VI, 2879; and VIIa, 991; Max von Laue, "Wilhelm Wien," in *Deutsches Biographisches Jahrbuch, X, das Jahr 1928* (Stuttgart–Berlin, 1931), 302–310, is a useful sketch; see also the obituary notices contributed by various authors in Wien's *Aus dem Leben und Wirken eines Physikers*, 139–189. Other sources include K. Reger, "Wilhelm Wien," in *Nobelpreisträger auf dem Wege ins Atomzeitalter* (Munich–Vienna, 1958), 233–246; and Max Steenbeck, *Wilhelm Wien und sein Einfluss auf die Physik seiner Zeit* (Berlin, 1964) (=Deutsche Akademie der Wissenschaften zu Berlin, Vorträge und Schriften, Heft 94, 1–21). On Wien's early scientific studies, see H. Kangro, *Vorgeschichte des Planckschen Strahlungsgesetzes . . .* (Wiesbaden, 1970), *passim*, esp. ch. 5.

HANS KANGRO

**WIENER, LUDWIG CHRISTIAN** (*b.* Darmstadt, Germany, 7 December 1826; *d.* Karlsruhe, Germany, 31 July 1896), *mathematics, physics, philosophy.*

In mathematics Christian Wiener did important work in descriptive geometry and the construction of mathematical models. As a physicist he studied chiefly molecular phenomena and atmospheric radiation. In his philosophical writings he advocated a point of view based on the methodology of natural science.

The son of a judge, Wiener attended the gymnasium in Darmstadt and from 1843 to 1847 studied engineering and architecture at the University of Giessen, where he passed the state architecture examination. In 1848 he obtained a post as teacher of physics, mechanics, hydraulics, and descriptive geometry at the Höhere Gewerbeschule (later the Technische Hochschule) of Darmstadt. Two years later he earned the Ph.D. and qualified as a *Privatdozent* in mathematics at the University of Giessen. To further his education he attended the Technical University in Karlsruhe, working for about a year under Ferdinand Redtenbacher, the professor of mechanical engineering. He returned to Giessen in the autumn of 1851; but the following year he accepted a professorship of descriptive geometry at the Technische Hochschule in Karlsruhe, retaining the position until 1896.

An able and respected teacher, Wiener trained a great number of students while conducting important research. Elected rector of the Technische Hochschule three times, he was also a member of the Gewerbeschulrat and the Oberschulrat of the state of Baden. Wiener was liked and esteemed for his upright character, his sense of justice, and his kindliness.

In his mathematical works Wiener frequently used direct intuition as an aid in carrying out proofs. This led him into the realm of aesthetics, as can be seen from his philosophical essay "Über die Schönheit der Linien" (1896), which contains an appendix on the relationship between mathematical continuity and the regularity of forms.

Wiener's chief work was the two-volume *Lehrbuch der darstellenden Geometrie* (1884–1887), based on his teaching experience and numerous publications on descriptive geometry. In the introduction to the *Lehrbuch* he presented a valuable historical survey, based on a firsthand study of the sources, that constituted an important supplement to Chasles's *Aperçu historique sur l'origine et le développement des méthodes en géométrie* (1837). Wiener treated the basic problems of descriptive geometry by a single method: a varied use of the principal lines of a plane. He also sought to simplify individual problems as much as possible and to find the easiest graphical solutions for them. He was not, however, concerned merely with graphical methods, of which he was a master. He was also interested in the problems and their solutions (such as shadow construction and brightness distribution), as well as in the development of the necessary geometric aids. For example, he used imaginary projection and developed a grid method that can be derived from the theory of cyclically projected point series.

Wiener also became known for his mathematical models. In 1869, at the suggestion of R. F. A. Clebsch, he constructed a plaster-of-Paris model of the third-order surface. He displayed his models at expositions of mathematical teaching aids in London (1876), Munich (1893), and Chicago (1893). In analysis he discussed and drew the Weierstrass function, which is everywhere continuous and yet at no point has a derivative.

Extending his works on descriptive geometry into physics, Wiener investigated the illumination conditions for various bodies. Thus, he calculated the amounts of solar radiation received at different latitudes and during the varying lengths of days in the course of the year. His numerical values are still fundamental for the study of atmospheric optics and of the effect of radiation on the earth's climate. In a posthumously published article Wiener examined the total radiation received by the atmosphere and considered problems related to color theory and strengths of perceptions.

In his studies on molecular physics, Wiener demonstrated by extremely careful observations that Brownian movement is an "internal motion peculiar to the liquid state." He developed an atomistic cosmology, which he set forth in *Atomlehre* (1869), the first volume of his chief philosophical work, *Die Grundzüge der Weltordnung*. He presupposed the causality of all natural phenomena and the existence of a real external world but, in accordance with a view widely held at the time, he still accepted the existence of an ether. In his treatment of crystalline forms Wiener developed the concept of the regular point system, which became important in crystallography.

Among the topics Wiener discussed in his writings on moral philosophy were will and morality. He defined free will as independence from external, determining circumstances only, thus precluding full independence—that is, absolute freedom. He opposed the view of some of his contemporaries that scientific research, with its analytic methods, could become a danger to man's sense of morality and beauty. Unlike his other publications, Wiener's philosophical works found only a limited audience.

## BIBLIOGRAPHY

I. ORIGINAL WORKS. Bibliographies of Wiener's approximately 100 scientific books and papers are in Poggendorff, II, 1322, and III, 1442; and in the unsigned *Zur Erinnerung an Dr. Christian Wiener* (see below).

Mathematical works include *Über Vielecke und Vielflache* (Leipzig, 1864); *Stereoskopische Photographie des Modells einer Fläche dritter Ordnung mit 27 reellen Geraden* (Leipzig, 1869); "Direkte Lösung der Aufgabe: Einen durch fünf Punkte oder durch fünf Tangenten gegebenen Kegelschnitt auf einen Umdrehungskegel zu legen," in *Zeitschrift für Mathematik und Physik*, **20** (1875), 317–325; "Geometrische und analytische Untersuchung der Weierstrass'schen Funktion," in *Journal für die reine und angewandte Mathematik*, **90** (1880), 221–252; and *Lehrbuch der darstellenden Geometrie*, 2 vols. (Leipzig, 1884–1887).

Writings in physics are "Erklärung des atomistischen Wesens des tropfbar-flüssigen Körperzustandes und Bestätigung desselben durch die sogenannten Molekularbewegungen," in *Annalen der Physik und Chemie*, **118** (1863), 79–94; "Über die Stärke der Bestrahlung der Erde durch die Sonne in ihren verschiedenen Breiten und Jahreszeiten," in *Zeitschrift für Mathematik und Physik*, **22** (1877), 341–368, also abridged in *Österreichische Zeitschrift für Meteorologie*, **14** (1879), 113–129; and "Die Helligkeit des klaren Himmels und die Beleuchtung durch Sonne, Himmel und Rückstrahlung,"

H. Wiener, O. Wiener, and W. Möbius, eds., 2 pts., *Nova acta Leopoldina*, **73**, no. 1 (1900), and **91**, no. 2 (1909).

On philosophy, see *Die Grundzüge der Weltordnung* (Leipzig–Heidelberg, 1863), 2nd ed., 2 vols.: I, *Atomlehre* (1869), II, *Die geistige Welt und der Ursprung der Dinge* (1869); and "Über die Schönheit der Linien," in *Abhandlungen des Naturwissenschaftlichen Vereins in Karlsruhe*, **11** (1896), 47–73.

II. SECONDARY LITERATURE. See the unsigned *Zur Erinnerung an Dr. Christian Wiener* (Karlsruhe, 1896); A. Brill and L. Sohnke, "Christian Wiener," in *Jahresberichte der Deutschen Mathematiker-Vereinigung*, **6** (1897), 46–69; and H. Wiener, "Wiener, Christian," in *Allgemeine deutsche Biographie*, XLII (1897), 790–792.

HANS-GÜNTHER KÖRBER

**WIENER, NORBERT** (*b.* Columbia, Missouri, 26 November 1894; *d.* Stockholm, Sweden, 18 March 1964), *mathematics*.

Wiener was the son of Leo Wiener, who was born in Byelostok, Russia, and Bertha Kahn. Although a child prodigy, he matured into a renowned mathematician rather slowly. At first he was taught by his father. He entered high school at the age of nine and graduated two years later. After four years in college, he enrolled at the Harvard Graduate School at the age of fifteen in order to study zoology. That soon turned out to be a wrong choice. He next tried philosophy at Cornell. "A philosopher in spite of himself," Wiener took a Ph.D. at Harvard in 1913 with a dissertation on the boundary between philosophy and mathematics. A Harvard traveling fellowship paid his way to Europe. Bertrand Russell was his chief mentor at Cambridge and advised him to learn more mathematics. Neither the examples of Hardy and Littlewood at Cambridge, however, nor those of Hilbert and Landau at Göttingen, converted him to mathematics. Back in the United States in 1915, Wiener tried various jobs teaching philosophy, mathematics, and engineering. In the spring of 1919 he got a position in the mathematics department of the Massachusetts Institute of Technology, not then particularly distinguished in that discipline. An assistant professor in 1924, associate in 1929, and full professor in 1932, he remained at MIT until his retirement. Although his genius contributed to establishing the institute's present reputation, he could never comfort himself over the failure of other American universities, and particularly of Harvard, to show much interest in him. He traveled a great deal, to Europe and to Asia, and his visits to Germany in the interwar years left their traces in many anecdotes told in Continental circles. His *Cybernetics* made him a public figure. President Lyndon Johnson awarded him the National Medal of Science two months before his death. He died during a trip to Sweden and left two daughters. His wife was the former Margaret Engemann.

In appearance and behavior, Norbert Wiener was a baroque figure, short, rotund, and myopic, combining these and many qualities in extreme degree. His conversation was a curious mixture of pomposity and wantonness. He was a poor listener. His self-praise was playful, convincing, and never offensive. He spoke many languages but was not easy to understand in any of them. He was a famously bad lecturer.

Wiener was a great mathematician who opened new perspectives onto fields in which the activity became intense, as it still is. Although most of his ideas have become standard knowledge, his original papers, and especially his books, remain difficult to read. His style was often chaotic. After proving at length a fact that would be too easy if set as an exercise for an intelligent sophomore, he would assume without proof a profound theorem that was seemingly unrelated to the preceding text, then continue with a proof containing puzzling but irrelevant terms, next interrupt it with a totally unrelated historical exposition, meanwhile quote something from the "last chapter" of the book that had actually been in the first, and so on. He would often treat unrelated questions consecutively, and although the discussion of any one of them might be lucid, rigorous, and beautiful, the reader is left puzzled by the lack of continuity. All too often Wiener could not resist the temptation to tell everything that cropped up in his comprehensive mind, and he often had difficulty in separating the relevant mathematics neatly from its scientific and social implications and even from his personal experiences. The reader to whom he appears to be addressing himself seems to alternate in a random order between the layman, the undergraduate student of mathematics, the average mathematician, and Wiener himself.

Wiener wrote a most unusual autobiography. Although it conveys an extremely egocentric view of the world, I find it an agreeable story and not offensive, because it is naturally frank and there is no pose, least of all that of false modesty. All in all it is abundantly clear that he never had the slightest idea of how he appeared in the eyes of others. His account of the ill-starred trip to Europe in 1926–1927 is a particularly good example. Although he says almost nothing about the work of the mathematicians whom he met, he recalled after twenty-five years meeting J. B. S. Haldane and setting him straight over an error in his book *The Gold-Makers*: Haldane had used a Danish name for a character supposed to be an Icelander (*I Am a Mathematician*, 160). In his autobiography Wiener comes through as a fundamentally good-natured person, realistic about his human responsibilities and serious enough to be a good friend, a good citizen, and a good cosmopolite. Despite his broad erudition, the philosophical interludes are no more than common sense, if not downright flat. Unlike many autobiographers, he never usurps the role of a prophet who long ago predicted the course that things have taken. A good biography ought to be written of him, one that would counterbalance his autobiography and do him more justice than anyone can do in a book about himself.

According to his own account, Wiener's understanding of modern mathematics began in 1918, when he came across works on integration, functionals, and differential equations among the books of a young Harvard student who had died. At that time he met I. A. Barnett, who by suggesting that he work on integration in function spaces, put Wiener on the track that would lead him to his greatest achievements, the first of which was differential space. It was already characteristic of Wiener's openness of mind that, rather than being satisfied with a general integration theory, he looked for physical embodiments to test the theory. The first he tried, turbulence, was a failure; but the next, Brownian motion (1921), studied earlier by Einstein, was a success. Wiener conceived a measure in the space of one-dimensional paths that leads to the application of probability concepts in that space (see *Selected Papers*, no. 2). The construction is surprisingly simple. Take the set of continuous functions $x(t)$ of $t \geqq 0$ with $x(0) = 0$ and require that the probability of $x$ passing for $t_i$ between $\alpha_i$ and $\beta_i$ ($i = 1, \ldots, k$) is provided by the Einstein-Smoluchowski formula that gives for the probability density of a point at $x$ staying at $y$ after a lapse of time $t$ the expression

$$(2 \pi t)^{\frac{1}{2}} \exp (-[y-x]^2/2t).$$

In later work Wiener made this measure more explicit by a measure-preserving mapping of the real number line on function space. He also proved that almost all paths are nondifferentiable and that almost all of them satisfy a Lipschitz condition of any degree $< 1/2$, although almost none does so with such a condition of degree $> 1/2$. "Differential space" is a strange term for this function space

with a measure, promising a measure defined not by finite but by differential methods. Although vaguely operative on the background, this idea was never made explicit by Wiener when he resumed use of the term "differential space" in later work.

In 1923–1925 Wiener published papers that greatly influenced potential theory: Dirichlet's problem, in its full generality (see *Selected Papers*, no. 3). The exterior problem of a compact set $K$ in 3-space led him to the capacitory potential of a measure with support $K$ as a basic tool.

From Brownian motion Wiener turned to the study of more general stochastic processes, and the mathematical needs of MIT's engineering department set him on the new track of harmonic analysis. His work during the next five years culminated in a long paper (1930) on generalized harmonic analysis (see *Selected Papers*, no. 4), which as a result of J. D. Tamarkin's collaboration is very well written. Rather than on the class $L^2$, Wiener focused on that of measurable functions $f$ with

$$\Phi(x) = \lim_{T \to \infty} \frac{1}{2T} \int_{-T}^{T} f(x+t)\bar{f}(t)dt$$

existing for all $x$, which is even broader than that of almost periodic functions. He borrowed the function $\Phi$ from physics as a key to harmonic analysis and connected it later to communication theory. Writing $\Phi$ as a Fourier transform,

$$\Phi(t) = (2\pi)^{-\frac{1}{2}} \int_{-\infty}^{\infty} e^{-itu} dS(u),$$

he obtained what is now called the spectral distribution $S$. The most difficult step was to connect $S$ to the integrated Fourier transform $g$ of $f$ by an analogue of the classical formula $S(t) = \int_{-\infty}^{t} |g(\lambda)|^2 d\lambda$. A brilliant example is: If $f(x) = \pm 1$ for $x_n \leqq x < x_{n+1}$, where the signs are fixed by spinning a coin, then the spectral distribution of $f$ is almost certainly continuous.

A key formula in this field was placed by Wiener on the cover of the second part of his autobiography:

$$\lim_{\epsilon \to 0} \frac{1}{2\epsilon} \int_{-\infty}^{\infty} (g(\omega+\epsilon) - g(\omega-\epsilon))^2 d\omega$$

$$= \frac{2}{\pi} \lim_{A \to \infty} \frac{1}{2A} \int_{-A}^{A} |f(t)|^2 dt.$$

When Wiener attempted to prove this, A. E. Ingham led him to what Hardy and Littlewood had called Tauberian theorems; but Wiener did more than adapt their results to his own needs. He gave a marvelous example of the unifying force of mathematical abstraction by recasting the Tauberian question as follows (see *Selected Papers*, no. 5): To prove the validity of

$$\lim_{x \to \infty} \int_{-\infty}^{\infty} K(x-y)f(y)\,dy = A \int_{-\infty}^{\infty} K(x)\,dx,$$

by which kind of more tractable kernel $K_1$, $K$ may be replaced. The answer is (for $K$ and $K_1 \in L_1$): If the Fourier transform of $K_1$ vanishes nowhere, the validity with $K_1$ implies that with $K$. Tauberian theorems have lost much of their interest today, but the argument by which Wiener proved his theorem is still vigorous. Wiener showed that in $L_1$ the linear span of the translates of a function is dense if its Fourier transform vanishes nowhere. This, again, rests on the remark that the Fourier transform class $L_1$ is closed with respect to division (as far as possible). Wiener's work in this area became the historical source of the theory of Banach algebras. The "Wiener problem," that is, the problem of deciding whether it is true that in $L_1$ a function $f_1$ belongs to the closure of the span of the translates of $f_2$ if and only if the Fourier transform of $f_1$ always vanishes together with that of $f_2$, greatly influenced modern harmonic analysis; it was proved to be wrong by Paul Malliavin in 1959.

Fourier transforms and Tauberian theorems were also the subject of Wiener and R. E. A. C. Paley's collaboration, which led to *Fourier Transforms* (1934). Another cooperative achievement was the study of the Wiener-Hopf equation (see *Selected Papers*, no. 6),

$$f(x) = \int_0^{\infty} K(x-y)f(y)\,dy,$$

generalizing Eberhard Hopf's investigation on radiation equilibrium. In *I Am a Mathematician* (p. 177), Wiener remarked that although originally accounting for the discontinuity of two physical media at $x = 0$, it can even better serve to embody the discontinuity of knowledge at the boundary of future and past. The previous work on the Wiener-Hopf equation became influential in Wiener's prediction theory.

Until the late 1930's stochastic processes, as exemplified by Brownian motion, and harmonic analysis were loose ends in the fabric of Wiener's thought. To be sure, they were not isolated from each other: the spectrally analyzed function $f$ was thought of as a single stochastic happening, and the earlier cited example shows that such a happening

could even be conceived as embedded in a stochastic process. Work of others in the 1930's shows the dawning of the idea of spectral treatment of stationary stochastic processes; at the end of the decade it became clear that the "Hilbert space trick" of ergodic theory could serve this aim also. Initially Wiener had neglected ergodic theory; in 1938–1939 he fully caught up (see *Selected Papers*, nos. 7–8), although in later work he did not avail himself of these methods as much as he might have done.

Communication theory, which for a long time had been Wiener's background thought, became more prominent in his achievements after 1940. From antiaircraft fire control and noise filtration in radar to control and communication in biological settings, it was technical problems that stimulated his research. Although linear prediction was investigated independently by A. N. Kolmogorov, Wiener's approach had the merit of dealing with prediction and filtering under one heading. If on the strength of ergodicity of the stationary stochastic process $f (f_t \in L_2)$, the covariances $\varphi(t) = (f_t, f_0)$ are supposed to be provided by the data of the past, linear predicting means estimating the future of $f$ by its projection on the linear span of the past $f_t$. On the other hand, linear filtering means separating the summands "message" and "noise" in $f_t = f_t^1 + f_t^2$, where again the autocovariances and cross covariances $\Phi(t) = (f_t, f_0)$ and $\Phi_1(t) = (f_t^1, f_0)$ are supposed to be known and the message is estimated by its projection on the linear span of the past signals $f_t$. Both tasks lead to Wiener-Hopf equations for a weighting distribution $w$,

$$\varphi(t+h) = \int_0^{\infty} \varphi(t-\tau)\,dw(\tau) \qquad (t \geqq 0),$$

$$\varphi_1(t+h) = \int_0^{\infty} \varphi(t-\tau)\,dw(\tau) \qquad (t \geqq 0),$$

respectively.

The implications of these fundamental concepts were elaborated in a wartime report that was belatedly published in 1949; it is still difficult to read, although its contents have become basic knowledge in communication theory. Nonlinear filtering was the subject of Wiener's unpublished memorandum (1949) that led to combined research at MIT, as reported by his close collaborator Y. W. Lee (see *Selected Papers*, pp. 17–33). A series of lectures on this subject was published in 1958. One of its main subjects is the use of an orthogonal development of nonlinear (polynomial) Volterra functionals by R. H. Cameron and W. T. Martin (1947) in a spectral theory and in the analysis and synthesis of nonlinear filters, which, rather than with trigonometric inputs, are probed with white Gaussian inputs.

After this brief exposition of Wiener's mathematics of communication, it remains to inspect the broad field that Wiener himself vaguely indicated as cybernetics; he tells how he coined this term, although it had not been unusual in the nineteenth century to indicate government theory. While studying antiaircraft fire control, Wiener may have conceived the idea of considering the operator as part of the steering mechanism and of applying to him such notions as feedback and stability, which had been devised for mechanical systems and electrical circuits. No doubt this kind of analogy had been operative in Wiener's mathematical work from the beginning and sometimes had even been productive. As time passed, such flashes of insight were more consciously put to use in a sort of biological research for which Wiener consulted all kinds of people, except mathematicians, whether or not they had anything to do with it. *Cybernetics, or the Control and Communication in the Animal and the Machine* (1948) is a rather eloquent report of these abortive attempts, in the sense that it shows there is not much to be reported. The value and influence of *Cybernetics*, and other publications of this kind, should not, however, be belittled. It has contributed to popularizing a way of thinking in communication theory terms, such as feedback, information, control, input, output, stability, homeostasis, prediction, and filtering. On the other hand, it also has contributed to spreading mistaken ideas of what mathematics really means. *Cybernetics* suggests that it means embellishing a nonmathematical text with terms and formulas from highbrow mathematics. This is a style that is too often imitated by those who have no idea of the meaning of the mathematical words they use. Almost all so-called applications of information theory are of this kind.

Even measured by Wiener's standards, *Cybernetics* is a badly organized work—a collection of misprints, wrong mathematical statements, mistaken formulas, splendid but unrelated ideas, and logical absurdities. It is sad that this work earned Wiener the greater part of his public renown, but this is an afterthought. At that time mathematical readers were more fascinated by the richness of its ideas than by its shortcomings. Few, if any, reviewers voiced serious criticism.

Wiener published more writings of this kind. The last was a booklet entitled *God and Golem, Inc.* It would have been more appropriate as the swan song of a lesser mathematician than Wiener.

### BIBLIOGRAPHY

I. ORIGINAL WORKS. Many of Wiener's writings were brought together in his *Selected Papers* (Cambridge, Mass., 1964), which includes contributions by Y. W. Lee, N. Levinson, and W. T. Martin. Among his works are *Fourier Transforms in the Complex Domain* (New York, 1934), written with Raymond E. A. C. Paley; *Cybernetics, or the Control and Communication in the Animal and the Machine* (Paris–Cambridge, Mass., 1948); *Extrapolation, Interpolation and Smoothing of Stationary Time Series, With Engineering Applications* (Cambridge, Mass.–New York–London, 1949); *Ex-Prodigy—My Childhood and Youth* (New York, 1953; Cambridge, Mass., 1955); *I Am a Mathematician—the Later Life of a Prodigy* (Garden City, N.Y., 1956; repr. Cambridge, Mass., 1964); *Nonlinear Problems in Random Theory* (Cambridge, Mass.–New York–London, 1958); *God and Golem, Inc.* (Cambridge, Mass., 1964); and *Differential Space, Quantum Systems, and Prediction* (Cambridge, Mass., 1966), written with Armand Siegel, Bayard Rankin, and William Ted Martin.

II. SECONDARY LITERATURE. See "Norbert Wiener," *Bulletin of the American Mathematical Society*, spec. iss., **72**, no. 1, pt. 2 (1966), with contributions by N. Levinson, W. Rosenblith and J. Wiesner, M. Brelot, J. P. Kahane, S. Mandelbrojt, M. Kac, J. L. Doob, P. Masani, and W. L. Root, with bibliography of 214 items (not including posthumous works). See also Constance Reid, *Hilbert* (Berlin, 1970), esp. 169–170.

HANS FREUDENTHAL

**WIENER, OTTO** (*b.* Karlsruhe, Germany, 15 June 1862; *d.* Leipzig, Germany, 18 January 1927), *physics*.

Wiener, whose ancestors included clergymen and jurists, was the son of Christian Wiener, a professor of descriptive geometry at the Technische Hochschule in Karlsruhe. His mother, the former Pauline Hausrath, was the sister of a Protestant theologian and died of typhus when Wiener was three.

Wiener studied physics first at Karlsruhe, then at Berlin, and finally at the University of Strasbourg, where he earned the Ph.D. in 1887 under August Kundt, whose private assistant he was. In 1890 he qualified as a lecturer with "Stehende Lichtwellen." The following year he was named *Dozent* for physics at the Technische Hochshule in Aachen, and in 1894 he was promoted to extraordinary professor. In the same year he married Lina Fenner, daughter of *Geheimrat* Georg Fenner of Hesse-Homburg. In 1895 Wiener accepted an offer of a full professorship at the University of Giessen, where all his efforts were absorbed in the construction and organization of a new physics institute. His experience in this undertaking subsequently proved very useful, when he became involved in a similar project at Leipzig, upon succeeding Gustav Wiedemann as professor of physics.

Wiener reached the summit of his scientific career at its beginning and spent the second half pursuing what proved to be a mirage: "a fundamental law of nature," as he put it, according to which all physical events could be derived from a universal ether and from the velocities and differences in velocities of its parts. In this view, even electrons and protons were considered to be only definite forms of motion: rotating ether rings. Wiener's publications on this subject, more sketches than reports of results, brought more opposition and ridicule than recognition and made him seem an "anti-Einstein" to many of his colleagues.

Wiener's name is linked with the experimental demonstration of standing light waves. In 1888 Heinrich Hertz, working in the physics institute of the Technische Hochschule of Karlsruhe, proved the existence of electromagnetic waves. Those he detected had lengths of about eight meters. A year later Wiener performed a similar experiment with light waves—electromagnetic waves—approximately ten million times shorter than those used by Hertz. In the simplest case these waves arise in front of a plane metal mirror from the interference of incident monochromatic waves with the reflected ones.

Wiener's research in this area was a result of the work he did for his doctoral dissertation, "Über die Phasenänderung des Lichtes bei der Reflexion und Methoden zur Dickenbestimmung dünner Blättchen" (1887). In the latter he had, at Kundt's suggestion, measured light absorption in transparently thin metal plates, obtained by cathode-ray evaporation. In order to evaluate the measurements, however, it was necessary to know the thickness of the plates and the change in the vibration phase resulting from reflection. This change could be determined only when the light was obliquely incident. Through this research Wiener became a pioneer in the physics and techniques of thin plates, a field of great importance today.

A major question remained unanswered: how the vibration phase changes when light is incident perpendicularly. Inspired by Hertz's work, Wiener hoped to find an answer and, if possible, to demonstrate standing light waves. He did, in fact, succeed in making visible nodes and antinodes separated by intervals of about $2 \cdot 10^{-5}$ centimeters in front of a plane silver plate on which monochromatic light shone perpendicularly. He achieved this with a suitably mounted photosensitive plate, like those used in photography, the thickness of which was about 1/30 the wavelengths. Wiener demonstrated conclusively that it was the nodes of the resulting light vibrations, and not antinodes, that lay in the mirror surface. Accordingly, the reflection of light must take place with phase inversion: this was the answer to his question. In addition the experiment revealed that only the electric portion of the electromagnetic light waves blackens the silver chloride in the photosensitive layer. Wiener's amazing success was acknowledged as a masterpiece of experimentation.

The standing waves soon found an application in Gabriel Lippmann's color photography. In this process the silver contained in suitably prepared photosensitive plates is separated into parallel planes by the standing light waves. When viewed in daylight, these planes transmit to the eye only those colors having wavelengths that match the distances between the planes, while the other wavelengths are eliminated through interference. Wiener worked on color photography and proved that the color effects observed in the plates produced by Daguerre (silver plates with a silver iodide layer) arose in the same way they do in Lippmann's plates. Wiener also had a predilection for technical problems, especially of bird flight, and was very interested in the developing subject of aeronautics.

## BIBLIOGRAPHY

I. ORIGINAL WORKS. A bibliography of Wiener's writings is in *Berichte. Sächsische Akademie der Wissenschaften*, **79** (1927), 119–121. Among his works are "Über die Phasenänderung des Lichts bei der Reflexion und Methoden zur Dickenbestimmung dünner Blättchen," in *Annalen der Physik und Chemie*, n.s. **31** (1887), 629–672, his doctoral dissertation; "Stehende Lichtwellen und die Schwingungsrichtung polarisierten Lichts," *ibid.*, n.s. **40** (1890), 203–243, 744; and "Farbenphotographie durch Körperfarben und mechanische Farbenanpassung in der Natur," *ibid.*, n.s. **55** (1895), 225–281. The Saxon Academy of Sciences, Leipzig, possesses more than 1,000 pages of a MS "Grundgesetz der Natur."

II. SECONDARY LITERATURE. See K. Lichtenecker, "Otto Wiener," in *Physikalische Zeitschrift*, **29** (1928), 73–78, with portrait; W. Möbius, "Otto Wiener gestorben," in *Zeitschrift für technische Physik*, **8** (1927), 129–131; and L. Weikmann, "Nachruf auf Otto Wiener," in *Berichte. Sächsische Akademie der Wissenschaften*, **79** (1927), 107–120, with portrait and bibliography.

FRITZ FRAUNBERGER

**WIESNER, JULIUS VON** (*b*. Tschechen, Moravia [now Czechoslovakia], 20 January 1838; *d*. Vienna, Austria, 9 October 1916), *plant anatomy, plant physiology*.

Wiesner was the youngest of eight children of Karl Wiesner, a shipping agent in Tschechen, and of Rosa Deutsch. Shortly after his birth the family moved to Brno, where Wiesner spent his youth and attended secondary school. He began his higher education at the Technical University of Brno and continued it at the University of Vienna, where he studied botany under E. Fenzl and Franz Unger, chemistry under Anton von Schrötter, physiology under Ernst Brücke, and physics under Andreas von Ettingshausen. He received the Ph.D. from Jena in 1860 and a year later qualified as academic lecturer at the Imperial-Royal Polytechnic Institute (now the Technical University) for Physiological Botany in Vienna, where in 1868 he was appointed associate professor. He became professor of plant physiology at the Forestry Institute of Mariabrunn in 1870 and, three years later, professor of plant anatomy and physiology at the University of Vienna, where he remained active until 1909.

Wiesner was rector of the University of Vienna during the academic year 1898–1899. Many scientific academies and learned societies elected him to membership: Vienna, Berlin, Paris, Munich, Rome, Turin, Göttingen, Uppsala, and Christiania (Oslo). He was awarded honorary doctorates by the technical universities of Brno and Vienna and by the universities of Uppsala and Glasgow. For many years Wiesner was a member of the Upper House, and when he retired from teaching in 1909, he was elevated to the hereditary nobility.

The Institute of Plant Physiology of the University of Vienna, of which Wiesner became director in 1873, was still located in a private house. Not until the fall of 1885 was it transferred to the newly built university, where it is still located. There Wiesner could bring to bear his talents as organizer and administrator, and the institution soon became known as one of the world's finest and best equipped plant physiology laboratories.

Led by his preference for applied research, Wiesner at first did work in technical microscopy and plant raw materials. His investigations on the microscopic characteristics of various fibers, on wood types and on how to demonstrate that a substance is wood, on tanning agents and on dyes, as well as on latexes, rubbers, resins, and balsams, were crowned by his integrated treatment of economically valuable plant materials in *Die Rohstoffe des Pflanzenreichs* (1873).

Wiesner also contributed work of enduring value in plant physiology with his studies of transpiration, the movements of plant organs, growth, and other phenomena of plant life. For decades he investigated the relationship between plants and light. In *Der Lichtgenuss der Pflanzen* he summarized his findings on the influence of the intensity and duration of sunlight in natural habitats on the distribution of plants and the development of their organs. Wiesner modified Bunsen and Roscoe's photographic method of light measurement to make it applicable to the requirements of plant physiology. He then undertook light measurements in Java, Egypt, Norway, and Spitsbergen, as well as in various parts of North America, thus providing the first survey of the light climate of the earth.

Wiesner also made valuable contributions to other fields. By examination of old Arabic and Central Asian papers, he demonstrated that six hundred years before the Arabs, the Chinese had known how to make paper from rags.

Wiesner had a lifelong interest in problems of natural philosophy. His book *Erschaffung, Entstehung, Entwicklung* was published a few weeks before his death.

*BIBLIOGRAPHY*

Wiesner published more than 200 articles in various journals. His books are *Einleitung in die technische Mikroskopie* (Vienna, 1867); *Gummiarten, Harze und Balsame* (Erlangen, 1869); *Die Entstehung des Chlorophylls in der Pflanze* (Vienna, 1877); *Elemente der wissenschaftlichen Botanik*, 3 vols. (I, Vienna, 1881; 2nd ed., 1885; 3rd ed., 1890; II, 1884; 2nd ed., 1891; III, 1889; 2nd ed., 1902; 3rd ed., 1913); *Die Elementarstruktur und das Wachstum der lebenden Substanz* (Vienna, 1892); *Die Rohstoffe des Pflanzenreichs*, 2 vols. (Leipzig, 1873; I, 2nd ed., 1900; II, 2nd ed., 1903; 3rd ed. enl., 3 vols. by J. Möller; 4th ed., by P. Krais and W. von Brehmer, 1927; 5th ed., by C. von Regel, Weinheim, 1962); *Der Lichtgenuss der Pflanzen* (Leipzig,

1907); and *Erschaffung, Entstehung, Entwicklung* (Leipzig, 1916).

A complete bibliography follows Hans Molisch's obituary of Wiesner in *Berichte der Deutschen botanischen Gesellschaft*, **34** (1916), 71–99.

RICHARD BIEBL

**WIGAND, ALBERT JULIUS WILHELM** (*b.* Treysa, Electoral Hesse, Germany, 21 April 1821; *d.* Marburg, Germany, 22 October 1886), *botany.*

The son of Johann Heinrich Friedrich Wigand, an apothecary, Wigand began the study of mathematics, science, and German philology at the University of Marburg in 1840. After a short period at the University of Berlin, where he studied botany under Karsten, he moved to Jena and became a pupil of Schleiden's. In fact, Wigand can be considered the last and most important member of Schleiden's school of botany. In 1846 he returned to Marburg and published his inaugural dissertation. In the same year he was appointed external university lecturer; in 1851, extraordinary professor; and in 1861, full professor of botany and director of the Botanical Garden and the pharmacognostic institute.

Wigand was active in various areas of botany; and all of his publications are characterized by a philosophical outlook that originated in his strong religious beliefs, although he always attempted to proceed inductively. In his inaugural dissertation he discussed the teratology of plants in the light of a general theory of metamorphosis, a subject to which he subsequently returned.

Strongly opposed to the view that ferns might have generative organs, Wigand mistakenly believed that both the antheridia and the archegonia must be functionless. With greater success he defended his views concerning the cuticula, the intercellular substance, and the structure of the cell wall. He stated that the wall between two cells is the result of chemical processes that lead to deposition of new material (apposition), an interpretation that appeared to be correct. His use of chemical substances for these microscopical investigations renders him a pioneer of microchemical staining techniques.

Wigand also was active in plant physiology, particularly in the study of tannin and the pigments of flowers, plant morphology, and plant systematics. In microbiology Wigand developed a theory of fermentation in which bacteria were morphologically and physiologically independent units, originating from the protoplasm of animal and plant cells in a state of decomposition (anamophosis of protoplasm). This theory was proposed because—on religious grounds—he could not accept the idea of spontaneous generation.

For similar reasons Wigand was one of Darwin's most ardent opponents in Germany, although he always tried to oppose Darwinian theory exclusively on scientific grounds. His own ideas on evolution were developed in *Genealogie der Urzellen* (1872).

Wigand's *Lehrbuch der Pharmakognosie* (1863), a manual for apothecaries, was written primarily from the practical point of view; another important pharmacognostic publication dealt with the origin of gums and resins (1863).

## BIBLIOGRAPHY

I. ORIGINAL WORKS. Many of Wigand's papers appeared in *Botanische Zeitung*, **7–29** (1849–1871), and in *Botanische Hefte*, **1–3** (1885–1888), the latter published by the Botanical Garden at Marburg. See also Royal Society *Catalogue of Scientific Papers*, VI, 363; VIII, 1238; XI, 806; XII, 783; and XIX, 608.

His earlier books include *Kritik und Geschichte der Lehre von der Metamorphose der Pflanze* (Leipzig, 1846), his inaugural dissertation; *Grundlegung der Pflanzenteratologie* (Marburg, 1850); *Intercellularsubstanz und Cuticula* (Brunswick, 1850); *Botanische Untersuchungen* (Brunswick, 1854); *Der Baum* (Brunswick, 1854); *Flora von Kurhessen und Nassau* (Marburg, 1859; 3rd ed., Kassel, 1879); *Lehrbuch der Pharmakognosie* (Berlin, 1863; 4th ed., 1887); and *Der botanische Garten von Marburg* (Marburg, 1867; 2nd ed., 1880).

Later publications include *Die Genealogie der Urzellen* (Brunswick, 1872); *Ueber die Auflösung der Arten durch natürliche Zuchtwahl* (Hannover, 1872); *Mikroskopische Untersuchungen* (Stuttgart, 1872); *Der Darwinismus und die Naturforschung Newtons und Cuviers*, 3 vols. (Brunswick, 1874–1877); *Die Alternative: Teleologie oder Zufall?* (Kassel, 1877); *Der Darwinismus, ein Zeichen der Zeit* (Heilbronn, 1878); *Entstehung und Fermentwirkung der Bakterien* (Marburg, 1884); and *Grundsätze aller Naturwissenschaft* (Marburg, 1886).

II. SECONDARY LITERATURE. See E. Dennert, "Julius Wilhelm Albert Wigand," in *Flora*, n.s. **44** (1886), 531–539; F. G. Kohl, "Albert Wigand," in *Botanisches Zentralblatt*, **28** (1886), 350–352, 381–384; A. Tschirch, "Julius Wilhelm Albert Wigand," in *Berichte der Deutschen botanischen Gesellschaft*, **5** (1887), xli–li; and B. Lehmann, *Julius Wilhelm Albert Wigand (1821–1886). Professor der Botanik und Pharmakognosie zu Marburg* (Marburg, 1973).

P. SMIT

**WILBRAND, JOHANN BERNHARD** (*b.* Clarholz, Germany, 8 March 1779; *d.* Giessen, Germany, 9 May 1846), *physiology.*

Wilbrand was one of the best-known adherents of Schelling's *Naturphilosophie.* Doggedly determined to accept only those facts compatible with his philosophical principles, he went so far as to deny Harvey's blood circulation and the gaseous exchange that occurs in the lungs. Despite his highly speculative ideas, however, he called for the comprehensive and factual observation of nature, because he deemed such empirically derived information essential in fleshing out the philosophical framework of his physiology.

Wilbrand was the only son of farmers who were serfs of a nearby cloister. After education by a local priest, he was sent to a Jesuit gymnasium in Münster. In 1800 he began to study theology and philosophy at the University of Münster, in order to secure a living as a clergyman. A year later Wilbrand transferred to the medical school to pursue his growing interest in the natural sciences. In the ensuing years he studied closely with the chemist Johann Bernhard Bodde (1760–1833), an ardent supporter of *Naturphilosophie.*

After being released from his serfdom in 1803, Wilbrand went to the University of Würzburg, ostensibly for clinical training at the Julius Hospital, since his previous medical education had been purely theoretical. Recommended by Bodde, he met the physician Ignaz Döllinger and the circle of students who attended the philosophical lectures given by Schelling, then a newly appointed member of the faculty. Wilbrand graduated in 1806 with a dissertation on respiration in which he rejected the existence of oxygen and carbon dioxide as independent substances. After receiving his medical degree, he spent several weeks at the Bamberg Hospital, studying the therapeutic methods based on John Brown's system of medicine (the Brunonian system).

Under the auspices of Count Spiegel Zum Desenberg, later archbishop of Cologne, and others, Wilbrand traveled to Paris, where he studied with Cuvier and Lamarck. Upon his return to Münster in 1807 he became an instructor at the medical school, where he lectured on medico-philosophical subjects.

In 1808 Wilbrand was appointed titular professor of comparative anatomy, physiology, and natural history at the University of Giessen. He became a prolific writer and a busy teacher, lecturing on botany, zoology, anatomy, physiology, and *Naturphilosophie.* His preeminence led to honors

and contacts with leading German intellectuals, including Goethe, who was interested in Wilbrand's use of the concept of metamorphosis.

In 1817 Wilbrand became director of the botanical gardens and zoo at Giessen. A few years later he received a medal from Friedrich Wilhelm III of Prussia for his schematic depiction of nature in atlas form: *Gemälde der organischen Natur in ihrer Verbreitung auf der Erde* (Giessen, 1821).

Wilbrand's work on human physiology admirably reflects the ideas expressed by the followers of Schelling's *Naturphilosophie* and the methods used to seek their verification. He based his highly speculative physiology on the belief that the organism was a complete psychophysiological entity endowed with opposite or contrasted principles responsible for its vital motions (polarity) and constantly undergoing structural transformations. The latter, in a sense, represented a metabolic process of solidification and liquefaction of organic matter. Wilbrand's methodology stressed the supremacy of the investigator's "mental eye," which could discern the fundamental pattern within nature from the confusing and abundant facts of observation, largely through the use of analogies.

During the 1820's and 1830's Wilbrand regularly attended the yearly meetings of the Gesellschaft Deutscher Naturforscher und Ärzte and often presented his papers at the sessions. As the empirical and inductive method gradually gained ascendancy in German medical circles, audiences became less sympathetic to his faltering philosophical efforts to maintain Schelling's grandiose conception of nature. Risking hostility and even ridicule, Wilbrand adamantly remained opposed to the new scientific research in biochemistry and biophysics, which he considered to be a distorted and piecemeal analysis. Paradoxically, his call for the observation of nature both in breadth and in depth was being heeded by the new generation of physicians, who refused to fetter their conclusions to *Naturphilosophie.*

## BIBLIOGRAPHY

I. Original Works. Wilbrand's best-known work is *Physiologie des Menschen* (Giessen, 1815). Among his philosophically oriented writings are *Darstellung der gesammten Organisation,* 2 vols. (Giessen, 1809), and *Ueber den Zusammenhang der Natur mit dem Uebersinnlichen* (Mainz, 1843). He also wrote two widely read textbooks: *Handbuch der Naturgeschichte des Thierreiches* (Giessen, 1829) and *Handbuch der vergleichenden Anatomie in ihrer nächsten Beziehung auf die Phy-*

*siologie* (Darmstadt, 1838). Wilbrand's *Selbstbiographie* (Giessen, 1831) provides glimpses of his career.

A number of Wilbrand's original documents exist in the family's archives in Darmstadt and have been catalogued by Dr. Axel Murken.

II. SECONDARY LITERATURE. Brief biographical sketches of Wilbrand are A. Murken, "Johann Bernhard Wilbrand (1779–1846), ein Mediziner und Philosoph aus Clarholz," in *Gütersloher Beiträge,* **8** (1967), 171–175; and K. E. Rothschuh, "Johann Bernhard Wilbrand, ein Münsterländer, Naturforscher und Arzt im Zeitalter der Romantik," in *Westfälische Nachrichten Beilage* (20 Nov. 1954), 93–95, 104; (24 Oct. 1957), 31–32.

Wilbrand's ideas regarding the circulation of the blood are mentioned in E. Hirschfeld, "Romantische Medizin," in *Kyklos,* **3** (1930), 29–31; and in Werner Leibbrand, *Die spekulative Medizin der Romantik* (Hamburg, 1956), 130–132. A more detailed analysis of his basic physiological ideas is C. Probst, "Johann Bernhard Wilbrand (1779–1846) und die Physiologie der Romantik," in *Sudhoffs Archiv,* **50** (1966), 157–178. Wilbrand's relationship with Goethe has been examined by Axel Murken, "Johann Bernhard Wilbrand (1779–1846), ein Naturwissenschaftler der Romantik und seine Beziehung zu J. W. von Goethe," in *Medizinische Monatsschrift,* **24** (1970), 165–170.

GUENTER B. RISSE

**WILCKE, JOHAN CARL** (*b*. Wismar, Germany, 6 September 1732; *d*. Stockholm, Sweden, 18 April 1796), *physics.*

Like many of the Swedish savants of the eighteenth century, including Samuel Klingenstierna and Mårten Strömer, his physics professors at the University of Uppsala, Wilcke came from a clerical family. His father, Samuel Wilcke, the son of a Pomeranian shoemaker, had educated himself for the ministry with the aid of generous patrons, especially F. A. Aepinus, professor of theology at the University of Rostock, whose children he tutored. In 1739 Samuel was called to minister to the German-speaking community in Stockholm, where he spent the remainder of his life.

Wilcke received his secondary education at the German school associated with his father's church. In 1750 he entered the University of Uppsala to prepare for the ministry. It was not theology, however, but mathematics and physics that aroused his interest; and for three terms he followed lectures on algebra, spherical trigonometry, mechanics, and experimental physics.

Hoping, perhaps, to save his son from science, Samuel Wilcke agreed to Johan Carl's wish to study at Rostock. The elder Aepinus having died,

Samuel counted on his former pupil, A. I. D. Aepinus, now holder of the Rostock chair of oratory, to urge the merits of the ministerial life. The scheme backfired. At Aepinus' home, where Wilcke boarded, lived the rhetorician's younger brother Franz, who, having rejected the family's plan to make him a physician,[1] taught mathematics at the university. The bond of common interest and sympathy that soon developed between Franz Aepinus and Wilcke accelerated Wilcke's drift from theology; and in 1753, when he matriculated at Göttingen, he no longer inscribed himself "theologus," as he had at Rostock, but as "mathematicus." Two years later A. I. D. Aepinus brought Samuel Wilcke to acquiesce in the *fait accompli,* perhaps made more palatable by the success of Franz Aepinus, who in the spring of 1755 became the astronomer of the Berlin Academy of Sciences.

**Electricity.** Wilcke joined Franz Aepinus in Berlin, where he devoted his newfound freedom to the study of physics, particularly to the agitated question of the contrary electricities. Were Dufay's vitreous and resinous electrifications differences only in degree, as Nollet insisted, or in kind, as the Franklinists claimed? Aepinus initially inclined toward Nollet, while Wilcke remained uncommitted, predisposed toward Franklin by certain experiments with the Leyden jar but arrested by Nollet's "apparently unanswerable" demonstration of the permeability of glass.[2] To resolve these uncertainties, Wilcke repeated all the experiments urged on either side; he prepared an annotated translation of Franklin's letters; and he found that, in most cases, Nollet's objections rested on misinterpretations of obscure, imprecise, or abbreviated passages in Franklin's work. As for Aepinus, he became an enthusiastic Franklinist when an experiment he designed to confirm Nollet failed.[3]

Not that Franklin's theory was unexceptionable. In his doctoral dissertation, defended at Rostock in 1757, and again in notes to his edition of Franklin, Wilcke showed that absolute insulation did not exist, that any electric per se could act the part of glass in the Leyden experiment, that the charges on the two coatings of the jar are not quite equal, and that substances are not innately vitreous or resinous.[4] This last point Wilcke owed to Canton, who had found that rough glass might be made minus or plus by rubbing with flannel or oiled silk, respectively. Recognizing that friction set up a competition for electrical matter, Wilcke hit on the idea of drawing up a winner's list, the entries being so placed that a given one became positive (or negative) when rubbed by those placed beneath (or above) it. His sequence, the first triboelectric series, consisted of smooth glass, wool, quills, wood, paper, sealing wax, white wax, rough glass, lead, sulfur, and metals other than lead.[5]

The most important result of Wilcke's Berlin period was the invention of the air condenser. Wilcke had consulted Aepinus—who had been studying the electricity of the tourmaline—about Franklin's version of Canton's induction experiments. Aepinus saw that the experimental arrangement amounted to an imperfect Leyden jar with air as dielectric; to check his insight he and Wilcke built a large air condenser (fifty-six square feet) that gave a shock comparable to that from a well-charged bottle. This demonstration threatened the already moribund theory of electrical atmospheres, which Franklin himself had not entirely discarded. While the repulsive force of the upper plate certainly reached the lower, its redundant electrical matter as certainly did not: for in that case the condenser, being shorted internally, could not have charged. Aepinus concluded for an instrumentalist theory of electricity, freely admitting action at a distance without specifying its cause. Indeed, he said, Franklinism must end in agnosticism: to save the simplest electrical phenomena, the particles of common matter must be supposed to repel one another at the same time that, according to the gravitational theory, they are mutually attractive.[6]

Wilcke did not embrace his friend's teachings altogether. He tentatively accepted the most bizarre of the new postulates, the mutual repulsion of matter particles, in order to conquer the enigma of the repulsion between negatively charged bodies; but he continued to ascribe the reciprocal recession of positive bodies to the pressure of their atmospheres. In Wilcke's asymmetric concept, positive atmospheres are material bodies, while negative ones are mere spheres of activity, spaces distorted by the presence of a deficient object.[7] Several years later (1763) Wilcke resolved this asymmetry by accepting and even championing the dualistic theory of Robert Symmer, which replaced the Franklinist negative state, or absence of electrical matter, with the presence of a second electrical fluid [6].

The productive collaboration ended in 1757 when Aepinus left Berlin for St. Petersburg. Wilcke had also received a Russian offer but declined it when Klingenstierna contrived to find him a position in Sweden, a lectureship (which in 1770 became a professorship) in experimental physics at the Royal Swedish Academy of Sciences. The position paid so poorly that Wilcke had to tutor for room and board. Not until 1777, when his salary had tripled, did he feel he could marry; he chose his housekeeper, Maria Christina Setterberg, who bore him no children to increase his expenses. Not until 1784, when he became secretary of the Academy, did his financial difficulties end. Some of Samuel Wilcke's misgivings about his son's career had been well taken.

Wilcke continued to work on electricity during his first year in Sweden [3]. His most characteristic efforts [4], on the location of charge in a dissectible plate condenser, anticipated the invention of the electrophorus; he observed that, having electrified the condenser, a plate could be removed, discharged, returned, grounded, and again removed, discharged, and so on, "without further electrification by the machine . . . as often as the trial is made." Wilcke explained these effects as inductive in 1762, some thirteen years before Volta described similar experiments without explanation; when he learned of the electrophorus, Wilcke immediately supplied its theory [13]. He acknowledged Volta's invention of a useful machine but rightly asserted priority in discovering its principle, a claim supported by most German-speaking electricians.[8]

Among Wilcke's other electrical researches his lengthy studies of the tourmaline [7] and of cyclones and waterspouts [15] deserve mention. The former are distinguished by careful examination of a multitude of delicate cases that established the validity of Aepinus' concept of electrical poles and corrected many previous errors of detail. The latter, although they do not in fact concern electricity, stemmed from Wilcke's conjecture that cyclonic winds might be driven by atmospheric electricity. With his usual care he gathered all available data on waterspouts and compared them with the behavior of vortices and whirlpools generated in the laboratory. His knowledge of the phenomena was not superseded during the nineteenth century.

**Heat.** Wilcke's best-known work was his independent discovery of latent heat [11], which, he said, followed from a chance observation made early in 1772. Wishing to remove snow from a small courtyard and expecting that, in obedience to Richmann's law (which states that the temperature $R$ of a mixture of two measures of water, $m_1$ and $m_2$, initially at temperatures $T_1$ and $T_2$, is $R = [m_1 T_1 + m_2 T_2]/[m_1 + m_2]$), hot water would melt more than its weight of snow, he was surprised to find the water of very little efficacy and concluded that the law did not hold for mixtures of ice and water. He therefore looked for a new rule. In a typical experiment Wilcke mixed hot water at temperature $T$ and melting snow, measured the resultant temperature $\theta$, and computed the difference between $\theta$ and $R$, the final temperature to be expected from Richmann's law if water at zero degrees had been used in place of the snow.

In the simplest case, when all masses were equal, the mean loss of heat $R - \theta$ was 36 3/28 degrees; hence, as Wilcke concluded, it requires somewhat more than seventy-two degrees of heat to melt unit mass of snow at zero degrees.[9] He observed that these seventy-two degrees disappear or, as we would say, become latent, in liquefying the ice, and that liquefaction occurs without change of temperature. Physically (according to Wilcke) the matter of heat, which, like Franklin's electrical fluid, is made up of mutually repellent particles attracted by common matter, insinuates itself between contiguous ice particles, transforming them into water; further heating causes the water to expand and raises its temperature.[10]

These experiments probably owed less to chance than Wilcke represented. In 1769, while pursuing an old hobby, the study of the shapes of snowflakes and ice crystals, he had made the "paradoxical" observation that water cooled below zero degrees warms on freezing [10]. As Oseen observes, the melting of the courtyard snow with warm water was probably an attempt to study the paradox: it was an experiment, not an accident.[11]

Wilcke returned to the problems of heat in the winter of 1780–1781, interrupting his study of waterspouts in order to follow up Joseph Black's concept of specific heat as reported in J. H. Magellan's *Nouvelle théorie du feu élémentaire* (1780). Wilcke had probably hit upon the same idea (although not the term) a few years earlier, perhaps in pursuing a note in Klingenstierna's *Inledning til naturkunnigheten* (1747), a translation of Musschenbroek's *Elementa physicae*. The note criticized Boerhaave's opinion, approved by Musschenbroek, that at equal temperatures all bodies contain equal amounts of heat by volume. In experiments apparently done in the 1770's, Wilcke showed that the sensible heats in bodies in thermal equilibrium were proportional neither to volume nor to mass; and, after a few false starts, he found how to measure relative heat capacities.[12] Immerse a mass of metal at temperature $T$ in an equal mass of ice-cold water and record the resultant equilibrium temperature $\theta$. Next calculate by Richmann's formula the amount of water $w$ at temperature $T$ that, when mixed with the same quantity of ice-

cold water (taken as unity for convenience), would yield the same resultant $\theta$:

$$\theta = \frac{wT + 1 \cdot 0}{w + 1}, \quad w = \frac{\theta}{T - \theta}.$$

Wilcke probably obtained $w$ for gold and lead before 1780. After seeing Magellan's book, he measured it for ten other substances [16]. Although his numerical results were not good (as in the experiments on latent heat he ignored the heat capacity of the calorimeter[13]), he understood that the $w$'s were the specific heat capacities that he and Black had sought. He also saw in them a further analogy between the properties of the matters of heat and electricity: for not only were they all subtle, elastic, and apparently weightless fluids, but each was retained in ponderable bodies by specific forces dependent upon the nature of the bodies [17].

**Miscellaneous Researches.** Between 1763, when he finished the electrical studies begun in Berlin, and 1772 Wilcke worked at terrestrial magnetism. He began by inventing a new declination compass [5] and immediately became its slave [14]; a few years later, about 1766, he designed a dipping needle that proved itself on a voyage to China [12]. Encouraged by its performance, he undertook the difficult task of selecting reliable data from conflicting published measurements of dip made with other instruments. The result, an important contribution [9], was a systematic isoclinal chart that showed a magnetic equator and indicated positions for the poles that approximated those obtained from mapping declination. In another important work [8], Wilcke showed that a soft iron needle may be magnetized naturally by placing it in the magnetic meridian, or artificially by setting it near a powerful lodestone; in either case the needle magnetized more readily if the discharge from a Leyden jar passed through it first. Wilcke explained that the discharge helped to rearrange the internal parts of the needle.

Like many leaders of Sweden's eighteenth-century scientific renaissance, Wilcke had a taste and talent for applied science. He improved many standard instruments: the magnetic needles, the air pump, the micrometer, the barometer, the eudiometer. He also made suggestions for ventilating ships, for cooking under pressure ("Papin's digester"), for life preservers, and—at the request of the government—for fortifying the harbor of Landskrona.

Wilcke was a dry, unsociable man, happiest when at work or when reading in the several nonscientific subjects that interested him: theology, travel, belles lettres, music. These qualities made his tenure as secretary of the Academy (1784–1796) a mixed success. A responsible and diligent bureaucrat, he kept up the Academy's correspondence, publications, and records, and tried to maintain its high standards, as exemplified in his own scientific work. But he lacked the spark and influence of his predecessor, the astronomer Pehr Wargentin. Wilcke was not the man to win the Academy public support or to change its direction when, in the 1780's, it grew increasingly anachronistic and isolated. It fell into a decline that, however, did not approach bottom until after his time.[14]

As a physicist Wilcke is distinguished, apart from his substantive contributions, by his emphasis on measurement, exactness, and reproducibility of results. Although not a mathematical physicist in the modern sense, he insisted upon the utility of mathematics and mathematical formulations in experimental philosophy. In these emphases he was by no means unique or original, but he was one of the first physicists to demonstrate their fruitfulness in his own work.[15]

## NOTES

1. J. C. Koppe, *Jetzlebendes gelehrtes Mecklenburg*, I (Rostock–Leipzig, 1783), 9–15.
2. F. U. T. Aepinus, *Recueil de différents mémoires sur la tourmaline* (St. Petersburg, 1762), 134; Wilcke, [2], intro., 388–389. The boldface numerals refer to items in the bibliography.
3. Aepinus, *Recueil*, 134–137; Wilcke, [2], 280–286, 348.
4. Wilcke, [2], 219–221, 271–272, 290, 308–309; and [1], 59–60, 81–83.
5. Wilcke, [1], 44–64.
6. Aepinus, *Tentamen theoriae electricitatis et magnetismi* (St. Petersburg, 1759), 5–7, 35–40, 75–83, 257–259; Wilcke, [2], 306–309.
7. Wilcke, [2], 221–224, 233–236, 262–263, 270–271, 307, 340–341.
8. G. C. Lichtenberg, *Briefe*, A. Leitzmann and C. Schüddekopf, eds., III (Leipzig, 1904), 203.
9. Let $L$ be latent heat, $M$ the mean of the experiments; then (since $R = T/2$), $T - 2\theta = 2M$, and $T - \theta = L + \theta$, whence $L = 2M = 72$ and 3/14 degrees. The value should be near 80.
10. Wilcke, [11], 105, 111; [16], 52.
11. Oseen, *Wilcke*, 156, 174–177.
12. This is an undated MS analyzed by Oseen, *Wilcke*, 232–234, 247–248.
13. McKie and Heathcote, *Specific and Latent Heats*, 86–87.
14. Lindroth, *Historia*, II, 20–26.
15. See Wilcke to W. C. G. Karsten, 1 July 1785, in Karsten, *Physisch-chemische Abhandlungen*, I (Halle, 1786), 118–119.

## BIBLIOGRAPHY

I. ORIGINAL WORKS. A bibliography of Wilcke's printed work and a catalog of his scientific MSS held at the Royal Swedish Academy of Sciences are given in C. W. Oseen, *Johan Carl Wilcke Experimental-fysiker* (Uppsala, 1939), 369–391. The Academy also has much administrative and scientific correspondence from Wilcke's secretaryship. Some scientific correspondence, notably that with C. W. Scheele, is printed in Oseen's biography. All Wilcke's scientific papers were published in Swedish in *Kungliga Svenska vetenskapsakademiens handlingar* (abbreviated below as *Handl.*) and translated into German in A. G. Kaestner, *Der königl. schwedischen Akademie der Wissenschaften, Abhandlungen aus der Naturlehre* (abbreviated below as *Abh.*); in the following bibliography the pages in Kaestner are given after the citation to the *Handlingar*.

Wilcke's most important works are [1] his thesis, *Disputatio physica experimentalis de electricitatibus contrariis* (Rostock, 1757); [2] his ed. of Franklin's letters, *Des Herrn Benjamin Franklins Esq. Briefe von der Electricität . . . nebst Anmerkungen* (Leipzig, 1758); [3] "Electriska rön och försök om den electriska laddningens och stötens åstadkommande vid flera kroppar än glas och porcellain," *Handl.*, **19** (1758), 250–282 (*Abh.*, **20**, 241–268); [4] "Ytterligare rön och försök om contraira electriciteterne vid laddningen och därtil hörande delar," *Handl.*, **23** (1762), 206–229, 245–266 (*Abh.*, **24**, 213–235, 253–274); [5] "Beskrifning på en ny declinations-compass," *Handl.*, **24** (1763), 143–153 (*Abh.*, **25**, 154–164); [6] "Electriska försök med phosphorus," *Handl.*, **24** (1763), 195–214 (*Abh.*, **25**, 207–226); [7] "Historien om tourmalin," *Handl.*, **27** (1766), 89–108, and **29** (1768), 3–25, 97–119 (*Abh.*, **28**, 95–113, and **30**, 3–26, 105–128); [8] "Afhandling om magnetiska kraftens upväckande genom electricitet," *Handl.*, **27** (1766), 294–315 (*Abh.*, **28**, 306–327); [9] "Försök til en magnetisk inclinations-charta," *Handl.*, **29** (1768), 193–225 (*Abh.*, **30**, 209–237); and [10] "Nya rön om vattnets frysning til snö-like is-figurer," *Handl.*, **30** (1769), 89–111 (*Abh.*, **31**, 87–108).

Also see [11] "Om snöns kyla vid smältningen," *Handl.*, **33** (1772), 97–120 (*Abh.*, **34**, 93–116); [12] "Om magnetiska inclinationen, med beskrifning på tvänne inclinations-compasser," *Handl.*, **33** (1772), 287–306 (*Abh.*, **34**, 285–302); [13] "Undersökning om de vid Herr Volta's nya elettrophoro-perpetuo förekommande electriska phenomener," *Handl.*, **38** (1777), 56–83, 128–144, 216–234 (*Abh.*, **39**, 54–78, 116–130, 200–216); [14] "Rön om magnet-nålens årliga och dagelige ändringar i Stockholm," *Handl.*, **38** (1777), 273–300 (*Abh.*, **39**, 259–284); [15] "Försök til uplysning om luft-hvirflar och sky-drag," *Handl.*, 2nd ser., **1** (1780), 1–18, 83–102, **3** (1782), 3–35, **6** (1785), 290–307, and **7** (1786), 3–20 (*Neue Abh.*, **1**, 3–18, 81–97, **3**, 3–31, **6**, 271–286, and **7**, 3–27); [16] "Rön om eldens specifiska myckenhet uti fasta kroppar, och des afmätande," *Handl.*, **2** (1781), 49–78 (*Neue Abh.*, **2**, 48–79; also *Journal de physique*, **26** [1785], 256–268, 381–389); and [17] "Rön om varmens spänstighet och fördeling, i anledning af ångors upstigande och kyla, uti förtunnad luft," *Handl.*, **2** (1781), 143–163 (*Neue Abh.*, **2**, 146–164).

II. Secondary Literature. The standard biography is Oseen's; for Wilcke's activities at the Academy, see also N. V. E. Nordenmark, *Pehr Wilhelm Wargentin* (Uppsala, 1939), and S. Lindroth, *Kungliga svenska vetenskapsakademiens historia 1739–1818* (Stockholm, 1967). A brief notice by Anna Beckman appears in S. Lindroth, ed., *Swedish Men of Science* (Stockholm, 1952), 122–130. For Wilcke's work in general, see Oseen; on heat, see also D. McKie and N. H. de V. Heathcote, *The Discovery of Specific and Latent Heats* (London, 1935), 78–108; and on electricity, J. Priestley, *The History and Present State of Electricity*, 3rd ed. (London, 1775), I, 272–276, 358–362, and II, 35–37; and E. Hoppe, *Geschichte der Elektrizität* (Leipzig, 1884).

J. L. Heilbron

**WILCZYNSKI, ERNEST JULIUS** (*b.* Hamburg, Germany, 13 November 1876; *d.* Denver, Colorado, 14 September 1932), *mathematics*.

Wilczynski was a son of Max Wilczynski and Friederike Hurwitz, who settled in Chicago when he was young. He returned to Germany for advanced study, receiving the Ph.D. from the University of Berlin in 1897 with a dissertation entitled "Hydrodynamische Untersuchungen mit Anwendung auf die Theorie der Sonnenrotation." Upon returning to the United States, he spent a year as a computer in the Office of the Nautical Almanac in Washington. In 1898 Wilczynski went to the University of California as an instructor; he rose to the rank of associate professor and served there until 1907. From 1903 to 1905 he was in Europe as assistant and associate of the Carnegie Institution of Washington, which provided the financial support that enabled him to write *Projective Differential Geometry of Curves and Ruled Surfaces* (1906). In 1906 he married Countess Ines Masola, of Verona. He was associate professor at the University of Illinois from 1907 to 1910 and at the University of Chicago from 1910 to 1914, achieving full professorship in the latter year.

Wilczynski's main work was in projective differential geometry, a subject of which he is generally considered the creator. A prolific worker, he published seventy-seven books and papers. He was also active in scientific organizations, serving as vice-president of the American Mathematical Society, as a member of the council of the Mathematical Association of America, and as an associate editor of the *Transactions of the American Mathematical Society*. Wilczynski won a prize (and was named laureate) of the Royal Belgian Academy in 1909, and in 1919 he was elected a member of the National Academy of Sciences.

What is now called classical differential geometry studied the local metric properties of geometrical configurations; projective differential geometry proposed similarly to study the local properties invariant under projective transformations. When Wilczynski started his work, about 1900, Halphen's projective differential geometry of curves already existed; but Wilczynski devised new methods, deepened the theory for curves, extended it to surfaces, and brought it to its present form.

In 1900, classical differential geometry was already a century old. Although it could still provide much interesting detail, it had lost its vitality; and by 1920 it had been declared dead. E. T. Bell has suggested that classical differential geometry lacked method and aim. Projective differential geometry, although it contained new points of view, was only a part of that larger subject and, therefore, shared its fate, although classical metric differential geometry is still a staple university course.

### BIBLIOGRAPHY

See E. T. Bell, *Development of Mathematics* (New York, 1940), 332; and E. P. Lane, "Ernest Julius Wilczynski," in *American Mathematical Monthly*, **39** (1932), 567–569, see also 500; and "Ernest Julius Wilczynski—In Memoriam," in *Bulletin of the American Mathematical Society*, **39** (1933), 7–14, with bibliography of 77 works published by Wilczynski from 1895 to 1923.

A. Seidenberg

**WILD, HEINRICH** (*b.* Uster, Zurich canton, Switzerland, 17 December 1833; *d.* Zurich, Switzerland, 5 September 1902), *meteorology*.

Wild studied at the universities of Königsberg and Heidelberg, and in 1857 received the Ph.D. at Zurich. In November 1858 he was appointed professor of physics and director of the observatory at the University of Bern. Ten years later he was invited to join the Academy of Sciences in St. Petersburg and to become director of its Central Astrophysical Observatory. In 1876 he founded the magnetometeorological observatory at Pavlovsk and remained its director until 1895.

Wild was an active meteorologist who played a major part in the development of the science in the latter half of the nineteenth century. He improved several instruments, including the anemograph, anemometer, atmometers, barometer, rain gauges, thermograph, several forms of theodolite, instruments for measurement of terrestrial magnetism, polarization photometer, and polaristrobometer. His modifications of these instruments significantly improved techniques for weather observation. He also was directly responsible for significantly extending the network of meteorological observation stations—almost as many in Switzerland as in Russia.

Wild was a member of several international meteorological commissions, including the International Polar Commission (1879–1891), and was largely responsible for the preparation of their reports. He also served on international commissions on the meter and on the reform of chronometric methods.

Wild wrote extensively, in both German and Russian, primarily on meteorological instruments and improved techniques for meteorological observations.

## BIBLIOGRAPHY

Wild's writings include "Études métrologiques," in *Mémoires de l'Académie impériale des sciences de St.-Pétersbourg*, 7th ser., **18** (1872), no. 8; *Bestimmung des Werthes der Siemen'schen Widerstands Einheit in absolutem electromagnetischen Masse* (St. Petersburg, 1884); and *Das Konstantinow'sche und magnetische Observatorium in Pawlowski* (St. Petersburg, 1895).

ASIT K. BISWAS
MARGARET R. BISWAS

**WILEY, HARVEY WASHINGTON** (*b.* Kent, Indiana, 18 October 1844; *d.* Washington, D.C., 30 June 1930), *chemistry.*

The son of Preston Prichard Wiley and Lucinda Maxwell, Wiley received his early education primarily from his father, who ran a subscription school during the seasons when farm work was not pressing. He received the B.A. from Hanover College in 1867, the M.D. from Indiana Medical College in 1871, and the B.S. from Lawrence Scientific School, Harvard, in 1873. In 1874 Wiley became professor of chemistry at Purdue University and served as Indiana state chemist, except for a short interlude of European study, until 1883, when he was appointed chief of the Division (later Bureau) of Chemistry of the U.S. Department of Agriculture.

By then Wiley had become well-known as an analytical chemist with expertise in sugar chemistry and technology. Although he continued the sugar studies in Washington, he was becoming concerned about the widespread adulteration of syrups available in the marketplace. This concern quickly spread to other foods. His agency undertook extensive analysis of commercial foods and reported widespread adulteration. Wiley became active in a campaign to bring about passage of pure food legislation by Congress, but his efforts were repeatedly frustrated.

In 1902 the Bureau of Chemistry undertook studies on the physiological effects of various chemical additives in human foods. These studies, made on human volunteers, raised doubts regarding the safety of salicylates, borates, formaldehyde, benzoates, saccharin, and copper salts in foods. Termed the "Poison Squad" experiments by newsmen, the studies attracted widespread interest.

The Food and Drug Act was finally passed in 1906, after scandals in the drug trade and in the meat-packing industry brought heavy public pressure on Congress for remedial action. The Bureau of Chemistry was charged with enforcement of the new law; but Wiley's efforts were frustrated as a consequence of industrial pressures on Secretary of Agriculture James Wilson, who steadily handicapped Wiley's work with bureaucratic obstructions. Of particular significance was the creation of the Referee Board of Consulting Scientific Experts, headed by Ira Remsen. This board repeated the studies on benzoates and other food additives, arriving at the conclusion that benzoates and saccharin were safe for use in foods, at least in limited amounts.

In 1912, shortly after being exonerated by a congressional committee of charges of alleged misuse of funds, Wiley decided that his enforcement powers had been undermined to such a degree that he could no longer be effective within the government. He resigned to become director of the Bureau of Foods, Sanitation, and Health for the magazine *Good Housekeeping*. Although he had hoped to use this position to educate the public, his efforts were largely ineffective.

Although he had a great deal of personal charm and was an effective public speaker, Wiley was also a forceful, determined, and uncompromising fighter for what he considered the best interests of the public. His firmness brought him many enemies, and his effectiveness declined steadily in the last three decades of his life. Nevertheless, his overall accomplishments were impressive. Besides his work for pure foods and drugs, Wiley was very active in the development of agricultural analysis and was a founder of the Association of Official

Agricultural Chemists in 1884, serving as its president in 1886. He served two terms as president of the American Chemical Society.

## BIBLIOGRAPHY

I. ORIGINAL WORKS. Wiley meticulously saved letters, diaries, notebooks, lecture MSS, newspaper clippings, and other papers. His personal papers are now preserved in the Manuscript Division of the Library of Congress. There also are extensive holdings of Wiley letters and related official material in the Bureau of Chemistry records in the National Archives. The National Archives also holds relevant material in the files of the secretary of agriculture, the office of the solicitor general, and the Food and Drug Administration; and there is some related material in the papers of presidents Theodore Roosevelt and William Howard Taft. For information on these holdings, see Oscar E. Anderson, Jr., *The Health of a Nation, Harvey Wiley and the Fight for Pure Food* (Chicago, 1958), *passim*, esp. 280–282.

There is no complete bibliography of Wiley's extensive published works. As chief of the Bureau of Chemistry he had responsibility for all of its publications and wrote many of them. The early work on sugar production is treated in the annual reports of Purdue University and in early bulletins and reports of the Bureau of Chemistry, U.S. Department of Agriculture (*Bulletin* nos. 2, 3, 5, 6, 8, 14, 17, 21). The extensive studies of food adulteration were published as "Foods and Food Adulterants," *Bulletin. Bureau of Chemistry. United States Department of Agriculture*, no. 13, 10 pts. (1887–1899). The "Poison Squad" experiments were published as "Influence of Food Preservatives and Food Adulterants," *ibid.*, no. 84, 6 pts. (1904–1908).

Wiley's work on analytical procedures was published in standard scientific journals and government bulletins until 1884, when he was active in organizing the Association of Official Agricultural Chemists. The Association's *Official Methods* were published by the Bureau of Chemistry as *Bulletin* no. 7 (1885) and were reprinted as *Bulletin* no. 107, with revisions, for many years thereafter. Through Wiley's influence, the Bureau of Chemistry provided extensive support to the Association for publication of proceedings, as well as manpower for checking proposed analytical methods. When Wiley was honorary president of the Association between 1912 and 1930, his annual addresses were published in *Journal of the Association of Official Agricultural Chemists*. His *Principles and Practice of Agricultural Analysis*, 3 vols. (Washington, D.C., 1894–1897), went through rev. eds. in 1906–1911 and 1926.

Other books by Wiley are *Foods and Their Adulteration* (Philadelphia, 1907; 2nd ed., 1911; 3rd ed., 1917); *1001 Tests of Foods, Beverages and Toilet Accessories* (New York, 1914); *The Lure of the Land* (New York, 1915); *Not by Bread Alone, The Principles of Human Nutrition* (New York, 1915); *Beverages and Their Adulteration* (Philadelphia, 1919); *History of a Crime Against the Food Law* (Washington, 1929); and *Harvey W. Wiley, an Autobiography* (Indianapolis, 1930). *History of a Crime*, which is strongly autobiographical, was written late in life, when Wiley was very ill, and reflects a personal bitterness that might have been more tempered had it been written earlier. The *Autobiography*, which was finished with the aid of O. K. Armstrong, gives less attention to the enforcement period, is less belligerent, and is perhaps more representative of the real Wiley, who combined firmness with charm.

II. SECONDARY LITERATURE. The best biography of Wiley is Oscar E. Anderson, Jr., *The Health of a Nation, Harvey W. Wiley and the Fight for Pure Food* (Chicago, 1958). M. Natenberg, *The Legacy of Dr. Wiley and the Administration of His Food and Drug Act* (Chicago, 1957), was written as a propaganda piece and has only minor value. The 1931 meeting of the Association of Official Agricultural Chemists commemorated Wiley—the memorials read by W. W. Skinner, C. A. Browne, W. G. Campbell, *et al.*, are published in *Journal of the Association of Official Agricultural Chemists*, **14** (1931), iii–xxii. Useful short biographies are W. D. Bigelow, "Harvey Washington Wiley," in *Industrial Engineering Chemistry*, **15** (1923), 88; C. A. Browne, "Harvey Washington Wiley," in *Dictionary of American Biography*, XX, 215–216; E. J. Dies, *Titans of the Soil* (Chapel Hill, N.C., 1949), 151–158; and A. J. Ihde, in E. Farber, ed., *Great Chemists* (New York, 1961), 813–819. There is extensive background material on the passage of the Pure Food and Drug Act in Mark Sullivan, *Our Times, The United States, 1900–1925* (New York, 1927), II, 471–551; and James Harvey Young, *The Toadstool Millionaires* (Princeton, 1961), 226–246. On the role of Wiley in the early enforcement of the Pure Food and Drug Act, see O. E. Anderson, Jr., "The Pure-Food Issue: A Republican Dilemma, 1906–1912," in *American Historical Review*, **61** (1956), 550–573.

AARON J. IHDE

**WILHELM IV, LANDGRAVE OF HESSE** (*b*. Kassel, Germany, 24 June 1532; *d*. Kassel, 25 August 1592), *astronomy*.

A contemporary of Peter Apian, Copernicus, Tycho Brahe, and Kepler, Wilhelm lived in the age of the greatest astronomical revolution since antiquity. He played scarcely any role in the resulting debates, however, for he was concerned primarily with the refining of the techniques of astronomical observation. At the court in Kassel he was tutored, chiefly in mathematics, by Rumold Mercator, the son of the geographer Gerardus Mercator. He became interested in astronomy after reading Apian's *Astronomicum Caesareum*, a splendid book although it was conceived within the conceptual framework of the old geocentric view. Wilhelm's manuscript copy of this work, which is still extant, contains handwritten planetary tables that obviously were drawn up at his request by Andreas Schöner. On the model of Apian's system of movable cardboard disks, Wilhelm devised an arrangement of metal plates that made possible the construction of the *Wilhelmsuhr* (1560–1561). This mechanical astronomical clock was so precise that the ephemerides could be read directly from it. Similar clocks were later produced in great quantities.

Satisfying the love of display then flourishing in most princely courts was not, however, Wilhelm's goal; his main goal was to further the study of astronomy. In the course of his own astronomical observations, he noted the great differences between the true positions of the stars and those calculated on the basis of Ptolemaic theory. He therefore decided to establish a new star catalog derived from actual observations, a project not realized since the time of Hipparchus. Wilhelm began making observations at his private observatory in Kassel and continued until 1567, when he became landgrave. Tycho Brahe, who was in Kassel for a few days in 1575, urged him to hire assistants to carry on the work. Accordingly, Wilhelm invited Christoph Rothmann to come to his court as mathematician and observer, and Joost Bürgi as mechanic.

Both these men did work of considerable scientific distinction while at Kassel. Bürgi constructed globe clocks, pendulum clocks, and mechanical computing devices. Later he became known as Kepler's friend at the court of Rudolf II in Prague. Rothmann was an industrious observer and computer and a resolute supporter of the Copernican world view, as can be seen from his correspondence with Tycho Brahe. The accuracy of the observations made by Wilhelm and Rothmann is astonishing. Their determination of the latitude of Kassel (51°19′) required a correction of only 10″ in the heyday of astronomical geography at the beginning of the nineteenth century.

Only a small part of Wilhelm's project of the Hessian star catalog was realized. Ultimately it included 179 of the 1,032 stars originally planned. (Wilhelm's observations furnished the data for 58 of these and Rothmann's for 121.) Wilhelm nevertheless deserves great credit for undertaking a program that became one of the major tasks of observational astronomy in the following decades, and without which the later development of celestial mechanics would have been inconceivable. He also introduced a new method for determining stellar positions: with his azimuthal quadrant he could determine the moment when a given star reaches a certain altitude. This process, in a slightly altered form, later developed into the basic method for determining stellar positions. Its superiority became evident, however, only with the development of much more accurate clocks than were available to Wilhelm. It was for this reason that Tycho Brahe criticized it.

Many of the instruments and clocks made for Wilhelm's Kassel observatory are preserved at the Astronomisch-Physikalische Kabinett in Kassel.

## BIBLIOGRAPHY

I. ORIGINAL WORKS. Tycho Brahe published selections of his scientific correspondence with Wilhelm IV and Rothmann in *Tychonis Brahe Dani epistolarum astronomicarum . . .* (Uraniborg, 1596). Portions of Wilhelm's political correspondence was printed in various other publications. A list of this material was prepared by W. Ribbeck for the article in *Allgemeine deutsche Biographie*, XLIII (Leipzig, 1898), 39. MS material can also be found under the heading "Landgräfliche Personalia Wilhelm IV Astronomica" in the state archive at Marburg.

II. SECONDARY LITERATURE. See P. A. Kirchvogel, "Landgraf Wilhelm IV von Hessen und sein astronomisches Automatenwerk," in *Index zur Geschichte der Medizin, Naturwissenschaften und Technik*, **1** (1953), 12–18; "Wilhelm IV, Tycho Brahe and Eberhard Baldewein—the Missing Instruments of the Kassel Observatory," in *Vistas in Astronomy*, **9** (1968), 109–121, which contains an extensive bibliography; F. Krafft, "Tycho Brahe," in *Die Grossen der Weltgeschichte*, V (Zurich, 1974), 297–345; B. Sticker, "Landgraf Wilhelm IV und die Anfänge der modernen astronomischen Messkunst," in *Sudhoffs Archiv*, **40** (1956), 15–25; and "Die wissenschaftlichen Bestrebungen des Landgrafen Wilhelm IV," in *Zeitschrift des Vereins für Hessische Geschichte und Landeskunde*, **67** (1956), 130–137; R. Wolf, *Geschichte der Astronomie* (Munich, 1877), 266 ff.; and F. X. von Zach, "Landgraf Wilhelm IV," in *Monatliche Correspondenz zur Beförderung der Erd- und Himmelskunde*, **12** (1805), 267–302.

DIETER B. HERRMANN

**WILHELMY, LUDWIG FERDINAND** (*b*. Stargard, Pomerania [now Poland], 25 December 1812; *d.* Berlin, Germany, 18 February 1864), *physics, chemistry.*

After completing his early schooling, Wilhelmy left Pomerania to study pharmacy in Berlin. He subsequently purchased an apothecary shop in his native state and joined his father in business. His desire for pure scientific research led him to sell the shop in 1843, however, and to study chemistry and physics at Berlin, Giessen, and Heidelberg. In 1846 Wilhelmy received the doctorate from Heidelberg on the basis of a dissertation on heat as a measure of cohesion. After traveling chiefly in Italy and Paris, where he studied with Regnault, he returned to Heidelberg and became a *Privatdozent* in 1849. He remained at the university for only five years; he then returned to private life in Berlin after a six-month stay in Munich, keeping busy with philosophical, mathematical, and physical studies. Wilhelmy never married, preferring to devote his entire attention to expanding his knowledge in all areas of learning. A skilled businessman, he had a warm heart and was always willing to assist a friend. Although shy with strangers, in his small circle of colleagues he was cheerful and witty, defending his peculiar views on many subjects with surprising liveliness.

As a student in Berlin, Wilhelmy joined Magnus in forming a physics colloquium that became the Physical Society in 1845. Among the members of this small circle of young investigators were Paul du Bois-Reymond, Clausius, Helmholtz, and Werner Siemens. Upon his return to Berlin ten years later, Wilhelmy found few of the original group remaining; and he consequently took the lead in directing the younger members. As leader of the Physical Society, he converted part of his Berlin home, as well as his summer villa in Heidelberg, into physics laboratories in 1860. His studies on capillary action, unfinished at his death, were carried out at his home laboratory.

Wilhelmy is best known as the first person to measure the velocity of a homogeneous chemical reaction. In 1850 he published a paper on the law of the action of acids on cane sugar, which went virtually unnoticed until Wilhelm Ostwald called attention to it thirty-four years later. Wilhelmy's procedure involved following the reaction with a polarimeter (widely used at the time of his investigations), which did not disturb the conditions of the reacting system. In the presence of a large amount (considered constant) of water, he found that the amount of sugar changed in any instant was proportional to the amount present, the acid being unchanged. In mathematical terms Wilhelmy presented the familiar law

$$-dZ/dt = MZS,$$

where $Z$ is the concentration of sugar, $t$ is time, $S$

is the acid concentration (presumed unchanging throughout the reaction), and $M$ is a constant today called the reaction velocity constant. He also investigated the temperature dependence of the reaction and assumed that it followed the same exponential law as concentration.

Wilhelmy's earlier physical studies, dealing with heat and utilizing differential equations, prepared the way for his key 1850 paper. In his dissertation (1846) he used Regnault's coefficients of expansion to calculate the force of cohesion and concluded that molecules are acted upon by two forces, heat and cohesion, the former tending to annihilate the latter. His conclusions are reminiscent of Lavoisier's ideas about *calorique*. Wilhelmy added to these conclusions the concept of the numerical equivalence of heat and energy, following J. R. Mayer's 1842 study of this equivalence. In a book published in 1851 Wilhelmy attempted to derive several general relationships among physical properties of compounds. He suggested, for example, that isomeric compounds of equal specific gravity and equal boiling points have equal coefficients of expansion. If the boiling points are different, the coefficients of expansion are inversely proportional to them. The book was meant to be an introduction to a work that would provide a complete understanding of the essence of natural forces, but this ambitious project was never completed.

## BIBLIOGRAPHY

I. ORIGINAL WORKS. Wilhelmy's important paper on the rate of inversion of sugar, "Ueber das Gesetz, nach welchem die Einwirkung der Säuren auf den Rohrzucker stattfindet," in *Annalen der Physik und Chemie*, **81** (1850), 413–433, 499–526, was reprinted as Ostwald's Klassiker der exacten Wissenschaften, no. 29 (Leipzig, 1891), which contains a complete list of Wilhelmy's ten publications. Portions of the paper were translated into English in Henry M. Leicester and H. S. Klickstein, *A Source Book in Chemistry 1400–1900* (New York, 1952), 396–400. In addition to his book on heat, *Versuch einer mathematisch-physikalischen Wärmetheorie* (Heidelberg, 1851), he published one other book, *Zur physikalischen Begründung der Physiologie und Psychologie* (Heidelberg, 1852).

II. SECONDARY LITERATURE. A short biographical sketch of Wilhelmy by Georg Quincke is in Ostwald's Klassiker (see above), 45–47. His work is discussed in Eduard Farber, "Early Studies Concerning Time in Chemical Reactions," in *Chymia*, **7** (1961), 135–148.

SHELDON J. KOPPERL

**WILKINS, JOHN** (*b.* Northamptonshire, England, 1614; *d.* London, England, 19 November 1672), *theology, science, scientific and academic administration and organization.*

Wilkins' career coincides with the most eventful period in modern English history—the years just before the Long Parliament to the decade after the Restoration and the formation of the Royal Society. It was not an easy time for an active man to retain influence and office, but Wilkins managed owing to his habit of prudence and a spirit of moderation and tolerance. In 1643 he subscribed to the Solemn League and Covenant and in 1649 he took the engagement of loyalty to the English Commonwealth. He was trusted by Cromwell, whom he advised on the need for a national church and episcopacy against presbytery. After the return of Charles II in 1660, he submitted to the Act of Uniformity and soon enjoyed the favor of the restored monarchy. Still, only the most unforgiving royalists ever questioned his integrity. Throughout his life, he gained and retained the friendship and respect of men of the most diverse political and religious persuasions. No doubt such personal qualities as charm, ready conversation, and energy played their part in his success, but the deeper reason would seem to lie in his commitment to beliefs that transcended the exclusive interests of any particular faction. From the first to the last, all his writings advocate scientific and religious views that by the time of his death had proved that they represented the temper of the times. The new science had triumphed, and the liberal Anglican theology known as latitudinarianism was, thanks to him, on the rise under such men as John Tillotson, Edward Stillingfleet, and Simon Patrick.

Both in print and action, Wilkins was committed to a set of principles and beliefs—generally known as natural theology—which he was the first fully to formulate and advocate in England. He never questioned the importance of the Bible and revelation as sources of faith, and in this respect his thought differs from what later became known as deism. But his writings are devoted to the argument that moral and religious philosophy can be grounded on natural religion, by which he understood what "men might know, and should be obliged unto, by the mere principles of reason, improved by consideration and experience, without the help of revelation."[1]

Owing to the omnipotence, benevolence, and wisdom of God, both the universe and man are so admirably contrived that man can ensure the welfare of his soul by the mature exercise of the faculty of reason, which is the defining quality of his nature. This faculty reveals to man the natural principles that govern creation, thus providing him with knowledge that "may conduce to the proving of a God, and making men religious," by making him understand that "such a great order and constancy amongst" the heavenly bodies "could not at first be made but by a wise providence, nor since preserved without a powerful inhabitant, nor so perpetually governed without a skillful guide."[2]

Similarly, man is endowed with a natural principle that makes him seek moral good "as a rational voluntary free agent,"[3] owing to his steady inclination "to seek his own well-being and happiness," so that "nothing properly is his duty, but what is really his interest," which is another argument "that the author of his being must be infinitely wise and powerful."[4] Man's natural desire for happiness is as certain as the descent of heavy bodies,[5] an example that Wilkins also used to illustrate the fixed laws that rule nature. Both man and nature are governed by laws that ensure the harmony of religion and science.

Consistent with these arguments, Wilkins stated the deistic principle that the salvation of the heathen is not a problem for man to decide; since "God has not thought fit to tell *us* how he will be pleased to deal with such persons, it is not fit for us to tell *Him* how he ought to deal with them."[6] In his writings, Wilkins often used the wise testimony of the ancients to support the knowledge and arguments advanced by the new science. Whether we call some of his writings scientific and others religious is a matter of emphasis; they all have the same aim: to guide man's conduct toward moral virtue, religious devotion, and ultimately the hope of salvation. The pursuit of happiness, even comfort, in this world is man's legitimate interest.

But reason alone is not sufficient. Man is also naturally "a sociable creature . . . having only these two advantages to his protection, Society and Reason . . . Adam in the state of innocence could not be happy, though in Paradise, without a companion."[7] This is a theme Wilkins stresses again and again; it is the foundation of his constant advocacy of conciliation, moderation, and tolerance, often in contexts that refer to "all that confusion and disorder, which seem to be in the affairs of these times."[8] The instrument that ensures the benefits of social intercourse is language: "Every rational creature, being of an imperfect and dependent happiness, is therefore naturally endowed with an ability to communicate his own thoughts and intentions; that so by mutual services, it might the better promote itself in the prosecution of its own well-being."[9] As useful knowledge, both natural and moral, is a function of cooperation, so successful cooperation is a function of communication; the improvement of natural knowledge and language is the response to the "two general curses inflicted on mankind," after the fall of Adam, "the one upon their labors, the other upon their language."[10] After the anniversary meeting of the Royal Society on 30 November 1667 (in which the annual election of officers also took place), Pepys recorded that some members went out for dinner, he himself choosing to sit next to Wilkins "and others whom I value." With his last work, *An Essay Towards a Real Character and a Philosophical Language*, then in the press, Wilkins stated that "man was certainly made for society, he being of all creatures the least armed for defence, and of all creatures in the world the young ones are not able to do anything to help themselves . . . and were it not for speech man would be a very mean creature." Wilkins is the chief source of the Royal Society doctrines about language and style; knowledge based on mere words and phrases has "in it this intrinsical imperfection, that 'tis only so far to be esteemed, as it conduces to the knowledge of things," words themselves being merely "the images of matter." To treat them otherwise is to fall into "Pygmalion's phrenzy."[11]

Wilkins' view of useful knowledge determined his attitude toward the three chief sources of authority: the Bible, antiquity, and books. Using arguments that today are perhaps best known from Galileo's *Letter to the Grand Duchess Christina*, Wilkins repeatedly rejected scriptural authority in natural philosophy, a principle to which all the new scientists were committed; if theology is allowed interference with philosophy, then the status of the latter is endangered as an independent source of the wisdom of the creator. In his first publication, Wilkins stated the principle in these terms: "It is not the endeavor of Moses or the prophets to discover any mathematical or philosophical subtleties; but rather to accommodate themselves to vulgar capacities, and ordinary speech, as nurses are wont to use their infants."[12] On scientific matters, he was also fond of citing contradictory scriptural passages, just as he criticized those among his contemporaries "who upon the invention of any new secret, will presently find out some obscure text or other to father it upon, as if the Holy Ghost must

needs take notice of every particular which their partial fancies did over-value."[13]

He treated classical authors in much the same way as the Bible, using citations to suit his purposes both for and against his own principles, those in the latter category being dismissed as contrary to reason and experience. But he rejected outright the superior authority of antiquity: "In such learning as may be increased by fresh experiments and new discoveries, it is we are the fathers, and of more authority than former ages, because we have the advantage of more time than they had."[14] He was aware that the vast public structures of the Egyptians, Hebrews, Greeks, and Romans might be used to argue against the inferiority of their mechanical knowledge; he answered that if we have nothing of the sort nowadays, the reason does not lie in our knowledge, for "mechanical discoveries are much more exact now," but rather in the fact that "we have not either the same motives to attempt such works, or the same means to effect them as the ancients had." By this he meant that great wealth and power, then concentrated in the hands of a few, were now more widely diffused. "There is now a greater equality amongst mankind and the flourishing of arts and sciences has so stirred up the sparks of men's natural nobility, and made them of such active and industrious spirits, as to free themselves in a great measure from that slavery, which those former and wilder nations were subjected unto."[15]

The belief in the leveling and ennobling effect of the new knowledge found expression in Wilkins' attitude toward "bookish" men and mere bookish learning. Antiquity having slighted the mere manual and practical arts as "base and common," such studies had come to be neglected for hundreds of years, with grave consequences for the well-being of man. But the mechanical arts are just as worthy as the old and honored liberal arts such as logic and rhetoric, indeed "that discipline which discovers the general causes, effects, and proprieties of things, may truly be esteemed as a species of philosophy." Since all studies ought "to conduce to practice as their proper end," book learning is often rightly considered mere "pedantry." Wilkins was eager to overcome the prejudice that studies pertaining to the mind deserve greater respect than those that deal with material things. It was in this spirit that he devoted his *Mathematical Magick* to practical mechanical devices and labor-saving inventions "whereby nature is in any way quickened or advanced in her defects," for these are in fact "so many essays, whereby men do naturally attempt to restore themselves from the first general curse inflicted upon their labors." Wilkins' scientific writings are all of a popular nature, written not for the learned, but for "such common artificers, as are well skilled in the practice of these arts, who may be much advantaged by the right understanding of their grounds and theory." For this reason he wrote in English, referring on the authority of Ramus to the German practice of public lectures given in the vernacular, "for the capacity of every unlettered ingenious artificer."[16] Though he defended the universities on several occasions, Wilkins was aware that they must justify their teaching in terms of real use and benefit to mankind, a view that made him one of the principal advocates of university reform at Oxford and Cambridge.[17]

Wilkins' scientific writings constitute a single, well-conceived educational program to reach a larger audience outside the confines of traditional learning, both to promote natural philosophy and to lend dignity to the practical arts. He announced this program in the opening of his first publication, saying that it was his desire to "raise up some more active spirit to a search after other hidden and unknown truths: since it must needs be a great impediment unto the growth of sciences, for men still to plod on upon beaten principles, as to be afraid of entertaining anything that may seem to contradict them."[18] In this task of popular education, Wilkins' importance can hardly be overestimated. He laid the foundation for the wide participation and interest that the Royal Society enjoyed during its formative years.

The means of this success was pedagogical flair, shown both in his capacity for clear and interesting exposition, always without any suggestion of condescension, and in the choice of subjects, which in the context of the times were sensational. Was the moon inhabited? Could man find a means of flying to it? Was it much like the earth with mountains and oceans? Was the earth a planet? Could man navigate under water, lift heavy weights with little effort, or communicate effectively by other means than ordinary speech? The very titles were catchy—he did not shun the title *Mathematical Magick*, although it was certainly against his principles to suggest that there was any magic in the study of natural philosophy.[19] His more serious purpose was to gain acceptance for the new science, to bring the work of Copernicus, Kepler, Galileo, Gilbert, Mersenne, and others to the attention of his countrymen. Against the authority of the Bible, antiquity, and book learning, he answered that "we must labor to find out what things are in themselves, by our own experience, and a thorough examination of their natures, not what another says of them." Natural religion will prevail; disorder, strife, and sectarianism will vanish when disputes are resolved by giving "soft words but hard arguments."[20] There is no important principle in Thomas Sprat's *History of the Royal Society* that had not earlier been argued by Wilkins. "The universal disposition of this age," wrote Sprat, "is bent upon a rational religion." In his first work Wilkins said that the opponents of new views too often submitted to authority, a point he enforced by saying that "our opposites . . . too often do *jurare in verba magistri*," thus citing the well-known line in Horace from which the Royal Society drew its motto *Nullis in verba*.[21]

There is, finally, another aspect of Wilkins' character that bears some relation to his career and influence: unlike most of his scientific and ecclesiastical associates, he was a man of the world. After their first meeting, Robert Boyle remarked that Wilkins' "entertainment did as well speak him a courtier as his discourse." Anthony à Wood observed that Wilkins was "bred in the court, and was a piece of a traveller, having twice seen the prince of Orange's court at the Hague, in his journey to, and return from, Heydelburg, whither he went to wait upon the prince elector palatine, whose chaplain he was in England."[22] Without such social attainments, Wilkins' sphere of activity would hardly have reached so far beyond his humble origins.

**Early Career.** Wilkins was born at the Northamptonshire house of his maternal grandfather, the puritan divine John Dod, who was known for an exposition of the Ten Commandments. His mother, Jane Dod, had four children in her marriage to Walter Wilkins, an Oxford goldsmith who died in 1625. John Aubrey reports that the father was "a very ingenious man with a very mechanical head. He was much for trying experiments, and his head ran much upon the perpetual motion." In a second marriage, to Francis Pope, Jane Dod had a son, Walter, who remained close to Wilkins.[23]

After schooling at home, Wilkins began grammar school at the age of nine under the noted Greek and Latin scholar Edward Sylvester, and in May 1627 he matriculated at New Inn Hall, Oxford (later united with Balliol College). He soon transferred to Magdalen Hall, where his tutor was the Baptist divine John Tombes. He graduated B.A.

20 October 1631, and gained the M.A. degree on 11 June 1634; at this time Wilkins was tutor in his college, one of his students being Walter Charleton, who thereby "profited much beyond his years in logic and philosophy."[24] A few years later he was ordained and became vicar of Fawsley. At this time he is reported to have become chaplain to William Fiennes, first viscount Saye and Seale, who was then a supporter of the Puritans and later sat in the Westminster Assembly. But in 1641 Wilkins dedicated his *Mercury* to George Lord Berkeley (1601–1658), signing himself "your lordship's servant and chaplain." His desire to move in high places was further gratified when he became chaplain to Charles Louis, the prince elector Palatine, the king's nephew. The elector lived in England during a good part of the 1640's, befriending the parliamentary party in the hope of securing the restitution of his lost possessions. During the early months of 1646, Wilkins was officially engaged as preacher at Gray's Inn; during these years he also preached at the Savoy.[25]

On 13 April 1648, the Parliamentary Visitors made Wilkins warden of Wadham College. The holder of this office was required to take the degree of doctor of divinity, but on 5 March 1649, the Visitors gave him a year's dispensation, since Wilkins was "at this time in attendance on the prince elector, and cannot in regard of that service have time to do his exercise, and all other things necessary unto that degree."[26] He took the degree on 19 December the same year. Since this occurred at the time when Charles Louis was returning to Heidelberg to take possession of the lands that had been restored to him as a consequence of the Peace of Westphalia, we may surmise that it was at this time that Wilkins made his visits to the Continent and to The Hague.[27]

Beyond these sparse facts, we have little information about Wilkins' life during his formative years. No doubt he spent most of them in Oxford and London. It was in London that he participated in the meetings that were devoted, as John Wallis recorded, to "what has been called the New Philosophy or Experimental Philosophy," these meetings having been convened at the suggestion of Theodore Haak. It is an interesting conjunction that they began during the Westminster Assembly, of which Wallis was then secretary. For a better view of Wilkins' early career, we have his writings and some reasonable conjectures about his associations.

Although published two years apart, the *Discovery* (1638) and the *Discourse* (1640) can be considered a single work. Addressed to the common reader, the primary aim was to make known and to defend the new world picture of Copernicus, Kepler, and Galileo by showing its agreement with reason and experience against subservience to Aristotelian doctrines and literal biblical interpretation. Kepler and especially Galileo's *Siderius nuncius* (1610) and Matthias Bernegger's Latin translation (1635) of the *Dialogue Concerning the Two Chief World Systems* are frequently cited, along with a wealth of other references from the literature that had appeared within the last generation. The work is polemical, but unlike Campanella's *Apologia pro Galileo* (1622), which is cited with approval, it constantly turns the reader's attention to the positive arguments that may be drawn from rational interpretation of observable phenomena. The central argument was borrowed from Galileo: the moon is not a shining disk or whatever else men have imagined, but a world with natural features much like the earth. And if so, then the moon might also be inhabited, although Wilkins does not find sufficient grounds to say what sort of beings the inhabitants are, thus neatly avoiding the touchy question of whether they are descendants of Adam. Further, if the moon shares natural features with the earth, then the argument could be extended to form a uniformitarian view of the constitution of the entire universe, thus breaking down the Aristotelian doctrine of fixed, hierarchical spheres that obey laws other than those of the sublunar world. In both the first and the second work, Wilkins is careful to warn the reader at the outset that he is not pretending to write a precise treatise expounding unquestionable truths; but though much might still be doubtful, he is confident that the hypotheses he defends will, against all prejudice, be granted conformity with observable phenomena and with simplicity of explanation. In the 1640 edition of the *Discovery*, Wilkins added the sensational idea that it might be possible to contrive a way of flying to the moon, thus taking up a suggestion already known in England from Francis Godwin's *Man in the Moone* (1638). In the latter part of the second work, Wilkins supports his argument for the movement of the earth by reference to William Gilbert's suggestion that the earth is a lodestone. Bacon had argued against Gilbert on that point. Both works make few and only general references to Bacon, quite insufficient to attribute any important inspiration to him.

The *Discovery* and the *Discourse* have a wealth of references to recent literature—at least some thirty in each, of which nearly a dozen are new in the second work. They suggest that Wilkins found his occasion in the controversy that grew up in the wake of Philip van Lansberge's *Commentationes in motum terrae, diurnum et annuum* (1630). This work was opposed by Libertus Fromondus both in *Anti-Aristarchus, sive orbis-terrae immobilis* (1631) and in *Vesta, sive Ant-Aristarchi vindex adversus Jac. Lansbergium* (1634), in which he defended the proscription of Copernican doctrine first issued by the congregation of cardinals in 1616 and reiterated in 1633. Fromondus was Wilkins' chief anti-Copernican opponent in both works; only the second work contains Alexander Ross's *Commentum de terrae motu circulari* (1634), which opposes both Lansberge and Nathaniel Carpenter. With a wide and mature command of the literature, Wilkins was engaged in international controversy. There can be no doubt that he succeeded in his aim of gaining acceptance for Copernicus, Kepler, and Galileo in England.[28]

We may wonder why Wilkins, still only in his middle twenties, took up the controversy with so much energy and conviction. In the *Discovery*, the "Epistle to the Reader" states that the work is "but the fruit of some lighter studies," finished in a few weeks; but the extensive reading adduced in both works could hardly have been so quickly mastered. The subject must have required longer preparation, perhaps during his student days and while he was tutor in his college. Henry Briggs, who died in 1630, was the first Savilian professor of geometry; in London he had been close to William Gilbert and Edward Wright, and in Oxford he became acquainted with John Pell and Theodore Haak, who was in Oxford during the later 1620's. Briggs was a strong Copernican and scorned astrology as "a system of groundless conceits," a view that was shared by his Savilian colleague in the astronomy chair, 1621–1643, John Bainbridge, who in London had belonged to the circle of Briggs and Nathaniel Carpenter. Both had been professors at Gresham College before coming to Oxford. It seems reasonable to assume that Wilkins had learned something from either or both of these men, who most closely illustrate the interest and orientation that characterized his career from the beginning.

Only a year later, in 1641, Wilkins published another book on a popular subject, entitled *Mercury, or the Secret and Swift Messenger, Showing How a Man May With Privacy and Speed Communicate His Thoughts to a Friend at Any Distance*. It mentions such old tricks as baking secret messages into loaves of bread, but Wilkins' chief interest was cryptography, of which he gives a wealth of examples, all ready for use. But he also deals with cryptology or secret communication by speaking, either by involving the sense in metaphors and allegories or by changing old words or inventing new ones as is done by thieves, gypsies, and lovers; and with "semeology," that is communication by signs and gestures, as used for instance by deaf-mutes. Thus *Mercury* is not merely a practical guide in the use and decoding of ciphers, but a broadly based discussion of the means of communication, or what today would be called semiotics. The opening chapter states the basic principle that men are born with a natural ability to communicate, capable of learning any language in the same manner as they can master "other arts and sciences"; but men are not born with a single language that is natural to all mankind, for if this were so men would retain it so that all men would have a "double language, which is evidently false." In other words, like Mersenne, Wilkins rejected the natural-language doctrine then advocated by Robert Fludd. Wilkins ridiculed cabalistic interpretations of the sort that was again to occupy him in controversy with John Webster, who attacked the universities for neglecting Jacob Boehme's mystical linguistic doctrines. At the same time, Wilkins saw that the Babelistic multiplicity of languages was a great hindrance to the promotion of arts and sciences, men now wasting much time merely learning words instead of addressing themselves directly to the study of things. Citing such well-known instances as Arabic numerals, astronomical and chemical signs, and musical notes, he devoted a chapter to the possibility of creating a universal character as a remedy for the confusion. It outlines the principles he was later to follow in his final work. At the end of *Mercury*, Wilkins notes that though his work can be used to serve unlawful purposes, it can also be used to uncover them. If the abuse of useful inventions is a reason for suppressing them, he observes, "there is not any art or science which might be lawfully professsed."[29]

After dealing with communication and the second curse on mankind in *Mercury*, Wilkins next turned to the remedies for the first curse, inflicted upon man's labors. This pattern shows how closely Wilkins, with most of his contemporaries, related his concerns to the biblical story of man's terrestrial life. His *Mathematical Magick* (1648) is divided in two parts: "Archimedes or Mechanical Powers" and "Daedalus or Mechanical Motions." These titles might suggest an emphasis on the theoretical problems that had occupied much of the literature on mechanics during the previous generation, but the work is almost wholly devoted to the practical uses of mechanical devices with only enough theory to give the reader a sense of scientific initiation and understanding. The address "To the Reader" explains that the present work forms part of the same educational efforts as Wilkins' previous publications by showing how "a divine power and wisdom might be discerned, even in those common arts which are so much despised." The book's aim was "real benefit," both for gentlemen in the improvement of their estates, as in the draining of mines and coalpits, and for "common artificers" in gaining a "right understanding of the grounds and theory" of the arts they practice. It is therefore a short book, a compendium of knowledge otherwise only available in large, expensive volumes in Latin rather than the vernacular, "for which these mechanical arts of all other are most proper."

The first part deals with the balance, lever, wheel, pulley, wedge, and screw in that order, all illustrated with line drawings and pictures. Then follow chapters that show how the combination of these devices may produce "infinite strength" so as to "pull up any oak by the roots with a hair, lift it up with a straw, or blow it up with one's breath," all illustrated with rather sensational pictures. The second part treats a miscellaneous collection of strange devices and possibilities, such as flying machines, moving and speaking statues, artificial spiders, the imitation of sounds made by birds and man, a land vehicle driven by sails, a submarine, Archimedes' screw, and perpetual motion. This is a strange, almost baroque assembly, but all of these subjects had already been discussed in the extensive literature on which Wilkins drew and a few years later a speaking statue was among the wonders shown to visitors at Wadham College. Automata were a legitimate scientific interest. There is little theory here, even scant hope of practical success, but much excitement. Learned fancies were being shared with a lay audience. It would be a mistake, however, to think that Wilkins was being frivolous. Even in the 1660's the Royal Society was not averse to the pursuit of such projects. There was as yet no clear distinction between what we consider good science and technology as opposed to fruitless speculation. The same scientific success that brought about the disenchantment of the universe also raised technological hopes that entered the realm of magic. Wilkins knew that wonder is the chief impulse to serious study and experiment.

A closer look at the sources of *Mathematical Magick* yields interesting information both about Wilkins' orientation and about the dating. It can easily be seen that many of the line drawings and illustrations are taken from other works along with the principles and devices they illustrate. The most recent work cited is John Greaves's description of the Egyptian pyramids, *Pyradomographia* (1646). But the works on which he chiefly relied were Guidobaldo del Monte's *Liber mechanicorum* (1577) and Marin Mersenne's *Cogitata physico-mathematica* (1644).[30] The use of Mersenne is much too extensive to have been introduced in a late revision; if therefore we take seriously Wilkins' statement in the dedication to Charles Louis that "this discourse was composed some years since, at my spare hours in the university," we must conclude that he devoted a good part of his time to university affairs during the mid- and late 1640's, a fact that may explain his sudden appointment to the wardenship of Wadham in 1648. Yet those affairs left him time to write the book, perform his official preaching duties in London, attend the early scientific meetings there, and serve as chaplain to the elector. Wilkins clearly managed his diverse functions with considerable energy.

Wilkins' explanation and illustration of the six traditional mechanical devices relied chiefly on Guidobaldo; a mere visual comparison of the handsome pages of the *Liber mechanicorum* with Wilkins' modest book makes this dependence obvious. Following Pappus, Guidobaldo had reduced all these devices to the same working principle as the lever—with the exception of the wedge, which he also discussed in terms of the inclined plane without making a clear choice between the two. Wilkins altogether omitted the inclined plane, but did not reduce the wedge to the lever principle as he did for the balance, wheel, pulley, and screw, presumably because he did not wish to burden his lay readers with the finer points of theory in a work which in any event limited to the barest minimum the mathematical principles offered by his sources.[31] In the order of the six devices, however, Wilkins followed Mersenne by treating the wheel before the pulley, but he did not use Mersenne's somewhat more complicated analyses. Thus the reader of *Mathematical Magick* would not have gained a sense of the long controversy over the proper understanding of these devices, revived in 1634 by Mersenne's *Les méchaniques de Galilée*.[32] From Mersenne, Wilkins also borrowed his account of the "glossocomus" or "engine of many wheels," with the analysis and illustration that show how it works like a series of interlocking levers.[33] In addition he cited works other than the *Tractatus mechanicus* from the *Cogitata*: on the bending and power of bows,[34] on the flattening of a bullet fired against a wall,[35] and on the submarine.[36]

Wilkins' debt to Mersenne is so heavy that it deserves closer attention. Mersenne is cited in the *Discovery*, the *Discourse*, and in *Mathematical Magick*. He is not mentioned in *Mercury*, but the general subject of this work forms the very core of Mersenne's own enquiries: the phenomena of communication, language, and the possibility of creating a philosophical language. It would be correct to say that Wilkins' scientific writings together present a popular version of Mersenne. The affinity of interests and orientation was too close to stem from common reliance on the same literature. The plurality of worlds was the only subject that separated them, but for Wilkins this was only a tentative suggestion of no systematic importance, confined to the *Discovery* and not repeated. Mersenne's position on the Copernican doctrine was sufficiently ambiguous not to create any problem.[37]

Mersenne and Wilkins shared the conviction that religion and morality have a rational basis, that the grounds of religious belief are not tied to the retention and defense of Aristotelian doctrines, that a rational explanation of nature is possible when firmly based on sense experience and experiment, that this explanation would be mechanical and quantitative, that man is essentially different from the animals by virtue of possessing reason, that man alone is capable of language and communication, and that the growth of knowledge is a function of communication. Both were opposed to magic and the irrational, and for this reason they opposed the belief in the magical and occult powers of words, a doctrine then chiefly associated with Jacob Boehme and Robert Fludd. Language is not part of nature, it can tell us nothing about the essences of things, and thus cannot give "real knowledge" about the things of creation. It is conventional and man-made—"a man is born without any of them, but yet capable of all," Wilkins said. If this were not so, then it would not be possible to maintain that reason and experience together form the exclusive source of scientific knowledge. Thus the nature of language is the crucial problem in the epistemology of the new science. This fact explains some evident similarities between Mersenne, Wilkins, and Locke; as Mersenne felt bound to engage in a sustained critique of Fludd, so Locke argued against Boehme and his English disciple John Webster with his doctrine of "innate

notions."[38] On these grounds Mersenne repeatedly argued that only God can know the essences of things and their true causes. Like Locke, he was convinced that certainty cannot be achieved in physics, "for we do not know the true reason of the effects we clearly see, and which we submit to our uses."[39]

Wilkins stated the same principle in 1649: "In our natural enquiries after the *efficient* causes of things, when our reason is at a stand, we are fain sometimes to sit down and satisfy ourselves in the notion of occult *qualities*, and therefore much more should be content to be ignorant of the *final cause* of things, which lie more deep and obscure than the other."[40] On this central doctrine, Mersenne and Wilkins disagreed with Bacon's goal of penetrating into "the nature of things." This principle severely limits the extent to which Bacon can be said to have guided and informed the new science in England. Bacon in fact played a small role in Wilkins' thought, in no way comparable to Mersenne's role. Mersenne and Wilkins also admired Gilbert on points that Bacon did not accept. As *Mathematical Magick* shows, Wilkins also followed Mersenne in taking an interest in automata; they focused attention on interesting problems. In all their conduct and affairs, both Mersenne and Wilkins showed admirable openness and tolerance, of men as well as of opinions. In spite of the dramatic outward differences of their lives, they offer a beautiful example of the unifying, even irenic effect of the new science, in accordance with their mutual aim.[41]

If with Wilkins' contemporaries we grant that he was the chief promoter of the new science in England—not only by virtue of his writings, but also owing to his personal encouragement of individuals and his success in the shaping of scientific organization before and after the official formation of the Royal Society—then his alliance with Mersenne has far-reaching consequences for the belief that the Rosicrucian enlightenment was the seed-bed of the sort of natural philosophy that it was the aim of the Royal Society to promote. No attempt to assess Wilkins' importance can ignore these problems. Fludd and Mersenne do not go together. The groups they represent are not separated by their interest in a philosophy of nature, but they are set apart by their basic methods and principles, and it is this latter criterion that is crucial. Neither does one owe anything to the other regarding the need for formal cooperation and exchange of knowledge in a college (whether invisible or not) or an academy, for this need had been advocated by Mersenne as early as 1623; it was met by Théophraste Renaudot's conferences as early as 1629 and by Mersenne's own Academia Parisiensis at least by 1635. The ubiquitous presence of Hartlib and others shows nothing except a shared interest in natural philosophy and its results, although this presence has been the chief prop of the Rosicrucian argument. The wide tolerance of men like Mersenne and Wilkins should not be construed to mean positive approval. It has been argued that Continental influences reached England through The Hague, owing to the presence there of the exiled Queen Elizabeth of Bohemia, who for well-known reasons made some political use of such men as Hartlib and John Dury (Durie) as well as their contacts with circles that may, at least in part, be called Rosicrucian. In these matters the queen relied heavily on the services of the roving ambassador Sir Thomas Roe. On these grounds it has been argued that John Wallis' account of the first London scientific meetings in 1645 "seems to give a curiously 'Palatinate' coloring to the origins of the Royal Society."[42]

The weakness of this argument is obvious: it ignores the fact that The Hague was the home of a very different intellectual group that had lively contacts with London. It was through these contacts that Mersenne became more widely known in England. During these years, from 1633 until his death in 1649, the English ambassador at The Hague was Sir William Boswell, whose chief business of course was not with the exiled Palatinate queen, but with the court of the House of Orange. A strong royalist and a Laudian, he was successful in preventing Dutch intervention in the Civil War during the 1640's. At the center of this group in The Hague was Constantijn Huygens, whose political, cultural, and intellectual importance is well known. Huygens' correspondence shows that he was on intimate terms with Boswell,[43] and they shared many scholarly interests, including musicology. As secretary to Prince Frederic Henry of Orange, Huygens was Boswell's main contact with the court. He corresponded with both Descartes and Mersenne, as did Boswell although those letters are lost. Huygens regularly transmitted mail from Mersenne in Paris to recipients in Holland, including Descartes; Boswell occasionally did likewise. Between mid-summer of 1639 and August 1640, Boswell lived in London, and it was during this period that Haak initiated his lively correspondence with Mersenne at the encouragement of Boswell, "with whom Haak seems to have enjoyed a long-lasting and close acquaintance," beginning

in 1638.[44] As was to be expected, it is evident that the contents of Mersenne's letters became widely known in London, just as these contacts were in part responsible for Mersenne's close English ties during the early 1640's.[45]

Having already cited Mersenne in his first two publications, Wilkins may have written *Mercury* on a hint from Mersenne transmitted through Haak. At the beginning of this book, Wilkins tells the reader that it was occasioned by a reading of Francis Godwin's *Nuncius inanimatus, or The Mysterious Messenger* (1629), which he had mentioned in the *Discovery*. It is tempting to think that his renewed interest in speedy and secret communication was related to the fact that Haak had sent Mersenne a copy of Godwin's little book, soon receiving the well-founded judgment that it "was indeed very animated because it teaches us nothing, saying not a word about its secret of communication. What is the use of writing, 'I know such and such things,' but not tell; that is to make fun of the readers."[46] In line with this critique, Wilkins' purpose in *Mercury* was precisely to remove linguistic mystification and the secrecy of ciphers by bringing the technique out in the open. It is no wonder that Wilkins kept informed about Mersenne, so that soon after its publication in 1644 he made the *Cogitata physico-mathematica* the main source of his *Mathematical Magick*. It was at this time, in 1645, that Haak called the first London meetings, which not only discussed scientific subjects but also performed experiments. Wallis' list of the topics shows no Rosicrucian inclination, and the meetings themselves were most likely suggested by the success of Mersenne's Academia Parisiensis.[47] It was the group around Huygens and Boswell at The Hague that exerted a decisive influence in England. The chief foreign vehicle of this influence was Mersenne, its chief beneficiary was Wilkins. The Royal Society is in large measure the record of the nature and success of this influence.[48]

**The Oxford Years.** In 1648 Wilkins entered upon the second stage of his career. Oxford had come under increasingly severe strains during the 1640's. College finances were in disarray, new admissions dropped precipitously, teaching duties were only fitfully performed, and the academic community was torn into factions aligning royalists and men of the old stamp against Parliamentarians, feuding over religious observances, the inviolability of college statutes, the curriculum, the proper conduct and morals of students and teachers, and even proper modes of personal appearance and attire. This situation was intensified by the frothy presence of extreme Anabaptist agitators who acknowledged no authority but their own private revelations. The crisis came to a head after the victorious Parliamentary forces under Fairfax entered the town. On 1 May 1647, Parliament passed an ordinance which empowered a committee to look after "the better regulating and reformation of the University of Oxford, and the several colleges and halls in the same, and for the due correction of offences, abuses, and disorders, especially of late times committed there."

Within the next year the Parliamentary Visitors came to Oxford, ejected the old warden of Wadham College, and appointed Wilkins, who took charge on 13 April 1648. It proved a wise choice. At the young age of thirty-four, he must have impressed the authorities by his accomplishments in the university and in his varied public offices as well as by his forceful advocacy of new learning, his moderation in religious affairs, his energy, and his extensive connections. Under the guidance of a man who was not considered a bigot, the college admissions soon rose steeply, including a large number of country gentlemen and "cavaliers," a fact that may also have helped improve the finances. It is universally acknowledged that Wadham was a distinguished college during Wilkins' wardenship. Among the new fellows of Wadham who came to Oxford from Cambridge were Seth Ward and Lawrence Rooke, "who was much addicted to experimental philosophy." They were joined by other men migrating from London and the scientific meetings there to continue their work in Oxford. They met at various places, including Wadham, where Wilkins created a laboratory. They included the nucleus of the future Royal Society: John Wallis, Jonathan Goddard, William Petty, Ralph Bathurst, Thomas Willis, and Robert Boyle, to whom Wilkins wrote on 6 September 1653: "I should exceedingly rejoice in your being stayed in England this winter, and the advantage of your conversation at Oxford, where you will be a means to quicken and direct our enquiries." Not long after, Boyle took up residence in Oxford.[49] The meetings were also attended by some of the able students who came to Wadham. The most brilliant was Christopher Wren, Wilkins' special protégé in his early career. Among the others were Wilkins' half-brother Walter Pope, Thomas Sprat, William Lloyd, William Neile, and Samuel Parker.

These men and their activities created an air of modernity and intellectual excitement in the university which suited Wilkins' desire to introduce the new philosophy in a manner that at the same time demanded discipline and significant achievement. He would hardly have been disturbed that his circle was in low repute among the Aristotelians, Galenists, and "those of the old stamp, that had been eminent for school and polemical divinity, and disputations and other polite parts of learning, [who] look upon them very inconsiderably, and their experiments as much below their profound learning and the professors of them."[50] This was precisely what reform was about and why so many sought Wilkins' advice and encouragement. When Oldenburg in the spring of 1656 settled in Oxford for a while, he was glad to find lodgings near Wilkins and Wadham, waxing poetic in his description of the new garden's "design and cultivation, where pleasure rivals utility and ingenuity industry."[51] Created at no small expense, the expansion and layout of this formal garden was one of Wilkins' first innovations. It was exquisitely executed with various mechanical wonders, a Doric temple, and, on a mound, a statue of Atlas carrying the world on his shoulders. The garden shows a characteristic aspect of Wilkins' knowledge and orientation, as does his fondness for music.[52] When the warden's friend, the royalist John Evelyn, visited Wadham in July 1654, he was fascinated by the curiosities he was shown. There were not only scientific instruments, but also a "hollow statue which gave a voice and uttered words" and transparent, elaborately adorned apiaries built in the shape of castles and palaces, but constructed so as to make it possible to take out the honey without destroying the bees.[53] In those days science and ingenuity were visual. While still at the Westminster School, Robert Hooke received a copy of *Mathematical Magick* as a gift from the author; and when a few years later he became a student at Oxford, he attended the scientific meetings and sought Wilkins' advice on his experiments on the art of flying and the making of artificial muscles.[54] Ten years later Hooke concluded the preface to *Micrographia* with an eloquent tribute to Wilkins, describing him as many must have seen him during those years:

> There is scarce any one invention, which this nation has produced in our age, but it has some way or other been set forward by his assistance. . . . He is indeed a man born for the good of mankind, and for the honor of his country. In the sweetness of whose behavior, in the calmness of his mind, in the unbounded goodness of his heart, we have an evident instance, what the true and the primitive unpassionate religion was, before it was soured by particular factions. . . . So I may thank God, that Dr. Wilkins was an Englishman, for wherever he had lived, there

had been the chief seat of generous knowledge and true philosophy.

In the midst of this busy life, Wilkins was also a member of several influential university committees, including the delegacy to which the governance of the university was entrusted by its chancellor, Oliver Cromwell, on 16 October 1652. In this work, Wilkins successfully sought to regain for the university and the colleges their lost autonomy, to mediate between contending factions, and to maintain order and discipline. He especially defended the university against the attacks of radical religious factions, both on the governance of the university and its curriculum. One such attack was Webster's *Academiarum examen* (1654), which Wilkins and Ward answered the same year in *Vindicae academiarum*. It opened with a letter by Wilkins, outlining and rejecting the three main charges. Contrary to Webster's accusations, the university was not a slavish follower of Aristotle but freely opposed him "as any contrary evidence does engage them, being ready to follow the banner of truth by whomsoever it shall be lifted up." Further, the university did not presume to teach what can proceed only from the spirit of God as Webster had charged. And it did not intend to direct its teachings according to the mystical linguistic doctrines of Boehme and "the highly illuminated fraternity of the Rosicrucians." Webster's trust in these authorities, said Wilkins, "may sufficiently convince what a kind of credulous fanatick reformer he is like to prove." Wilkins remained committed to the principles he shared with Mersenne.[55]

There appears to be good reason to accept Tillotson's assessment of Wilkins' achievement in the life of the university: "It is so well known to many worthy persons yet living, and has been so often acknowledged even by his enemies, that in the late times of confusion, almost all that was preserved and kept up of ingenuity and learning, of good order and government in the University of Oxford, was chiefly owing to his prudent conduct and encouragement."[56]

In the spring of 1656, Wilkins married Cromwell's sister, Robina French, which is said to have strengthened his hand with the Lord Protector in the interests of the university.[57]

**Cambridge.** In 1659 Wilkins made a sudden change of the sort that energetic men, confident of their powers, are prone to make when they, after success in one place, see an opportunity to apply their talents in new territory. After Cromwell's death, Wilkins had become a close adviser to Richard Cromwell, who appointed him master of Trinity College, Cambridge, "thinking he would be as serviceable in that, as he had been in the other university."[58] He took possession in late summer, resigning from the wardenship of Wadham on 3 September 1659. His tenure lasted barely a year. After the king's return to England in May 1660, Henry Ferne was made master, having successfully pressed a claim on the basis of a promise made by Charles I. The reason given was that the statutes did not allow a married master, but without Ferne's intervention this circumstance would hardly have prevented continuation. In a letter of July 1660, "numerously signed," the fellows of Trinity both offered their congratulations on the restoration and requested the reconfirmation of Wilkins, "appointed at their earnest petition, on the death of Dr. Arrowsmith, in 1658."[59]

During his brief association with Cambridge, Wilkins entered the circle of a group of men with whom he, in spite of some differences, had so much in common that he came to be considered one of them. With the Cambridge Platonists, he shared the outlook that was just then coming to be known as latitudinarianism: a commitment to tolerance and comprehension in church affairs, respect for learning, and the principle that the right understanding of religion, both revealed and natural, is essentially governed by reason. At the time of the Act of Uniformity a few years later, Richard Baxter wrote a succinct description of these men. He divided the conformists into three groups: the zealots, those who submitted for a variety of personal and other reasons, and

> those called latitudinarians, who were mostly Cambridge men, Platonists or Cartesians, and many of them Arminians with some additions, having more charitable thoughts than others of the salvation of the heathens and infidels. . . . These were ingenious men and scholars, and of universal principles, and free; abhorring at first the imposition of these little things, but thinking them not great enough to stick at when imposed.[60]

Wilkins' departure from Cambridge was felt as a loss by many, one of them being Isaac Barrow, whom Wilkins helped to the geometry professorship at Gresham College in 1662, the year before Barrow assumed the Lucasian chair at Cambridge. With an uncertain future behind him, Wilkins now gravitated to London and the culmination of his career as the energetic center of the Royal Society.

**The Royal Society and the Last Years.** In 1660 began the third and last stage of Wilkins' career.

He did not have to wait long for ecclesiastical preferment. On 28 January 1661, he was again elected preacher at Gray's Inn,[61] and at the end of the year George Lord Berkeley (1628–1698) presented him with the living of Cranford, Middlesex.[62] On 11 April 1662 he became vicar of St. Lawrence Jewry in London, a living that was in the king's gift; thus he soon gained royal favor.[63] During the 1660's, he held a plurality of other ecclesiastical offices until in 1668 he became bishop of Chester.[64] Wilkins preached regularly at St. Lawrence Jewry, but his main sphere of activity was elsewhere.

During the late 1650's scientific meetings were held at Gresham College. After attending a lecture by Wren on 28 November 1660, the group gathered to discuss a plan for the founding of "a college for the promoting of physico-mathematical experimental learning." It is an unmistakable sign of Wilkins' importance that he was on this occasion appointed to the chair; within the next two weeks, Oldenburg wrote that Wilkins had been elected "president of the new English Academy very recently founded here under the patronage of the king for the advancement of the sciences."[65] Wilkins was still styled president in the first months of the new year, but on 6 March 1661 Sir Robert Moray was chosen president, no doubt owing to his close associations with the king, whose favor was eagerly and successfully sought during the first years. The rest is a familiar story. The society gained its first official charter under royal patronage a few years later, many new members joined, and an astonishing and ceaseless round of activities got under way, lasting with undiminished energy until about the time of Wilkins' death in November 1672, when attendance at meetings began to drop off and a state of seeming exhaustion set in, no doubt in part owing to a financial crisis. It is hard to say whether this decline was related to the loss of Wilkins, but the coincidence is striking.[66]

The records of these years show that Wilkins was busier than any other member in the affairs of the society. From the beginning until his death, he was each year reelected to the council, being also one of the two secretaries, another elective office, until he became bishop of Chester. He was occasionally called vice-president, although the statutes made no provision for such an office. While secretary, he attended practically every meeting and at most of them he was busy doing something: providing recent information, proposing experiments, being put in charge of this and that, appointed to special committees, asked for advice, engaged in fund-raising, and preparing suitably interesting doings for the king's visits. He proposed a very large number of candidates for membership, suggested that Robert Hooke be made curator of the collections, and proposed Nehemiah Grew as curator for the anatomy of plants.[67] At the same time he also supervised the writing of Sprat's *History of the Royal Society* (1667).[68] During the plague in the summer of 1665, Wilkins, Hooke, and William Petty removed to Durdans near Epsom in Surrey to carry out experiments on "improved chariots" and other mechanical devices; their results were reported to the society the following year. This was one of the several subjects of *Mathematical Magick* that occupied the society during the 1660's.[69]

At the beginning of 1668, Wilkins once more became involved in church affairs. After the fall of Clarendon, during the closing months of the previous year, the way was open for an attempt to bring at least some groups of nonconformists into communion with the church, a policy Wilkins had long supported in accordance with the promise made by the king in the Declaration of Breda shortly before his return to England. It was also advocated by the duke of Buckingham, now the king's first minister. Richard Baxter was approached, but he found himself unable to accept the initial terms of negotiation and requested instead that "two learned peaceable divines" be nominated "to treat with us, till we agreed on the fittest terms." One of them was Wilkins, who drew up a proposal that was revised during further deliberations. Baxter's detailed account shows that Wilkins was a skillful negotiator who tried his best to find a compromise that would satisfy all parties. This proved impossible, and when it became known that a bill for comprehension was ready, Parliament refused to accept it.[70] But Wilkins had Buckingham's patronage, and when the see of Chester fell vacant in August, he was soon appointed and duly consecrated on 14 November 1668.[71] In a diocese known for its large number of Dissenters, he was as lenient to nonconformists as his predecessor had been severe, many being brought into communion with the church owing to his "soft interpretation of the terms of conformity," while others who did not conform were still allowed to preach.[72] Early in 1669, Pepys heard that Wilkins, "my friend . . . shall be removed to Winchester and be Lord Treasurer." Although he discounted this rumor, he added that Wilkins was "a mighty rising man, as being a Latitudinarian, and the Duke of Buckingham's great friend."[73] In the midst of all his activities during the 1660's, Wilkins had also found time to prepare his greatest work, *An Essay Towards a Real Character and a Philosophical Language*, which with the official imprimatur of the Royal Society was presented to it on 7 May 1668.[74]

The *Essay* is the largest and most complete work in a long tradition of speculation and effort to create an artificial language that would, in a contemporary phrase, "repair the ruins of Babel." On one level a mere universal language would accomplish this aim by removing the obstacle that ordinary languages place in the way of common communication, whether in religion, commerce, or science. The universal use of a single language, for example, Latin, would meet this problem, but as Latin lost ground during the early half of the seventeenth century, especially in scientific writings, the need for other solutions was felt with greater urgency. As knowledge grew, in large measure aided by the introduction of common, conceptual, nonverbal symbols (much like Arabic numerals), there seemed to be new hope for the idea of a different sort of language, generally traced back to Ramón Lull, which would refer directly to what knowledge and thought are about, rather than using the imperfect medium of ordinary languages. There was wide agreement with Bacon that in these languages words were a perpetual source of philosophical error, being "framed and applied according to the conceit and capacities of the vulgar sort."[75]

The traditional model for such a language, often cited in the seventeenth century, was the language Adam spoke when he named the animals in his perfect state of knowledge before the fall. In the cabalist tradition, in Boehme and Fludd, it was believed that this language could somehow be recaptured. It was, for instance, seriously believed by some that it could be found by a sort of etymological distillation from all existing languages of the hitherto hidden but original elements of the Adamic language, on the assumption that this language was Hebrew, that Hebrew was the source of all other languages, and that these elements expressed the natures or essences of things. This was the mystical way, repeatedly rejected by Mersenne as nonsense; only God can know the essences of things.

But granting that man can grasp the order of creation by sense experience and reason, it would seem possible for man to comprehend and codify this knowledge in an artificial language based on the study of things. Within the more limited range of fallen man, this language would be a substitute for the lost Adamic language; if complete, it would express all man's knowledge in a methodical, rationally ordered fashion that mirrored the fabric of nature. It would be philosophical and scientific without error. On the practical level, it could be expressed in written or spoken symbols or both. Unlike a universal language, in which knowledge was still tied to the "cheat or words," to use another contemporary phrase, it would deal directly with things. This, it was hoped, would not only make knowledge easier and quicker to attain; it would cause a vast increase in knowledge.

These hopes were sustained by an optimism for which nothing seemed unattainable, similar to other expectations that strike us as equally chimerical, for instance the perpetuum mobile and the squaring of the circle. During the first half of the seventeenth century, a wealth of texts toyed with the possibility of a philosophical language, most of them on the level of groping speculation which never reached articulate statement of basic principles. In addition to these texts, there were many rumors about men who were working on such projects. They were typically surrounded by great secrecy, and there were several instances of offers to reveal the secret for great sums of money. The philosophical language was the exact equivalent of the philosopher's stone. Leibniz brought more conviction, energy, and intelligence to this problem; yet even he never spelled out its full meaning.[76]

Wilkins based his plan on a few basic principles. He assumed that "as men do generally agree in the same principle of reason, so do they likewise agree in the same internal notion or apprehension of things." Now, if the common notions of men could be tied to common marks, written or spoken, then mankind would be "freed from that curse in the confusion of tongues, with all the unhappy consequences of it." These marks would "signify things, and not words," conjoined "with certain invariable rules for all such grammatical derivations and inflexions, and such only, as are natural and necessary," all contrived so "as to have such a dependence upon, and relation to, one another, as might be suitable to the nature of the things and notions which they represented." Thus the various marks, with their modifications, would follow an ordered and rational analysis of knowledge. The advantage would be immense, for "besides [being] the best way to helping the memory by a natural method, the understanding likewise would be highly improved; and we should, by learning the character and the names of things, be instructed likewise in their natures."[77]

Wilkins decided, somewhat arbitrarily he admitted, on forty basic genera, which with "differences" and "species" would produce the marks that would give an inventory of the world, so to speak. Thus "world" is a genus (in the "effabie" language represented by *da*), which by addition of the second difference, denoting "celestial" (with the effable sign *d*) produces the notion "heaven" (*dad*). "Earth" has the same elements, but to it must be added the mark for the seventh species, denoting this "globe of sea and land." This mark is *y*, so that the effable sign for earth is *dady*. As was soon observed by several critics, this entire system was after all closely tied to English words. Yet, postulating that it followed a natural method, Wilkins believed that it could be mastered in one month.[78] This belief reveals something about the *Essay*'s ancestry, for this was precisely the claim being made by mystical projectors, who, however, had the good reason for their claim that they assumed a strict interpretation of the macrocosm-microcosm harmony. For them, once the Babelistic confusion of ordinary words and false concepts was stripped away, man would regain the Adamic nakedness of pure and complete knowledge. With pure intellect thus restored, the need for memory would vanish; the small traces of it still required would be caused by the last imperfections in the system, much as friction cannot be entirely overcome.

The *Essay* was tainted by its ancestry. In *Mercury*, Wilkins had outlined some of its principles, although only for the creation of a universal language. In the *Vindicae academiarum*, having ridiculed Webster's mystical advocacy of a genuinely natural, Adamic language, Seth Ward suddenly, as if unrelated to the subject, had said: "It did presently occur to me, that by the help of logic and mathematics this might soon receive a mighty advantage." He then briefly outlined the plan Wilkins executed. "Such a language as this," Ward said, "where every word were a definition and contained the nature of the thing, might not unjustly be termed a natural language, and would afford that which the cabalists and Rosicrucians have vainly sought for in the Hebrew, and in the names assigned by Adam."[79] The evidence shows that it was soon after and with the help of Ward that Wilkins began work on his philosophical language, as he openly admits in the "Epistle to the Reader" in the *Essay*. In rather awkward fashion Wilkins straddled two traditions that in the minds of most

observers could not be brought together. Mersenne had clearly outlined the plan of such a language, but stayed clear of the mystical implications; and, in the event, he seems not to have had faith in its practicality, although he took an interest in its theoretical aspects, much as he did in automata.[80] In the *Essay* Wilkins also modified his optimistic statements with great diffidence about the entire plan and avowals of its tentative, incomplete execution, inviting the Royal Society to appoint a committee to examine it and make suggestions for its improvement. It was fortunate for his reputation that the *Essay* came at the end of Wilkins' career.[81]

The publication of the *Essay* put the Royal Society in a difficult situation. Written by one of its best-known members, encouraged and published under its auspices, it caused a crisis of prestige. It had been much talked about before publication, and it was soon distributed both in England and on the Continent. Yet none of the scientific members of the society had much, if any, faith in it, with the exception of Hooke, who mastered it and continued to take great interest in it.[82] Following Wilkins' wishes, the society immediately set up a committee to report on the *Essay*, but within the society this committee was never heard from again.[83] It was, however, decided that the society's "repository" under Hooke would be organized according to the *Essay*.[84] In its outward relations, the society talked up the *Essay* with much exaggeration. Thus after Christiaan Huygens had voiced his doubts to Moray, the latter quickly wrote back that the character was easy to master; the king had already done so and everyone was now following his example.[85]

Outside the Royal Society, a group of men (some of whom were fellows) continued to seek to improve and perfect the philosophical language, but with the exception of Hooke, these were men without scientific prestige in the society.[86] Having himself already written on similar plans, Leibniz soon learned about the *Essay*; he admired it greatly, although he still found it short of his own requirements. In 1680 he wrote of this admiration to Haak, but added that something "much greater and more useful could be made of it, insofar as algebraic characters are superior to chemical signs."[87] But so far as the Royal Society was concerned, the *Essay* was quietly forgotten.

The *Essay* did have one important effect; it set John Ray to work on botanical classification. Wilkins had lost all his belongings in the Great Fire of London, including part of the as yet unpublished manuscript of the *Essay*.[88] But eager to finish it, he enlisted the help of Francis Willoughby and John Ray in October 1666. They prepared the zoological and botanical tables. Ray was at the time perhaps Wilkins' most intimate and devoted friend; he immediately went to work, spending much of the next year helping Wilkins, on several occasions spending extended periods with him at Chester. But he admitted at the same time that the project did not suit him.

> I was constrained in arranging the tables not to follow the lead of nature, but to accommodate the plants to the author's prescribed system. . . . What possible hope was there that a method of that sort would be satisfactory, and not manifestly imperfect and ridiculous? I frankly and openly admit that it was, for I care for truth more than for my own reputation.[89]

It is a good question whether Wilkins knew of this criticism, which went to the heart of the matter; the *Essay* did not, as he had intended, follow the "method of nature." After publication, Ray helped Wilkins in amending the tables of natural history, just as he also at Wilkins' request made a Latin translation.[90] Later Ray brought his classifications to a perfection that he had not found it possible to achieve within the system of the *Essay*.[91]

Wilkins was now spending most of his time at Chester, with frequent journeys to London. Suffering from "fits of the stone," he unsuccessfully sought a cure at Scarborough Spa during the summer of 1672. On 10 August 1672, Lord Berkeley, recently arrived from Dublin, was nobly entertained by Wilkins at dinner in the bishop's palace at Chester.[92] On 30 October Wilkins was in London, where he attended, for the last time, a meeting of the Royal Society.[93] But the attacks persisted. Hooke and others administered medication, but to no avail. On 19 November 1672, Wilkins died at the house of John Tillotson, who had married his stepdaughter. At his death he is reported to have said that he was "prepared for the great experiment." The funeral sermon was preached by William Lloyd at the Guildhall Chapel on 12 December; the funeral was attended by a very large crowd, "though it proved a wet day, yet his corpse was very honorably attended . . . there were above forty coaches with six horses, besides a great number of others." He was buried in the church of St. Lawrence Jewry.[94]

In his own time Wilkins' stature and influence were very considerable. He was committed to a policy of tolerance that allowed compromise both in political and ecclesiastical affairs, based on the conviction that natural and revealed religion together with the new science proved a benevolent, providential order which, if rightly understood, ensured that mankind could live happily and peacefully, even prosperously, in this world. For this reason, his influence was divided between such men as Hooke, Boyle, and Ray on the one hand, Tillotson, Stillingfleet, and Patrick on the other. In this sense he shaped the temper of England in the latter half of the seventeenth century and left a significant impression on the eighteenth. His influence was acknowledged by John Ray both in the *Wisdom of God Manifested in the Works of the Creation* (1691) and *A Persuasive to a Holy Life* (1700), with the telling subtitle, "From the Happiness Which Attends It Both in This World and in the World to Come." In science, Hooke's tribute in the *Micrographia* leaves no doubt of Wilkins' importance, although he did not make any direct contribution to science. Even those, like Anthony à Wood, whose party loyalties made them caustic critics of men with similar careers, were sparing in their criticism of Wilkins. The age is full of testimonies that are echoed in Gilbert Burnet's summary of Wilkins' character: "He was naturally ambitious, but was the wisest clergyman I ever knew. He was a lover of mankind, and had a delight in doing good."

*NOTES*

1. *Of the Principles and Duties of Natural Religion*, 8th ed. (London, 1722), p. 34; 1st ed. (London 1675). It was published from Wilkins' papers by his literary executor, John Tillotson, who in the preface explains that the first 12 chapters (pp. 1–165) were left ready for the press by Wilkins. They constitute the greater part of bk. I, entitled *Of the Reasonableness of the Principles and Duties of Natural Religion*. The rest was put together by Tillotson from "the materials left for that purpose," including all of bk. II, *Of the Wisdom of Practicing the Duties of Natural Religion*. There are two references (pp. 48, 55) to Tillotson's sermon *Of the Wisdom of Being Religious* (1664), but these may be insertions and thus do not necessarily determine the time of composition. William Lloyd's *Sermon Preach'd at the Funeral of the Right Reverend Father in God, John Wilkins, D. D., Late Bishop of Chester* is included.
2. *A Discourse Concerning a New Planet, Tending to Prove, That 'Tis Probable Our Earth Is One of the Planets* (London, 1640), in *The Mathematical and Philosophical Works*, 2 vols. (London, 1802), I, 257. The *Discourse* comprises I, 131–261; it was published anonymously.
3. *Principles and Duties*, p. 17.
4. *Ibid.*, p. 73.
5. *Ibid.*, p. 17. Marin Mersenne had used the same metaphor: "Les Méchaniques peuvent enseigner à bien vivre, soit en imitant les corps pesans qui cherchent tousjours leur centre dans celuy de la terre comme l'esprit de l'homme doit chercher le sien dans l'essence divine qui est la source de tous les esprits." Dedication in *Les méchaniques de Gailée*, Bernard Rochot, ed. (Paris, 1966), p. 14.
6. *Ibid.*, p. 346.

7. *Sermons Preach'd Upon Several Occasions*, 2nd ed. (London, 1701), p. 236, 1st ed. (London, 1677, repr. 1680, 1682). There is a preface by the editor, John Tillotson. The axiom that man is a sociable creature is credited to Aristotle and, as often in Wilkins, supported by reference to the Stoics, especially Seneca.

8. *A Discourse Concerning the Beauty of Providence in all the Rugged Passages of It* (London, 1649), p. 65. Similar references occur in *Sermons*. The text of the 9th sermon (pp. 263–287) is Ecclesiastes 4:9–"Two are better than one." Its opening words call Ecclesiastes "a discourse from the most profound principles of reason and philosophy." Like Isaac Barrow, Wilkins had a marked preference for the Wisdom Books (see H. R. McAdoo, *The Spirit of Anglicanism* [London, 1965], p. 239). The 11th sermon (pp. 327–357) and 12th sermon (pp. 359–390) inculcate public spiritedness and cooperation; the theme of the 13th sermon (pp. 391–427) is moderation, followed by a sermon on the evils of vengeance and wrath.

9. *Mercury, or the Secret and Swift Messenger* (London, 1641; 2nd ed., 1694), in *Mathematical and Philosophical Works*, II, 1. *Mercury* comprises II, 1–87; it was published anonymously.

10. *Mercury*, II, 53; these are the opening words of ch. 13, "Concerning an Universal Character, That May Be Legible to All Nations and Languages."

11. *Sermons*, p. 184. The nature of language and the sociability of man were discussed in one of Théophraste Renaudot's conferences, 21 May 1635, with views that agree with Mersenne and Wilkins. *Recueil général des questions traictées ès Conférences du Bureau d'Adresse*, II (Paris, 1660), 458–463; 1st ed. (Paris, 1636). Wilkins had great influence on prose style, both in scientific discourse and in sermons. This is succinctly pointed out by Gilbert Burnet, *History of his Own Time*, 6 vols., 2nd ed. enlarged (Oxford, 1833), I, 347–348. See also Francis Christensen, "John Wilkins and the Royal Society Reform of Prose Style," in *Modern Language Quarterly*, 7 (1946), 179–187, 279–290, and esp. W. S. Howell, *Eighteenth-Century British Logic and Rhetoric* (Princeton, 1971), pp. 448–502. Wilkins' basic stylistic doctrine is already stated in the last section of *Ecclesiastes, or a Discourse Concerning the Gift of Preaching as It Falls Under the Rules of Art*. This section, "Concerning Expression," says that "obscurities in the discourse is an argument of ignorance in the mind. The greatest learning is to be seen in the greatest plainness. The more clearly we understand anything ourselves, the more easily we can expound it to others. When the notion itself is good, the best way to set it off, is in the most obvious plain expression," 3rd ed. (1651), p. 128; 1st ed. (1646). This was Wilkins' most popular work, often reprinted and steadily expanded, also after his death, having reached at least ten printings and its 7th ed. by 1693.

12. *The Discovery of a World in the Moon, Or, a Discourse Tending to Prove, That 'tis Probable There May Be Another Habitable World in That Planet* (London, 1638), in *Mathematical and Philosophical Works*, I, 19. The *Discovery* comprises I, 1–130; it was published anonymously. The 1640 printing contains chapter 14 on the possibility of flying to the moon. Since 1640, the *Discovery* and the *Discourse* have been published together; there was a 5th ed. in 1684. As Wilkins indicates, the words quoted here are taken from Edward Wright's preface to William Gilbert's *De Magnete* (1600). On the same point, Wilkins also refers to John Calvin's *Commentaries on the First Book of Moses, Called Genesis* (see the translation by John King [Edinburgh, 1847], pp. 84–87, 141, 177, 256). I see no evidence that Wilkins knew Galileo's *Letter* with its closely similar arguments, first published in Italian with Latin translation in 1636. In 1640 Wilkins devoted chs. 3–6 of the *Discourse* (I, 149–203) to the same issue, again citing Calvin (now

including the *Commentary on the Psalms*), many passages from the Bible and the Church Fathers, and also such modern writers as Girolamo Zanchi, Franciscus Valesius, Christoph Clavius, Gaspar Sanctius, and Mersenne. Their religious and scientific allegiances were diverse: Sanctius and Clavius were Jesuits, the latter a friend of Galileo but opponent of Copernican astronomy; Zanchi studied at Padua and died at Heidelberg where he served the Palatine rulers; Valesius was a Spanish physician; Mersenne, often cited by Wilkins, took an ambiguous attitude toward Copernicus, but found no scriptural evidence for a charge of heresy, as Wilkins pointed out in the *Discourse* (I.160). Cf. William S. Hine, "Mersenne and Copernicanism," *Isis*, 64 (1973), 18–32. Zanchi (1516–1590) was a Reformed theologian of pronounced irenic tendencies. His use by Wilkins at this time is noteworthy because he was also, along with especially Hugo Grotius, an authority with William Chillingworth in the *Religion of Protestants* (1638). See the excellent study by Robert R. Orr, *Reason and Authority, the Thought of William Chillingworth* (Oxford, 1967). There are other suggestive similarities between Chillingworth and Wilkins. Thus *Principles and Duties*, p. 27, cites the last section in bk. II of Grotius' *De veritate religionis Christianae* for the very same purpose as Chillingworth in *Religion*, ch. 6, sect. 51.

13. *Discourse*, I, 172.

14. *Ibid.*, I, 138. Cf. *Discovery*, "To the Reader": "It is a false conceit for us to think that amongst the ancient variety and search of opinions, the best has still prevailed." (In the *Mathematical and Philosophical Works* [1802] this "To the Reader" is placed at the front of vol. I, before "The Life of the Author.") Mersenne makes the same point in *Questions inouyes* (Paris, 1634), pp. 144–148.

15. *Mathematical Magick, or the Wonders That May Be Performed by Mechanical Geometry* (London, 1648), in *Mathematical and Philosophical Works*, II, 127,131. *Mathematical Magick* comprises II, 89–260, but the dedication to the prince elector Palatine and "To the Reader" are placed at the very front of vol. I. There was a 4th ed. in 1691.

16. *Mathematical Magick*, "To the Reader." For the other points, often repeated in his writings, see the opening chapters, *ibid*. (II, 91–97); cf. *Sermons*, p. 254.

17. *Sermons*, p. 254.

18. *Discovery*, "To the Reader."

19. *Mathematical Magick*, "To the Reader," points out that the title was suggested by Cornelius Agrippa, *De vanitate scientiarum*, ch. 42.

20. *Discourse*, I, 136–137, 134.

21. *Discovery*, I, 14. The full line in Epistle I, 14, reads *Nullius addictus jurare in verba magistri* ("Not pledged to echo the opinions of any master") but the entire context of lines 10–18 is relevant. It was John Evelyn who suggested the motto. In "Praefatio ad lectorem" of the *Quaestiones in Genesim*, Mersenne had recalled the same Horatian passage for precisely the same purpose, against Aristotelian authority and in favor of our own experience of phenomena; Wilkins cited this work in the *Discovery* and in the *Discourse*. See Robert Lenoble, *Mersenne ou la naissance du mécanisme* (Paris, 1943), p. 224; cf. p. 222.

22. R. E. W. Maddison, *The Life of the Honourable Robert Boyle* (London, 1969), p. 85 (Boyle to Hartlib, 14 September 1655); Anthony à Wood, *Athenae Oxonienses*, Philip Bliss, ed., III (London, 1817), col. 971. Wood's information is also in Walter Pope, *Life of Seth Ward* (London, 1697), p. 29.

23. The information often given that Wilkins was born at Fawsley, Northamptonshire, is not certain; see Barbara J. Shapiro, *John Wilkins 1614–1672. An Intellectual Biography* (Berkeley, 1969), pp. 12–13, 254–255.

24. Wood, *op. cit.*, IV (1820), col. 752. Edward Sylvester also taught Chillingworth.

25. Reginald J. Fletcher, *The Pension Book of Gray's Inn, 1569–1669* (London, 1901), pp. 355–357. There is good reason to accept the explanation that it was Wilkins' "skill in the mathematics that chiefly recommended him" to Charles Louis, "his Electoral highness being a great lover and favourer of those sciences, in which he must needs have been very agreeable to his Chaplain, who was entirely of the same turn and temper." See vol. VI (1756), 4266, in *Biographia Britannica*, 7 vols. (London, 1747–1766); this very full and well-informed article is the best biographical account of Wilkins (it covers pp. 4266–4275 and was most likely the work of Thomas Birch).

26. Montague Burrows, ed., *The Register of the Visitors of the University of Oxford from AD 1647 to AD 1658* (London, 1881), p. 22, Camden Society, n.s. 29.

27. It is not clear whether Wilkins made two journeys during 1648–1649, or whether one of them occurred earlier or, less likely, later. Charles Louis spent most of the years between 1644 and his return (May 1649) in England. In 1644 he was invited to attend the sessions of the Westminster Assembly (Bulstrode Whitelocke, *Memorials* [London, 1732], p. 108). Wilkins was formally accepted by the Assembly on 25 September 1643.

28. It is hard to accept Grant McColley's argument that Campanella's *Apologia* is the main source of both the *Discovery* and the *Discourse*. The reason is not merely that the two writers had little in common except their defense of Galileo, but especially that Wilkins used the important literature published since the *Apologia* (1622), including Galileo's own *Dialogue* in the Latin translation (1635). See "The Debt of Bishop Wilkins to the *Apologia pro Galileo* of Tomaso Campanella," in *Annals of Science*, **4** (1939), 150–168. Campanella, *The Defence of Galileo*, tr. by Grant McColley, in *Smith College Studies in History*, **22**, nos. 3–4 (April–July 1937), intro. McColley, "The Ross-Wilkins Controversy," in *Annals of Science*, **3** (1938), 153–189. All these items have much useful information, although they are committed to a view of conflict between science and religion that is now outmoded. Hartlib's "Ephemerides" indicate that Campanella was in London during 1635. Ross answered Wilkins in *The New Planet no Planet* (London, 1646). The entry on Wilkins in *Biographia Britannica* plausibly suggests that the *Discourse* was not merely a treatise on the new astronomy but written as a defense of Galileo: "It was the first just treatise of its kind, and more effectually exposed the folly and absurdity as well as cruelty of the proceedings in the Inquisition by taking no direct notice of them" (*op. cit.*, p. 4268). It is remarkable that Wilkins' defense on the question of biblical authority uses the same arguments as Galileo in the *Letter to the Grand Duchess*, which was presumably not known to Wilkins.

29. Like his two previous books, *Mercury* cites a wealth of sources, both ancient and modern, with some fifty in the latter category. Among the most important are Johannes Trithemius, *De polygraphia* and *De stenographia*, Hermannus Hugo, *De origine scribendi* (1617), and Gustaphus Selenus, *De cryptographia* (1624), the name is a pseudonym for the learned Duke August of Braunschweig-Lüneburg. In 1630 John Pell had written "'A Key to Unlock the Meaning of Johannes Trithemius' in His Steganography; Which Key Mr. Pell the Same Year Imparted to Mr. Samuel Hartlib." (See Wood, *Fasti Oxonienses*, Philip Bliss, ed. [London, 1815], I, 463.) Like the *Discovery* and the *Discourse*, *Mercury* was published anonymously, but the dedication is signed "J. W." It has five commendatory poems at the front, two of them addressing the author as their friend: Richard Hatton, who entered Magdalen Hall, Oxford, on 7 July 1637; and Richart West, who matriculated at Christ Church, Oxford, on 15 February 1633; both presumably knew Wilkins at Oxford, which adds a little to the sparse information we have of Wilkins' life during those

years. Another poem is by Sir Francis Kynaston, the center of a literary coterie at court, who in 1635 founded Musaeum Minerva, an academy for young noblemen. Wilkins was clearly getting known in wider circles.

30. Among other recent works are Pierre Gassendi, *Vita Peireskii* (1641), A. Kircher, *De magnete* (1643), and Mario Bettini, *Apiaria universae philosophia mathematicae, quibus paradoxa et nova pleraque machinamenta ad usus eximios traducta et facillimis demonstrationibus confirmata exhibentur*, 2 vols. (Bologna, 1641–1642).

31. Wilkins mentions Guidobaldo among his chief sources. An abbreviated version of the *Mechanicorum Liber* is in *Mechanics in Sixteenth-Century Italy*, tr. and annotated by Stillman Drake and I. E. Drabkin (University of Wisconsin Press, 1960), pp. 239–328. It includes, on a reduced scale, the line drawings and illustrations of the original. In the final pages of *Mathematical Magick*, Wilkins discussed Archimedes' screw with reference to Guidobaldo's *De cochlea* (1615). This device also interested Mersenne.

32. The only point on which Wilkins may be indebted to Galileo is the subject "concerning the proportion of slowness and swiftness in mechanical motions" (*Mathematical Magick*, II, 146–148), which shows similarity with chapters 1 and 5 of *Les méchaniques* (see Rochot, ed., pp. 23–25, 32–34), but it is possible that Wilkins could also have found this in some other source. In that work Galileo did not deal with the wedge, but explained the rest on the principle of the lever. The Mersenne work in question is *Tractatus mechanicus theoricus et practicus* (96 pp.) contained in the *Cogitata physico-mathematica*, which was ready from the press on 1 April 1644. This collective volume also contains other pieces to which Wilkins refers. Mersenne explained the screw in terms of the inclined plane, the balance and the wheel in terms of the lever, and the pulley and the wedge in terms that combined the lever and the inclined plane. During the 1630's, Descartes also treated these devices in a number of letters to Mersenne (about August-October 1630 and again at greater length on 13 July 1638) (see C. de Waard *et al.*, eds., Mersenne, *Correspondance*, II [1937], 602–620, and VII [1962], 347–375); and in the letter to Constantijn Huygens 5 October 1637 (Descartes, *Correspondance*, Ch. Adam and G. Milhaud, eds. II [Paris, 1939], 31–41). These letters do not all offer the same explanations, but Descartes had a low opinion of Guidobaldo's reduction of the pulley to the lever principle, while Galileo found Guidobaldo the best of all writers on these subjects (see Rochot, ed., p. 77).

33. *Mathematical Magick*, II, 137, 135, 138, 148; cf. *Tractatus*, pp. 39–43. Mersenne's term is *glossocomus*. With the same name, this device was also discussed and explained on the principle of interlocking levers, with illustration, in Bettini, *Apiaria*, I, pt. 4, 31–34, with reference to the source in bk. VIII of Pappus, *Mathematicae collectiones* (1588). This book gave an account of the mechanics of Hero of Alexandria, of which the full text was not known until the late nineteenth century. Pappus attributed the term *glossocomus* to Hero, who is also the source of other terms in the technical vocabulary of mechanics. First published in the late sixteenth century, both his *Automata* and *Pneumatics* were very influential, clearly seen, for instance, in Salomon de Caus, *Les raisons des forces mouvantes avec diverses machines tant utilles que plaisantes. Aus quelles sont adjoints plusieurs desseings de grottes et fontaines* (Frankfurt, 1615). Book I, theorem XVI, on the lifting of heavy burdens by the multiplication of forces, has an illustration that bears a striking resemblance to Wilkins' illustration in *Mathematical Magick*, II, 143. De Caus' garden designs found expression in the garden at Wadham College, for instance the mound with a statue (cf. de Caus, bk. II, problem X; bk. I, problem XII, deals with perpetual motion). In John Bate, *The Mysteries of Nature and Art* (London, 1634), bk. I, "Of Water Works," is a popular ex-

position of Hero's *Pneumatics*, with illustrations from the Italian edition, showing how to make mechanical chirping birds and the like, all subjects that also fascinated Mersenne and Wilkins, who was clearly much indebted to this tradition stemming from Hero. De Caus was active in England and Heidelberg in the early seventeenth century. On de Caus, see C. S. Maks, *Salomon de Caus 1576–1626* (Paris, 1935).

34. *Ibid.*, II, 162; cf. Mersenne, *Ballistica et acontismologia* in *Cogitata*.

35. *Ibid.*, II, 174; cf. *De hydraulicus et pneumaticus phaenomenis*, pp. 149–153.

36. *Ibid.*, II, 188–194, "Concerning the Possibility of Framing an Ark for Submarine Navigations"; cf. *De hydraulicus*, pp. 207–208, and *Tractatus de magnetis proprietatibus*, pp. 251–259. In the former, Mersenne, like Wilkins, referred to the submarine constructed by Cornelis Drebbel, who was also known for his work on other devices, including the perpetuum mobile; the name recurs elsewhere in Mersenne. Already in 1634, Mersenne had asked in question 21 of the *Questions inouyes*, pp. 84–89, "Peut-on faire des navires, et des bateaux qui nagent entre deux eaux." The same work opened with one of Wilkins' favorite topics, "A sçavoir si l'art de voller est possible," a problem that recurs in the *Cogitata* (e.g., *Tractatus mechanicus*, p. 41). It is curious that Wilkins already in the *Discovery* (I, 118) had discussed why a man under water does not feel the weight of the water above him, a subject Mersenne treated in the *De hydraulicus*, pp. 204–206. *Mathematical Magick* (II,192) credits information about an especially accomplished French diver to a note to *Tractatus de magnetis*, placed in the pagination of *Harmoniae liber*, p. 368 (also part of the *Cogitata*). For the greater part of his career, Drebbel was active in England, where he died in 1633. During his stay in London in the early 1620's, Constantijn Huygens was intimately acquainted with Drebbel's projects and inventions, which were also widely discussed later in the century by Boyle, Wren, and Hooke, in addition to Wilkins. See Gerrit Tierie, *Cornelis Drebbel (1572–1633)* (Paris–Amsterdam, 1932); and L. E. Harris, *The Two Netherlanders Humphrey Bradley and Cornelis Drebbel* (Cambridge, 1961), pp. 119–227.

37. See Hine, cited at end of note 12. Some time around 1660, Isaac Newton took extensive notes from the *Mathematical Magick*; see Frank E. Manuel, *A Portrait of Isaac Newton* (Cambridge, Mass., 1968), pp. 11, 49. The same notebook also has long excerpts from Bate, *Mysteries*, bk. III, "Of Drawing, Washing, Limming, Painting, and Engraving." See E. N. da C. Andrade, "Newton's Early Notebook," in *Nature*, **135** (1935), 360.

38. The term is in Webster's *Academiarum examen* (1654); see Aarsleff, "Leibniz on Locke on Language," in *American Philosophical Quarterly*, **1** (1964), 180.

39. *Questions inouyes*, pp. 69–74, where Mersenne also argues that certainty is possible in mathematics since it deals with quantities, it is "une science de l'imagination, ou de pure intelligence, comme la métaphysique, qui ne se soucie pas d'autre objet que du possible absolut."

40. *Discourse Concerning the Beauty of Providence*, p. 71. Belonging to the year of the king's execution, this sermon argued that, "we may infer, how all that confusion and disorder, which seems to be in the affairs of these times, is not so much in the things themselves, as in our mistake of them" (p. 65); it is characteristic of Mersenne and Wilkins that moral and religious arguments jostle statements of scientific principle. In this text Wilkins often cites the Stoics, especially Seneca.

41. For an excellent introduction to Mersenne, see A. C. Crombie's article in *Dictionary of Scientific Biography*, IX (1974), 316–322.

42. Frances Yates, *The Rosicrucian Enlightenment* (London, 1972), p. 182; cf. p. 183: "We have thus here a chain of tradition leading from the Rosicrucian movement to the antecedents of the Royal Society." See also p. 175 and the reference to H. R. Trevor-Roper there.

43. Boswell has a brief entry in the *Dictionary of National Biography*; there is a much fuller life in *Autobiography of Thomas Raymond and Memoirs of the Family of Guise of Elmore* (London, 1917), G. Davis, ed., pp. 69–80 (Camden Society, third series, vol. 18). Boswell was one of the literary executors of Bacon's estate, possessing among other things the important writings edited by Isaac Gruter, *Francisci Baconi de Verulamio scripta in naturali et universali philosophiâ* (Amsterdam, 1653). In 1651, Gruter published another manuscript in Boswell's possession, William Gilbert, *De mundo nostro sublunari philosophia nova*, often known as "Physiologia nova." Bacon used this work in some of his writings, though without citation. Mersenne knew of this work, writing to John Pell, on 20 January 1640, that Gilbert had written on "Selenography or the geography of the moon, which however has not been published" (*Correspondance*, IX [1965], 52). The most likely source of this information is surely Boswell. Boswell also had a collection of John Dee's papers, some of which he intended to publish himself (C. H. Josten, ed., *Elias Ashmole 1617–1692*, 5 vols. [Oxford, 1966], II, 1242; IV, 1372). This was known to Hartlib, who recorded it in the "Ephemerides" in 1639; he said there and later repeated (see Davies, p. 77) that Boswell attributed "all his proficiency in learning whatever it be, to the goodness" of Dee's Preface to Euclid. There is no compelling reason to believe that respect for that Preface means commitment to cabalistic doctrines; it is perhaps wiser to accept Leibniz' opinion that Edward Kelley was an impostor who abused Dee. Boswell was secretary to Lord Herbert of Cherbury in 1620 while the latter was ambassador at Paris. There are references to Boswell in *De Briefwisseling van Constantijn Huygens (1608–1687)*, J. A. Worp, ed., 6 vols. (The Hague, 1911–1917). (These are vols. XV, XIX, XXI, XXIV, XXVIII, XXXII in the series *Rijks geschiedkundige Publicatiën*.) The Mersenne *Correspondance* is of primary importance.

44. Pamela Barnett, *Theodore Haak* (The Hague, 1962), p. 32. Wood, *Athenae Oxonienses*, IV, 280, has an instructive list of Haak's "many great and learned acquaintance," including John Williams, John Selden, Henry Briggs, John Pell, Wilkins, and Boswell, "who encouraged him to keep and continue his correspondence with the learned Mersennus, and others of later time." Wood says of Boswell: "He was a learned man, a great encourager of learning, zealous for the Church of England, faithful in the execution of his embassy, and highly valued by eminent persons" (*Fasti*, I, 332). In the 1640's, Haak and Boswell helped Pell to academic appointments in Holland.

45. In 1639 and 1640, Hartlib's "Ephemerides" show knowledge of the Mersenne-Haak correspondence; during Boswell's stay in London at this time, there is also information about him. For information about Haak, see the entry in *Dictionary of Scientific Biography*, IV (1972), 606–608.

46. *Correspondance*, XI (1970), 412 (to Haak, 4 September 1640). Mersenne also wrote to Haak on other subjects that occur in Wilkins, e.g., universal language, underwater navigation, and flying (XI, 417, 408, 435). On 16 November 1640, he wrote to Haak: "Vous avez raison de dire, que ni Dieu, ni les sciences ne sont point liées aux langues, et en effet, chacune est capable d'expliquer toute chose." This statement expresses both his own and Wilkins' rejection of mystical linguistic doctrines (XI, 420).

47. Christoph J. Scriba, "The Autobiography of John Wallis," in *Notes and Records of the Royal Society*, **25** (1970), 40.

48. During the mid-1640's both Wilkins and Haak, himself a native Palatine, were associated with Charles Louis. Both his mother's and his own letters have been extensively published; the letters give no indication that Rosicrucian influ-

ence could have come from that source, or even that the writers had any interest in it. An informative recent article is G. A. Benrath, "Die konfessionellen Unionsbestrebungen des Kurfürsten Karld Ludwigs von der Pfalz (d. 1680)," in *Zeitschrift für die Geschichte des Oberrheins*, **116** (1968), 187–252.

49. Boyle, *Works*, Thomas Birch, ed., 6 vols. (London, 1772), VI, 633; this is one of the few Wilkins letters on record. At this time, Wilkins found a place at Wadham for the instrument maker Christopher Brooke (or Brookes), "purposely to encourage his ingenuity" (see Wood, *Fasti*, I, 403; also E. G. R. Taylor, *The Mathematical Practitioners of Tudor and Stuart England* [Cambridge, 1954], p. 234; this book has a valuable alphabetical collection of brief biographies [pp. 165–307], followed by a list of works in chronological order [pp. 311–441]).

50. Anthony à Wood, *The History of the Antiquities of the Colleges and Halls in the University of Oxford*, John Gutch, ed., 2 vols (Oxford, 1792–1796), II, pt. 1, 633–634. Though seen with a somewhat prejudiced eye, this is one of the chief sources for the history of Oxford in this period, with the relevant material on pp. 501–708. Another important source is Montague Burrows, *Register of the Visitors*. The handiest narrative source is Charles Edward Mallet, *A History of the University of Oxford*, 3 vols. (London, 1924–1926). See esp. vol. II, *The Sixteenth and Seventeenth Centuries* (1924).

51. *Correspondence*, A. R. and M. B. Hall, eds., I, 94 (letter to Edward Lawrence, April 1656).

52. See T. G. Jackson, *Wadham College* (Oxford, 1843), on the gardens (with illustration), pp. 211–212, on music, p. 117; there is an account of a famous musical evening at Wadham in "The Life of Anthony à Wood," in *Athenae Oxonienses*, I (1813), xxxii.

53. *Diary*, E. S. de Beer, ed., III, 105–110 (1–13 July 1654).

54. R. T. Gunther, *Early Science at Oxford*, VI (Oxford, 1930), *The Life and Work of Robert Hooke*, pp. 5–9.

55. The two pieces have been reprinted in Allen G. Debus, *Science and Education in the Seventeenth Century: the Webster-Ward Debate* (London, 1970). In his letter to Ward, Wilkins nearly verbatim repeats some passages from the opening chapter of his *Discourse Concerning the Gift of Prayer* (1651; 9th ed., 1718) on the three gifts requisite in a minister.

56. "To the Reader," in *Sermons*. Tillotson was specifically rejecting some critical remarks in Wood's *Historia et Antiquitates Oxoniensis* (1674), which was a Latin version done by John Fell from Wood's English manuscript. Wood was much displeased with this version, both because of its bad Latin and because Fell had taken the liberty of inserting his own comments, of which the depreciation of Wilkins was one. In the late summer of 1654, some of the Wadham fellows made official complaint about Wilkins' conduct of college affairs, but after due consideration the charges were rejected by the Visitors; it is not clear what the issue was. See Burrows, *Register*, pp. 394–397.

57. She had previously been married to Peter French of Christ Church, also a man of some importance in the university. Tillotson married a daughter of that marriage. It is an often repeated error that Wilkins on this occasion gained permission to marry from Cromwell, then chancellor of the university; the Wadham statutes had already been altered in 1651 so as to permit the warden to marry—one wonders whether Wilkins contemplated marriage at that time or whether he was acting on principle. See Jackson, *Wadham College*, p. 116. In June 1670, Wilkins was the only bishop to favor a divorce act, then pending (see Edmund Ludlow, *Memoirs*, C. H. Firth, ed., 2 vols. [Oxford, 1894], II, 503). Robina Wilkins died in 1689; she and Wilkins had no children.

58. Mark Noble, *Memoirs of the Protectoral-House of Cromwell*, 2 vols. (London, 1787), I, 314.

59. *Calendar of State Papers*, *Domestic*, 1660. In preparation for the appointment, Wilkins had been incorporated doctor of divinity at Cambridge on 18 March 1659.

60. *Reliquiae Baxterianae* (London, 1696), pt. I, p. 386. Baxter especially sought the churches where he "heard a learned minister that had not obtruded himself upon the people, but was chosen by them, and preached well (as Dr. Wilkins, Dr. Tillotson . . .)" (*ibid.*, p. 537). Gilbert Burnet made the same point, counting Benjamin Whichcote, Ralph Cudworth, Henry More, and John Worthington along with Wilkins among "the divines called Latitudinarians." "At Cambridge," he wrote, Wilkins "joined with those who studied to propagate better thoughts, to take men off from being in parties, or from narrow notions, from superstitious conceits, and a fierceness about opinions" (*History of His Own Time*, I, 340). I see no reason at all for the opinion, heard in the eighteenth century and repeated by John Tulloch, that Wilkins "was a Calvinist . . . of a somewhat strict type" (*Rational Theology and Christian Philosophy in England in the Seventeenth Century*, 2 vols. [Edinburgh, 1872], II, 442). The terms "latitude-men," "latitudinarian," and "latitudinarianism" first occurred in the 1660's in a pejorative sense, but were soon adopted as the common term. In 1662, the term was used to refer to the men we call the Cambridge Platonists with stress on the connection between them and the mechanical philosophy. (The generic term Cambridge Platonists did not occur until after the middle of the nineteenth century.) See the pamphlet by S. P., *A Brief Account of the New Sect of Latitude-Men Together With Some Reflections on the New Philosophy*. (S. P. is traditionally identified as Simon Patrick, who was also the first English translator (1680) of Grotius' *De veritate*.) There is an illuminating contemporary account in Edward Fowler, *The Principles and Practices of Certain Moderate Divines of the Church of England (Greatly Misunderstood) Truly Represented and Defended* (London, 1670). Thus this book was published soon after the failure of the bill for comprehension. Fowler calls the latitudinarians "persons of great moderation" and says they are also called "rational preachers" and "moral preachers." He names More, Cudworth, John Worthington, Joseph Mede, and Chillingworth. John Beardmore said that Wilkins "was looked upon as the head of the *Latitudinarians*, as they were then stiled." See "Some Memorials of the Most Reverend Dr. John Tillotson . . . Written Upon the News of His Death [1694] by J. B.," in Thomas Birch, *The Life of the Most Reverend Dr. John Tillotson*, 2nd ed. (London, 1753), p. 390. The term "latitude" is given prominence by Chillingworth: "This Deifying of our own Interpretations, and tyrannous inforcing them upon others; this Restraining of the World of God from that latitude and generality, and the Understandings of Men from that liberty, wherein Christ and the Apostles left them, is, and hath been the only Fountain of all the Schisms of the Church . . . the common Incendiary of Christendom" (*Religion of Protestants*, ch. 4, sect. 16; in this passage Chillingworth cites the agreement of Zanchi). The two chief influences on Tillotson were Chillingworth and Wilkins. Ernst Cassirer's *Die Platonische Renaissance in England und die Schule von Cambridge* (Leipzig–Berlin, 1932), opens with the surprising opinion that the Cambridge Platonists were hostile to the new mechanical philosophy and had little understanding of it. With characteristic misjudgment, R. F. Jones believed that Samuel Parker's *A Free and Impartial Censure of the Platonick Philosophy* (Oxford, 1666) was "a vigorous attack" on the Cambridge Platonists; in agreement with the common use of the term "Platonic" at that time, it was a critique of the chief opponents of the new philosophy, *i.e.*, enthusiasts and Rosicrucians of the sort illustrated by John Webster, whose *Academiarum Examen* Jones, astonishingly, calls "the most important expression of the new scientific outlook between Bacon and the Restoration" (*Ancients and Moderns* [paper-

back ed., 1965], pp. 188, 108). For reliable information and interpretation, see Marjorie Nicolson, "Christ's College and the Latitude-Men," in *Modern Philology*, **27** (1929), 35–53, and McAdoo, *The Spirit of Anglicanism*.

61. Fletcher, *Pension Book*, 435–436.

62. White Kennett, *Historical Register* (London, 1706), p. 576. Wilkins succeeded Thomas Fuller on 10 December 1661. The appointment shows Wilkins' life-long association with the Berkeley family, this George Berkeley being the son of the man to whom *Mercury* was dedicated.

63. Kennett, p. 658; Wilkins succeeded Seth Ward, who became bishop of Exeter.

64. Some of these offices are listed in R. B. Gardiner, *The Registers of Wadham College*, pt. I, 1613–1719 (London, 1889), p. 171.

65. *Correspondence*, I, 406 (Oldenburg to Boreel, 13 December 1660). The term "physico-mathematical" may have been heard before, but it brings to mind the title of Mersenne's *Cogitata physico-mathematica*; was it perhaps Wilkins who had brought in the proposal?

66. Wilkins willed £400 to the Society.

67. Among the candidates Wilkins proposed were Haak, John Hoskins, Francis Willoughby, Edward Bysshe, George Smyth, Thomas Sprat, Henry Power, Henry More, John Ray, and Anthony Lowther; they were all elected; he also proposed Ralph Cudworth, who for some reason never joined. *The Record of the Royal Society of London*, 4th ed. (London, 1940), does not list Cudworth among the members, contrary to statements in the recent literature, e.g., J. A. Passmore, *Ralph Cudworth* (Cambridge, 1951), p. 2; and McAdoo, p. 121.

68. I have dealt with that important function in the entry on Thomas Sprat in *Dictionary of Scientific Biography*, XII (1975), 580–587.

69. Thomas Birch, *History of the Royal Society*, 4 vols. (London, 1756–1757), II, 30, 41, 60, 63, 66, 74, 89. Durdans was the property of Lord Berkeley. On his return from Oxford on 7 September 1665, Evelyn stopped at "Durdans by the way, where I found Dr. Wilkins, Sir William Petty and Mr. Hooke contriving chariots, new rigs for ships, a wheel for one to run races in, and other mechanical inventions, and perhaps three such persons together were not to be found elsewhere in Europe, for parts and ingenuity." Samuel Pepys was interested in the same matter; see entries in his *Diary* under 11 and 22 January 1666. See also letter from Hooke to Boyle, 8 July 1665, in Gunther, *Early Science*, VI, 248.

70. Baxter, *Reliquiae*, pt. III, pp. 23 ff; Burnet, *History*, I, 477. On the Comprehension scheme, see Norman Sykes, *From Sheldon to Secker. Aspects of English Church History 1660–1678* (Cambridge, 1959), pp. 71–75. At this time Sir Matthew Hale and Wilkins "came to contract a firm and familiar friendship," so close that "there was an intimacy and freedom in [Hale's] converse with Bishop Wilkins that was singular to him alone." See Gilbert Burnet, *The Life and Death of Sir Matthew Hale, Kt. Sometime Lord Chief Justice of His Majesty's Court of King's Bench* (London, 1700). Hale was also close to James Ussher and Baxter.

71. Burnet, *History*, I, 464; Evelyn's description in *Diary* under that date. Benjamin Whichcote succeeded Wilkins as vicar of St. Lawrence Jewry.

72. Kennett, *Register*, pp. 815, 817, 921.

73. Pepys, *Diary*, 16 March 1669.

74. In a meeting of the Royal Society on 29 October 1662, "Dr. Wilkins was put in mind to prosecute his design of an *universal language*" (Birch, *History*, I, 119).

75. Aarsleff, "Leibniz on Locke on Language," p. 178.

76. Albert Heinekamp, "Ars characteristica und natürliche Sprache bei Leibniz," in *Tijdschrift voor Filosofie*, **34** (1972), 452; this article is an excellent treatment of the subject. The classic treatment is Louis Couturat, *La logique de Leibniz* (Paris, 1901), esp. chs. 2–5. A briefer discussion is

found in L. Couturat and L. Leau, *Histoire de la langue universelle* (Paris, 1907), with a section on Wilkins, pp. 19–22. Paolo Rossi, *Clavis universalis, arti mnemoniche e logica combinatoria da Lullo a Leibniz* (Milan, 1960), is the best history of the subject. In the literature, both primary and secondary, the *locus classicus* for the philosophical language is Descartes's letter to Mersenne, 20 November 1629 (Mersenne, *Correspondance*, II, 323–339), written in response to a project of which Mersenne had sent him a copy. The subject is often mentioned in the Mersenne correspondence, but unfortunately the notes, usually so informative, attached both to the Descartes letter and others on the same subject are very confused; this confusion has gradually been cleared up in recent volumes. It is an index of the low conceptual level of much recent secondary writing on this popular topic that it fails to make the distinction between a merely universal and a philosophical language; this has made it possible for some to argue that the philosophical language came about by a sort of evolutionary growth of stenography.

77. Wilkins, *Essay*, pp. 20–21.

78. *Ibid.*, pp. 51–52, 398, 454.

79. Debus, pp. 214–216 (original pagination, also given there, pp. 20–22). Ward's basic outline does not state anything that had not been said earlier.

80. For the relevant passages in Mersenne, see references given in notes 50–51 to the entry on Mersenne in *Dictionary of Scientific Biography*, IX, 322. Cf. Lenoble, *Mersenne*, pp. 514–518; Eberhard Knobloch, "Marin Mersenne's Beitrag zur Kombinatorik," in *Südhoffs Archiv*, **58** (1974), 356–379.

81. There are useful illustrations in E. N. da C. Andrade, "The Real Character of Bishop Wilkins," in *Annals of Science*, **1** (1936), 1–12. An informative account is Jonathan Cohen, "On the Project of a Universal Character," in *Mind*, **63** (1954), 49–63. Although weak on the intellectual and philosophical context there is much useful detail on contemporary projects in Vivian Salmon, *The Works of Francis Lodwick. A Study of his Writings in the intellectual Context of the Seventeenth Century* (London, 1972). In a monograph entitled *Zum Weltsprachenproblem in England im 17. Jahrhundert. G. Dalgarno's 'Ars signorum' und J. Wilkins' 'Essay' (1668)* (Heidelberg, 1929; *Anglistische Forschungen*, Heft 69), Otto Funke argued that Bacon was the inspiration for such projects and that Wilkins was in large measure indebted to Dalgarno. Funke does not consider Mersenne. In a useful article on "The Evolution of Dalgarno's *Ars Signorum*," in *Studies in Language and Literature in Honour of Margaret Schlauch* (Warsaw, 1966), pp. 353–371, Vivian Salmon, along somewhat similar lines, argued that "without Dalgarno, Wilkins would never have begun the task which led to the *Essay*" (p. 370); the evidence, including troublesome questions of dating and personal relationships, does not warrant that conclusion. Neither Funke nor Salmon considered the cogent contemporary discussion in Robert Plot's *Natural History of Oxfordshire* (London, 1677), pp. 282–285, which concludes that the question must be left open. Anthony à Wood is the source of the persistent belief that Wilkins cribbed from Dalgarno's *Ars signorum*, saying that the author showed it, before it went to press, to Wilkins, "who from thence taking a hint of a greater matter, carried it on, and brought it up to that which you see extant" (*Athenae Oxonienses*, III, 970; this opinion is repeated in the entry on Wilkins in the *Dictionary of National Biography*). Benjamin DeMott has unconvincingly argued for strong Comenian influence on Wilkins ("Comenius and the Real Character in England," in *Publications of the Modern Language Association*, **70** [1955], 1068–1081; "The Sources and Development of John Wilkins' Philosophical Language," in *Journal of English and Germanic Philology*, **57** [1958], 1–13). He rests his argument chiefly on the claim for the irenic religious effect of

the philosophical language, but this is a common claim that cannot be used for such identification, but the fundamental difficulty is that what Comenius had to say on this subject was not original. DeMott ignores Mersenne. Salmon argues against DeMott in "Language-Planning in Seventeenth-century England," *In Memory of J. R. Firth* (London, 1966), pp. 370–397. R. F. Jones, "Science and Language in England of the Mid-Seventeenth Century," in Jones, *The Seventeenth Century* (Stanford, 1951; original publ. 1932), was always a poor guide and is now thoroughly outmoded. Jorge Luis Borges' quaint essay "The Analytical Language of John Wilkins" has brought Wilkins and the *Essay* to the attention of the literati (in *Other Inquisitions 1937–1952*, Ruth L. C. Sims, trans. [New York, 1966], pp. 106–110). See also the entries on Boehme, in *Dictionary of Scientific Biography*, II (1970), 222–224; and on Comenius, *ibid.*, III (1971), 359–363.

82. R. T. Gunther, *Early Science in Oxford*, vol. VIII, *The Cutler Lectures of Robert Hooke* (Oxford, 1931), pp. 150–152, with illustration (reproduced in Andrade). Hooke found it "so truly philosophical, and so perfectly and thoroughly methodical, that there seems to be nothing wanting to make it have the utmost perfection." Hooke's faith in the philosophical language is closely related to his belief in demonstrability in natural science, a belief not shared by his scientific colleagues in the Royal Society.

83. Since this is true also of other committees appointed by the Society during these years, the failure to report cannot be taken as evidence one way or the other.

84. This had been suggested by Wilkins in the "Epistle dedicatory" of the *Essay*. See also Sprat, *History of the Royal Society*, p. 251. Hooke called memory a "repository." His conception intimates a link with the mnemonic tradition; in John Willis' *The Art of Memory* (London, 1621; later reissued), *repository* is the word for the memory device of "an imaginary house or building."

85. Huygens, *Oeuvres*, VI, 397 (Huygens to Moray, 30 March 1669); *ibid.*, p. 425 (Moray to Huygens, 16 April 1669).

86. This correspondence is in the Aubrey MSS in the Bodleian Library, Oxford. They have recently been examined by Vivian Salmon in "John Wilkins' *Essay* (1668): Critics and Continuators," in *Historiographia Linguistica*, 1 (1974), 147–163. Great efforts were made to elicit a plan from Seth Ward, but when it finally came it was found disappointing, inclining "too much to Lullius" (MS Aubrey 13, fol. 113v, Thomas Pigott to Aubrey at Hooke's, Oxford, 14 April 1678).

87. Leibniz, *Philosophische Schriften*, C. I. Gerhardt, ed., 7 vols. (Berlin, 1875–1890), VII, 16.

88. On this occasion Seth Ward helped Wilkins to a precentorship at Exeter; see Pope, *Life of Seth Ward*, p. 56.

89. Ray to Martin Lister (7 May 1669), quoted in Charles E. Raven, *John Ray* (London, 1950), p. 182. Ray repeats this judgment in several other letters of the same years.

90. Several Continental scholars, including Leibniz, had called for a translation. Ray's translation is known to have been in the archives of the Royal Society for more than a century, but has since been lost. As late as May 1678, Aubrey wrote to Ray: "I have at length gotten my desire, viz. an able Frenchman to translate the real Character into French. It is Dr. Lewis du Moulin." W. Derham, *Philosophical Letters of Ray* (London, 1718), p. 144.

91. There is an illuminating discussion of these problems in Phillip R. Sloan, "John Locke, John Ray, and the Problem of Natural System," in *Journal of the History of Biology*, 5 (1972), 1–53. Locke said in the *Essay*: "I am not so vain to think that anyone can pretend to attempt the perfect reforming the languages of the world, no, not so much as of his own country, without making himself ridiculous" (Book III, ch. II, paragraph 2). This represents the general view of the Royal Society. There is cogent criticism of Wilkins'

*Essay* in *Reflections Upon Learning* (1699) by the antiquary and critic of the new science, Thomas Baker; see *Reflections*, 4th ed. (1708), pp. 21–22.

92. *Calendar of State Papers, Domestic,* 1672.

93. *Diary of Robert Hooke*, 1672–1680, Henry W. Robinson and Walter Adams, eds. (London, 1935), p. 11.

94. The death is reported in Hooke's *Diary* under 19 November: "Lord Bishop of Chester died about 9 in the morning of a suppression of the urine." On the next day, he had more details: "Dr. Needham brought in account of Lord Chester's having no stoppage in his uriters nor defect in the kidneys. There was only found 2 small stones in one kidney and some little gravel in one uriter but neither big enough to stop the water. 'Twas believed his opiates and some other medicines killed him, there being no visible cause of his death, he died very quickly and with little pain, lament of all." The cause of Wilkins' death continued to be a matter of debate. In 1695, the physician Edward Baynard published "An Account of the Probable Causes of the Pain in Rheumatisms; as also of the Cure of a Total Suppression of Urine, not caused by a Stone, by the Use of Acids," in *Philosophical Transactions of the Royal Society*, 19 (Jan.–Feb. 1695), 19–20. Baynard suggests that Wilkins' case was falsely diagnosed.

## BIBLIOGRAPHY

I. ORIGINAL WORKS. In addition to the works in the notes, see the following: *A Sermon Preached Before the King on March 7, 1669* (London, 1669). *A Sermon Preached Before the King on March 19, 1671* (London, 1671). These two sermons are not reprinted in Tillotson's collection of fifteen sermons.

When the *Discovery* and the *Discourse* were first published together, in 1640, they appeared under the title *A Discourse Concerning a New World and Another Planet in Two Books*. Several of Wilkins' works have been issued in reprints in recent years. *The Mathematical and Philosophical Works* (London, 1708) is the first collection of the works covered by that title. They are here placed in chronological order of publication with separate paginations and title pages. This edition opens with a "Life of the Author and an Account of His Writings," and closes with "An Abstract of Dr. Wilkins' *Essay Towards a Real Character and a Philosophical Language*." The contents are the same as in the 1802 edition.

II. SECONDARY LITERATURE. This literature is given in the notes. Our knowledge of Wilkins' life derives chiefly from the early biographical writings: William Lloyd's funeral sermon; Walter Pope, *The Life of Seth Ward . . . With a Brief Account of Bishop Wilkins, Mr. Lawrence Rooke, Dr. Isaac Barrow, Dr. Turberville, and Others* (London, 1697); John Aubrey, "John Wilkins," in *Aubrey's Brief Lives*, Oliver Lawson Dick, ed., (Ann Arbor, 1957), pp. 319–320; A. à Wood, *Athenae Oxonienses*, Bliss, ed., III (1817), cols. 967–971, but this rich source has much relevant information scattered throughout the four volumes. This is also true of Wood, *Fasti Oxonienses*, and *History of the Antiquities of the Colleges and Halls in the University of Oxford*, John Gutch, ed. See also Pierre Bayle, *A General Dictionary,*

*Historical and Critical. . .* , John Peter Bernard, Thomas Birch, John Lockman, eds., 10 vols. (London, 1734–1741), X, 160–164. The best biographical entry on Wilkins is the one in *Biographia Britannica*; see n. 25. It is much better than the entry in the *Dictionary of National Biography*. (In the article on Thomas Sprat in the *Dictionary of Scientific Biography* I attributed independent value to the biographical notice of Wilkins entered at the time of his death in Birch, *History of the Royal Society*, III, 67–68; I now believe that this notice was inserted by Birch.) These sources have formed the bases of entries in biographical reference works since the eighteenth century, with the accretion of more or less reliable anecdotal matter from other sources.

Since Wilkins was so widely known in his own time, he is mentioned in most contemporary records, some published long ago and some only recently, such as the diaries of John Evelyn and Samuel Pepys, Birch's *History of the Royal Society*, the correspondence of Henry Oldenburg, and *The Diary and Correspondence of Dr. John Worthington*, James Crossley, ed., 2 vols in three parts (Manchester, 1847, 1855, 1886, with vol. II, part II edited by R. C. Christie). (These are vols. 13, 36, and 114 in the publications of the Chetham Society.)

On Wilkins and Wadham College, the most important treatment is Jackson's *Wadham College*, but see also J. Wells, *Wadham College* (London, 1898), pp. 69–87. Patrick A. W. Henderson, *The Life and Times of John Wilkins* (London, 1910), is chiefly about Wadham College. The best modern biography is Dorothy Stimson, "Dr. Wilkins and the Royal Society," in *Journal of Modern History*, 3 (1931), 539–563. Neither J. G. Crowther, *Founders of British Science* (London, 1960), nor E. J. Bowen and Sir Harold Hartley, "John Wilkins," in *The Royal Society, Its Origins and Founders*, Sir Harold Hartley, ed. (London, 1960), pp. 47–56, offer anything new, and they are not reliable. For some reason, the subject of Wilkins at large has proved an open field for guesswork, partisan interpretation, and free anecdotal accretion. The intellectual history of England in the mid-seventeenth century has been treated in a number of recent books that show great diversity of interpretation, e.g., Christopher Hill, *Intellectual Origins of the English Revolution* (Oxford, 1965), and Frances A. Yates, *The Rosicrucian Enlightenment* (London, 1972); this literature tends to be occupied with polemics rather than substance. Barbara J. Shapiro, *John Wilkins 1614–1672. An Intellectual Biography* (Berkeley, 1969), has some new biographical information, but does not meet its claim to being an intellectual biography. Based on a small part of the relevant literature, Henry G. van Leeuwen presents an illuminating discussion of his subject in *The Problem of Certainty in English Thought 1630–1690* (The Hague, 1963). He argues that Chillingworth's discussion was followed by Tillotson, which is correct, but then postulates that Wilkins and Glanvill, learning from Tillotson, "secularized" the argument for the benefit of science

and the Royal Society. Simple chronology is enough to refute that interpretation. The deeper problem, however, is that van Leeuwen ignores Wilkins' early writings except *Mercury*, and that he makes a distinction between religion and science (as is also clearly shown in the notion of secularization) that is not warranted by the texts and the intellectual framework of the time; the term "natural religion" should be a sufficient reminder of that fact. (Van Leeuwen also states that *Mathematical Magick* was composed, "like most of [Wilkins'] earlier works, during his school days" [p. 56].) Shapiro rightly argues against van Leeuwen (pp. 232–316); see also Shapiro, "Latitudinarianism and Science in Seventeenth-Century England," in *Past and Present*, no. 40 (July 1968), 16–41. Marjorie Hope Nicolson's *Voyages to the Moon* (New York, 1948) is the classic treatment of a subject that has come to be associated with Wilkins. There is an excellent account of Wilkins in H. R. McAdoo, *The Spirit of Anglicanism. A Survey of Anglican Theological Method in the Seventeenth Century* (London, 1965), esp. pp. 203–231; it is the most important recent treatment of Wilkins. See also the bibliographies under the entries for Theodore Haak and Thomas Sprat in the *Dictionary of Scientific Biography*.

I have also used material contained in five lectures given under the auspices of the Program in the History and Philosophy of Science at Princeton University in the spring of 1964, entitled "Language, Man, and Knowledge in the 16th and 17th Centuries."

HANS AARSLEFF

**WILKS, SAMUEL STANLEY** (*b.* Little Elm, Texas, 17 June 1906; *d.* Princeton, New Jersey, 7 March 1964), *mathematical statistics*.

Wilks was the eldest of the three children of Chance C. and Bertha May Gammon Wilks. His father trained for a career in banking but after a few years chose to operate a 250-acre farm near Little Elm. His mother had a talent for music and art and instilled her own lively curiosity in her three sons.[1] Wilks obtained his grade-school education in a one-room schoolhouse and attended high school in Denton, where during his final year he skipped study hall regularly in order to take a mathematics course at North Texas State Teachers College, where he received an A.B. in architecture in 1926.

Believing his eyesight inadequate for architecture, Wilks embarked on a career in mathematics. During the school year 1926–1927, he taught mathematics and manual training in a public school in Austin, Texas, and began graduate study of mathematics at the University of Texas. He continued his studies as a part-time instructor in 1927–1928, received an M.A. in mathematics in

1928, and remained as an instructor during the academic year 1928–1929.

Granted a two-year fellowship by the University of Iowa, in the summer of 1929 Wilks began a program of study and research leading to receipt, in June 1931, of a Ph.D. in mathematics. National research fellowships enabled him to continue research and training in mathematical statistics at Columbia University (1931–1932), University College, London (1932), and Cambridge University (1933). Wilks's scientific career was subsequently centered at Princeton, where he rose from instructor in mathematics (1933) to professor of mathematical statistics (1944).

Wilks married Gena Orr, of Denton, in September 1931; they had one son, Stanley Neal Wilks. He was a member of the American Philosophical Society, the International Statistical Institute, and the American Academy of Arts and Sciences, and a fellow of the American Association for the Advancement of Science. He also belonged to most major societies in his field.

Wilks's education was extraordinary for the number of prominent people involved in it. At the University of Texas, his first course in advanced mathematics was set theory, taught by R. L. Moore, noted for his researches in topology, his unusual methods of teaching, and his contempt for applied mathematics. Having a strong practical bent, however, Wilks was more interested in probability and statistics, taught by Edward L. Dodd; known for his researches on mathematical and statistical properties of various types of means, Dodd encouraged Wilks to pursue further study of these subjects at the University of Iowa (now the State University of Iowa).

At Iowa, Wilks was introduced by Henry L. Rietz to "the theory of small samples" pioneered by "Student" (W. S. Gossett) and fully developed by R. A. Fisher, and to statistical methods employed in experimental psychology and educational testing by E. F. Lindquist.

Wilks chose Columbia University for his first year of postdoctoral study and research because Harold Hotelling, a pioneer in multivariate analysis and the person in the United States most versed in the "Student"-Fisher theory of small samples, had just been appointed professor there in the economics department. At Columbia, Wilks attended the lectures at Teachers College of Charles E. Spearman, considered the father of factor analysis, and became acquainted with the work at Bell Telephone Laboratories of Walter A. Shewhart, originator of statistical quality control of manufacturing processes.

Wilks spent the first part of his second year writing a joint paper with Egon S. Pearson in the department of Karl Pearson at University College, London. At Cambridge University he worked with John Wishart who had been a research assistant to both Karl Pearson and Fisher, and whose work in multivariate analysis was close to Wilks's main interest.

Wilks's first ten published papers were contributions to the branch of statistical theory and methodology known as multivariate analysis, and it was to this area that he made his greatest contributions. His doctoral dissertation, written under Henry L. Rietz, provided the small-sample theory for answering a number of questions arising in use of the technique of "matched" groups in experimental work in educational psychology. It was preceded by a short note, "The Standard Error of the Means of 'Matched' Samples" (1931). This note and dissertation are the first in a long series of papers on topics in multivariate analysis suggested to Wilks by problems in experimental psychology and educational testing.

It was, however, his paper, "Certain Generalizations in the Analysis of Variance," that immediately established Wilks's stature. In this paper he defined the "generalized variance" of a sample of $n$ individuals from a multivariate population, constructed multivariate generalizations of the correlation ratio and coefficient of multiple correlation, deduced the moments of the sampling distributions of these and other related functions in random samples from a normal multivariate population from Wishart's generalized product moment distribution (1928), constructed the likelihood ratio criterion for testing the null hypothesis that $k$ multivariate samples of sizes $n_1, n_2, \cdots, n_k$ are random samples from a common multivariate normal population (now called Wilks's $\Lambda$ criterion) and derived its sampling distribution under the null hypothesis, and similarly explored various other multivariate likelihood ratio criteria.

Three other papers written in 1931–1932 concerned derivation of the sampling distributions of estimates of the parameters of a bivariate normal distribution from "fragmentary samples"—that is, when some of the individuals in a sample yield observations on both variables, $x$ and $y$, and some only on $x$, or on $y$, alone; derivation of the distribution of the multiple correlation coefficient in samples from a normal population with a nonzero multiple correlation coefficient directly from Wishart's generalized product moment distribution (1928) without using the geometrical notions and an invariance property utilized by Fisher in his derivation (1928); and derivation of an exact expression for the standard error of an observed "tetrad difference," an outgrowth of attending Spearman's lectures.

"Methods of Statistical Analysis . . . for *k* Samples of Two Variables" (1933), written with E. S. Pearson, and "Moment-Generating Operators for Determinants of Product Moments . . ." (1934) are the products of Wilks's year in England. The first consists of elaboration in greater detail for the bivariate normal case of the techniques developed for the multivariate normal in his "Certain Generalizations . . .," and reflects his and Pearson's growing interest in industrial applications by including a worked example based on data from W. A. Shewhart (1931). The second may be regarded as an extension of the work of J. Wishart and M. S. Bartlett, who had just completed an "independent" derivation of Wishart's product moment distribution "by purely algebraic methods" when Wilks arrived in Cambridge. His next important contribution to multivariate analysis, "On the Independence of *k* Sets of Normally Distributed . . . Variables" (1935), appears to have been written to meet a need encountered in his work with the College Entrance Examination Board, as do many of his later contributions to multivariate analysis.

In addition to his extensive and penetrating studies of likelihood ratio tests for various hypotheses relating to multivariate normal distributions, Wilks made similar investigations (1935) relating to multinomial distributions and to independence in two-, three-, and higher-dimensional contingency tables. He also provided (1938) a compact proof of the basic theorem on the large-sample distribution of the likelihood ratio criterion for testing "composite" statistical hypotheses—that is, when the "null hypothesis" tested specifies the values of, say, only *m* out of the *h* parameters of the probability distribution concerned. Jerzy Neyman's basic paper on the theory confidence-interval estimation appeared in 1937. The following year Wilks showed that under fairly general conditions confidence intervals for a parameter of a probability distribution based upon its maximum-likelihood estimator are, on the average, the shortest obtainable in large samples.

In response to a need expressed by Shewhart,

Wilks in 1941 laid the foundations of the theory of statistical "tolerance limits," which actually are confidence limits, in the sense of Neyman's theory—not, however, for the value of some parameter of the distribution sampled, as in Neyman's development but, rather, for the location of a specified fraction of the distribution sampled. He showed that a suitably selected pair of ordered observations ("order statistics") in a sample of sufficient size from an arbitrary continuous distribution provides a pair of limits (statistical "tolerance limits") to which there corresponds a stated chance that at least a specified fraction of the underlying distribution is contained between these limits, thus providing the "distribution-free" solution needed when the assumption of an underlying normal distribution of industrial production is unwarranted. Wilks also derived the corresponding parametric solution of maximum efficiency in the case of sampling from a normal distribution (based on the sample mean and standard deviation) and an expression for the relative efficiency of the distribution-free solution in this case.

In 1942 Wilks developed formulas for the probabilities that at least a fraction $N_0/N$ of a second random sample of $N$ observations from an arbitrary continuous distribution (a) would lie above the $r$th "order statistic" ($r$th observation in increasing order of size), $1 \leq r \leq n$, in a first random sample of size $n$ from the same distribution, or (b) would be included between the $r$th and $s$th order statistics, $1 \leq r < s \leq n$, of the first sample; and illustrated the application of these results to the setting of one- and two-sided statistical tolerance limits. This work was Wilks's earliest contribution to "nonparametric" or "distribution-free" methods of statistical inference, an area of research of which he provided an extensive review in depth in "Order Statistics" (1948).

Wilks was a founder of the Institute of Mathematical Statistics (1935) and remained an active member. The Institute took full responsibility for the *Annals of Mathematical Statistics*, and Wilks became editor, with the June 1938 issue.[2] He served through the December 1949 issue, guiding the development of the *Annals* from a marginal journal, with a small subscription list, to the foremost publication in its field.

Although Wilks became an instructor in the department of mathematics at Princeton University at the beginning of the academic year 1933–1934, he did not give a formal course in statistics at Princeton until 1936, owing to a prior commitment that the university had made with an instructor in the department of economics and social institutions who had been sent off at university expense to develop a course on "modern statistical theory" two years before; and owing to the need for resolution by the university's administration of an equitable division of responsibility for the teaching of statistics between that department (which theretofore had been solely responsible for all teaching of statistics) and the department of mathematics.[3] Wilks was promoted to assistant professor in 1936. In the fall term he taught a graduate course, the substance of which he published as his *Lectures . . . on . . . Statistical Inference, 1936–37 . . .*; and in the spring of 1937 he gave an undergraduate course, quite possibly the first carefully formulated college undergraduate course in mathematical statistics based on one term of calculus.

Wilks's service to the federal government began with his appointment in 1936 as a collaborator in the Soil Conservation Program of the U.S. Department of Agriculture. He continued to serve the government as a member of the Applied Mathematics Panel, National Defense Research Committee, Office of Scientific Research and Development; chairman of the mathematics panel, Research and Development Board, Defense Department; adviser to the Selective Service System and the Bureau of the Budget; a member of various committees of the National Science Foundation, the National Academy of Sciences, and NASA; and an academic member of the Army Mathematics Advisory Panel. In 1947 he was awarded the Presidential Certificate of Merit for his contributions to antisubmarine warfare and the solution of convoy problems.

Wilks was deeply interested in the whole spectrum of mathematical education. In "Personnel and Training Problems in Statistics" (1947) he outlined the growing use of statistical methods, the demand for personnel, and problems of training, and made recommendations that served as a guide in the rapid growth of university centers of training in statistics after World War II. Drawing on his experience at Princeton, he urged, in "Teaching Statistical Inference in Elementary Mathematics Courses" (1958), teaching the principles of statistical inference to freshmen and sophomores, and further proposed revamping high school curricula in mathematics and the sciences to provide instruction in probability, statistics, logic, and other modern mathematical subjects. During his last few years he worked with an experimental program in a

school at Princeton that introduced mathematics at the elementary level, down to kindergarten.

## NOTES

1. An unfortunate consequence of the father's predilection for alliteration in naming his sons is that publications of Samuel Stanley and Syrrel Singleton Wilks (a physiologist and expert in aerospace medicine) are sometimes lumped together under "S. S. Wilks" in bibliographic works, such as *Science Citation Index.*

2. For a fuller account of the founding and early years of the *Annals of Mathematical Statistics,* see the letter from Harry C. Carver, dated 14 Apr. 1972, to professor [W. J.] Hall, reproduced in *Bulletin of the Institute of Mathematical Statistics,* **2**, no. 1 (Jan. 1973), 11–14; and Allen T. Craig, "Our Silver Anniversary," in *Annals of Mathematical Statistics,* **31**, no. 4 (Dec. 1960), 835–837.

3. The background of this delay and its ultimate resolution are discussed in detail by Churchill Eisenhart, in "Samuel S. Wilks and the Army Experiment Design Conference Series," an address at the twentieth Conference on the Design of Experiments in Army Research, Development and Testing, held at Fort Belvoir, Va., 23–25 Oct. 1974, published in the *Proceedings* of this conference (U.S. Army Research Office Report 75–2 June 1975), 1–47. This account also contains material unavailable elsewhere on Wilks's family and early career, together with extensive notes on the American institutions and personages that played important roles in it.

## BIBLIOGRAPHY

I. ORIGINAL WORKS. "The Publications of S. S. Wilks," prepared by T. W. Anderson, in *Annals of Mathematical Statistics,* **36**, no. 1 (Feb. 1965), 24–27, which gives bibliographic details for five books, forty-eight articles, and twelve "other writings," appears to be complete with respect to the first two categories but not to the last. All forty-eight articles are repr. in T. W. Anderson, *S. S. Wilks: Collected Papers—Contributions to Mathematical Statistics* (New York, 1967), as are Anderson's lists of Wilks's publications, in rearranged form (xxvii–xxxiii). Particulars on thirty-one additional "other writings" are given by Churchill Eisenhart, "A Supplementary List of Publications of S. S. Wilks," in *American Statistician,* **29**, no. 1 (Feb. 1975), 25–27.

Among the more important of Wilks's publications are three holograph books: *Lectures by S. S. Wilks on the Theory of Statistical Inference 1936–1937, Princeton University* (Ann Arbor, Mich., 1937); *Elementary Statistical Analysis* (Princeton, 1948), quite conceivably the first carefully developed undergraduate course in mathematical statistics based on one term of calculus; and *Mathematical Statistics* (New York, 1962), a far more advanced, comprehensive treatment—*Mathematical Statistics* (Princeton, 1943) was an early version of some of the same material, prepared partly with the help of his students. He also wrote *Introductory Probability and Statistical Inference: An Experimental Course*

(New York, 1957; rev. ed., Princeton, 1959; Spanish trans., Rosario, Argentina, 1961), with E. C. Douglas, F. Mosteller, R. S. Pieters, D. E. Richmond, R. E. K. Rourke, and G. B. Thomas; and *Introductory Engineering Statistics* (New York, 1965; 2nd ed., 1971), with Irwin Guttman (2nd ed. with Guttman and J. S. Hunter).

Of his research papers, the most notable are "The Standard Error of the Means of 'Matched' Samples," in *Journal of Educational Psychology*, **22**, no. 3 (Mar. 1931), 205–208, repr. as paper 1 in *Collected Papers*; "On the Distributions of Statistics in Samples From a Normal Population of Two Variables With Matched Sampling of One Variable," in *Metron*, **9**, nos. 3–4 (Mar. 1932), 87–126, repr. as paper 2 in *Collected Papers*, his doctoral dissertation; "Certain Generalizations in the Analysis of Variance," in *Biometrika*, **24**, pts. 3–4 (Nov. 1932), 471–494, repr. as paper 6 in *Collected Papers*; "Methods of Statistical Analysis Appropriate for *k* Samples of Two Variables," *ibid.*, **25**, pts. 3–4 (Dec. 1933), 353–378, repr. as paper 7 in *Collected Papers*, written with E. S. Pearson; "Moment-Generating Operators for Determinants of Product Moments in Samples From a Normal System," in *Annals of Mathematics*, 2nd ser., **35**, no. 2 (Apr. 1934), 312–340, repr. as paper 8 in *Collected Papers*; "On the Independence of *k* Sets of Normally Distributed Statistical Variables," in *Econometrica*, **3**, no. 3 (July 1935), 309–326, repr. as paper 9 in *Collected Papers*; "The Likelihood Test of Independence in Contingency Tables," in *Annals of Mathematical Statistics*, **6**, no. 4 (Dec. 1935), 190–196, repr. as paper 11 in *Collected Papers*; "The Large-Sample Distribution of the Likelihood Ratio for Testing Composite Hypotheses," *ibid.*, **9**, no. 1 (Mar. 1938), 60–62, repr. as paper 14 in *Collected Papers*; and "Weighting Systems for Linear Functions of Correlated Variables When There Is No Dependent Variable," in *Psychometrika*, **3**, no. 1 (Mar. 1938), 23–40, repr. as paper 16 in *Collected Papers*.

See also "Shortest Average Confidence Intervals From Large Samples," in *Annals of Mathematical Statistics*, **9**, no. 3 (Sept. 1938), 166–175, repr. as paper 17 in *Collected Papers*; "An Optimum Property of Confidence Regions Associated With the Likelihood Function," *ibid.*, **10**, no. 4 (Dec. 1939), 225–235, repr. as paper 20 in *Collected Papers*, written with J. F. Daly; "Determination of Sample Sizes for Setting Tolerance Limits," *ibid.*, **12**, no. 1 (Mar. 1941), 91–96, repr. as paper 23 in *Collected Papers*; "Statistical Prediction With Special Reference to the Problem of Tolerance Limits," *ibid.*, **13**, no. 4 (Dec. 1942), 400–409, repr. as paper 26 in *Collected Papers*; "Sample Criteria for Testing Equality of Means, Equality of Variances, and Equality of Covariances in a Normal Multivariate Population," *ibid.*, **17**, no. 3 (Sept. 1946), 257–281, repr. as paper 28 in *Collected Papers*; "Order Statistics," in *Bulletin of the American Mathematical Society*, **54**, no. 1 (Jan. 1948), 6–50, repr. as paper 32 in *Collected Papers*; and "Multivariate Statistical Outliers," in *Sankhya*, **25A**, pt. 4 (Dec. 1963), 407–426, repr. as paper 48 in *Collected Papers*.

Two important papers on teaching and training in statistics are "Personnel and Training Problems in Statistics," in *American Mathematical Monthly*, **54**, no. 9 (Nov. 1947), 525–528; and "Teaching Statistical Inference in Elementary Mathematics Courses," *ibid.*, **65**, no. 3 (Mar. 1958), 143–152.

Following Wilks's death, his "working papers on subjects requiring statistical analysis; letters, reports and papers relating to professional organizations," were donated by his widow and Princeton University to the American Philosophical Society; for further details see *Guide to the Archives and Manuscript Collections of the American Philosophical Society* (Philadelphia, 1966), 146. Another dozen items of correspondence (1946, 1961–1962) are preserved in the Leonard J. Savage Papers (MS group 695), Sterling Memorial Library, Yale University. Wilks's professional books and journals have been placed in the S. S. Wilks Room in New Fine Hall, Princeton University.

II. SECONDARY LITERATURE. The biography of Wilks by Frederick Mosteller in *International Encyclopedia of the Social Sciences*, XVI (New York, 1968), 550–553, provides an informative summary of the highlights of Wilks's life, work, and impact in diverse professional roles. Wilks's research contributions and other writings are reviewed in the comprehensive obituary by T. W. Anderson in *Annals of Mathematical Statistics*, **36**, no. 1 (Feb. 1965), 1–23 (repr. in *S. S. Wilks: Collected Papers*), which is preceded by a photograph—not in *Collected Papers*—of Wilks at his desk. A less technical but equally full account of Wilks's life and work is Frederick Mosteller, "Samuel S. Wilks: Statesman of Statistics," in *American Statistician*, **18**, no. 2 (Apr. 1964), 11–17; there is some additional illuminating information in the obituaries by W. G. Cochran, in *Review of the International Statistical Institute*, **32**, nos. 1–2 (June 1964), 189–191; and John W. Tukey, in *Yearbook, American Philosophical Society* for 1964 (1965), 147–154. The obituary in *Estadística* (Washington, D.C.), **22**, no. 83 (June 1964), 338–340, tells of his activities in connection with the Inter-American Statistical Institute.

The eight articles that constitute "Memorial to Samuel S. Wilks" in *Journal of the American Statistical Association*, **60**, no. 312 (Dec. 1965), 938–966, are rich sources of further information, insight, and perspective: Frederick F. Stephan and John W. Tukey, "Sam Wilks in Princeton," 939–944; Frederick Mosteller, "His Writings in Applied Statistics," 944–953; Alex M. Mood, "His Philosophy About His Work," 953–955; Morris H. Hansen, "His Contributions to Government," 955–957; Leslie E. Simon, "His Stimulus to Army Statistics," 957–962; Morris H. Hansen, "His Contributions to the American Statistical Association," 962–964; W. J. Dixon, "His Editorship of the *Annals of Mathematical Statistics*," 964–965; and the unsigned "The Wilks Award," 965–966.

Other publications cited or mentioned in the text are: R. A. Fisher, "On the Mathematical Foundations of Theoretical Statistics," in *Philosophical Transactions of the Royal Society*, **222A**, no. 602 (19 Apr. 1922), 309–368; and "The General Sampling Distribution of the Multiple Correlation Coefficient," in *Proceedings of the Royal Society*, **121A**, no. A788 (1 Dec. 1928), 654–673; E. F. Lindquist, "The Significance of a Difference Between 'Matched' Groups," in *Journal of Educational Psychology*, **22** (Mar. 1931), 197–204; J. Neyman, "Outline of a Theory of Statistical Estimation Based on the Classical Theory of Probability," in *Philosophical Transactions of the Royal Society*, **236A**, no. 767 (30 Aug. 1937), 333–380, repr. as paper no. 20 in *A Selection of Early Statistical Papers of J. Neyman* (Cambridge–Berkeley–Los Angeles, 1967); J. Neyman and E. S. Pearson, "On the Use and Interpretation of Certain Test Criteria. Part I," in *Biometrika*, **20A**, pts. 1–2 (July 1928), 175–240, repr. as paper no. 1 in *Joint Statistical Papers of J. Neyman and E. S. Pearson* (Cambridge–Berkeley–Los Angeles, 1967); "On the Use and Interpretation of Certain Test Criteria. Part II," *ibid.*, pts. 3–4 (Dec. 1928), 263–294, repr. as paper no. 2 in *Joint . . . Papers*; and "On the Problem of *k* Samples," in *Bulletin international de l'Académie polonaise des sciences et des lettres*, no. 6A (June 1931), 460–481, repr. as paper no. 4 in *Joint . . . Papers*; Walter A. Shewhart, *Economic Control of Quality of Manufactured Product* (New York, 1931), 42; J. Wishart, "The Generalized Product Moment Distribution in Samples From a Normal Multivariate Population," in *Biometrika*, **20A**, pts. 1–2 (July 1928), 32–52; and J. Wishart and M. S. Bartlett, "The Generalized Product Moment Distribution in a Normal System," in *Proceedings of the Cambridge Philosophical Society. Mathematical and Physical Sciences*, **29**, pt. 2 (10 May 1933), 260–270.

CHURCHILL EISENHART

[Contribution of the National Bureau of Standards, not subject to copyright.]

**WILLDENOW, KARL LUDWIG** (*b.* Berlin, Germany, 22 August 1765; *d.* Berlin, 10 July 1812), *botany, historical phytogeography.*

As a botanist in the Linnaean tradition, Willdenow was concerned chiefly with description and classification, although he also helped lay the foundations for the new field of phytogeography that emerged in the early nineteenth century. He was introduced to the study of plants by his father, Karl Johann Willdenow, a Berlin apothecary, and by the botanist Johann Gottlieb Gleditsch. He also was taught chemistry by his father's friend and colleague Martin Heinrich Klaproth. After receiving his early formal education at a Berlin Gymnasium,

Willdenow studied at the pharmacy school conducted by Johann Christoph Wiegleb at Langensalza. He completed the course in 1785 and then went on to study medicine at Halle, receiving the M.D. in 1789. In 1790 he married Henriette Louise Habermass and took over his father's establishment in Berlin.

By this time Willdenow had already published a flora of Berlin (1787), and for several years he had been conducting informal botanical lessons and field trips in and around the city. One of those whom he introduced to the subject, in 1788, was Alexander von Humboldt, who became a lifelong friend and occasional scientific collaborator. Willdenow greatly extended his educational influence in 1792 with the publication of *Grundriss der Kräuterkunde*, a basic textbook intended to replace Linnaeus' obsolete *Philosophia botanica* (1751). The *Grundriss* was a great success and long remained a standard text, going through numerous editions in several languages.

Willdenow's growing reputation brought him membership in the Berlin Academy of Sciences in 1794, and in 1801 he became its principal botanist. He was named professor of natural history at the Berlin Medical-Surgical College in 1798, at which time he gave up his apothecary shop. In 1801 Willdenow became curator of the Berlin Botanical Garden, which he developed from modest proportions into one of the most comprehensive in Europe, introducing numerous exotic species into its collection. He also continued to add to his own herbarium, which numbered more than 20,000 dried specimens at the time of his death and is still preserved at the Berlin Botanical Garden. In 1810 he was named professor of botany at the new University of Berlin, but he died before formally taking up the duties.

Willdenow lived in an age of worldwide geographical exploration; and although he rarely traveled outside Germany, and never outside Europe, he corresponded with many explorers, who provided him with thousands of botanical specimens for his collections and research. Humboldt, for example, gave him the nearly 400 plants that he collected in Spain in 1799; and it was to Willdenow that he turned for assistance in describing and classifying the thousands of new species that he and Bonpland brought back from their long South American expedition. In 1810 Willdenow traveled to Paris to help Humboldt; but the work was interrupted by an illness that forced him to return to Berlin, where he died in 1812. Willdenow also had undertaken a thorough revision of Linnaeus' *Species plantarum*, a massive project that was incomplete in five volumes at the time of his death.

Although Willdenow's own researches were primarily taxonomic, he recognized that plants also fall into distinct geographical groups and advocated the systematic investigation of various regularities of plant distribution. Some aspects of the subject had been treated by earlier botanists, especially Linnaeus and his students; but Willdenow was one of the first to conceive of a separate and clearly historical botanical discipline dealing with plant distribution in relation to climatic, geographical, geological, migrational, and other factors. He discussed this discipline under the heading "History of Plants" in the first edition of *Grundriss der Kräuterkunde*, and substantially revised and expanded the section in subsequent editions. (The following account is based primarily on the second edition.)

Willdenow understood the scope of the history of plants "to include the influence of climate on vegetation, the changes that plants have probably endured during the revolutions of our globe, the distribution of plants over the earth, their migrations, and, finally, the means by which Nature has provided for their preservation." Under the first heading he included the role of climate in defining the great floral regions of the earth, the climatic adaptations of plant species as limiting factors to their distribution, and the ability of climate to influence the relative number of plant species found in a given region as well as their general characteristics, such as size and shape. In discussing the changes of plants, Willdenow refuted Linnaeus' theory that new plant species can arise through the hybridization of old ones, and he defended the idea that many species have become extinct over the course of time as a result of geological and climatic change.

Regarding the distribution of species, Willdenow proposed a theory that attempted to relate the present division of the earth into floristic regions to its geological history, as then understood. Accepting the view that the earth was originally covered by a vast sea from which only the highest mountain ranges emerged, he suggested that God had populated these mountain archipelagoes with all the plant species that would ever exist, creating each species in only one place. Then, as the seas receded, the plants descended from the mountains and spread to the surrounding lowlands until they encountered some barrier to further migration. It is because each mountain range had a unique set of species that the earth is still divided into more or less distinct floral regions that cannot be explained through climate alone. As Willdenow demonstrated at length, however, there are numerous means by which plants and their seeds can be transported over even the most formidable barriers, so that considerable mixing of the original floras has occurred and continues to occur. He thus recognized that the present distribution of plants is the result of historical processes and suggested that by studying the present pattern it should be possible to reconstruct both the primeval distribution and the processes that have led to the present one. He himself did not pursue this and other aspects of the history of plants in great detail; but it was partly due to his influence that others, especially Humboldt, went on to establish the field of phytogeography on a comprehensive basis.

## BIBLIOGRAPHY

I. ORIGINAL WORKS. Willdenow's principal books include *Florae Berolinensis prodromus* (Berlin, 1787); *Tractatus botanico-medicus de Achilleis* (Halle, 1789); *Historia amaranthorum* (Zurich, 1790); *Grundriss der Kräuterkunde* (Berlin, 1792; 2nd. ed., 1798), also in English as *Principles of Botany* (Edinburgh, 1805); *Berlinische Baumzucht* (Berlin, 1796); *Species plantarum*, 5 vols. (Berlin, 1797–1810); *Anleitung zum Selbststudium der Botanik* (Berlin, 1804); *Hortus Berolinensis*, 2 vols. (Berlin, 1806–1809); and *Enumeratio horti regii botanici Berolinensis* (Berlin, 1809; supp., 1813). Most of Willdenow's numerous articles are listed in the Royal Society *Catalogue of Scientific Papers*, VI, 372–374.

II. SECONDARY LITERATURE. Willdenow's friend and colleague D. F. L. von Schlechtendal gave an account of his activities as head of the Berlin Botanical Garden in his intro. to the supp. of the *Enumeratio* (1813), iii–x; he published a fuller *éloge* in *Magazin für der neuesten Entdeckungen in der gesammten Naturkunde*, **6** (1814), v–xvi. Also useful are Clemens König, "Karl Ludwig Willdenow," in *Allgemeine deutsche Biographie*, XLIII (Leipzig, 1898), 252–254; and Max Lenz, *Geschichte der königlichen Friedrich-Wilhelms-Universität zu Berlin*, I (Halle, 1910), 247–249. John Ise and Fritz G. Lange, eds., *Die Jugendbriefe Alexander von Humboldts 1787–1799* (Berlin, 1973); and E. T. Hamy, ed., *Lettres américaines d'Alexandre de Humboldt (1798–1807)* (Paris, 1905), contain a number of important letters from Humboldt to Willdenow as well as many references to him. See also Hanno Beck, *Alexander von Humboldt*, 2 vols. (Wiesbaden, 1959–1961), *passim*, esp. I, 16–17, and II, 65–68; Wolfgang-Hagen Hein, "Alexander von Humboldt und Karl Ludwig Willdenow," in *Pharmazeutische Zeitung*, **104** (1959), 467–471; and Clemens König, "Die historische Entwicklung der pflanzengeographische Ideen Humboldts," in *Naturwissenschaftliche Wochenschrift*, **10** (1895), 77–81, 95–98, 117–124 (not examined).

JEROME J. BYLEBYL

**WILLIAM HEYTESBURY.** See Heytesbury, William.

**WILLIAM OF AUVERGNE,** also known as **Guilielmus Arvernus** or **Alvernus** (*b*. Aurillac, Auvergne [now Cantal], France, between 1180 and 1190; *d*. Paris, France, 30 March 1249), *philosophy, theology.*

After a brief teaching career at Paris, where he was made a master of theology in 1223, William was named bishop of Paris in 1228, a post he held until his death; thus he is sometimes called William of Paris. Like a famous successor, Étienne Tempier, he meddled in the affairs of the university, but generally with a more positive attitude toward the pagan learning that was then being introduced there. He did not think highly of the Jews, however, and was among those responsible for the public burning of the Talmud at Paris in June 1242.

As a Christian philosopher William may be characterized as the last eminent French theologian, completing the tradition of Abailard and Bernard of Clairvaux; and as the first great scholastic, setting the stage for Alexander of Hales, Albertus Magnus, and their disciples. Alexander and Albertus were at Paris with him, as was Roger Bacon, who mentions having heard him lecture on the active intellect.[1] William was also friendly with Robert Grosseteste, bishop of Lincoln, and is mentioned as a possible source of the latter's "metaphysics of light." Because of his insistence on the primacy of being and his use of an Avicennian teaching on essence and existence taken over later by Thomas Aquinas, William is sometimes seen as a forerunner of Aquinas. Actually William was more in the tradition of Augustine, Boethius, and the School of Chartres; and many of his teachings were combated energetically by Aquinas.

While setting himself to destroy the errors of the pagans, William insisted on a careful study of their writings. He was particularly interested in Ibn Sīnā, although he also cited al-Karajī, al-Ghazzali, al-Fārābī, Ibn Rushd, al-Battānī, Abū Maʿshar, Altāf Husain Hālī, al-Biṭrūjī, and al-Farghānī; and he knew of the writings ascribed to Hermes Trismegistus. References to these authors occur mainly in William's *De universo*, the part of his monu-mental *Magisterium divinale* devoted to the world of nature, composed around 1231–1236. *De universo* serves as an intermediary between the early medieval writings on cosmology of Isidore of Seville and Bede and the great encyclopedias of Vincent of Beauvais and Albertus Magnus that appeared later in the century. Apart from the insight it provides into William's sparse knowledge of astronomy and cosmology, it is of considerable value for its accounts and critiques of medieval magic and so-called experimental science; William, in fact, speaks often of "experiments," but without any of the modern connotations of this expression.

The *De universo* is divided into two parts, each containing three subdivisions. The first part considers creation as a whole and treats in some detail of the material universe, while the second part is devoted almost entirely to the spiritual universe, that is, the world of intelligences, angels, and demons. William upholds the Christian doctrine of creation against the Manichaeans, insisting on the unity of the universe and arguing against a plurality of worlds and any void existing between them.[2] He teaches that the heavens and the elements were created at the same time,[3] and that the heavenly bodies have no proper movements independent of the celestial spheres in which they are imbedded,[4] the latter consideration leading him to discourse on the relative thickness of the various spheres.[5] In general he endorses the astronomical system of al-Biṭrūjī, against that of Ptolemy, without manifesting an adequate grasp of either.[6] There are also Platonic overtones in his exposition, as when he explains the motion of the heavens in terms of a power emanating from al-Biṭrūjī's ninth sphere, somewhat like the World Soul of the *Timaeus*,[7] and which he also likens to the phenomenon of magnetic induction.[8] He is explicit that the Holy Spirit is in no way to be identified with the soul of the world.[9]

The second part of *De universo* opens with an account of Aristotle's intelligences and a repudiation of them as movers of the heavens.[10] William teaches also that angels are not necessary to account for the differences in velocities of the heavenly bodies.[11] While discussing the motion of separated substances, he treats incidentally of the speed of illumination, holding that the operation of light is not instantaneous.[12] He inveighs against the excesses of judicial astrology, although he admits the existence of remarkable phenomena, "which some physicians and certain natural philosophers refer to as empirical."[13] William distinguishes between natural magic and black magic, allowing that the former is based on the hidden properties of natural substances and is wrong only if used for evil purposes, whereas the latter involves the intervention of demons and is itself evil.[14] Like most medievals William is exceedingly credulous in accepting and recounting the many marvelous and occult workings of nature of which he has heard or read in earlier authors. He lists detailed prescriptions against the practice of magic in another part of his *Magisterium divinale* entitled *De legibus*; this prohibits the cult of the stars and heavenly bodies and the idolatry of elements, statues, and similar objects.[15]

## NOTES

1. *Opus tertium*, cap. 23; see *The 'Opus Majus' of Roger Bacon*, J. H. Bridges, ed., I (Oxford, 1897), p. xxvii.
2. *De universo*, Primae partis prima pars, cc. 13–16, in *Opera omnia* (Paris, 1674), I, pp. 607–611.
3. *Ibid.*, cc. 28–29, pp. 624–625.
4. *Ibid.*, c. 44, pp. 648–653.
5. *Ibid.*, c. 45, p. 654.
6. *Ibid.*, c. 44, pp. 651–653.
7. *Ibid.*, Primae partis tertia pars, c. 28, pp. 798–801.
8. *Ibid.*, c. 29, pp. 801–803; see Duhem, *Le système du monde*, III, pp. 258–260.
9. *De universo*, Primae partis tertia pars, c. 33, p. 806.
10. *Ibid.*, Secundae partis prima pars, c. 45, p. 843.
11. *Ibid.*, Secundae partis secunda pars, c. 97, pp. 951–952.
12. *Ibid.*, c. 101, pp. 953–954.
13. ". . . exemplis occultarum operationum et mirabilium, quaeque nonnulli medicorum et etiam quidam philosophorum naturalium empirica vocant," *ibid.*, c. 76, p. 929.
14. *Ibid.*, Secundae partis tertia pars, cc. 7–8, pp. 1029–1035; c. 18, pp. 1049–1050.
15. *Opera omnia* (Paris, 1674), vol. I, pp. 18–102, esp. 44, 77, 81, and 86.

## BIBLIOGRAPHY

I. ORIGINAL WORKS. William's *Opera omnia* has appeared in various Latin editions, all incomplete: (Nuremberg, 1496); 2 vols. (Paris, 1516, 1574); 2 vols. (Venice, 1591); 2 vols. (Orleans, 1674); and 2 vols. (Paris, 1674; repr., Frankfurt am Main, 1963). The sermons contained in vol. II of the latter edition and attributed to William of Auvergne are actually those of the Dominican William Peraldus (Perrauld or Perault). An important treatise has been edited by J. R. O'Donnell, as "Tractatus magistri Guillelmi Alvernensis *De bono et malo*," in *Mediaeval Studies*, **8** (1946), 245–299, and **16** (1954), 219–271; other writings and sermons still remain unedited.

II. SECONDARY LITERATURE. For a brief biography of William and a bibliography, see J. R. O'Donnell, in *New Catholic Encyclopedia*, XIV (New York, 1967), 921. On William's philosophy, see Étienne Gilson, *History of Christian Philosophy in the Middle Ages* (New York–London, 1955), 250–258, 658–660, with bibliography. William's contributions viewed in relation to the history of science are detailed in George Sarton, *Introduction to the History of Science*, II, pt. 2 (Baltimore, 1931), 588; E. J. Dijksterhuis, *The Mechanization of the World Picture*, C. Dikshoorn, trans. (Oxford, 1961), 139, *passim*; L. Thorndike, *A History of Magic and Experimental Science*, II (New York, 1923), 338–371; Pierre Duhem, *Le système du monde*, III (Paris, 1915), 249–260, and V (Paris, 1917), 260–285; and *Études sur Léonard de Vinci*, II (Paris, 1909), 408–410. A valuable study of William's teaching on the soul and on psychology is E. A. Moody, "William of Auvergne and His Treatise *De Anima*," in his *Studies in Medieval Philosophy, Science, and Logic, Collected Papers 1933–1969* (Berkeley, Calif., 1975), 1–109.

WILLIAM A. WALLACE, O.P.

**WILLIAM OF MOERBEKE.** See **Moerbeke, William of.**

**WILLIAM OF OCKHAM.** See **Ockham, William of.**

**WILLIAM OF SAINT-CLOUD** (*fl.* France, end of the thirteenth century), *astronomy*.

All of the very little that is known about William of Saint-Cloud comes from his own writings. The earliest recorded date of his activity is 1285, when he observed a conjunction of Saturn and Jupiter (28 December), an event to which he alludes in his *Almanach*. He was undoubtedly well received in French court circles, for his calendar is dedicated to Queen Marie of Brabant, widow of Philip III (The Bold); and he translated it into French at the request of Jeanne of Navarre, wife of Philip IV (The Fair).[1] There is no substantial evidence to support the hypothesis that William of Saint-Cloud is identical with a certain Simon of Saint-Cloud, canon of Meaux and a steward of the queen. Simon is mentioned several times in archival documents. Nor are there grounds for calling William of Saint-Cloud by the name of Lefebvre.[2]

William of Saint-Cloud's known works are devoted entirely to astronomy. The treatise on the *Directorium*, or "adrescoir," is the oldest of his preserved writings; it is referred to in the *Calendrier de la reine*. The instrument described in it is a magnetic compass with a graduation in unequal hours; it is provided with a table for computing the duration of diurnal arcs.

The text accompanying Queen Marie's calendar deals with problems relating to the daily movement of the sun and to the astronomy of the *primum mobile* (inequality of days and nights according to the season and the geographic latitude; division of the inhabited world into "climats"), as well as to the nineteen-year lunar cycle. Beyond the information usually found in such works (the number of the decemnovennial cycle coordinated with the day of the month in which the new moon occurs during the year designated by this number; ferial letters; saints' days; entry of the sun into the signs of the zodiac), the calendar also furnishes more technical data: the height of the sun at noon, duration of diurnal and nocturnal arcs, and hours of the new moon. The most notable aspect of this work is William's firm resolve to establish his calendar on a purely astronomical basis. As a result, he contradicted the ecclesiastical calendrical computation, emphasizing its inadequacy and errors. For example, he presented—along with the traditional decemnovennial cycle (which he was still obliged to give since the rules of the ecclesiastical computation had not been abrogated)—another cycle that conformed to the scientific data of the astronomical tables and that he designated by the letters from *a* to *t*. Toward the same end, he appended a table that permits the user to make corrections—beyond the first solar cycle of four years—in the dates of the entry of the sun into the signs of the zodiac. The base year of the calendar is 1292 (not, as P. Duhem stated, 1296).

The starting point of William's *Almanach* is also the year 1292. The purpose of this work was to furnish the effective positions of the planets, in contradistinction to the astronomical tables which gave only the elements for computing these positions. The introductory text is neither a theory of the planets, nor, properly speaking, canons (which, moreover, are scarcely necessary in an almanac), but rather an account of the observations and considerations on which the book is based. William takes this opportunity to point out the errors he has detected in the astronomical tables he used and to show how he has corrected them. The tables that he subjects to this criticism are those of Toledo (used in the Arab calendar) and of Toulouse (in which the preceding tables are applied to the Christian calendar). Nevertheless, in the end he adopted the tables of Toulouse, although not without making slightly arbitrary corrections in some of the mean movements listed in them.

In discussing the movement of the eighth sphere, William verified by calculation and observation the value he assigned to it for the year 1290. Noting that this value differs by nearly a degree from the one that would result from applying Thābit ibn Qurra's theory of accession and recession, he rejected the latter and opted for the Ptolemaic theory of simple precession. He recorded, however, the different values that astronomers assigned to the amplitude of that precession.

The *Almanach* gives the daily planetary positions for a period of twenty years beginning with 1292. For the sun and the moon, all the positions are accurate to within a minute. This same degree of accuracy is achieved for the positions of the outer planets every ten days and for the positions of the inner planets every five days. The latitude of the moon is also given.

William's *Almanach* makes no reference to the Alphonsine tables. Yet Duhem, on the basis of a text printed with the works of Nicolas of Cusa, which he attributed to William, concluded that the latter was among the first, if not the first, in Paris, to know of and use the Alphonsine tables. (William supposedly learned about them a few years after composing his *Almanach*.) Nothing is less certain. Duhem's analysis of this short text is insufficiently critical. Moreover, it seems certain that the Alphonsine tables were not introduced into Parisian astronomy before 1320,[3] after which date it is not certain that William of Saint-Cloud was still alive.

The works of William had only a limited diffusion, undoubtedly because they were based on astronomical data (the tables of Toledo and Toulouse) that was soon superseded by the Alphonsine tables. Nonetheless, William holds a very significant place in the history of medieval astronomy. The many observations he made and the conclusions he drew from them, together with his criticism of the available tabular material, make him a genuine precursor, perhaps even the chief inspiration, of the Parisian astronomers of the first half of the fourteenth century.

*NOTES*

1. E. Zinner, *Verzeichnis der astronomischen Handschriften des deutschen Kulturgebietes* (Munich, 1925), p. 413, mistakenly speaks of a Queen Elisabeth. Further, Zinner (*ibid.,* nos. 2578–2594) confused William of Saint-Cloud with William the Englishman, the Marseilles author of *De urina non visa* and of several other astronomical texts, who lived in the first half of the thirteenth century.
2. A. d'Avezac, "Note sur Guillaume de Saint-Cloud," in *Mémoires de l'Institut national de France, Académie des inscriptions et belles-lettres,* **29,** pt. 1 (1877), 8–10, and in *Académie des inscriptions et belles-lettres, comptes-rendus des séances 1869,* 29–31.
3. See the article on John of Murs, in *Dictionary of Scientific Biography,* VII.

*BIBLIOGRAPHY*

I. ORIGINAL WORKS. The treatises of William of Saint-Cloud are all unpublished. The MS of the directorium or "adrescoir" ("Presens ingenium directivum (*sic*) vocitavi . . .") is Paris Arsenal 1037, fol. 7v–8v, together with the French trans. ("Très haute dame ci sont les proufis que l'en puet avoir . . ."). The Latin text is in verse. Another very summary French version, without the table of hours, can also be found in Paris Arsenal 2872, fol. 21v.

The calendar in Latin ("Testante Vegecio in libro suo de re militari . . .") is in: Florence Laur. XXX.24, fol. 99–109v and 110–123; Paris Arsenal 534, fol. 91–106; Paris lat.7281, fol. 145–148 (text only); Paris lat. 15171, fol. 88–101. Calendar in French ("Si come Vegeces tesmoigne en son livre . . .") in: Paris Arsenal 2872, fol. 1–21. Another French version, with a reduced commentary, is in Rennes 593, fol. 1–7.

The MSS of the almanac ("Cum intentio mea sit componere almanac . . .") contain either the text only or the tables only; the text is in: Cues 215, fol. 24–31v; Paris lat.7281, fol. 141–144v; Paris nouv. acq. lat. 1242, fol. 41–44; summary note in Cues 212, fol. 405–406; the tables are in: Vatican lat. 4572; Paris lat. 16210.

The MS Erfurt 4° 355, fol. 44v preserves a star table "verified at Saint-Cloud near Paris in 1294" that may well be by William.

II. SECONDARY LITERATURE. On William and his work, see E. Littré, in *Histoire littéraire de la France*, XXV (Paris, 1869), 63–74; P. Duhem, *Le système du monde*, IV (Paris, 1916), 10–24.

EMMANUEL POULLE

**WILLIAM OF SHERWOOD**, also **Shyreswood, Shirewode** (*fl.* Oxford, thirteenth century), *logic.*

William was active as a master of logic at a time when that subject was making remarkable progress. He probably was born in Nottinghamshire between 1200 and 1210 and is most likely to have studied at Oxford or Paris, or both. His only extant works are treatises on logic explicitly attributed to him in the manuscripts: the *Introductio in logicam*, a compendium af Aristotelian-Boethian logic together with the main topics of terminist logic; and *Syncategoremata*, a more advanced treatise on the semantic and logical properties of syncategorematic words (words that have special logical-semantic effects on subjects, predicates, or their combinations). The Paris manuscript B.N. Lat. 16.617 contains, besides the works mentioned above, four logical treatises, three of which may in all probability be ascribed to William: the first of two treatises entitled *De insolubilibus* (works dealing with the paradoxes of self-reference, as in the proposition "What I am saying now is false"); *De obligationibus*, a work on the rules to be observed in formal disputations (its authenticity is certain); and *Petitiones contrariorum*, on the solution of logical puzzles, called *sophismata* in medieval usage, that arise from hidden ambiguity in the premises of an inference. The last three works have not been printed so far.

William's teaching at the University of Paris is uncertain and cannot be deduced, as is usually done, from any influence on Paris logicians and metaphysicians, since such influence cannot be shown. It is certain, however, that he was an active master at Oxford sometime before 27 January 1249, when his name is found in a deed. He certainly was there during the great disturbance between the northern and the Irish scholars. William was treasurer of the cathedral church of Lincoln at least from about 1256 to 1265. He is mentioned as rector of Aylesbury, in Buckinghamshire, in October 1266 and of Attleborough, Norfolk. He must have died sometime between 1266 and 1271.

As a writer of a compendium on logic, William can be compared with two other authors of such works, Peter of Spain (*ca.* 1205–1277) and Lambert of Auxerre, who wrote his compendium between 1253 and 1257. Accurate investigations have shown that they worked quite independently of each other; the dissimilarities are numerous, and the resemblances can be explained by the authors' sharing a common tradition of logical teaching.

William's compendium, unlike that by Peter of Spain, was not very influential in later times. His impact on his contemporaries can be deduced only from a passage in Roger Bacon's *Opus tertium* (1267), in which William is described as "one of the famous wise men in Christendom" who was "much wiser than Albert the Great in what is called *philosophia communis*" (logic); Bacon even calls him the greatest logician. Elsewhere (*Compendium studii philosophie*, written in 1271 or 1272) Bacon mentions William as one of the wise and solid philosophers and theologians of the older generation. His evaluation of William as a first-rate logician is the more remarkable since his opinion of contemporary philosophers tended to be disdainful. The importance of William's work in the development of logic has not yet been fully investigated.

*BIBLIOGRAPHY*

I. ORIGINAL WORKS. The *Introductiones in logicam* was edited by M. Grabmann as *Sitzungsberichte der Bayerischen Akademie der Wissenschaften zu München,*

Phil.-hist. Abt. (1937), no. 10 (unreliable), and was translated by Norman Kretzmann as *William of Sherwood's Introduction to Logic* (Minneapolis, 1968), with introd. and notes. The *Syncategoremata* was edited by J. R. O'Donnell, in *Mediaeval Studies*, **3** (1941), 46–93.

II. SECONDARY LITERATURE. Kretzmann's introd. to his trans. is fundamental for evidence on William's career. On William as a logician, see the work of Kretzmann and also L. M. de Rijk, *Logica modernorum*, II, *The Origin and Early Development of the Theory of Supposition* (Assen, Netherlands, 1967), 567–591; and "The Development of *Suppositio naturalis* in Mediaeval Logic, I: Natural Supposition as Non-Contextual Supposition," in *Vivarium*, **9** (1971), 71–107.

L. M. DE RIJK

**WILLIAMS, HENRY SHALER** (*b*. Ithaca, New York, 6 March 1847; *d*. Havana, Cuba, 31 July 1918), *paleontology, stratigraphy.*

Williams was a member of a family long prominent in Ithaca. Interested in natural science from an early age, he received the Ph.B from the Sheffield Scientific School in 1868 and the Ph.D. from Yale in 1871. After a few years in his father's business he joined the faculty of geology at Cornell University. Of an independent mind regarding geology, he vigorously commenced paleontological and stratigraphical studies on the Devonian rocks of central New York; and during the next twelve years he not only described these rocks and their fossils in detail but also demonstrated that the true relationships to time (correlation) could be shown only by careful paleontological analysis. Williams quickly became aware of the connection between facies changes and the evolution and shifting of fossil faunas, a theme that occupied much of his work and one on which he published many papers, culminating in his monograph on recurrent *Tropidoleptus* zones (1913). He extended his work on the Middle Paleozoic strata over much of the eastern United States as an associate of the U.S. Geological Survey.

Williams' major contribution to the philosophical aspects of paleontology and stratigraphy was his book *Geological Biology* (1895). Ahead of its time, its ideas had little impact; but it is now recognized as a minor classic. From analyses of the fossil record Williams made a perceptive and striking estimate of the relative lengths of time involved in the great geological periods, estimates that correspond closely to those based on the radiometric methods of the twentieth century.

In 1892 Williams returned to Yale as Silliman professor of geology, succeeding James Dwight Dana. In 1904 he returned to Cornell, where he continued his research until he retired in 1912. In 1888 he was one of the leading founders of the Geological Society of America, two years after he had organized the Society of the Sigma Xi.

*BIBLIOGRAPHY*

I. ORIGINAL WORKS. Williams wrote more than ninety books and papers, among which the most important are "The *Cuboides* Zone and Its Fauna; a Discussion of the Methods of Correlation," in *Bulletin of the Geological Society of America*, **1** (1890), 481–500; "Correlation Papers: Devonian and Carboniferous," in *Bulletin of the United States Geological Survey*, **80** (1891); "Dual Nomenclature in Geological Classification," in *Journal of Geology*, **2** (1894), 145–160; *Geological Biology, an Introduction to the Geological History of Organisms* (New York, 1895); "Fossil Faunas and Their Use in Correlating Geological Formations," in *American Journal of Science*, **163** (1902), 417–432; "Shifting of Faunas as a Problem of Stratigraphic Geology," in *Bulletin of the Geological Society of America*, **14** (1903); and "Recurrent *Tropidoleptus* Zones of the Upper Devonian in New York," in *Professional Papers. United States Geological Survey*, **79** (1913).

II. SECONDARY LITERATURE. See H. F. Cleland, "Memorial of Henry Shaler Williams," in *Bulletin of the Geological Society of America*, **30** (1919), 47–65, with portrait and bibliography of published works; H. E. Gregory, "Professor Williams at Yale," in *Science*, **49** (1919), 63–65; Charles Schuchert, "Henry Shaler Williams, an Appreciation of His Work in Stratigraphy," in *American Journal of Science*, **196** (1918), 682–687; and Stuart Weller, "Henry Shaler Williams," in *Journal of Geology*, **26** (1918), 698–700.

JOHN W. WELLS

**WILLIAMS, ROBERT RUNNELS** (*b*. Nellore, India, 16 February 1886; *d*. Summit, New Jersey, 2 October 1965), *chemistry, nutrition.*

Williams was the son of Robert Runnels Williams, a Baptist missionary, and Alice Evelyn Mills. He was educated at Ottawa University in Kansas and the University of Chicago, receiving the B.S. from Chicago in 1907 and the M.S. in 1908. An honorary D.Sc. was conferred on him by Ottawa University in 1935; six other universities so honored him later. In 1909 he became a chemist with the Bureau of Science in Manila, where he undertook a search for the substance in rice polishings that was a curative for beriberi. The search, identification, and medical use of the substance became the major objective of his entire career.

By the time he returned to the United States in 1914, to take a position with the Bureau of Chemistry of the U.S. Department of Agriculture, Williams had established that the active substance was a nitrogenous base. When the United States entered World War I, he was briefly involved with chemical warfare investigations and was later to work for the Bureau of Aircraft Production. After the war he left government service, because the low salary made it difficult to support his wife and four children.

Williams worked briefly in 1919 for the Melcho Chemical Company of Bayonne, New Jersey, developing a process for recovering chemicals from petroleum refinery gases. Between 1919 and 1925 he did research on submarine insulating materials for the Western Electric Company, and in 1925 he became director of the chemistry laboratories at the Bell Telephone Laboratories, a position he held until 1946.

During the 1920's and 1930's Williams pursued his research on the anti-beriberi factor (ultimately named vitamin $B_1$) in his spare time. Working at night in a laboratory in his garage, he slowly improved the concentration of his products. In the meantime, B. C. P. Jansen and W. F. Donath obtained the pure substance in very low yield (1926). In 1927 Williams secured research support from the Carnegie Corporation and was given laboratory space at Columbia University. By 1933 he and his co-workers had obtained pure crystals of vitamin $B_1$. By using quinine for the elution of the vitamin from fuller's earth, he developed a procedure that gave better yields than those obtained by other workers in the field.

Once the pure compound was available, Williams found that sulfurous acid cleavage gave a pyrimidine and a thiazole fraction. These were identified, and in 1935 a tentative formula for the structure was published; soon thereafter the compound, named thiamine, was synthesized. Commercial synthesis soon followed.

In 1933 Williams had severed his connections with the Carnegie Corporation as a result of a disagreement regarding patent policy. He subsequently assigned his patents to Research Corporation, a foundation set up by Frederick Cottrell in 1912 to develop scientific patents and use the proceeds for further research. In 1946 Williams became director of grants for Research Corporation, and in 1951 he was made director. Personal profits from Williams'

patents were set aside in the Williams-Waterman Fund for the Combat of Dietary Disease, the income being used to support nutritional research and field programs to combat malnutrition.

In 1940 Williams became chairman of the Cereal Committee of the Food and Nutrition Board of the National Research Council. As a wartime measure he promoted the enrichment of flour and bread with thiamine, other vitamins, iron, and calcium.

Williams' younger brother, Roger John (*b.* 1893) discovered pantothenic acid and did extensive nutritional research, especially on the vitamin B complex. The brothers were jointly honored by receipt of the Charles Frederick Chandler Medal of Columbia University in 1942.

## BIBLIOGRAPHY

I. ORIGINAL WORKS. *Toward the Conquest of Beriberi* (Cambridge, Mass., 1961), although a historical account of the study of the disease and the vitamin preventing it, is somewhat autobiographical because Williams was deeply involved in the isolation and synthesis of thiamine. As autobiography, however, it is limited almost entirely to his vitamin research and the use of the synthetic product in controlling the disease, especially in the Philippines; there is very little other personal history. The story of the patents and the use of the income therefrom is treated in *The Williams-Waterman Fund for the Combat of Dietary Diseases: A History of the Period 1935 Through 1955* (New York, 1956). Williams was coauthor with Tom D. Spies of *Vitamin $B_1$ (Thiamine) and Its Use in Medicine* (New York, 1938). The program on flour enrichment is described in "Enrichment of Flour and Bread. A History of the Movement," *Bulletin of the National Research Council,* no. 110 (1944), written with R. M. Wilder. The research on the isolation, proof of structure, and synthesis of thiamine was published mostly in *Journal of the American Chemical Society*. Particularly significant are "Larger Yields of Crystalline Antineuritic Vitamin," in *Journal of the American Chemical Society,* **56** (1934), 1187–1191, written with R. E. Waterman and J. C. Keresztesy; "Structure of Vitamin $B_1$," *ibid.,* **57** (1935), 229–230, and **58** (1936), 1063–1064; "Studies of Crystalline Vitamin $B_1$. III. Cleavage of the Vitamin With Sulfite," *ibid.,* 536–537, written with R. E. Waterman, J. C. Keresztesy, and E. R. Buchman; "Studies . . . $B_1$. VIII. Sulfite Cleavage. Chemistry of the Acidic Product," *ibid.,* 1093–1095, written with E. R. Buchman and A. E. Ruehle; and "Studies . . . $B_1$. XI. Sulfite Cleavage. Chemistry of the Basic Part," *ibid.,* 1849–1851, written with E. R. Buchman and J. C. Keresztesy.

II. SECONDARY LITERATURE. The only significant short biography of Williams appears in *National Cyclo-*

*paedia of American Biography*, current vol. F (1942), 204–205. Also see *McGraw-Hill Modern Men of Science*, I (New York, 1966), 537.

AARON J. IHDE

**WILLIAMSON, ALEXANDER WILLIAM** (*b.* Wandsworth, London, England, 1 May 1824; *d.* Hindhead, Surrey, England, 6 May 1904), *organic chemistry.*

Although he published little, Williamson was the most influential chemist in Great Britain during the period 1850–1870, two critical decades in which chemists released themselves from the stranglehold of Berzelius' electrochemical dualism, forged a unitary system of inorganic and organic chemistry, created a rational system of atomic weights, developed concepts of valence and structure, and organized themselves professionally. In all these changes and developments Williamson was a leader, as researcher, teacher, critic, and elder statesman.

Williamson was the second of three children of Alexander Williamson, a clerk at East India House who was a friend of the economist James Mill, and Antonia McAndrew, a merchant's daughter. Throughout his life he was racked by severe physical disabilities: a semiparalyzed left arm, a blind right eye, and a myopic left one. These deficiencies undoubtedly promoted his later disenchantment with detailed laboratory work and encouraged his theoretical and speculative powers, which had been stimulated by his philosophical education. In 1840, following schooling and private instruction at Kensington, Paris, and Dijon, Williamson began medical training at the University of Heidelberg, where he was encouraged to study chemistry by Leopold Gmelin. From 1844 to 1846 he worked with Liebig at Giessen, where he published his first papers on bleaching salts, ozone, and Prussian blue. Apparently he had independent means, and from 1846 to 1849 he established a private research laboratory in Paris, where he fraternized with Laurent, Gerhardt, Wurtz, and Dumas and, on the recommendation of his older childhood friend John Stuart Mill, took private lessons in mathematics from Auguste Comte. The latter regarded Williamson as one of his most promising converts to positivism, but in England Williamson proved a disappointing disciple and advocate.

In 1849, encouraged by Graham and supported by Liebig, Dumas, Laurent, and Hofmann, Williamson applied for the vacant chair of practical chemistry at University College, London. On Graham's retirement from the chair of general chemistry in 1855 Williamson, rather unfortunately, took both titles. He remained at University College until his retirement to farming in the countryside at Hindhead in 1887. As far as active research was concerned, however, Williamson's retirement dated from the completion of his etherification studies in 1854. The reasons for this are complex. Certainly the falling off of his research was not due to any loss of mental power, nor entirely to his absorption in academic politics (where his agitation for university science degrees was successful in 1870), nor yet to his involvement in the affairs of the Chemical and Royal Societies or the British Association for the Advancement of Science. The apparent decline of his work did, however, accompany the development of other practical and engineering interests that ultimately proved fruitless technically and financially, and for which little documentary evidence survives. The only positive results of these enthusiasms were pedagogic: Williamson insisted that his chemistry classes take conducted tours of industrial plants, and he was instrumental in creating a chair of applied chemistry (chemical engineering) at University College.

Many private letters refer to Williamson's superior and acute intellectual powers. Kekulé, who was in London from 1854 to 1855, found his friendship and ideas "excellent schooling for making the mind independent," while Odling was always proud to have followed in his footsteps. Acquaintances were sometimes repelled by his tendency to make cutting remarks; and in arguments he constantly interrupted, so that his opponent's meaning could not be fully expressed. He was a forceful and dogmatic critic of papers at the Chemical Society, for which he established the valuable system of monthly abstracts of British and foreign papers in 1871. Basically, however, he was a kindly man whose sociability, and that of his wife Emma Catherine Key, made him the natural choice as British host to the first Japanese noblemen who came to England to learn Western ways in 1863.

Williamson announced his elegant theory of etherification to the British Association at Edinburgh in August 1850. At this time there were various rival theories concerning the structures of alcohol and ethyl ether, but in all cases ether was supposed to be formed by the loss of water from alcohol. Williamson's initial intention, however, was not to clarify a muddled theoretical situation but to develop practical methods for preparing the homologous higher alcohols. To his "astonishment," when he used Hofmann's alkyl radical substitution technique and reacted ethyl iodide with a solution of potassium in alcohol (potassium ethylate [ethoxide]), he obtained ordinary ethyl ether instead of an ethylated alcohol (Williamson's synthesis).

Influenced by his familiarity with the work of Laurent and Gerhardt, Williamson saw that the relationship between alcohol and ether could not be one of the loss or addition of water but, rather, of substitution, since ether contains two ethyl radicals but the same quantity of oxygen as alcohol. Since equal molecular magnitudes were involved, the formulas of these substances had to be expressed in terms of the French chemists' formula for water, $H_2O$ (instead of HO or $H_4O_2$):

$$C^2H^5I + \genfrac{}{}{0pt}{}{C^2H^5}{K}O = \genfrac{}{}{0pt}{}{C^2H^5}{C^2H^5}O + KI \ (C = 12).$$

Williamson saw, however, that this result might still be explained according to a four-volume formulation ($H_4O_2$) if it were supposed that both potassium ethylate and ethyl iodide contained ether:

$$\genfrac{}{}{0pt}{}{C^4H^{10}O}{K^2O} + C^4H^{10}I^2 = 2(C^4H^{10}O) + 2KI.$$

This possibility was disproved by using methyl (instead of ethyl) iodide, in which case a mixed ether was formed, not a mixture of ethyl ether and methyl ether:

$$CH^3I + \genfrac{}{}{0pt}{}{C^2H^5}{K}O = \genfrac{}{}{0pt}{}{C^2H^5}{CH^3}O + KI,$$

$$\text{not} \quad \genfrac{}{}{0pt}{}{C^2H^6I^2}{K^2O} + C^4H^{10}O = C^4H^{10}O + C^2H^6O + 2KI.$$
$$\qquad\qquad\qquad\quad\text{ethyl}\quad\text{methyl}$$
$$\qquad\qquad\qquad\quad\text{ether}\quad\text{ether}$$

These views were confirmed independently by G. C. Chancel in 1850.

Williamson also explained the process of continuous etherification by the action of sulfuric acid on alcohol. According to the contact theory of Mitscherlich and Berzelius, the sulfuric acid acted merely as a catalyst in this reaction; but according to Liebig's chemical theory, ether was produced only after the intermediate formation of ethyl hydrogen sulfate. The latter, argued Williamson, played a role in the double decomposition analogous to that of potassium ethylate in his synthesis of ether. He represented the exchanges in two stages:

$$\text{I.} \quad \genfrac{}{}{0pt}{}{\genfrac{}{}{0pt}{}{H}{H}SO^4}{\genfrac{}{}{0pt}{}{C^2H^5}{H}O} \quad \genfrac{}{}{0pt}{}{\genfrac{}{}{0pt}{}{C^2H^5}{H}SO^4}{\genfrac{}{}{0pt}{}{H}{H}O} \qquad \text{II.} \quad \genfrac{}{}{0pt}{}{\genfrac{}{}{0pt}{}{C^2H^5}{H}SO^4}{\genfrac{}{}{0pt}{}{H}{C^2H^5}O} \quad \genfrac{}{}{0pt}{}{\genfrac{}{}{0pt}{}{H}{H}SO^4}{\genfrac{}{}{0pt}{}{C^2H^5}{C^2H^5}O}$$

The sulfuric acid produced in II was recycled for further decompositions.

Williamson's impressive study has been rightly seen as laying the foundation for twentieth-century mechanistic studies. Historically it had a number of important consequences. First, Williamson completely rejected the notion of a catalytic force and opted for chemical intermediates in catalyzed reactions. In this stand he echoed Comte, for whom catalysis was a metaphysical fancy improper to the positive stage that chemistry was achieving. Second, Williamson was led to visualize atoms and molecules in motion, and not as the static particles of traditional Daltonism. The mechanism of etherification was inconceivable unless it was viewed as a process of continuous atomic exchange. Such a viewpoint proved to be a major step toward the reunification of chemistry with physics via the kinetic theory of gases, the ionic theory of electrolytes, and the revival of Berthollet's law of mass action. Williamson developed his views on dynamic atomism only in a series of lectures; confirmatory experiments with slow double decompositions were abandoned after a severe explosion. Finally, and most important, the study suggested that analogies for the structures of both organic and inorganic substances should be based on the inorganic type, water.

Echoing Laurent's use in 1846 of a water analogy, Williamson argued in 1851 that "water may be assumed as a very general type and standard of comparison, by viewing other bodies as formed from it by the replacement of one or more atoms of hydrogen in water by the equivalent of various simple or compound radicals" (*Papers on Etherification*, 40). For instance,

$$\genfrac{}{}{0pt}{}{H}{H}O \quad \genfrac{}{}{0pt}{}{C_2H_5}{H}O \quad \genfrac{}{}{0pt}{}{C_2H_5}{C_2H_5}O \quad \genfrac{}{}{0pt}{}{C_2H_3O}{H}O \quad \genfrac{}{}{0pt}{}{C_2H_3O}{C_2H_5}O.$$
$$\text{water}\quad\begin{matrix}\text{ethyl}\\\text{alcohol}\end{matrix}\quad\begin{matrix}\text{ethyl}\\\text{ether}\end{matrix}\quad\begin{matrix}\text{acetic}\\\text{acid}\end{matrix}\quad\begin{matrix}\text{ethyl}\\\text{acetate}\end{matrix}$$

Through the work of Odling and Gerhardt this formal analogy with water completed the unification of organic and inorganic chemistry (the "new type theory"); and through the admission of valence by Frankland, Kekulé, and Odling it permitted the emergence of the real structural formulas that Williamson saw as the ultimate goal of positive chemistry. The use of multiples of water, suggested by Williamson in 1851, gave a ready explanation for differences of basicity and was confirmed by him in 1856, when the chlorination of sulfuric acid produced chlorosulfonic acid:

$$\begin{bmatrix} HO \\ HO \\ HO \\ H \end{bmatrix} \quad \begin{matrix} HO \\ SO_2 O \\ H \end{matrix} O \xrightarrow{PCl_5} \begin{matrix} HO \\ SO_2 O \\ Cl \end{matrix} .$$

Similarly, his "prediction" of a class of anhydrous organic acids formed by the replacement of the H of acetic acid was dramatically confirmed by Gerhardt in 1852, when he reacted acetyl chloride with potassium acetate:

$$\begin{matrix} C_2H_3O \\ K \end{matrix} O + C_2H_3OCl = \begin{matrix} C_2H_3O \\ C_2H_3O \end{matrix} O + \quad \begin{matrix} KCl. \\ \text{acetic} \\ \text{anhydride} \end{matrix}$$

During the 1860's Williamson, who was a devout atomist, did much to eradicate the predominant skepticism of his fellow chemists. His proselytism culminated in a famous clash with his friend B. C. Brodie, Jr., at the Chemical Society in 1869. Brodie's interest in notation and nomenclature was shared by Williamson, who faced the problems involved when writing his chemistry textbook (1865). In 1864 he introduced parentheses into formulas to enclose reaction-invariant groups, such as $Ca(CO_3)_3$; abolished the Berzelian "plus" sign in compounds; and proposed the suffix "-ic" for the base of all salts (including hydrogen) to avoid circumlocution—for instance, "sodic chloride" for "chloride of sodium" and "hydric sulphate" for "sulphuric acid." Although the latter convention was adopted by several British chemists, it did not survive into the twentieth century.

## BIBLIOGRAPHY

I. ORIGINAL WORKS. Thirty-five papers by Williamson are recorded in Royal Society, *Catalogue of Scientific Papers*, VI, 379–380; VIII, 1244–1245; XI, 817; XIX, 637. The major ones are conveniently collected as *Papers on Etherification and on the Constitution of Salts*, Alembic Club Reprint no. 16 (Edinburgh, 1902; reiss., 1949). This reprint unfortunately does not include "On Dr. Kolbe's Additive Formulae," in *Journal of the Chemical Society*, 7 (1855), 122–129, published in reply to A. W. H. Kolbe, "Critical Remarks on Williamson's Water, Ether and Salt Theories," *ibid.*, 111–121—German original in *Justus Liebigs Annalen der Chemie*, 90 (1854), 44–61. These papers exemplify the clash between the type and radical theories. Williamson published two books: a political tract written with his father-in-law,

T. Hewitt Key, *Invasion Invited by the Defenceless State of England* (London, 1858); and *Chemistry for Students* (Oxford, 1865; 2nd ed., 1868; 3rd ed., 1873), for which *Problems From Williamson's Chemistry With Solutions* (Oxford, 1866) was also issued.

Williamson's correspondence with Brodie is printed in W. H. Brock, ed., *The Atomic Debates* (Leicester, 1967), 95–96, 119–120. The bulk of Williamson's papers, which were in the possession of his son, Dr. Oliver Key Williamson, were stolen during a native rebellion in Africa (private information from J. Harris, 1963). For surviving letters and referee's reports, consult the Royal Society, Royal Institution, and Imperial College Archives, London.

II. SECONDARY LITERATURE. There are two detailed and very fine obituaries by Williamson's pupils: Edmund Divers, in *Proceedings of the Royal Society*, 78A (1907), xxiv–xliv, with portrait; and G. Carey Foster, in *Journal of the Chemical Society*, 87 (1905), 605–618; the German trans. in *Berichte der Deutschen Chemischen Gesellschaft*, 44 (1911), 2253–2269, has an unusual photograph. Williamson's relationship with Comte is discussed by W. M. Simon, "Comte's English Disciples," in *Victorian Studies*, 8 (1964–1965), 161–162; and by Brock (see above), 145–152, who also treats Williamson's atomism extensively. For Williamson's friendship with Laurent and Gerhardt, see the nonindexed E. Grimaux and C. Gerhardt, Jr., *Charles Gerhardt: sa vie, son oeuvre, sa correspondance* (Paris, 1900), 218, 220–221 (letter of 1851), 240–243, 249–250, 263–264, 412–413, and 558; and with Kekulé, see R. Anschütz, *August Kekulé*, I (Berlin, 1929), *passim*. The context of Williamson's work is fully discussed in J. R. Partington, *A History of Chemistry*, IV (London, 1964), ch. 14; J. S. Rowe, "Chemical Studies at University College, London" (Ph.D. diss., London, 1955), 211–328e; and C. A. Russell, *A History of Valence* (Leicester, 1971), ch. 3. See also J. Harris and W. H. Brock, "From Giessen to Gower Street: Towards a Biography of Williamson," in *Annals of Science*, 31 (1974), 95–130.

W. H. BROCK

**WILLIAMSON, WILLIAM CRAWFORD** (*b.* Scarborough, Yorkshire, England, 24 November 1816; *d.* Clapham Common, England, 23 June 1895), *botany, geology, zoology, paleontology.*

Williamson's father, John Williamson, was an accomplished gardener and naturalist who for many years served as curator of the Scarborough Museum, Yorkshire. His close friendships with the geologists John Phillips and William Smith greatly aided and influenced young Williamson. His mother was Elizabeth Crawford, the daughter of a jeweler and lapidary of Scarborough. As a boy Williamson was devoted to his maternal grandfather, from whom he learned the art of cutting and polishing stones.

Williamson was married in June 1842 to Sophia Wood, who died in 1871. Three years later he married Annie C. Heaton; their son Herbert became a painter. A member and officer of several leading scientific societies, he was elected to fellowship of the Royal Society in 1854 and received its gold medal in 1874.

Williamson's activity ranged widely over the field of natural history in his research, teaching, and popular lecturing. With considerable success he bridged two ages in science—from the early 1800's, when a natural scientist was expected to deal with nearly all natural phenomena, to the close of the century, with its rapidly developing specialization. He is best remembered today by students of paleobotany for his series of studies of the fossil plants of the British coalfields, in which he laid a large part of the foundations of our knowledge of the earliest pteridophytes as well as of the early seed plants.

Most of Williamson's scientific publications present data that he discovered and recorded with brilliance and efficiency. In addition, his *Reminiscences* constitutes a delightful and informative record of a vanished way of life that had a real bearing on the development of biological and geological science in the nineteenth century.

Because of poor health, Williamson's education was inadequate. At the age of six he was sent to William Potter's school and studied Latin and English. He received his only real instruction from the Reverend Thomas Irving at the Thornton grammar school, which he attended for only six months. When he was fifteen Williamson's parents decided that he would benefit from education in France. He arrived at the school, which was located at Bourbourg, near Calais, but found that there were no vacancies; and it was only with difficulty that he obtained admission as a special student. The school was attended mostly by English boys and English was the spoken language. He learned little and returned home in less than a year, disillusioned.

In the meantime Williamson's parents had determined that he should prepare for a medical career, a decision that had somewhat happier results than his French venture. His medical studies began in 1832 with a three-year apprenticeship to Thomas Weddell, a general practitioner in Scarborough. Such doctors were rarely paid for visits to their patients; rather, their income was derived from the sale of the drugs that were prescribed. The preparation of these medications was one of the chief responsibilities of the apprentice. His other duties consisted of delivering the drugs and preparing the annual bills. Although he claimed that he learned little with Weddell that could not have been mastered in a few weeks in an apothecary's shop, Williamson did have considerable free time to extend his field studies of rocks, fossils, and plants of the surrounding area and to read scientific literature.

Through his father, Williamson had met, at a very early age, such great naturalists as Murchison, Sedgwick, Lyell, and Buckland. At the age of sixteen or seventeen, while apprenticed to Weddell, he was invited to prepare many of the illustrations for Lindley and Hutton's *Fossil Flora of Great Britain*, a renowned compilation of the day that is still used as a reference work.

In 1835, through the aid of a Dr. Phillips of Manchester, Williamson was appointed curator of the Manchester Natural History Society, with an annual stipend of £110. He resigned this position in June 1838 in order to enter medical school in Manchester. Faced with the necessity of obtaining funds to pay his school fees and living expenses, Williamson gave a series of lectures in nearby towns. Teaching, particularly popular lecturing, was clearly a great joy to him; and he was adept at presenting his vast scientific knowledge in an understandable fashion to a variety of audiences.

Medical instruction in Manchester was mediocre at best and, determined to avail himself of what seemed to be the best that Britain could offer, Williamson entered University College, London, in September 1840. He was not disappointed and quickly became aware that with such teachers as Quain in anatomy, Sharpey in physiology, Robert Liston and Astley Cooper in surgery, C. B. Williams in medicine, Graham in chemistry, and Lindley in botany, "no man with brains could fail to learn" (*Reminiscences*, p. 86). Although Williamson had prepared drawings for Lindley some years before, the two had never met; and Lindley was quite surprised to find that he had had so youthful a collaborator. Williamson's medical studies progressed well, but his other interests were not abandoned; he found time to attend meetings of the Geological Society of London, where he furthered his acquaintances with Sedgwick, Murchison, Greenough, James Yates, and Basil Hall.

On 1 January 1842 Williamson returned to Manchester, mounted a brass plate on the door of a house at the corner of Wilton Street and Oxford Road, and started his medical practice. While attending an afternoon tea with a friend of his wife, he met a young man who asked whether he had read Mantell's recently published *Medals of Creation*. Later, in reading this work, Williamson was attracted by the author's report that native chalk consisted largely of microscopic fossil shells; this observation led him to initiate one of his most important scientific studies of diatoms, desmids, and Foraminifera, and opened up other lines of research involving microscopy.

In 1851 Williamson was elected first professor of natural history and geology at the newly founded Owens College in Manchester; and for about nineteen years he taught the courses in botany, comparative anatomy, geology, and paleontology. As the amount of knowledge and the college enrollment increased, he was relieved of teaching geology by the appointment of William Boyd Dawkins in 1872; and in 1880 Arthur Milnes Marshall joined the staff as zoologist, leaving Williamson free to devote more time to botany.

He continued to conduct his busy medical practice along with his academic duties. Having a special interest in ear ailments, Williamson spent some time in Ménière's consulting rooms at Paris, learning his techniques and the use of new instruments; and he also studied in London. After returning to Manchester, he helped raise funds for the establishment of an institution for aural ailments.

One of Williamson's earliest investigations was concerned with a tumulus—a Bronze Age grave—found at Gristhorpe Cliff, a few miles south of Scarborough. Although others were also involved, Williamson played a leading part in the excavation and laboratory treatment of the remains; and his report was published in Scarborough in 1834—before he was eighteen. The article attracted the attention of Buckland, who reprinted part of it in a weekly journal. Interest in the paper led to the publication of a second edition in 1836, and in 1872 Williamson prepared a third, revised edition.

In 1842 Williamson was given a small sample of sediment from the Levant in which he found Foraminifera. Similar material was received from other sources, including samples from Charles Darwin, who had recently returned from the *Beagle* voyage. These studies produced an article published in the *Memoirs of the Manchester Literary and Philosophical Society* that was a pioneering contribution to the understanding of the part that Foraminifera played in the formation of geological deposits. In 1851–1852 Williamson conducted a very meticulous and time-consuming study of *Volvox globator*, a motile, spherical colony of green cells, barely visible with the naked eye, that is commonly found in fresh waters. He observed asexual reproduction, apparently for the first time, and discovered basic facts about the mode of connection of the several hundred cells that make up the plant.

In 1849 and 1851 Williamson published two papers in the *Philosophical Transactions of the Royal Society* on the cellular structure and development of the teeth and bones of fish. As a developmental study this pioneering research was highly regarded and was instrumental in his election to the Royal Society.

Williamson's greatest contribution dealt with the petrified plants found in the Upper Carboniferous coal seams of Lancashire and Yorkshire. Sometime in the 1840's collectors began to bring him specimens of "coal balls," aggregations of petrified plants found in the coal itself that included fragments of stems, leaves, seeds, and other reproductive parts sometimes preserved in excellent cellular detail. As representative samples of the vegetation of the Carboniferous, "coal balls" presented an unparalleled source of information, and Williamson took full advantage of it. The challenge was to prepare the plant materials for study and to fit the parts together so as to reconstruct the trees that forested so much of the northern hemisphere some 200 million years ago.

Williamson's contribution in this area is the more remarkable because he prepared his own thin sections of the fossil material and drew most of the numerous illustrations for his text. The main body of this research was published in the *Philosophical Transactions of the Royal Society* in nineteen parts (1871–1893). At the outset Williamson was probably unaware of the magnitude of the task; and he encountered some difficulty when he submitted the first part under the title "On the Organization of the Fossil Plants of the Coal-Measures. Part I," because an editor complained that it would obligate the publication of more than one part. His "coal ball" investigations supplied much basic information on the early evolution of the pteridophytes and the more primitive seed plant groups, and were continued by many investigators in Europe and the United States. The nineteen papers may not contain outstanding writing, but they are a sound record on which later workers have been able to reconstruct, to a considerable degree, the vegetation of the Carboniferous landscapes.

Williamson served as president of the Manchester Scientific Students' Association, the Manchester Literary and Philosophical Society, and the

Union of Yorkshire Naturalists. He received the gold medal of the Royal Society in 1874 and the Wollaston Medal of the Geological Society in 1890. The University of Edinburgh awarded him the LL.D. in 1883, and he was elected an honorary member of the Göttingen Academy of Sciences and the Royal Swedish Academy of Sciences.

It is sad that in 1892, at the age of seventy-six and after forty-one years of service to Owens College, Williamson's application for a pension was refused by the College Council—on the grounds that it might establish a precedent. He retired to the London suburb of Clapham Common. As his strength declined, and with much fossil plant research left to do, Williamson invited D. H. Scott, a young botanist from Kew Gardens, to collaborate with him. Scott carried on the work for many years and became a major figure in paleontology.

*BIBLIOGRAPHY*

I. ORIGINAL WORKS. Williamson's autobiography is *Reminiscences of a Yorkshire Naturalist* (London, 1896), edited by his wife. In addition to several popular lectures on scientific subjects, he also published *On the Recent Foraminifera of Great Britain* (London, 1858); and *A Monograph on the Morphology and Histology of Stigmaria ficoides* (London, 1887). The Royal Society *Catalogue of Scientific Papers*, VI, 380–381; VIII, 1245–1246; XI, 817–818; and XIX, 638–639; lists 106 articles, including two papers written with D. H. Scott.

Works cited in the text are *Description of the Tumulus Lately Opened at Gristhorpe* (Scarborough, 1834; 2nd ed., 1836; 3rd ed., rev., 1872); "On Some of the Microscopical Objects Found in the Mud of the Levant and Other Deposits, With Remarks on the Mode of Formation of Calcareous and Infusorial Siliceous Rocks," in *Memoirs of the Manchester Literary and Philosophical Society*, 2nd ser., **8** (1848), 1–128; "On the Microscopic Structure of the Scales and Dermal Teeth of Some Ganoid and Placoid Fishes," in *Philosophical Transactions of the Royal Society*, **139** (1849), 435–476; "The Structure and Development of the Scales and Bones of Fishes," *ibid.*, **141** (1851), 643–702: "On the *Volvox globator*," in *Memoirs of the Manchester Literary and Philosophical Society*, 2nd ser., **9** (1851), 321–339; and in *Transactions of the Royal Microscopical Society of London*, n.s. **1** (1853), 45–56; and "On the Organization of the Fossil Plants of the Coal-Measures," 19 pts., in *Philosophical Transactions of the Royal Society*, **161–184B** (1871–1893), his most important work.

II. SECONDARY LITERATURE. On Williamson and his work, see Charles Bailey, "Memoir of Professor Williamson," in *Report and Proceedings of the Manchester Scientific Students' Association* for 1886, 1–8; the unsigned "In Memoriam. William Crawford Williamson," in *Proceedings of the Yorkshire Geological and Polytechnic Society*, n.s. **8** (1899), 95–111; H. D. Scott, "Williamson's Researches on the Carboniferous Flora," in *Science Progress*, **4** (1895), 253–272; and L. F. Ward, "Saporta and Williamson and Their Work in Paleobotany," in *Science*, n.s. **2** (1895), 141–150.

Further biographical details may be found in *Mémoires de la Société de physique et d'histoire naturelle de Genève*, **32** (1894–1897), pt. 2, xi–xii; *Geological Magazine*, **2** (1895), 383–384; *Journal of Botany, British and Foreign*, **33** (1895), 298–300; *Journal of the Royal Microscopical Society* (1895), 478; *Leopoldina*, **31** (1895), 169; *Nature*, **52** (1895), 441–443; *Canadian Record of Science*, **6** (1896), 443–447; *Memoirs and Proceedings of the Manchester Literary and Philosophical Society*, 4th ser., **10** (1896), 112–125; and *Proceedings of the Royal Society*, **60** (1897), xxvii–xxxii.

HENRY N. ANDREWS

**WILLIAM THE ENGLISHMAN** (*fl.* France, thirteenth century), *astronomy, astrology.*

All that is known of William's life is that he was a physician who lived in Marseilles during the first half of the thirteenth century. Of the works that have been variously attributed to him, four, *De urina non visa*, an *Astrologia*, a *Summa super quarto libro metheorum*, and a treatise on the *astrolabium Arzachelis*, or saphea, may be considered to be his with some certainty. All four may be dated between 1220 and 1231. A number of other works may be less clearly ascribed to William.

Of the tracts known to be by William (Guillelmus Anglicus civis Marsiliensis), the first, *De urina non visa* ("Ne vel ignorancie vel potius invidie redarguar mi germane. . ."), is a brief argument that an astrologer's prognostication of an illness, based on astral conjunctions, may have the same validity as that of a physician who has been able to observe the symptomatology of the patient. William here cites the case of a patient whom he himself had examined, and for whom he had made the astrological prediction that he would live for another two months and eight days; his prediction proved correct. The planetary positions upon which he based it indicate that the diagnosis could have been made only in the last days of the year 1219; the *De urina non visa* cannot have been written before 1220, and the date 1219 that occurs in one manuscript must have meant *anno completo*.[1]

The text of William's *Astrologia* is undated, but a manuscript in the Biblioteca Capitular Colombina in Seville ascribes it to 1220. This treatise, which begins "Quoniam astrologie speculatio prima figuram ipsius. . .," is a theory of the planets that follows, like a commentary, the canons of the Toledan Tables, although they are never referred to specifically. The work opens with a description of the astrolabe and some of its uses, then reviews the principles of stereographic projection, together with a note on the construction of an *instrument azimutal* for taking meridian altitudes. William does not give any exact information about the eccentricities of the planets, the length of the radii of the epicycles, or the duration of their revolutions; his materials on the conjunctions of the sun and moon and on eclipses is, however, developed at some length. The examination of the movement of the eighth sphere—that is, the motion of "accession and recession"—was discussed at the end of the treatise, as in the canons of al-Zarqālī.

The only known manuscript of the *Summa super quarto libro metheorum*, which begins "Rerum corruptibilium effectus ut ad nutum et voluntatem . . .," gives 1230 as the date of the text. This rather brief text is organized into three parts, of which the first deals with terrestrial phenomena, both those originating within the earth (water, gems, and minerals) and those found upon its surface (as, for example, alums and salts). The second section treats of aerial, or meteorological matters, including evaporation, dew, rain and snow, ice, winds, earthquakes, and rainbows, while the concluding portion discusses the ethereal region of shooting stars, thunder, lightning, and comets. William drew the hypothesis that the Flood had resulted from the joining together of the waters that fall from the sky and the waters that well up from the depths of the earth. He further attributed the *passiones etheris* to vapors rising from the earth, the nature of the phenomenon being dependent upon the nature and form of the ascendant vapor—thus, dry vapors moving directly upward create shooting stars.

William's treatise on the saphea, or *astrolabium Arzachelis*, beginning "Siderei motus et effectus motuum speculator . . .," represents the introduction of this instrument into the Latin West. Invented in the eleventh century by 'Alī ibn Khalaf or by al-Zarqālī,[2] the saphea is, like the astrolabe, conceived on the principle of the stereographic projection of both the movable sphere of the stars and the zodiac and a fixed sphere of celestial reference; it differs from the astrolabe in that the pole of projection is one of the points of intersection of the ecliptic and the zodiac, while the plane of projection is that of the colure of the solstices.

Contrary to what is generally believed, William's treatise on the saphea is not an abridgment of al-Zarqālī's, which became known in the Latin West only through Ibn Tibbon's translation of 1263. It is likely that William knew of this kind of projection only by hearsay and had never seen it put into practice, since the method he himself proposes—and upon which he says he worked for six years—is at best rather clumsy. William attempted to construct the almucantars of the horizon by piercing small holes on the limb of his instrument and holding strings parallel to the diameter by which this horizon was projected. Thus the instrument he describes is characterized by both the stereographic projection proper to the saphea and by the orthographic projection invented by J. de Rojas in the middle of the sixteenth century.[3] The saphea devised by al-Zarqālī, which became known to the West in 1263, used the almucantars of the equator as a provisional coordinate system: a reference point could then be selected on this system and moved to that of the horizon by means of a ruler. He remained true to the tradition of the astrolabe, inscribing twenty stars on his saphea although they have no purpose on it. Their positions were taken directly from al-Zarqālī's table, which had been established according to Ptolemy's positions, with the addition to the longitudes of a constant of 14°7'.[4]

In addition to these works, a number of others attributed to William remain problematical. Confusions and improbable identifications with other Williams, notably Guillaume Grisaunt and William of Aragon[5] have further wrongly extended the list. A *De virtute aquile* attributed to a "Guillelmus Anglicus" is known in only one manuscript.[6] While the sixteenth-century bibliographer John Bale composed a list of nine titles, of which six are given with their incipits,[7] only one corresponds to a genuine work, the *Astrologia*. The other works ascribed by Bale to William are all to some degree suspect. A *De quadratura circuli* ("Aristoteles in eo qui de categoriis . . .") is found in other manuscripts only under the name of Campanus;[8] a *De motu capitis* ("Motum accessionis et recessionis. . .") and a *De magnitudine solis* ("Dico quod sol apparet mag. . .") have not been located; a *De qualitatibus signorum* ("Cum humana corpora sint omnia. . .") has been erroneously cited by E. Zinner in a manuscript at Bamberg which does not contain the incipit given;[9] a *De significatione signorum* cannot be identified for lack of an incipit; a *De urina non visa* has an aberrant incipit ("De corpore quidem humano Satur. . ."); and a *De judicio patientis* and a *De causa ignorancie* are probably doublets of the *De urina*.[10]

The attribution to a "W. A." by Wellcome manuscript 175 of a pseudotranslation of Abū-l-gāsim 'Ammor's (Conamusoli) *De infirmitate oculorum* likewise cannot be maintained,[11] while the *De stellis fixis* that P. Duhem has put forward as William's translation of a treatise by al-Zarqālī is in fact only the star table appended to the treatise on the saphea. The *Scripta Marsiliensis* or *Scripta super canones Azarchelis* (beginning "Cum," or "Quoniam, cujuslibet actionis; liber iste scilicet canones tabularum. . ."),[12] a commentary on the canons of the Toledan Tables, cannot be by William, although sometimes ascribed to him, since it alludes to the turquet, and therefore cannot have been written earlier than the end of the thirteenth century. (The first treatise on this instrument was in fact written by either Francon of Poland in 1284 or by Bernard of Verdun at a slightly earlier date.)[13] It is further worth noting that the *Scripta Marsiliensis* suggests, especially in certain aspects of the development of its treatment of the movement of the eighth sphere, the commentary on these same canons written by John of Sicily in 1291.[14]

## NOTES

1. L. Thorndike, *A History of Magic and Experimental Science*, II, 485–486, n. 5. Simon de Phares, *Recueil des plus célèbres astrologues . . .*, E. Wickersheimer, ed. (Paris, 1929), 180, 191, devoted two accounts to William the Englishman: one for the beginning of the twelfth century, in which he also attributed to the author of the *De urina non visa* a prediction of the destruction of Liège, and one for 1219, in which he alludes to a "book of astrology" the first words of which ("De ignorantie . . .") recall those of *De urina*.

2. J.-M. Millás Vallicrosa, *Estudios sobre Azarquiel* (Madrid–Granada, 1943–1950), 438–447. On the theory of the saphea, see S. García Franco, *Catalogo crítico de astrolabios existentes en España* (Madrid, 1945), 64–65; H. Michel, *Traité de l'astrolabe* (Paris, 1947), 95–97.

3. Michel, *op. cit.*, 20, 105–107; and F. Maddison, *Hugo Helt and the Rojas Astrolabe Projection* (Coimbra, 1966; *Agrupamento de Estudos de Cartografia Antiga, no. 12*).

4. The MS tradition of William's star table is so mediocre that its origin is difficult to uncover; on this table see P. Kunitzsch, *Typen von Sternverzeichnissen in astronomischen Handschriften des 10. bis 14. Jahrhunderts* (Wiesbaden, 1966), 77.

5. Thorndike, *op. cit.*, 301.

6. *Ibid.*, 487.

7. J. Bale, *Scriptorum illustrium Majoris Brytannie*, I (Basel, 1557), 446; the same information can be found in Bale's *Index Britanniae scriptorum*, R. L. Poole and M. Bateson, eds. (Oxford, 1902), 114–115.

8. This attribution is examined and the text is edited by M.

Clagett, *Archimedes in the Middle Ages*, I (Madison, Wis., 1964), 581–609; to the twelve MSS cited add Columbia University Smith add. 1, fols. 138v–139.

9. E. Zinner, *Verzeichnis des astronomischen Handschriften des deutschen Kulturgebietes* (Munich, 1925), 4034.

10. J. Bale, *Scriptorum*, II (1559), 46, also notes a Guillelmus Anglicus who is the author of a *De incarnatione verbi* and of a *Commentarium de anima* that are hardly likely to be by the citizen of Marseilles. C. H. Lohr, "Medieval Latin Aristotle Commentaries," in *Traditio*, **24** (1968), 194, who has not identified this William, does not indicate the author of the commentary on the fourth book of the *Meteorology*.

11. See G. Sarton, *Introduction to the History of Science*, I (Baltimore, 1927), 729.

12. A short extract was published by M. Curtze, "Urkunden zur Geschichte des Trigonometrie im christlichen Mittelalter," in *Bibliotheca mathematica*, 3rd ser., **1** (1900), 321–416: no. 3 (347–353), "Aus den Scripta Marsiliensis super canones Azarchelis." MSS are Berlin F.246, fols. 144–154v; Erfurt F.394, fols. 111v–119.

13. E. Poulle, "Bernard de Verdun et le turquet," in *Isis*, **55** (1964), 200–208.

14. The following text (188–190) that Sédillot published does not belong to the treatise of William the Englishman; it is the first chapter of Ibn Tibbon's translation (in 1263) of the treatise by al-Zarqālī.

## BIBLIOGRAPHY

I. ORIGINAL WORKS. The *De urina non visa* is preserved in numerous MSS; to those cited in L. Thorndike, *A History of Magic and Experimental Science*, II (New York, 1923), 485–486, add Berlin F.246, fols. 252v–254v; Cracow 551, fols. 122–124; Oxford, Hertford Coll. 4, fols. 44–46v. A French trans. of this text is cited by J. Camus, "Un manuscrit namurois du XV^e siècle," in *Revue des langues romanes*, **38** (1895), 31–32. The *Astrologia* is preserved in the following MSS: Erfurt F.394, fols. 136–140v; Erfurt 4° 357, fols. 1–21; Paris lat. 7298, fols. 111v–124v; Seville 5-I-25, fols. I–33; Vienna 5311, fols. 42–51v. Of the *Summa super quarto libro metheorum*, only one MS is known: Paris lat. 6552, fols. 39v–41v.

As for the treatise on the saphea, the section on its construction was published by L. A. Sédillot, "Mémoire sur les instruments astronomiques des Arabes," in *Mémoires présentés par divers savants à l'Académie des inscriptions et belles-lettres*, 1st ser., **1** (1844), 185–188, text repr. in R. T. Gunther, *The Astrolabes of the World*, I (Oxford, 1932), 259–262; and that on its uses by P. Tannery, "Le traité du quadrant de maître Robert Anglès," in *Notices et extraits des manuscrits de la Bibliothèque nationale*, **35**, pt. 2 (1897), 75–80, repr. in his *Mémoires scientifiques*, V, 190–197.

II. SECONDARY LITERATURE. Brief accounts of William are in P. Duhem, *Le système du monde*, III (Paris, 1915), 287–291; L. Thorndike, *A History of Magic and Experimental Science*, II (New York, 1923), 485–487; E. Wickersheimer, *Dictionnaire biographique des médecins en France au moyen âge* (Paris, 1936), 224–225;

and C. H. Talbot and E. A. Hammond, *The Medical Practitioners in Medieval England* (London, 1965), 381–382.

EMMANUEL POULLE

**WILLIS, BAILEY** (*b.* Idlewild-on-Hudson, New York, 31 March 1857; *d.* Palo Alto, California, 19 February 1949), *geology.*

The early schooling of Bailey Willis, son of poet Nathaniel Parker Willis, was a haphazard mixture of private tutoring, some classroom instruction, and listening to the literary repartee engendered by his father's friends and work. After Nathaniel Willis' death in 1868, the boy's maternal grandfather, Arctic explorer Joseph Grinnell, decided that his bright grandson should have the advantage of more rigorous schooling. So at the age of thirteen Bailey was enrolled in a German boarding school under stern Prussian professors who encouraged concentration on studies by liberal application of the rattan switch. Fortified by four years of this preparation, young Willis returned to New York in 1874, and enrolled at Columbia University, where he received degrees in mining engineering (1878) and civil engineering (1879).

In 1880 the Northern Pacific Railway hired Willis as geologist, and sent him to explore for coal in the forest wilderness of Washington Territory. East of his area towered Mount Rainier, then known by its Indian name, Tacoma. This glacier-clad volcano claimed Willis' interest for the rest of his life; his first two scientific publications are about it, and he pioneered a new climbing route to its summit via glaciers on its north side. In 1894 Willis submitted documents to Congress that led, in 1899, to establishment of Mount Rainier National Park.

In 1882 Willis married Altena Holstein Grinnell; she died four years later, leaving an infant daughter. In 1898 Willis married Margaret Delight Baker; three children were born of this union. Willis was frequently away from home, engaged in geologic field work or foreign exploration. Margaret Baker Willis saved all his letters written during these travels. From these letters, after his retirement, came three partly autobiographical books: *Living Africa* (1930), *A Yanqui in Patagonia* (1947), and *Friendly China* (1949).

Willis was employed by the U.S. Geological Survey from 1882 to 1915, except for one year (1903–1904) spent in geologic exploration in China, and four years (1910–1914) helping the Argentine government start a geological survey and plan irrigation projects. During his career with the U.S. Geological Survey Willis published more than sixty scientific papers including several long monographs. One of many papers that received wide attention came from Willis' deep interest in the complexly folded rocks of the Appalachian Mountains. Trained as an engineer, Willis longed to simulate the great Appalachian folds in the laboratory. He built a "pressure box" and began experiments. After initial failures Willis recognized that materials used in his small pressure box must be scaled down in strength if they were to behave like the huge masses of rock deformed by compression in the crust of the earth. Using plastic materials, and also by loading his artificial strata under a cover of loose lead shot, he made artificial "mountains" with folds that closely resembled those of the Appalachians. His report "The Mechanics of Appalachian Structure" (1893) brought Willis international fame, especially in Europe, where experimental geology was gaining in interest.

In 1915 Willis joined the Stanford University faculty as professor and chairman of the geology department. During his years as professor, and those after retiring at sixty-five, Willis' geologic interests became more firmly entrenched in structural geology and seismology. His textbook *Geologic Structures* (1923) and more than seventy papers dealing with continental genesis, rift valleys, faults, and earthquakes were published during this period. So familiar did Willis become in many California towns on his search for knowledge about earthquakes, that he was known throughout the state as the "earthquake professor." He tried to get California politicians to pass an enforceable building code outlawing the shoddy construction that had compounded damage during earthquakes. His rueful assessment of this effort was "I didn't get the building code, but I certainly did increase earthquake insurance rates."

Willis received his first honorary doctorate in 1910 from the University of Berlin for the Appalachian experiments and for his research in China. Later he was elected to the National Academy of Sciences and the American Philosophical Society. Belgium awarded him the Legion of Honor in 1936, and he won the Penrose Medal of the Geological Society of America in 1944.

*BIBLIOGRAPHY*

I. ORIGINAL WORKS. A complete bibliography of Willis' publications is in *Bulletin of the Geological Society* of America, **73** (1962), 68–72. Some of his better-known works are "Canyons and Glaciers. A Journey to the Ice Fields of Mount Tacoma," in *Northwest*, **1**, no. 2 (1883), repr. with slight modification, in E. S. Meany, *Mount Rainier. A Record of Exploration* (New York, 1916), 142–149; "Mount Tacoma in Washington Territory," in *Proceedings of the Newport Natural History Society*, **2** (1884), 13–21; "Conditions of Sedimentary Depositions," in *Journal of Geology*, **1** (1893), 476–520; "Conditions of Appalachian Faulting," in *American Journal of Science*, **46** (1893), 257–268, written with C. W. Hayes; "The Mechanics of Appalachian Structure," in *Report of the United States Geological Survey*, **13**, pt. 2 (1893), 211–281; "Some Coal Fields of Puget Sound," *ibid.*, **18**, pt. 3 (1898), 393–436; "A Symposium on the Classification and Nomenclature of Geologic Time-divisions," in *Journal of Geology*, **6** (1898), 345–347; "The Mount Rainier National Park," in *Forester*, **5** (1899), 97–102; "Individuals of Stratigraphic Classification," in *Journal of Geology*, **9** (1901), 557–569; "Stratigraphy and Structure, Lewis and Livingston Ranges, Montana," in *Bulletin of the Geological Society of America*, **13** (1902), 305–352; "Physiography and Deformation of the Wenatchee-Chelan District, Cascade Range," in *Professional Papers. United States Geological Survey*, no. 19 (1903), 41–97; *Carte géologique de l'Amérique du Nord*, prepared for Congrès Géologique Internationale, 10th session (Mexico, 1906); and "Research in China," in *Publications. Carnegie Institution of Washington*, no. 54 (1907), written with E. Blackwelder, R. H. Sargent, and F. Hirth.

Other works are *Outline of Geologic History With Special Reference to North America* (Chicago, 1910), written with R. D. Salisbury; "Index to the Stratigraphy of North America," in *Professional Papers. United States Geological Survey*, no. 71 (1912); *Northern Patagonia* (New York, 1914); "Discoidal Structure of the Lithosphere," in *Bulletin of the Geological Society of America*, **31** (1920), 247–302; *Fault Map of the State of California* (1922), compiled with H. O. Wood, from data assembled by the Seismological Society of America; *Geologic Structures* (New York, 1923); "Dead Sea Problem: Rift Valley or Ramp Valley?" in *Bulletin of the Geological Society of America*, **39** (1928), 490–542; "Continental Genesis," *ibid.*, **40** (1929), 281–336; "African Rift Valleys—a Geological Study," in *Carnegie Institution Washington News Service Bulletin*, no. 2 (1930), 27–34; *Living Africa. A Geologist's Wandering Through the Rift Valleys* (New York, 1930); "Isthmian Links," in *Bulletin of the Geological Society of America*, **43** (1932), 917–952; "African Plateaus and Rift Valleys," in *Publications. Carnegie Institution of Washington*, no. 470 (1936); "Asthenolith (Melting Spot) Theory," in *Bulletin of the Geological Society of America*, **49** (1938), 603–614; "San Andreas Rift, California," in *Journal of Geology*, **46** (1938), 1017–1057; "Eruptivity and Mountain Building," in *Bulletin of the Geological Society of America*, **52** (1941), 1643–1683, written with Robin Willis; *A Yanqui in Patagonia* (Stanford, 1947);

and *Friendly China: Two Thousand Miles Afoot Among the Chinese* (Stanford, 1949).

II. SECONDARY LITERATURE. On Willis and his work, see E. Blackwelder, "Bailey Willis, 1857–1949," in *Biographical Memoirs. National Academy of Sciences*, **35** (1961), 333–350; Philip B. King, "Bailey Willis," in *Dictionary of American Biography*, supp. 4 (1974), 896–897; and Aaron C. Waters, "Memorial to Bailey Willis, 1857–1949," in *Bulletin of the Geological Society of America*, **73** (1962).

AARON C. WATERS

**WILLIS, ROBERT** (*b.* London, England, 27 February 1800; *d.* Cambridge, England, 28 February 1875), *engineering, medieval archaeology.*

The son and grandson of distinguished physicians, Willis was educated privately until he entered Gonville and Caius College, Cambridge, where he obtained the B.A. and was elected fellow in 1826. The next year he was ordained deacon and priest. In 1837 he succeeded William Farish as Jacksonian professor of natural and experimental philosophy at Cambridge, a position he held until his death. His major contributions were to the kinematics of mechanisms and the study of the architecture of the Middle Ages.

As Jacksonian professor, Willis delivered lectures on "mechanical philosophy" and applied his considerable inventive skills to the improvement of a set of machine parts for the construction of demonstration models. By modifying Farish's original concepts, Willis reportedly was able to popularize what may well have been the first mechanical model-building kit. His lectures formed the basis for his book, *Principles of Mechanism* (1841).

Willis was one of the first clearly to enunciate the importance of excluding causal forces in the study of the motion of machinery. He introduced the term "kinematics," as an anglicized version of the French *cinématique*, thereby originating the English name of the branch of mechanics that deals with the geometry of motion without regard to the forces causing it. He felt it was important to change the study of machinery from a descriptive to an analytic science. Although his analytical treatments were modest by modern standards, Willis' advocacy of a systematic approach to the design of machine mechanisms anticipated and encouraged the subsequent development of kinematic analysis and synthesis of mechanisms. He organized mechanisms according to an original classification scheme, little of which is in use today although it was quite popular until almost 1900.

By 1870, when an enlarged second edition of his book was published, Willis was able to point out that all (thirteen) books on mechanisms published (in England and France) in the previous twenty-two years utilized his classifications and nomenclature. The present ideas on classification, however, are derived mainly from Franz Reuleaux, who published his landmark book in the year of Willis' death. Of lasting value was Willis' chapter on gear teeth, taken from an earlier paper (1838). In this outstanding work he introduced the idea of manufacturing sets of interchangeable gears, pointed out the convenience of 14.5° involute gear teeth (in common use today), and described his invention of a device to facilitate the approximate layout of gear teeth. (He coined the name "odontograph," which has become the generic term for devices used to assist in that process.) His book remains the earliest attempt to develop a complete treatment of the science of machine kinematics.

Willis studied architecture and archaeology with great enthusiasm and expertise, becoming an authority on medieval Latin and construction techniques. In 1835 he published an essay that is reputed to have been the first work to call serious attention to the Gothic style of architecture. He then invented a device (the "cymograph") for copying architectural moldings. Subsequently he published studies detailing the original construction and the later modifications to the cathedrals of Hereford, Canterbury, Winchester, York, Chichester, and Worcester and the abbey churches of Glastonbury and Sherborne. To all these works he brought such great skills in antiquarian research and keen insight that most of these works are still regarded as the definitive studies of these churches. He continued his archaeological writings until his health became seriously impaired, several years before his death.

Willis' earliest works include an analysis of a well-known mechanical chess player, which he correctly proved was a hoax (1821), and three papers applying mathematical analysis to the flow of air. The last of these (1828–1829) describes the action of the larynx. As a result of this work he was elected to the Royal Society (1830). Willis served on government commissions in such diverse fields as structures and astronomy, and participated in two international expositions. He held honorary membership in and medals from various learned societies, and in 1862 was president of the British Association for the Advancement of Science.

## BIBLIOGRAPHY

I. ORIGINAL WORKS. A complete list of works published during Willis' lifetime is given in his book, *Principles of Mechanism*, 2nd ed., enl. (London, 1870), the title page of which contains a list of his honors and more prominent affiliations. Eleven years after Willis' death his nephew and biographer, John Willis Clark, completed and published Willis' *The Architectural History of the University and Colleges of Cambridge*, 4 vols. (Cambridge, 1886), written with T. W. Clark.

II. SECONDARY LITERATURE. *Dictionary of National Biography*, XXI, 492–494, contains an excellent biography by John Willis Clark. Abbreviated biographical data are in J. A. Venn, *Alumni Cantabrigienses*, pt. II, VI (Cambridge, 1954). Venn includes some items that Clark omits, and differs with Clark on several minor dates. For a historical perspective on Willis' mechanism work see R. S. Hartenberg and J. Denavit, *Kinematics of Linkages* (New York, 1964), 16, 70–75; and E. S. Ferguson, "Kinematics of Mechanisms From the Time of Watt," *Contributions. Museum of History and Technology, United States National Museum*, paper 27 (Washington, D.C., 1962). For historical perspective on Willis' architectural studies one apparently must consult books on the various cathedrals. See, for example, the intro. to H. R. Williamson, *Canterbury Cathedral* (London, 1953).

BERNARD ROTH

**WILLIS, THOMAS** (*b*. Great Bedwyn, Wiltshire, England, 27 January 1621; *d*. London, England, 11 November 1675), *anatomy, medicine*.

Thomas was the eldest of three sons of Rachel Howell and Thomas Willis, the steward of the manor at Great Bedwyn. Before his mother's death in 1631, the family moved to North Hinksey, Berkshire, where the mother had property. The proximity to Oxford (a mile and a half) enabled young Willis to be schooled there with Edward Sylvester, who numbered John Wilkins among his former pupils. He matriculated in the university from Christ Church on 3 March 1637, and worked as a servitor to one of the cathedral canons while proceeding B.A. (19 June 1639) and M.A. (18 June 1642). His father's death in 1643 left Thomas head of the family, and his own partisan military service in the losing royalist cause during the siege of Oxford forestalled his career in the church. He turned to medicine, taking his B.Med. and license to practice on 8 December 1646.

Almost from the beginning of his medical career, Willis evinced an interest in science, first in mathematics but increasingly in chemistry and anatomy.

He and two Trinity fellows, Ralph Bathurst and John Lydall, carried out chemical experiments in Willis' Christ Church rooms in the late 1640's. When other eminent scientists—Wilkins, William Petty, John Wallis, Seth Ward, and Jonathan Goddard—were appointed to Oxford positions during the years 1648–1651, Willis and his friends joined them and others in forming a philosophical "Clubb" to meet weekly and perform experiments *in rota*. By the mid-1650's the club had grown to include Robert Boyle, Christopher Wren, Thomas Millington, and Robert Hooke, the last of whom Willis hired out of Christ Church as a chemical assistant, later recommending him for the same position with Boyle.

Willis and his friends also did anatomical dissections. A clinical notebook kept by Willis (*ca.* 1651) recorded not only his careful case notes, but also the results of occasional postmortems. In the famous case of Anne Green, convicted and hanged at Oxford for infanticide in late 1650, Willis, Petty, Bathurst, and others assembled for a dissection, only to find the cadaver still very much alive.

Working within this milieu, Willis completed by 1656 his first scientific work, *De fermentatione*. During the late 1650's he supplemented this with a major work on fevers, *De febribus*, and a shorter piece on urine, *Dissertatio epistolica de urinis*, written to Bathurst; they were published in 1659 as *Diatribae duae medico-philosophicae*.

In *De fermentatione* Willis argued that all bodies are composed of five kinds of particles: those of spirit, sulfur, salt, water, and earth, in order of decreasing activity. Any body containing a mixture of these particles is capable of fermentation, which Willis defined as an intestine (internal) motion of a body's chemical particles leading to the perfection or transformation of that body. According to this process must becomes wine and wort becomes beer; liquids coagulate, or solids precipitate from them; food is converted into chyme, and thence into blood. Animals and plants grow by the process of fermentation, just as they are corrupted by it after their deaths.

But for the physician, the most important kinds of fermentation take place in the fluids of the human body, most especially the blood. Accepting Harvey's theory, he proposed a reason for the circulation: as the blood and its dissolved food pass through the heart, a ferment implanted there excites a fermentation, or "accension," by which heat is generated and the food converted into nutrient blood.

Willis' theories were new versions of ideas widely discussed on the Continent during the 1640's and 1650's, but with the important difference that Willis cast his explanations into the atomistic and chemical terms that Boyle had made so popular among his Oxford friends. Helmont had proposed that numerous physiological processes are carried out by fermentation, but had used that term to denote an animistic function of the soul. Descartes and the Dutch Cartesian Hogelande had written of a ferment in the heart, but not in such chemical and corpuscular detail.

But Willis was a practitioner as well as a theorist, and the second tract of 1659, *De febribus*, exemplifies what was to be the enduring characteristic of his published works: the concern to use anatomy, physiology, and chemistry to explain clinical findings. Harvey's discovery of the circulation, Willis said, necessitated a new theory of fevers based upon knowledge of fermentation. Fever was nothing but the natural exothermic fermentation of the heart, excited to a preternatural degree by foreign materials introduced into the blood. After speculations on the mechanisms that might be involved in this derangement, Willis filled the remainder of the tract with detailed descriptions of fevers drawn from his own casebooks. His characterizations of epidemics were particularly acute, reporting in detail the first English outbreak of war-typhus, among the Oxford troops in 1643, cases of plague in 1645, measles and smallpox in 1649 and 1654, and influenza in 1657 and 1658. He also recorded what seems to be the first reliable clinical description of typhoid fever. To a great degree he, rather than Sydenham or Morton, began the tradition of English epidemiology.

Willis' life changed radically after the restoration of Charles II in 1660. Wilkins and other friends moved to London and founded the Royal Society. Willis remained in Oxford, and both his growing scientific reputation, and his unswerving loyalty to king and church, were rewarded by his appointment at the university as Sedleian professor of natural philosophy. He graduated D.Med. on 30 October 1660, and began regular lectures on natural philosophy and medicine, which attracted a large audience.

The notes for some of these lectures were copied out by Willis' assistant from Christ Church, Richard Lower, and later extracted by Lower's friend John Locke. They show the degree to which Willis ignored the statutory injunction to teach only from Aristotle. Rather, he lectured on neurological topics: sense and motion, the cerebellum, sleeping and waking, pleasure and pain, as well as the clinical effects of neurological changes in diseases such as convulsions, epilepsy, hysteria, vertigo, lethargy, and paralysis.

But, as he remarked later in the preface to *Cerebri anatome*, he was dissatisfied with the excessively speculative nature of these lectures, and in late 1661 he and Lower began a series of dissections of the brain with a view toward clarifying such questions. Lower wrote to Boyle in early 1662 that Willis found "most parts of the brain imperfectly described," and intended "to make a whole new draught thereof, with the several uses of the distinct parts." Thomas Millington contributed to the discussions, and just before the completion of the book in July 1663, Wren executed a magnificent series of drawings to illustrate the text.

The *Cerebri anatome*, published early in 1664, is the foundation document of the anatomy of the central and autonomic nervous systems. It greatly surpassed, in the detail and precision of its descriptions, the fragmentary treatments of the brain that had preceded it. As a text it continued to be used until the late eighteenth century, and was mandatory background reading for neuroanatomists until the mid-nineteenth century.

Willis' description and classification of the pairs of cranial nerves superseded those of Falloppio (1561), and remained in widespread use until those of Sömmering (1778) replaced them in the late eighteenth century. Willis recognized ten such nerves. His first six are those used today: olfactory, optic, oculomotor, trochlear, trigeminal, and abducens. His seventh cranial nerve included both the facial and auditory (VII and VIII), while his eighth combined the glossopharyngeal and vagus (IX and X) with the cranial root of the spinal accessory (XI). Willis' ninth cranial nerve is the hypoglossal (XII), and his tenth is the modern first cervical. He described and delineated the spinal root of the accessory (XI) nerve, not numbering it separately, but pointing out how it accompanies and then diverges from the vagus. The distribution of all cranial nerves is described in great detail.

Willis' aim in tracing out the cranial nerves was rather more physiological than anatomical: they fitted closely into his ideas of cerebral and cerebellar localization. Most classical and Renaissance anatomists had believed that the three commonly recognized mental functions, sense, imagination, and memory, were carried out by animal spirits inhabiting the cerebrospinal fluid that filled the system of cerebral ventricles. While he accepted the action of animal spirits, Willis rejected ventricular localization on the grounds that distinctions of function could better be maintained by animal spirits acting within the solid portions of the brain.

Willis believed that voluntary functions are localized in the cerebrum. Animal spirits intended for these functions are generated in the grey cerebral cortex from the arterial blood, which continually bathed the cerebrum. These spirits pass inward into the white medullary matter, where they are differentiated and distributed into tracts for separate kinds of voluntary action. Those concerned with sense are localized in the corpora striata, those with imagination (intelligence) in the corpus callosum, and those with memory distribute back outward into the cerebral cortex.

According to Willis, sense impressions are carried inward to the corpora striata, where an inward perception arises. If the impression is carried farther on to the corpus callosum, then imagination results. If the fluctuation of spirits are struck back out to the cortex, memory of the event or idea is created. If impressions are reflected back out to the voluntary muscles directly from the corpora striata, then a "reflex" action could occur without conscious volition—a concept of the reflex considerably more sophisticated than that which Descartes had propounded a few years earlier.

In performing these functions the spirits transmit their information as successive wave fronts along predetermined medullary tracts. And just as ripples from several sources in a pond can cross unchanged, so also can the same tracts carry both sensory (afferent) and motor (efferent) impulses.

Involuntary functions are carried out in an analogous way by the cerebellum and its attendant structures, the corpora quadrigemina and the medulla oblongata. Spirits for these functions are generated from the blood in the cerebellar cortex, then flow into the underlying medullary structures, where they interact to regulate heartbeat, respiration, and digestion. Therefore it is proper that four pairs of cranial nerves (modern V–X) which have involuntary functions should have their origins near the cerebellum.

These involuntary actions are performed especially by what Willis called the "intercostal" and "vagal" nerves—respectively the modern sympathetic and parasympathetic divisions of the autonomic nervous system. The former Willis believed to have an intracranial origin, arising indirectly from the V and VI nerves, while the latter come directly from the vagus (X). He traced in great detail how these two systems, and their attendant spinal ganglia, innervate all the major organs of the thorax and abdomen. By this pathway the cerebellum and medulla could effect the regulation of involuntary functions and, in turn, the states of the viscera could affect the higher conscious functions of the central cerebrum and the higher brain stem.

Good follower of Harvey that he was, Willis did not neglect to trace how all these structures are bathed and nourished by the circulating blood. In preparing the book, Lower wrote in a letter to Boyle (4 June 1663), Willis had been especially struck by a postmortem in which a man dying of an unrelated disease exhibited a completely occluded right carotid artery. Yet blood continued to flow to both cerebral hemispheres, and the patient had complained only of a headache on the left side, where the carotid artery had been enlarged by the increased blood flow. To account for this, Willis traced out the circle of anastomosed arteries at the base of the brain by which, if any carotid or vertebral arteries were blocked, the remaining ones could maintain full blood flow to all parts of the brain. Willis and Lower confirmed this by tying both carotids in a spaniel, to no ill effect. They further demonstrated it by using a technique of injection developed in Oxford a few years earlier by Wren and Boyle; they syringed ink into one artery, and observed it flowing out from the others. The "circle of Willis," as it has since been known, is clearly delineated in the Wren drawings in the *Cerebri anatome.* Although an anatomical description of the circle had been published by Wepfer in 1658, Willis was the first to grasp and demonstrate its physiological and pathological significance.

Many of Willis' deepest insights derived from an unparalleled knowledge of the comparative anatomy of the nervous system. In writing *Cerebri anatome* he drew conclusions from dissections of fish, birds, and more than a dozen different mammals. From these he suggested that the convolutional complexity of the human cerebral cortex is correlated with man's greater intelligence. He observed that the cerebellum has a uniformity of appearance in mammals that accords well with its function as a source of animal spirits for involuntary actions. He rejected the Cartesian suggestion that the pineal gland is the seat of the soul because he saw its presence not just in man, but also in other quadrupeds, birds, and fish.

The *Cerebri anatome,* and to a lesser degree the *Diatribae duae,* established the lines of research with which Willis occupied the remainder of his scientific life. The action of the nervous system and the composition and function of the blood were his two primary foci. He explored anatomical structures (usually with the assistance of a junior collaborator such as Lower, or his successors Edmund King and John Masters), postulated a series of conclusions about their functions, deduced from them his explanations of malfunction in the course of disease, and illustrated his conclusions with case histories and postmortems.

Before leaving Oxford in late 1667 to set up a large and lucrative practice in London, Willis brought out his *Pathologiae cerebri et nervosi generis specimen,* the clinical study that he had promised as a companion volume to the *Cerebri anatome.* He based his analysis of convulsive diseases upon the belief that muscle contraction results from the explosive mixing of two types of particles: saline-spirituous particles from the nerves, and nitrosulfurous particles from arterial blood. When spirits of too heterogeneous a nature are supplied by the nervous system, the muscle contraction is too powerful and uncontrolled, thus causing convulsive symptoms. Thus, he argued, epilepsy originates in the central cerebrum, not in the meninges. Or too few particles could be supplied by the nerves, resulting in weak contractions, a condition he illustrated with the first clinical description of myasthenia gravis. Convulsive coughs and asthma, hysterical and hypochondriacal disorders, even scurvy, he saw as nervous afflictions.

In 1670 he published another set of tracts elaborating his earlier ideas on metabolic heat and muscular contraction. He accepted Lower's contention, advanced in the *Tractatus de corde* (1669), that the heart is merely a muscle and does not have an innate ferment. Therefore, the body's heat must come from an "accension" or fermentative process lodged in the blood itself. This process demands both a sulfurous fuel, derived from food, and nitrous particles derived from the air. It is exactly analogous to inorganic combustion. Here Willis was both elaborating his and Bathurst's earlier ideas on the metabolic function of air, and adding to them ideas about aerial "nitrous particles" published by his Oxford confreres Boyle, Hooke, Lower, and John Mayow, during the 1660's.

These same themes, joined to others also adumbrated in the *Cerebri anatome,* were the core of his anatomical and clinical study *De anima brutorum,* published in 1672. Man, he said, has two souls: a corporeal, mortal soul which he shares with animals, and a rational, immortal one which is uniquely human. The corporeal, or "brutish," soul consists of two parts: one lodged in the blood is responsible for vital functions, the other located in the nervous system is responsible for functions of action and sensation. The vital soul in the blood performs nourishment by taking up and distributing food particles, and produces heat and vitality by "burning" some of these with the nitrous particles derived from the air. In explaining the functions of the sensitive soul, he recapitulated many of the neurophysiological concepts first introduced in *Cerebri anatome*, especially those of localization, and extended these to invertebrates with some of the first detailed dissections of the earthworm, oyster, and lobster. He traced in detail how vibratory impressions from the five senses are transmitted through the plenum of animal spirits which inhabit the nervous system, and how these impulses are interpreted, processed, and stored in specialized parts of the cerebrum and medulla oblongata.

As in previous books, Willis was not satisfied with anatomical investigation and speculative interpretation. He goes on to argue, with the aid of extensive case histories and numerous postmortems, how a broad range of disorders are due to derangement of the neural portion of the corporeal soul. Sleeping and waking, headache, lethargy, narcolepsy, coma, nightmare, vertigo, apoplexy, delirium, frenzy, and paralysis—all are of neurological, rather than supernatural or humoral, origins.

Willis' last work, the *Pharmaceutice rationalis*, was cast from the same mold. In its two parts, brought out in 1674 and 1675, he summarized the anatomy and physiology of the thoracic and abdominal organs, hypothesized mechanisms of their pathology, and filled pages with case histories, therapies, and postmortems. Many observations testify to his acute clinical judgment. He discovered the superficial lymphatics of the lungs, distinguished acute tuberculosis from the chronic fibroid type, and gave the first clinical and pathological account of emphysema. He described extrasystoles of the heart, aortic stenosis, heart failure in chronic bronchitis, and emboli lodging in the pulmonary artery. He was the first European to note the sweet taste of the urine in diabetes mellitus, and described the pains and weakness of diabetic polyneuritis. He made original observations on the muscle layers of the stomach wall, and devised the use of a whalebone probang to treat achalasia of the cardia.

Unfortunately, Willis was scarcely able to enjoy the acclaim that greeted his later works. Tending a busy London practice, he was unable— and perhaps disinclined—to participate in the activities of the Royal Society and the Royal College of Physicians. His personal life was touched with tragedy: six of his eight children died before adolescence; his first wife, the sister of John Fell, dean of Christ Church, died in 1670; and both of his brothers predeceased him. Willis died of pneumonia on 11 November 1675, and was buried in the north transept of Westminster Abbey. He was survived by his second wife.

Willis has often been castigated for the unremittingly speculative nature of much of his writings, but that is to judge him by the scientific taste of the present century. He saw himself as a physician whose lasting contribution would be to formulate a series of corpuscular explanations that would link anatomical fact with clinical practice. A number of these hypotheses were, even if incorrect, extremely fruitful. His notion of animal heat arising from a fermentation in the blood, fed by a nitrous aerial agent, was elaborated by Mayow into a concept of respiration and metabolism that foreshadowed Lavoisier's discovery of oxygen a century later. Willis' ideas of cerebral localization were the impetus for a line of experimental work traceable into the early nineteenth century. His notion of the corporeal soul in the nervous system, and the disorders to which it was prone, was both a contribution to comparative psychology and the beginning of modern concepts of neurology. His speculations on the involuntary functions of the "intercostal" and "vagal" nerves provided the foundation of our knowledge of the autonomic nervous system. Yet if these ideas were more subject to correction than his easily verifiable conclusions on cerebral and cerebellar structure, cerebral circulation, and the cranial nerves, they were no less important a part of his *oeuvre*. Willis accomplished much, not in spite of his penchant for speculation, but because of it. He attempted, with an energy and insight unsurpassed in the seventeenth century, to construct a medical system that encompassed not only his own anatomical discoveries and acute clinical observations, but set them within the emerging Harveian physiology and the new corpuscular natural philosophy.

*BIBLIOGRAPHY*

I. ORIGINAL WORKS. Willis' clinical notebook (*ca.* 1651) is MS 799ᴬ in the Wellcome Medical Historical Library, London. *Diatribae duae medico-philosophicae, quarum prior agit de fermentatione . . . altera de febribus* (London, 1659) had a 2nd ed., with additions, in 1662. Locke's extracts from Lower's transcript of Willis' lectures are in the Bodleian Library, Oxford, MS

Locke f. 19, pp. 1–82, *passim. Cerebri anatome: cui accessit nervorum descriptio et usus* (London, 1664) was published that year first in a quarto and then in an octavo ed.; a trans. is available in modern facs. (Montreal, 1964). *Pathologiae cerebri, et nervosi generis specimen* (Oxford, 1667) contains a frontispiece portrait of Willis, aetatis suae 45, drawn by Loggan. The two tracts *De sanguinis accensione* and *De motu musculari* were published with *Affectionum quae dicuntur hystericae & hypochondriacae pathologia spasmodica vindicata* (London, 1670). *De anima brutorum* (Oxford, 1672) is available in a facs. of a 17th-century trans. *Pharmaceutice rationalis* was published in two pts.: I (Oxford, 1674), II (Oxford, 1675), published posthumously. Willis' *Opera omnia* was published immediately after his death (Geneva, 1676) and reprinted several times in the succeeding decades. These often contain a tract *De ratione motus muscularum* which was misattributed to Willis; it was published anonymously by William Croone (London, 1664). All of Willis' works, with the exception of *Affectionum*, were translated by Samuel Pordage and published in one volume as *Practice of Physick* (London, 1684).

II. Secondary Literature. Hansruedi Isler, *Thomas Willis, 1621–1675: Doctor and Scientist* (New York, 1968), is the only full-length historical treatment of Willis. Audrey B. Davis, *Circulation Physiology and Medical Chemistry in England 1650–1680* (Lawrence, Kans., 1973), sheds much light on Willis' chemical ideas. The fundamental study by Alfred Meyer and Raymond Hierons, "On Thomas Willis's Concepts of Neurophysiology," in *Medical History,* **9** (1965), 1–15, 142–155, has an extensive bibliography which provides the best entree into the literature on specialized topics of Willis' life and work.

Robert G. Frank, Jr.

**WILLISTON, SAMUEL WENDELL** (*b.* Roxbury, Massachusetts, 10 July 1851; *d.* Chicago, Illinois, 30 August 1918), *vertebrate paleontology, entomology, medicine.*

The fourth child of Samuel Williston—an unschooled blacksmith—and Jane A. Turner, Williston developed an early passion for books and education. Infected by the concern of New Englanders over the fate of Kansas in the turmoil leading to the Civil War, the family moved in 1857 to Manhattan, Kansas, where the young man entered Kansas State Agricultural College in 1866. The inspiring professor of natural sciences Benjamin Franklin Mudge introduced him to science. At the college "there were no laboratories of any kind, no microscopes and but few instruments. The college catalogue of about that time . . . gravely mentions

an electrical machine, three Leyden jars and six test-tubes!" (Williston, "Recollections" [1916]). Williston discovered Darwin's writings on evolution and lectured on them, for which he was denounced by the local church.

In 1874, two years after Williston received his B.S., Mudge invited him to join a fossil-collecting trip to western Kansas for Othniel Charles Marsh of Yale. Two summers of collecting led to Williston's direct employment by Marsh until 1885, as a leader of fossil-collecting expeditions in the western United States and as a laboratory assistant in New Haven, Connecticut. He worked at each of the first three American quarries of giant dinosaurs in Colorado and Wyoming soon after their almost simultaneous discovery in 1877.

Torn by uncertainties over which career to pursue, Williston, while working for Marsh, also earned an M.D. (1880) and a Ph.D. in entomology (1885), both from Yale. He married Annie Isabel Hathaway in 1881; they had five children.

Williston's contributions to medicine were chiefly in public health and education. From 1886 to 1890 he taught anatomy at Yale. In 1887 and 1888 he was health officer of New Haven; and from 1888 to 1890 he studied the pollution of rivers for the state of Connecticut. In 1891 he served on the Kansas State Board of Health and helped to establish the licensing and medical registration of doctors there. He was instrumental in establishing the medical school at the University of Kansas and became its first dean (1898–1902).

In 1890 Williston became a professor of geology and paleontology at the University of Kansas. He immediately began his own expeditions for vertebrate fossils, concentrating on the productive Cretaceous deposits of western Kansas and later on those of eastern Wyoming.

Williston entered paleontology when it was advancing beyond the stage of descriptive classification and was ready for synthesis. Georges Cuvier had described fossil remains, and Richard Owen had proposed the term *Dinosauria* before 1850. But the fossil remains in America were more extensive than those of Europe, and Darwin's theory of evolution provided impetus to the exploration of the past. Joseph Leidy had described American fossils, mainly from the east coast. When advancing railroads opened the American West to travel in the 1850's and 1860's, Marsh and Edward Drinker Cope competed for collections of fossil vertebrates from many different geologic horizons. They described many species and began the classification of the early reptiles and mammals.

In Kansas, Williston concentrated on mosasaurs, plesiosaurs, and pterodactyls, assembling the known information and describing new species. His detailed observations of the structure and anatomy of these animals enabled him to discuss their probable habits. He also found and described many other single fossils, publishing extensively in the *Kansas University Quarterly* throughout the 1890's. He contributed summary articles on the fossil birds, dinosaurs, crocodiles, mosasaurs, and turtles to the geological survey of Kansas (1898).

His acceptance of a professorship at the University of Chicago in 1902 soon changed the direction of his research, perhaps because of the Permian fossils already in the university collection. Williston collected extensively in the Permian red beds of Texas and New Mexico, ably aided by his preparator, Paul C. Miller. Rich pockets of fossils produced a wealth of labyrinthodont amphibians and reptiles from the early beginnings of the reptiles; indeed, some of the genera discussed by Williston (e.g., *Seymouria*) cannot be positively assigned to either one of these classes. His descriptions and synthesis of the classification of these primitive vertebrates stand as his major contribution to paleontology. Always fascinated by anatomy, he presented a number of carefully drawn restorations of the animals he described, many of his papers appearing in the *Journal of Geology* between 1902 and 1918.

While at the University of Chicago, Williston did not ignore the fossil groups that he had previously studied; in addition to single papers, he published his highly readable *Water Reptiles of the Past and Present* (1914). His knowledge of the broad spectrum of the reptiles led him to surveys of the evolution of the class and provided a firm foundation for later paleontologists. *The Osteology of the Reptiles* (1925), in preparation at the time of his death and completed at his request by William K. Gregory, summarized his classification.

Williston was president of the Kansas Academy of Science in 1897, president of Sigma Xi from 1901 to 1904, and delegate to the Ninth International Congress of Zoology at Monaco in 1913. He also received an Sc.D. from Yale in 1913, and in 1915 was elected to the National Academy of Sciences.

Williston's early indecision on his own career, combined with what he considered the tyranny of Marsh as an employer (Marsh did not want his employees to publish articles on paleontology), had led him into entomology and medicine. He began collecting beetles first as a diversion on field trips

in 1876, but he soon concluded that the order was already too widely known for a beginner to make a name for himself. Quite arbitrarily he selected flies as a hobby for study and he found his diversion highly rewarding. The Diptera of North America had been scarcely touched at this time (the 1870's), and Williston, through persistence and research in European publications, was able to classify the multitudinous members of the order. He also found his subjects readily available: on picnics, field trips, vacations, and even in the classroom while he lectured on paleontology. Although he never taught courses in entomology, he published a great many papers on Diptera and presented his classification of the order in three successive editions of *The Manual of North American Diptera* (1888; 2nd ed., 1896; 3rd. ed., 1908), the last edition of which was liberally illustrated by himself. He was consulted by entomologists throughout the world and received many specimens for identification.

Williston was an outstanding teacher and beloved by his students. His broad interests and keen enthusiasm influenced many students who later became prominent in a variety of fields, such as Clarence E. McClung, Ermine Cowles Case, and Barnum Brown.

## BIBLIOGRAPHY

I. ORIGINAL WORKS. Williston published more than 300 papers and books; about half on paleontology and geology; about 100 on entomology; and the remainder on education, zoology, and public health.

Many of the short papers in paleontology are of value for descriptions of species and for the discussions of phylogenetic relationships. His individual papers on fossil birds, dinosaurs, crocodiles, mosasaurs, and turtles of Kansas in 1898 (*University Geological Survey of Kansas*, 4 [1898]) are of special value.

Significant review papers on specific Cretaceous vertebrate fossil groups include "Kansas Pterodactyls, Part I," in *Kansas University Quarterly*, 1 (1892), 1–13; "Kansas Pterodactyls, Part II," *ibid.*, 2 (1893), 79–81; "Range and Distribution of the Mosasaurs, With Remarks on Synonymy," *ibid.*, A ser., 6 (1897), 177–185; "Mosasaurs" (1898), cited above; "North American Plesiosaurs, Part I," in *Publications. Field Museum of Natural History*, Geological ser., 73 (1903), 1–77; and "North American Plesiosaurs: Trinacromerum," in *Journal of Geology*, 16 (1908), 715–736.

On Permian amphibians and reptiles, see *American Permian Vertebrates* (Chicago, 1911), a summary of the then-known information on this group morphologically and taxonomically; "Primitive Reptiles: A Review," in *Journal of Morphology*, 23 (1912), 637–663, enlarges the relationships of these animals to a worldwide scale and presents the characters necessary to the classification; "Permocarboniferous Vertebrates From New Mexico," in *Publications. Carnegie Institution of Washington*, **181** (1913), offers the results of Williston's collections and description of species in the New Mexico red beds; "Synopsis of the American Permocarboniferous Tetrapoda," in *Contributions From the Walker Museum*, **1** (1916), 193–236, is a final summary of the group that Williston knew better than anyone else at the time of his death.

On reptile classification, see *Water Reptiles of the Past and Present* (Chicago, 1914), with detailed information on the classification, habits, and special adaptations of all aquatic reptiles in their respective geologic periods; "The Phylogeny and Classification of Reptiles," in *Journal of Geology*, **25** (1917), 411–421, which contains Williston's final published graphical classification of the terrestrial vertebrates; and *The Osteology of the Reptiles*, W. K. Gregory, ed. (Cambridge, 1925), a valuable posthumous work, illustrated by extensive line drawings done by him in his final years.

Williston's major contributions in entomology were the three successive editions of *The Manual of North American Diptera* (published in New Haven, with slightly different titles in 1888 and 1896; 3rd ed., 1908). His earlier "Synopsis of North American Syrphidae," in *Bulletin. United States National Museum*, no. 31 (1886), is an exhaustive treatise of that family. South American, Central American, and West Indian Diptera were described in several monographs, reference to which can be found in Shor and in Lull (see below).

II. SECONDARY LITERATURE. Williston's childhood, youth, and the circumstances leading to his entry into paleontology are contained in his MS "Recollections," written in 1916; the MS is included in Elizabeth N. Shor's *Fossils and Flies* (Norman, Okla., 1971), as is an account of the remainder of Williston's life, scientific accomplishments, and a complete bibliography. Brief summaries of Williston's life are in "A Tribute to the Life and Work of Samuel Wendell Williston," *Sigma Xi Quarterly*, **7**, no. 1 (1919); and in Richard S. Lull, "Bibliographical Memoir, Samuel Wendell Williston," in *Memoirs of the National Academy of Sciences*, **17** (1924), 115–141. The latter includes a detailed summary of Williston's paleontological contributions and an almost complete bibliography.

All memorials to Williston prior to Shor give the date of his birth as 1852 instead of 1851, because of an indecipherable date in "Recollections." A birth certificate from Boston (which now includes Roxbury), Mass., confirms the birth date of 1851.

ELIZABETH NOBLE SHOR

**WILLSTÄTTER, RICHARD** (*b.* Karlsruhe, Germany, 13 August 1872; *d.* Locarno, Switzerland, 3 August 1942), *organic chemistry*.

Willstätter was the son of Max and Sophie Ulmann Willstätter. Raised in a well-to-do German-Jewish mercantile family, Willstätter attended school in Karlsruhe and then at the Realgymnasium in Nuremberg. Upon graduation in 1890, he entered the University of Munich. It was there that he came under the influence of Adolf von Baeyer, who took great interest in Willstätter's career, and recommended him to his colleague A. Einhorn, with whom Willstätter did his research for the Ph.D. (1894). Two years later Willstätter became *Privatdozent*, and in 1902 he was appointed extraordinary professor in Baeyer's institute. The following year he married Sophie Leser; they had two children before her untimely death in 1908. In 1905 he became professor of chemistry at the Eidgenössische Technische Hochschule in Zurich, but left in 1912 to become director of the new Kaiser-Wilhelm Institute of Chemistry in Berlin-Dahlem.

In 1916 Willstätter succeeded Baeyer as professor of chemistry at the University of Munich, but resigned in 1924 in protest of the vote of the faculty to deny V. M. Goldschmidt appointment as the successor of Groth. After 1925 most of Willstätter's research was conducted by Margarete Rohdewald in a laboratory provided by Wieland, Willstätter's successor at Munich. With the rise of Hitler, and the threat of arrest during the anti-Semitic campaign of 1938, Willstätter had to leave Germany; after considerable difficulty, he succeeded in emigrating to Switzerland in March 1939.

Willstätter's doctoral work with Einhorn dealt with the structure of cocaine, for which the latter had proposed a formula in 1893. After the completion of his Ph.D., Willstätter continued to work on the tropine alkaloids related to cocaine; and through a series of brilliant chemical degradative and synthetic researches during 1894–1898, he demonstrated that earlier formulas were incorrect and that these alkaloids belonged to a family of bicyclic compounds having a seven-member ring. During succeeding years he returned occasionally to the tropine alkaloids; thus, in 1918, he described an elegant synthesis of ecgonine. His studies in this field also led him to prepare cyclooctatetraene in 1913.

Another area of organic chemistry that Willstätter illuminated early in his career was the chemistry of quinones and quinone imines. In 1905 he prepared the hitherto unknown *o*-benzoquinone, and the succeeding seven years saw a series of important studies on the Wurster dyes, formed by the oxidation of *p*-phenylenediamines, and on "aniline black," a product of the oxidation of aniline.

The high point of Willstätter's chemical work was attained during 1905–1914, in his studies on chlorophyll and the anthocyanins. Although there had been much earlier work on chlorophyll—and its chemical relation to the porphyrin of hemoglobin was appreciated—it was Willstätter who laid the groundwork for the later complete elucidation of the structure of chlorophyll by Hans Fischer. Willstätter separated chlorophyll from green plants into two components (chlorophyll *a* and *b*), and showed them to be magnesium complexes of a porphyrin derivative (pheophytin) in which one of the two carboxyl groups is esterified by a long-chain alcohol (phytol). Through a series of chemical degradations with acid and alkali, Willstätter and his associates produced a series of well-characterized chemical intermediates on the way to the simpler porphyrins. During the course of his work on chlorophyll, he found that in the presence of ethanol, an enzyme present in plant tissue (chlorophyllase) catalyzes the transesterification of phytol by ethanol. This observation awakened his interest in enzymes, the principal subject of his last researches. The work on the chemistry of chlorophyll was followed, during 1915–1916, by studies on its role in photosynthesis, and on the assimilation by green plants of carbon dioxide; but these researches did not lead to clear-cut conclusions.

Willstätter's studies on the anthocyanin pigments of flowers, in particular on cyanin and pelargonin, led to his establishment of their structures as oxonium salts derived from hydroxychromanes, whose hydroxyl groups are linked to sugar units. These brilliant studies were terminated by the advent of World War I but served as the basis for the further development of the subject by R. Robinson. In 1915 Willstätter was awarded the Nobel Prize for chemistry in recognition of his "pioneer researches on plant pigments, especially chlorophyll."

With the resumption of his work after the war, Willstätter turned his attention to the nature of enzymes. From 1918 to 1925 he and his associates attempted to develop methods for the purification of a variety of enzymes: peroxidase, lipase, trypsin, and amylase. An important consequence of these efforts was the introduction, into enzyme chemistry, of reproducible adsorption methods (for example, the use of aluminum hydroxide) and of improved assay procedures for the determination of enzymic activity. Willstätter advocated the idea that enzymes are substances of low molecular weight that are merely adsorbed on colloidal carriers; he also questioned J. B. Sumner's claim (1926) to have isolated the enzyme urease in the form of a crystalline protein the integrity of which was essential for catalytic activity. Although some of Willstätter's students (notably E. Waldschmidt-Leitz) continued to defend his view into the 1930's, the isolation of pepsin and other enzymes as crystalline proteins led to its rejection. In his final years of research, with M. Rohdewald, Willstätter studied the biochemical transformation of glycogen and the role of polysaccharides in alcoholic fermentation; this work did not have a significant impact.

*BIBLIOGRAPHY*

I. ORIGINAL WORKS. Willstätter's works include *Untersuchungen über Chlorophyll* (Berlin, 1913), written with Arthur Stoll, trans. by F. M. Schertz and A. R. Merz, as *Investigations on Chlorophyll* (Lancaster, Pa., 1928). Willstätter and Stoll also collected their papers on photosynthesis, in *Untersuchungen über die Assimilation der Kohlensäure* (Berlin, 1918). The papers on enzymes are collected in *Untersuchungen über Enzyme*, 2 vols. (Berlin, 1928); see also *Problems and Methods in Enzyme Research* (Ithaca, N.Y., 1927). Willstätter wrote an autobiography, *Aus meinem Leben*, A. Stoll, ed. (Weinheim, 1948), trans. by L. S. Hornig as *From My Life* (New York, 1965).

II. SECONDARY LITERATURE. Appreciations of Willstätter's work are R. Huisgen, in *Journal of Chemical Education*, **38** (1961), 10–15; R. Robinson, in *Journal of the Chemical Society* (1953), 999–1026; and in *Obituary Notices of Fellows of the Royal Society*, **8** (1953), 609–634; and J. Renz, *Helvetica Chimica Acta*, **56** (1973), 1–14.

JOSEPH S. FRUTON

**WILLUGHBY, FRANCIS** (*b*. Middleton, Warwickshire, England, 22 November 1635; *d*. Middleton, 3 July 1672), *natural history*.

Willughby was the third child but only son of Sir Francis Willughby and his wife Cassandra, daughter of Thomas Ridgeway, earl of Londonderry. The Willughbys[1] of Wollaton, Nottinghamshire, and Middleton, Warwickshire, were country gentry with estates in many English counties. Francis was educated at Sutton Coldfield School, and in September 1652 entered Trinity College, Cambridge, where John Ray was a lecturer and where their lifelong association began. Upon graduation in 1656, Willughby continued his scientific studies, possibly at Cambridge, in the late 1650's[2]; and for a time in 1660 he was reading books on natural history at the Bodleian Library in Oxford. In 1663 he became one of the original fellows of the Royal Society of London.

During the summer of 1660, Willughby and Ray probably carried out their first tour together through northern England and the Isle of Man collecting botanical specimens. Accompanied by Philip Skippon, they made another tour through Wales and the west country in 1662. These tours were the prelude to a more ambitious journey. Their intentions had now widened into a comprehensive consideration of plants, birds, fish, animals, and insects. Sailing from Dover to Calais on 18 April 1663, Willughby, with Ray, Skippon, and Nathaniel Bacon, traveled through the Low Countries and Germany into Italy, where they spent the winter of 1663–1664 at Padua. It was there that they visited the botanical gardens and studied anatomy at the university, where Willughby matriculated in January 1664. At Naples, Willughby left the party and traveled through Spain before returning to England late in 1664. Besides collecting specimens, he purchased paintings or engravings of flowers, birds, fish, small mammals, and reptiles.

While Ray and Skippon were still abroad in March 1665, Willughby tapped birch trees and noted the behavior of the rising sap.[3] In 1669 and succeeding years he expanded and continued these experiments with Ray. Willughby reported his observations on leaf-cutting bees and on ichneumon wasps to the Royal Society in 1670 and 1671. When his father died in December 1665, Willughby continued to live with his mother at Middleton, where in the winter of 1666–1667 Ray assisted him in the arrangement and labeling of the collection of specimens. Resuming their field explorations in the summer, they toured southwest England.

In January 1668 Willughby married Emma Barnard, the younger daughter of Sir Henry Barnard; they had two sons and a daughter. Willughby had suffered periods of ill health and was naturally inclined to a studious life, but this did not deter him from undertaking strenuous journeys. At the time of his death he was planning to visit North America to study the animals there.

Willughby's work in natural history is inseparable from that of Ray, Skippon, and Francis Jessop. His name is associated particularly with birds, fish, animals, and insects, but his surviving collection shows that his botanical work was not insignificant. When Willughby died Ray was at Middleton,

and he remained there until the winter of 1675–1676, ostensibly as a trustee under Willughby's will and as tutor to his children, but primarily working on his collections. When compiling Willughby's *Ornithologia* (1676) and *Historia piscium* (1686), Ray supplemented Willughby's material with that of himself and other naturalists. Similarly, Ray's *Historia plantarum* and more especially his writings on animals and insects incorporated Willughby's observations. They were following in the footsteps of Jean and Gaspard Bauhin, Aldrovandi, Gesner, and Rondelet, to whose nomenclature they largely adhered. They consciously adopted a systematic approach, compiling detailed descriptions based on personal observation. Willughby's contribution was twofold: he gave encouragement and financial support to Ray; and he contributed his own fieldwork, experiments and observations, and his collection of plants, birds, and fishes. Willughby's work was incomplete partly on account of his early death, and partly, perhaps, on account of the wide-ranging interests of the man who could compile notes on the history of his family or gather information on contemporary games with the same assiduity as he collected his specimens.[4] It was left to Ray, with the help of Skippon and Jessop, his co-trustees, to assemble the material into a methodical presentable form.

*NOTES*

1. There were many variants of the name. The modern spelling "Willoughby" was adopted by the naturalist's son Thomas, first Baron Middleton.
2. Willughby's commonplace book on a wide variety of religious, classical, and scientific subjects includes chemical experiments, some headed "Mr. Wrays," dated 1658 and 1659. Middleton MS MiLM 15.
3. *Ibid.*, botanical notes.
4. Middleton MSS MiLM 13 (notes based on the family archives) and MiLM 14 (a book on games); compare his lists of vocabularies in many languages compiled on the Welsh and continental tours, Mi 4/149a/3.1–16.

*BIBLIOGRAPHY*

I. Original Works. Original MSS of and relating to Willughby, and his botanical specimens, are in the Middleton collection deposited in the Library Manuscripts Department of the University of Nottingham. Reports on the flow of sap in trees, leaf-cutting bees, and ichneumon wasps are in *Philosophical Transactions of the Royal Society of London*, **4**, no. 48 (1669), 963; no. 57 (1670), 1165; **5**, no. 58 (1670), 1199; no. 65 (1670), 2100; **6**, no. 70 (1671), 2125; no. 74 (1671), 2221; no. 76 (1671), 2279.

Other works are *Observations, Topographical, Moral and Physical Made in a Journey Through the Low-Countries, Germany, Italy and France . . . by John Ray, Fellow of the Royal Society. Whereunto Is Added a Brief Account of Francis Willughby Esq.; His Voyage Through a Great Part of Spain* (London, 1673); *Francisci Willughbeii de Middleton in agro Waricensi, armigeri, e Regia Societate, Ornithologiae, libri tres . . . totum opus recognovit, digessit, supplevit Joannes Raius* (London, 1676), trans. into English as *The Ornithology of Francis Willughby of Middleton in the County of Warwick, Esq., Fellow of the Royal Society in Three Books . . . by John Ray, Fellow of the Royal Society* (London, 1678); and *Francisci Willughbeii armig. de Historia piscium libri quatuor . . . totum opus recognovit, coaptavit, supplevit, librum etiam primum et secundum integros adjecit Joannes Raius et Societate Regia* (Oxford, 1686).

II. SECONDARY LITERATURE. On Willughby and his work, see W. Blunt, *The Art of Botanical Illustration* (London, 1950), 68, which describes the book of flower paintings (Middleton MS MiLM22); G. S. Boulger in *Dictionary of National Biography,* XXI, 525–528; C. Brown, *Lives of Nottinghamshire Worthies* (London, 1882), 207–211; L. C. Miall, *The Early Naturalists, Their Lives and Work (1530–1789)* (London, 1912), 99–130; C. E. Raven, *John Ray Naturalist, His Life and Works* (Cambridge, 1942; 2nd ed., 1950); M. A. Welch, "Francis Willoughby, F. R. S. (1635–1672)," in *Journal of the Society for the Bibliography of Natural History,* 6, pt. 2 (1972), 71–85, which includes a descriptive archival list of the material in the Middleton collection; and A. C. Wood, ed., *The Continuation of the History of the Willoughby Family by Cassandra Duchess of Chandos* (Windsor, 1958), which is a printed edition of the contemporary account by the naturalist's daughter (Middleton MS MiLM 37).

MARY A. WELCH

**WILSING, JOHANNES** (*b.* Berlin, Germany, 8 September 1856; *d.* Potsdam, Germany, 23 December 1943), *astronomy.*

Wilsing received his doctorate from the University of Berlin in 1880 and the following year became assistant at the Potsdam Astrophysical Observatory. In 1893 he received the post of observer and, in 1898, chief observer. He retired in 1921.

Wilsing conducted many observations concerning problems in astrophysics, a relatively new branch of astronomy at the time. He observed the velocity of rotation of the sun and offered a hydrodynamic explanation of its variation with latitude. Several of his studies deal with the influence on astrophysical measurements of systematic errors, such as atmospheric dispersion or optical and mechanical deficiencies of telescopes. He also observed novae, nebulae, and double stars.

Several of Wilsing's publications deal with methods, such as the derivation of the surface temperature of a star from photometric measurements of its spectrum. In calculating the diameters of stars, he used the laws of radiation and the measured values of the surface temperature, from which the radiating area can be computed. Although this method was not new in principle, Wilsing was the first to apply it systematically. His results were confirmed some years later, when the first interferometric measurements of stellar diameters were made.

*BIBLIOGRAPHY*

I. ORIGINAL WORKS. Wilsing's writings include *Determination of the Mean Density of the Earth by Means of a Pendulum Principle,* J. H. Gore, trans. (Washington, 1890); "Über die Helligkeitsverteilung im Sonnenspektrum nach Messungen an Spektrogrammen," which is *Publikationen des Astrophysikalischen Observatoriums zu Potsdam,* 22, no. 66 (1913); and "Messungen der Farben, der Helligkeiten und der Durchmesser der Sterne mit Anwendung der Planckschen Strahlungsgleichung," *ibid.,* 24, no. 76 (1920).

See also the Royal Society *Catalogue of Scientific Papers,* XIX, 644–645, which lists 38 memoirs published to 1900; and Poggendorff, IV, 1645–1646; V, 1376–1377; VI, 2896; and VIIa, 1015.

II. SECONDARY LITERATURE. See E. von der Pahlen, *Lehrbuch der Stellarstatistik* (Leipzig, 1937); and M. Waldmeier, *Ergebnisse und Probleme der Sonnenforschung* (Leipzig, 1941).

F. SCHMEIDLER

**WILSON, ALEXANDER** (*b.* St. Andrews, Scotland, 1714; *d.* Edinburgh, Scotland, 18 October 1786), *astronomy.*

Wilson was the son of Patrick Wilson, the town clerk of St. Andrews, and of Clara Fairfoul. He was very young when his father died, and he was brought up under the care of his mother. He studied at the College of St. Andrews, receiving an M.A. in 1733. He then was apprenticed to a surgeon-apothecary, first in St. Andrews, later in London. A chance visit to a typefoundry brought about a change in his career. Struck by an idea for an improved method of making type, he returned to St. Andrews in 1739 and set up a typefoundry there in 1742 with the assistance of a friend. The foundry was enlarged and moved to Camlachie, near Glasgow, in 1744. Since his student days Wilson had maintained an active interest in astronomy, and in 1760 was appointed—mainly through the influence of the duke of Argyll—first professor of practical astronomy at the University of Glasgow. He retained this post until 1784.

In 1774 Wilson published some observations, which showed that sunspots were depressions in the luminous matter surrounding the sun. This was not an entirely original hypothesis, for it had been suggested earlier by Christoph Scheiner, Philippe de La Hire, and Jacques Cassini. Nevertheless, Wilson's use of strict geometrical reasoning in his demonstration made his argument very forceful, and led to a renewed burst of enthusiasm for sunspot observations.

By carefully studying the apparent change in appearance of a spot as it crossed the solar disk, Wilson observed that the penumbra appeared narrowest on the side of it that was nearest the center of the sun, and widest on the side nearest the edge. He noted that this could be explained as an effect of perspective if the spot were a funnel-shaped depression, with the umbra corresponding to the bottom of the funnel and the penumbra to the sloping sides. Going beyond his observational data, Wilson conjectured that the sun was an immense dark globe surrounded by a thin shell of luminous matter. According to this view, sunspots were excavations in the luminous matter caused "by the working of some sort of elastic vapour, which is generated within the dark globe."

Wilson's interpretation of sunspots was challenged by Lalande in France, but supported by Sir William Herschel in England. Herschel then developed the interpretation into a general description of the solar constitution, which remained standard until the advent of spectroscopic investigations.

Wilson also speculated on a question posed by Newton in his *Opticks* (4th ed. [London, 1730], query 28): "What hinders the fixed stars from falling upon one another?" His answer, published in a short anonymous tract entitled *Thoughts on General Gravitation*, was that the entire universe partook in a periodic motion around some "grand centre of general gravitation."

Wilson was awarded an honorary M.D. from St. Andrews in 1763, and was one of the original members of the Royal Society of Edinburgh. In 1752 he married Jean Sharp. His portrait, a medallion by James Tassie, hangs in the National Portrait Gallery, Edinburgh.

## BIBLIOGRAPHY

I. ORIGINAL WORKS. Wilson's works are "Observations of the Transit of Venus Over the Sun," in *Philo-sophical Transactions of the Royal Society*, **59** (1769), 333–338; "An Account of the Remarkable Cold Observed at Glasgow, in the Month of January, 1768," *ibid.*, **61** (1771), 326–331; *A Specimen of Some of the Printing Types Cast in the Foundry of Alexander Wilson and Sons* (Glasgow[?], 1772); "Observations on the Solar Spots," in *Philosophical Transactions of the Royal Society*, **64** (1774), 1–30; "An Improvement Proposed in the Cross Wires of Telescopes," *ibid.*, **64** (1774), 105–107; *Thoughts on General Gravitation, and Views Thence Arising as to the State of the Universe* (n.p., 1777[?]); and "An Answer to the Objectives Stated by M. De la Lande, in the Memoirs of the French Academy for the Year 1776, Against the Solar Spots Being Excavations in the Luminous Matter of the Sun, Together With a Short Examination of the Views Entertained by Him Upon that Subject," in *Philosophical Transactions of the Royal Society*, **73** (1783), 144–168.

II. SECONDARY LITERATURE. For a brief biographical sketch of Wilson's life, see the article by George Stronach in the *Dictionary of National Biography*, XXI, 545–546.

Good but brief accounts of Wilson's theories can be found in Agnes M. Clerke, *A Popular History of Astronomy During the Nineteenth Century* (Edinburgh–New York, 1886), and Robert Grant, *History of Physical Astronomy From the Earliest Ages to the Middle of the Nineteenth Century* (London, 1852).

HOWARD PLOTKIN

**WILSON, ALEXANDER** (*b.* Paisley, Scotland, 6 July 1766; *d.* Philadelphia, Pennsylvania, 23 August 1813), *ornithology.*

Wilson's background was so remote from scientific interests that his emergence in the last five years of his life as an ornithologist, and as founder of the science in America, is one of the most remarkable aspects of his extraordinary career. His father was a smuggler who, after his marriage to Mary McNab—comely and pious "and in every way (in a good sense) a superior person"—reformed and become a prosperous silk gauze weaver and loom operator in Paisley. Alexander, their third child and only son, was baptized by Paisley's most famous citizen, the Reverend John Witherspoon, later president of Princeton and a leading figure in the American Revolution. The boy studied at the Paisley Grammar School, and since he was precocious was intended for the ministry and placed in charge of a divinity student—the only formal education he received. From an early age he read widely, since the relatively high cultural standard of Paisley made books readily available.

Wilson's mother died when he was ten years old, and his father, marrying again almost immediately, returned to smuggling. Wilson was placed on a farm as a herd boy, and at thirteen was apprenticed to a weaver, William Duncan, the husband of his sister Mary. When he ended his apprenticeship at the age of sixteen, he became a peddler, tramping country roads across Scotland with a pack of cloth that he had woven with his brother-in-law. He wrote poetry, especially after the publication of Burns's first book in 1786 awakened Scottish intellectuals to the poetry of the common life and language around them; and he sketched and made his own designs for the cloth he wove. Both efforts were evidence of a powerful creative impulse seeking an outlet, but could scarcely be said to foreshadow the assured prose and the superb bird paintings that distinguished *The American Ornithology*. Nor was Wilson's home environment one that fostered scrupulously exact observation. His father took over an ancient, half-ruined castle, the Tower of Auchinbathie, near Lochwinnoch, where he operated illegal stills and hired weavers to work smuggled silk. Smuggling was not so sternly condemned in the west of Scotland as to make the household disreputable, but secrecy and the rural underworld prevented the development of disciplined habits such as the *Ornithology* was to require of Wilson.

After painful struggles with finances and his self-distrust, Wilson published a volume of poetry in 1790. It gained him favorable notice without improving his station in life. Thomas Crichton, Paisley's most eminent man of letters, characterized Wilson's poems accurately: "For original ideas, a masculine superiority of language, high graphic and descriptive character—especially his Scottish poems—they will stand a fair comparison with any of our Scottish poets, Burns not excepted. But Wilson is far short of that poet in fine poetic imagination." Wilson's masterpiece, *Watty and Meg*, a popular favorite for generations, was attributed to Burns, a fair indication of its hold on the public.

*Watty and Meg* was published anonymously, Wilson being in prison at the time. He was jailed during an obscure dispute, in a period of great social stress, with William Sharp, a wealthy Paisley mill owner. Wilson published a poem "The Shark" accusing Sharp of stealthily lengthening the measuring devices by which his employees were paid, all weaving then being piecework. Shortly before the poem appeared Sharp received an anonymous letter containing an offer to suppress the poem for a payment of five guineas, which made the charge

against Wilson not libel, but blackmail. Wilson was arrested, roughly handled, convicted, ordered to beg the pardon of God and Mr. Sharp, to burn the poem in the public square, and to pay fines and damages amounting to £60 sterling—more than a weaver's annual earnings. These were reduced on appeal, but Wilson was in and out of court and jail for two years; and his friends, who signed peace bonds, were threatened with ruin if he became involved in conflict with any of His Majesty's servants, something that became increasingly likely in that time of riot and disorder. His love affair with Martha McLean, a Paisley girl of a well-to-do family, was broken off. Sir William Jardine in his otherwise laudatory biography of Wilson held the Sharp episode to be the only disreputable act of Wilson's career. Alexander Grosart, a Paisley historian, concluded that the charge in the original poem had been true, and would have been aired in a trial for libel; the charge of blackmail prevented any such disclosure. Wilson was utterly disheartened when he sailed for America in May 1794, telling Crichton, "I must get out of my mind."

Against the waste and disorder of his years in Scotland, Wilson's achievement in *The American Ornithology* became phenomenal. The development of the work in his mind can be traced in personal notes scattered throughout the *Ornithology* and in Wilson's poems and letters after he settled near Philadelphia. He had an initial interest in birds as game and the folklore and hunting skills they involved, inspired by the immense flights of ducks and geese over the school in which he taught (1796–1801) at Milestown near the Delaware. There was also a growing awareness of the wealth and variety of the bird life in the wilderness, marked especially during his long journeys on foot to a farm in western New York, which he had purchased for the family of his sister Mary, whose husband had abandoned her. As he sketched from life the birds his students brought him, Wilson developed his skill in drawing. His observations became more exact as he studied the hummingbirds, orioles, owls, grosbeaks, finches, and hawks that he kept as pets and watched in the woods and fields. As early as 1803 he wrote to Crichton that he was beginning to draw all of America's finest birds. During the four years (1802–1806) he taught at Gray's Ferry, his vague plans came into focus through his association with the venerable naturalist William Bartram, whose home in Bartram's garden, Kingsessing, Pennsylvania, was near his school; but he was still so little prepared that he asked Bartram to identify some of the birds he sketched. "I am miserably deficient in many requirements," he wrote Bartram, in reference to the *Ornithology*. "Botany, Mineralogy and Drawing I most ardently wish to be instructed in. . . . Can I make any progress in Botany, sufficient to enable me to be useful, and what would be the most proper way to proceed?"

Wilson was forty years old when he left teaching to try to classify scientifically and to describe accurately and picture in faithful color all the species of birds in America. His plan called for a ten-volume work to be sold by subscription for $120 a set. Samuel Bradford, a Philadelphia publisher, agreed to bring out one volume, and to continue the series if Wilson could secure 200 subscribers on the strength of that sample. Volume I, which included such familiar birds as the bluejay, the Baltimore oriole, and the robin, with two to six birds pictured on each of ten colored plates, appeared in the fall of 1808. With this in hand Wilson set out through the northeastern states, signing up subscribers, the first of the great journeys that carried him more than ten thousand miles in the next five years. The southern trip that followed was more successful. With the encouragement of President Thomas Jefferson, who subscribed and urged others to do so, Wilson made his way through the South to Savannah, signing up 250 subscribers and collecting specimens to be pictured in later volumes. He also formed lasting relations with naturalists, including Stephen Elliott and John Abbot, who provided him with specimens and accurate information he could not otherwise have obtained. Forty-two birds were included in Volume II, and when that book was in the hands of the printer in January 1810, Wilson set out on an amazing journey, six wilderness months down the Ohio by rowboat and over the Natchez Trace by horseback, to New Orleans, some three thousand miles, at a cost of $455, but returning a treasury of heretofore unknown species, and enough new subscribers to bring the total to more than 450.

At Louisville, according to Audubon's later recollections, Wilson tried to induce him to become a subscriber, and became depressed when Audubon showed him his own portfolio of bird drawings that were superior to those in Wilson's book. Wilson himself made no mention of the encounter in his letters or in the long account of his journey he published after his return to Philadelphia in *The Port Folio*. Doubt was cast on Audubon's account during his long conflict with George Ord, one of Wilson's literary executors. In a pioneering study of Wilson, Elsa Guerdrum Allen concluded that

Audubon's ambitions were awakened by his first view of Wilson's book. In any case it is unlikely that Wilson would have reacted so strongly at the sight of a more accomplished artist's work in his own field; John Abbot was also a technically trained artist whose bird paintings are of very high quality, and Wilson remained on close terms with Abbot. The distinction of Wilson's work is in the unity of his paintings and his text, and when individual works are inferior to Audubon's splendid and spectacular plates (although in many cases, such as the snowy owl and the Mississippi kite, Wilson's work is plainly superior), Wilson's birds are always birds rather than decorations, supplementing and adding to the text, in an unparalleled catalog of nature: his birds are really wild.

Wilson's third volume appeared in February 1811, and the fourth only seven months later; both were editions of 500 copies. "I have sacrificed everything to print my *Ornithology*," Wilson wrote to the botanist André Michaux. Except for the engraver Alexander Lawson, who cut most of the plates, Wilson worked almost without assistance. He oversaw all details; hired and supervised the colorists; secured virtually all of the subscribers; familiarized himself with the scientific literature of each species; pictured each bird; and composed his brief, engaging, and exact descriptions that are often masterpieces of nature writing.

Before his death of dysentery at the age of forty-seven, Wilson had completed eight volumes of the *Ornithology*, and the drawings for the ninth volume; he had painted and described 264 species. He added forty-eight new species to those previously known to exist in the United States, prepared good life histories for ninety-four species, and maintained a standard so exacting that in a century and a half only a score of minor errors have been found in the *Ornithology*. Francis Herrick, the biographer of Audubon, wrote, "When we consider that Wilson's entire working period on the *Ornithology* was not over ten years . . . the achievement of this man is little short of marvelous"—an accurate appraisal, except that the period was nearer five years than ten.

During the economic stress of the War of 1812, Wilson's colorists left him, Bradford's interest in the *Ornithology* ebbed, and Wilson, forced to color many of the plates himself, also acted as a collector of the money due from subscribers. His social life had long since ceased to exist (although he was elected to membership in the American Philosophical Society in 1813) apart from his friendship with the family of Jacob Miller, a wealthy landowner he had known in his schoolteaching days at Miles-town. The only intimate relation during days of unceasing but often inspired work was with Sarah Miller, the daughter of the family, fifteen years younger than Wilson, to whom he was reportedly engaged and to whom he left everything he owned, including the rights to the *Ornithology*.

## BIBLIOGRAPHY

I. ORIGINAL WORKS. Virtually all of Wilson's nature writing is included in *The American Ornithology*, 9 vols. (Philadelphia, 1808–1813), and most of his journals, travel accounts, and many letters are in *Poems and Literary Prose of Alexander Wilson*, the Reverend Alexander B. Grosart, ed., 2 vols. (Paisley, 1876).

II. SECONDARY LITERATURE. George Ord prepared a biographical introduction to the 9th vol. of the *Ornithology*, 2nd ed. (1824–1825), which was supplanted by a much fuller work by Sir William Jardine as the introduction to the 3-vol. edition of the *Ornithology*, prepared "with additions" by Charles Lucien Bonaparte (London, 1832).

Other biographies include Elsa Guerdrum Allen, *The History of American Ornithology Before Audubon* (New York, 1969); Robert Cantwell, *Alexander Wilson, Naturalist and Pioneer* (Philadelphia, 1961); Thomas Crichton, *Biographical Sketch of the Late Alexander Wilson* (Paisley, 1819); W. M. Hetherington, *Memoir of Alexander Wilson* (Edinburgh, 1831); William B. O. Peabody, *Life of Alexander Wilson* (Boston, 1839); Emerson Stringham, *Alexander Wilson, a Founder of Scientific Ornithology* (Kerrville, Tex. 1958); and James Southall Wilson, *Alexander Wilson, Poet-Naturalist* (New York, 1906).

ROBERT CANTWELL

**WILSON, BENJAMIN** (*b*. Leeds, England, 1721; *d*. Bloomsbury, London, England, 6 June 1788), *electricity*.

Wilson was born in the latter part of 1721, the youngest of the fourteen children of Major Wilson, "the most considerable merchant in Leeds," and Elizabeth Yates. His father's house at Mill Hill, near Leeds, was decorated by Jacques Parmentier, a French artist, and it was to his influence that Wilson attributed the origin of his own interest in art. Later in his youth Wilson studied for a year with another French artist, Longueville, who was working on commissioned historical paintings in the neighborhood.

The Wilson family became impoverished while Benjamin was still under twenty, and the boy went to London, on foot, to find employment. He worked as a clerk, in poor circumstances, continuing his artistic studies whenever occasion offered. During this period, Wilson, by his own account, read widely in the field of experimental philosophy. This interest was channeled toward the novel science of electricity through his friendship with the apothecary William Watson, who was awarded the Copley Medal of the Royal Society in 1745 for his electrical experiments. Wilson also corresponded from 1745 with John Smeaton, the civil engineer. As his own ideas on electricity developed, Wilson came to know Martin Folkes, president of the Royal Society from 1741 to 1753, who advised the young painter to begin his career in Ireland, so that he could return to London a master of his craft. Consequently, Wilson went to Ireland for a short period in 1746, and again from 1748 to 1750.

While in Dublin in 1746, Wilson was allowed to use the experimental room in Trinity College, which resulted in his first publication, *An Essay Towards an Explication of the Phaenomena of Electricity Deduced From the Aether of Sir Isaac Newton*. His second, longer stay in Ireland permitted the writing of *A Treatise on Electricity* (1750), published in London after his return. It was no doubt as a result of this work that Wilson was elected a fellow of the Royal Society on 5 December 1751.

Upon his return from Ireland, Wilson took a seven-year lease of the house in Great Queen Street, Lincoln's Inn Fields, previously occupied by Sir Godfrey Kneller. Wilson was mainly employed in portrait painting, having as sitters many of the men of science whom he came to know through his interest in electricity, including at least eight fellows of the Royal Society. He also painted the actor David Garrick and the poet Thomas Gray, whom he had met at Cambridge in 1747. Wilson also showed some skill at engraving, and produced a famous caricature in February 1766 (at the time of the repeal of the Stamp Act), which, selling for one shilling a copy, brought him £100 in four days. Wilson won the patronage of the duke of York, and upon the death, in 1764, of William Hogarth, who was a friend of Wilson's, the duke gave him Hogarth's appointment of sergeant-painter. Wilson's career as a painter was both successful and remunerative, but he was, unfortunately, fond of speculation, and was declared a defaulter on the Stock Exchange in 1766.

Wilson's scientific interests were almost exclusively concerned with electricity. Following his two publications in 1746 and 1750, he invented and exhibited a large electrical apparatus. With the physician Benjamin Hoadly, he carried out electrical research, the results of which were published in *Observations on a Series of Electrical Experiments* (1756). The purpose of these three books was to assert the identity of electricity, in particular the Franklinian single electric fluid, with the Newtonian aether, as postulated in the English edition of the *Opticks*. In 1757 Wilson visited France and repeated many of his experiments at St. Germain-en-Laye. The culmination of this period of research was the award to Wilson of the Royal Society's Copley Medal in 1760.

The most remarkable of Wilson's scientific activities was his public controversy with Franklin on the question of whether lightning conductors should be round or pointed at the top. Wilson held that "thunder rods" should be round-headed, for, recognizing quite correctly that a pointed metal rod attracts lightning, he believed that if these rods were erected on buildings, they would actually cause the lightning to strike. Wilson was nominated by the Royal Society to serve on a committee to regulate the erection of lightning conductors on St. Paul's Cathedral, and was later asked by the Board of Ordnance to inspect the gunpowder magazines at Purfleet. In 1773, a Royal Society committee, on which he also sat, considered the problem of the magazine, and finally advised the erection of a pointed rod on the summit of the building, Wilson being the sole dissenter. Wilson continued the dispute, publicly disagreeing with the opinion of the Royal Society, and the arguments of such noted scientists as Franklin, Cavendish, and Nairne. Finally, in July 1777, Wilson arranged a huge demonstration before King George III in the Pantheon in Oxford Street. He certainly convinced the king, who declared that Wilson's arguments were sufficient to persuade the apple-women in the street. The scientific world took a different view, for Wilson had continued the dispute beyond the bounds of reason, and the editors of the abridgment of the *Philosophical Transactions* were strongly critical: "But he has been chiefly distinguished as the ostensible person whose perverse conduct in the affair of the conductors of lightning produced such shameful discord and dissensions in the Royal Society, as continued for many years after, to the great detriment of science" (*The Philosophical Transactions of the Royal Society, Abridged, 1755 to 1763*, XI [London, 1809], p. 15).

One commission that united Wilson's interests in science and in painting was the task, entrusted to him by James Short, of producing a map of the moon. Wilson would have received 100 guineas

had he completed the task, but, because of the strain on his eyesight and because working at night gave him constant colds, he was unable to finish the map. The contact between the two men was not, however, without practical outcome, for Wilson painted a portrait of Short, and also one of his fellow telescope-maker, John Dollond.

Wilson's electrical studies brought him into correspondence with foreign scientists throughout Europe. He was a member of four European academies, including the Istituto delle Scienze ed Arti Liberali at Bologna, where he was the first Englishman to be so honored.

In 1771 Wilson married a Miss Hetherington, and the couple had seven children. Wilson's third son was General Sir Robert Thomas Wilson, whose *Life*, published in 1862 by Herbert Randolph, contains an abridgment of Benjamin Wilson's manuscript autobiography, which he had most strictly directed should not be published.

## BIBLIOGRAPHY

I. Original Works. Wilson initially published most of his work in *Philosophical Transactions of the Royal Society*; some of these papers have been reprinted, and are included here. See *An Essay Towards an Explication of the Phaenomena of Electricity, Deduced From the Aether of Sir Isaac Newton* (London, 1746); *A Treatise on Electricity* (London, 1750); *Observations on a Series of Electrical Experiments* (London, 1756), written with Benjamin Hoadly; *A Letter to Mr. Apinus on the Electricity of Tourmaline, With Observations on Mr. Aepinus's Work on the Same Subject* (London, 1764); *A Letter to the Marquess of Rockingham, With Some Observations on the Effects of Lightning* (London, 1765); *Observations Upon Lightning, and the Method of Securing Buildings From Its Effects, in a Letter, by B. Wilson and Others* (London, 1773); *Further Observations Upon Lightning, Together With Some Experiments* (London, 1774); *A Series of Experiments on the Subject of Phosphori, and Their Prismatic Colours: in Which Are Discovered, Some New Properties of Light* (London, 1775; 2nd ed., 1776); *A Letter, From F. Beccaria to Mr. Wilson, Concerning the Light Exhibited in the Dark by the Bologna Phosphorus, Made According to Mr. Canton's Method, and Illuminated Through Coloured Glasses*, printed with *To the Reverend Father Beccaria, Professor of Natural Philosophy at Turin. B. Wilson London 23 September 1776* (n.p., n.d.); *An Account of Experiments Made at the Pantheon, On the Nature and Use of Conductors: to Which Are Added, Some New Experiments With the Leyden Phial* (London, 1778; 2nd ed., 1788); *A Letter To Mr. Euler, Professor of Philosophy, and Member of the Imperial Academy of Sciences at Petersbourg*, . . . (London, 1779); and *A Short View of Electricity* (London, 1780).

There is a typescript copy of Wilson's *Memoirs* on deposit at the National Portrait Gallery, London. These *Memoirs* Wilson never intended for publication, but they were drawn on by H. Randolph (see below). A volume of letters to and papers of Wilson is in the British Museum, Add. MS. 30094.

II. SECONDARY LITERATURE. See Herbert Randolph, *The Life of Sir Robert Wilson* (London, 1862); G. J. Symons, ed., *Lightning Rod Conference. Report of the Delegates . . .* (London, 1882); G. L'E. Turner, "A Portrait of James Short, F.R.S., Attributable to Benjamin Wilson, F.R.S.," in *Notes and Records of the Royal Society of London*, **22** (1967), 105–112. For an account of Wilson's theory of electricity, and for a contemporary criticism, see R. W. Home, "Some Manuscripts on Electrical and Other Subjects Attributed to Thomas Bayes, F.R.S.," *Notes and Records of the Royal Society*, **29**, no. 1 (October 1974), 81–90 (especially pp. 84–87).

G. L'E. TURNER

**WILSON, CHARLES THOMSON REES** (*b*. near Glencorse, Midlothian, Scotland, 14 February 1869; *d*. Carlops, Peeblesshire, Scotland, 15 November 1959), *atomic physics, meteorological physics*.

Wilson's father, John Wilson, was well-known in Scotland for his experiments in sheep farming; his mother, the former Annie Clark Harper, came from a Glasgow family of thread manufacturers. John Wilson died when Charles, the youngest of his eight children by two marriages, was four years old; and Mrs. Wilson then moved to Manchester. The family was not well off, and Wilson owed his university education to the kindness and financial support of his half brother William, a successful businessman in Calcutta.

Wilson attended Greenheyes Collegiate School in Manchester; and even then he showed an interest in natural science, preparing specimens for observation under the microscope. At the age of fifteen he entered Owens College, Manchester, registering as a medical student but taking a B.Sc. degree when he was eighteen. A further year was spent studying philosophy and the classics, after which Wilson won an entrance scholarship to Sidney Sussex College, Cambridge. By this time all thought of medicine had been abandoned, and he had determined to become a physicist. The years following receipt of his degree and the death of his half brother William (1892) were difficult ones, for he had to help support his mother, yet longed to devote himself to research. Wilson taught for a short time at Bradford Grammar School in York-shire but was drawn again to continue his experimental work at Cambridge, making just enough to live on by serving as demonstrator for medical students. It was at this time that Rutherford, Townsend, and McClelland became research students at the Cavendish Laboratory; and Wilson joined them in the famous discussions over tea.

In 1896 Wilson was awarded the Clerk Maxwell studentship for three years. After a year of work on atmospheric electricity problems for the Meteorological Council, he was elected in 1900 a fellow of Sidney Sussex College, and was appointed a university lecturer and demonstrator. For the two university posts his annual salaries were, respectively, £100 and £50; his duties were to take charge of the teaching of advanced practical physics and to lecture to the part II physics class on light, which was a new course. Wilson's influence on the teaching of experimental physics at Cambridge was considerable, his chief innovation being to give his students minor research problems to solve in the laboratory, rather than carry out textbook experiments. From 1925 to 1934 Wilson was Jacksonian professor of natural philosophy at Cambridge.

The Royal Society elected Wilson a fellow in 1900, and awarded him the Hughes Medal in 1911, a Royal Medal in 1922, and the Copley Medal in 1935. A Nobel Prize for physics was awarded jointly to Wilson and A. H. Compton in 1927 for their work on the scattering of high-energy photons. Wilson was appointed Companion of Honour by the king in 1937, and held honorary degrees from Aberdeen, Glasgow, Manchester, Liverpool, London, and Cambridge.

At the age of thirty-nine Wilson married Jessie Fraser Dick; the couple had a son and two daughters. Soon after his retirement from the Jacksonian chair, Wilson left Cambridge and returned to Scotland. The twenty-three years of his retirement were extremely active. He continued climbing well into his eighties, and at eighty-six traveled in an airplane for the first time. He died after a short illness at his cottage a few miles from his birthplace.

Wilson attributed the shaping of his research career to his experiences on holiday in the Highlands:

In September 1894 I spent a few weeks in the Observatory . . . on the summit of Ben Nevis . . . . The wonderful optical phenomena shown when the sun shone on the clouds surrounding the hill-top, and especially the coloured rings surrounding the sun (coronas) or surrounding the shadow cast by the hill-top or observer on mist or cloud (glories), greatly excited my interest and made me wish to imitate them in the laboratory.[1]

Elsewhere he wrote: ". . . It is hardly necessary for me to say that these experiments might have had little result had it not been that they were made in the Cavendish Laboratory at the beginning of the wonderful years of the discovery of the electron, X-rays and radioactivity."[2] Such was the initial impetus behind Wilson's work. J. J. Thomson assessed his achievement thus:

This work of C. T. R. Wilson, proceeding . . . since 1895, has rarely been equalled as an example of ingenuity, insight, skill in manipulation, unfailing patience and dogged determination. . . . The beautiful photographs that he published [of the tracks of atomic particles] required years of unremitting work before they were brought to the standard he obtained. . . . It is to him that we owe the creation of a method which has been of inestimable value to the progress of science.[3]

Wilson well exemplifies the British experimental scientist whose inspiration was found not in mathematical concepts but in the observation of natural phenomena. Early in 1895 he posed himself a set of questions on cloud formation, and in March of that year he began to build the first apparatus to condense water vapor in dust-free air (see Fig. 1). By August he had established that the critical volume-ratio limit for drop formation in clean conditions was $V_2/V_1 = 1.25$. In February 1896, shortly after the discovery of X rays by Röntgen, Wilson used a primitive X-ray tube, made by J. J. Thomson's assistant, to irradiate the expansion chamber. At the same volume ratio as before, a dense fog was produced by the X rays, which led Wilson to suppose that the condensation nuclei were ions, to which the conductivity of a gas exposed to X rays was attributed by Thomson and Rutherford. By the spring of 1899 he wrote a summary of his work: "General results of all the experiments. *Negative* ions *begin* to be caught about $V_2/V_1 = 1.25$ and *all* appear to be caught when $V_2/V_1 = 1.28$. Density of negative fog shows no increase from this point onwards. *Positive* ions begin to be visible about $V_2/V_1 = 1.31$. Fogs are constant and identical with the negative from 1.35 upwards."[4]

The phenomena discovered empirically by Wilson may, briefly, be explained as follows. When air saturated with water vapor is suddenly cooled by

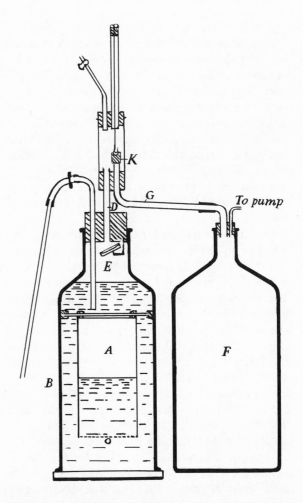

FIGURE 1. Wilson's 1895 apparatus. The gas to be expanded is in the glass vessel A, which itself is placed inside a glass bottle B, which is partially filled with water so as to trap the gas in the inner vessel. The air above the water in the bottle is connected with an evacuated vessel F by tubes D and G, to which are fitted valves E and K, the latter of which is normally closed. When this valve is quickly opened, the air at the top of the bottle B rushes into the evacuated vessel F and the water in B rises until it fills the top of the bottle, and by doing so, closes the valve E, so stopping further expansion of the gas in A. By suitably adjusting the initial volume of the gas in A and the amount of water in B, the relative expansion of the gas in A can be precisely controlled.

an adiabatic expansion, it becomes supersaturated. In this condition, condensation into droplets will occur, provided there are nuclei present. Dust particles allow drops to form immediately, and so Wilson carefully eliminated all gross matter from his apparatus. Negative ions act as nuclei at an expansion ratio of 1.25 (fourfold supersaturation), and positive ions become nuclei at 1.31 (sixfold supersaturation). At about 1.38 (eightfold supersaturation) air molecules themselves will act as drop nuclei in the absence of all others. The vapor pressure of a spherical drop is greater than that of a plane surface in inverse proportion to the radius of the drop, so that if a very small drop forms, it will reevaporate immediately. A nucleus gives the necessary larger radius to assist the persistence of a drop. The surface tension of the liquid of the drop also is important, because it acts to contract the drop and thus reduce the radius. If a drop carries an electric charge, this acts contrary to the surface tension, tending to enlarge the drop. Because of a characteristic of the skin of a water drop, negative ions are more effective than positive ions in nucleation.

Wilson continued to experiment with ultraviolet radiation and other techniques for producing condensation effects, but soon concentrated on atmospheric electricity, not returning to the cloud chamber until December 1910. He designed an improved chamber with new methods of illumination and the possibility of photographing the results. At this time Wilson realized that it might be possible to reveal the track of an $\alpha$ ray by condensing water drops onto the ions produced by its passage. During March 1911 he saw this effect produced in his apparatus. Thus, the elucidation of phenomena seen in the Scottish hills led to the possibility of studying the processes of radioactivity, and the Wilson cloud chamber became an important piece of laboratory equipment. But it was in the study of cosmic rays that it achieved its full power, particularly in the refined form developed by Patrick Blackett, in which it was possible to study particles of very high energy and the production of electron-positron pairs with the chamber situated in a strong magnetic field.

The study of atmospheric electricity was dramatically thrust upon Wilson by the experience of his hair standing on end while at the summit of Ben Nevis in June 1895. The subsequent lightning flash impressed on him the magnitude of the electric field of a thundercloud. In his experiments he used captive balloons and kites to measure the strength of the electric field at various heights. He also developed a sensitive electrometer and voltameter, as well as a capillary electrometer for the measurement of the earth's electric field and air-earth currents. In fine weather there is always an electric field directed toward the earth that has a potential gradient of 100–200 volts per meter. The total negative charge on the whole earth is about 500,000 coulombs. The current from the upper atmosphere to the earth is sufficient to discharge the earth in a matter of minutes, so the problem is to account for the maintenance of the earth's charge.

Equilibrium probably is kept by the thunderstorm, the global incidence of which is about two thousand at any given time.

The theory put forward by Wilson to explain the electric structure of a thundercloud implied that the top would be positively charged and the bottom negatively charged. He thought that larger drops would be found on negatively charged nuclei, causing them to fall faster than those positively charged. Wilson's last scientific paper, "A Theory of Thundercloud Electricity," was communicated to the Royal Society in 1956, when he was the oldest fellow. Although his theory is not complete, it certainly was a crucial contribution to a problem that has yet to be fully solved.

Work on the conductivity of air was done by Wilson in 1900, using very well insulated electroscopes. They always showed a residual leakage that was the same in daylight and in darkness, and for positive or negative charge. Having described his results, Wilson made the significant statement: "Experiments were now carried out to test whether the production of ions in dust-free air could be explained as being due to radiation from sources . . . outside our atmosphere, possibly radiation like Röntgen rays or like cathode rays, but of enormously greater penetrating power."[5] This ingenious hypothesis was tested in 1911 by Victor Hess, who took an electroscope up in a balloon, thereby discovering that after an initial fall, the conductivity of air increased with altitude. To explain this effect, Hess postulated the existence of "cosmic radiation."

*NOTES*

1. Nobel lecture, Stockholm, 12 Dec. 1927.
2. "Ben Nevis Sixty Years Ago," in *Weather*, **9** (1954), 310.
3. J. J. Thomson, *Recollections and Reflections* (London, 1936), 419–420.
4. From laboratory notebook A3 in the library of the Royal Society, cited by Dee and Wormell, "Index . . .," 57.
5. "On the Leakage of Electricity Through Dust-Free Air," in *Proceedings of the Cambridge Philosophical Society*, **11** (1900–1902), 32.

*BIBLIOGRAPHY*

I. ORIGINAL WORKS. Wilson published 45 papers between 1895 and 1956, a third of them in *Proceedings of the Cambridge Philosophical Society*, and the majority of the remainder in *Proceedings of the Royal Society*, ser. A. A complete list of the papers is printed in Blackett (below), 294 f., and in Dee and Wormell (below), 65 f. An autobiographical account is "Reminiscences of My

Early Years," in *Notes and Records. Royal Society of London*, **14** (1960), 163–173. MS laboratory records for 1895–1940 are in the library of the Royal Society.

II. SECONDARY LITERATURE. See P. M. S. Blackett, "Charles Thomson Rees Wilson 1869–1959," in *Biographical Memoirs of Fellows of the Royal Society*, **6** (1960), 269–295; and P. I. Dee and T. W. Wormell, "An Index to C. T. R. Wilson's Laboratory Records and Notebooks in the Library of the Royal Society," in *Notes and Records. Royal Society of London*, **18** (1963), 54–66.

G. L'E. TURNER

**WILSON, EDMUND BEECHER** (*b.* Geneva, Illinois, 19 October 1856; *d.* New York, N.Y., 3 March 1939), *cytology, embryology, heredity.*

Wilson was among the most important and prolific biologists in the last part of the nineteenth and first part of the twentieth centuries. As an investigator of remarkable observational and analytical skill, he contributed significantly to an understanding of the structure and function of the cell. As a meticulous and exhaustive encyclopedist, he brought together and organized vast quantities of research related to the cell—its structural, hereditary, and developmental aspects. Wilson's *The Cell in Development and Inheritance* (1896) is a monument to his comprehensive and profound understanding of major biological problems of the time, many of which are still unsolved. Born three years before the publication of Darwin's *Origin of Species*, Wilson grew up in an era during which biology was transformed from a science dominated by natural history into one that was more and more concerned with rigorous and quantitative experimental analysis. His own work played a significant part in this transition.

Wilson was the son of Caroline Clarke and Isaac G. Wilson. His father, a graduate of Brown University and Harvard Law School, had gone west in the 1840's to open a law practice. In later years he served as county judge, circuit court judge, and finally as chief justice of the Appellate Court of Chicago. Wilson's maternal ancestors were descended from Thomas Clarke, reputed mate of the Mayflower who had settled at Plymouth, Massachusetts, in 1623. After the financial crash of 1837, Scotto Clarke (Wilson's grandfather) moved from Boston to Geneva, Illinois, with his four children, of whom Caroline was the second youngest. She and Isaac Wilson were married in 1843 and had five children: Frank, Ellen, Charles, Edmund, and Harriet.

Wilson grew up in a cultured atmosphere that encouraged his two lifelong interests: the study of living things and music. When his father was appointed a circuit court judge in 1859, Wilson's parents moved to Chicago and he was "adopted" by his mother's sister, Mrs. Charles Patten of Geneva. Thus, from an early age Wilson had two homes, both of which encouraged his varied interests and provided him with, as he wrote, "four parents between whom I hardly distinguished in point of love and loyalty." During his childhood he spent considerable time in the countryside around Geneva collecting specimens, which he stored in a special room provided for him in the Patten house. In the fall of 1872 his uncle suggested that young Wilson (he was not quite sixteen) take over the small country school that his brother Charles had taught the year before. Living with his aunt and uncle in Oswego, Illinois, he spent a year teaching everything from arithmetic to reading. It was a rewarding experience and strongly supported his desire for further education. Inspired by a cousin, Samuel Clarke, who was then attending Antioch College in Ohio, Wilson decided in the summer of 1873 to apply for admission to that institution. At Antioch he received his first formal instruction in zoology, botany, Latin, geometry, trigonometry, and chemistry, the latter with laboratory work that he found especially appealing. He paid his way partly by odd jobs, one of which was manufacturing the gas by which the college was lit. Instead of returning to Antioch the following fall, however, Wilson decided to begin a career in science by attending the Sheffield Scientific School at Yale, about which he had heard so much from Sam Clarke, who was enrolled there. Realizing that he lacked the proper background to enter Yale, he decided to live with his parents in Chicago for the next year (1874–1875) and attend the (old) University of Chicago for additional preparation.

Wilson entered the Sheffield Scientific School in 1875, and during his first year he took courses in zoology with A. E. Verrill and in embryology with Sidney I. Smith. At Yale he also had his first real exposure to the study of heredity and evolution, through a series of lectures given by William Henry Brewer, who made an indelible impression on Wilson and his classmates by lecturing "with the utmost fire and vehemence."[1] After receiving the bachelor's degree (Ph.B.) in 1878, Wilson was invited to remain at Sheffield as a graduate student and assistant, which he did for one year; but soon Samuel Clarke once again found new and exciting horizons, this time at the newly opened Johns

Hopkins University, where he was then enrolled. Clarke's letters were so enthusiastic that Wilson and his close friend William T. Sedgwick, who also completed his studies at Yale, applied for and received fellowships to Hopkins beginning in the fall of 1878.

Wilson's three years at Hopkins opened up a wholly new world—that of original investigation: he studied with the physiologist H. Newell Martin and the morphologist William Keith Brooks, both of whom emphasized research by continually pointing out the many unsolved problems in contemporary biology. Wilson received his Ph.D. in 1881, then remained at Hopkins for another year as assistant. In the spring of 1882 he went abroad for further study. For several months he was at Cambridge, where he met Michael Foster, William Bateson, and T. H. Huxley. Wilson then proceeded to Leipzig, where he worked in the laboratory of the invertebrate zoologist Rudolf Leuckart and attended lectures by the mechanistic physiologist Carl Ludwig. After leaving Leipzig he headed south to the zoological station at Naples. Through an arrangement with Williams College, where Samuel Clarke was then teaching, Wilson obtained a table in the laboratory for part of the year 1882–1883. The Naples station made a deep and lasting impression on him, for he met and became close friends with Anton Dohrn, the director, and with a number of embryologists and invertebrate zoologists, including Edouard Meyer and Arnold Lang. Like his friend T. H. Morgan, Wilson found that his first experience at the Naples station was one of the most exciting of his life, and set the direction for much of his future thinking about biological research. Many years later he wrote: "It was a rich combination of serious effort, new friendships, incomparable beauty of scenery, a strange and piquant civilization, a new and charming language, new vistas of scientific work opening before me; in short, a realization of my wildest, most unreal dreams."[2]

On his return from Naples, Wilson taught for one year (1883–1884) at Williams College, replacing his cousin Sam Clarke, who was on leave to spend the year at Naples. The following year (1884–1885) he held a lectureship at the Massachusetts Institute of Technology, where he worked closely with his friend Sedgwick on a biology textbook they had begun planning several years earlier. In 1885 Wilson accepted an offer to head the biology department at Bryn Mawr College, where he remained until 1891, when he was appointed adjunct professor of zoology and chairman of the zoology department at Columbia. He remained at Columbia for the rest of his career, retiring as Da Costa professor of zoology in 1928.

Before assuming his official duties at Columbia, Wilson spent a year abroad, the first half with Theodor Boveri at Munich and the second half at Naples with the experimental embryologists Hans Driesch and Curt Herbst. During this and later years Wilson spent considerable time at marine stations and on collecting trips. His long association with the Marine Biological Laboratory, Woods Hole, Massachusetts (both as investigator and as trustee), and the Chesapeake Zoological Laboratory of Johns Hopkins were part and parcel of the importance he attached to studying living specimens, and especially marine forms as material for basic biological investigation.

A well-liked and eminently respected teacher, Wilson was known for his deep personal interest in his students. His lectures were highly polished and meticulously researched, possessing a balanced structure that demonstrated his strong sense of organization and aesthetics. Wilson's success as a teacher stemmed partly from his enormous erudition and from the warm and articulate manner in which he conveyed his enthusiasms. He taught students at Columbia, both graduate and undergraduate, to see biology as a whole, as a series of fields—such as heredity, evolution, and embryology—at a time when many workers saw only separate disciplines. Among Wilson's graduate students (or those who took some courses with him) at Columbia were G. N. Calkins, A. P. Mathews, C. E. McClung, H. J. Muller, Franz Schrader, and W. S. Sutton.

Music was of intense interest to Wilson throughout his life. He was a cellist of outstanding accomplishment, being, in the words of one contemporary musician, "the foremost non-professional player in New York."[3] To Wilson music was a solace, no less nor more beautiful than a living organism or a cell—something to which he owed, in his own words, some of the greatest pleasures of his life. In addition he loved sailing and skippered numerous collecting and pleasure expeditions out of Woods Hole, Bermuda, and other ports. He was also a linguist of considerable ability, with a knowledge of German, French, Italian, Spanish, and Arabic.

In 1904 Wilson married Anne Maynard Kidder, daughter of Jerome Henry Kidder, a friend of Spencer Fullerton Baird. Wilson had first met her at Woods Hole, where her family spent nearly every summer. The Wilsons had one daughter, Nancy, who became a professional cellist.

Although Wilson always worked concurrently on a variety of problems, his career can be divided roughly into three periods, each of which was dominated by a particular set of interests: 1879–1891, descriptive embryology and morphology (including studies of cell lineage); 1891–1903, experimental embryology (including the organization of the egg, the effects of various substances on differentiation, and artificial parthenogenesis); and 1903–1938, heredity (including the relation of Mendelism to cytology, sex determination, and evolution). To Wilson these various topics converged in a single problem: How does the individual organism lie implicit in the fertilized (or even unfertilized) egg? This problem could be broken down into a number of subsidiary and more specific questions: What is the mechanism by which the likeness of the parents is transmitted to the offspring? How is hereditary information transformed into a complete adult during embryonic development? How do the cell nucleus and its hereditary components direct the day-to-day activity of cells? How does the interaction between parts—nucleus and cytoplasm, egg and sperm, one embryonic tissue layer and another, the whole embryo and its environment—influence the final form of the adult organism? Early in his career Wilson saw that answers to all of these questions bring the investigator down to the level of the cell. He felt it was impossible fully to understand larger problems, such as those occurring on the tissue, organ, organismic, or population level, without a thorough knowledge of the cell—its structure, organization, and functions.

As a student of William Keith Brooks, Wilson was schooled in the aims and methods of morphology. Morphology, a discipline prominent in the late nineteenth century, utilized a variety of areas—embryology, systematics, comparative anatomy, cytology, heredity, and physiology—to determine phylogenetic relationships. Problems of embryology, for example, were not considered so much for their own value but, rather, for whatever light they might throw on the evolutionary history of various species. Although Wilson's later work, particularly after 1891, gradually moved away from such overriding concern with phylogeny, his early papers strongly showed the influence of Brooks, whom he found an inspiring teacher. Brooks let his students alone, and Wilson was able to pursue whatever leads he wanted in the laboratory. Brooks also taught his students to think of biology in terms of problems still to be solved, rather than as a static and accumulated body of facts. He had a distinct philosophical bent that led him to think of problems—biological or nonbiological—in a large framework. He seldom accepted any conclusion on its own, always examining not only the evidence on which it was based but also the underlying philosophical assumptions and points of view. Wilson wrote of his experience with Brooks: "It was through informal talks and discussions in the laboratory, at his house, and later at the summer laboratories by the sea that I absorbed new ideas, new problems, points of view, etc. . . . From him I learned how closely biological problems are bound up with philosophical considerations. He taught me to read Aristotle, Bacon, Hume, Berkeley, Huxley; to think about the phenomena of life instead of merely trying to record and classify them."[4]

**Descriptive Embryology and Morphology: 1879–1891.** Although Wilson published two papers on the systematics of Pycnogonida (sea spiders) in 1879 and 1881, the result of work he had carried out for the Ph.B. at Yale, his earliest work of importance involved studies on the embryology and morphology of the coelenterate *Renilla*. This work was undertaken for his doctoral dissertation and consisted of comparing serial sections of embryos to determine the cellular changes occurring during development. Among other things, he observed that despite the regular division of the nuclei, the cytoplasmic cleavage of the egg was variable, either definitely segmenting the egg surface from the beginning or being relatively unexpressed until as late as the fourth division, when simultaneous formation of all cell boundaries might occur. By observing the development of various members of the *Renilla* colony (not all polyps were the same morphologically), Wilson drew some interesting physiological, ontogenetic, and phylogenetic conclusions. His presentation of the *Renilla* work won the commendation of Huxley when Wilson was in England in 1882, and Huxley had the young man read the paper before the Royal Society (it was published in the *Philosophical Transactions* in 1883).[5]

During the two years following Wilson's return to the United States, his teaching duties at Williams College and M.I.T. provided little opportunity for continuing his research. He did, however, complete the writing of a textbook, *General Biology*, with Sedgwick, based upon ideas they both developed from observing H. Newell Martin's approach to introductory biology at Johns Hopkins. *General Biology*, published in 1886, was an attempt to treat the study of living organisms from a more analytical and integrated viewpoint than had been customary. To this end Wilson and Sedgwick treated life as a manifestation of chemical and physical laws; the properties of life were a result of the properties of its constituent atoms and molecules. They also included both plant and animal material in their discussion, and tried to show how all organic processes involved an interaction of the living system with its environment. *General Biology* provides one of the earliest examples of Wilson's broad perspective on biological problems, and as a textbook it was influential in bringing a new approach to the taxonomically and phylogenetically oriented introductory courses offered in most universities around the turn of the century.

After taking up his duties at Bryn Mawr in 1885, Wilson continued his studies on the cellular and morphological basis of early development with work on two annelids: *Lumbricus*, the earthworm, and *Nereis*, a marine polychaete. In his reports on *Lumbricus* (1887, 1889, 1890), he focused particularly on the origin of the mesoderm. He traced early development (cleavage through gastrula) in detail and demonstrated that the mesoderm is formed in a spiral or, as it was called, "mosaic" manner — that is, certain cells were set aside quite early to form the mesodermal tissues. These cells began to proliferate at the gastrula stage and all mesodermal tissues originated from them. Wilson's work on *Lumbricus* settled an existing controversy on the nature of mesoderm origin and showed, in conjunction with the subsequent work on *Nereis*, that spiral cleavage probably was characteristic of all annelids.

The earthworm proved to be a less than satisfactory organism for such studies, however, because it was difficult to follow the cells during successive cleavages. Following the lead of E. A. Andrews of Johns Hopkins, who had first pointed out the favorable nature of *Nereis* larvae (obtained at Woods Hole) for early embryological studies (these organisms show highly precise, regular, and easily observable cleavage patterns), Wilson carried out an exhaustive study of these forms. The *Nereis* work, published in 1890 and 1892 (although carried out mostly between 1885 and 1890), was a landmark both in the history of modern biology and in Wilson's career.

To study early cleavage Wilson developed to a high degree a method known as "cell lineage." It involved following the cell-by-cell development of young embryos from fertilization to blastula, cataloging the exact position of every daughter cell. From such studies it was possible to determine the exact ancestry of every cell in a blastula, and thus to determine the pattern by which cell division had occurred. Cell lineage studies are enormously intricate and detailed, and require considerable patience and observational skill (see Figure 1). The purpose of these studies was to apply the methods of comparative embryology to very early stages of development in different species. By accurately determining which cells in the early embryo came from which "lineage," for example, Wilson was able to show that triploblastic animals (those having three germ layers) fall into two large groups in terms of the mode of mesodermal formation. One group, including the annelids, arthropods, and mollusks, showed the spiral or mosaic pattern he had observed in the earthworm. The other group, including the echinoderms, primitive chordates, and vertebrates, showed a pattern called "radial," in which the mesoderm originates from pouches in the archenteron of the gastrula. Thus, cell lineage provided a means of establishing homologies in very early embryonic development that often were obscured in later stages. The work on *Lumbricus* and *Nereis* confirmed the study of cell lineage as an important embryological and morphological tool. It also established Wilson's reputation as a biologist of considerable observational skill and interpretive ability.

Wilson's detailed work also showed, however, that the problem of homologies, as many biologists were beinning to suspect, was more complex than had originally been thought when Ernst Haeckel proposed the biogenetic law in 1866. Although there might be many similarities among large animal phyla in cleavage patterns, there were some very important differences: structures obviously homologous in later embryonic stages sometimes derived from noncorresponding cells of earlier stages. Cell lineage patterns, like any other embryonic patterns, were not absolute criteria, and could suggest phylogenetic relationships only in the broadest outlines. Wilson recognized that embryonic processes (and structures) undergo evolution just as adults do, and that the present pattern of an organism's development is not a fossilized repetition of its ancestral history.

The choice of problems in Wilson's early work was largely influenced by the aims and methods of the morphologists, such as Brooks, under whom he was trained. Yet whatever problem he studied

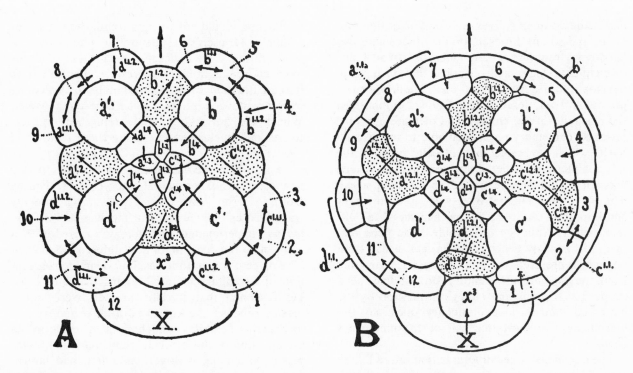

FIGURE 1.   Cell lineage study of young embryo of the marine worm *Nereis*. Letters and numbers indicate generational relationships; arrows indicate cleavage patterns. SOURCE: E. B. Wilson, "Cell Lineage of *Nereis*," in *Journal of Morphology,* **6** (1892), 396.

always showed the distinct mark of his personality: a meticulous attention to detail and an eye for larger issues. At the same time, interested as he was in the grander problems of evolution, or the "nature" of life, he rigorously avoided flights of fancy or ungrounded speculation. He could work on cell lineage as a means of understanding evolutionary relationships, without committing himself unalterably to a strict and rigid interpretation of embryological homologies. To Wilson, the primary process in biological investigation was the accurate determination of what happened in any phenomenon. Once the process or structure was described and observed to be repeatable, then it could be related to larger issues and theories—the understandings—of how life is organized.

**Experimental Embryology and Cytology: 1891– 1903.** Wilson's first year as adjunct professor of zoology at Columbia was spent on leave in Europe (1891–1892). During the first half he worked with Theodor Boveri at Munich, and during the second half at the zoological station in Naples. From Boveri he learned much about the chromosomes and their relation to normal or abnormal development. He imbibed Boveri's concern for the importance of the chromosomes in cell division and in determining the course of development. By the time Wilson reached Munich, Boveri had al-

ready concluded that the nucleus—specifically the chromosomes—was the most important element in determining an organism's heredity. Further, Boveri argued that the chromosomes should be expected to influence development specifically—a thesis he was finally able to demonstrate in 1901 with experiments on doubly and triply fertilized sea urchin eggs. Particularly important during his stay in Munich were what Wilson learned about cytology and the strong personal relationship he developed with Boveri. To Wilson, Boveri was "far more than a brilliant scientific discoverer and teacher. He was a many-sided man, gifted in many directions, an excellent musician, a good amateur painter, and we found many points of contact far outside of the realm of science."[6] Wilson dedicated his major work, *The Cell in Development and Inheritance* (1896), to Boveri; and they remained close friends until Boveri's death in 1915.

At Naples, Wilson was exposed to the new experimental embryology through the work of Hans Driesch and Curt Herbst, both of whom were testing Wilhelm Roux's mosaic theory of development, put forth in 1888. Roux claimed that during cleavage, hereditary material is qualitatively divided among the daughter cells so that by the time the organism is fully differentiated, each cell has only one type of determinant (muscle cells have only muscle determinants, liver cells only liver determinants, and so on). Driesch, on the other hand, isolated cells from very young embryos—two-, four-, or eight-cell stage—and observed that each could develop into a normal larva, contradicting Roux's premises. To Driesch, these findings emphasized the plasticity of the embryo and of the embryonic process. The embryo remained able to reconstruct itself, which suggested that all cells retained the full complement of hereditary information, which was not qualitatively restricted, as Roux supposed. The Roux-Driesch controversy focused on a new and important question: the mechanism of cell differentiation. Although this problem had been recognized for many generations (in fact, it had been implicit in preformation and epigenesis arguments from the seventeenth century on), it had been eclipsed as a prominent biological question by the increased interest in evolutionary questions (by morphology) in the latter half of the nineteenth century.

The questions of cell differentiation raised by the Roux-Driesch controversy greatly stimulated Wilson's imagination, and turned his attention away from the more morphologically oriented studies and toward more critical questions of experimental embryology. Although he never abandoned the older methods of observation or the study of cell lineage, he began to see that embryology had important questions in its own right. Characteristically, Wilson kept his balance in the cross fire between the Roux and Driesch camps. He realized from his previous work on *Nereis* that although developmental processes are indeed determined, they also are plastic—they constantly reveal an interplay between the hereditary characteristics of the organism and the total environmental conditions to which it is exposed. The manner of development of a part, Wilson wrote in 1899, is "a manifestation of the general formative energy acting at a particular point under given conditions—the formative processes in special parts [being] definitely correlated with the organization of the entire mass."[7] He was acutely aware that embryonic parts continually interact, to differing degrees at various stages and varying from species to species.[8] Although he reserved his final judgment until more critical evidence was available (unlike many other biologists, who quickly took sides), from the early 1890's Wilson tended to agree with Driesch in opposing the seemingly very simplistic nature of the mosaic theory.[9] The Roux theory was mechanically possible and logically consistent, but

to Wilson it could not account for all the facts—for example, Driesch's results or the phenomena of regeneration. Like Driesch, he saw that embryos have enormous abilities to restore themselves to normal function even if profoundly disturbed by experimental conditions. Unlike Driesch, however, Wilson did not take ultimate refuge in mystical forces and entelechies to explain these restorative capacities.

Exposure to the problems and methods of the new school of experimental embryology (called by Roux's term, *Entwicklungsmechanik*, roughly translated as "developmental mechanics," or simply as "experimental embryology") raised in Wilson's mind the question of how differentiation *does* take place if it is not the result of a simple segregation of hereditary material among daughter cells. He reasoned that if differentiation were not a mosaic process, the key to both its regularity and its amazing flexibility somehow must reside in the organization of the egg cell, particularly the cytoplasm. Assuming, as Boveri and others had shown, that every daughter cell receives the same number and kind of chromosomes as the parent cell, he concluded that differentiation must be triggered by variations in the cytoplasm in which each nucleus lies. Thus, the egg cell's cytoplasm must be "preorganized" in such a way that regional localization of substances exists before cleavage begins. How the cytoplasm became structured in the first place was utter speculation, yet on the assumption of preorganization in the egg, Wilson could explain why some species seemed to show mosaic, and others nonmosaic, patterns of development. Those species appearing to have mosaic development simply showed cytoplasmic regionalization at a much earlier time in the embryo's life than those that seemed to be nonmosaic.

The concept of "prelocalization," or "formative substances," was strongly criticized by numerous workers, including T. H. Morgan, who objected that the idea simply pushed the problem of differentiation back another step by postulating that it had already taken place within the cytoplasm of the egg. Since there was no satisfactory explanation of how this localization was attained, the concept of cytoplasmic differentiation in the ovum seemed to be without substance. Yet Wilson retained a conviction that prelocalization was to some extent a reality, for his studies suggested that the cytoplasm was not a homogeneous mix but was, in fact, quite diverse in its local composition. Although it is recognized today that eggs (indeed, all cells) have regional localization, such as polarity or gradients of distribution of certain substances, it has become clear that in many species the organization of the cytoplasm has little to do with the process of differentiation.

As a result of his work with Boveri, Wilson developed a strong interest in the cytological events surrounding cell division, particularly those involved in the maturation of the egg. On returning to the United States, he took up the study of chromosome movements, particularly spindle formation and the origin of the centrosomes (today called cell centrioles). In a lengthy study done with his pupil A. P. Mathews (1895), Wilson produced solid evidence against Hermann Fol's widely held theory of the "quadrille of the centers." (Fol maintained that the sperm and egg centrosomes fuse after fertilization, then divide, moving through the cytoplasm, like dancers changing partners in the eighteenth-century square dance quadrille, to form the two poles of the spindle apparatus.) Wilson showed that in echinoderms (especially the sea urchin) the poles were formed only by division of the sperm's centrosome. He went on to demonstrate in later papers that the centrosomes were formed within the cytoplasm, not within the nucleus, as had previously been thought. Close observation of the movements and doubling of centrosomes convinced Wilson that the replication of these bodies did not cause, and was not caused by, the replication of the chromosomes. The doubling of both sets of structures probably responded, he maintained, to some underlying rhythm in the cell's activity. He demonstrated this clearly by comparing rhythmic changes in protoplasmic activity in fragments of fertilized eggs of the marine mollusk *Dentalium*. Parallel rhythmic changes could be observed in the fragments and in nucleated portions of the same egg, even though the two parts were no longer physically associated.

During his initial decade at Columbia, Wilson prepared the first edition of *The Cell in Development and Inheritance* (1896), the basis of which was a series of lectures he gave in 1892–1893. *The Cell* was much more than a compilation of all the relevant information on various parts of the cell and various cell processes. It was not only a synthesis of a great deal of information (the bibliography in itself represents a prodigious effort) but also reflected Wilson's wide-ranging and balanced views of contemporary problems, and his special emphasis on the function of cytology in elucidating such topics as embryology, heredity, evolution,

and general physiology. The primary aim of the work, according to Wilson, was no less grandiose than "to bring the cell-theory and the evolution-theory into organic connection."[10] He believed that a fundamental understanding of the cell in all its aspects (structure, development, and physiological functions) would provide a better understanding of those fundamental processes—heredity, variation, and differentiation—on which evolution was ultimately based.

The book is organized to lead the reader to appreciate the role of the cell—the nucleus and chromosomes—in heredity. The opening chapter deals with cell structure in broad overview, the second with cell division. The following three chapters deal with the germ cells: their structure and mode of origin, the phenomenon of fertilization, and the maturation divisions by which the gametes are prepared for fertilization. The sixth chapter deals with cell organization—the structure of chromosomes and the evidence for their "individuality"—and with centrosome origin and astral formation. The seventh chapter reviews the physiological properties of the cell, and the eighth treats the maturation of the ovum and the general laws of cell division of which it is an expression. In the final chapter Wilson considers the basic phenomena of development (as elucidated by Roux, Driesch, Herbst, Chabry, and others) in terms of cell structure and function.

The central conclusion of the book is in the eighth and ninth chapters, where Wilson focused on an in-depth study of the cleavage of the fertilized egg and on the various experimental results that shed light on the underlying processes by which cleavage could produce cell differentiation. Thus, at the end of the book Wilson was able to muster many lines of evidence to demonstrate the key point: "that the nucleus contains the physical basis of inheritance; and that chromatin, its essential constituent, is the idioplasm postulated on Nägeli's theory."[11] Several lines of evidence led Wilson to place the seat of heredity within the cell nucleus and particularly in the chromosomes. First, the persistent accuracy with which the chromosomes replicate and are distributed, in contrast with the often random division of the cytoplasm by region, indicates the importance of ensuring that each daughter cell receives a full complement of chromosomes. Although Wilson had not abandoned the idea of cell prelocalization, he recognized that compartmentalization of the cytoplasm through cleavage was a much less precise process than distribution of the chromosomes. The greater precision of the chromosome distribution mechanism suggested that it was intimately related to the hereditary process, which by definition must be a regular and highly accurate phenomenon.

Second, the work of Boveri in particular (1887) had suggested that chromosomes maintain their individuality and continuity from one cell generation to the next. Contrary to an idea prevalent in the 1870's and 1880's, he and others had shown that the chromosomes do not disintegrate between divisions, but have the same spatial arrangement after interphase as before. Although Wilson was not willing to conclude that the physical structure of the chromosomes was necessarily maintained unbroken from interphase to interphase, he did argue that all evidence pointed to the maintenance of hereditary integrity.

Third, abundant cytological evidence showed that while sperm and egg had enormously different cytoplasmic components (the sperm has virtually no cytoplasm), they seemed, on the whole, to affect the heredity of the offspring equally. Thus it would appear, Wilson pointed out, that the cytoplasm had relatively little hereditary function.

Fourth, experiments by M. Nussbaum, Gruber, Verworn, and others on many different types of cells (including Protozoa) indicated that enucleated cells did not function normally. Whatever the exact function of the nucleus, it was necessary to the normal maintenance of cell activity. It seemed evident that the control that the nucleus appeared to exert over the entire cell must be an expression of the cell's heredity.

Even in 1896 Wilson recognized that the control of the nucleus over the cytoplasm was ultimately a matter of chemical interactions. Too little was known about the chemistry of chromatin for him to formulate a specific idea about how this might work, but he did maintain that the nucleus was the seat of constructive (anabolic), and the cytoplasm of destructive (catabolic), processes. This view came directly from Claude Bernard, who some twenty years earlier (1878) had postulated a similar division of chemical labor between nucleus and cytoplasm.[12] To Wilson, inheritance (associated with the nucleus) "is the recurrence through the transmission from generation to generation of a specific substance or idioplasm which we have seen reason to identify with chromatin. If the nucleus be the formative center of the cell, if nutritive substances be elaborated by or under the influence of the nucleus while they are built into the living fabric, then the specific character of the cytoplasm is determined by that of the nucleus."[13]

Yet Wilson was aware enough of biological phenomena in general to recognize that the cytoplasm also must profoundly influence the nucleus. The nucleus could not function, after all, if it did not have a cytoplasm upon which to act. But more than that, he saw that as the nucleus altered the cytoplasm (by building up certain substances), of necessity it also altered its own environment. Chemical change—interaction and modification—was always occurring between the nucleus and cytoplasm in a living cell. Development was nothing more than a highly ordered example of this interaction, in which the expression of hereditary information in each cell nucleus was successively altered as cleavage and morphogenetic changes occurred. To Wilson, the nucleus and the cytoplasm were intimately involved in the cell's chemistry, heredity, and development. They had different but complementary functions, and had to be understood in relation to each other. Neither could, or should, be viewed in isolation.

*The Cell* went through three editions and numerous reprintings. It is estimated that this book has been the single most influential treatise on cytology during the twentieth century. Many of the problems that Wilson clearly outlined (such as the relationship between the nucleus and cytoplasm in cell differentiation) are still being investigated. And no one has succeeded in posing those problems more clearly than he did in his many writings, particularly in *The Cell*. In reading *The Cell*, one is impressed not only by Wilson's skill as a summarizer (an encyclopedist in the best sense of the word) but also with the enormous patience and effort on the part of hundreds of other workers as well, who over the past century have contributed to the growing knowledge of cell structure and function.

**Studies on Chromosomes and Heredity: 1903–1912.** Historically, one of the most important functions of *The Cell* was to pave the way for a more rapid acceptance of Mendelian theory, once it was reintroduced to the scientific community in 1900. By focusing attention on the cell nucleus, and particularly on the chromosomes as the seat of heredity, Wilson prepared many biologists—especially cytologists—to see the relationship between Mendel's laws and the events of maturation of the sperm and egg. Recognition of the possible parallel between the segregation and random assortment of Mendelian "factors" (later called "genes") and the chromosome reduction division (meiosis) that occurs during gametogenesis ultimately provided a material basis for the science of genetics.

Although two of the rediscoverers of Mendel's work—Carl Correns and Hugo de Vries—had offered a chromosomal interpretation of their own and Mendel's findings shortly after 1900, it was not based on much observational evidence. In 1900, however, H. von Winiwarter reported the occurrence of synapsis in early reduction division; and in 1901 T. H. Montgomery discovered that the chromosomes are present in germ cell nuclei (prior to reduction division) as pairs of homologues. With these observations Wilson and his group were ready by 1901 to seek possible connections between Mendelism and cytology. In fact, it was one of Wilson's graduate students, Walter S. Sutton, who made the connection first and most cogently (1902). In studying synapsis (the intertwining of the two chromosomes in a homologous pair of chromosomes), Sutton showed that the visible behavior of the chromosomes afforded an explanation of the first and second Mendelian laws. His careful studies of chromosomal pairing provided cytological evidence that the chromosomes segregating in reduction division are the two members of a homologous pair, not any two random chromosomes. Thus each chromosome could be considered as the counterpart of a Mendelian factor, or at least a bearer of one factor. Wilson quickly came to see the importance of Sutton's work, and supported his conclusions.

In 1902 another former student of Wilson's, Clarence E. McClung, pointed out that the unpaired "accessory" chromosome (later called the X by Wilson), long known to exist in the males of some arthropods, might offer a clue to how sex was inherited. Wilson was intrigued by McClung's work and set out to study the occurrence and distribution of the accessory chromosome in a number of species, mostly insects. In 1905 Wilson and, independently, Nettie M. Stevens of Bryn Mawr published extensive cytological evidence suggesting a chromosomal basis for sex determination.[14] These works provided the missing link between cytology and heredity. Wilson and Stevens concluded that females normally have a chromosome complement of XX and males have one of XY. In oögenesis and spermatogenesis, the X and X (for oögenesis) and the X and Y (for spermatogenesis) separate, and end up, by meiotic division, in separate gametes. All eggs thus have a single X chromosome, while sperm can have either an X or a Y. When a Y-bearing sperm fertilizes an egg, the off-

spring is a male (XY); when an X-bearing sperm fertilizes an egg, the offspring is a female (XX).

Wilson and Stevens recognized that a few groups of organisms have variations (or reversals) of this scheme—for instance, species that normally lack a Y or in which the females are XY and the males XX (the latter case is true for moths, butterflies, and birds). The 1905 papers by Wilson and Stevens not only cleared up a long-standing controversy on the nature of sex determination (for example, whether it was hereditarily or environmentally induced) but also were the first reports that any specific hereditary trait (or set of characteristics, such as those associated with sex) could be identified with one specific pair of chromosomes.

Wilson pursued studies on the chromosomes, particularly in relation to sex inheritance, over the next seven years (1905–1912), producing a series of eight papers entitled "Studies on Chromosomes." In general these papers worked out the chromosomal theory of sex determination (essentially as it is understood today) in great detail, and supported its Mendelian nature. Among other things, Wilson showed that the Y chromosomes in different insect species are of widely different sizes in comparison with the X; in some species the X and Y are of virtually equal size, whereas in others the Y is very small, and in still others it is nonexistent. He also observed that in a species where the female is normally XX, some females have the combination XXY and some males have only a single X and no Y. Wilson interpreted these cases as having resulted from the failure of the X and the Y to separate during spermatogenesis in the organism's male parent. When the same phenomenon was observed in *Drosophila* by C. B. Bridges in 1913, he and Wilson jointly coined the term "nondisjunction" for the failure of two homologues to segregate during meiosis. These and other results led Wilson to postulate that the Y chromosome had degenerated over the course of evolutionary history. He felt it represented either inactive chromatin material or an excess that was duplicated elsewhere in the chromosome group.[15] Wilson considered the X to be the active member of the sex chromosome pair, and therefore the causal agent of sex determination. Although we know today that the matter is not so simple, he was essentially correct in judging that the Y has little actual hereditary function, in relation to sex or anything else.

Wilson speculated that the difference between

the X and the Y might be due to the presence on the X (or associated with it) of a specific chemical substance (perhaps an enzyme) that produces a definite reaction on the part of the developing individual.[16] Surprisingly, his idea that a chromosome might carry out its hereditary function by producing enzymes is close to the modern conception that genes (located on chromosomes) code for enzymes that catalyze specific biochemical reactions. Although Wilson was the first to point out, repeatedly, that too little was known about the chemistry of living cells to formulate any meaningful theory of how characteristics were determined, he saw the importance of phrasing hereditary or developmental problems in chemical terms.

Wilson's studies on chromosomes provided the important cytological foundation upon which T. H. Morgan's later chromosome theory of inheritance was based. In 1910 Morgan, Wilson's close friend and colleague in the zoology department at Columbia, discovered a white-eyed male *Drosophila* in his laboratory culture (*Drosophila* normally have red eyes). Although initially skeptical of the Mendelian theory, Morgan found that Mendel's assumptions provided the best means of accounting for the hereditary pattern observed in the white-eye condition. Moreover, he saw that white eyes seemed to occur mostly but not exclusively in males, a fact that could be explained only by assuming that the "factor" for eye color was located on the X chromosome. Wilson quickly saw the implications of this work, and in 1911 he used Morgan's findings as further support for a chromosomal interpretation of sex. He also saw immediately what later came to be called sex-linked inheritance. Thus, the keystone to the chromosome theory of inheritance was laid in the Columbia laboratory, where Morgan from the animal-breeding side, and Wilson from the cytological side, provided evidence that hereditary units exist as material entities located on chromosomes in the nucleus.

Aside from his intellectual contribution to the chromosome theory of heredity, Wilson was influential as a strong supporter of Morgan and his group as they expanded the *Drosophila* work. As head of the zoology department, he encouraged all the "fly room" workers, especially graduate students, by his persistent interest in the work and by the obvious connections it bore to his earlier work on chromosomes. Most of the students who worked with Morgan (Muller, A. H. Sturtevant, Bridges, Edgar Altenberg) had been Columbia undergraduates and had taken Wilson's courses or used his textbook in the introductory course taught

by G. N. Calkins and James H. McGregor. In his teaching from 1906 on, Wilson particularly emphasized the relations between Mendelian heredity, chromosomes, and evolutionary theory, using as the text for his second-level one-semester course on heredity R. H. Lock's provocative book *Variation, Heredity and Evolution* (1906). Far ahead of its time, Lock's book treated Mendelian heredity, cytology, and Darwinian evolution in a completely integrated fashion, something few biologists did until after 1915.

Thus many of the students who came to work with Morgan after 1910 had been prepared by Wilson to see clearly the relationships between chromosomes, Mendelian theory, and the concept of natural selection in a way that not even Morgan himself was able to accomplish at the time. Wilson also supported the *Drosophila* group by incorporating its findings into his own work, and by championing the new ideas long before many other biologists began to follow Morgan's lead. Although neither Wilson, Morgan, nor any other biologists at the time could "see" that Mendelian genes were parts of chromosomes, or that crossing-over and exchange of chromosome parts actually took place as the *Drosophila* group postulated, Wilson felt that the conclusions were sound because they were consistent and fitted all the data. In a lecture in 1913, he pointed out that although the hypothesis of crossing-over and chromosome mapping techniques based on it were bold ventures, they were justified because, pragmatically, they worked; that is, they accounted for all the data better than any other explanations. To Wilson it was by just such venturesome ideas that new possibilities of discovery were opened.[17]

Recognizing the importance to Morgan's work of testing the assumption of crossing-over (in meiotic divisions), Wilson set out in 1912 (study VIII) to examine the cytological evidence for such a process. Obtaining preparations of germ tissue from F. A. Janssens (who had originated the hypothesis of crossing-over in 1909), A. and K. E. Schreiner, and McClung, Wilson showed that synapsis seemed to be a real phenomenon—that is, homologous chromosomes do appear to come together and wrap around each other prior to the first meiotic division. The evidence was not clear enough, however, to show any signs of the actual exchange of chromosome parts. It was not until 1931 that techniques were developed sufficiently for such workers with animals as Curt Stern and with plants as Barbara McClintock and Harriet Creighton to observe actual exchanges between strands and thus provide final proof that crossing-over was a real phenomenon.

The years between 1902 and 1912 marked the zenith of Wilson's creative period. The eight studies on chromosomes were brilliant examples of his observational and analytical skill. In this work his broad-reaching mind incisively drew the connections between Mendelian theory and cytology, long before many other workers (including Morgan) were prepared to make the same bold leaps. The chromosomal concept of Mendelian heredity was a logical view for Wilson to maintain because it provided the link he had intuitively held for many years between the cell, heredity, and development. The main theme enunciated in *The Cell* (1896) was being realized in actuality by the parallel studies on chromosomes in Wilson's laboratory and on the process of heredity in Morgan's.

**Later Work: 1912–1938.** Wilson's studies after 1912 were variations of a single basic question: What cell constituents other than the chromosomes affect the hereditary process? There were really two aspects to this question. One was that of extrachromosomal inheritance: the replicative function of such organelles as chloroplasts or mitochondria, which by 1920 were known to be able to reproduce themselves without nuclear control. The other question was the effect of the cytoplasm on the expression of genetic potential in the nucleus. In investigating the former, Wilson studied various cytoplasmic bodies in scorpions and insects: the Golgi bodies, chondriosomes (today called mitochondria), and vacuomes (today, vacuoles). From these observations he concluded that at least the Golgi bodies and chondriosomes increase in size and fragment, so that daughter cells get equal numbers with each division. Nevertheless, he maintained that these cytoplasmic bodies do not have genetic individuality as chromosomes do—they are all very much alike, and must be derived from the same genetic ancestry, with little or no divergence.[18] In investigating the effect of the cytoplasm on expression of genetic potential, Wilson steadfastly stated his earlier view that it is impossible to make any rigid distinction between the nucleus and cytoplasm. What was important was to attempt to determine the precise ways in which the nucleus influenced the cytoplasm, and vice versa; in that way not only would it be possible to achieve a clearer understanding of how the cell functions to maintain itself day by day, but also it would be possible to see more clearly how such phenomena as cell differentiation might be brought about.

In his later years Wilson came more and more to view the cell as a plastic, ever-changing structure, continually building itself up and tearing itself down, a constant dialectic between stability and change, heredity and variation, maintenance and differentiation. In the flux of materials and changing structures, the constancy in cell life was an underlying organization of molecules and intramolecular associations that produced life.

The culminating work of Wilson's later years was the complete revision and expansion of *The Cell* into a third edition (1925). So much information had accumulated regarding cytological phenomena in the quarter-century since the second edition that only Wilson, with his encyclopedic mind and incisive judgment, could have undertaken, let alone completed, such a task. Although Wilson's health showed signs of decline after 1920, he nonetheless worked tirelessly on what was a monumental undertaking for a man in his mid-sixties. The completed volume of over 1,200 pages was published when Wilson was sixty-nine. "In it," wrote H. J. Muller, "virtually the whole of cytology from the time of its birth more than half a century before, stood integrated."[19] The revised edition, under the title *The Cell in Development and Heredity*, was awarded the Daniel Giraud Elliot Medal of the National Academy of Sciences (1928) and the gold medal of the Linnean Society of London (1928). Perhaps the most significant testimony to its value is that it is still found on the bookshelves of cytologists, not only as a useful reference source for older literature but also because many of the problems it posed are still being investigated. The electron microscope, with all the resolution of fine detail and astounding discoveries it has made possible, has not yet solved many of the questions and problems that Wilson raised. Developments in cytology since 1925 have expanded upon, but not contradicted, the underlying concepts that he wove so skillfully into the fabric of *The Cell*.

In all three editions of *The Cell* Wilson related the phenomena of heredity, cell structure and function, and development to organic evolution and adaptation. To him the central problem of evolution as posed by Darwin was how hereditary variations come about. In 1896 he recognized the importance of August Weismann's conception of the continuity of the germ plasm, and much of his future cytological work on chromosomes served to support the basic idea of a separation of germ and somatoplasm. Wilson's insight into this problem lay in his recognition that heredity was a cellular phenomenon—something that Darwin and his fol-

433

VINCENNES PUBLIC LIBRARY
VINCENNES, INDIANA

lowers also had recognized. The Darwinian theory of pangenesis was, after all, only a cellular mechanism for how variations could occur. From his early studies of cells and his growing awareness that the nucleus was the locale of a cell's heredity, Wilson rejected the pangenesis theory. Because cell heredity was localized in the nucleus, specifically in the chromosomes, and because each set of chromosomes had continuity—that is, it transmitted its effects only vertically from one generation to the next—somatic variations could not be transmitted to the germ cells of the same organism.

By his further work on chromosome structure and variation, approached cytologically and framed in Mendelian terms, Wilson tried to show how new heritable variations arose and could be acted upon by selection. The most significant support that he gave to the Darwinian theory was his conviction that heredity (and its correlate, variation) was ultimately a cellular (chromosomal) phenomenon. By emphasizing this relationship and by providing, through cytological studies, a material basis for Mendelian heredity, Wilson paved the way for a comprehensive theory of evolution, which emerged after 1930.[20]

Despite his strong interest in evolution, Wilson was somewhat skeptical of certain aspects of the Darwinian theory of natural selection. Like many of his contemporaries, he greatly admired Darwin's work as a naturalist and his synthetic powers as expressed in *The Origin of Species*. He felt, however, that Darwin had placed too much emphasis on evolution by the accumulation of small variations (what Darwin called "individual differences") that could not be shown to be inherited. By failing to distinguish adequately between inherited and acquired variations, Darwin had not provided a mechanism for the origin of adaptations. Wilson also was bothered by the emphasis that Darwin's theory placed on "chance" in the origin of species. Strongly influenced as he was by his old teacher, he stated in 1907 that Brooks's epigram was true, that "the essence of life is not protoplasm but purpose."[21] Wilson did not believe in teleological principles or in vitalistic driving forces in evolution. Nevertheless, like many biologists raised in the era of Haeckel, Weismann, and the other German Darwinians, it was difficult for him to believe that purpose was altogether lacking in evolutionary processes. The evolution of adaptations as intricate and functional as the vertebrate eye, simply by the accumulation of numerous *chance* variations, seemed to defy reason. As late as 1930 Wilson wrote: "[I am] not yet quite ready

to admit that higgledy-piggledy can provide an adequate explanation of organic adaptations."[22] Yet when confronted with alternative explanations of adaptation, Wilson always found himself forced to return to Darwin. In 1915 he wrote, "We have made it the mode to minimize Darwin's theory . . . but . . . we should take heed how we underestimate the one really simple and intelligible explanation of organic adaptation, inadequate though it may now seem, that has thus far been placed in our hands."[23]

**Wilson's Scientific Methodology.** Although Wilson was trained as a morphologist, he embraced the quantitative and experimental side of biology early in his career, following his 1891–1893 stay in Europe, particularly at the Naples station. Along with a number of younger biologists around the end of the nineteenth century, he felt that for biology to make any progress, it had to avoid vapid speculation and the construction of all-embracing theories that had no basis in empirical evidence. To him careful observation, hypothesis formulation, and experimentation were the only true means of reaching valid conclusions. Experiment alone was never enough—experiments had to be designed to test something, and that something was a particular hypothesis. In Wilson's view, however, hypotheses had to be testable. If they were not, then oversimplified and misleading ideas could gain a vast following, as had happened with the speculative theories of Haeckel and Weismann. The strong advocacy that Wilson and many of his contemporaries (including T. H. Morgan, Ross G. Harrison, Jacques Loeb) made in behalf of experimental biology was in some part a reaction to the nonexperimental, speculative methodology characteristic of a previous generation.

Behind Wilson's experimentalism lay a firm belief that "the scientific method is the mechanistic method."[24] By mechanistic he meant, as did most of the younger workers at the time, that phenomena should be subject to experimental analysis and that biological processes should be investigated in physicochemical terms. Wilson did not argue that the only meaningful explanation of a biological process was one couched in terms of chemical equations. He knew full well that such explanations were not then possible for most biological phenomena, yet he firmly believed that they should be sought as much as chemical theory and technology would allow. He was not a crude mechanist and could not share the extreme mechanical bias of Jacques Loeb. Nevertheless, he felt that until biologists could understand the complex events characterizing cell life in chemical terms, they could not gain much understanding of the nature of life or its immense complexities.

Philosophically, Wilson believed that the scientific method was the only way to understand the world—inside or outside the laboratory; but he did not think that scientific truths are final truths, for truth itself, he claimed, is relative. To Wilson the fundamental concepts of science had no finality. "The profound significance of what we call natural laws lies in the fact that they tersely sum up our experience of the world at any given moment . . . ."[25] Science was for him a creative process, the ideas running in advance, to some extent, of the hard facts. Wilson's own artistic and aesthetic sense allowed him to see science as no different, in its creative aspects, from music, art, or literature: "At every point the material world overflows with half-revealed meanings about which science is forever weaving her imaginative fabrics; and at their best these have all the freedom, boldness and beauty of true works of art."[26] Wilson the musician and Wilson the cytologist were one and the same person, applying different skills at different times but with the same aesthetic delight and by the same intellectual methods. For Wilson internal beauty had to be matched with external reality. Music to him was not simply a theory—it was the reality of notes played on an instrument, filling a room and affecting human beings. Science also was not theories—fossilized answers—it was the reality of what could be observed, predicted, and repeated by living, imaginative people. Both music and biology had their theoretical sides, but the theories had meaning only as they were applied in practice on a day-to-day basis.

In his teaching, as in his investigation and his writing, Wilson emphasized that science was not accumulated knowledge, but a process of reasoning, understanding, and testing that understanding against natural phenomena. He saw life as a whole, in all its manifest complexities, harmonies, and apparent inconsistencies. He was willing to let an issue rest unresolved rather than propose a solution that was untested or untestable. Yet in his emphasis on process, he saw the human side of science—that it was ultimately the activity of human beings, not monuments of static information. Externally, he lived the life of the classic reserved scholar; but beneath this formality was a fire that, as Muller put it, was rigorously channeled into self-discipline. Nevertheless, it was this fire that shone through even the most meticulous pages of cell lineage studies, or the most detailed analysis of mitotic patterns. It transformed details into the comprehensive and exciting fabric of biological ideas that Wilson wove throughout his life.

## NOTES

1. T. H. Morgan, "Edmund Beecher Wilson," 318.
2. *Ibid.*, 320.
3. H. J. Muller, "Edmund B. Wilson—an Appreciation," 166.
4. Morgan, *op. cit.*, 319.
5. E. B. Wilson, "The Development of *Renilla*."
6. Morgan, *op. cit.*, 321.
7. Muller, *op. cit.*, 17.
8. E. B. Wilson, "Amphioxus and the Mosaic Theory of Development," in *Journal of Morphology*, 8 (1893), 579–638, esp. 636–638.
9. The "mosaic theory" of Roux and Weismann is not to be confused with the "mosaic" or spiral pattern of cleavage Wilson had discussed in his earlier (1887, 1889, 1890) work on annelid embryology. The Roux-Weismann "mosaic" theory held that differentiation during ontogeny was caused by the qualitative nuclear division of hereditary material during cleavage; as development progressed, cells gradually lost more and more hereditary potential in terms of the kinds of adult tissues they could form.
10. E. B. Wilson, *The Cell in Development and Inheritance*, intro., 11.
11. *Ibid.*, 302.
12. *Ibid.*, 247; Bernard's work is in his *Leçons sur les phénomènes de la vie . . .*, I (Paris, 1878), 523.
13. Muller, *op. cit.*, 35.
14. E. B. Wilson, "The Chromosomes in Relation to the Determination of Sex in Insects"; N. M. Stevens, "Studies in Spermatogenesis With Especial Reference to the 'Accessory Chromosome,'" *Publications. Carnegie Institution of Washington*, no. 36 (1905).
15. E. B. Wilson, "Studies on Chromosomes. V. The Chromosomes of *Metapodius*, a Contribution to the Hypothesis of the Genetic Continuity of Chromosomes."
16. *Ibid.*
17. Muller, *op. cit.*, 156.
18. *Ibid.*, 160.
19. *Ibid.*, 161.
20. For Wilson's more explicit attempts to discuss cytology and Darwinism, see his "The Cell in Relation to Heredity and Evolution"; and his "Biology."
21. Muller, *op. cit.*, 153.
22. *Ibid.*, 153–154.
23. *Ibid.*, 153.
24. *Ibid.*, 24.
25. E. B. Wilson, "Science and Liberal Education," in *Science*, 42 (1915), 625–630.
26. *Ibid.*

## BIBLIOGRAPHY

I. ORIGINAL WORKS. There is no complete, or even selected, collection of Wilson's writings, although a bound set of his reprints, with only minor omissions, is in the library of the Marine Biological Laboratory, Woods Hole, Mass. A complete bibliography is in T. H. Morgan's obituary (see below).

Wilson's books are *General Biology* (New York, 1886), written with William T. Sedgwick; *An Atlas of Fertilization and Karyokinesis of the Ovum* (New York,

1895); *The Cell in Development and Inheritance* (New York, 1896; 2nd ed., 1900; 3rd ed., rev. and enl., *The Cell in Development and Heredity*, 1925)—1st ed. repr., with intro. by H. J. Muller, as Sources of Science, no. 30 (New York, 1966).

Among his most important journal articles are "A Problem of Morphology as Illustrated by the Development of the Earthworm" (abstract), in *Johns Hopkins University Circulars* (May 1880), 66; "The Development of *Renilla*," in *Philosophical Transactions of the Royal Society*, **174** (1883), 723–815; "The Embryology of the Earthworm," in *Journal of Morphology*, **3** (1889), 387–462; "The Cell-Lineage of *Nereis*. A Contribution to the Cytogeny of the Annelid Body," *ibid.*, **6** (1892), 361–480; "The Mosaic Theory of Development," in *Biological Lectures. Marine Biological Laboratory, Woods Hole, 1893* (1894), 1–14; "Maturation, Fertilization, and Polarity in the Echinoderm Egg. New Light on the 'Quadrille of the Centers,'" in *Journal of Morphology*, **10** (1895), 319–342, written with A. P. Mathews; "On Cleavage and Mosaic-Work," in *Archiv für Entwicklungsmechanik der Organismen*, **3** (1896), 19–26; "The Structure of Protoplasm," in *Biological Lectures, Woods Hole Marine Biological Laboratories for 1898* (1899), 1–20; "Cell Lineage and Ancestral Reminiscence," *ibid.*, 21–42; "Some Aspects of Recent Biological Research," in *International Monthly* (June 1900), 1–22; "Mendel's Principles of Heredity and the Maturation of the Germ-Cells," in *Science*, **16** (1902), 991–993; "Mr. Cook on Evolution, Cytology and Mendel's Laws," in *Popular Science Monthly* (Nov. 1903), 188–189; "The Problem of Development," in *Science*, **21** (1905), 281–294, presidential address, New York Academy of Sciences, 19 Dec. 1904; and "The Chromosomes in Relation to the Determination of Sex in Insects," *ibid.*, **22** (1905), 500–502.

Wilson's eight "Studies on Chromosomes" are in *Journal of Experimental Zoology*, **2** (1905), 371–405; II. "The Paired Microchromosomes, Idiochromosomes and Heterotropic Chromosomes in *Hemiptera*," *ibid.*, 507–545; III. "The Sexual Differences of the Chromosome-Groups in *Hemiptera*, With Some Considerations on the Determination and Inheritance of Sex," **3** (1906), 1–40; IV. "The 'Accessory' Chromosome in *Syromastes* and *Pyrrochoris* With a Comparative Review of the Types of Sexual Differences of the Chromosome Groups," **6** (1909), 69–99; V. "The Chromosomes of *Metapodius*, a Contribution to the Hypothesis of the Genetic Continuity of Chromosomes," *ibid.*, 147–205; VI. "A New Type of Chromosome Combination in *Metapodius*," **9** (1910), 53–78; VII. "A Review of the Chromosomes of *Nezara*; With Some More General Considerations," **12**, (1911), 71–110; VIII. "Observations on the Maturation-Phenomena in Certain *Hemiptera* and Other Forms, With Considerations on Synapsis and Reduction," **13** (1912), 345–448.

Other papers are "Mendelian Inheritance and the Purity of the Gametes," in *Science*, **23** (1906), 112–113; "Recent Studies of Heredity," in *Harvey Lectures* (1906–1907), 200; "Notes on the Chromosome Groups of *Metapodius* and *Banasa*," in *Biological Bulletin*, **12** (1907), 303–313; "Differences in the Chromosome-Groups of Closely Related Species and Varieties, and Their Possible Bearing on the 'Physiological Species,'" in *Proceedings, Seventh International Congress of Zoology* (1909), 1–2; "The Cell in Relation to Heredity and Evolution," *Fifty Years of Darwinism* (New York, 1909), 92–113; "The Chromosomes in Relation to the Determination of Sex," in *Science Progress*, **16** (1910), 570–592; "Some Aspects of Cytology in Relation to the Study of Genetics," in *American Naturalist*, **46** (1912), 57–67; "Observations on Synapsis and Reduction," in *Science*, **35** (1912), 470–471; "The Bearing of Cytological Research on Heredity," in *Proceedings of the Royal Society*, **88** (1914), 333–352, the Croonian lecture for 1914; "Chiasmatype and Crossing Over," in *American Naturalist*, **54** (1920), 193–219, written with T. H. Morgan; "The Physical Basis of Life," in *Science*, **57** (1923), 277–286; and "Biology," in *A Quarter Century of Learning: 1904–1929* (New York, 1931), 241–260.

II. SECONDARY LITERATURE. The standard obituary is T. H. Morgan, "Edmund Beecher Wilson, 1856–1939," in *Biographical Memoirs. National Academy of Sciences*, **21** (1941), 315–342, condensed in *Science*, **89** (1939), 258–259; also *New York Times* (4 Mar. 1939), 15, col. 1.

Perhaps the best single evaluation of Wilson's life and especially of his career, and the source that has been particularly helpful in preparing this article, is H. J. Muller, "Edmund B. Wilson—an Appreciation," in *American Naturalist*, **77** (1943), 5–37, 142–172. Muller's familiarity with Wilson's work is thorough, and his assessment of Wilson's place in the history of twentieth-century biology is authoritative. A shorter version of this "appreciation" is in Muller's intro. to the 1966 repr. of *The Cell in Development and Inheritance*.

Despite his importance to twentieth-century biology (and American science especially), there is a surprising lack of biographical or critical material on Wilson's life and work.

GARLAND E. ALLEN

**WILSON, EDWIN BIDWELL** (*b.* Hartford, Connecticut, 25 April 1879; *d.* Brookline, Massachusetts, 28 December 1964), *mathematics, physics, statistics, public health.*

The son of a schoolteacher, Wilson graduated B.A. from Harvard in 1899 and Ph.D. from Yale two years later. He studied for a while in Paris, taught mathematics at Yale, and then moved to the Massachusetts Institute of Technology, becoming head of the department of physics there in 1917. Five years later he was appointed professor of vital statistics at the Harvard School of Public Health. Wilson's work in that capacity earned him two presidencies in 1929: of the American Statistical Association and the Social Sciences Research Council, New York. Following his retirement in 1945 he acted as consultant to the Office of Naval Research. Throughout his long and varied career (among other things he was managing editor of the *Proceedings of the National Academy of Sciences*, Washington, for half a century) Wilson combined a quiet if somewhat crotchety Yankee charm with a firm sense of high standards in research and exposition.

In each of his fields Wilson made characteristic contributions. As a student of Willard Gibbs at Yale, he codified the great physicist's lectures on vector analysis into a textbook. This beautiful work, published when Wilson was only twenty-two years old, had a profound and lasting influence on the notation for and use of vector analysis. Meantime, Wilson's mind and pen began to range over many other areas of mathematics, including the foundations of projective and differential geometry; and in 1903 he criticized, with bold sharpness, Hilbert's "so-called foundations" of geometry. In 1912 Wilson published a comprehensive text on advanced calculus that was the first really modern book of its kind in the United States. Immediately successful, it had no rival for many years. Wilson's interest in theoretical physics, inspired by Gibbs, resulted in papers on mechanics and relativity. World War I led him to study aerodynamics, in which he gave a course; and he did research on the theory of the effects of gusts on airplane flight. Outcomes of this work were the publication of a book on aeronautics in 1920 and the stimulation of a group of students who were to make a mark in that field.

Early in the 1920's Wilson began to think carefully about probability and statistics. Because of his Harvard professorship he naturally focused on vital statistics, but he also pondered the theory of errors and its relation to quantitative biology and astronomy. In this field he was both innovative and evangelical—constantly drawing attention to the role of statistics in biology and urging the recruitment of full-time statisticians.

A major contribution to inferential statistics was Wilson's restructuring of interval estimation. For long before his time it had been vaguely implicit that the attachment of a standard error to a point estimate was a crude interval estimate. Thus, noting, say, that a series of observations yielded $129 \pm 22$ mm. as the mean length of a sample of Armadillidiidae, the researcher could add that the true (parametric) value lay, with a probability of about 2/3, in the interval 107–151. In an admirably concise note published in 1927, Wilson pointed out that, logically, a true value cannot have a probable location. He also showed how a rigorous and unelliptic statement could be made about the probability that an estimated interval will embrace the (fixed) parameter. This interval was essentially what became known as a confidence interval, as rediscovered and developed by Jerzy Neyman and his school. The priority must, however, be given to Wilson.

In studying cumulative population growth, and in handling quantal-response bioassay (which involves "all-or-none" reactions of members of a biological population to an agent), Wilson was an early and effective advocate of the logistic function, $P = (1 + \exp[-(\alpha + \beta X)])^{-1}$, where $P$ is the probability of response to the amount $X$ of the agent, and $\alpha$ and $\beta$ are parameters. He published methods of handling data that fitted this function, and thus of estimating the potency of the agent.

Wilson exhibited a constructively critical mind, quick to expose flaws and errors. Each of his books was an effective and timely exposition of a major subject, and his best papers made lasting impressions. He contributed to many disciplines other than his specialties, including epidemiology, sociology, and economics. His greatest originality may have been reached in his papers on statistics—which, interestingly, was a subject he did not explore deeply until middle age.

*BIBLIOGRAPHY*

Wilson's three important books are *Vector Analysis* (New York, 1901); *Advanced Calculus* (Boston, 1912); and *Aeronautics* (New York, 1920). Some noteworthy papers are "The So-Called Foundations of Geometry," in *Archiv der Mathematik und Physik*, **6** (1903), 104–122; "The Space-Time Manifold of Relativity; the non-Euclidean Geometry of Mechanics and Electromagnetics," in *Proceedings of the American Academy of Arts and Sciences*, **48** (1912), 389–507, written with G. N. Lewis; "Differential Geometry of Two-Dimensional Surfaces in Hyperspace," *ibid.*, **52** (1916), 270–386, written with C. L. E. Moore; "Probable Inference, the Law of Succession, and Statistical Inference," in *Journal of the American Statistical Association*, **22** (1927), 209–212; "Periodogram of American Business Activity," in *Quarterly Journal of Economics*, **48** (1934), 375–417; and "The Determination of LD-50 and Its Sampling Error in Bioassay," in *Proceedings of the National Academy of Sciences of the United States of America*, **29** (1943), 79–85, 114–120, 257–262, written with Jane Worcester.

A full account of Wilson's life and work, by Jerome Hunsaker and Saunders Mac Lane, is in *Biographical Memoirs. National Academy of Sciences*, **43** (1973), 285–320, with bibliography.

NORMAN T. GRIDGEMAN
SAUNDERS MAC LANE

**WILSON, JOHN** (*b*. Applethwaite, Westmorland, England, 6 August 1741; *d*. Kendal, Westmorland, 18 October 1793), *mathematics.*

Wilson was educated at Kendal and at Peterhouse, Cambridge, where in the mathematical tripos of 1761 he was senior wrangler. He was elected a fellow of Peterhouse in 1764 and a fellow of the Royal Society in 1782. As an undergraduate he attracted notice in the university by his defense of Waring, then Lucasian professor of mathematics, against adverse criticism of the latter's *Miscellanea analytica* (1762).

As a private tutor at Cambridge, Wilson had a high reputation; but after a short period of teaching, he was called to the bar in 1766 and acquired a considerable practice on the northern circuit. In 1786 he was raised to the bench of the Court of Common Pleas; later he served for a short time as one of the commissioners for the great seal, between the retirement of Lord Edward Thurlow from the office of lord chancellor and the appointment of Lord Loughborough.

Wilson's name is given to the theorem that if $p$ is a prime number, then $1 + (p-1)!$ is divisible by $p$. The first published statement of the theorem was by Waring in his *Meditationes algebraicae* (1770), although manuscripts in the Hannover Library show that the result had been found by Leibniz. Waring ascribed the theorem to Wilson but did not prove it; the first published proof was given by Lagrange (1773), who provided a direct proof from which Fermat's theorem (1640), first proved by Euler in 1736, can be deduced: If $p$ is a prime and $a$ is not divisible by $p$, then $a^{p-1} - 1$ is divisible by $p$. Lagrange also showed that Wilson's theorem can be deduced from Fermat's theorem, and that the converse of Wilson's theorem is true: if $n$ divides $1 + (n-1)!$, then $n$ is a prime.

In a series of letters exchanged between Sir Frederick Pollock and Augustus De Morgan, published by W. W. Rouse Ball, Pollock described the mathematical work done at Cambridge in the first decade of the nineteenth century, and asserted that Wilson's theorem was a guess that neither he nor Waring could prove.

Wilson's result has been generalized to provide a series of theorems relating to the symmetric functions of the integers $1, 2, \cdots, p - 1$, and in other ways. The history of the theorem and its generalizations is given in detail by L. E. Dickson.

*BIBLIOGRAPHY*

For Wilson's life, see *Dictionary of National Biography*, XXI, p. 578; and Atkinson, *Worthies of Westmorland*, II (London, 1850); for personal details, Augustus De Morgan, *Budget of Paradoxes*, 2nd ed. (Chicago–London, 1915); W. W. Rouse Ball, *A History of the Study of Mathematics at Cambridge* (Cambridge, 1889).

For Wilson's theorem, see the following, listed chronologically: E. Waring, *Meditationes algebraicae* (Cambridge, 1770); J. L. Lagrange, in *Nouveaux mémoires de l'Académie de Berlin* (1773); and L. E. Dickson, *History of the Theory of Numbers*, I (repr. New York, 1934), ch. 3.

T. A. A. BROADBENT

**WINCHELL FAMILY** (founded in America by British immigrant Robert Winchell, who lived in Windsor, Connecticut, from 1635 until his death in 1669). The descendants spread from Connecticut to eastern New York, where the eighth-generation brothers Alexander Winchell (1824–1891) and Newton Horace Winchell (1839–1914) were born in Dutchess County. Alexander married and settled in Michigan. Newton Horace joined his older brother in Michigan, married, and eventually moved to Minnesota. Among the five children of the ninth generation two sons were born: Horace Vaughn Winchell (1865–1923), who married one of Alexander Winchell's daughters, and Alexander Newton Winchell (1874–1958).

The family is unique in its contributions to geology over four generations. They were leaders in the broad organization of geology as a professional science in America and in the establishment of the first American journal devoted solely to geology. Members have been prominent in education, state and national government, and civic activities.

They have published numerous scientific papers, reports, and books, as well as popular communications, in geology, mineralogy, petrology, mining, mining law, archaeology, ethnology, and religion.

*BIBLIOGRAPHY*

N. H. Winchell and A. N. Winchell, *The Winchell Genealogy, the Ancestry and Children of Those Born to the Winchell Name in America Since 1635*, 2nd ed. (Minneapolis, Minn., 1917).

**WINCHELL, ALEXANDER** (*b.* Northeast, New York, 31 December 1824; *d.* Ann Arbor, Michigan, 19 February 1891), *geology, education.*

Winchell was the son of Horace and Caroline McAllister Winchell, both of whom were schoolteachers. After graduation from Wesleyan University in 1847, he was appointed teacher of natural science at Pennington Male Seminary in New Jersey, where he studied the local flora and languages, and conducted experiments with electricity. Subsequent teaching positions were Amenia Seminary (New York), Newbern Academy (Alabama), and Mesopotamia Female Seminary (Eutow, Alabama). Winchell was president of Masonic University (Selma, Alabama) and was professor at the University of Michigan, first of physics and engineering (1853–1855), and later, when a chair was established, of geology, zoology, and botany (1855–1873). During his tenure at the University of Michigan he served on the State Geological Survey (1859–1861, 1869–1871). While chancellor and then professor of geology at Syracuse University (1873–1874), Winchell accepted a professorship in geology, zoology, and botany at Vanderbilt University. The latter chair was abolished in 1878, allegedly for economic reasons; it is believed, however, that the action was taken by the university board of trust because of his views on evolution. In 1879 he was recalled to the University of Michigan as professor of geology and paleontology, and remained there until his death.

Winchell's main impact was his role in organizing geology as a science in America. By popularizing its principles as having both economic and cultural value, he influenced legislation establishing geological surveys. In addition to his teaching, lecturing, and voluminous writing, he made important scientific observations in a great many fields, mainly stratigraphy and paleontology. He described seven new genera and 304 new species of organisms, mostly fossil. Winchell established the basin shape of the strata in Michigan and predicted the economic development of salt in the Saginaw Valley. Much effort went into the description of a series of strata called the Marshall group that encompassed many previously described beds and required a strong defense. He was particularly interested in the oil-bearing formation of Michigan and the ancient (Archean) rocks of Minnesota. Other geological work included studies on glacia-tion, pedology, geochronology, hydrology, and sedimentology.

Winchell's second major contribution was in bridging the alleged gap between science and religion. He defended the Christian Scriptures and sought rational interpretations that harmonized with scientific observations. He revived the seventeenth-century idea of preadamites and presented an anthropological account of the evolution of the human family without, in his view, contravening the Scriptures. Winchell's greatest endeavor resulted in a highly imaginative world history that brought together cosmology and geology. His published bibliography lists 255 titles, but his personal list of compositions numbers 566. Other scientific subjects to which he contributed include astronomy, climatology, meteorology, and zoology.

Winchell's brother Newton Horace described him as a man of strong personality and convictions, physically strong, and deft in mechanical construction. Audiences were inspired and entertained by his popular scientific lectures. He wrote poetry, mostly unpublished, and mastered at least seven languages. Winchell has been called the father of the Geological Society of America, founded in 1888, of which he was president in 1891, and was one of the founders of *American Geologist* (1888). He married Julia F. Lines of Utica, New York, a teacher of instrumental music, on 5 December 1849. Of their six children only two daughters lived to maturity.

*BIBLIOGRAPHY*

Winchell's writings on geology are *First Biennial Report of the Progress of the Geological Survey of Michigan, Embracing Observations on the Geology, Zoology, and Botany of the Lower Peninsula* (Lansing, 1861); "On the Saliferous Rocks and Salt Springs of Michigan," in *American Journal of Science*, 2nd ser., **34** (1862), 307–311; "Description of Fossils From the Marshall and Huron Groups of Michigan," in *Proceedings of the Academy of Natural Sciences of Philadelphia*, **14** (1862), 405–430; *The Oil Region of Michigan. Description of the Baker Tract, Situated in the Heart of the Oil Region of Michigan* (Detroit, 1864); *The Grand Traverse Region. A Report on the Geological and Industrial Resources of the Counties of Antrim, Grand Traverse, Benzie, and Leelanaw, in the Lower Peninsula of Michigan* (Ann Arbor, 1866); "On the Geological Age and Equivalents of the Marshall Group," in *Proceedings of the American Philosophical Society*, **11** (1871), 245–260; *Geological Studies, or Elements of Geology* (Chicago, 1886); "The Taconic Question," in *American Geologist*, **1** (1888), 347–363; and "American Opinion on the Older Rocks," in *Report of the Minnesota Geological Survey*, **18** (1891), 65–226.

His works on evolution are *Sketches of Creation* (New York, 1870); *The Doctrine of Evolution* (New York, 1874); *Reconciliation of Science and Religion* (New York, 1877); *Preadamites* (Chicago, 1880); *Sparks From a Geologist's Hammer* (Chicago, 1881); and *World Life or Comparative Geology* (Chicago, 1883).


**WINCHELL, ALEXANDER NEWTON** (*b*. Minneapolis, Minnesota, 2 March 1874; *d*. New Haven, Connecticut, 7 June 1958), *mineralogy, petrology, education.*

Winchell was the youngest son of Newton Horace and Charlotte Sophia Imus Winchell. He received the B.S. degree in 1896 and the M.S. in 1897 from the University of Minnesota, where his mineralogical studies were directed by Charles P. Berkey. Following a year as instructor in physics at Central High School, Minneapolis, he married and went to the University of Paris to pursue advanced studies in mineralogy and petrology under Alfred Lacroix. Winchell received the D.Sc. from the University of Paris in 1900 and then took a post at the Montana School of Mines. In 1907 he moved to the University of Wisconsin, becoming full professor in 1908, and remained there until his retirement in 1944. In 1934 he was given a semester's leave of absence to study X-ray methods under Linus Pauling at the California Institute of Technology and under W. H. Taylor and W. L. Bragg at the University of Manchester. His promotion to chairman of the department of geology at the University of Wisconsin also was effective in 1934.

Winchell was associated with the U.S. Geological Survey from 1901 to 1910. After moving to Connecticut in 1948, he was made an honorary fellow in geology at Yale University. He served as visiting professor of mineralogy at the University of Virginia (1948–1949) and at Columbia University (1949–1950), and was resident mineral consultant at the Stamford laboratory of the American Cyanamid Company for three years. His remaining years were devoted to reviewing geological literature and revising his books.

Winchell's major contribution to geology is his well-known, and still widely used, three-volume *Elements of Optical Mineralogy*. The first volume was an outgrowth of a book that his father and himself published in 1909. That book was the first presentation in English of the principles and methods of optical mineralogy, and its expanded revision quickly became a major textbook. Four additional revised editions followed. The second volume dealt with the description of minerals and underwent three revisions, the last in collaboration with his youngest son, Horace. The third volume, on determinative tables, was revised once. These volumes contain the compilation and correlation of vast amounts of data relating the optical and physical properties of crystals to their composition. Three-fourths of the approximately 120 diagrams in the book giving graphical representation of these relations were developed by Winchell. He made significant contributions to the understanding of such major mineral groups as the feldspars, pyroxenes, melilites, amphiboles, micas, chlorites, zeolites, and scapolites. He also compiled a text on the optical properties of synthetic minerals and one on organic crystals, as well as an elementary textbook on mineralogy. These books made the methods of mineralogy available to chemists, ceramists, and other research scientists.

Winchell's second major contribution to geology was in the field of petrology. He studied Keweenawan igneous rocks, the relationship of igneous rocks to the occurrence of ores, and limestone alteration, and devised a graphical classification of rocks. Petrological field observations from Montana, Oregon, Nevada, and Utah are recorded.

Winchell devoted forty-four years to the teaching of mineralogy. He was an inspiring teacher with boundless patience, always ready and available to answer students' questions. He was friend and counselor to students, earnest in discussion and a source of support.

Winchell served as president of the Mineralogical Society of America in 1932 and as vice-president of the Geological Society of America in the same year. The former society awarded him its highest award, the Roebling Medal, in 1955.

Serious games were Winchell's principal hobbies: chess, bridge, Russian bank, anagrams, and crossword puzzles. He pursued his early university interest in history and was an active member of a poetry club. After retirement he enjoyed traveling in North America.

He married Clare Edith Christello of Minneapolis on 29 May 1898. They had five children, most of whom carried on the family tradition in geology directly or indirectly, through marriage to geologists. Two years after the death of his wife in 1932, he married Florence Mabel Sylvester, granddaughter of Alexander Winchell.

*BIBLIOGRAPHY*

Winchell's textbooks are *Elements of Optical Mineralogy*, 3 vols.: I, *Principles and Methods* (5th ed., New York, 1937), II, *Descriptions of Minerals* (4th ed., New York, 1951), written with H. Winchell; III, *Determinative Tables* (2nd ed., New York, 1939); *Microscopic Characters of Artificial Inorganic Solid Substances or Artificial Minerals* (New York, 1931); *Optical Properties of Organic Compounds*, 2nd ed. (New York, 1954); and *Elements of Mineralogy* (New York, 1942).

On the optical properties of major mineral groups, see "Studies in the Pyroxene Group," in *American Journal of Science*, 5th ser., **6** (1923), 504–520; "The Composition of Melilite," *ibid.*, **8** (1924), 375–384; "Studies in the Amphibole Group," *ibid.*, **7** (1924), 287–310; "Studies in the Mica Group," *ibid.*, **9** (1925), 309–327, 415–430; "Studies in the Feldspar Group," in *Journal of Geology*, **34** (1925), 714–727; and "Chlorite as a Polycomponent System," in *American Journal of Science*, 5th ser., **11** (1926), 282–300.

Petrological studies are "Mineralogical and Petrographic Study of the Gabbroid Rocks of Minnesota," in *American Geologist*, **19** (1900), 336–339; "Review of Nomenclature of Keweenawan Igneous Rocks," in *Journal of Geology*, **16** (1908), 765–774; "Discussion of Igneous Rocks as Related to Occurrence of Ores," in American Institute of Mining Engineers, *Ore-Deposits* (New York, 1913), 303–304; "Rock Classification on Three Co-ordinates," in *Journal of Geology*, **21** (1913), 208–223; *Petrology and Mineral Resources of Jackson and Josephine Counties, Oregon* (Salem, 1914); and "Petrographic Studies of Limestone Alteration at Bingham," in *Transactions of the American Institute of Mining and Metallurgical Engineers*, **70** (1924), 884–903.

Historical studies are "Minnesota's Northern Boundary," in Minnesota Historical Society Collections, **8**, pt. 2 (1896), 184–212; and "Minnesota's Eastern, Southern, and Western Boundaries," *ibid.*, **10** (1905), 1–11.

**WINCHELL, HORACE VAUGHN** (*b.* Galesburg, Michigan, 1 November 1865; *d.* Los Angeles, California, 28 July 1923), *geology, mining engineering.*

Winchell was the oldest son of Newton Horace and Charlotte Sophia Imus Winchell. He studied at the University of Minnesota and then at the University of Michigan, from which he graduated in 1889. Apparently he was greatly influenced by his uncle Alexander Winchell, under whom he studied, as well as by his father to follow the natural sciences. Winchell's first geological work was for the Minnesota State Geological Survey; his father, the state geologist, assigned him to study the Mesabi Range, where promising sources of iron ore had just been discovered.

Winchell next worked for the Minnesota Mining Company, until the panic of 1893 terminated exploration. He and F. F. Sharpless then formed a partnership as consulting geologists; however, depression in the mining industry and work in the West led to its early dissolution. In 1898 he became geologist for Anaconda Copper Mining Company and, in 1906, geologist for the Northern Pacific Railroad. In 1908 Winchell broadened his consulting practice and established an independent office in Minneapolis. His assignments took him to Alaska, Mexico, South America, Europe, and Russia, where he witnessed the Kerensky revolution in February 1917. He retired to Los Angeles in 1921.

Winchell's contributions to science differ greatly from those of his father and his uncle even though his early career was devoted to the observational and theoretical aspects of geology, in close association with his father. Field studies on the drift-covered Mesabi Range outlined the importance of that area as a source of iron ore and led to an acceptable theory of the origin of the ores. A *Bulletin of the Minnesota Geological Survey* on the iron ores of the state, published with his father (1891), and another report published in 1893 especially on the Mesabi Range, influenced the development of the most productive iron ore deposits in America. The iron-bearing strata originated, according to Winchell and his father, as a chemical precipitate from Precambrian ocean waters; however, the algal and bacterial structures found later suggest some involvement of organic life forms. Winchell favored the view that the soft ore bodies resulted from the alteration of the strata by surface waters (secondary enrichment), and his early experience on the iron ranges influenced his thinking with regard to other ore deposits around the world.

In 1898 Winchell turned to the practical applications of the then-evolving science of geology to mining and engineering problems, and eventually to mining law. A geological staff was organized at the Anaconda Copper Mining Company, and his success in advising the engineers on the development of the Butte, Montana, mine no doubt encouraged other companies to set up similar departments. Winchell's policies of geological investigation and continuity of geological mapping in connection with mining operations proved highly profitable. In 1903 he published the conclusion that the upper levels of the Butte copper ore were the result of secondary enrichment, basing that view on geological field studies and laboratory experiments carried out with the assistance of C. F. Tolman, Jr. The concept of secondary enrichment had already been well established, but Winchell's role in its development was recognized.

Turning to private consulting practice in 1908, Winchell became more involved in the legal problems accompanying mining. He was particularly interested in the statutes attending extralateral rights, those governing mining claims, and ownership of mineral properties in the public domain. His concern for the public good and appreciation of the need for development of new resources was great. One of his friends and biographers records his occasional bitterness toward the hostile and critical attitude of some of his fellow scientists, who held such service to humanity in low regard in comparison with the contributions of pure science.

Winchell helped found, and for about five years served as editor of, *Economic Geology*, which was in effect a continuation of the *American Geologist* (the latter established primarily through the efforts of his father in 1888). He also was one of three American associate editors of *Zeitschrift für praktische Geologie* from 1896 until the United States entered World War I. He was president of the American Institute of Mining Engineers in 1919, succeeding Herbert Hoover.

In his younger years Winchell gained national recognition as a whist player and represented Minneapolis in championship contests. Golf was his chief outdoor recreation. He acquired a valuable library on mining geology that after his death was given to the Engineering Societies Library in New York by his wife and the Anaconda Company. He married his cousin, Ida Belle Winchell, on 15 January 1890. One child was born but survived only six months.

## BIBLIOGRAPHY

Scientific observations are "On a Possible Chemical Origin of the Iron Ores on the Keewatin in Minnesota," in *American Geologist*, **4** (1889), 291–300, written with N. H. Winchell; "The Iron Ores of Minnesota; Their Geology, Discovery, Development, Qualities, Origin, and Comparison With Those of Other Districts," *Bulletin of the Minnesota Geological and Natural History Survey*, no. 6 (1891), written with N. H. Winchell; "The Mesabi Iron Range," in *Transactions of the American Institute of Mining Engineers*, **21** (1893), 644–686; "The Lake Superior Iron Ore Region, United States of America," in *Transactions of the Federal Institute of Mining Engineers* (London), **13** (1897), 493–562; "Synthesis of Chalcocite and Its Genesis at Butte, Montana,"

in *Bulletin of the Geological Society of America*, **14** (1903), 269–276; and "The Genesis of Ores in the Light of Modern Theory," in *Popular Science Monthly*, **72** (1908), 534–542.

Legal contributions are "Mining Laws," in *Transactions of the Canadian Mining Institute*, **15** (1912), 535–551; "Why the Mining Laws Should Be Revised," in *Transactions of the American Institute of Mining Engineers*, **48** (1915), 361–385; "Apex Litigation. Jim Butler Versus West End," in *Mining and Scientific Press*, **110** (1915), 763–765; "Mining Laws," in Robert Peele, ed., *Mining Engineers' Handbook* (New York, 1917), 1465–1514; and "Uniform Mining Law for North America," in *Transactions of the American Institute of Mining Engineers*, **61** (1919), 696–705.

**WINCHELL, NEWTON HORACE** (*b.* Northeast, New York, 17 December 1839; *d.* Minneapolis, Minnesota, 2 May 1914), *geology, archaeology.*

Winchell was the son of Horace and Caroline McAllister Winchell, both of whom were schoolteachers. At the age of sixteen he began teaching in public schools and continued that career after entering the University of Michigan in 1857. His studies and teaching were interrupted by military service in the Civil War, and he graduated in 1866. Winchell served as principal and superintendent of local schools in Michigan between 1866 and 1870. He accepted a position as assistant to his brother Alexander on the Michigan State Geological Survey and, later, to John Strong Newberry on the Ohio State Geological Survey. In 1872 he was appointed state geologist of Minnesota, a post he held for twenty-eight years. While state geologist Winchell was also professor of geology and curator of the museum at Michigan State University; he relinquished most of those duties, however, after about seven years. The last nine years of his life were devoted to the Minnesota Historical Society.

In contrast with his brother Alexander, Winchell confined his scientific work mainly to original research rather than teaching and lecturing. His principal contributions to geology are recorded in twenty-four *Reports* and ten *Bulletins of the Minnesota Geological and Natural History Survey*. With a group of assistants he surveyed, mapped, and reported on every county in the state. The great iron ore deposits of the Mesabi and Vermilion ranges, as well as the Marquette, Gogebic, and Cuyuna ranges, were studied in detail. In addition, building-stone resources, copper deposits, lignite and anthracite beds, water supply, salt wells, and drift soils were examined in the course of the survey. Winchell's interpretations of the structure of the Lake Superior region and of the origin of the iron ores was in conflict with that of the geologists of the U.S. Geological Survey.

Winchell also contributed to the ornithological, entomological, and botanic studies of Minnesota. Although his geological work was carried out almost exclusively in that state, he prepared the first geologic map of the interior of the Black Hills as a member of Custer's expedition in 1874. With the aid of his younger son, Alexander Newton, Winchell wrote *Elements of Optical Mineralogy*, revised editions of which are still used. Aid on other projects was given by his older son, Horace Vaughn Winchell, and his son-in-law, Ulysses S. Grant, the geologist.

Contributions to archaeology were among Winchell's earliest studies, and these were related to his glaciological work. His detailed and accurate conception of the waning of the great ice sheets and the contemporaneous existence of man produced considerable debate. Most noteworthy was his estimate of the time of the last stage of the Glacial Period by approximating the rate of recession of St. Anthony's Falls, cutting the Mississippi River gorge from Fort Snelling to the present site of the falls in Minneapolis. The duration of postglacial time was estimated as about eight thousand years, assuming that the gorge was the result of postglacial erosion. Winchell assembled data on thousands of Indian mounds and concluded that they were the work of the immediate ancestors of the present Indian tribes and were not constructed by a prior race of distinct culture. His geological knowledge aided him in determining that paleolithic man in America antedated the Kansan stage of glaciation.

Winchell was appointed by President Grover Cleveland as a member of the Federal Assay Commission in 1886. He was one of the founders of the Minnesota Academy of Sciences in 1873 and served three terms as its president. The first steps in the organization of the Geological Society of America were instigated by Winchell in 1881, and he served as its president in 1902. In cooperation with his brother Alexander and other geologists, in 1888 he established the *American Geologist*, which he edited for eighteen years. The initial purpose of the journal was to provide a nonpartisan publication free from the influence of the national geological survey, which was viewed as encroaching on the domain of the state geological surveys. The causes for concern evaporated, and the magazine turned to then-current geological problems. In 1905 the magazine was incorporated

with, enlarged, and published as *Economic Geology*, the title it still bears.

Winchell married Charlotte Sophia Imus of Galesburg, Michigan, on 24 August 1864. Of their five children, their sons Alexander Newton and Horace Vaughn became prominent geologists and one daughter, Avis, married a successful geologist, Ulysses Sherman Grant.

*BIBLIOGRAPHY*

Winchell's writings include "Report of a Reconnaissance of the Black Hills of Dakota in 1874," in *Geological Report* . . . (1875), 21–65; *The Geology of Minnesota; Final Report of the Geological and Natural History Survey of Minnesota*, 6 vols. (Minneapolis, 1884–1901); "The So-Called Huronian Rocks in the Vicinity of Sudbury, Ontario," in *Bulletin of the Minnesota Academy of Sciences*, **3** (1889), 183–185; "The Iron Ores of Minnesota; Their Geology, Discovery, Development, Qualities, Origin, and Comparison With Those of Other Mining Districts," *Bulletin of the Minnesota Geological and Natural History Survey*, no. 6 (1891), written with H. V. Winchell; "Was Man in America in the Glacial Period?," in *Bulletin of the Geological Society of America*, **14** (1903), 133–152; *Elements of Optical Mineralogy*, 3 vols. (New York, 1909), written with A. N. Winchell; *The Aborigines of Minnesota* (St. Paul, Minn., 1911); and "The Weathering of Aboriginal Stone Artifacts; a Consideration of the Paleoliths of Kansas," *Collections of the Minnesota Historical Society*, **16**, pt. 1 (1913).

H. S. YODER, JR.

**WINDAUS, ADOLF OTTO REINHOLD** (*b.* Berlin, Germany, 25 December 1876; *d.* Göttingen, Germany, 9 June 1959), *chemistry*.

Windaus came from a family that had a strong technological background. The ancestors of his father, Adolf, had been weavers and clothing manufacturers for two hundred years. The family of his mother, Margarete Elster, consisted mostly of artisans and craftsmen. A few of his ancestors had held academic positions, but none had been physicians or scientists.

The boy received his elementary education at the French Gymnasium in Berlin, where almost no science was taught and the emphasis was on literature. In his final year, however, Windaus learned of the bacteriological work done by Koch and Pasteur, and was much impressed with the benefits of their studies for humanity. He therefore decided upon a career in medicine, thereby disappointing his widowed mother, who had hoped that he would enter the family business.

Windaus entered the University of Berlin in 1895 and almost at once began to attend Emil Fischer's lectures on chemistry. He was particularly struck by the physiological applications of Fischer's work and began to develop what later became the basis for his approach to chemistry, an interest in the general physiological mechanisms of the compounds he studied. Windaus was awarded the bachelor's degree in 1897 and then decided to attend the University of Freiburg im Breisgau, where Heinrich Kiliani taught chemistry. For a time Windaus continued his medical studies, but he began to neglect medicine more and more, and finally gave it up entirely. At Kiliani's suggestion he started to study the chemistry of the glycosides of digitalis, and in 1899 he received the Ph.D. with a dissertation on those substances. The next year was spent in military service at Berlin, but during the summer semester Windaus was able to assist Fischer in a study of the formation of quaternary ammonium compounds from aniline. At the end of 1901 he returned to Freiburg to devote himself entirely to chemistry.

Kiliani suggested that Windaus begin a study of cholesterol, a compound about which almost nothing was known. Windaus felt that a substance so widely distributed in animal cells, and in related forms in plants, must have close connections with other physiologically important compounds. He thus entered on studies that occupied much of the rest of his life. In 1903 he presented his inaugural dissertation, "Cholesterin," and became a *Privatdozent* at Freiburg, with promotion to a professorship three years later.

In 1913 Windaus accepted the chair of medical chemistry at Innsbruck, where he remained for two years. In 1915 he was called to the University of Göttingen as successor to Otto Wallach. Until his retirement he was professor of chemistry and director of the chemical laboratory at Göttingen. Windaus continued active research even during the period of National Socialism. Although he was not in sympathy with the Hitler regime, he was allowed to continue his work because of the reputation he had established. He ceased active investigation in 1938, and after his retirement in 1944 he published no further papers.

The course of Windaus' scientific activity was determined by his early studies on digitalis and cholesterol. His work always had some relation to natural products; and although he was mainly concerned with the structure of cholesterol, he investi-

gated many other sterols and established the membership of these substances in a group that he called the "sterines." In 1908 Windaus found that cholesterol formed an insoluble compound with digitonin. This explained the action of cholesterol in preventing the hemolytic activity shown by the saponins, of which digitonin was one. Thereafter he included studies of the structure of the saponins in his research program.

During this period Windaus' friend Heinrich Wieland, at Munich, was studying the structure of the bile acids; and among the derivatives of these substances he had prepared a compound that he called cholanic acid. In 1919 Windaus prepared the same acid from cholesterol, thus demonstrating the close chemical relationship between the sterines and the bile acids. The results obtained by the workers at Göttingen and Munich could now be combined. Active study at the two institutions finally led to the determination of the correct structure for the sterol ring in 1932.

Even before the structure of cholesterol was completely established, there had been indications that the substance was involved in some way in vitamin activity. By the early 1920's it was known that rickets could be cured by administration of certain fish liver oils. The study of vitamins was widespread at the time, and it was assumed that the liver oils contained a specific substance, called vitamin D, that was responsible for the cure. It also had been found, however, that exposure of the patient to ultraviolet light could bring about a cure. The studies of A. F. Hess had established this fact firmly. A dilemma thus arose: Was a chemical or a physical process responsible for the favorable effect? Most physiologists assumed that two different processes were involved. It was believed that the vitamin cured rickets specifically, just as vitamin C cured scurvy, but that exposure to ultraviolet light raised the general level of resistance to the disease.

In 1924 Harry Steenbock and Alfred Hess independently showed that exposure of certain foods to ultraviolet light made them active in curing rickets. This indicated that some compound was photochemically converted into vitamin D, and thus the concept of a provitamin was developed. Hess found that the provitamin occurred in the sterine fraction of the irradiated foods, and in 1925 he sought Windaus as a collaborator in determining the chemical nature of the vitamin and its precursor. Windaus was eager to accept the invitation because of his approach to the general chemistry of natural products. Although many chemists believed that he was concerned only with cholesterol, he said that he was not interested in the chemical composition of any particular substance, but only in the major relationships between natural products. The collaboration between Hess (in New York City) and Windaus resulted in the development at Göttingen of an active center for vitamin research. Rosenheim (in London) soon joined the project, and the results of studies in the three cities confirmed each other.

It was at first thought that cholesterol was the provitamin, since irradiation of a supposedly pure sample produced an active product. When a more highly purified sample failed to yield the same result, it was recognized that this idea was incorrect. Robert Pohl, working at Göttingen, showed by a study of absorption spectra that a very small amount of an impurity was present in the original cholesterol sample; and in 1927 Hess and Windaus identified the impurity as the fungus sterol ergosterol. Windaus soon demonstrated that the conversion of ergosterol to the vitamin involved an isomerization. Attempts to isolate the pure vitamin apparently were successful when a crystalline compound was obtained, but later it was shown that this was a molecular compound of the vitamin with another sterol. By this time the molecular compound had been so well established that the name vitamin $D_1$ was applied to it; and when a pure vitamin finally was isolated from irradiated ergosterol, it was called vitamin $D_2$, or calciferol.

It was assumed that ergosterol was the only provitamin, but Windaus continued to seek other sterols that could serve as precursors of vitamin D. In 1932 he and his co-workers prepared 7-dehydrocholesterol and showed that it also was a provitamin. The name vitamin $D_2$ was retained for the substance obtained from ergosterol, and the new vitamin was named $D_3$. It proved to be even more important than vitamin $D_2$, since it was obtained by activation of a sterol synthesized by the animal body. Hans Brockmann, working in Windaus' laboratory, confirmed this fact when he isolated pure vitamin $D_3$ from tuna liver oil.

Knowledge of the structure of the various D vitamins soon followed. During the rest of his working life, Windaus was occupied with a study of the structural features necessary for a sterol to qualify as a provitamin, and with determining the course of the photochemical reactions by which activation of the provitamins occurs. He identified and characterized the other compounds formed in these reactions: lumisterol, tachysterol, and the suprasterols.

By 1927 the work on the structure and chemistry of the sterols and of vitamin D, although by no means complete, had proceeded so far that the importance of the results was clear. The brilliance of the contributions made by Wieland and Windaus was equally obvious. In 1927 Wieland was awarded the Nobel Prize in chemistry for his work on the bile acids, and in 1928 the same prize was given to Windaus for his studies on the constitution of the sterols and their connection with other substances occurring in nature.

As soon as the sterol ring structure was determined (1932), it became possible to assign structures to many other biologically important sterols. Adolf Butenandt, an assistant to Windaus, was able almost at once to present the structures of the male and female sex hormones, even though he had only 25 mg. of the male hormone available for study. Adrenal cortical hormones, saponins, glycosides, and even the poisonous substances found in the skin of certain toads (substances that Windaus had done much to characterize) were found to belong to the same group; and the term "sterine" was replaced by the more significant name "steroid."

Another important result of Windaus' studies on steroid structure arose from his discovery that in saturated derivatives of cholesterol there is a type of isomerism due to the cis- or trans-fusion of two saturated rings. This opened the field of the stereochemistry of condensed ring systems, a subject developed in detail by another student of Windaus', Walther Hückel.

At the time of his early work on cholesterol, Windaus also had undertaken a study, in collaboration with the biochemist Franz Knoop, of the reaction of sugars with ammonia. They hoped to convert the sugars into amino acids, and thus to establish the possibility of converting carbohydrates into proteins. To Windaus' surprise, when he treated glucose with ammoniacal zinc hydroxide, he obtained derivatives of imidazole. From a study of these compounds he discovered that the amino acid histidine was an imidazole derivative. In the course of this work he discovered the physiologically very important compound histamine, which became commercially available as a result of his work. These investigations brought Windaus into contact with the chemical industry, and he retained close connections with industrial chemists for the rest of his life. Chemical concerns supplied him with many of the substances he needed in his research and often suggested problems.

After his early work on the imidazoles, Windaus abandoned this line of research until 1929. He was induced to return to the field because two Dutch chemists, B. C. P. Jansen and W. F. Donath, had claimed that the antineuritic vitamin, $B_1$ or thiamin, contained an imidazole ring. In their analysis, however, they had overlooked the presence of sulfur in the compound. On the basis of a correct analysis, Windaus was able to assign the proper empirical formula and to show that the compound contained not an imidazole, but a thiazole and a pyrimidine ring. He isolated the pure vitamin $B_1$ from yeast, and his work helped greatly in the final synthesis of the vitamin by Robert R. Williams.

Windaus' other major field of research was the determination of the structure of colchicene, a substance that proved to have strong mutagenic properties for plants.

Although Windaus had been almost alone in his early investigations on cholesterol, the field he had pioneered quickly became a major branch of organic chemistry and biochemistry. He always worked closely with his colleagues in Germany and abroad, and gave his students great freedom in their research, as well as full credit for their contributions.

Besides the Nobel Prize, Windaus received many honorary degrees and memberships in scientific societies. He was awarded the Baeyer, Pasteur, and Goethe medals. Windaus served on the editorial board of *Justus Liebigs Annalen der Chemie*; and volumes **603** and **604** of that journal were dedicated to him in 1957, to celebrate his eightieth birthday.

*BIBLIOGRAPHY*

Windaus' scientific papers are listed in Poggendorff, V, 1380; VI, 2901–2902; VIIa, 1016–1018.

The most complete biography is the Windaus memorial lecture by Adolf Butenandt, in *Proceedings of the Chemical Society* (1961), 131–138. Further details are in Gulbrand Lunde, "The 1927 and 1928 Chemistry Prize Winners, Wieland and Windaus," in *Journal of Chemical Education*, **7** (1930), 1767–1777. A survey of the significance of the work on steroids and its relation to the work of others is H. H. Inhoffen, "50 Jahre Sterin-Chemie," in *Naturwissenschaften*, **38** (1951), 553–558.

Henry M. Leicester

**WING, VINCENT** (*b.* North Luffenham, Rutland, England, 19 April 1619; *d.* North Luffenham, 30 September 1668), *astronomy*.

Wing's father, for whom he was named, was a small landowner. Young Wing had little formal education and began earning his living at an early age as a surveyor, almanac compiler, astrologer, and prolific writer of astromical works. His almanacs were the most popular of their time; and, in Flamsteed's judgment, Wing produced "our exactest ephemerides." He was an eager polemicist and frequently was involved in public disputes over astronomical and astrological matters.

Wing's career as an astronomer mirrors the development of astronomical thought during the seventeenth century. His first book, *Urania practica* (1649), asserted the stability of the earth and was Ptolemaic in spirit. A published attack on it by Jeremy Shakerley may have led to Wing's conversion to Copernicanism. By 1651 he had accepted the fundamentals of Keplerian astronomy as modified by Ismael Boulliau.

Like many astronomers in the second half of the seventeenth century, Wing, following Boulliau and Seth Ward, opted for an "empty-focus" variant of Kepler's second law, holding that a planet moving in an elliptical orbit describes equal angles in equal times about the focus not occupied by the sun. In works published in 1651 and 1656 Wing, adopting Boulliau's method, had his elliptical orbits, including that of the moon, generated in purely geometrical fashion by circles and epicycles. In his posthumously published *Astronomia Britannica*, however, he discarded the epicycles in favor of a refined version of the theory proposed by Ward in the latter's *Astronomia geometrica* (1656), in which the elliptical orbits were assumed to be physically generated. Wing's celestial mechanics contained a mixture of Cartesian and Keplerian components, with a rotating sun and celestial vortex pushing the planets around in their orbits.

*BIBLIOGRAPHY*

I. Original Works. Wing produced a great many almanacs, ephemerides, and astrological pamphlets. His chief works are *Urania practica* (London, 1649; 2nd ed., 1652); *Ens fictum Shakerley, His In-artificial Anatomy of Urania practica* (London, 1649), written with William Leybourn; *Harmonicon coeleste: Or the Coelestial Harmony of the Visible World* (London, 1651); *Astronomia instaurata: Or a New and Compendious Restauration of Astronomy* (London, 1656); *Geodates practicus: Or the Art of Surveying* (London, 1664); *Examen astronomiae Carolinae* (London, 1665); and *Astronomia Britannica* (London, 1669).

II. SECONDARY LITERATURE. See J. B. J. Delambre, *Histoire de l'astronomie moderne*, II (Paris, 1821), 519–524; and John Gadbury, *A Brief Relation of the Life and Death of the Late Famous Mathematician and Astrologer, Mr. Vincent Wing* (London, 1670).

WILBUR APPLEBAUM

**WINKLER, CLEMENS** (*b.* Freiberg, Germany, 26 December 1838; *d.* Dresden, Germany, 8 October 1904), *technical chemistry, analytical chemistry.*

Winkler was the son of Kurt Winkler, a pupil of Berzelius, N. G. Sefström, and Gahn, who managed a large cobalt works. Before entering the School of Mines at Freiberg, he spent his school vacations in his father's laboratory, where he learned accuracy and cleanliness in the Berzelius tradition.

Winkler entered the cobalt trade and soon became interested in the use of sulfur gases from the smelting furnaces as a raw material in preparing sulfuric acid. This involved refining the methods of industrial gas analysis, and to this end he developed the Winkler gas burette; he also published the first comprehensive book on the subject (1876). Extending his work on sulfuric acid, Winkler prepared oleum (required by dyestuff makers) from chamber acid by means of a contact process. Chamber acid was decomposed at red heat to yield oxygen and sulfur dioxide, which were converted to sulfur trioxide over platinized asbestos. This was a significant advance, since previous workers had attempted to use finely divided metals or oxides without the asbestos support. The weakness of Winkler's process lay in the gases being formed and used in stoichiometric proportions; his paper, however, was published in 1875, four years before the law of mass action was enunciated in its final form.

In 1885 a rich vein of argyrodite was discovered, and the mineral was submitted to Winkler for complete analysis. In repeated experiments his totals were consistent at 93 percent, and his early training in mineral analysis under his father convinced him that some hitherto unrecognized element must be present. In 1886 he showed that the substance was Mendeleev's predicted ekasilicon, which he named germanium.

Winkler was professor of analytical and technical chemistry at the Freiberg School of Mines from 1873 to 1902. At a time when most German chemical effort was concentrated in the organic field, he made many contributions to inorganic and analytical chemistry through his patient teaching and his prolific writing.

*BIBLIOGRAPHY*

I. ORIGINAL WORKS. The Royal Society *Catalogue of Scientific Papers*, VI, 396, VIII, 1251–1252, XI, 824–825, and XIX, 662, lists 91 publications. The following are relevant to the present article: "Versuche über die Ueberführung der schwefligen Säure in Schwefelsäureanhydrid durch Contact wirkung behufs Darstellung von rauchender Schwefelsäure," in *Dinglers polytechnisches Journal*, **218** (1875), 128, on the contact process for sulfuric acid; and "Germaniun, Ge, ein neues, nichtmetallisches Element," in *Berichte der Deutschen chemischen Gesellschaft,* **19** (1886), 210, on germanium. The book on gas analysis is *Anleitung zur chemischen Untersuchung der Industrie-gase* (Freiberg, 1876), which is supplemented by "Beiträge zur technischen Gasanalyse," in *Zeitschrift für analytische Chemie*, **28** (1889), 269–289. Those who wish to savor Winkler's literary style should read "Über die Entdeckung neuer Elemente," in *Berichte der Deutschen chemischen Gesellschaft*, **30** (1897), 6–21.

II. SECONDARY LITERATURE. There is no complete biography in English. The definitive life is Otto Brunck, in *Berichte der Deutschen chemischen Gesellschaft*, **39** (1906), pt. 4, 4491–4548. A shorter version by Brunck is in G. Bugge, *Das Buch der grossen Chemiker*, II (Berlin, 1930), 336–350.

The best English account of the sulfuric acid process is in G. Lunge, *Sulphuric Acid and Alkali*, 4th ed., I (London, 1913), in which 46 index references are given. Winkler's work on gas analysis has 25 index references in G. Lunge, *Technical Gas Analysis* (London, 1914). The discovery of germanium is described in M. E. Weekes, *Discovery of the Elements*, 4th ed. (Easton, Pa., 1939), 319–323.

W. A. CAMPBELL

**WINKLER, LAJOS WILHELM** (*b.* Arad, Hungary [now Rumania], 21 May 1863; *d.* Budapest, Hungary, 14 April 1939), *chemistry.*

One of nine children of Vilmos Winkler, a wholesaler, Winkler worked as an assistant pharmacist in a chemist's shop in Arad and then studied chemistry and pharmacology at the University of Budapest. He received the degree in pharmacology in 1885 and soon afterward was offered an assistant professorship at the university's chemical institute by Károly Than, a former student of Bunsen and a founder of scientific chemistry in Hungary.

Research at the institute was then focused primarily on the chemical composition of Hungarian mineral waters, the main concern being dissolved gases. Winkler's own interest centered on the quantitative determination of dissolved oxygen in water, which provided the subject of his doctoral dissertation at the University of Budapest in 1888. The Winkler method, as it is now known, laid the foundation of his scientific reputation.

Winkler subsequently participated in the preparation of volumes II–IV of the *Pharmacopoeia Hungarica*, of which Than was editor-in-chief. For this work he developed analytical methods that can be used even in simply furnished laboratories, and his practical sense and keen critical ability enabled him to create a number of techniques of enduring value, in particular his colorimetric titration method of determining the contamination of water by metals, such as iron, lead, and copper, and by ammonia, hydrogen sulfide, silica, and other contaminants, and his method of determining iodine concentration. In 1896 he was elected corresponding member of the Hungarian Academy of Sciences and, in 1922, full member. Than's department was divided into two professorships following his death in 1908; Winkler became professor of analytics and pharmacology, as well as director of the first chemistry department at the University of Budapest.

Winkler opened new areas in analytical chemistry, and the methods that he elaborated were summarized in *Die chemische Analyse* (1931–1936). In addition to his work in high-precision gravimetry and the analysis of gases, water, and pharmaceuticals, he also investigated the absorption coefficients of gases in various solvents and devised instruments for their measurement that still provide reliable data. The results of his work on gas, which covered nearly twenty years, became internationally known with their inclusion in Hans Landolt and Richard Börnstein's *Physikalisch-chemische Tabellen* (1883), replacing Bunsen's values. His figures have not been superseded.

To a considerable extent, the success of Winkler's methods for the determination of halogens can be regarded as responsible for the subsequent development of halogen analysis as an almost exclusively Hungarian field of investigation, and many of his pupils conducted work in that area. Winkler's techniques reflect the importance of strictly maintaining the prescribed experimental conditions in all reproducible methods. The application of the fundamental principle of reproducibility—in analytical chemistry as in the natural sciences—constitutes one of his most outstanding accomplishments.

## BIBLIOGRAPHY

A list of more than 200 of Winkler's works, compiled by L. Szebellédy, was published in *Winkler Lajos dr. emlékezete* (Budapest, 1940), 17–26. His writings include his dissertation, "Die Bestimmungen des in Wasser gelösten Sauerstoffs," in *Berichte der Deutschen chemischen Gesellschaft*, **21** (1889), 2843–2855; *Die chemische Analyse*, XXIX, XXX (Stuttgart, 1931–1936); and *Ausgewählte Untersuchungsverfahren für das chemische Laboratorium*, 2 vols. (Stuttgart, 1931–1936).

On Winkler's life and work, see E. Schulek, "L. W. Winkler, 1863–1939," in *Talanta*, **10** (1963), 423–428.

I. DE GRAAF BIERBRAUWER-WURTZ

**WINLOCK, JOSEPH** (*b*. Shelby County, Kentucky, 6 February 1826; *d*. Cambridge, Massachusetts, 11 June 1875), *astronomy, mathematics*.

Immediately upon graduation from Shelby College in 1845, Winlock was appointed professor of mathematics and astronomy in that school. At the meeting in 1851 of the American Association for the Advancement of Science, Winlock met Benjamin Peirce; thenceforth he was esteemed and promoted by the scientific lazzaroni. In 1852 he moved to Cambridge, as a computer for the *American Ephemeris and Nautical Almanac*. Using the refracting telescope from Shelby set up in the Cloverden Observatory in Cambridge, Winlock and B. A. Gould made astronomical observations. In 1857 Winlock was appointed professor of mathematics at the U.S. Naval Observatory. The following year he was promoted to superintendent of the Nautical Almanac office, which position he resigned in 1859 to take charge of the mathematics department of the U.S. Naval Academy. Following the outbreak of the Civil War, Winlock again took superintendence of the Nautical Almanac. In 1863 he was made an original member of the National Academy of Sciences. In 1866, backed by the "Coast Survey Clique," he was appointed Phillips professor of astronomy and director of the Harvard College Observatory. In 1871 the professorship of geodesy in the Lawrence Scientific School was added to his duties.

While at Harvard, Winlock's primary concern was to develop and obtain more accurate and efficient instruments. In this he was quite successful. Had he lived longer he would probably have used them to even better advantage than he did. Troughton & Simms, after extensive collaboration with Winlock, supplied a large and improved meridian circle. With this the Harvard zone of stars for the Astronomische Gesellschaft was determined; after Winlock's death the observations were continued by William A. Rogers, and the computations by Winlock's oldest daughter, Anna.

Among Winlock's several contributions to solar photography was the development of fixed-horizontal long-focus refracting telescopes. One of these instruments, installed at Harvard in 1870, took daily pictures of the sun. Similar telescopes were used by the eight U.S. government-sponsored expeditions to record the 1874 transit of Venus. Also worthy of mention are Winlock's particularly detailed photographs of the solar corona during the eclipse of 1869. Celestial spectroscopy also received Winlock's attention, and he obtained several fine spectroscopes for the observatory. To take the fullest possible advantage offered by the 1870 solar eclipse, Winlock devised a mechanical method of recording the positions of spectral lines. Throughout his tenure at Harvard he collaborated with the Coast Survey on both astronomical and geographical projects.

## BIBLIOGRAPHY

The Royal Society of London, *Catalogue of Scientific Papers,* Poggendorff, and the *Bibliographie Générale de l'Astronomie* list about two dozen Winlock papers. Winlock's influence as an astronomer, both his own work and the work he inspired in others, is best seen in the *Annals* of the Harvard College Observatory. Vols. **5, 6, 7,** published by Winlock, contain work done by his predecessors, W. C. Bond and G. P. Bond. Published after Winlock's death, vol. **8,** pt. 1, "Historical Account of the Astronomical Observatory of Harvard College," details the instrumental additions and improvements engineered by Winlock; pt. 2 contains "Astronomical Engravings of the Moon, Planets, etc.; Prepared [by L. Trouvelot] at the Astronomical Observatory of Harvard College Under the Direction of the Late Joseph Winlock, A.M." Vol. **9** contains C. S. Peirce's photometrical researches, also supported by Winlock. Vols. **10, 12, 14, 16, 25, 35,** and **36** contain astrometric catalogs prepared by William A. Rogers under the direction of Winlock and his successor, E. C. Pickering (in many cases these observations had been begun by Winlock). Vol. **13** contains micrometric observations from 1866 to 1881, made under, and in some cases by, Winlock and Pickering.

The most extensive obituary is in *Proceedings of the American Academy of Arts and Sciences*, **11** (1875–1876), 339–350, republished verbatim in *Biographical Memoirs of the National Academy of Sciences*, **1** (Washington, D.C., 1875). See also *Nature*, **12** (1875), 191–192; *American Journal of Science*, **10** (1875), 159–160 (quoted in *Scientific American*); *Dictionary of American Biography*, XX (New York, 1936); and the various published histories of the Harvard College Observatory.

DEBORAH JEAN WARNER

**WINSLØW, JACOB** (or **JACQUES-BÉNIGNE**) (*b.* Odense, Denmark, 17 April 1669; *d.* Paris, France, 3 April 1760), *anatomy.*

Winsløw was the eldest of the thirteen children of Peder Jacobsen Winsløw, dean of the Protestant Church of Our Lady in Odense, and Martha Bruun, whose own father had held the same post. He received his early education from his father, who was learned in both linguistics and archaeology, and at the Odense secondary school. He entered the University of Copenhagen to study theology in 1687. Although he delivered several sermons, Winsløw was soon attracted to the natural sciences, inspired by Oliger Jacobaeus and Caspar Bartholin the younger. From 1691 to 1696 he attended Borch's College and worked under the county barber-surgeon Johannes de Buchwald. Although Buchwald was the best surgeon in Copenhagen, Winsløw concentrated on anatomy, since the sight of blood alarmed him; he himself never performed an operation. He soon became Bartholin's prosector, and the latter was so pleased with his public anatomical demonstrations that he promoted him anatomicus regius, a post held by Winsløw's granduncle, Niels Stensen, some twenty years before.

In 1697 Winsløw was awarded a royal grant and accompanied Buchwald to the Netherlands, where he not only studied anatomy, but also received practical training in clinical medicine, surgery, and obstetrics, including private instruction with a midwife. These studies, together with his association with a number of Dutch scientists—including Johann Rau, Pieter Verduyn, and Hendrik van Deventer—convinced him of the value of the practical application of basic anatomical and physiological investigations.

Winsløw stayed in the Netherlands for fourteen months, then moved to Paris, where he began to study anatomy and surgery with J.-G. Duverney. A spiritual crisis intervened, however, inspired by discussions with his friend Ole Worm and by the treatises of Jacques-Bénigne Bossuet. After a series of conversations with the latter, in 1699 Winsløw converted to Roman Catholicism (taking his baptismal name Bénigne from Bossuet), whereupon his subsidy from the Danish government was terminated. With the help of Bossuet and other Catholic patrons he was soon able to resume his work with Duverney, and in 1704 Winsløw became a medical licentiate at the Hôtel Dieu and was authorized to practice as a physician in the city of Paris. Duverney made him his assistant in anatomy and surgery at the Jardin du Roi.

Winsløw became a member of the Académie Royale des Sciences in 1708; he also maintained a busy medical practice, was appointed physician at the Hôpital Général and at Bicêtre in 1709, assumed Duverney's duties at the Jardin du Roi in 1721, and was made *docteur-régent* of the Paris Faculty of Medicine in 1728. In 1743 Winsløw became full professor of anatomy at the Jardin du Roi; he held this post until 1758, when he was obliged to retire because of extreme deafness. On 18 February 1745 Winsløw dedicated the new anatomical theater of the Paris Faculty of Medicine, a building that still stands at 13 rue de la Bûcherie. Although in the address he made upon that occasion he referred to himself as being merely the successor of Riolan, Bartholin, and Stensen, he was in fact regarded as the greatest European anatomist of his day, and attracted a number of able students, including Albrecht von Haller.

Winsløw's own anatomical studies combined a talent for making observations with systematic thoroughness. Between 1711 and 1743 he published nearly thirty treatises, on a variety of subjects, in the *Mémoires de l'Académie royale des sciences*. Among these works was a series of investigations, published between 1715 and 1726, of the course of the various muscles, in which Winsløw showed that a single muscle does not function alone as a flexor or supinator, but rather that muscles work in groups as synergists, and always in relation to antagonists. In another tract of 1715 he described the foramen between the greater and lesser sacs of the peritoneum that is now named for him.

In "Sur les mouvements de la tête, du col et du reste de l'épine du dos" of 1730, Winsløw was the first to describe exactly the function of the small intervertebral joints, while in " . . . certaines mouvements avec les deux mains à la fois . . . plus facilement en sens contraire qu'en même sens" (1739), he noted that this effect is caused by nerve crossings in the brain and spinal cord, and not by any action of the muscles. In 1742 he published an account, based on comparative anatomical studies, of the function of the digastric muscles in opening the mouth through lowering the mandible. He also found occasion, in two articles published between 1740 and 1742, to inveigh against the formidable corsets worn by women at that time, and between 1733 and 1743 published a series of treatises on

monsters, in which he demonstrated that congenital malformations resulted from faulty predispositions and were not lesions of a normal fetus.

Winsløw's best-known work was his *Exposition anatomique de la structure du corps humain*, first published in 1732, then in a large number of subsequent editions and translations. The *Exposition* was the first treatise on descriptive anatomy, and, in its elimination of extraneous physiological details and hypothetical explanations, represented a pioneer work of exact scientific research. It was used by students and surgeons well into the following century. In it, following Stensen, Winsløw introduced a number of exact new terms, still used today, including the *corpora quadrigemina anteriora et posteriora* (formerly called *nates* and *testes*) and, for the ganglion chain, the "grand sympathetic nerve," the smaller branches being the "lesser sympathetic nerves."

Winsløw remained in Paris for the rest of his life, although he was invited on several occasions to return to Denmark. Only one of his treatises, *Mortis incertae signa* (1740), was translated into Danish (1868).

## BIBLIOGRAPHY

I. Original Works. There is a full list of Winsløw's works in H. Ehrencron-Müller, *Forfatterlexikon*, IX (Copenhagen, 1932), 124–128. His major writings are *Exposition anatomique de la structure du corps humain* (Paris, 1732; many later eds., 4 vols., 1732–1776); English trans. by G. Douglas, *An Anatomical Exposition of the Structure of the Human Body*, 2 vols. (London, 1733); German trans. by Georg Matthiae, *Anatomische Abhandlung von dem Bau des menschlichen Leibes*, 4 vols. (Berlin, 1733); enl. ed. by Bernhard Siegfried Albinus, 5 vols. (Basel, 1754); Latin trans. by E. Gallico, *Expositio anatomica structurae corporis humani*, 4 vols. (Frankfurt–Leipzig, 1758), also in 2 vols. (Venice, 1758); Italian trans., *Esposizione anatomica della struttura del corpo humano*, 4 vols. (Bologna, 1743; Naples, 1746, 1763, 1775; Venice, 1747, 1767); and *Quaestio medico-chirurgica . . . an mortis incertae signa minus incerta a chirurgicis, quam ab aliis experimentis* (Paris, 1740), also in French (Paris, 1742), Italian (Naples, 1744, 1775), Swedish (Stockholm, 1751), German (Leipzig, 1754), and Danish (Sorø, 1868). His autobiography is *L'autobiographie de J.-B. Winsløw*, Vilhelm Maar, ed. (Paris–Copenhagen, 1912).

II. Secondary Literature. See E. Hintzsche, *Albrecht v. Haller Tagebuch der Studienreise nach London, Paris* (Bern, 1968), 35; V. Maar, "Lidt om J.-B. Winsløw," in *Festskrift til Julius Petersen, V. Meisen, Prominent Danish Scientists* (Copenhagen, 1932), 53–60; R. Schär, *Albrecht von Hallers neue anatomisch-*

*physiologische Befunde* (Bern, 1958), 50; E. Snorrason, *L'anatomiste J.-B. Winslow, 1669–1760* (Copenhagen, 1969); and T. Vetter, "La vie active de Jacques-Benigne Winslow," in *Nordisk medicin* (1971), 107–129.

E. SNORRASON

**WINTHROP, JOHN** (*b.* Groton, Suffolk, England, 12 February 1606; *d.* Boston, Massachusetts, 5 April 1676), *natural philosophy, medicine.*

Winthrop, who has frequently been called John Winthrop, Jr., by historians to distinguish him from his father, was the son of John Winthrop and Mary Forth. Born into the Puritan landed gentry, he studied for two years at Trinity College, Dublin, read law at the Inner Temple, and toured Europe. In 1631 he married his cousin Martha Fones and emigrated to the Massachusetts Bay Colony, following his father, who had been chosen governor of the Puritan company.

Thereafter the younger Winthrop held various colonial offices, culminating in a long tenure as governor of Connecticut. His first wife died in 1634, and he married Elizabeth Reade the following year. Winthrop's moderate but fluctuating means gave him a certain degree of independence, and in his spare time he was able to undertake a wide range of scientific activities and to carry on an extensive correspondence with other investigators.

To meet the needs of New England's settlers and in the hope of providing commodities for export, Winthrop frequently searched for mineral resources. He used processes familiar from reading and observation to produce iron, salt, indigo, saltpeter, and other substances, and he promoted the development of a graphite mine. With the exception of his infant iron and graphite industries, which eventually were brought to fruition by others, these efforts did not achieve lasting success. Nevertheless, Winthrop is widely recognized as one of the founders of American industrial chemistry.

Winthrop was a devoted student of the Hermetic philosophy, which helped to form his early attitudes toward science. Little is known about his alchemical experiments, which began during his residence at the Inner Temple and continued, at least peripatetically, for a long while. Although there is no evidence that Winthrop ever claimed the alchemical secret, he had the reputation of an "adept." Circumstantial evidence has involved him in the problem of the authorship of the treatises on the theory and practice of alchemy published un-

der the pseudonym "Eirenaeus Philalethes," even though George Starkey probably used Winthrop only as an inspiration for the American adept from whom he claimed to have obtained some of the manuscripts. Winthrop amassed a large collection of alchemical and other scientific books within a general library of considerable extent. Portions of it are in various repositories.

Winthrop's medical records show that although he dispensed a wide variety of herbal preparations, he depended heavily on chemical medicines, especially antimonials and niter. At first his practice was limited to family and friends, but as word of his skill and willingness spread, he received medical requests from many parts of New England. Frequently his remedies were given free to the poor; and at his death Winthrop was undoubtedly New England's foremost physician.

His astronomical observations were of little consequence, although in 1660 Winthrop was operating what was probably the first large telescope in the American colonies, a ten-foot refractor. Several years later he was using a smaller instrument, and in 1668 he was attempting to perfect a telescope with a focal length of eight or ten feet.

Winthrop's letters reveal his interest in scientific phenomena as diverse as waterspouts and the metamorphosis of insects. During one of his voyages to England and Europe, he was admitted in 1662 to the group soon to be chartered as the Royal Society, and he was the first fellow resident in North America. While in London (1661–1663) he read papers on diverse subjects at the Society's meetings and was a faithful correspondent after returning to New England. Several of his communications were printed in the *Philosophical Transactions*. Although Winthrop contributed little to the history of scientific thought, he was the first scientific investigator of note in British America.

*BIBLIOGRAPHY*

I. ORIGINAL WORKS. Most of Winthrop's scientific observations were reported in his correspondence, now being printed by the Massachusetts Historical Society as part of *The Winthrop Papers* (Boston, 1929–    ). Earlier selections of his letters are cited below. Cromwell Mortimer, secretary of the Royal Society, asserted that Winthrop wrote "several learned Pieces . . . in Natural Philosophy; which indeed his innate Modesty would not suffer him to publish immediately, and when prevailed on by Friends to impart some of them to the Public, he concealed his Name, not being solicitous of the Reputation they might reflect on their Author" (*Philosophical*

*Transactions of the Royal Society,* **40** [1737–1738]). The only publications traditionally credited to Winthrop are excerpts from his letters in *Philosophical Transactions of the Royal Society,* **5** (1670), 1151–1153; and **6** (1671), 2221–2224; as well as a paper, "The Description, Culture, and Use of Maiz," *ibid.,* **12** (1678), 1065–1069, presented to the Royal Society in 1662.

II. SECONDARY LITERATURE. The first extensive biography is Robert C. Black, *The Younger John Winthrop* (New York–London, 1966). The only full-length study of Winthrop's scientific activities is Ronald S. Wilkinson, *The Younger John Winthrop and Seventeenth-Century Science* ([London], 1975). E. N. Hartley, *Ironworks on the Saugus* (Norman, Okla., 1957), examines his ironmaking endeavors. Among other specific modern studies are Ronald S. Wilkinson, "'Hermes Christianus': John Winthrop, Jr. and Chemical Medicine in Seventeenth Century New England," in Allen Debus, ed., *Science, Medicine and Society in the Renaissance: Essays to Honor Walter Pagel* (New York, 1972), I, 221–241; John W. Streeter, "John Winthrop, Junior, and the Fifth Satellite of Jupiter," in *Isis,* **39** (1948), 159–163; supplemented by Ronald S. Wilkinson, "John Winthrop, Jr. and America's First Telescopes," in *New England Quarterly,* **35** (1962), 520–523; and Ronald S. Wilkinson, "The Alchemical Library of John Winthrop, Jr. and His Descendants in Colonial America," in *Ambix,* **11** (1963), 33–51, and **13** (1966), 139–186.

RONALD S. WILKINSON

**WINTHROP, JOHN** (*b.* Boston, Massachusetts, 19 December 1714; *d.* Cambridge, Massachusetts, 3 May 1779), *astronomy, mathematics.*

One of sixteen children of Adam Winthrop and Anne Wainwright, John Winthrop was born into a New England family that was already famous both politically and scientifically. His great-granduncle and namesake, the son of Winthrop the elder, who immigrated to Massachusetts in 1630, was a founding member of the Royal Society of London, and governor of Connecticut from 1660 until his death in 1676. He was a notable administrator of the new settlements and a practical student of chemistry. It is interesting to note that one of his communications to the Royal Society concerned a fifth satellite of Jupiter. Here he anticipated his descendant's far more extensive astronomical studies.

Winthrop attended the Boston Latin School and Harvard College, from which he graduated in 1732. For the next six years he lived at home and studied privately to such effect that in 1738, at the age of twenty-four, he was appointed the second Hollis professor of mathematics and natural philosophy at Harvard, succeeding Isaac Greenwood.

His duties included giving illustrated public lectures and taking charge of the considerable collection of philosophical instruments in Harvard Hall, used for demonstrations.

During his long tenure of the Hollis chair, which ceased only with his death, Winthrop established the first experimental physics laboratory in America; taught the laws of mechanics, optics, and astronomy according to Newton's principles; and introduced into the mathematics curriculum the study of the calculus. Perhaps his most important work for Harvard followed the disastrous fire that destroyed Harvard Hall on the night of 24 January 1764. The fire gutted the last of Harvard's original buildings and wiped out the valuable collection of scientific instruments. It fell to Winthrop to arrange for the replacement of the collection, which he was well equipped to do, both because of his scientific knowledge and because of his family connections and many friends on both sides of the Atlantic. The most active and influential of these friends was Franklin, who knew many of the finest instrument makers in London. The first orders for new apparatus went to London in June 1764, and over the next few years, instruments bearing such names as John Ellicott, Jeremiah Sisson, James Short, Peter Dollond, Benjamin Martin, Edward Nairne, and George Adams were dispatched to Harvard. The two major shipments were valued together at about £540. Among the instruments were two telescopes produced by Short. Winthrop himself owned a telescope by Short (made *ca.* 1755), which appears in the portrait of him painted by John Singleton Copley about 1773.

After 1739 Winthrop carried out many astronomical observations, the majority of which were reported in the *Philosophical Transactions of the Royal Society.* He observed the transits of Mercury in 1740, 1743, and again in 1769; and he used his observations to help determine the difference in longitude between Cambridge, Massachusetts, and Greenwich, England. In April 1759 he delivered lectures on the return of Halley's comet of 1682. Perhaps his most important astronomical work was concerned with the two transits of Venus in 1761 and 1769, which engaged astronomers all over the world. For the 1761 transit Winthrop organized an expedition from Harvard to St. John's, Newfoundland, which provided the material for one of his most important papers. In 1769 he published the results of further work in *Two Lectures on the Parallax and Distance of the Sun, as Deducible From the Transit of Venus.* Winthrop was also interested in magnetism and meteorology, and carried out systematic observations over a period of twenty years, reporting in 1756 on the effects of the severe earthquake in New England.

A number of honors were awarded to Winthrop in his later years. On 27 June 1765 he was proposed as a fellow of the Royal Society at the instigation of Franklin; Short was another of his supporters. Winthrop must have been closely associated with both men at this time, over replacement instruments for his college, and in work on the transits of Venus. Not only did Short make telescopes for observatories throughout the world, but he was also closely concerned with the Royal Society's plans for observing the phenomena. Winthrop's election was delayed until February 1766, when the ballot finally took place. Franklin signed a bond for his contributions, and the Harvard records show that his fees, not exceeding fifty-two shillings, were paid out of the treasury of the society in return for his placing a volume of the *Philosophical Transactions* annually in the library. In 1769 Winthrop became a member of the American Philosophical Society. He received the honorary degrees of LL.D. from the University of Edinburgh and from Harvard in 1771 and 1773, respectively.

Winthrop's first wife, whom he married in 1746, was Rebecca Townsend; and three years after her death in 1756, he married Hannah Fayerweather, a widow, who survived him. Winthrop was an ardent patriot, and a friend and adviser of George Washington. His career maintained the family tradition of public service allied with learning.

## BIBLIOGRAPHY

I. ORIGINAL WORKS. Winthrop's works include "Concerning the Transit of Mercury Over the Sun, April 21, 1740 and of an Eclipse of the Moon, Dec. 21, 1740," in *Philosophical Transactions of the Royal Society*, **42** (1742–1743), 572–578; "An Account of the Earthquake Felt in New England, and the Neighbouring Parts of America, on the 18th of November 1755," *ibid.*, **50** (1757–1758), 1–18; "An Account of a Meteor Seen in New England, and of a Whirlwind Felt in That Country," *ibid.*, **52** (1761–1762), 6–16; "An Account of Several Fiery Meteors Seen in North America," *ibid.*, **54** (1764), 185–188; "Extract of a Letter . . . to James Short," *ibid.*, 277–278, on longitude and the equation of time; "Observations on the Transit of Venus, June 6, 1761, at St. John's, Newfoundland," *ibid.*, 279–283; "Cogitata de Cometis," *ibid.*, **57** (1767), 132–154; "Observations of the Transit of Venus Over the Sun, June 3, 1769," *ibid.*, **59** (1769), 351–358; "Observations of the Transit of Mercury Over the Sun, Oc-

tober 25, 1743," *ibid.*, 505–506; "Extract of a Letter . . . to B. Franklin," *ibid.*, **60** (1770), 358–362, on the transit of Venus and the aberration of light; "Observations of the Transit of Mercury Over the Sun, November 9th, 1769," *ibid.*, **61** (1771), 51–52; and "Remarks Upon a Passage in Castillione's Life of Sir Isaac Newton," *ibid.*, **64** (1774), 153–157.

Some of the material in the above papers was published separately including *Relation of a Voyage From Boston to Newfoundland for the Observation of the Transit of Venus, June 6, 1761* (Boston, 1761); and *Two Lectures on the Parallax and Distance of the Sun, as Deducible From the Transit of Venus. Read in Holden-Chapel at Harvard-College in Cambridge, New England, in March 1769* (Boston, 1769).

II. SECONDARY LITERATURE. On Winthrop and his work, see I. Bernard Cohen, *Some Early Tools of American Science. An Account of the Early Scientific Instruments and Mineralogical and Biological Collections in Harvard University* (Cambridge, Mass., 1950), *passim* (225 ff.); Raymond Phineas Stearns, "Colonial Fellows of the Royal Society of London, 1661–1788," in *Notes and Records of the Royal Society of London*, **8** (1951), 178–246; Raymond Phineas Stearns, *Science in the British Colonies of America* (Urbana, Ill., 1970), esp. 642–670; G. L'E. Turner, "The Apparatus of Science," in *History of Science*, **9** (1970), 129–138, an essay review of David P. Wheatland, *The Apparatus of Science at Harvard 1766–1800. Collection of Historical Scientific Instruments, Harvard University* (Cambridge, Mass., 1968), written with Barbara Carson; and *Dictionary of American Biography*, X, pp. 414–416.

G. L'E. TURNER

**WINTNER, AUREL** (*b*. Budapest, Hungary, 8 April 1903; *d*. Baltimore, Maryland, 15 January 1958), *mathematics*.

Wintner studied mathematics at the University of Leipzig from 1927 to 1929. During that period he was an editorial assistant for *Mathematische Zeitschrift* and *Jahrbuch über die Fortschritte der Mathematik*, serving under the direction of Leon Lichtenstein, who for many years was editor of those journals. This period of apprenticeship had a profound influence on Wintner, and he often expressed his gratitude for his training under Lichtenstein.

Wintner's mathematical reputation was established by a series of papers on the Hill lunar theory that gave the first mathematically rigorous proof of the convergence of George Hill's method involving infinitely many unknowns. He received the Ph.D. at Leipzig in 1929, then spent a semester in Rome as a Rockefeller fellow and another in Copenhagen, where he worked with Elis Stromgren. As a result of that collaboration, Wintner was able to provide a theoretical basis for Stromgren's "natural termination principle" for orbit periods, which was an empirical analysis of the degeneration of periodic orbits.

In 1929 Wintner published *Spektraltheorie der unendlichen Matrizen*, which contains the first proofs of the basic facts in Hilbert space—the fundamental mathematical construct in the then-developing physical theory of quantum mechanics. Unfortunately, Wintner's fundamental contributions to this subject were (and are) not adequately appreciated because he formulated his results in the language of matrices rather than in the more abstract language of operators, made popular by von Neumann. This lack of recognition embittered Wintner and made him suspicious of the (genuine) merits of the more abstract developments in recent mathematics.

In 1930 Wintner married the daughter of Otto Hölder, one of his teachers at Leipzig. In the same year he joined the faculty of the Johns Hopkins University, where he remained until his death. In 1944 he became an editor of *American Journal of Mathematics*, to which he devoted most of his energy, both through his scientific contributions (a substantial part of his most valuable work after he came to America was published there) and through his editorial work.

Wintner's work in America covered the entire range of classical analysis, from probability and analytic number theory to differential equations and basic questions in local differential geometry. Much of his work from 1936 to 1958 was done in collaboration with his student and colleague Philip Hartman. He published several papers with Norbert Wiener in a branch of probability theory that is now coming back into fashion. He also produced works with several other mathematicians. In 1941 Wintner published *Analytical Foundations of Celestial Mechanics*, which combines great astronomical and mathematical scholarship with deep and meticulous analysis. He is best known for this work.

Wintner, a man of high moral principles, opposed direct government support of scholarly research, for fear of interference. He not only accepted considerable financial hardship by personally refusing such support but also was willing to forgo fruitful scientific collaboration in order to maintain his ideals.

SHLOMO STERNBERG

**WISLICENUS, JOHANNES** (*b.* Klein-Eichstedt, near Querfurt, Germany, 24 June 1835; *d.* Leipzig, Germany, 5 December 1902), *chemistry.*

Wislicenus was a student at the University of Halle in 1853 when his father, a Lutheran pastor of liberal religious and political views, was ordered arrested for the publication of a biblical study. The family fled to the United States, where Wislicenus became an assistant in the analytical laboratory at Harvard. When the family returned to Europe in 1856, he completed his studies at Halle. Subsequently he was professor of chemistry at the Zurich Oberen Industrieschule (1861), associate (1864) and full professor (1867) at the University of Zurich, and professor (1870) at the Eidgenössische Technische Hochschule in Zurich. He succeeded Adolf Strecker at Würzburg in 1872 and Kolbe at Leipzig in 1885.

Wislicenus' first papers were joint publications with Wilhelm Heintz, professor of chemistry at Halle. They studied the condensation of aldehydes with ammonia and isolated the base oxytetraldin in 1858. At Zurich he and his colleague Adolf Fick investigated the origin of muscle energy. According to Liebig, proteins produced force and their oxidation furnished the energy for muscle power. Carbohydrates and fats produced only heat. In 1865 Wislicenus and Fick tested this theory by climbing the Faulhorn in the Swiss Alps, calculating the work done during the ascent and measuring the amount of nitrogen in the urine excreted. They proved that the oxidation of protein contributed little to muscle energy and concluded that protein was used mainly in the growth and maintenance of tissues, carbohydrate and fat oxidation being the source of muscle energy.

Between 1863 and 1873 Wislicenus studied lactic and paralactic acids. These two acids and a third, hydracrylic acid, were monobasic acids with the formula $C_3H_6O_3$. Wislicenus observed that lactic acid was optically active but paralactic acid was not. In 1863 he represented them according to the type theory, their radicals being in a different order:

$$\begin{cases} CH_3 \\ CH(OH) \\ CO(OH) \end{cases} \quad \begin{cases} CH_2(OH) \\ CH_2 \\ CO(OH) \end{cases}$$

When structural formulas came into use during the 1860's, he proposed that the two acids had identical structures. By 1873 Wislicenus established that lactic acid and paralactic acid were both $\alpha$-hydroxypropionic acid, while hydracrylic acid was $\beta$-hydroxypropionic acid. He was the first to establish the structural identity of two different substances, and argued that ordinary structural formulas were inadequate: the two acids must be represented by three-dimensional formulas that indicate the different arrangement of the atoms in space. Wislicenus called this type of isomerism "geometrical isomerism."

In 1874 van't Hoff presented his theory of the tetrahedral carbon atom and asserted that it occurred to him after reading Wislicenus' paper of the previous year. Wislicenus enthusiastically accepted van't Hoff's theory and wrote to him in 1875 for permission to have *La chimie dans l'espace* translated into German. He later contributed an introduction to the German edition.

Wislicenus was the leader in applying and extending the ideas of van't Hoff and Le Bel, and his successes helped to bring chemists to the new field of stereochemistry. There was, however, no serious attempt to apply the theory of the tetrahedral carbon atom to cases other than optical isomers. Van't Hoff had suggested that doubly linked carbon atoms could be represented by two tetrahedrons with one edge in common and that possibilities for isomerism occurred when two or more of the radicals attached to these carbon atoms differed.

In 1887 Wislicenus published an important paper on the stereoisomerism of unsaturated carbon compounds, extending the hypothesis along the lines suggested by van't Hoff and also considering the attractive-repulsive forces of the atoms in order to determine the most probable geometric configuration of the atoms in the molecule. He showed how the interpretation of maleic and fumaric acids as geometric isomers explained their chemical transformations. In addition he determined the configurations of many unsaturated isomeric carbon compounds and investigated geometric isomerism in cyclic compounds.

Wislicenus contributed to several areas of organic chemistry. He introduced molecular silver as a synthetic agent, preparing adipic acid from $\beta$-iodopropionic acid in 1869. Other syntheses include hydantoin (1873), glutaric acid (1878), vinyl ether (1878), cyclic ketones (1893), and vinyl acetic acid (1899). In a long series of researches on acetoacetic ester and its derivatives, he established the conditions for their hydrolysis, showing that acid hydrolysis produced a ketone, alcohol, and carbon dioxide, and alkaline hydrolysis a fatty acid and alcohol (1878). Wislicenus elucidated the structure of acetoacetic ester by replacing hydrogen with sodium. The ethyl sodioacetoacetate combined with an alkyl iodide gave high yields of a substituted acetoacetic ester that could accept another sodium atom and exchange it for a second alkyl group.

## BIBLIOGRAPHY

I. ORIGINAL WORKS. Wislicenus' study of the geometric isomerism of unsaturated compounds is "Über die räumliche Anordnung der Atome in organischen Molekülen und ihre Bestimmung in geometrischisomeren ungesättigten Verbindung," in *Abhandlungen der K. Sächsischen Gesellschaft der Wissenschaften*, math.-phys. Kl., **14** (1887), 1–78, translated by George M. Richardson in *Foundations of Stereochemistry: Memoirs by Pasteur, Van't Hoff, Le Bel and Wislicenus* (New York, 1901), 65–132. Wislicenus rewrote Strecker's textbook, originally based on an earlier work of Regnault, *Regnault-Strecker's Kurzes Lehrbuch der Chemie*, 2 vols. (Brunswick, 1874–1881); there is an English version of the organic chemistry part: *A. Strecker's Short Textbook of Organic Chemistry by Dr. J. Wislicenus*, translated and edited by W. R. Hodgkinson and A. J. Greenaway (London, 1881).

Significant papers include "Über ein basisches Zersetzungsproduck des Aldehydammoniaks," in *Annalen der Physik und Chemie*, **105** (1858), 577–597, written with W. Heintz; "Studien zur Geschichte der Milchsäure und ihrer Homologen," in *Justus Liebigs Annalen der Chemie*, **125** (1863), 41–70; **133** (1865), 257–287; and **146** (1868), 145–161; "On the Origin of Muscular Power," in *Philosophical Magazine*, 4th ser., **31** (1866), 485–503, written with A. Fick; "Synthetische Untersuchungen über die Säuren der Reihe $C_nH_{2n}$ (CO · OH)$_2$," in *Annalen der Chemie*, **149** (1869), 215–224; "Über die isomeren Milchsäuren," *ibid.*, **166** (1873), 3–64; "Über die optisch-active Milchsäuren der Fleischflüssigkeit, die Paramilchsäure," *ibid.*, **167** (1873), 302–346; "Über Acetessigestersynthesen," *ibid.*, **186** (1877), 161–228; "Spaltung des Acetessigester und seiner Alkylsubstitutionsproducte durch Basen," *ibid.*, **190** (1878), 257–281; "Über Vinyläthyläther," *ibid.*, **192** (1878), 106–128; "Untersuchungen zur Bestimmung der räumliche Atomlagerung," *ibid.*, **246** (1888), 53–96, **248** (1888), 281–355, and **250** (1889), 224–254; and "Über Ringketone," *ibid.*, **275** (1893), 309–382.

II. SECONDARY LITERATURE. There are two detailed accounts of Wislicenus' work: Ernst Beckmann, "Johannes Wislicenus," in *Berichte der Deutschen chemischen Gesellschaft*, **37** (1904), 4861–4946, which includes a bibliography; and William Henry Perkin, Jr., "The Wislicenus Memorial Lecture," in *Memorial Lectures Delivered Before the Chemical Society*, II (London, 1914), 59–92, which originally appeared in *Journal of the Chemical Society*, **87** (1905), 501–534.

ALBERT B. COSTA

**WISTAR, CASPAR** (*b.* Philadelphia, Pennsylvania, 13 September 1761; *d.* Philadelphia, 22 January 1818), *anatomy.*

Fifth of eight children of Richard Wistar, proprietor of a glass factory at Salem, New Jersey, and his wife, Sarah Wyatt, both of whom were Quakers, Wistar attended Friends' schools in Philadelphia and, moved, it is said, by the sufferings of the wounded at the battle of Germantown in 1777, determined to study medicine. After a preceptorship with Dr. John Redman, he entered the University of the State of Pennsylvania in 1779, and was graduated Bachelor of Medicine three years later. Although he had some difficulty in obtaining permission of the Quaker monthly meeting to go abroad, because he had fought a duel, Wistar went to England, where he studied anatomy in London under John Hunter. At Edinburgh he so impressed his instructors that, had university regulations not prevented, they would have allowed him to take a degree after only one year's study. Wistar was equally respected by his fellow students, who elected him an annual president of both the Royal Medical Society (a student organization) and the Edinburgh Natural History Society, to the latter of which he read a paper on moisture in the atmosphere. His graduation thesis, *De animo demisso* (1786), was said to have given "unspeakable relief" to several Scottish hypochondriacs; and Dr. Charles Stuart of Edinburgh urged that it be translated and printed in London. After a short visit to the Continent, Wistar returned home in 1787.

As a practitioner Wistar was slow and deliberate, but accurate; he lacked the temperament for surgery. During the Philadelphia yellow fever epidemic of 1793 he remained in the city, giving Benjamin Rush aid and support; but, falling ill himself, he allowed Adam Kuhn to treat him. Thereafter he abandoned Rush's heroic prescriptions of bleeding and purging and so lost his friendship. Wistar was an attending physician of the Philadelphia Dispensary in 1786, a physician to the Pennsylvania Hospital in 1793–1810, and in 1809 founder of a vaccine society that vaccinated 1,102 persons in its first year. Ill health forced him to give up much of his practice several years before his death.

As a medical teacher Wistar was professor of chemistry at the College of Philadelphia[1] in 1789, then adjunct professor of anatomy, surgery, and midwifery at the new University of Pennsylvania in 1792; after 1810 he taught only anatomy. Through hard work he made himself an effective lecturer, and introduced two innovations in instruction: in class he employed large-scale models of the small parts of the human structure; and he divided the students into small groups ("bone classes"), giving each an assortment of bones and preparations to study and identify. As a further aid he prepared *A System of Anatomy for the Use of Students of Medicine* (2 vols., Philadelphia, 1811). Drawing heavily on John Innes, Monro, and Bichat, this manual went into nine editions and was pronounced by Charles Caldwell, who was not given to praising his contemporaries, as "without rival, in any language." It was John Syng Dorsey's judgment of Wistar that "no one could fail to become an Anatomist who diligently attended his lectures." Wistar's only original contribution to anatomy was an account, read in 1814, of the sphenoid sinuses ("Observations on Those Processes of the Ethnoid Bone Which Originally Form the Sphenoidal Sinuses," in *Transactions of the American Philosophical Society*, n.s. **1** [1818], 371–374). In his latter years he wrote several papers on paleontological remains from Big Bone Lick (near Burlington), Kentucky.

Wistar married twice: in 1788 Isabella Marshall, who died in 1790; and in 1798 Elizabeth Mifflin, who died in 1840, by whom he had a daughter and two sons, one of whom became a physician. Concerned since young manhood about slavery, Wistar was president of the Pennsylvania Abolition Society when he died. He was equally sensitive to the plight of the American Indians and was one of the first in the United States to appreciate their eloquence, examples of which he used to read aloud to his family. In the American Philosophical Society, to which he was elected in 1787, he succeeded Thomas Jefferson as president (1815–1818). His portrait was painted by Bass Otis, and William Rush carved a bust; and he is otherwise remembered by the lovely flowering shrub that Thomas Nuttall named for him,[2] as well as for his agreeable informal suppers for friends and distinguished strangers, which, institutionalized after his death as the Wistar Association, continue little changed to this day.

### NOTES

1. The College of Philadelphia was chartered in 1755, and flourished until 1779, when it was abolished by legislative act and its endowments and property were given to a new institution called the University of the State of Pennsylvania. In 1789 the confiscated properties were restored to the ousted trustees of the defunct College, and the institution was revived under its old name. Thus in 1789 there were two collegiate institutions in Philadelphia: the College of Philadelphia and the University of the State of Pennsylvania. In 1791

the two institutions were united under a new charter and name as the University of Pennsylvania.

2. Nuttall named the plant for his friend Caspar Wistar, but spelled it Wister. That would not cause any complication but for the fact that one branch of the family in Philadelphia spells its name Wister; and in the mid-nineteenth century, after the principals were dead, Charles J. Wister, Jr., claimed that Nuttall had named the plant for *his* father, who (to make the argument plausible) was an amateur of natural history. The generally accepted version is that the wisteria was named for Caspar Wistar and really should be spelled wistaria.

*BIBLIOGRAPHY*

I. ORIGINAL WORKS. In addition to those cited in the text, Wistar's writings include *Eulogium on Doctor William Shippen . . .* (Philadelphia, 1818); several articles in *Transactions of the American Philosophical Society*; and one (on scurvy) in *Philadelphia Medical and Physical Journal*, **2**, pt. 2 (1806). His letter "To the Physicians of Philadelphia" on yellow fever is in the Philadelphia *General Advertiser* (26 Sept. 1793); the controversy with Rush continues in issues of 4 Oct. and 1 and 8 Nov. 1793. Miscellaneous MS letters and papers are at the Historical Society of Pennsylvania, the College of Physicians of Philadelphia, and the American Philosophical Society Library.

II. SECONDARY LITERATURE. Contemporary eulogies and memoirs by Charles Caldwell, *An Elogium on Caspar Wistar, M.D.* (Philadelphia, 1818), David Hosack, *Tribute to the Memory of the Late Caspar Wistar, M.D.* (New York, 1818), and William Tilghman, *An Elogium in Commemoration of Dr. Caspar Wistar* (Philadelphia, 1818), are the principal sources. Within a few weeks of Wistar's death Tilghman asked professional colleagues, friends, and family for information and judgments; the replies, preserved at the College of Physicians of Philadelphia, contain more data than the printed eulogy. Sketches of Wistar in Samuel D. Gross, ed., *Lives of Eminent American Physicians and Surgeons of the Nineteenth Century* (Philadelphia, 1861); and James Thacher, *American Medical Biography* (Boston, 1828), add little to the 1818 eulogies. William S. Middleton, "Caspar Wistar, Junior," in *Annals of Medical History*, **4** (1922), 64–76, contains the essential facts. On Rush's relations with Wistar, see *Letters of Benjamin Rush*, L. H. Butterfield, ed., 2 vols. (Princeton, 1950).

WHITFIELD J. BELL, JR.

**WITELO** (*b.* Poland, *ca.* 1230/1235; *d. after ca.* 1275), *optics, natural philosophy.*

**Life.** Very little is known of Witelo's life. His homeland and national origins must be inferred from scattered remarks in his *Perspectiva*. There he refers to "our homeland, namely Poland" and mentions the city of Vratizlavia (Wrocław) and the nearby towns of Borek and Liegnitz,[1] thus reveal-ing an intimate knowledge of the environs of Breslau (Wrocław) in Silesia, which suggests that he probably was born and raised there. In the preface to the *Perspectiva*, Witelo refers to himself as "the son of Thuringians and Poles," from which it may be gathered that on the paternal side he was descended from the Germans of Thuringia who colonized Silesia in the twelfth and thirteenth centuries, while on the maternal side he was of Polish descent.

Witelo's education and adult life likewise must be reconstructed from the most fragmentary evidence. It may be surmised, from a reference to time spent in Paris and a description of a nocturnal brawl that occurred there in 1253, that he received his undergraduate education at the University of Paris in the early 1250's. He must, therefore, have been born in the early or middle 1230's. In the 1260's Witelo was studying canon law at Padua, as revealed by his reference to an event that occurred in Padua in 1262 or 1265.[2] His presence in Padua also is indicated by the explicit of his *Tractatus de primaria causa penitentie et de natura demonum* (written during his stay in Padua), in which he is referred to as "Witilo, student in canon law."[3] It is evident, however, that at Padua he was not totally preoccupied with his legal studies, for he wrote the *Tractatus* during an Easter recess, and, according to Birkenmajer, it reflects the teachings of Plato, Galen, Ibn Sīnā, Aristotle, Ibn Rushd, Euclid, and Ibn al-Haytham (Alhazen).[4]

Late in 1268 or early in 1269, Witelo appeared in Viterbo, where he became acquainted with William of Moerbeke, papal confessor and translator of philosophical and scientific works from Greek to Latin, to whom Witelo later dedicated the *Perspectiva*. We know nothing further of Witelo's movements unless he is to be identified with the person of that name who served as chaplain to King Ottocar II of Bohemia and who was sent on a mission to Pope Gregory X in 1274.[5] The Bern manuscript of Witelo's *Perspectiva* refers to the author as "Magister Witelo de Viconia," which has given rise to speculation that Witelo retired to the Premonstratensian abbey of Vicogne during his declining years.[6]

It is apparent that Witelo's *Perspectiva* was not composed before 1270, since it draws on Hero of Alexandria's *Catoptrica*, the translation of which was completed by Moerbeke on 31 December 1269. Because such an immense work probably was not written in less than several years, it is unlikely that Witelo died before the mid-1270's.

There continues to be a good deal of confusion

regarding Witelo's name. In the printed editions of the *Perspectiva*, the author's name is spelled "Vitellio" or "Vitello"; and a number of historians have adopted this orthography. Maximilien Curtze and Clemens Baeumker have demonstrated, however, that early manuscripts of the *Perspectiva* give overwhelming support to the form "Witelo."[7] They have argued, further, that "Witelo" is a diminutive of "Wito" or "Wido," a given name commonly encountered in Thuringian documents of the thirteenth century. Family names were uncommon in thirteenth-century Poland, and there is no evidence to suggest that Witelo had one.

**Works.** Witelo's known extant works are *Perspectiva* and *De primaria causa penitentie et de natura demonum*. In addition he refers in the *Perspectiva* to several other treatises of his, none of which can now be identified: *De elementatis conclusionibus, Philosophia naturalis, Scientia motuum celestium, Naturales anime passiones,* and *De ordine entium*.[8] These titles reveal the range of Witelo's interests in natural philosophy. Nevertheless, since only the *Perspectiva* has been the object of detailed study, his reputation rests almost solely on his work in optics.

Optics in the latter half of the thirteenth century was hardly (if at all) an experimental endeavor;[9] the principal task was to master an abundance of literature on the subject. By far the most important optical treatise in Witelo's day was Ibn al-Haytham's *Optics* or *De aspectibus*, rendered into Latin by an unidentified translator late in the twelfth or early in the thirteenth century. Although Witelo never refers to Ibn al-Haytham by name, there can be no doubt that the latter was his chief source: Witelo normally treats the same topics in the same fashion and sometimes even in the same words; occasionally he omits or inserts a topic, and often he seeks to clarify or supplement one of Ibn al-Haytham's points by further elaboration or an improved demonstration, but in very few respects does he escape the general framework inherited through the latter's *Optics*.[10]

Yet other influences are evident. It is beyond dispute that Witelo used the *Optica* of Ptolemy, whose table of refraction he reproduces; the *Catoptrica* of Hero, whose principle of minimum distance he employs to explain reflection at equal angles; and the *De speculis comburentibus* (anonymous in the thirteenth century, but now attributed to Ibn al-Haytham), from which he drew his analysis of paraboloidal mirrors. There can be little doubt that he also was familiar with the widely circulated *Optica (De visu)* of Euclid, *Ca-*

*toptrica (De speculis)* of Pseudo-Euclid, *De aspectibus* of al-Kindī, and the physiological and psychological works of Galen, Ḥunayn ibn Isḥāq, Ibn Sīnā, and Ibn Rushd. As for Latin authors, Alexander Birkenmajer has argued that Witelo was strongly influenced by Robert Grosseteste's *De lineis angulis et figuris* and Roger Bacon's *De multiplicatione specierum*.[11] In addition, it is certain that he knew Bacon's *Opus maius* and possible that he knew John Pecham's *Perspectiva communis*.[12] Witelo also relied on a number of ancient mathematical works, including those of Euclid and Apollonius of Perga, and perhaps of Eutocius, Archimedes, Theon of Alexandria, and Pappus.

Witelo's *Perspectiva* is an immense folio volume of nearly five hundred pages in the three printed editions, and no detailed analysis of its contents has ever been made. It will be possible, in the remainder of this article, only to trace its most significant features. The scope of the *Perspectiva* is revealed by the following outline of its contents: Book I consists of definitions, postulates, and 137 geometrical theorems, which provide the mathematical principles required for the optical demonstrations of the remaining nine books. In this book Witelo skillfully summarizes the aspects of the geometrical achievement of antiquity that are relevant to his own geometrical optics. Book II deals with the nature of radiation, the propagation of light and color in straight or refracted lines, shadows, and the problem of pinhole images. Book III is concerned with the physiology, psychology, and geometry of monocular and binocular vision by means of rectilinear radiation.

Book IV treats the perception of the twenty visible intentions other than light and color, including size, shape, remoteness, corporeity, roughness, darkness, and beauty. It also deals with errors in the perception of these intentions—principally errors in judging distance, shape, and relative size. This book is thus largely psychological in tone, although it includes a number of matters that fall into the realm of traditional geometrical perspective. In book V, Witelo considers vision by reflected rays, beginning with the nature and geometrical laws of reflection and proceeding to a detailed analysis of plane mirrors. Image formation in curved mirrors occupies books VI through IX of the *Perspectiva*—convex spherical mirrors in book VI, convex cylindrical and conical mirrors in book VII, concave spherical mirrors in book VIII, and concave cylindrical, conical, and paraboloidal mirrors in book IX. Book X is concerned with vision by rays refracted at plane or spherical interfaces; it also includes a discussion of the rainbow and other meteorological phenomena.

The most essential feature of any optical system might seem to be its theory of the nature of light. Witelo's concerns were principally geometrical, however, and he formulated no systematic account of the nature of light. From scattered remarks throughout the *Perspectiva* (particularly its preface) one can hope at the very most to classify him within a broad tradition on this question. He writes in the preface: "Sensible light is the intermediary of corporeal influences"; "Light is a corporeal form"; and "Light is the first of all sensible forms." It is apparent from such remarks that light is regarded as the intermediary in certain natural actions—an instance of the multiplication of forms. Light is thus one particular manifestation of a more general phenomenon, the propagation of force or influence from one natural body to another. But although light is only one instance of natural action, it is the instance most accessible to the senses and most amenable to analysis; therefore it serves, for Witelo, as the paradigm for the investigation of all natural actions. Thus he writes, at the conclusion of his quantitative analysis of refraction, "These are the things that occur to lights and colors and universally to all forms in their diffusion through transparent bodies and in the refraction that occurs in all of them."[13] And in the preface he remarks, "The investigation [in general, of the action of one body on another] properly proceeds by means of visible entities." It is evident, then, that Witelo falls very generally into the Neoplatonic tradition traceable from Plotinus through Ibn Gabirol to Grosseteste and Bacon. For Witelo, as for these predecessors, every natural body propagates its power to surrounding bodies, of which propagation light is the principal example. Moreover, Witelo would seem to follow Grosseteste and Bacon in perceiving that optics thus becomes the fundamental science of nature.

A second essential feature of any optical system, about which Witelo says somewhat more, is the propagation of light or visible forms. According to Witelo, light is always propagated rectilinearly unless it encounters a reflecting or refracting surface. This fact, he claims, can be verified experimentally; and he even describes the required apparatus. The same apparatus had already been described by Ibn al-Haytham, however, and there is no reason to believe that Witelo personally verified the rectilinear propagation of light by experimental means. Witelo is uninformative on the physical mechanism of propagation, but one can surmise from his use of terms like "multiplication" and "diffusion" that his view was not far from that of Roger Bacon. He departs from Ibn al-Haytham and Bacon and most of the ancient optical tradition on the temporal aspects of propagation, arguing that light requires no time for propagation through an extended medium. He proceeds on logical grounds, reducing to absurdity the claim that the propagation of light requires time. Witelo is unable to maintain this position, however, and later admits that "every light passing through a transparent body tranverses it with an exceedingly swift and insensible motion. And yet the motion occurs more swiftly through more transparent bodies than through less transparent bodies."[14]

The applicability of geometry to optical problems follows from the principle of rectilinear propagation: light proceeding along straight lines, subject only to the rules of reflection and refraction, clearly is amenable to geometrical analysis. Witelo draws a careful distinction, however, between the one-dimensional lines employed in a geometrical analysis of optical phenomena and actual rays (or radial lines) of light. The latter are real physical lines traversed by the smallest visible light, and "in the least light that can be supposed, there is width. . . . Therefore in a radial line along which light is diffused, there is some width."[15] Nevertheless, "in the middle of that [radial line] is an imaginary mathematical line, parallel to which are all the other mathematical lines in that natural line."[16] And since the mathematical lines always fall within the natural radial lines, the former adequately represent the actual path of light, and it is proper to employ them in optical demonstrations.[17]

It was still a matter of debate in the thirteenth century whether rays issue only from the visible object or whether, in addition, there is an emission from the observer's eye that assists in the act of sight. Witelo follows Ibn al-Haytham (and departs from Grosseteste, Bacon, and Pecham) in acknowledging no emission of visual rays from the eye; sight is due solely to the forms of light and color issuing in all directions from every point (or small part) of the visible object and entering the observer's eye to produce visual sensations.

Witelo also follows Ibn al-Haytham (and the entire ancient and medieval optical tradition) in declaring that the sensitive organ of the eye is the glacial humor (or crystalline lens), which occupies the central position. Sight occurs, therefore, when the forms of light and color are arranged on the surface of the crystalline lens in the same order as the points of the visible object from which they issued: on the surface of the crystalline lens there is a "union of the visible forms and the soul's organ,"[18] which constitutes the act of sight. But how is it possible for light to be arranged on the surface of the lens exactly as on the surface of the object, since light issues in all directions from every point of the object? Witelo supplies precisely the same answer as Ibn al-Haytham, Bacon, and Pecham: only unrefracted light is strong enough to be efficacious in sight, and there is but one unrefracted ray issuing from each point of the visible object—the ray proceeding toward the center of curvature of the humors and tunics of the eye. The collection of all such unrefracted rays maintains its configuration between the visible object and the glacial humor and consequently forms, on the surface of the latter, an exact image (albeit reduced in size) of the visible object. Yet the act of sight is not completed in the glacial humor; the forms it receives pass through to the optic nerve and thence to the anterior part of the brain, where the nerves from the two eyes intersect to form the "common nerve," the residence of the visual power or *ultimum sentiens*, where a final judgment is made.

The geometrical structure that Witelo builds upon the conception of rays and mathematical lines naturally encompasses problems of geometrical perspective and image formation by reflection and refraction, but it also extends to the anatomy of the eye and the act of sight. He describes the eye in traditional terms, as a composite of three humors—glacial or crystalline, vitreous, and albugineous (aqueous)—and four tunics—uvea, cornea, conjunctiva or consolidativa, and aranea or retina. Geometrical considerations predominate in Witelo's descriptions of these tunics and humors: all are spherical in form; all tunics and humors anterior to the glacial humor must have concentric surfaces, so that a ray perpendicular to one is perpendicular to the rest and passes through all of them without refraction; and the glacial and vitreous humors have precisely the necessary shapes and relative densities to refract the rays converging toward the center of the eye before they actually intersect, and to conduct them through the vitreous humor and optic nerve without alteration or inversion.

Books V–IX of the *Perspectiva* are devoted to the science of catoptrics. The foundation of this science is the law of reflection, which Witelo derives from the principle of minimum distance: since nature does nothing in vain, it "always acts along the shortest lines."[19] Following Hero of Alexandria, Witelo demonstrates that the shortest lines connecting two points and a reflecting surface are those that make equal angles with the surface.[20] He also argues that the plane formed by the incident and reflected rays is perpendicular to the surface of reflection (or, in the case of curved mirrors, its tangent), and that an object seen by reflection appears to be located where the backward extension of the ray incident on the eye intersects the perpendicular dropped from the visible object to the reflecting surface.

Employing these three rules and the principles of geometry, Witelo proceeds to solve a series of very abstruse problems in reflection, drawn primarily (but not entirely) from Ptolemy and Ibn al-Haytham. This is the most substantial section of the *Perspectiva*, occupying much of books V–IX and some 200 pages in the printed editions. Witelo deals skillfully with such problems as inversion and reversal of images, determination of precise size and location of images formed by concave and convex mirrors of various shapes, and computation of the number of images of a given object visible in a concave spherical mirror. Not until the seventeenth century was his catoptrics excelled in the West.

Book X of the *Perspectiva* deals with the refraction of light. In book II, Witelo had described an instrument for gathering quantitative data on the propagation of light, and in book X he claims to have used the same instrument in the formulation of tables of refraction. In fact, there is ample evidence that this claim is untrue. In the first place, the upper half of the table is taken directly from Ptolemy's *Optica*.[21] Second, the values appearing in the table are not those given by experiment, but sets of numbers conforming to a regular progression—the differences between successive angles of refraction (corresponding to angles of incidence taken at 10° intervals) form an arithmetic progression with a common difference of one-half degree. Finally, the lower half of the table was computed by Witelo from the values in the upper half by erroneous application of the reciprocal law; consequently it includes preposterous results, such as angles of refraction (measured from the perpendicular) greater than 90° and no recognition whatsoever of total internal reflection.

Nevertheless, at the qualitative level Witelo is fully cognizant of the principal phenomena of refraction: light passing obliquely from a less dense to a more dense medium is refracted toward the perpendicular, while light passing in the reverse direction is refracted away from the perpendicular. But Witelo is not content with a quantitative or qualitative description of the geometrical phenomena of refraction; he also presents a mechanical explanation based on the varying resistance offered to the passage of light by different transparent substances, the idea that ease of traversing a medium is associated with proximity to the perpendicular, and the principle that light is so refracted at a transparent interface as to most nearly preserve uniformity of strength or action in the two media. In the course of this analysis, Witelo resolves the oblique motion of light into components perpendicular and parallel to the refracting interface.[22]

**Influence.** It is difficult to separate Witelo's influence on the history of late medieval and early modern optics from that of Ibn al-Haytham, particularly after their works were published in a single volume in 1572. One can affirm in general that their writings, along with John Pecham's *Perspectiva communis*, served as the standard textbooks on optics until well into the seventeenth century. More specifically, it is possible to establish Witelo's influence on Henry of Hesse, Blasius of Parma, and Nicole Oresme in the fourteenth century; Lorenzo Ghiberti, Johannes Regiomontanus, and Leonardo da Vinci in the fifteenth century; Giambattista della Porta, Francesco Maurolico, Giovanni Battista Benedetti, Tycho Brahe, William Gilbert, Simon Stevin, and Thomas Harriot in the sixteenth century; and Kepler, Galileo, Willebrord Snell, Descartes, and Francesco Grimaldi in the seventeenth century.[23]

## NOTES

1. Bk. X, theor. 74; bk. IV, theor. 28.
2. The former date is in Alexander Birkenmajer's "Witelo e lo studio di Padova," 156; the latter is in Lynn Thorndike's *History of Magic and Experimental Science*, V, 86.
3. Birkenmajer, *op. cit.*, 160. Thorndike regards this as a single work, while Birkenmajer treats it as two separate treatises.
4. *Ibid.*, 162.
5. *Ibid.*, 157.
6. Alternatively, it has been suggested that "Viconia" may be a misreading of "Vitovia," a Polish village (which is not, however, near Wrocław); see Clemens Baeumker, "Zur Biographie," 360.
7. Maximilien Curtze, "Sur l'orthographe," 49–66; Baeumker, *Witelo*, 190–200.
8. Some of these titles are less than certain: in several cases one cannot be sure that Witelo is claiming authorship; in others it is not clear whether the title applies to a chapter or to an entire treatise. For more detail, see Baeumker, *Witelo*, 239–244. *De intelligentiis*, formerly ascribed to Witelo, is now generally attributed to Adam Pulchrae Mulieris (*fl.* 1225). On the possibility that certain MSS of Euclid's *De visu* actually contain Witelo's recension of this treatise, see Wilfred R. Theisen, "The Medieval Tradition of Euclid's *Optics*" (Ph.D. diss., Univ. of Wis., 1972), 58–60; David C. Lindberg, intro. to facs. repr. of Risner ed., xi, xxvii.
9. If there is an exception to this generalization, it seems to be in the science of the rainbow, where both Witelo and Dietrich von Freiberg claim to have used spherical containers filled with water to simulate a raindrop.
10. The appellation "Alhazen's ape," later applied to Witelo by Giambattista della Porta, is unfortunate, since it ignores Witelo's frequent attempts to revise or supplement Ibn al-Haytham and the constant use of his own critical powers.
11. Alexander Birkenmajer, "Robert Grosseteste and Richard Fournival," in *Mediaevalia et humanistica*, **5** (1948), 36.
12. In bk. X, theor. 78, Witelo refers to those who maintain that the sum of the altitudes of the sun and rainbow is 42°, the precise value given by Bacon in pt. VI of the *Opus maius*. As I have argued in my ed. of Pecham's *Perspectiva communis* and elsewhere, it is possible that Witelo borrowed from Pecham, but more likely that Pecham borrowed from Witelo.
13. Bk. X, theor. 8.
14. Bk. II, theor. 47.
15. Bk. II, theor. 3.
16. *Ibid.*
17. Yet Witelo recognizes that not only the imaginary mathematical lines, but even radial lines, are fictions and that radiation is actually continuous; see, for example, bk. X, theor. 3. Nevertheless, analysis into rays and imaginary lines is a legitimate technique for the solution of most optical problems.
18. Bk. III, theor. 6.
19. Bk. V, theor. 5.
20. Bk. I, theor. 17–18; bk. V, theor. 18.
21. Witelo's table appears in bk. X, theor. 8, a trans. of which appears in Edward Grant, *A Source Book in Medieval Science* (Cambridge, Mass., 1974), 424–426.
22. Bk. II, theor. 47.
23. Witelo's influence is treated more fully in the intro. to the facs. repr. of the Risner ed., xxi–xxv.

## BIBLIOGRAPHY

I. ORIGINAL WORKS. Witelo's most important extant work is the *Perspectiva*, first published under the title *Optica* (Nuremberg, 1535; 1551) and, with Ibn al-Haytham's *Optics*, in a volume edited by Friedrich Risner, entitled *Opticae thesaurus* (Basel, 1572; facs. repr., New York, 1972). There is no modern ed. except for a few sections edited by Clemens Baeumker in his *Witelo* and a critical ed. and English trans. of bk. I (with analysis and commentary) by Sabetai Unguru, "Witelo as a Mathematician: A Study in XIIIth Century Mathematics" (Ph.D. diss., Univ. of Wis., 1970). The extant MSS of the *Perspectiva* are listed in the intro. to the facs. repr. of Risner's *Opticae thesaurus*. A comparison of early MSS with the three printed eds. reveals that the latter are quite accurate.

Witelo's *De primaria causa penitentie et de natura demonum* (regarded as two separate works by Birkenmajer) is extant in British Museum, MS Sloane 2156 (15th century), fols. 148r–154v; and Paris, B.N. MS Lat. 14796 (15th century), fols. 86v–97v (abbreviated version). Birkenmajer has edited the latter MS in his "Études sur Witelo, I" (see below).

II. SECONDARY LITERATURE. The major studies of Witelo are Clemens Baeumker, *Witelo, ein Philosoph und Naturforscher des XIII. Jahrhunderts*, which is *Beiträge zur Geschichte der Philosophie des Mittelalters*,

III, pt. 2 (Münster, 1908); and Aleksander Birkenmajer, "Études sur Witelo," which appear in his *Études d'histoire des sciences en Pologne* (Wrocław, 1972), 97–434. Portions of Baeumker's analysis are vitiated by his erroneous attribution of *De intelligentiis* to Witelo, and it is absolutely essential that close attention be paid to Birkenmajer's cautions, reservations, and corrections. The first and fourth of Birkenmajer's "Études sur Witelo" were previously published as "Studja nad Witelonem, I," in *Archiwum komisji do badania historji filozofji w polsce*, **2**, pt. 1 (1921), 1–149; and "Witelo e lo studio di Padova," in *Omaggio dell'Accademia polacca di scienze e lettere all'Università di Padova nel settimo centenario della sua fondazione* (Cracow, 1922), 147–168.

On Witelo's life, in addition to Baeumker's *Witelo* and Birkenmajer's "Études sur Witelo," see Baeumker, "Zur Biographie des Philosophen und Naturforschers Witelo," in *Historisches Jahrbuch der Görres-Gesellschaft*, **33** (1912), 359–361; Maximilien Curtze, "Sur l'orthographe du nom et sur la patrie de Witelo (Vitellion)," in *Bullettino di bibliografia e di storia delle scienze matematiche e fisiche*, **4** (1871), 49–77; and David C. Lindberg, "Lines of Influence in Thirteenth-Century Optics: Bacon, Witelo, and Pecham," in *Speculum*, **46** (1971), 72–75, 77–83; and intro. to the facs. repr. of the Risner ed. (New York, 1972), vii–xiii.

Studies of particular aspects of Witelo's thought appear in Carl B. Boyer, *The Rainbow: From Myth to Mathematics* (New York, 1959), ch. IV; A. C. Crombie, *Robert Grosseteste and the Origins of Experimental Science 1100–1700* (Oxford, 1953), 213–232; David C. Lindberg, "The Theory of Pinhole Images From Antiquity to the Thirteenth Century," in *Archive for History of Exact Sciences*, **5**, pt. 2 (1968), 154–176; and "The Cause of Refraction in Medieval Optics," in *British Journal for the History of Science*, **4** (1968–1969), 23–38; and Sabetai Unguru, "Witelo and Thirteenth-Century Mathematics: An Assessment of His Contributions," in *Isis*, **63** (1972), 496–508. Witelo's *De natura demonum* has been summarized briefly by Lynn Thorndike in *A History of Magic and Experimental Science*, V (New York, 1941), 86–89.

DAVID C. LINDBERG

**WITHAM, HENRY** (*b*. Minsteracres, Northumberland, England, 1779; *d*. Lartington Hall, Yorkshire, England, 28 November 1844), *geology, paleobotany.*

Witham was the second son of John Silvertop and Catherine Lawson of Brough, Yorkshire. He married Eliza Witham of Headlam, a niece and coheiress of William Witham of Cliffe, Yorkshire, and took the name and arms of Witham. He became the first Roman Catholic high sheriff of County Durham; and his son Thomas, a Roman Catholic

priest, inherited the Lartington estate after the deaths of his three brothers.

Witham's interest in geology and paleobotany was expressed in the founding in 1829 of the Natural History Society of Northumberland, Durham, and Newcastle upon Tyne, of which he was a founder-member and vice-president. He was also a member of the Wernerian Natural History Society and of the Royal Society of Edinburgh. Witham read the paper "On the Vegetation of the First Period of an Ancient World" before the Wernerian Society on 5 December 1829. In Edinburgh he became acquainted with William Nicol, whose method of making thin rock sections led to a revolution in both paleobotany and petrology. This technique was a development of that used by George Sanderson, an Edinburgh lapidary. Witham's Edinburgh connections also led to his "Description of a Fossil Tree Discovered in the Quarry of Craigleith" (1831). Three specimens were found, and the first was removed to the grounds of the Natural History Museum at South Kensington. Witham employed the Aberdeen botanist William MacGillivray to illustrate this paper and his *Observations on Fossil Vegetables* (1831).

In Newcastle, Witham met N. J. Winch and W. Hutton, both interested in botany and geology. Winch wrote on the geology of Northumberland (1816) and the Tweed banks (1831). Witham subscribed to J. Lindley and Hutton's *Fossil Flora* (1831–1837) and dedicated his *Observations on Fossil Vegetables* to Hutton. Their common interest was partly stimulated by the great development of mining at that time.

Witham was the first investigator of *Lepidodendron harcourtii*, *Pitus withami* (the Craigleith tree), *P. antiqua* and *P. primaeva* (the Lennel Braes trees), *Cordaites brandlingi* (the Wideopen tree), and *Anabathra pulcherrima* (a petrified xylem cylinder of *Stigmaria*).

His interpretation of the *Pitus* trees was that they were fossil gymnosperms and not vascular cryptogams. Hence his greatest achievement was to show that gymnosperms were prevalent in Lower Carboniferous rocks.

*BIBLIOGRAPHY*

I. ORIGINAL WORKS. Witham's writings include "Vegetation of the First Period of an Ancient World," in *Philosophical Magazine*, 2nd ser., **7** (1830), 28–29; "On the Vegetable Fossils Found at Lennel Braes, Near Coldstream, Upon the Banks of the River Tweed in Berwickshire," *ibid.*, **8** (1830), 16–21; "On the Red

Sandstones of Berwickshire, Particularly Those at the Mouth of the River Tweed," in *Transactions of the Natural History Society of Northumberland* . . ., **1** (1831), 172–183; "Description of a Fossil Tree Discovered in the Quarry of Craigleith," *ibid.*, 294–301; *Observations on Fossil Vegetables, Accompanied by Representations of Their Internal Structure as Seen Through the Microscope* (Edinburgh–London, 1831), repr. as *The Internal Structure of Fossil Vegetables Found in the Carboniferous and Oolitic Deposits of Great Britain, Described and Illustrated* (Edinburgh–London, 1833); "On the *Lepidodendron harcourtii*," in *Transactions of the Natural History Society of Northumberland* . . ., **2** (1838), 236–238; and "On the Effects Produced by a Greenstone Dyke Upon the Coal, in Passing Over Cockfield Fell, in the County of Durham," *ibid.*, 343–345.

II. SECONDARY LITERATURE. See J. Lindley and W. Hutton, *Fossil Flora of Great Britain*, 3 vols. (London, 1831–1837); A. G. Long, "The Fossil Plants of Berwickshire: Part 1," in *History of the Berwickshire Naturalists' Club*, **34** (1959), 248–273; A. G. MacGregor and R. J. A. Eckford, "The Upper Old Red and Lower Carboniferous Sediments of Teviotdale and Tweedside, and the Stones of the Abbeys of the Scottish Borderland," in *Transactions of the Edinburgh Geological Society*, **14** (1948), 230–252; F. W. Oliver, ed., D. H. Scott, "William Crawford Williamson (1816–95)," in *Makers of British Botany* (Cambridge, 1913), 243–260; D. H. Scott, *Extinct Plants and Problems of Evolution* (London, 1924), 150; and N. J. Winch, "Observations on the Geology of Northumberland and Durham," in *Transactions of the Geological Society*, **4** (1816), 1–101; and "Remarks on the Geology of the Banks of the Tweed," in *Transactions of the Natural History Society of Northumberland* . . ., **1** (1831), 117–131.

ALBERT G. LONG

WITHERING, WILLIAM (*b.* Wellington, Shropshire, England, March 1741; *d.* Birmingham, England, 6 October 1799), *medicine, botany, natural history.*

Withering was the only son of a prosperous Wellington apothecary. He entered the University of Edinburgh in 1762, graduating M.D. in 1766. In 1767 he settled into a relatively quiet country practice at Stafford. Upon the death of Dr. William Small in 1775, Withering removed to Birmingham and soon had one of the largest provincial practices of his day. He was active in Birmingham's vigorous Lunar Society, other members of which included Joseph Priestley, Erasmus Darwin, Josiah Wedgwood, Matthew Boulton, and James Watt. Withering was elected a fellow of the Royal Society in 1784. He was also a fellow of the Linnean

Society and a foreign corresponding member of the Royal Academy of Sciences of Lisbon. He visited Portugal twice in search of a salubrious climate which would slow the progressive deterioration of the chronic pulmonary condition (probably tuberculosis) from which he suffered the last fifteen years of his life. It ultimately caused his death at the age of fifty-eight.

Withering always remained primarily a practicing physician. Nevertheless, he had broad scientific interests and published significant work in botany, mineralogy, chemistry, and medicine. His botanical investigations began as a systematic collection of the flora indigenous to the Stafford area. He eventually extended his herbarium to include plants from all parts of Great Britain. His first major publication, *A Botanical Arrangement of all the Vegetables Naturally Growing in Great Britain* (1776), was little more than a translation of the portions of Linnaeus' writings relevant to English botany. As Withering acquired more botanical experience, however, his *Botanical Arrangement* became increasingly based on his first-hand observations. In the last edition published during his lifetime (1796), Withering effected a number of important taxonomic changes in the Linnaean system. He also surveyed the British cryptogams, a class of plants imperfectly described by Linnaeus.

As a botanist Withering rarely penetrated beyond the descriptive level; yet his *Botanical Arrangement* was the product of many years' patient, methodical study. It remained a standard British flora long after his death. Between 1805 and 1830 Withering's son added four editions to the three that Withering had published.

Although Withering's botanical interests were confined principally to indigenous British plants, his reputation on the Continent was such that the French botanist L'Héritier de Brutelle named a genus of plants (of the Solanaceae family) *Witheringia*. In 1796 the German mineralogist Abraham Gottlob Werner also commemorated Withering's name when he called barium carbonate "witherite." Withering had in 1782 first demonstrated that naturally occurring barium carbonate is a compound distinct from other barium salts, such as the sulfite and the oxide. Withering also published several other chemical and mineralogical papers, chiefly in the *Philosophical Transactions*, including "Experiments on Different Kinds of Marl" (1773) and "An Analysis of Two Mineral Substances, Viz. the Rowley Rag-Stone and the Toad-Stone" (1784). His chemical investigations were obviously nourished by his close friendship with

Priestley, who communicated some of Withering's early papers to the Royal Society. Withering was opposed to the phlogiston theory, which he satirized in a verse essay "The Life and Death of Phlogiston," read before the Lunar Society in 1796. He never published his experiments on phlogiston, however, and though he mentioned in a letter having "given up my pursuits upon *Phlogiston* to Dr. Priestley," the latter obviously found Withering's strictures on the theory unconvincing.

In 1783 Withering translated Torbern Bergman's *Sciagraphia regni mineralis* as the *Outlines of Mineralogy*, to which he added notes. He also chemically analyzed the waters at various spas in England and Portugal.

Withering maintained a lifelong interest in climate. He kept an extensive meteorological journal, from which his son printed extracts in 1822. Withering was especially interested—personally and professionally—in the effects of different climates on patients suffering from consumption. He rather grimly concluded (after twice wintering in Portugal) that the dry Portuguese weather is ineffectual in such cases.

In addition to his scientific publications, Withering left two significant medical treatises. In his *Account of the Scarlet Fever and Sore Throat* he moved from a brief description of a 1778 Birmingham epidemic of scarlet fever to a more general consideration of the causes, diagnosis, and treatment of the disease. He insisted on its contagiousness and noted the occasional development of generalized edema shortly after the disappearance of the fever.

In 1785 Withering published his *Account of the Foxglove, and Some of Its Medical Uses*, which is a genuine classic of clinical medicine. In it he summarized a decade's careful study of digitalis, the cardiotonic glycoside obtained from the leaves of the foxglove (*Digitalis purpurea*). Withering honestly recorded both successes and failures in his trials with the drug, and the gradual development of his skill in using digitalis may be followed in the chronological series of 163 cases reported in his book. Withering learned to employ digitalis only in selected cases of edema (dropsy). He stressed that care must be taken in adjusting the dose, and he accurately described the signs and symptoms of digitalis toxicity and established clear guidelines for its rational use. Despite Withering's modest but definite claims for the efficacy of the foxglove, the drug became for nineteenth-century clinicians a kind of panacea. It was prescribed (in dangerously large doses) for a variety of conditions. Only in the past few decades has the real merit of Withering's work on the foxglove been recognized. The place of digitalis in the contemporary pharmacopoeia remarkably vindicates Withering's prediction that "TIME will fix the real value upon this discovery."

His published medical writings amply demonstrate that Withering's reputation as a practitioner was justified. The breadth of his extraprofessional interests made him a proper member of the group of savants who constituted the Birmingham Lunar Society.

## BIBLIOGRAPHY

I. Original Works. Withering's principal publications include the following: *A Botanical Arrangement*, 2 vols. (London, 1776); the 3rd ed., 4 vols. (Birmingham, 1796), is the most important. *An Account of the Scarlet Fever and Sore Throat* (London, 1779; 2nd ed. 1793; German trans., 1781). *An Account of the Foxglove, and Some of Its Medical Uses* (Birmingham, 1785). A limited facs. ed. was brought out in 1948. *A Chemical Analysis of the Water at Caldas da Rainha* (Lisbon, 1795).

There are in addition minor medical tracts and letters, Withering's translation of Bergman's *Sciagraphia regni mineralis*, and papers in the *Philosophical Transactions*, the *Transactions of the Linnean Society*, and *Annals of Medicine*. A convenient bibliography is given in *The Miscellaneous Tracts of the Late William Withering, M.D. F.R.S.*, ed. by his son, 2 vols. (London, 1822), 207–209. This work reprints virtually all of Withering's writings, with the exception of the *Botanical Arrangement* and Withering's Edinburgh thesis *De angina gangraenosa* (Edinburgh, 1766). The latter has recently been translated by Charles D. O'Malley, *Journal of the History of Medicine*, **8** (1953), 16–45.

II. Secondary Literature. The standard account of Withering's life remains the *Memoir* by his son, included in the *Miscellaneous Tracts* (see above). There is a full-scale modern biography by T. Whitmore Peck and K. Douglas Wilkinson, *William Withering of Birmingham* (Bristol–London, 1950). It includes a number of previously unpublished letters and a short bibliography. A recent paper has summarized Withering's work on digitalis, J. W. Estes and P. D. White, "William Withering and the Purple Foxglove," in *Scientific American*, **212** (1965), 110–119. See also John F. Fulton, "The Place of William Withering in Scientific Medicine," in *Journal of the History of Medicine*, **8** (1953), 1–15. For the later history of digitalis therapy, see E. H. Ackerknecht, "Aspects of the History of Therapeutics," in *Bulletin of the History of Medicine*, **36** (1962), 389–419. Some of Withering's work on mineralogy is discussed by Frederick D. Zeeman, "William Withering as a Mineralogist, the Story of Witherite," *ibid.*, **24** (1950), 530–538.

Withering's relations with various members of the

Lunar Society may be best approached through Robert Schofield's study, *The Lunar Society of Birmingham* (Oxford, 1963), with a splendid bibliography of published and manuscript materials.

WILLIAM F. BYNUM

**WITT, JAN DE** (*b*. Dordrecht, Netherlands, 24 September 1625; *d*. The Hague, Netherlands, 20 August 1672), *mathematics.*

De Witt was the son of Jacob de Witt, burgomeister of Dordrecht, and Anna van de Corput. Both families were prominent members of the regent class which governed the towns and provinces of the Netherlands. He entered Dordrecht Latin school in 1636, and went to the University of Leiden in 1641. There he studied law, leaving for France in 1645 to take his degree at Angers. At Leiden he studied mathematics privately with Frans van Schooten the Younger, and received from him an excellent training in Cartesian mathematics. De Witt was a talented mathematician who had little time to devote to mathematics. He became pensionary of Dordrecht in 1650, and grand pensionary of Holland in 1653, making him the leader of the States Party, and, in effect, the prime minister of the Netherlands. He was a statesman of unusual ability and strength of character who guided the affairs of the United Provinces during the twenty-year interregnum in the Stadtholdership during the minority of William of Orange. This was one of the most critical periods in Dutch history, with the three Anglo-Dutch wars; the hostility of the Orange faction culminated in the murder of de Witt and his brother Cornelis by a mob in 1672.

De Witt's most important mathematical work was his *Elementa curvarum linearum*, written before 1650 and printed in Van Schooten's second Latin edition of Descartes's *Géométrie* (1659–1661). It is in two books: the first, a synthetic treatment of the geometric theory found in the early books of Apollonius' *Conics*; and the second, one of the first systematic developments of the analytic geometry of the straight line and conic. In the first book the *symptomae* (expressed as proportions) of the parabola, ellipse, and hyperbola are derived as plane loci, rather than as sections of the cone. His locus definitions of the ellipse are familiar to us today: the eccentric angle construction (a point fixed with respect to a rotating segment); the trammel construction (a fixed point on a given segment moving on two intersecting lines); and the "string" construction, based on the two-focus definition. For the hyperbola and parabola the locus is con-

structed as the intersection of corresponding members of two pencils of lines, one parallel and one concurrent. In modern terms these are interesting unintentional examples of the Steiner-Chasles projective definition of the conics, where the vertex of one pencil is at infinity.

De Witt is credited with introducing the term "directrix" for the parabola, but it is clear from his derivation that he does not use the term for the fixed line of our focus-directrix definition. Given fixed lines *DB* and *EF* intersecting at *D*, with *B* the pole and *EF* the directrix: for any point *H* on *EF*, if ∠*HBL* is constructed equal to ∠*FDB*, a line through *H* parallel to *BD* cuts *BL* in *G*, a point on the locus. *AC* is drawn through *B* with ∠DBC = ∠BDF, cutting *HG* in *I*, and *GK* is drawn parallel to *AC*. Since triangles *BDH* and *GKB* are similar, $(BI)^2 = (BD)(BK)$ or $y^2 = px$, a parabola with vertex at *B*, abscissa *BK* = *x*, and ordinate *KG* = *y*. If *EF* is perpendicular to *DB*, a rectangular coordinate system results, but *EF* is not our directrix.

In the first book of the *Elementa* de Witt not only freed the conics from the cone with his kinematic constructions, but satisfied the Cartesian criteria of constructibility. This book was written, as he reported to van Schooten, to give a background for the new analytic development of the second book. He began the analytic treatment by showing that equations of the first degree represent straight lines. As was usual at the time he did not use negative coordinates, graphing only segments or rays in the first quadrant. He carefully explained the actual construction of the lines for arbitrary coeffi-

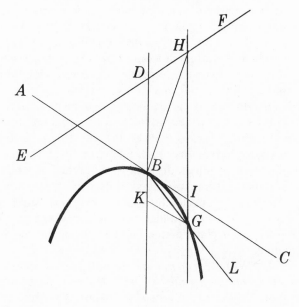

FIGURE 1

cients since they would be needed in his transformations reducing general quadratic equations to type conics. For each conic de Witt began with simplified equations equivalent to his standard forms in book I, and then used translations and rotations to reduce more complicated equations to the canonical forms. For example, in the hyperbola

$$yy + \frac{2bxy}{a} + 2cy = \frac{fxx}{a} + ex + dd$$

he lets

$$z = y + \frac{b}{a}x + c$$

and then

$$v = x + h$$

where $h$ is the coefficient of the linear term in $x$ after the first substitution, giving

$$\frac{aazz}{fa + bb} = vv - hh + \frac{aadd + aacc}{fa + bb},$$

a standard hyperbola which cuts the new $v$ or $z$ axes according as $hh$ is greater than or less than $\frac{aadd + aacc}{fa + bb}$. Although de Witt seems to be aware of the characteristic of the general quadratic equation in choosing his examples, he does not explicitly mention its use to determine the type of conic except in the case of the parabola. There he states that, if the terms of the second degree are a perfect square, the equation represents a parabola.

The last chapter is a summing up of the various transformations showing how to construct the graphs of all equations of second degree. Each case of positive and negative coefficients must be handled separately in a drawing, but the discussion for each curve is completely general, and both original and transformed axes are drawn.

In addition to the algebraic simplifications of the curves to normal form, book II contains the usual focus-directrix property of the parabola, and the analytic derivations of the ellipse and hyperbola as the locus of points the sum or difference of whose distances from two fixed points is a constant. These are done in the modern manner, squaring twice, with the explicit use of the Pythagorean theorem in place of the more recent distance formula.

De Witt's *Elementa* and John Wallis' *Tractatus de sectionibus conicis* (1655) are considered the first textbooks in analytic geometry. Although Wallis raised the question of priority, their approaches were different and completely independent. Wallis first defined the conics as second-degree equations and deduced the properties of the curves from the equations, while de Witt defined them geometrically in the plane, and then showed that quadratic equations could be reduced to his normal forms.

Christiaan Huygens once wrote John Wallis of de Witt: "Could he have spared all his strength for mathematical works, he would have surpassed us all." His geometry was his only contribution to pure mathematics, but he turned his mathematical interests to the financial problems of the province of Holland throughout his long tenure as grand pensionary. The chief means of raising money for the States was by life or fixed annuities. In 1665 de Witt succeeded in reducing the interest rate from 5 to 4 percent and established a sinking fund with the interest saved by the conversion accumulated at compound interest to be applied to the debt of Holland, which could thus be paid in forty-one years. The second Anglo-Dutch War (1665–1667), however, defeated this scheme. The English wars were a perpetual financial drain, and more than half of the expenditure of the province of Holland (which had to defray the costs of the war almost alone) was swallowed up in interest payments.

In April 1671 it was resolved to negotiate funds by life annuities, thereby limiting the debt to one generation. De Witt prepared a treatise for the States of Holland demonstrating mathematically that life annuities were being offered at too high a rate of interest in comparison with fixed annuities. For many years the rule-of-thumb rates for life annuities had been twice the standard rate of interest. Holland had recently reduced the rate of interest to twenty-five years' purchase (4 percent) and was selling life annuities at fourteen years' purchase ($7\frac{2}{7}$ percent). De Witt wanted to raise the price to sixteen years' purchase ($6\frac{1}{4}$ percent). His *Waerdye van Lyf-renten naer proportie van Los-renten* (July, 1671) is certainly among the first attempts to apply the theory of probability to economic problems. It was written as a political paper, and remained buried in the archives for almost two hundred years. Since its discovery and publication by Frederick Hendriks in 1852 there have been many articles (some of which are listed in the bibliography) explaining or criticizing it on the basis of modern actuarial science. It is actually a very simple and ingenious dissertation based only on the use of the principle of mathematical expectation to form equal contracts.

De Witt listed the present values at 4 percent of annuity payments of 10,000,000 stuyvers (to avoid decimals) per half year, and summed the mathematical expectations using hypothetical mortality rates for different ages. He first presupposed that a man is equally likely to die in the first or last half of any year, and then, since annuities were generally purchased on young lives, extended this to any half year of the "years of full vigor" from age three to fifty-three. For simplicity he considered the first hundred half years equally destructive or mortal, although he stated that the likelihood of decease is actually smaller in the first years. So too, he stopped at age eighty, although many live beyond that age. In the next ten years, fifty-three to sixty-three, the chance of dying does not exceed more than in the proportion of 3 to 2 the chance of dying in the first period; from sixty-three to seventy-three, the chance of dying is not more than 2 to 1; and from seventy-three to eighty, not more than 3 to 1.

De Witt gives many examples to explain the use of the concept of mathematical expectation. The following one is basic to his later calculations, and has been overlooked by many commentators. Consider a man of forty and a man of fifty-eight. According to his presuppositions the chances of the older man dying compared with the younger man are as 3 to 2. An equal contract could be devised: if the person of fifty-eight dies in six months, the younger man inherits 2,000 florins, but if the man of forty dies in six months, the elder inherits 3,000 florins. That is, the chance of the man of fifty-eight gaining 3,000 florins. is as 2 to 3, or, in terms of de Witt's annuity calculations, the chance of receiving a particular annuity payment in the second period is two-thirds that in the first period.

From this reasoning de Witt's calculations are straightforward: He sums the present values for the first hundred half years; two-thirds the present values for the next twenty half years; for the next twenty, one-half the present values; and one-third for the last fourteen. All these are summed and the average taken, giving a little more than sixteen florins as the present value of one florin of annuity on a young and healthy life. If the method had been applied to actual mortality tables, the labor would have been formidable. Later in 1671 de Witt and Jan Hudde corresponded on the problem of survivorship annuities on more than one life, and here both used actual mortality figures taken from the annuity records of Holland. Working with several groups of at least a hundred persons of a given age de Witt developed appropriate rates for annui-

ties on two lives. These were extended a posteriori to any number of lives by a Pascal triangle, with a promise to Hudde to establish the results a priori. This was the culmination of de Witt's work with annuities, but for political reasons he suggested to Hudde that the public not be informed of the results of their study, since they were willing to buy annuities on more than one life at the current rate, which was favorable to the government.

## BIBLIOGRAPHY

I. ORIGINAL WORKS. *Elementa curvarum linearum*, in Frans van Schooten's Latin ed. of Descartes's *Géométrie, Geometria a Renato Descartes* (Amsterdam, 1659–1661). *Waerdye van Lyf-renten naer proportie van Los-renten* (The Hague, 1671; facs. ed. Haarlem, 1879). Six volumes of letters in *Werken van het Historisch Genootschap te Utrecht*, 3d ser., XVIII, XXV, XXXI, XXXIII, XLII, XLIV (1906–1922). Volume XXXIII contains letters to and from mathematicians including the letters to Jan Hudde on annuities on more than one life.

II. SECONDARY LITERATURE. Of the many biographies of de Witt, Nicolaas Japikse, *Johan de Witt* (Amsterdam, 1915), is indispensable. Still valuable is G. A. Lefèvre-Pontalis, *Jean de Witt, Grand Pensionnaire de Hollande*, 2 vols. (Paris, 1884); English trans., S. F. Stephenson and A. Stephenson (London, 1885). For a reliable discussion of the period, and the relations between de Witt and William III, see Pieter Geyl, *The Netherlands in the Seventeenth Century, Part Two 1648–1715* (London, 1964), and his *Oranje en Stuart* (Utrecht, 1939), English trans., Arnold Pomerans (London, 1969). For the geometry see P. van Geer, "Johan de Witt als Wiskundige," in *Nieuw Archief voor Wiskundige*, 2nd ser., **11** (1915), 98–126; and C. B. Boyer, *History of Analytic Geometry* (New York, 1956).

An English translation of the work on life annuities can be found in Frederick Hendriks, "Contributions to the History of Insurance . . . a Restoration of the Grand Pensionary De Witt's Treatise on Life Annuities," in *The Assurance Magazine* (now *Journal of the Institute of Actuaries*), **2** (1852), 230–258. Vols. **3** (1901), **10** (1908), and **11** (1909) of the *Archief voor Verzekeringe Wetenschap* contain articles offering varying criticisms and explanations of de Witt's writings on annuities.

JOY B. EASTON

**WITTGENSTEIN, LUDWIG (JOSEF JOHANN)** (*b.* Vienna, Austria, 26 April 1889; *d.* Cambridge, England, 29 April 1951), *philosophy*.

Wittgenstein was one of the most imaginative and original thinkers of the twentieth century, a legend during his lifetime and an enduring influence since. To his numerous admirers and followers, his work marks a decisive turn in the history of philosophy and in all fields of investigation to which philosophical method is pertinent.

Ludwig Wittgenstein, as he always called himself, was the youngest of eight children. His father, an engineer and a successful steel magnate, was a prominent patron of the arts in Vienna. Wittgenstein was never at home in this worldly and sophisticated setting; and his life and work alike show the imprint of a deeply serious temperament, radically at odds with the compromises of bourgeois society.

Educated privately until he was fourteen, Wittgenstein spent only three years at school (in Linz) before entering the Technical Institute at Berlin-Charlottenburg with a view to becoming an engineer. As a research student at Manchester University (1908–1911) he made original contributions to the design of a jet-reaction propeller for airplanes. His interests having turned to the foundations of mathematics and to logic, in 1911, on the advice of Gottlob Frege, he became a student of Bertrand Russell's at Cambridge University. In 1913–1914, while living in solitude in Norway, he was already composing the *Tractatus*, although it was not published until 1921. During the period 1919–1926 Wittgenstein studied for and obtained a diploma qualifying him for elementary school teaching, and eventually taught in a number of small village schools in Austria. For a while he worked as a gardener's assistant at a convent near Vienna. He also designed and built, for one of his sisters, a remarkable house that is still standing (at the time this article was written) in the Kundmanngasse (and declared a national monument by the Austrian government). In 1929, Wittgenstein returned to Cambridge, was made a fellow of Trinity College, and began the famous succession of informal classes through which his philosophical views gradually became known. Ten years later he was appointed professor of philosophy in succession to G. E. Moore. He worked in a medical school and a medical laboratory during World War II and resigned his professorship in 1947. He died of cancer four years later.

The last two decades of Wittgenstein's life were filled with unremitting intellectual work. His many manuscripts include, in addition to his masterpiece, the *Philosophical Investigations* (which he left almost ready for press), several full-length books, and thousands of pages of additional materials. His last finished piece of work, *On Certainty* (composed in 1950–1951), shows him in full possession of penetrating powers of insight and expression.

Wittgenstein's later work stands in sharp contrast with and opposition to the conceptions presented in the *Tractatus*. That book, written in short, epigrammatic paragraphs carefully arranged in quasi-logical form (with a special system of decimal references marking the relative subordination of successive items), remains cryptic on essential points and lends itself to a variety of different interpretations. A central theme is the delineation of the essential characteristics that any language or symbol system must manifest. It would therefore not be unfair to call it a "Critique of Pure Language." Wittgenstein's celebrated "picture theory of language" insists upon the presence in language, as the root of its semantic power, of an isomorphism between sentences and the possible states of affairs to which they ultimately refer. Reality must be composed of "facts"—patterned clusters of ultimate simples or "objects"—each standing in one–one correspondence to the simple names that underlie the superficial complexity of ordinary language. Thus the "logical form" of reality (roughly speaking, the patterns of possible co-occurrence of the simple "objects") must be reflected in the "logic of language" (the corresponding patterns of co-occurrence of the semantic elements).

It was part of the originality of this version of "logical atomism" to reject any possibility of the representation, from some external standpoint, of the "logical form" itself. The "logic" of reality and its linguistic mirror must "*show* itself," through the impossibility of "saying" what *cannot* be said: the limits of language are the "limits of thought." What philosophers have tried to say about metaphysics, transcendental ethics and aesthetics, and theology turns out to consist of pseudo propositions that are "nonsense." The book accordingly ends with the much quoted line, "Whereof one cannot speak, one must be silent." (This article must necessarily omit reference to Wittgenstein's important technical contributions to the foundations of logic, focusing on the notion of "tautology"; to probability theory; and to the philosophy of science.)

Some hostile critics, such as Karl Popper, have regarded the conclusion of the *Tractatus* as a self-refutation, which reduces the book itself to the sort of "nonsense" that cannot be "said"; other readers, notably early members of the Vienna Circle, have sought to purge the *Tractatus* of its allegedly irrelevant "mystical" intrusions and to quarry from it a positivistic critique of metaphysics. But a more sympathetic reading would treat it as a peculiar sort of demonstration ("showing") of how a powerful conception of the necessary relations between symbolism and reality, pushed to its logical consequences, results in an impasse, from which there is no escape except through a revolution in perspective and approach. From this standpoint the *Tractatus* is a prime example of what Wittgenstein later came to call a "metaphysical cramp," an obsession with a single conception of what the metaphysical situation *must be*—and the natural springboard for his subsequent revolution in method.

Although there is considerable continuity between the *Tractatus* and the later masterpiece, the *Philosophical Investigations* (completed some twenty-five years later), the second work reads at first sight like a wholesale rejection of the earlier methodology. In the *Investigations*, the earlier interest in the one and only "logical form," manifested in every adequate linguistic or symbolic system, is rejected as arising from a distorted metaphysical conception. Attention shifts to language as it is used in concrete social practices, constituted partly by rules of syntax and application, but even more importantly by a background "agreement in the form of life" that shows itself in practice but is not reducible to formal principles. The a priori considerations that dominated the *Tractatus* are replaced by meticulous attention to the "natural history" of language, the complex and various ways in which men actually communicate and express their thoughts. The prime philosophical error is to impose upon this motley of speech practices some a priori model of what language *must* be like. Wittgenstein shows, by detailed discussion of questions that have been the staple of philosophical dispute for two thousand years, how such oversimplified impositions generate *insolubilia*. He hoped to have shown how such "philosophical sickness" can yield to rational treatment.

Wittgenstein's later work introduced a number of special notions that continue to be of high value, despite their often cryptic and controversial character. Among them are the notions of a "language game" (a deliberately simplified model of speech practice, introduced for the sake of comparison), of a "criterion" of use, and of "family resemblances" (the overlapping pattern of relations that hold together the items referred to by some general term).

Wittgenstein's later methods of investigation are "dialectical," in the sense of proceeding repeatedly from the real or fancied philosophical difficulties of an imaginary interlocutor. His writings provide tantalizing glimpses of his incomparable style of face-to-face philosophizing with friends and pupils.

Despite a lifelong interest in science and its relations to philosophy, Wittgenstein did comparatively little work on the philosophy of science (although the *Tractatus* contains some important contributions). On the philosophy of mathematics, on the other hand, he left voluminous manuscripts, still in process of publication and critical evaluation.

It is misleading to assign to Wittgenstein, as is too often done, the stock labels "behaviorist" or "positivist." His life was devoted, with exemplary single-mindedness, to discovering a radically new way of leading men out of the darkness of conceptual confusion.

### BIBLIOGRAPHY

I. ORIGINAL WORKS. All of Wittgenstein's works, except the first and third, were published posthumously. Since he composed in German, translations are, at his desire, published with the original German text facing. Exceptions to this are indicated below.

1. *Tractatus Logico-Philosophicus*, translated by D. F. Pears and B. F. McGuinness, with intro. by Bertrand Russell (London, 1961). The trans. by C. K. Ogden in the original English ed. (London, 1922), although faulty in places, still deserves attention. There also have been translations into Italian, Russian, French, Finnish, Swedish, Danish, and Chinese.

2. *The Blue and Brown Books*, with a preface by Rush Rhees (Oxford, 1958). Originally dictated in English (1933–1935) for the use of Wittgenstein's pupils. Although superseded by the *Investigations*, still the best introduction to the later work.

3. *Notebooks 1914–1916*, translated by G. E. M. Anscombe, edited by Anscombe and G. H. von Wright (Oxford, 1961). Surviving parts of the notebooks used in preparing the *Tractatus*. An indispensable aid to the study of that work.

4. *Philosophical Investigations*, translated by G. E. M. Anscombe, edited by Anscombe and Rush Rhees (London, 1953). The great masterpiece of Wittgenstein's later thought.

5. *Remarks on the Foundations of Mathematics*, translated by G. E. M. Anscombe (Oxford, 1956). Compiled from MSS by the literary executors, G. H. von Wright, Rush Rhees, and G. E. M. Anscombe.

6. *Philosophische Bemerkungen* (Oxford, 1964). German text only. Composed 1929–1930.

7. *Zettel*, translated by G. E. M. Anscombe (Oxford, 1966). Based on notes arranged as for a book.

8. *Philosophische Grammatik* (Oxford, 1969), translated by Anthony Kenny, edited by Rush Rhees, as *Philosophical Grammar* (Berkeley, Calif., 1974).

9. *On Certainty*, translated by G. E. M. Anscombe (Oxford, 1969). Composed in 1950–1951.

10. *Ludwig Wittgenstein und der Wiener Kreis*, B. F.

McGuinness, ed. (Oxford, 1967). Conversations with Moritz Schlick, based upon verbatim shorthand reports by Friedrich Waismann.

11. *Lectures and Conversations on Aesthetics, Psychology and Religious Belief*, Cyril Barrett, ed. (Oxford, 1966).

Other sets of lecture notes, some of them transcribed verbatim, are in private circulation.

Almost all of Wittgenstein's voluminous MSS are preserved in the library of Trinity College, Cambridge. The entire *Nachlass* has been microfilmed by Cornell University Library, Ithaca, New York, from which microfilm copies and Xeroxes can be purchased. A detailed guide to the Cornell collection is in G. H. von Wright, "The Wittgenstein Papers," in *Philosophical Review*, **78** (1969), 483–503.

A very full bibliography of primary and secondary writings is in K. T. Fann, *Wittgenstein's Conception of Philosophy* (Oxford–Berkeley, 1969), with a supp. by Fann in *Revue internationale de philosophie*, **23** (1969), 363–370.

II. Secondary Literature. For Wittgenstein's life and teaching, see especially Norman Malcolm, *Ludwig Wittgenstein: A Memoir*, rev. ed. (London, 1966), which also contains a biographical sketch by G. H. von Wright and a photograph. An authorized biography by B. F. McGuinness is in course of preparation.

Among the many commentaries on the *Tractatus* are G. E. M. Anscombe, *An Introduction to Wittgenstein's Tractatus* (London, 1959), the earliest and in some ways the most useful; Max Black, *A Companion to Wittgenstein's Tractatus* (Cambridge–Ithaca, N.Y., 1964), an elaborate exegesis; J. Griffin, *Wittgenstein's Logical Atomism* (London, 1964), which stresses the influence of Heinrich Hertz; and E. Stenius, *Wittgenstein's Tractatus* (Oxford, 1960), a penetrating but controversial analysis.

For the later work; see especially Norman Malcolm, "Wittgenstein's *Philosophical Investigations*," in *Philosophical Review*, **63** (1954), 530–559; and Peter Winch, ed., *Studies in the Philosophy of Wittgenstein* (London, 1969). A useful comprehensive anthology is K. T. Fann, ed., *Ludwig Wittgenstein: The Man and His Philosophy* (New York, 1967).

Possible applications to science are well illustrated in W. H. Watson, *Understanding Physics Today* (Cambridge, 1963).

MAX BLACK

**WITTICH** (or **WITTICHIUS**), **PAUL** (*b*. Breslau, Silesia [now Wrocław, Poland], 1555 [?]; *d*. Breslau, 9 January 1587), *mathematics*.

Little is known about Wittich's life. In the summer of 1580, with a letter of introduction from Hagecius, he went for a short time to Uraniborg to work with Tycho Brahe.[1] He soon showed himself to be a skillful mathematician, for with Tycho he discovered—or, more precisely, rediscovered—the method of prostaphaeresis, by which the products and quotients of trigonometric functions appearing in trigonometric formulas can be replaced by simpler sums and differences.[2] The two formulas involved in this method are $\sin a \cdot \sin b = \frac{1}{2}(\cos [a - b] - \cos [a + b])$ and $\cos a \cdot \cos b = \frac{1}{2}(\cos [a - b] + \cos [a + b])$.

The individual contributions of Tycho Brahe and Wittich cannot be established with certainty, but that of Wittich, who was the better mathematician, was probably the greater.[3] A letter is extant in which Tycho reported on this period of collaboration, during which each freely and fully shared his results with the other.[4] It is therefore understandable that he was very angry with Wittich when he learned that the method of prostaphaeresis had become known in Kassel, which Wittich had visited in 1584, and that Nicolai Reymers Bär (Ursus) had published it as his own discovery in 1588.[5]

Actually, Ursus also had been at Uraniborg in 1584 and had secretly noted down the method, although he did not discover the proof, which Brahe kept more carefully concealed. Wittich, who taught mathematics in Breslau from 1582 to 1584, was in Kassel in 1584.[6] There he described to Joost Bürgi, the clockmaker for Landgrave Wilhelm IV, the instruments used by Tycho in his observatory,[7] which Bürgi reproduced and improved. Wittich also showed him the proof of prostaphaeresis; and it was from Bürgi that Ursus learned the *mysteria triangulorum*. Wittich left Kassel before 1586 and died in Breslau at the beginning of 1587. On learning of Wittich's death, Tycho regretted that he had doubted his honesty.[8]

The method of prostaphaeresis originated with Johann Werner, who developed it in conjunction with the law of cosines for sides of a spherical triangle. In Regiomontanus' formulation the law reads: sinvers $A$: sinvers $a$ − sinvers $[b - c] = r^2$: $(\sin b \cdot \sin c)$.[9] If one eliminates the *sinus versus* and takes $r = sinus\ totus = 1$, the result is

$$\frac{1}{\cos A} = \frac{\sin b \cdot \sin c}{\cos a - \cos b \cdot \cos c}.$$

Here Werner, who preserved the *sinus versus*, used the first formula of prostaphaeresis in handling the term $\sin b \cdot \sin c$; whereas Tycho and Wittich also knew the cosine law with the term $\cos b \cdot \cos c$.[10] They also used prostaphaeresis for problems that Werner solved without this method.[11]

It is unlikely that Tycho and Wittich ever saw Werner's *De triangulis sphaericis libri quatuor*. Its manuscript, which Rheticus wanted to publish at Cracow in 1557, was not printed until 1907.[12] On the other hand, Tycho knew that such a work existed and sought, unsuccessfully, to obtain a copy of it.[13] He and Wittich might, therefore, have been encouraged by this knowledge to work out the details of such a method, which Ursus stole and published in 1588.[14]

In 1580 Tycho and Wittich probably had not seen Viète's *Canon mathematicus* of 1579. Further evidence on this point is provided by Longomontanus, who was Tycho's assistant at Uraniborg from 1589 to 1597.[15] The method of converting products to sums or differences was further developed by Bürgi, Clavius, and Jöstel, among others. Specifically, Bürgi took as his starting point the relationship between arithmetic and geometric series and introduced logarithms.[16] He thereby definitively replaced the older method with an improved one that Pitiscus called *modus Byrgii*.[17] Kepler, who was thoroughly acquainted with Tycho's computations, mentions the *negotium prostaphaereticum Wittichianum* in his book on optics (1604).[18]

## NOTES

1. Wittich, who left Uraniborg because of a matter concerning an inheritance, carried with him a letter from Brahe to Hagecius dated 4 Nov. 1580. Since Brahe received no answer, Wittich was suspected of not having delivered it. Hagecius later cleared up the matter (23 Sept. 1582). On this point see Brahe, *Opera*, VII, 72.
2. In the letter of 4 Nov. 1580 Brahe speaks of their efforts to develop this method, "quae per προσταφαίρεσιν procedit absque taediosa multiplicatione et divisione." *Ibid.*, 58.
3. See R. Wolf, *Handbuch der Astronomie*, 227 f.
4. See Brahe's letter to Hagecius of 14 Mar. 1592. Brahe, *Opera*, VII, 323.
5. See Brahe's letter to Hagecius of 1 July 1586, in which he writes that Wittich "agit sane minus sincere mecum." *Ibid.*, 108.
6. See J. L. E. Dreyer, *Tycho Brahe*, 121, n. 4.
7. Among these were the mural quadrant with transverse calibration. On this see C. D. Hellman, "Brahe," 405.
8. See his letter of 14 Jan. 1595: "nec vivum nec defunctum suis privavi honoribus." *Opera*, VI, 327.
9. See A. von Braunmühl, *Vorlesungen über Geschichte der Trigonometrie*, 131; and J. Tropfke, *Geschichte der Elementar-Mathematik*, 139 ff.
10. In the process *cos* is replaced by the *sin* of the complement. See A. A. Björnbo, "Ioannis Verneri . . . ," 169; and M. Cantor, *Vorlesungen über Geschichte der Mathematik*, 642f. Ibn Yūnus also knew prostaphaeresis for the operation involving cos *a* · cos *b*. See G. Sarton, *Introduction to the History of Science*, 716 ff. Traces of the law can be found in a special case in Indian mathematics (see Braunmühl, 41), and in a more complete form in the work of al-Battānī (see Sarton, *op. cit.*, 603; and Braunmühl, *op. cit.*, 53). Peuerbach also knew this law and derived it independently in *Compositio tabule altitudinis solis ad omnes horas* (in Codex Vindobonensis 5203, fols. 54r–55r).

11. See Björnbo, *op. cit.*, 169.
12. It was published by Björnbo with the preface by Rheticus that was printed in 1557.
13. See Tycho's letter to Hagecius of 25 Aug. 1585. *Opera*, VII, 95.
14. See Björnbo, *op. cit.*, 171.
15. See Dreyer, *op. cit.*, 361, n. 3, and 383.
16. Even before Stifel's *Arithmetica integra* (1544) others, including Chuquet and Heinrich Grammateus, compared the two types of series. On this point see L. Nový, "Bürgi," 602.
17. See Bartholomeo Pitiscus, *Trigonometriae sive de dimensione triangulorum libri quinque*, 3rd ed. (Frankfurt, 1612), 177.
18. Kepler, *Gesammelte Werke*, II (Munich, 1939), 336.

## BIBLIOGRAPHY

See A. A. Björnbo, "Ioannis Verneri De triangulis sphaericis libri quatuor, de meteoroscopiis libri sex cum prooemio Georgii Ioachimi Rhetici. I. De triangulis sphaericis," in *Abhandlungen zur Geschichte der mathematischen Wissenschaften*, **24** (1907), 150–175; A. von Braunmühl, *Vorlesungen über Geschichte der Trigonometrie*, I (Leipzig, 1900), 256; 260; and "Zur Geschichte der prosthaphaeretischen Methode in der Trigonometrie," in *Abhandlungen zur Geschichte der Mathematik*, **9** (1899), 15–29; M. Cantor, *Vorlesungen über Geschichte der Mathematik*, 2nd ed., II (Leipzig, 1913), 937; J. L. E. Dreyer, *Tycho Brahe, a Picture of Scientific Life and Work in the Sixteenth Century* (Edinburgh, 1890; New York, 1963), 405; and *Tychonis Brahe Opera omnia*, XV (Copenhagen, 1913; 1929), 50; C. D. Hellman, "Brahe," in *Dictionary of Scientific Biography*, II, 401–416; L. Nový, "Bürgi," *ibid.*, 602–603; G. Sarton, *Introduction to the History of Science*, I (Baltimore, 1927); J. Tropfke, *Geschichte der Elementar-Mathematik*, 2nd ed., V (Berlin–Leipzig, 1923), 108 ff; and R. Wolf, *Handbuch der Astronomie, ihrer Geschichte und Litteratur*, I (Zurich, 1890).

KURT VOGEL

**WOEPCKE, FRANZ** (*b*. Dessau, Germany, 6 May 1826; *d*. Paris, France, 25 March 1864), *mathematics, Oriental studies*.

Woepcke was the son of Ernst Woepcke, the Wittenberg postmaster, and Karolina Chapon. He studied mathematics and physics at Berlin from 1843 to 1847, receiving the Ph.D. *magna cum laude* in the latter year for a work on sundials in antiquity. In addition to pure mathematics, he was particularly interested in its history, a subject that Humboldt encouraged him to pursue.[1] In the mid-nineteenth century very little was known of the Arab contribution to the development of mathematics. Many Latin translations from the Arabic had existed since the twelfth century; but the texts themselves were not accessible, and further research was thus effectively blocked.[2] Woepcke therefore went to Bonn in 1848 to learn Arabic.[3] After qualifying as *Privatdozent* in the spring of 1850, he went to Leiden, where there were many Arabic manuscripts, and in May of the same year, to Paris, then the center of Oriental studies in Europe.[4] In Paris he studied Persian (under Julius von Mohl) and Sanskrit (under P. O. Foucaux), as well as mathematics (under J. Liouville).

Woepcke interrupted his stay in Paris only from 1856 to 1858, when he taught mathematics and physics at the French Gymnasium in Berlin. He resigned his post because it left him no time for research. His tireless work on Arabic and Persian manuscripts enabled Woepcke to publish some thirty texts.[5] His edition of al-Khayyāmī's *Algebra*, which appeared in 1851, was followed in 1853 by a selection from al-Karajī's *Algebra*. In 1861 and 1863 Woepcke worked on manuscripts in Oxford and in London. He was obliged to return to Paris in December 1863 because his health, always weak, was failing rapidly. He died at the age of thirty-seven and was buried in Père Lachaise cemetery.

Woepcke's contemporaries praised him as modest but confident in his own judgment and as an enemy of all superficiality.[6] He valued only facts and left the working out of unproved conclusions to others.

A member of many learned societies, Woepcke made an outstanding contribution to the knowledge of Eastern contributions in the history of mathematics. Although he investigated many specific problems in various fields, his studies centered on the algebra of the Arabs (its symbolism and the determination of its Greek and Indian components) and on the Indian and Arab influence on the West (the spread of Hindu numerals and methods and the sources of the work of Leonardo Fibonacci).[7] He also attempted to reconstruct lost texts of Apollonius and Euclid on the basis of Arab manuscripts.[8]

Woepcke's own mathematical research dealt mainly with curves and surfaces, equations of the *n*th degree, and function theory. He also translated into French works by J. Steiner (central curves) and by Weierstrass (theory of Abelian functions). Because of Woepcke's early death, many of his editorial projects—for which he had already copied or translated the Arabic texts—were left unfinished or were continued by others.[9] Among the material that came into the possession of Boncompagni were 174 letters and a codex with twenty-five unpublished works, including selections from texts, translations, and notes.[10]

## NOTES

1. In 1851 Woepcke translated Humboldt's *Über die bei verschiedenen Völkern üblichen Systeme von Zahlzeichen* (1829) into French.
2. Exceptions were the *Algebra* of al-Khwārizmī, edited by Frederic Rosen (London, 1831), and the *Jawāmiʿ* of al-Farghānī edited by Jacob Golius (Amsterdam, 1669).
3. He studied Arabic under G. W. F. Freytag and J. Gildemeister, as well as astronomy under F. W. A. Argelander.
4. Among the scholars who had worked there were Silvestre de Sacy, J. J. Sédillot, and L. A. Sédillot. See G. Sarton, *Introduction to the History of Science*, I, 665, 667, 717; II, 622.
5. See E. Narducci, "Intorno alla vita ed agli scritti di Francesco Woepcke," 123.
6. *Ibid.*, 123 ff.
7. His investigations include Leonardo Fibonacci's solution of the third-degree equation, two Arab approximation methods for determining sine 1°, Indian methods for calculating the sine, ancient methods of multiplication, and astrolabes. On Woepcke's works see Sarton, *op. cit.*, I, 600 (Thābit ibn Qurra), 663 (number symbols in a MS of 970), 667 (Abu'l-Wafā'), 718 (Abū Jaʿfar ibn al-Ḥusain), 719 (al-Karkhī); II, 401 (Muḥammad ibn al-Ḥusain); III, 1765 (al-Qalasādī), 1766 (spread of Hindu numerals and algebraic symbolism).
8. *Ibid.*, I, 154, 174; also R. C. Archibald, *Euclid's Book on Divisions of Figures With a Restoration Based on Woepcke's Text and on the Practica Geometriae of Leonardo Pisano* (Cambridge, 1915), 9–13.
9. Baron de Slane (see Sarton, I, 665; II, 401) edited works on al-Qūhī, al-Sijzī, and Muḥammad ibn al-Ḥusain (dealing with universal compasses for all conic sections); and Aristide Marre (see Sarton, II, 1000) edited the *Talkhīṣ* of Ibn al-Bannāʾ—for Woepcke's preliminary work on this text see Narducci, *op. cit.*, 129, 151.
10. See Narducci, *op. cit.*, 151 f.

## BIBLIOGRAPHY

I. ORIGINAL WORKS. There are complete bibliographies in Narducci (see below), 133–152; and in Poggendorff, II, 1353–1354, and III, 1458. His writings include *Disquisitiones archaeologico-mathematicae circa solaria veterum* (Berlin, 1847), his doctoral dissertation; *L'Algèbre d'Omar Alkhayyāmī* (Paris, 1851); *Extrait du Fakhrī, Traité d'algèbre par Aboū Bekr Mohammed ben Alhaçan Alkarkhī* (Paris, 1853); *Sur l'introduction de l'arithmétique indienne en Occident*, (Rome, 1859); and "Recherches sur plusieurs ouvrages de Léonard de Pise . . . et sur les rapports qui existent entre ces ouvrages et les travaux mathématiques des arabes," in *Atti dell'Accademia pontificia dei Nuovi Lincei*, **10** (1856–1857), 236–248; **12** (1858–1859), 399–438; and **14** (1860–1861), 211–227, 241–269, 301–356.

II. SECONDARY LITERATURE. See J. Fück, *Die ara-*

*bischen Studien in Europa* (Leipzig, 1955), 204; E. Narducci, "Intorno alla vita ed agli scritti di Francesco Woepcke," in *Bullettino di bibliografia e di storia delle scienze matematiche e fisiche*, **2** (1869), 119–152; and G. Sarton, *Introduction to the History of Science*, 3 vols. (Baltimore, 1927–1948).

KURT VOGEL

**WÖHLER, AUGUST** (*b.* Soltau, Germany, 22 June 1819; *d.* Hannover, Germany, 21 March 1914), *material testing*.

Wöhler came from a Protestant family from the small town of Soltau in the Luneburg Heath. His father, Georg Heinrich Wöhler, was a teacher at and rector of the local school, where Wöhler studied for a time. To encourage his mathematical gifts, the boy was sent to the technical college (which later became the Technische Hochschule) in Hannover, headed at the time by the technologist Karl Karmarsch. Having very successfully completed his studies with the aid of a scholarship, Wöhler began a short period of practical training. In 1840 he joined the Borsig engineering works in Berlin, where he gained practical experience in the construction of railway lines. After returning briefly to Hannover in 1843, he went to Belgium to learn how to operate a locomotive and then became an engineer on the first Hannoverian railroad (Hannover to Lehrte). In 1844 Wöhler was promoted to administrative engineer, and in 1847 he became chief superintendent of rolling stock on the Lower Silesia-Brandenburg Railroad (Berlin to Frankfurt-an-der-Oder to Breslau), which was taken over by the state in 1854. His brilliant work in this post was of lasting influence. In 1874 he was named imperial railway director and was placed on the newly created management board of the Imperial Railways in Strasbourg, on which he remained until 1889. His many awards included an honorary doctorate in engineering.

Wöhler's important scientific achievements originated in the problems he encountered while working for the railroads. They consisted in the study and description of the dynamic strength of engineering materials and, more generally, in the creation of modern techniques for testing materials.

In 1852 the Prussian minister of commerce, industry, and public works appointed Wöhler to a commission established to investigate the causes of axle breakage and train derailments. Wöhler's first publications dealt with the theory of elasticity. In 1855 he derived the formulas for calculating the sag of lattice girders, commonly called the equation of three moments (*Zeitschrift für Bauwesen*, **5**, 122–166); these formulas were published two years before the work of Clapeyron, for whom they are often named. At the same time Wöhler recommended that bridge girders be supported at one end on roller bearings to absorb thermal expansion—a precaution that became universal practice.

Wöhler gained broad recognition through his fatigue bending tests, for which he constructed the experimental apparatus. In them the tested material, usually iron or steel, was subjected to a sequence of stresses that bent or turned it back and forth millions of times. Wöhler distinguished between static, increasing, and alternating loads; and he arrived at universally valid results, known as Wöhler's laws. They can be understood from a consideration of the fatigue strength diagram, a curve that shows the dependence of the time strength of a given construction material on the number of load-application cycles borne. The first of Wöhler's four laws states (in his formulation of 1870): "The failure of the material can . . . occur through constantly repeated vibrations, no single one of which reaches the absolute rupture limit. The differences of the tensions, which frame the vibrations, are decisive for failure of cohesion" (*Zeitschrift für Bauwesen*, **20**, 83).

Wöhler's results, illustrated by pieces broken in fatigue tests, were presented at the Paris Exposition in 1867, at which his work first came to the attention of the English (see *Engineering*, **2** [1867], 160). Also in 1867 Wöhler urged the "introduction of a government-approved classification for iron and steel" and the establishment of a government bureau for testing materials. These proposals were not implemented until sometime later, and then only gradually; but they greatly promoted the development of uniform quality in the manufacture of construction materials, as well as progress toward an "honest trade" in them.

*BIBLIOGRAPHY*

I. ORIGINAL WORKS. A list of Wöhler's writings is in R. Blaum, "August Wöhler" (see below). Between 1851 and 1898 Wöhler published 42 articles in German technical periodicals. The most important include "Theorie rechteckiger eiserner Brückenbalken mit Gitterwänden und mit Blechwänden," in *Zeitschrift für Bauwesen*, **5** (1855), 122–166; "Resultate der in der Central-Werkstatt der Niederschlesisch-Märkischen Eisenbahn zu Frankfurt a. d. O. angestellten Versuche über die relative Festigkeit von Eisen, Stahl und Kupfer," *ibid.*, **16** (1866), 67–84; and "Über die Festigkeitsversuche mit Eisen und Stahl," *ibid.*, **20** (1870), 73–106.

II. SECONDARY LITERATURE. See R. Blaum, "August Wöhler," in *Beiträge zur Geschichte der Technik und Industrie*, **8** (1918), 35–55, with bibliography and portrait; and "August Wöhler," in *Deutsches biographisches Jahrbuch*, Überleitungsband I (Stuttgart, 1925), 103–107; F. G. Braune, "Zum 150. Geburtstag von August Wöhler," in *Technik*, **24** (1969), 400–402; A. J. Kennedy, "Fatigue Since Wöhler: A Century of Research," in *Engineering* (London), **186** (1958), 781–782; L. Troske, "August Wöhler," in *Zentralblatt der Bauverwaltung*, **34** (1914), 242–244, with portrait and bibliography; and W. Ruske, "August Wöhler (1819–1914) zur 150. Wiederkehr seines Geburtstages," in *Materialprüfung*, **11** (1969), 181–188.

LUDOLF VON MACKENSEN

**WÖHLER, FRIEDRICH** (*b.* Eschersheim, near Frankfurt-am-Main, Germany, 31 July 1800; *d.* Göttingen, Germany, 23 September 1882), *chemistry*.

For three generations the Wöhlers had been equerries to the electors of Hesse. Wöhler's mother, Anna Katharina Schröder, was the daughter of a professor of philosophy; his father, Anton August Wöhler, left Hesse and became a farmer, then a court official and leading citizen at Frankfurt. Wöhler attended the public school but had extra instruction in Latin, French, and music so that he could attend the Gymnasium from 1814 to 1820. After a year at the University of Marburg and two years at Heidelberg he qualified in 1823 for the M.D., specializing in gynecology. In 1828 he married a cousin, Franziska Wöhler, who bore him two children before her death in 1832; in 1834 he married Julie Pfeiffer, the daughter of a banker, by whom he had four children.

Wöhler's teaching career began at an industrial school in Berlin (1825–1831). He next became professor at a similar institution in Kassel (1831–1836), and he finally settled as professor of chemistry at Göttingen (1836–1882). He was elected foreign member of the Royal Society in 1854 and was awarded its Copley Medal in 1872. From 1864 he was a foreign associate of the Institut de France and an officer of the Legion of Honor.

From childhood Wöhler had a passionate interest in practical chemistry and the collection of minerals. At Heidelberg, Leopold Gmelin encouraged him to experiment on cyanates and, since it

was essential for Germans to go abroad for systematic training in chemistry, he recommended Wöhler to Berzelius in Stockholm. Here Wöhler received a year's rigorous training in mineral analysis and formed a firm friendship with Berzelius. The friendship lasted until the latter's death in 1848 and can be followed through a voluminous correspondence. For over twenty years Wöhler translated Berzelius' influential and often controversial annual reports, occasionally modifying their polemical tone but not their content. He also translated three editions of Berzelius' *Lehrbuch der Chemie*, a labor undertaken for both love and money. Berzelius' influence depended on accurate and prompt translation of his work, and Wöhler wrote an elementary textbook of inorganic chemistry that had fifteen editions in his lifetime and was translated into French, Dutch, Danish, and Swedish; a textbook of organic chemistry that reached thirteen editions; and a textbook of analytical methods that was translated into English.

Wöhler became acquainted with his lifelong friend Liebig as a result of what seemed in 1825 to be a minor squabble over the interpretation of analytical results but became a classic example of a new phenomenon that Berzelius in 1830 called isomerism: both silver cyanate and silver fulminate correspond to the empirical formula AgCNO. Liebig had studied the explosive fulminate and at first rejected Wöhler's 1824 results for the stable cyanate. In the 1820's most chemists assumed that only one chemical compound corresponded to one set of analytical percentages. Wöhler and Liebig exchanged letters, often visited each other, and sometimes took vacations together from 1829 until Liebig's death in 1873.

Wöhler's interest in cyanates led to a historic preparation of "artificial" urea, the circumstances of which are best described in his letter to Berzelius of 22 February 1828:

> I can no longer, as it were, hold back my chemical urine; and I have to let out that I can make urea without needing a kidney, whether of man or dog: the ammonium salt of cyanic acid is urea.
>
> Perhaps you can remember the experiments that I performed in those happy days when I was still working with you, when I found that whenever one tried to combine cyanic acid with ammonia a white crystalline solid appeared that behaved like neither cyanic acid nor ammonia . . . . I took this up again as a subject that would fit into a short time interval, a small undertaking that would quickly be completed and—thank God—would not require a single weighing.
>
> The supposed ammonium cyanate was easily ob-

tained by reacting lead cyanate with ammonia solution. . . . Four-sided right-angled prisms, beautifully crystalline, were obtained. When these were treated with acids, no cyanic acid was liberated, and with alkali, no trace of ammonia. But with nitric acid lustrous flakes of an easily crystallized compound, strongly acid in character, were formed; I was disposed to accept this as a new acid because when it was heated, neither nitric nor nitrous acid was evolved, but a great deal of ammonia. Then I found that if it were saturated with alkali, the so-called ammonium cyanate reappeared; and this could be extracted with alcohol. Now, quite suddenly I had it! All that was needed was to compare urea from urine with this urea from a cyanate.

The letter goes on to describe how the discovery adds to the pairs of substances of similar composition but of different properties already known. "It is noticeable that in making cyanates (and in making ammonia) we always have to start with an organic substance. . . ."

In his published paper Wöhler referred to his work of 1823, in which he had shown that cyanogen and aqueous ammonia yielded oxalic acid and a white crystalline solid that he now realized was urea.[1] This, and his new method, he considered to be remarkable examples of the preparation "by art" of a substance of animal origin from inorganic materials.

In a widely quoted obituary, A. W. Hofmann grossly exaggerated the impact of Wöhler's discovery on his contemporaries; there are in fact few references to the discovery in papers or letters of the time. J. H. Brooke and others refer to the literature and indicate the place of Wöhler's discovery in the history of the decay of vitalism and the establishment of isomerism.[2]

Wöhler's period in Berlin was remarkable not only for the preparation of urea but also for the extraction of aluminum.[3] In Lavoisier's *Traité* of 1789 there is a list of earths, including alumina: although he was confident that the fixed alkalies (soda and potash) were compound, he was less certain of the earths. In 1807 Davy succeeded in decomposing soda and potash, and in 1808 he attempted electrolysis of the earths. In his footnotes to the printed lecture the history is reviewed.[4] Meanwhile, Berzelius succeeded in using mercury as a cathode for the electrolysis of most lime and barytes; but alumina would not yield aluminum for him or for Davy, even though the latter tried many ingenious variations. With hindsight one can perhaps see that Davy almost certainly obtained aluminum in several very impure forms: as an amalgam, as a solution in potassium, fused into molten glass, and in iron alloys. Faraday and James Stodart in 1822 made an aluminum-in-iron alloy by reduction with coal and iron. In 1824 Berzelius succeeded in extracting silicon by heating potassium with potassium fluosilicate, the potassium probably being provided by Wöhler; the method failed for aluminum.

In 1825 H. C. Oersted showed a specimen of metal, which he believed was aluminum, to the Academy of Sciences in Copenhagen (the specimen is not now available). He certainly prepared aluminum chloride by a new method, but it seems unlikely that the metal was pure aluminum; an alloy of aluminum and potassium seems probable. Oersted, a friend of Wöhler's, never published a claim and made no objection when Wöhler tacitly assumed priority in 1827 or when he published further details in 1845. Recently, however, claims have been made for Oersted's priority.[5]

On 10 October 1827 Wöhler wrote to Berzelius: "Oersted has told me that he does not intend to carry on with his experiments with aluminum chloride. I have already made a first repetition of his researches. . . ." Later he said, "Like Oersted, I decomposed it [aluminum chloride] with potassium amalgam and distilled the product. When the mercury had gone, an iron-black lump of metal remained; but on strong heating it distilled as a green vapor." In a paper of 1827, Wöhler emphasized that he was not saying the extraction was impossible by Oersted's method, but that he could not repeat the process and had a better one. Oersted had, he stated, given up the work and had given him permission to go ahead—an important ethical consideration. He praised Oersted's "most ingenious method" for the preparation of the aluminum chloride from which the metal could be extracted.

Wöhler's technique was to cover a small quantity of potassium in a platinum crucible with excess aluminum chloride and to heat the covered crucible gently to start the vigorous reaction. Nothing remained to react with water to produce alkalies when the reaction mixture was put into water. Other workers possibly had failed with similar methods because alkalies would react with the finely divided metallic product. Wöhler proved that his metal contained no potassium and described its chemical properties in considerable detail, especially its reactions with other elements, acids, and alkalies; footnotes contain many references to other metals.

In 1845 Wöhler published a supplementary paper to amplify his descriptions of 1827.

Later in the nineteenth century, when aluminum became a common metal, Wöhler was honored by Napoleon III. Twentieth-century controversies over priority in the extraction of pure aluminum have added little to history except nationalistic claims. Wöhler subsequently used the same technique to extract beryllium and what he thought was yttrium from their chlorides.

From the first letters exchanged between Wöhler and Liebig the possibility of a joint work was discussed; but when it came, it was not, as might have been expected, on cyanates but, rather, on mellitic acid. In 1825 Wöhler became interested in the mineral honeystone sent to him by Heinrich Rose. (Its true structure, as the aluminum salt of mellitic acid—$C_6(COOH)_6$—was established by Adolf von Baeyer in 1865.) He isolated the pure acid, a calcium salt, and other metallic derivatives; and qualitative observations led him to believe that the acid contained little or no hydrogen and might be related to benzoic acid. (By "the acid," workers at that time usually meant the acid anhydride.) Liebig took over the practical work in 1829, and a joint paper eventually was published. Wöhler returned to the subject in 1839; was helped by Berzelius with supplies of the rare material in 1840; and prepared the ammonium salt, an amide, euchronic acid, and some unidentified colored derivatives.

In January 1830, Liebig wrote to Wöhler that he would prefer their joint work to be on cyanates instead of honeystone. While he was still a student Wöhler had already published four papers on cyanates; one on mercuric thiocyanate ("Pharaoh's serpent") and perthionic acid, two more after his year with Berzelius, and a fourth in 1829 on the products of dry distillation of urea and uric acid. Urea yielded an acid that he recognized as cyanic acid, already discovered and named by Serullas. But whereas Serullas gave $C_2N_2O_2$ as an empirical formula. Wöhler decided that the acid of the cyanates must be $C_2N_2O$. Liebig and Wöhler set to work separately, Wöhler doing the preparation and Liebig the analyses. They struggled for a year and were remarkably successful in sorting out the complex products of dry distillation of urea. In 1845 they returned to the study of the product obtained when cyanic acid reacts with alcohol and decided, with irony, to call it allophanic ether (literally, "unexpected" ether).

The correspondence shows that a joint paper consisting of miscellaneous observations in inorganic chemistry was based solely on Wöhler's work. From the letters that each exchanged with Berzelius it can be seen that at this time both men were considering a study of oil obtained by pressing bitter almonds. Wöhler suggested it to Liebig as a joint study, and they began to collect materials. After Wöhler's first wife died in June 1832, he went for about seven weeks to Giessen and worked feverishly with Liebig: although they published other joint works, this was the only time they actually shared a laboratory. A letter to Berzelius shows that in the first four weeks, they had carried out most of the experimental work and tentatively drawn what were to be their final conclusions.

In 1832 the two workers left open the relationship between the oil and the material from which it was extracted. In their classic paper—which was actually written by Wöhler although Liebig is listed as coauthor—they summarized their achievements: ". . . we make the general assertion that as a result of our experiments, it is established that there is a body, composed of three elements, that remains stable in the presence of reagents and that can be regarded not only as the radical of benzoic acid but, perhaps with slight variations, as the radical of a large number of similar compounds."[6]

Wöhler and Liebig overcame considerable practical and theoretical difficulties. They had, for example, no thermometer that could measure temperatures over 130° C. Misunderstanding over the relative atomic weights of heavy metals and oxygen led to formulas double the modern ones (for instance, $C^{14}H^{10}O^2$ instead of $C_7H_5O$ for the benzoyl radical); their analysis of benzoic acid therefore gave a result different from that established by Berzelius. The last of these difficulties was overcome after correspondence with Berzelius and analysis of the silver salt. They established the relation between the oil (now called benzeldehyde) and its aerial oxidation product (already known as benzoic acid). Then the reaction of the oil with potassium hydroxide was studied and a new "oil" (now called benzyl alcohol) extracted with potassium benzoate.

By passing chlorine through the oil, Wöhler and Liebig obtained benzoyl chloride, which they converted into the bromide and iodide; they also studied its reaction with alkalies, water, alcohol, and dry ammonia gas. Among many derivatives they obtained were benzoyl sulfide, benzoyl cyanide, benzamide, ethyl benzoate, benzonitrile, and benzoin. They did not analyze all of these, and some of their tentative formulas are incorrect; but the paper established beyond doubt what they claimed: the existence of a body that was constant from one compound to another. Incidentally, many of the compounds they first prepared and described (such as benzoyl chloride) were important in the future development of organic chemistry. Berzelius was prepared to accept the benzoyl radical, oxygen included; but he later felt that oxygen could not possibly be present in an electropositive radical and withdrew his support for such a view.

When Wöhler moved to Göttingen in 1836, he wrote to Liebig and proposed a joint study of amygdalin. Within two days of sending this letter he mailed another showing that he had virtually solved the problem. In 1830 P. J. Robiquet and Antoine Boutron-Charlard had found that crushed bitter almonds smell of bitter almonds only when moistened and that, from the crushed nuts, fats, a resin, a liquid sugar, and the substance they called amygdalin could be extracted by addition of boiling alcohol. Wöhler showed in 1836 that the crystalline amygdalin could be decomposed by a vegetable emulsion, providing the emulsion had not been coagulated by boiling. Liebig took over the quantitative work and showed that a sugar was the other product of the decomposition. Amygdalin, the first example of a glycoside, was the subject of a joint paper.

Wöhler and Liebig collaborated on one more major piece of work, a study of uric acid. Wöhler suggested the subject, and the idea seems to have come from his medical interests. Uric acid was not easily obtainable—snake excrement was the only substantial source—and relationships with urea and allantoin were suspected by Wöhler. As a student he had won a prize in 1828 for an essay on the conversion in the human body of chemicals taken orally and excreted in urine. The technique adopted by Liebig and Wöhler was to subject uric acid, and the derivatives they prepared, to oxidation and reduction by reagents of different concentrations and strengths. Wöhler seems to have been the first to heat reagents together in sealed glass tubes, but after an explosion he thought metal ones safer.

Their 100-page paper described fourteen new compounds and their preparation and analysis.[7] An attempt to establish a new radical called "uril" ($C_8N_4O_4$) was less successful. Perhaps even more significant than the sophisticated, practical and theoretical organic chemistry was the new spirit revealed. Writing to Berzelius in 1828, Wöhler was doubtful whether animal substances could be prepared in the laboratory. In 1832 he began the paper on the benzoyl radical with a description of organic chemistry as "the dark region of organic nature." But in 1838 his work with Liebig led him to write (at Liebig's suggestion):

> The philosophy of chemistry will conclude from this work that it must be held not only as probable but [as] certain that all organic substances, insofar as they no longer belong to the organism, will be prepared in the laboratory. Sugar, salicin, morphine will be produced artificially. It is true that the route to these end products is not yet clear to us, because the intermediaries from which these materials develop are still unknown, but we shall learn to know them.

Although the two friends published further joint papers, they did no more major investigations together, Liebig turning to agricultural and physiological chemistry and Wöhler to inorganic studies. Although at the age of forty Wöhler had published only a quarter of the papers he was to present, none of the later ones was as important for the development of chemistry as those before 1840. As professor of chemistry and pharmacy, director of the laboratories, and inspector general of all the apothecaries in the kingdom of Hannover, he had to spend a great deal of time from 1836 to 1848 on inspection tours of apothecary shops. During these years translation of Berzelius' texts also took much time. The school of chemistry at Göttingen grew steadily, and Wöhler estimated that about 1,750 students heard his lectures between 1845 and 1852, 2,950 between 1853 and 1859, and 3,550 between 1860 and 1866. He thus had all the duties of a government official, translator, and teacher, as well as father of a growing family; and later in his life he told Kolbe that he had not kept up with theoretical developments. Nevertheless, during his forty-six years as professor at Göttingen he produced a stream of interesting papers.

Wöhler was always fascinated by geological samples, which were sent to him from all over the world by friends and ex-students. Meteorites were equally absorbing, and he published some fifty papers on minerals, meteorites, and their analyses: he noted the passivity of meteoric iron. Wöhler's lively curiosity and ingenuity shine through these papers, as well as through the fifteen papers on general analytical methods.

In organic chemistry Wöhler studied quinone and hydroquinone, established the relationship between them, and discovered quinhydrone (which he compared for beauty of color with the feathers of the hummingbird). He distrusted theoretical speculation and in 1840 published a paper under the pseudonym S. C. H. Windler satirizing Dumas's substitution theory. Had he allowed the developing theories to guide his research, it is possible that his time spent on organic chemistry might have been more fruitful: many of his papers are on topics already absorbed into the current theories (such as chloroform) or too far beyond the tide of research to affect it (such as alkaloids). Like other workers, including Berzelius, he spent time on ill-characterized substances of biological or medicinal interest that failed to yield clear chemical results even to his superb manipulative technique.

Mid-nineteenth-century inorganic chemistry was relatively static, and many workers simply collected data and prepared new compounds. Their interest was in the materials themselves: rocks, crystals, or chemicals. There is hardly a metal for which Wöhler did not prepare new salts, and he was particularly fond of colored derivatives. Some of his methods, such as the preparation of phosphorus by heating calcined bones with sand, have since been developed industrially. He was the first to make acetylene from calcium carbide (1862), by heating together zinc, calcium, and carbon. Copper-colored cubic crystals from blast-furnace slag, which had been thought to be metallic titanium, were shown by Wöhler in 1850 to be a compound of titanium, carbon, and nitrogen.

Working with Deville, Wöhler used aluminum to extract crystalline boron from boric acid, and crystalline silicon from potassium fluosilicate. Heinrich Buff consulted Wöhler about the gas, which ignited explosively and spontaneously in air, that he obtained during the electrolysis of dilute acids with aluminum electrodes. Wöhler realized that the aluminum contained silicon and went on to discover and describe silicon hydride. Wöhler and Buff were the first to prepare organosilicon compounds, silicon chloroform, iodoform, and bromoform.

Unlike his close friends Liebig and Berzelius—and, indeed, many of the eminent chemists of the time—Wöhler rarely made enemies, kept a cool good humor, avoided rancorous argument, and did his best to bring together even such immovable objects and irresistible forces as Berzelius and Liebig. His efforts to counsel Liebig to lead a quieter life were unsuccessful.

Wöhler was popular with students from throughout the world. An account of his American pupils, many of whom obtained important chemical posts, was published.[8] His most distinguished student probably was Hermann Kolbe, who became professor at Marburg and remained a close friend until

Wöhler's death. Unlike Liebig, Wöhler remained interested in what went on his laboratory even in old age.

## NOTES

1. "Über künstliche Bildung des Harnstoffs," in *Annalen der Physik und Chemie*, 2nd ser., **12** (1828), 253–256.
2. John H. Brooke, "Wöhlers Urea and Its Vital Force?—A Verdict From the Chemists," in *Ambix*, **15** (1968), 84–114. The significance of the preparation of urea from inorganic sources has been pressed by (among others) W. H. J. Warren, in "Contemporary Reception of Wöhler's Discovery of the Synthesis of Urea," in *Journal of Chemical Education*, **5** (1928), 1539–1552; and dismissed by the following: D. McKie, "Wöhler's Synthetic Urea and the Rejection of Vitalism, a Chemical Legend," in *Nature*, **153** (1944), 608–610; P. Mendelssohn-Bartholdy, "Wöhler's Work on Urea," *ibid.*, **154** (1944), 150–151; and E. Campaigne, "Wöhler and the Overthrow of Vitalism," in *Journal of Chemical Education*, **32** (1955), 403, an attempt to reestablish the significance of the discovery. A balanced review of the literature is in T. O. Lipman, "Wöhler's Preparation of Urea and the Fate of Vitalism," *ibid.*, **41** (1964), 452–458.
3. "Über das Aluminium," in *Annalen der Physik und Chemie*, 2nd ser., **11** (1827), 146–161.
4. Humphry Davy, "Electrochemical Researches on the Decomposition of the Earths . . .," in *Philosophical Transactions of the Royal Society*, **98** (1808), 333–370.
5. N. Bjerrum's claim for Oersted in "Die Entdeckung des Aluminiums," in *Zeitschrift für angewandte Chemie*, **39** (1926), 316–317, was countered by K. Goldschmidt in "Nochmals die Entdeckung des Aluminiums," *ibid.*, 375–376. Oersted's notes were published by Kirstine Meyer, in *H. C. Oersted Naturvidenskabelige skrifter*, II (Copenhagen, 1920), 467–470.
6. "Untersuchungen über das Radikal der Benzoesäure," in *Justus Liebigs Annalen der Chemie*, **1** (1832), 249–282, written with Liebig; also reprinted separately as Ostwalds Klassiker der Exacten Wissenschaften, no. 22 (Leipzig, 1891).
7. "Untersuchungen über die Natur der Harnsäure," in *Justus Liebigs Annalen der Chemie*, **26** (1838), 241–340, written with Liebig.
8. H. S. van Klooster, "Friedrich Wöhler and His American Pupils," in *Journal of Chemical Education*, **21** (1944), 158–170.

## BIBLIOGRAPHY

I. ORIGINAL WORKS. A. W. Hofmann's complete bibliography of Wöhler's publications (see below) includes details of the translations of his books. The Royal Society *Catalogue of Scientific Papers*, VI, 410–419; VIII, 1258–1259; XI, 836–837; and XII, 790; lists all the translations of the papers.

Wöhler's books include *Grundriss der unorganischen Chemie* (Berlin, 1831; 15th ed., 1873); *Grundriss der organischen Chemie* (Berlin, 1840; 13th ed., 1882); *Beispiele zur Übung in der analytischen Chemie* (Göttingen, 1849), published anonymously; *Practische Übungen in der chemischen Analyse* (Göttingen, 1853), also published anonymously; and *Die Mineralanalyse in Beispielen* (Göttingen, 1861), published as a 2nd ed. of the last work.

Wöhler's translation of Berzelius' *Lärbok i kemien* appeared as *Lehrbuch der Chemie*, 4 vols. (Dresden, 1825–1831); the 3rd ed., rev., appeared in 10 vols. (Dresden, 1833–1841); and the 4th ed. in 10 vols. (Dresden–Leipzig, 1835–1841). Vols. 4–20 of Berzelius' annual surveys of progress in the sciences, *Årsberättelser öfver Vetenskapernas Framsteg*, 27 vols. (Stockholm, 1822–1848), were also translated by Wöhler.

The voluminous correspondence between Wöhler and Berzelius was published almost in its entirety by O. Wallach, ed., *Briefwechsel zwischen J. Berzelius und F. Wöhler*, 2 vols. (Wiesbaden, 1901), with scholarly footnotes.

Extracts from the Liebig-Wöhler correspondence were published six years after Wöhler's death. Wöhler selected and often polished the extracts, probably intending publication as a tribute to his friend: A. W. Hofmann, ed., *Aus Justus Liebig's und Friedrich Wöhler's Briefwechsel 1829–1873*, 2 vols. (Brunswick, 1888). The extracts represent perhaps a quarter of the total correspondence, the bulk of which is at the Bayerische Staatsbibliothek, Munich. Wöhler's (and Liebig's) publisher, Vieweg, in Brunswick, has about 100 letters exchanged between the two men. The Deutsches Museum, Munich, and the University Library, Göttingen, hold letters exchanged by Wöhler and other chemists, such as Kolbe and Bunsen.

II. SECONDARY LITERATURE. A. W. Hofmann, "Zur Erinnerung an Friedrich Wöhler," in *Berichte der Deutschen chemischen Gesellschaft*, **15** (1882), 3127–3290; and Johannes Valentin, *Friedrich Wöhler* (Stuttgart, 1949), 159–170, both include bibliographies of Wöhler's writings. See also Th. Kunzmann, *Die Bedeutung der wissenschaftlichen Tätigkeit Friedrich Wöhler's für die Entwicklung der Deutschen chemischen Industrie* (Berlin, 1830), which gives a list of papers published by Wöhler's students between 1837 and 1863; and Poggendorff, VII A (1970), 779–783, with a full list of papers published on Wöhler and his work.

ROBIN KEEN

**WOLF, CHARLES JOSEPH ÉTIENNE** (*b.* Vorges, near Laon, Aisne, France, 9 November 1827; *d.* St.-Servan, Ille-et-Vilaine, France, 4 July 1918), *astronomy, history of science.*

Wolf, whose family included a number of teachers and professors, entered the École Normale Supérieure in 1848. *Agrégé* in science three years later, he taught at the *lycée* in Nîmes and later at the one in Metz. His initial research, a study of capillarity as a function of temperature, earned him a doctorate in physical sciences in 1856. He was then named professor of physics at the Faculty of Sciences of the University of Montpellier, where

in 1862 he demonstrated that the spectra of incandescent bodies, then thought to be rigorously stable, vary when the temperature of the body rises.

Also in 1862, Le Verrier had Wolf named astronomer at the Paris observatory. Assigned at first to the Service Méridien, Wolf studied the personal equation affecting meridian observations and built an apparatus for determining it. He also worked on the electric synchronization of astronomical clocks, perfecting a device that was later adopted for the clocks of Paris.

Wolf was transferred to the Service des Équatoriaux, where, in collaboration with Rayet, he photographed the penumbra of the moon during the eclipse of October 1865. Shortly afterward he observed the spectrum of a nova and noted that it contained bright lines, a new phenomenon that he subsequently sought to detect in the spectra of other stars. For this purpose, Wolf devised a direct-view spectroscope, with neither slit nor lens, that could immediately be substituted for the eyepiece of a telescope when a star was sighted. With this instrument the user could quickly carry out a spectroscopic exploration of the sky. In 1867 Wolf and Rayet discovered three stars exhibiting the phenomenon they were seeking; these were the first examples of what are called Wolf-Rayet stars, also known as stars of spectral type W.

Of Wolf's thirty or so published notes and articles we shall mention only two of the most important. In 1869, exploiting data gathered during the transit of Mercury in the preceding year, he definitively solved the problem of the "black drop," a phenomenon that occurs at the moment when the image of a planet comes into contact with the solar limb, making it difficult to determine the instant of contact. He showed that the phenomenon, which Lalande had attributed to irradiation, is purely instrumental and can be eliminated by the use of a sufficiently large objective that is free from aberration. From 1873 to 1875 Wolf studied the Pleiades, which serve as standards for astrometrical measurements. He established the first general catalog of the cluster (1877), containing the positions and magnitudes of 571 stars.

Appointed *professeur suppléant* of astronomy at the Paris Faculty of Sciences in 1875, Wolf was named titular professor in 1892. He left the observatory in the latter year and retired from teaching in 1901. Toward the end of his career Wolf became especially interested in the history of science. In the *Bulletin astronomique* of 1884 and 1885 he published seven articles on cosmogonic hypotheses and later collected them in a book that also contained his own complete French translation of Kant's *Universal Natural History and Theory of the Heavens*. He also studied ancient standards of weights and lengths and the history of the pendulum. His most remarkable work, *Histoire de l'Observatoire de Paris*, is still the only full-length account of that institution. Drawing on original documents, he related "the history of the buildings and of their successive transformations, of the instruments used there, of the astronomers who lived there, and of the administration under which they lived."

Wolf was deeply religious, austere but kindly. He often spent vacations in the house where he was born. Obliged to leave it in 1914 because of the German invasion, he took refuge in St.-Servan, where he died a few months before his native city was reconquered. Wolf was elected to the Académie des Sciences in 1883 and served as its president in 1898.

*BIBLIOGRAPHY*

I. Original Works. Wolf's physical works are "Influence de la température sur les phénomènes qui se passent dans les tubes capillaires," in *Annales de chimie et de physique*, **49** (1857), 230–279; "Sur les spectres des métaux alcalins," in *Comptes rendus . . . de l'Académie des sciences*, **55** (1862), 334–336, written with M. Diacon; and "Sur le pouvoir réflecteur des miroirs en verre argenté," in *Journal de physique théorique et appliquée*, **1** (1872), 81–86.

His writings on instruments and their use include "Recherches sur l'équation personnelle . . .," in *Annales de l'Observatoire de Paris, Mémoires*, **8** (1865), 153–208; "Description d'un nouveau spectroscope," in *Comptes rendus . . . de l'Académie des sciences*, **65** (1867), 292–293; "Description du sidérostat de Foucault," in *Annales scientifiques de l'École normale supérieure*, 2nd ser., **1** (1872), 51–84; "Les applications de l'électricité à l'astronomie," in *Bulletin de la Société internationale des électriciens*, **2** (1885), 105–125; and "Comparaison des divers systèmes de synchronisation des horloges astronomiques," in *Comptes rendus . . . de l'Académie des sciences*, **105** (1887), 1155–1159.

Among his astronomical writings are "Sur le passage de Mercure du 4 novembre 1868 . . .," in *Comptes rendus . . . de l'Académie des sciences*, **68** (1869), 181–183, written with C. André; "Description du groupe des Pléiades," in *Annales de l'Observatoire de Paris, Mémoires*, **14**, pt. 1 (1877), A1–A81; *Les hypothèses cosmogoniques* (Paris, 1886); and *Astronomie et géodésie*, H. Le Barbier and P. Bourguignon, eds. (Paris, 1891). The discovery of the Wolf-Rayet stars is discussed in Jacques R. Lévy, "Rayet," in *DSB*, XI, 319–321. Various observations are reported in some twenty notes in *Comptes rendus . . . de l'Académie des sciences*, **62–107** (1866–1888).

The history of science is treated in "Étalons de poids et mesures de l'Observatoire . . .," in *Annales de l'Observatoire de Paris*, **17** (1883), C1–C78; "Rôle de Lavoisier . . . système métrique," in *Comptes rendus . . . de l'Académie des sciences*, **102** (1886), 1279–1284; *Travaux relatifs à la théorie et aux applications du pendule*, 2 vols. (Paris, 1889–1891); and *Histoire de l'Observatoire de Paris de sa fondation à 1793* (Paris, 1902). Wolf also wrote seven notes, mainly on ancient standards of length, that appeared in *Comptes rendus . . . de l'Académie des sciences*, **95–125** (1882–1897).

II. Secondary Literature. See G. Bigourdan, "Notice sur la vie et les travaux de M. Ch. Wolf," in *Comptes rendus . . . de l'Académie des sciences*, **167** (1918), 46–48; and an anonymous "Notice nécrologique," in *Astronomie*, **32** (1918), 255–256; and P. Painlevé, "Annonce de la mort de Ch. Wolf," in *Comptes rendus . . . de l'Académie des sciences*, **167** (1918), 45–46.

Jacques R. Lévy

**WOLF, JOHANN RUDOLF** (*b.* Fällanden, near Zurich, Switzerland, 7 July 1816; *d.* Zurich, 6 December 1893), *astronomy, history of science.*

Wolf, the son of Johannes Wolf, a minister, and Regula Gossweiler, came from an old Zurich family, the Windeggen-Wolfs, who had been citizens of that city since the fourteenth century. He was educated at the Zurich Industrieschule and at the newly founded university, where his teachers included K. H. Gräffe and J. L. Raabe. He continued his studies at Vienna (1836–1838) under J. J. von Littrow and J. A. von Ettingshausen, and at Berlin (1838) under Encke, Dirichlet, and Steiner. In 1839 Wolf went to Bern to teach mathematics and physics, and from 1844 to 1855 he also was professor of astronomy at the university. In the latter year he accepted a double appointment at Zurich as professor of astronomy at the Eidgenössische Technische Hochschule and the university. Through his efforts an observatory was constructed at Zurich and opened in 1864.

Wolf's most important achievement was the reliable determination of the lengths of sunspot periods and of their relationship to the variation in terrestrial magnetism. After Schwabe announced that he had detected a period of about ten years, Edward Sabine, Alfred Gautier, and Wolf discovered, simultaneously and independently of each other, that this period paralleled the variations in the earth's magnetic elements. By exploiting older data, Wolf gathered enough solar observations to establish, in 1852, a mean value of 11.1 years for the duration of a period. He also determined the epochs of all the maxima and minima from 1610 on; and until his death he continued to publish regular reports on his determinations of the relative numbers of the sunspots (see his *Geschichte der Astronomie*, secs. 188, 235).

Wolf also made a significant contribution to the study of the history of science. His works in this field are a rich source of historical data, and by virtue of his astonishingly wide-ranging studies they are exceptionally reliable. Moreover, they are very concise. Among his scholarly achievements was the discovery that the correspondence of Johann I Bernoulli, augmented by that of the younger Bernoullis, had been sold shortly before 1800, in part to the Stockholm Academy and in part to the prince of Gotha. As a result, O. Spiess was able to make the correspondence accessible to scholars. Wolf's own correspondence was stored with his other papers at the Zurich observatory and, unfortunately, his successor, lacking space, disposed of it (see Spiess's preface to *Der Briefwechsel von Johann Bernoulli*, 35, n. 1).

Wolf founded the *Vierteljahrsschrift der Naturforschenden Gesellschaft in Zürich* in 1856 and served as its editor until his death. Upon the establishment of the Zurich Polytechnikum he was named head librarian; during his tenure he assembled a valuable collection of early printed books on astronomy, mathematics, and other branches of science.

## BIBLIOGRAPHY

I. Original Works. Wolf's writings include "Über den gelehrten Briefwechsel der Bernoulli," in *Mitteilungen der Naturforschenden Gesellschaft in Bern*, no. 109 (1848), 1–7; *Handbuch der Mathematik, Physik, Geodäsie und Astronomie*, 2 vols. (Zurich, 1869–1872); "Die Correspondenz von Johannes Bernoulli," in *Vierteljahrsschrift der Naturforschenden Gesellschaft in Zürich*, **21** (1876), 384–386; *Geschichte der Astronomie* (Munich, 1877), vol. XVI of *Geschichte der Wissenschaften in Deutschland*; and *Handbuch der Astronomie, ihre Geschichte und Literatur*, 2 vols. (Zurich, 1890–1893).

The Zurich observatory has Wolf's journal for 1816–1841, which consists of 141 MS pages. Wolf's contributions to *Biographien zur Kulturgeschichte der Schweiz*, 4 vols. (Zurich, 1858–1862), were continued in 475 articles subsequently published in *Vierteljahrsschrift der Naturforschenden Gesellschaft in Zürich*, **6–39** (1861–1894).

II. Secondary Literature. See Heinz Balmer, "Rudolf Wolf und seine Briefsammlung," in *Librarium*, **8**, no. 2 (1965), 95–105; and Alvin Jaeggli, "Die Berufung des Astronomen Joh. Rudolf Wolf nach Zürich 1855," Eidgenössische Technische Hochschule (Zurich), Bibliothek, Schriftenreihe no. 11 (1968).

Obituaries are collected in *Reden, gehalten bei den Trauerfeierlichkeiten für Herrn Dr. J. R. Wolf* (Zurich, 1894). A list of additional obituaries, some with bibliography and portrait, is in *Vierteljahrsschrift der Naturforschenden Gesellschaft in Zürich*, **46** (1901), 333.

See also *Der Briefwechsel von Johann Bernoulli*, O. Spiess, ed., I (Basel, 1955), foreword, 35, n. 1.

J. J. Burckhardt

**WOLF, MAXIMILIAN FRANZ JOSEPH CORNELIUS** (*b.* Heidelberg, Germany, 21 June 1863; *d.* Heidelberg, 3 October 1932), *astronomy.*

Wolf was the son of Franz Wolf and Elise Helwerth. He became interested in astronomy in his youth and in 1885 his father, a rich physician, constructed a private observatory for him. Wolf received the Ph.D. at Heidelberg in 1888, with a dissertation on celestial mechanics written under the direction of Leo Königsberger; he then went to Stockholm, where for the next two years he continued his studies with Gylden. His dissertation on asteroids, influenced by Gylden, was published in Stockholm, and won him a post as academic lecturer when he returned to the University of Heidelberg. He remained there for the rest of his life, and was professor of astrophysics and astronomy from 1901 until 1932.

Working in his private observatory, Wolf soon became famous for his innovative photographic methods. He used a wide-angle lens to investigate the diffuse nebulae of our galaxy and invented a technique for discovering asteroids through the streaks they made on time-exposure plates. These investigations brought him into contact with a number of American astronomers, especially E. E. Barnard, and in 1893 Wolf visited United States observatories. He returned with plans to build a new observatory at Heidelberg, since his own, located in the center of town, was inadequate; the grand duke of Baden was interested in Wolf's ideas, and under his patronage an observatory was begun on the Königstuhl. Catherine Wolfe Bruce, of New York City, who was also interested in Wolf's work, made him the generous gift of the sixteen-inch double telescope that provided the foundation for his continuing investigations.

At the new Baden Observatory, Wolf and his

collaborators discovered hundreds of new asteroids and determined their positions by means of a visual refractor—a method that produced more exact results than those derivable photographically from plates made with a wide-angle objective. From 1906 on, Wolf also used a reflector to obtain spectrographs of the galactic nebulae. He began by studying the shapes of the gaseous nebulae—as they were then called—but soon became interested in their relationships to surrounding stars. Observing that many of the extended dark nebulae show dark patches, or "cavities," as he called them, Wolf counted the number of stars in such dark areas and demonstrated by the statistics of stellar magnitudes that the cavities were clouds of cosmic dust. Since it was possible for him to make spectrophotographs of only the brighter single stars, he made use of red filters on his reflector to view an extended celestial region.

As a result of these investigations Wolf was early able to recognize the difference between the gaseous and planetary nebulae, on the one hand, and the spiral nebulae, on the other. He reached this distinction through both spectral analysis and the study of the systematic distribution of the spiral nebulae relative to the mean plane of the galaxy. By 1911 he had offered a number of conclusions that were later generally adopted.

Wolf also studied single stars, comparing two plates of the same celestial region, photographed at different times, to find variable stars of substantial proper motion. In these investigations he often made use of the stereocomparator, an instrument that he and Pulfrich had invented. Wolf was of the view that, in general, the instrument creates the science, as could best be seen in the development of astronomy; throughout his career, he therefore paid particular attention to instrumentation. He further wished to establish an observatory in a more favorable climate than that of central Europe, and, with his friend A. F. Lindemann (the father of the British physicist Lord Cherwell), investigated sites around the Mediterranean—without, however, finding any more suitable.

Wolf was an exceptional teacher as well as researcher, and attracted students from all over the world, including Luigi Carnera, R. S. Dugan, August Kopff, and Heinrich Vogt. His lectures were vivid, and he often illustrated them with slides. In addition to his students, Wolf had friends all over the world, particularly in the United States; he was therefore much affected by World War I, and following the war was active in attempting to restore scientific relationships between America and Germany.

Wolf received many honors and awards. He was also highly esteemed by amateur astronomers, from whom he often received requests for celestial photographs. It is characteristic of his generosity that he was often able to oblige them, even though he prepared all copies and slides of his photographs himself.

## BIBLIOGRAPHY

I. ORIGINAL WORKS. Wolf's works include "Photographic Observations of Minor Planets," in *Astronomy and Astrophysics*, **12** (1893), 779; "Reflector and Portrait Lens in Celestial Photography," in *Nature*, **55** (1897), 582; *Königstuhlnebellisten*, I–XVI (1902–1928); "Stereoskopische Bestimmung der relativen Eigenbewegung von Fixsternen," in *Astronomische Nachrichten*, **171** (1906), 321–326; "Spektren von Gsnebeln," in *Vierteljahrsschrift der Astronomischen Gesellschaft*, **43** (1908), 208; "Die Spektra zweier planetarischer Nebel, Heidelberg," in *Sitzungsberichte der Akademie der Wissenschaften in Wien*, pt. 2A (1911); "Auffindung und Messung von Eigenbewegungen durch Stereoeffekt," in *Vierteljahrsschrift der Astronomischen Gesellschaft*, **51** (1916), 113; "Die Sternleeren beim Amerikanebel," in *Astronomische Nachrichten*, **223** (1924), 89; and "Die Sternleeren bei S. Monocerotis," in *Seeliger-Festschrift* (1924), 312.

II. SECONDARY LITERATURE. On Wolf and his work, see H.-C. Freiesleben, Max Wolf, *Der Bahnbrecher der Himmelsphotographie*, Grosse Naturforscher, no. 26 (Stuttgart, 1962), which includes a comprehensive bibliography of Wolf's publications, 232–238.

H.-CHRIST. FREIESLEBEN

**WOLFF, CASPAR FRIEDRICH** (*b*. Berlin, Germany, 18 January 1734; *d*. St. Petersburg, Russia [now Leningrad, U.S.S.R.], 22 February 1794), *biology*.

For a detailed account of his life and work, see Supplement.

**WOLFF, CHRISTIAN** (*b*. Breslau, Silesia [now Wrocław, Poland], 24 January 1679; *d*. Halle, Germany, 9 April 1754), *philosophy*.

During his school years at Breslau, Wolff became acquainted with Cartesian ideas, although he concentrated at first on the writings of the Scholastics. He then became interested in logic, which ultimately left him dissatisfied because it lacked any sustained account of an "art of discovery." This view of logic, together with a lifelong search for certainty in matters scientific and philosophical, led to his interest in mathematics, not for its own sake but for its methodological implications. After three years at Jena, Wolff received the master's degree from Leipzig in 1702, becoming first a lecturer in mathematics and then, in 1706, professor of mathematics and natural science at the University of Halle. He was recommended for the latter post by Leibniz, with whom he had established a correspondence and whose philosophical ideas, although somewhat modified and vulgarized, subsequently became the cornerstone of his own philosophical writings.

At Halle, Wolff lectured on mathematics and algebra, building and fortification, as well as experimental and theoretical physics; a glimpse of the kind of courses given may be obtained from one of the earliest writings of this period, his popular handbook *Anfangsgründe aller mathematischen Wissenschaften* (1710). Gradually the interest in logic supervened, leading in 1713 to publication of *Vernünftige Gedanken von den Kräften des menschlichen Verstandes* (the so-called "German Logic"); and by 1719 his philosophical lecturing, which had become the focus of his university activities, found its first full expression in *Vernünftige Gedanken von Gott, der Welt und der Seele des Menschen . . .* (the "German Metaphysics"), which testifies to the leading influence of Leibniz. Although the form of these works is characteristically Scholastic, the importance of their publication in German, rather than Latin, cannot be overrated; by creating a German philosophical vocabulary, it led to a great spread of philosophical interest in eighteenth-century Germany that reinforced the general movement toward deism, determinism, and free thought incipient in these writings.

Indeed, Wolff's deterministic tendencies led to his dismissal from Halle in 1723, after which he taught at the University of Marburg, where he published another set of writings, this time in Latin, many of them corresponding to the earlier German versions but more formal and Scholastic in appearance and with an impressive complex of definitions, theorems, and demonstrations, as instanced in the important volumes on ontology and general cosmology. As Wolff's fame spread, he received invitations to return to Prussia and to go to Berlin; but he finally settled again at Halle,

where he continued to write on law, moral philosophy, and related subjects.

Wolff was essentially a popularizer and (to some extent inspired by Leibniz) sought to effect a formal synthesis between Scholasticism, the new mathematical methods, and more recent scientific conceptions. From Leibniz he also inherited the emphasis on certain philosophical ideas, such as the principles of contradiction and of sufficient reason, as well as the central attention given to the notion of possibility in their metaphysical writings. Round these conceptions Wolff organized a vast philosophical system; if it was not original, and was rather eclectic, it nevertheless set the tone and produced the form in which questions were to be debated by contemporaries and successors down to the time of Kant. The tone is that of a seeming rationalism that nevertheless tries to incorporate the empirical and theoretical results of recent scientific and mathematical innovations. Indeed, it was Wolff's respect for the mathematical method, as he understood it, that inspired the form of his writing, with its strict definitions and syllogistic development.

Limiting ourselves here to aspects of Wolff's philosophy of physical science, we find one of his basic models, both in ontology and in methodology, to be analysis and synthesis. Analysis yields the set of irreducible predicates of a thing which provide the ground or reason for its possibility; that there must be a ground is postulated by the principle of sufficient reason. This principle in turn falls under the principle of contradiction, since it would be self-contradictory (Wolff holds) to posit anything without a sufficient reason. He thus fails to distinguish in principle between logical and empirical possibility. Although mere possibility of finite things does not entail their existence, existence is stated to be merely "the complement of possibility," God being the ground of both actuality and possibility. To know that something exists, however, requires recourse to experience, both direct and inferential, through the giving of reasons; the reference to reason again permits a convenient slide from *ratio cognoscendi* to *ratio essendi*, and from logical to real possibility.

These doctrines quite naturally lead to Wolff's deterministic formulations of his cosmological principles, which emphasize the rational connections between things, given as sequences or coexistences; these formal themes were later directly echoed in Kant's writings. The visible world is a machine, operating in accordance with the laws of motion: almost one-third of the *Cosmologia generalis* treats these laws. In his physics Wolff is an outspoken corpuscularian, although the ultimate elements, the *atomi naturae*, are neither extended nor divisible. All that can be said a priori is that the properties of composites derive from their elementary constituents; empirical knowledge is limited to the properties of the composites. Thus the a priori part evidently provides no more than the mechanist-determinist theme, although modified by the Leibnizian idea of a competing teleological explanation of things.

Wolff's doctrine of space as the order of things existing simultaneously, although having some resemblance to Leibniz's theories, is more uncompromisingly kinetic. Space is mere phenomenon, both in the sense that it is secondary and ontologically derivative from coexisting substances, and in that it is perceived only "confusedly." Also, since the notion of substances as coexisting presupposes their mutual interaction, it is the latter conception that is ontologically basic. Wolff's bodily substances, being essentially centers of action, are also more uncompromisingly purely physical than Leibniz's monads; in all this, Wolff's views foreshadow the basic positions taken by Kant in his early writings down to about 1760. Similarly, Wolff's theory of time makes time reducible to the order of successive things in a continuous series; time is not given without the latter, he states expressly.

*BIBLIOGRAPHY*

I. ORIGINAL WORKS. The latest standard edition of Wolff's works is Christian Wolff, *Gesammelte Werke*, J. École, J. E. Hofmann, M. Thomann, and H. W. Arndt, eds. (Hildesheim, 1962–    ), German writings in 11 vols., Latin writings in 35 vols., containing major bibliographies of and on Wolff's writings.

Wolff's chief writings bearing on mathematics and the methodology and philosophy of science include the following in German: *Vernünftige Gedanken von den Kräften des menschlichen Verstandes* (Halle, 1713); *Auszug aus den Anfangsgründen aller mathematischen Wissenschaften* (Halle, 1717); *Vernünftige Gedanken von Gott, der Welt und der Seele der Menschen . . .* (Frankfurt–Leipzig, 1720); *Vernünftige Gedanken von den Wirkungen der Natur* (Halle, 1723); *Vernünftige Gedanken von den Absichten der natürlichen Dinge* (Frankfurt, 1724); and *Vernünftige Gedanken von dem Gebrauch der Theile in Menschen, Tieren und Pflanzen* (Frankfurt, 1725).

Latin works are *Philosophia rationalis sive logica* (Frankfurt–Leipzig, 1728); *Philosophia prima, sive ontologia* (Frankfurt, 1729); and *Cosmologia generalis* (Frankfurt, 1731).

An English trans. is *Discursus preliminaris de philosophia in genere*, translated by R. J. Blackwell (Indianapolis, 1963).

II. SECONDARY LITERATURE. The following, listed chronologically, concern Wolff's scientific and methodological ideas: J. E. Erdmann, *Grundriss der Geschichte der Philosophie*, II (Berlin, 1866), §290, 187–196; E. Kohlmeyer, *Kosmos und Kosmogonie bei Christian Wolff* (Göttingen, 1911); H. Lüthje, "Christian Wolffs Philosophiebegriff," in *Kant-Studien*, **30** (1923), 39–56; H. J. de Vleeschauwer, "La genèse de la méthode mathématique de Wolff," in *Revue belge de philologie et d'histoire*, **11** (1931), 651–677; M. Campo, *Christian Wolff e il razionalismo precritico*, 2 vols. (Milan, 1939); H. Heimsoeth, "Christian Wolffs Ontologie und die Prinzipienforschung Immanuel Kants," in *Studien zur Philosophie Immanuel Kants*, supp. no. 71 (1956), 1–92; J. École, "Un essai d'explication rationelle du monde ou la *Cosmologia generalis* de Christian Wolff," in *Giornale di metafisica*, **18** (1963), 622–650; and "Cosmologie wolffienne et dynamique leibnitienne," in *Études philosophiques*, n.s. **19** (1964), 3–9; J. V. Burns, *Dynamism in the Cosmology of Christian Wolff* (New York, 1966); L. W. Beck, *Early German Philosophy* (Cambridge, Mass., 1969), ch. 11, 256–272; and Tore Frängsmyr, "Christian Wolff's Mathematical Method," in *Journal of the History of Ideas*, **36** (1975), 653–668.

GERD BUCHDAHL

**WOLLASTON, FRANCIS** (*b*. London, England, 23 November 1731; *d*. Chislehurst, Kent, England, 31 October 1815), *astronomy*.

Wollaston was the eldest son of Mary Fauquier and Francis Wollaston. With his brother Charlton, he matriculated at Sidney Sussex College, Cambridge, in June 1748. He graduated LL.B. in 1754. With the intention of practicing law, he entered Lincoln's Inn on 24 November 1750, but he soon decided to enter the church, and was ordained deacon in 1754 and priest in 1755. In 1758 Simon Fanshawe presented him to the living of Dengie, in Essex, and in the same year he married Althea Hyde, by whom he had ten daughters and seven sons, one of whom was William Hyde Wollaston. In 1761 he became rector of East Dereham, in Norfolk (where his father had a summer residence). In 1769 he was made rector of Chislehurst in Kent and elected a fellow of the Royal Society. Other ecclesiastical benefices followed, but he continued to live at Chislehurst. His wife died there in 1798.

Wollaston's first book, *Address to the Clergy of the Church of England in Particular and to All Christians in General Proposing an Application for Relief, etc.*, was offered in support of a parliamentary bill of 1772, proposing to remove the obligation placed on members of the universities to subscribe to the Thirty-nine Articles of religion, and to replace it with a simple declaration of faith in the scriptures. The obligation had been established by the Ecclesiastical Commission of 1562, which agreed on the articles. Wollaston's support was of no avail and the university tests were not abolished until 1871. Two other books written during the next two years with a view to mild reform of the church seem likewise to have been little noticed, but not to have stood in the way of preferment.

Wollaston's serious interest in astronomy was, as he explained, calculated to remove him to a "distance from the misrepresentations of narrow-minded bigots."[1] At Chislehurst he had a private observatory built at the top of a square brick house. Here he used a telescope with a triple object-glass, made for him in 1771 by Peter Dollond. The telescope passed to his son, and thence to the Royal Astronomical Society. With the Dollond telescope Wollaston saw and described the great spot and belts of Jupiter, although he recorded no colors (1772). He equipped his observatory with a thermometer and barometer, and presented papers to the Royal Society on the variation in the rate of his astronomical clock with corresponding atmospheric conditions. He was not able to correlate these quantities in any significant way.

Wollaston long entertained the hope that astronomers might collaborate on a general plan for improving star catalogues and drafting them in a way that would facilitate the measurement of small stellar movements. In 1789 he published a very substantial collection of comparative catalogues with a preface announcing his plan and discussing the many previous catalogues on which he based his coordinates, which were reduced to 1 January 1790. As an essay in history, what he wrote was not altogether reliable, as S. P. Rigaud pointed out in connection with Wollaston's remarks on Bradley.[2] His catalogue was much used by William Herschel.[3]

Wollaston produced a number of ideas for new instruments, but he tended to make exaggerated claims for them, and none was of any great moment. He saw the merits of the transit circle, having worked with a small one (fourteen-inch focal length) from before 1772, but tried in vain to persuade first Jesse Ramsden and then Edward Troughton to make a larger one to his design. Finally, in 1781, William Cary began work, according to Wollaston's plan, on an altazimuth instrument (for the method of equal altitudes). Another instrument of his was a "universal meridian dial," for any latitude, on which he wrote a pamphlet; but

in doing so he added little to the art of dialing. Wollaston's most important contribution to astronomy was not made at a fundamental level, but was rather his publication of two or three useful practical aids to the ordinary astronomer and navigator, one of which was the comparative catalogue already mentioned. The second was a catalogue of circumpolar stars (1800), made with his transit instrument, by way of practicing what he had preached in his first book of 1789. The instrument is described at the end of the catalogue, together with explanations of the tables and formulas for calculating from them. His third important contribution, a collection of ten plates depicting the heavens "as they appear to the naked eye," was published by John Cary Sr., whose firm was renowned for its maps, atlases, and globes.

Although the date of birth given above is that which Wollaston himself gives in his autobiography, he makes a curious remark on the second page of his *Fasciculus astronomicus* of 1800, to the effect that the observations it embodies were made with "the eye of an old man, turned threescore before he engaged in the work."

*NOTES*

1. *The Secret History of a Private Man*, p. 54.
2. *Miscellaneous Works of James Bradley* (Oxford, 1832), p. 59.
3. J. L. E. Dreyer, ed., *Scientific Papers of Sir William Herschel* (London, 1912), p. 40.

*BIBLIOGRAPHY*

Wollaston's chief works are *A Specimen of a General Astronomical Catalogue, Arranged in Zones of North Polar Distance* . . . (London, 1789); *Directions for Making an Universal Meridian Dial Capable of Being Set to Any Latitude, Which Shall Give the Mean-Solar Time of Noon, by Inspection, Without any Calculation Whatsoever* (London, 1793); *Fasciculus astronomicus, Containing Observations of the Northern Circumpolar Region; Together With Some Account of the Instrument With Which They Were Made* . . . (London, 1800); *A Portraiture of the Heavens as They Appear to the Naked Eye* (London, 1811).

References to papers in the *Philosophical Transactions* of the Royal Society will be found in the printed books. In 1795 Wollaston printed privately for his friends a short autobiography written in the third person, *The Secret History of a Private Man*, which is rare. It contains an interesting account of the way in which his proposed reforms of 1772 were received in different quarters and is largely a justification of his behavior as a minister of the English church. There are letters from him in the British Museum (Add. MSS. 32887, f. 501; 32888, f. 198; 32892, f.155; 32896, f. 360; 32902, f. 330). A combined entry on Francis and his youngest brother, George, written by E. I. Carlyle, is in *Dictionary of National Biography*. There are references to genealogies of the family in the *DNB* entry on William Wollaston.

J. D. NORTH

**WOLLASTON, WILLIAM HYDE** (*b*. East Dereham, Norfolk, England, 6 August 1766; *d*. London, England, 22 December 1828), *chemistry, optics, physiology.*

Wollaston's family had become well known through their interests in science and theology. His great-grandfather, William Wollaston, was the author of *Religion of Nature Delineated*, a widely read work on natural religion published in 1724. His father, Francis Wollaston, a vicar and fellow of the Royal Society, was interested in astronomy and compiled a catalog of stars, *Fasciculus astronomicus*, which appeared in 1800. The famous physician William Heberden was his uncle. His father's brother, Charlton Wollaston, who died before William's birth, was a physician to the royal household.

William went to school at Charterhouse and in 1782 entered Caius College, Cambridge, as a medical student. There he pursued his favorite field, botany, but also studied some astronomy and, most important for his future work, became interested in chemistry. He attended the lectures of Isaac Milner, Jacksonian professor of chemistry, and performed experiments in the laboratory of his elder brother, Francis, who then held a lectureship in mathematics and who later lectured in chemistry, succeeding Milner in 1792. His interest in chemistry was also stimulated by Smithson Tennant, who was also studying medicine. William graduated in 1787 and then completed his medical studies in London. He first practiced in Huntingdon in 1792, but after a few months he went to Bury St. Edmunds. He became a fellow of the Royal Society in 1793. Four years later he moved to London. In 1800, either because of his failure in a contest for the appointment of physician to St. George's Hospital or through his dislike of the profession, he abandoned medicine and turned his attention to the other sciences. In 1802 he was awarded the Copley Medal of the Royal Society for his published papers. He became secretary of the Royal Society in 1804. As a member of numerous committees he gave advice on matters of sci-

entific interest. He was associated with the attempts to bring uniformity into the system of weights and measures and recommended the introduction of the imperial gallon, which was accepted in 1824. Between 1818 and 1828 he was an active member of the Board of Longitude, and was particularly concerned with nautical instruments. In 1820 he was president of the Royal Society, for the interim period before Humphry Davy's election. In 1823 he was elected foreign associate of the Académie des Sciences. Shortly before his death on 22 December 1828, he made notable donations for scientific research. He gave two thousand pounds to the Royal Society for promoting research, so initiating the Donation Fund. He also invested one thousand pounds in the name of the Geological Society, of which he had been a member since 1812. The proceeds from the first year's income were used to cast a die for a medal bearing Wollaston's head. The "Wollaston Medal," first awarded to William Smith in 1832, has continued to be an annual prize of the Society.

In the same year that he left the medical profession Wollaston formed a partnership with Tennant which was to bring him fame and wealth. Tennant had traveled to Sweden and met J. G. Gahn, an adept of chemical analysis on the small scale. This may well have been the source of Wollaston's practice of working with unusually small quantities, a distinctive feature of his chemical operations. When Berzelius visited England he was astonished at the extent to which Wollaston had developed this art. In a letter to Gahn[1] he remarked that the whole of Wollaston's chemical apparatus consisted of no more than a few bottles standing on a small wooden board with a handle. The bottles contained the common reagents and were so stoppered that their contents could be extracted in drops. Substances were investigated on a small piece of glass. A good example of Wollaston's small-scale chemistry was his introduction of the standard laboratory test for magnesium by the precipitation of magnesium ammonium phosphate, assisted by the scratching of a glass point.[2] But his skill was best demonstrated in his important investigations on the platinum metals.

Wollaston and Tennant were both interested in platinum, which continued to resist the efforts of chemists (particularly intensive since the middle of the eighteenth century) to produce it in a satisfactory malleable state in which it might be worked. Tennant bought a large quantity of crude platinum ore, and the partners began work on the intractable metal. Tennant was soon able to announce his discovery of osmium and iridium, new elements in the crude ore; but Wollaston was the harder worker, and it was through his continuing experiments, conducted in his private laboratory, into which he was reluctant to admit anyone, that the difficult practical problem was solved.

It had become common practice to refine the crude ore by dissolving it in aqua regia and then to precipitate platinum by means of ammonium chloride, with which it forms an insoluble complex salt. To recover any platinum still in solution Wollaston added bars of iron, and treated the precipitate as before with aqua regia and ammonium chloride. Adding iron for the second time, he obtained a precipitate with unexpected properties. When it was treated with nitric acid, a red solution formed. This gave an amalgam when treated with mercury, which in turn was decomposed by heat, leaving a white metal. The new metal, which he had discovered by July 1802, he first called "ceresium" after the recently discovered asteroid. But he soon changed the name to "palladium," after Pallas, another asteroid.

Instead of reporting his discovery openly Wollaston sent out anonymous printed notices in April 1803, describing the properties of the new metal and advertising its sale at a Soho shop. This attracted the attention of Richard Chenevix, a chemist, who suspected fraud from the way in which the discovery was announced. He bought the advertised stock and performed many experiments. In spite of his conviction that palladium was an alloy of known metals, none of his many attempts to analyze it succeeded. He claimed, however, that he had synthesized palladium by mixing a solution containing mercuric oxide and platinum in aqua regia with a solution of ferrous sulfate. When heated, this mixture produced a precipitate that fused into a button, supposedly indistinguishable from palladium, though it was in fact a compound of platinum with silicon and boron contained in the powdered charcoal used for the fusion. Chenevix concluded that palladium was an alloy of platinum and mercury. He felt he had found the key to reducing the number of the elements, whose recent rapid increase had led him to suspect their real simplicity. One critic, congratulating Chenevix, pointed out that the pursuit of alchemical transmutations was not as ridiculous as it had seemed.[3] Wollaston replied, again anonymously, offering a prize of twenty pounds to anyone who could synthesize palladium. The repeated failures to achieve this result soon convinced chemists that palladium was a genuine new metal. In 1804 Wollaston announced his discovery of rhodium in the crude platinum ore. Yet he withheld the identity of the discoverer of palladium until February 1805. He mentioned his fears of competing workers anticipating his discoveries, but he never fully explained his curious behavior, which according to Banks, the president of the Royal Society, had brought him into disfavor with scientists who were "open and communicative."

It was Wollaston's skill in working with small quantities that made possible the isolation and characterization of the new metals rhodium and palladium. For these metals are only present in platinum ore in small amounts. From one thousand grains of crude ore he had extracted five grains of palladium and four grains of rhodium. Vauquelin, who was working with much larger quantities of platinum ore at the same time, thought that Wollaston's achievement "seems at first incredible."[4]

In 1805 Wollaston stated that he had at last found a way to make platinum malleable, but he gave no details of his process until shortly before his death in 1828. His paper earned him the Royal Medal of the Royal Society. No one had yet succeeded in fusing platinum in large quantities. Previous workers had tried the effects of heat and pressure on the platinum sponge, obtained by the ignition of the complex ammonium salt. Through trial and error, and a careful attention to detail in the treatment of his material, Wollaston brought remarkable refinements to this method. His techniques included the slow thermal decomposition of the ammonium salt, the avoidance of burnishing by gently powdering the platinum sponge, sieving, and sedimentation. This process produced a uniform powder, essential to the production of malleable platinum. Impurities were removed by washing and forming a compact mass under water. The cake so formed was powerfully compressed by a toggle press. Finally the compact metal was carefully dried and forged. These details of Wollaston's process constitute the fundamental procedures of modern powder metallurgy. His process was not immediately adopted in industry; but it was followed, at least in part, by Liebig at the Giessen laboratory.[5] Today it is recognized as a standard method for producing compact metals from powder.

Wollaston sold the laboratory apparatus which he made from his malleable platinum. He drew very fine platinum wires by a process that is still used, and superintended the construction of platinum vessels for the concentration of sulfuric acid. These are the earliest platinum boilers known. They were sold to manufacturers. According to one estimate, Wollaston's profit up to 1826 from the sale of articles of platinum and the other platinum metals was £15,000.[6]

In theoretical chemistry Wollaston influenced the way in which the new atomic theory of Dalton was received. His own attitude to atomic chemistry varied remarkably between bold speculation and complete skepticism. In 1808 he described his experiments on carbonates, sulfates, and oxalates, which proved that the composition of these substances was regulated by the law of multiple proportions. These additional instances of the law were easily verifiable and were often mentioned as standard examples. Wollaston accepted that his findings were merely particular instances of Dalton's assertion that the atoms of elements united one to one, or by some simple multiple relation. He speculated on the possible atomic composition of the oxalates of potash. With brilliant intuition he predicted that arithmetical relations between atoms would be insufficient to explain chemical combination, and that spatial considerations would have to be introduced. He stated that a compound of four particles of one type and one of another would be stable if the four surrounding particles were arranged tetrahedrally. This surmise was confirmed much later in the century with the development of the stereochemistry of the carbon atom.

Wollaston therefore appeared to accept Dalton's theory, pointing to its possible extension. Yet already there was a hint of reservation in his statement that the "virtual extent"[7] of the particles was spherical. He discussed this idea in more detail in his paper on the structure of crystals, which was read in 1812. He remarked that the existence of ultimate physical atoms was not established and that virtually spherical particles, consisting of mathematical points surrounded by forces of attraction and repulsion, would explain the structure of crystals equally well.[8] This theory of unextended point centers of force, invented by Bošković in the eighteenth century, had already interested Davy. Later Faraday would accept it in favor of the extended massy atoms of Dalton.

In 1813 Wollaston discussed the atomic theory in a way that was to have a surprisingly wide appeal. His tone was totally different from that of his earlier treatment of the subject. He complained justifiably that there was no known way to establish the numbers of atoms present in particular compounds, but he went on to say that in any case such questions were "purely theoretical" and unnecessary for practical chemistry. He therefore proposed to draw up a scale, based on the most reliable analyses available, which would express the proportions in which the common chemical substances combined. This summary of chemical facts would provide chemists with immediate answers to the routine problems of laboratory work. Referring all combinations to a standard oxygen unit of 10, he calculated the combining proportions of various substances, and distributed their names and values on a sliding rule, along a line logarithmically divided from 10 to 320. He was thus able to compute mechanically chemical proportions that before had been obtained only by lengthy multiplication and division. Chemists were not yet employing tables of logarithms for their calculations. According to Wollaston the numbers that he had given to each substance were reliable and not "warped" by the atomic theory. He called these values "equivalents." This use of the term earlier introduced by Cavendish was unfortunate for it implied that every chemical has a fixed equivalent, an erroneous conception that persisted until Laurent, thirty years later, pointed out how chemical equivalence varies with function.

Abandoning atoms and conjectures Wollaston had attempted to strip chemistry of all but the factual content of experimental results. There appeared to remain a purely descriptive chemistry, a body of recipes for producing desired effects, summarized on an instrument. Yet this was an illusion. Chemists, particularly in England, succumbed to this apparently factual presentation. They did not detect the intrusion of hypothesis, which later prevented Comte from recognizing Wollaston's treatment as fully positivistic, saying that it amounted to no more than a "mere artifice of language."[9] In his calculation of representational numbers Wollaston had in fact made assumptions about composition of exactly the same arbitrary nature that he had objected to in Dalton. For example he assumed that the two oxides of carbon consisted of one equivalent of carbon united to one and two equivalents of oxygen. The same hypotheses crept, apparently unnoticed, into Davy's calculations of "proportional numbers"; they too relied on tacit suppositions on the constitution of oxides. Like Wollaston, he presented his numbers as deduced from experiment and free from theoretical assumptions. The skepticism of Davy and Wollaston was accepted by English chemists as embodying a sound philosophy and for many years dictated their reactions to Dalton's theory. A typical statement came from William Brande, who welcomed Wollaston's treatment of chemistry as "divested of all hypothetical aspect."[10] One fellow of the Royal Society objected that Wollaston and not Dalton should have been given the Royal Medal, for he had done for the atomic theory what Watt had done for the steam engine: he had rendered it useful.[11] Perhaps the clearest indication of Wollaston's influence appeared in the new *Chemical Dictionary* of Andrew Ure, containing the entry "Atomic Theory. See Equivalents (Chemical)."[12] Wollaston's "equivalents" continued to be used in this sense until the middle of the century. Chemists were convinced that equivalents expressed the unalterable facts of chemical proportions. Reluctant to introduce theories of matter into their science, or to accept calculations of atomic weights (Berzelius conceded these were based on unproved suppositions of atomic constitution and were therefore subject to revision), they felt the language of equivalents was safest. This circumstance accounts for the preference later given to Gmelin's equivalents over Berzelius' system of atomic weights. There was even a tendency to use "equivalent" and "atom" synonymously. According to this usage, "atom" was regarded as a convenient alternative to "proportion" or "equivalent," and carried no theoretical implications. It was left for later generations of chemists to distinguish between equivalents, atoms, and molecules, and to show how atomic weights could be unambiguously determined.

Wollaston's chemical slide rule, in some form, was in general use in laboratories for over twenty years. The instrument was reportedly sold in the bookstores of New York and Vienna. Schweigger, the editor of the *Journal für Chemie und Physik*, reproduced two copies of Wollaston's scale in one issue, so that one copy could be cut out and pasted on a slider.[13] Berzelius said that he used the instrument constantly. Faraday, in his practical manual, described it as a commonly used calculating device.[14] But the instrument began to fall into disuse around 1840 on account of the increasing demands for more accurate calculations. In 1842 Thomas Graham said that Wollaston's instrument was "not of much practical value" and gave instead the logarithms of atomic weights.[15]

In 1822, in spite of his earlier firm skepticism, Wollaston returned by a most unusual route to the full acceptance of Dalton's theory. With startling boldness he asserted that conclusive tests on the existence of atoms could be made through the observation of planets. He argued that the particles of the atmosphere of the earth were subject to the opposing forces of their mutual repulsion and gravity. If there were a limit to the divisibility of atmo-

spheric matter, the weight of these ultimate particles would prevent further atmospheric expansion. But if matter were endlessly divisible into lighter and lighter particles, the force of repulsion would overcome gravity. Then the atmosphere of the earth would not terminate at a finite height, but would expand freely into celestial space and collect about the planets through gravitational attraction. Wollaston therefore believed that the classical problem of the divisibility of matter could be decided by a crucial test in astronomy. In May 1821 Venus was passing very close to the sun in superior conjunction. He carefully followed the path of the planet with a small telescope. He was unable to detect any apparent retardation in the motion of Venus that might be attributable to refraction by the solar atmosphere. He added that Jupiter possessed no sensible atmosphere, since the occultation of its satellites was also unretarded. He was in no doubt that the atmosphere of the earth was of finite extent. Therefore he concluded that it was composed of ultimate atoms. He argued that since the laws of definite proportions were true for all kinds of matter, not just the elastic atmosphere but all substances could be regarded as composed of indivisible atoms. He asserted that the equivalents of chemistry really did express the relative weights of atoms, but curiously he made no mention of the problem, which had earlier troubled him, of estimating the numbers of atoms that entered into combination.

There was a surprising delay before the weakness of Wollaston's logic was exposed. Meanwhile the popular expositions of the atomic theory given by Turner and Daubeny accepted the attractive new argument as a clear proof of atomism. Graham pointed out that the atmosphere of the earth could be limited simply through condensation at low temperatures and that Wollaston's explanation in terms of atoms was unnecessary.[16] But it was not realized until much later that Wollaston had put forward a circular argument.[17] He had assumed from the start that if there were atmospheric particles of limited divisibility, these must be the ultimate Daltonian atoms that participated in chemical change; but the particles of oxygen and nitrogen in the atmosphere need not be monatomic. The carbon dioxide and water vapor of the atmosphere were clearly not chemically simple particles. In fact, the height of an atmosphere is controlled by the weight of polyatomic molecular particles, and by the temperature.

In general, chemists did not share Wollaston's concern to test the divisibility of matter. They were content to deal with combining weights as they found them, without speculating on their further divisibility outside of chemistry. Wollaston's paper continued to be referred to in connection with the existence of a universal ether.[18]

Some of Wollaston's best work was in crystallography, another field of study intimately connected with the structure of matter. The fundamental laws of crystallography had been discovered toward the end of the eighteenth century. In part this was the work of Haüy, who had created a system of crystallography in a spirit of mathematical idealism. It was a problem for Haüy's contemporaries to determine how far the details of his thought, inspired by a belief in the simplicity of nature, were representative of reality. Haüy had constructed algebraic formulas that related the various occurring crystalline forms of a given substance to the primitive form, which could be extracted by mechanical cleavage from each of them. For example, the primitive form of calcium carbonate was a rhomboid, which could be extracted from the secondary forms with hexagonal and pentagonal faces by appropriate cleavages. Once the dimensions of the primitive form were known it was possible to deduce the angles of any related secondary form. Where the primitive form was a regular solid, such as the cube, the required dimensions could be inferred from considerations of symmetry; but with less regular forms such as the obtuse rhomboid the dimensional ratios had to be calculated from measurements of angles. This was approximately performed by the contact goniometer, which consisted of a hinged pair of arms attached to a protractor. It was difficult to make the arms coincide with the crystal faces, and Haüy never claimed an accuracy beyond twenty or thirty minutes of arc. Within this wide margin afforded by approximate measurement, Haüy was able to consider various possible dimensional ratios and select those that most satisfied his metaphysical beliefs. He asserted that the dimensions of the regular solids, which were correctly expressed as ratios of square roots of small integers, reflected Nature's simplicity. This, he argued, must be discernible in the irregular forms also. Accordingly, in his discussion of these he chose the simplest possible ratios consonant with measurement, and then adjusted the angles by calculation.

In 1809 Wollaston described his newly invented reflective goniometer, which allowed a far greater accuracy in the measurement of crystals. It consisted of a graduated circle, vertically fixed on a horizontal axle. The crystal was attached by wax to a small leveling device joined to the axle. An object was viewed by reflection in one face of the crystal, and then the crystal was rotated until the same object appeared in the adjacent face. The angle through which the graduated circle had moved was read off. This procedure gave the angle of the crystal to the nearest five minutes. In this way Wollaston showed the angle of rhomboidal calcium carbonate to differ by over thirty minutes from that given by Haüy. He detected even greater discrepancies in other carbonates, but if he had shown the way he was not prepared to carry out the extensive determinations needed to correct Haüy's data. Doing so was largely the work of William Phillips, a printer and bookseller, whom Wollaston had instructed in the use of his instrument. Employing the new goniometer with graduations of half-minutes, Phillips compiled the most accurate body of crystal data that had hitherto existed. The results showed that Haüy's values for the irregular primitive forms, based on conceptions of simplicity, were incorrect. By 1824 several continental authorities, including Mohs and Mitscherlich, had rejected Haüy's data. It was fitting that John Herschel later mentioned Wollaston's goniometer as an illustration of the influence of instrumentation on the progress of science.[19] The modern goniometer is the result of extensive refinements of Wollaston's original design.

Haüy had concluded, from the polyhedral fragments produced in cleavage, that the crystal kingdom was constructed from three molecular forms: the tetrahedron, the triangular prism, and the parallelepiped. His conclusions were criticized by others, including Wollaston, who objected that a stable crystal could not result from such arrangements as the grouping of tetrahedral particles hanging together at their edges. Regarding this as precarious masonry, Wollaston in 1812 proposed alternative spherical crystal units, joined together as closely as possible by mutual attraction. His close-packed formations of triangularly arranged spheres imitated the commonly occurring crystal forms. From a rhomboid of spheres, tetrahedral groups of spheres could be removed, leaving an octahedron. This accounted for the cleavage of rhomboidal fluorspar. Wollaston was surprised to learn that the beginnings of his theory were to be found in the thirteenth observation of Hooke's *Micrographia*. He also constructed other forms from spheroids, earlier considered by Huygens. The most original part of his theory concerned the cubic form. He explained this in terms of two different kinds of sphere, whch he referred to as "black and white balls," so arranged that each black ball was equidistant from all surrounding white balls; balls of the same type were also equidistant from each other. This produced a cube from two interpenetrating tetrahedra. In the twentieth century the lattice structure of sodium chloride was shown to be of this type; but in 1812 Wollaston's theory was an unverifiable speculation.

The most enthusiastic supporter of Wollaston's theory was John Daniell, professor of chemistry at King's College, London. He brought forward various arguments, none of which was successful, to show that this theory was the only one that would explain the facts of crystallography. For example, he tried to interpret his observations on crystal etching in this way. Etched forms are indicative of crystal symmetry, but they could not have provided the crucial data on internal structure that Daniell believed he had found. The American mineralogist James Dana also adopted Wollaston's spheres and spheroids but grouped them differently according to supposed discrete polarities. This development represented some steps toward the conception of the space lattice.

Discussions of the type initiated by Haüy and Wollaston were not favorably received in the early nineteenth century. At the time crystallography was largely concerned with the geometrical treatment of external symmetry. The important physical study of internal structure was not revived until the middle of the century. Wollaston's speculations provided an early example of how, in the absence of direct experimental investigation, remarkably close approximations to the actual internal structure of crystals could be derived through the arrangement of spheres.

The mineral wollastonite was named by a French admirer of Wollaston's work in crystallography.[20]

A large part of Wollaston's published work was devoted to optics, notably in the design of instruments. His early papers on atmospheric refraction discussed the phenomena of the mirage. His theoretical treatment was muddled and made no advance on existing theories, which had similarly exaggerated the effects of water vapor. But his imitation of the phenomena by mixing liquids of different density was frequently referred to.[21] Further, his own careful observations across heated surfaces and description of a mirage, which he was surprised to observe while sitting in a boat near Chelsea, provided Biot with data for his mathematical treatment of the phenomenon.[22] Wollaston was particularly interested in such irregular refraction for the difficulties it created in navigation. Altitudes were taken with reference to the horizon, and the necessary dip correction was difficult to assess in cases of unusual refraction close to the horizon. He therefore designed a dip sector, a modified sextant, which allowed the dip to be measured by simultaneous observation of opposite points of the horizon. The commissioners of the Admiralty directed Ross, and later Parry, to make observations on the dip of the horizon during their arctic voyages, taking with them Wollaston's instrument.[23] But they reported that the dip sector was of limited use, since the atmospheric conditions were not uniform on the opposite sides of the horizon. Wollaston Island, in Baffin Bay, was named for him by Ross; it was the first of several arctic christenings in his honor.[24]

In 1802 Wollaston introduced the important method of determining refractive indices by total internal reflection. The alternative method of minimum deviation, however, continued to be used in the early part of the century. His observations on an impure spectrum led him to conclude that there were only four colors in the solar spectrum. This influenced Thomas Young, who was led by it to alter his own theory of color vision. At the same time Wollaston discovered the dark lines in the solar spectrum, later to be known as Fraunhofer lines. Also in 1802 he presented convincing experimental support for Huygens' wave theory. Using the technique he had invented, he measured the refractive index of Iceland spar in different directions and showed that for different planes of incidence the extraordinary ray was refracted exactly as Huygens' theory predicted. He did not commit himself, however, to a firm statement of belief in the wave theory. This later brought Wollaston charges of timidity and undue caution; but there was no reason why he should have gone further, particularly since Young's impressive evidence had not yet appeared.

In 1803 he described his "periscopic spectacles," designed to allow clear vision in oblique directions. He substituted meniscus lenses for the generally used biconvex and biconcave forms. Contemporary opticians were mistaken in supposing the elimination of spherical aberration to be the prime consideration in the design of spectacles. As Wollaston correctly pointed out, the eye looks through only a small part of the lens at any instant, and the chief requirement is sharp vision in all directions. Meniscus lenses had been recommended since the seventeenth century. It is uncertain to what extent Wollaston's spectacles were used; the general introduction of meniscus spectacles did not occur until after the work of F. Ostwalt at the close of the nineteenth century.

In 1807 Wollaston described his camera lucida, a quadrilateral glass prism, which by two total internal reflections sent horizontal rays from an object vertically upward into the eye viewing above the prism. This device was widely used as an aid in drawing.[25] It was also commonly attached to the eyepiece of microscopes for sketching images. He also improved the camera obscura by introducing a meniscus lens and an aperture, so reducing the curvature of image of a laterally extended object. In this form it was employed as an early camera by Niepce and Daguerre.

His well-known microscopic doublet was described posthumously. Dissatisfied with the performance of the compound microscope, which was soon to receive essential improvements from Lister, Wollaston proposed the use of a combination of two planoconvex lenses to reduce the aberration of the simple microscope. This suggestion had been occasionally adopted since the seventeenth century, and more recently John Herschel had worked out formulas for the aberration of spherical surfaces in combination. But Herschel's suggestion of a biconvex lens combined with a concavo-convex type presented difficulties in grinding. Wollaston's doublets were easier to make, particularly since two surfaces were plane. The improved resolution impressed workers and led to further developments. A diaphragm was placed between the lenses, and triplet combinations were introduced. While there were continuing attempts to improve the compound microscope, the simple microscope, improved through Wollaston's suggestions, continued to be used. His improvements in illumination, involving the reduction of glare by a type of field stop, were also adopted.

Although he left the medical profession Wollaston continued to be interested in physiology. In 1797 he characterized the principal constituents of urinary calculi, and in 1812 identified a new and rare type of stone, which he called "cystic oxide" since it occurred in the bladder. This was later renamed cystine, the first of the amino acids to be discovered. Fourcroy and Vauquelin reported similar investigations, but unaccountably gave no recognition to Wollaston. This led Alexander Marcet, a physician, to set matters right in a popular work dedicated to Wollaston, his friend.[26]

In his Croonian lecture of 1809 Wollaston stated for the first time the vibratory character of muscular action. He had been led to this discovery by considering the sound heard when a finger is put in the ear, which he compared to the sound of distant carriages. He reproduced the sound by rubbing a pencil over notches on a board and thus determined the frequency of the vibration. With one finger against his ear he found the number of notches which the pencil had to pass over in five seconds to produce the same sound. His value of 20–30 vibrations per second was later shown by Helmholtz to be the first overtone of the fundamental frequency of muscular murmur.

In 1811 he announced that in spite of the known presence of sugar in the urine of diabetics he had failed to detect it in the blood taken from victims of this disease. He adopted the eccentric theory, proposed by Charles Darwin (d. 1778), the son of Erasmus Darwin, that there existed an unknown route between the stomach and bladder, allowing the sugar to avoid the blood and pass directly into the urine. The failure to detect the sugar was due to the use of stale specimens. Claude Bernard later pointed out that quick tests on fresh serum were essential, since sugar is unstable in blood.

In 1820 Wollaston read an interesting paper on the physiology of the ear. Hiding in the library of Sir Henry Bunbury he had produced high notes from pipes and looked to see which of the company present had heard them. He discovered that there was a sharply defined upper limit to audibility and that this varied noticeably with the individual. He also speculated that some insects might communicate by high notes inaudible to humans. His correct conclusions were challenged by the French authority Savart, who erroneously stated that the inaudibility of the high notes was due, not to their frequency, but to their low intensity.

In 1824 Wollaston discussed a traditional problem in physiology, that of binocular vision. In the eighteenth century it had been debated whether this faculty of combining two images was inherited or acquired. Newton had argued for the former possibility in the fifteenth query of his *Opticks*, postulating an arrangement of the optic nerves in which corresponding points of the retinas were connected by nerve fibers that joined before entering the brain. The same theory was proposed by Wollaston, who supposed it to be new. The intricate structure of the human chiasma was still not known. Wollaston was led to adopt the correct arrangement of "semi-decussation," also given by Newton, as a result of his experiences of hemianopia, a disease in which there is a loss of sight in symmetrical parts of each eye. This relation of hemianopia to semi-decussation had also been noticed before; but Wollaston's was the fullest description of the disease that had yet appeared. As a theory of binocular vision it was opposed by those who favored alternative nervous arrangements in the chiasma, and by those who continued to insist that an explanation in terms of acquisition was required. The invention of Wheatstone's stereoscope emphasized the psychological character of binocular vision which had been ignored in the physiological explanations of Newton and Wollaston.

Wollaston and Humphry Davy both died within a few months of each other. It became common to contrast the soaring poetic imagination of Davy with the cautious approach of Wollaston. It is clear from his letters to Young that Wollaston warned against speculation and advised staying close to the facts. It is equally clear from his work that he did not practice what he preached. George Peacock, the Victorian biographer of Young, said of Wollaston that "posterity is not likely to maintain the same high estimate of his powers which was made by his contemporaries."[27] There is growing evidence that this prediction will not stand.

## NOTES

1. *Jac. Berzelius Bref*, H. D. Söderbaum, ed., IV, pt. 9 (Uppsala, 1912–1941), p. 73.
2. W. Saunders, *A Treatise on the Chemical History and Medical Powers of Some of the Most Celebrated Mineral Waters*, 2nd ed. (London, 1805), 391–392.
3. "Inquiries Concerning the Nature of a Metallic Substance, Lately Sold in London . . .," in *Edinburgh Review*, 4 (1804), 168.
4. N. Vauquelin, "Mémoire sur le palladium et le rhodium," in *Annales de chimie*, 88 (1813), 170.
5. J. Pelouze, "Note sur la fabrication du platine," in *Annales de chimie et de physique*, 62 (1836), 443–444.
6. L. F. Gilbert, "W. H. Wollaston MSS at Cambridge," in *Notes and Records of the Royal Society*, 9 (1952), 326.
7. Wollaston, "On Super-acid and Sub-acid Salts," in *Philosophical Transactions of the Royal Society*, 98 (1808), 101.
8. Wollaston, "The Bakerian Lecture. On the Elementary Particles of Certain Crystals," *ibid.*, 103 (1813), 61.
9. A. Comte, *Cours de philosophie positive*, III (Paris, 1830–1842), 149.
10. "Proceedings of the Royal Institution," in *Quarterly Journal of Literature, Science and the Arts*, 21 (1826), 109–110.
11. "On the Recent Adjudgment of the Royal Medals . . .," *ibid.*, 1 (1827), 15.
12. A. Ure, *A Dictionary of Chemistry* (London, 1821).
13. "Synoptische Scale der chemischen Aequivalente," in *Journal für Chemie und Physik*, 12 (1814), 105.
14. Faraday, *Chemical Manipulation* (London, 1827), p. 551.
15. T. Graham, *Elements of Chemistry* (London, 1842), 117, 1071.
16. T. Graham, "On the Finite Extent of the Atmosphere," in *Philosophical Magazine*, 1 (1827), 107–109.
17. G. Wilson, "On Wollaston's Argument From the Limitation of the Atmosphere, as to the Finite Divisibility of Mat-

ter," in *Transactions of the Royal Society of Edinburgh*, 16 (1849), 79–86.
18. A. v. Humboldt, *Kosmos*, III (Stuttgart–Tübingen, 1845–1862), p. 52.
19. J. F. W. Herschel, *Preliminary Discourse on the Study of Natural Philosophy* (London, 1833), p. 354.
20. S. Léman, "Meionite," in *Nouveau dictionnaire d'histoire naturelle*, XX (Paris, 1816–1819), 28–31.
21. A similar treatment is given in the fifty-eighth observation of Hooke's *Micrographia*.
22. J. Biot, "Recherches sur les réfractions extraordinaires," in *Mémoires de l'Institut national des sciences et arts*, 10 (1810), 6–7.
23. J. Ross, *A Voyage of Discovery . . .* (London, 1819), pp. xviii, 10, app.
24. *Ibid.*, p. 206.
25. B. Hall, *Forty Etchings From Sketches Made With the Camera Lucida in North America in 1827 and 1828* (Edinburgh–London, 1829).
26. A. Marcet, *An Essay on the Chemical History and Medical Treatment of Calculous Disorders* (London, 1817).
27. G. Peacock, *Life of Thomas Young* (London, 1855), p. 470.

## BIBLIOGRAPHY

I. ORIGINAL WORKS. In 1949 a collection of Wollaston's notebooks was discovered in the Department of Mineralogy and Petrology, Cambridge. A report containing the essential new information is L. F. Gilbert, "W. H. Wollaston MSS. at Cambridge," in *Notes and Records of the Royal Society of London*, 9 (1952), 311–332. There are also some of his notes and letters in the Science Museum, London, concerning his work on the production of rhodium alloys, platinum wires, and boilers. Additional information on the controversy over palladium is contained in the letters between Chenevix and Banks in volumes XIV and XV of the Dawson Turner copies of the Banks correspondence, Natural History Museum, London. Wollaston's activities on the Board of Longitude are recorded in the minutes of the board at the Royal Greenwich Observatory, Herstmonceux Castle, Sussex. The Royal Society possesses some of Wollaston's letters to Thomas Young, in which he stated his reluctance to speculate. One of these has been published in D. Turner, "Thomas Young on the Eye and Vision," in *Science, Medicine and History*, E. A. Underwood, ed., II (Oxford, 1953), 251. Other letters, in which he commented on the wave theory of light, can be found in T. Young, *Miscellaneous Works*, G. Peacock, ed., I (London, 1855), 233, 261.

Wollaston's published scientific work appeared in the journals. The list given in the Royal Society *Catalogue of Scientific Papers* is almost complete. The following are not mentioned there: "On Gouty and Urinary Concretions," in *Philosophical Transactions of the Royal Society*, 87 (1797), 386–400; "Report from the Select Committee on Weights and Measures," in *Parliamentary Papers*, 3 (1813–1814), 140–141; and "Instructions for the Adjustments and Use of the Instruments Intended for the Northern Expeditions," in *Journal of Science and the Arts*, 5 (1818), 223–226. Some interesting information on the background of Wollaston's work was related by a close acquaintance, the Reverend H. Hasted, in his "Reminiscences of Dr. Wollaston," in *Proceedings of the Bury and West Suffolk Archaeological Institute*, **1** (1849), 121–134.

II. SECONDARY LITERATURE. No satisfactory study of Wollaston's work as a whole has yet been published. A discussion of his work on the platinum metals is included in D. Mc. Donald's excellent *A History of Platinum from the Earliest Times to the Eighteen-eighties* (London, 1960). Useful as general introductions to nineteenth-century crystallography are L. Sohncke, *Entwickelung einer Theorie der Krystallstruktur* (Leipzig, 1879), pp. 5–18; and P. H. von Groth, *Entwickelungsgeschichte der Mineralogischen Wissenschaften* (Berlin, 1926). Wollaston's work in crystallography has been discussed in D. C. Goodman, "Problems in Crystallography in the Nineteenth Century," in *Ambix*, **16** (1969), 152–166. For his fluctuating views on atoms, see D. C. Goodman, "Wollaston and the Atomic Theory of Dalton," in *Historical Studies in the Physical Sciences*, **1** (1969), 37–59. Wollaston's meniscus lenses have been discussed by M. v. Rohr, who states that Wollaston's spectacles were sold in Vienna by Voigtländer. See his "Der grosse Streit bei des Einführung des periskopischen Brillengläses," in *Central-Zeitung für Optik und Mechanik*, **43** (1922), 490–491; "Contributions to the History of English Opticians in the First Half of the Nineteenth Century (With Special Reference to Spectacle History)," in *Transactions of the Optical Society*, **28** (1926–1927), 117–144; and "Meniscus Spectacle Lenses," in *British Journal of Physiological Optics*, **6** (1932), 183–187. Another useful article is H. C. King. "The Life and Optical Work of W. H. Wollaston," in *British Journal of Physiological Optics*, **11** (1954), 10–31. A Herschel MS, which tells of the intrigues involving Wollaston in the election of a successor to Banks, has been discussed in L. F. Gilbert, "The Election to the Presidency of the Royal Society in 1820," in *Notes and Records of the Royal Society*, **11** (1955), 256–279.

D. C. GOODMAN

**WOLTMAN, REINHARD** (*b.* Axstedt, Germany, December 1757; *d.* Hamburg, Germany, 20 April 1837), *hydraulics*.

The son of a farmer, Woltman, while quite young, taught school, presumably at Axstedt. Within a short time, however, he was transferred to the part of the Ritzebüttel district that borders on the North Sea between the Elbe and Weser rivers, an area where the shore-erosion problem constitutes a challenge to the best hydraulic engineers. During the previous century its protection facilities had been destroyed by storms and floods at least seven times. Developing stronger means of protection became an early and primary objective of Woltman's career.

In May 1779, Woltman was appointed an under-inspector and clerical employee in the office responsible for erecting and maintaining the erosion-control structures. The following year he began taking courses in mathematics and architecture at Hamburg, and later at the universities of Kiel and Göttingen. Woltman subsequently made a journey during which he met skilled workers in hydraulics at Frankfurt, Strasbourg, Paris, Cherbourg, Calais, Dover, London, and Holland. Upon his return to Ritzebüttel on 20 November 1784, he began work on the local erosion problem.

Woltman's first book, *Theorie und Gebrauch des hydrometrischen Flügels* (1790), drew attention to the extensive use in England and Holland of wind and water power. That, he contended, should be done in the Hamburg area, and added that if his idea was adopted, frequent measurements of wind and water velocities could provide data of great value. The remainder of his book was devoted largely to the instruments he had designed for that purpose.

The four-volume *Beiträge zur hydraulischen Architektur* (1791–1799) immediately attracted attention in the scientific community with the first volume, which concerned the management of dikes and reinforcing shorelines. In 1792 Woltman became a member of the Hollandsche Maatschappij der Wetenschappen, at Haarlem; and the Bataafsch Genootschap der Proefondervindelijke Wijsbegeerle, at Rotterdam; and was offered membership in the Königliche Gesellschaft der Wissenschaften, at Prague. In the following year he received an offer to join the Königliche Akademie der Wissenschaften, at Göttingen.

On 1 October 1797 Woltman married Johanna Schuback, the daughter of his first patron. They had five children.

Antoine Chézy (1718–1798) and Pierre Du Buat, contemporaries of Woltman's, conceived what may have been the earliest valid equations concerning the velocity of flowing water. Woltman probably never heard of Chézy, whose formula attracted little attention until 1897, when Clemens Herschel wrote an article about it. Du Buat's work (published in 1779 under the title *Principes d'hydraulique*), however, received immediate and highly favorable attention. Its velocity equation was so complicated and so difficult to apply that Woltman recommended a much simpler one. Much of its simplification was made possible by experiments that Woltman had conducted and that justified the use of powers (exponents) for velocity ranging from 1.75 (for pipes) to 2 (for open channels).

Those values, as noted by Hunter Rouse, "are precisely the limits now accepted."

The invention of Woltman's water current meter in 1790 brought him the most lasting fame. One of the original models has been preserved at the Deutsches Museum in Munich, and a replica of it is on display at the National Museum of History and Technology in Washington, D.C.

Just before he constructed the current meter, Woltman had designed two anemometers, one of which was intended to be mounted on a standard and the other to be held in one's hand. These, he admitted, were largely patterned after C. G. Schober's anemometer (described in the 1752 editions of the *Hamburgisches Magazin*). After numerous futile attempts to evaluate, both experimentally and mathematically, the relationship between the speed of their rotors and the velocity of the wind, he decided to calibrate them in still water. That procedure was successful, and it convinced him that with only a minor change (reducing the rotor to about one-third of its original size), the device would be suitable for measuring the velocity of water flowing in rivers. He thereupon ordered his mechanic (a man named Steinmetz, in Cuxhaven) to build such a model. The ancestry of practically all of the propeller-type current meters in use today can be traced to that particular model.

For many years after Woltman announced that meter's invention, most of the improved versions of it were called "Woltman meters" as a courtesy to him (a commendable practice, but one that unfortunately has resulted in his having erroneously been credited in many modern textbooks and magazines with having built a better instrument than he actually designed). A somewhat similar practice is presently being carried on with respect to the type of meters that measure the amount of water flowing through pipes supplying homes and office buildings. In some instances modern engineers have applied the Woltman principle of operation to such meters, and have identified them as "Woltman meters."

*BIBLIOGRAPHY*

I. ORIGINAL WORKS. Woltman's first published work was *Theorie und Gebrauch des hydrometrischen Flügels oder eine zuverlässige Methode die Geschwindigkeit der Winde und strömenden Gewässer zu beobachten* (Hamburg, 1790). His other major work was *Beiträge zur hydraulischen Architektur*, 4 vols. (Göttingen, 1791–1799).

II. SECONDARY LITERATURE. *Allegemeine deutsche Biographie*, XLIV, 192–199, lists the titles of several additional works by Woltman relating to canals, navigation, and shore protection. Also see Hegell, "Die Urform des Woltmanschen Flügels," in *Zeitschrift des Verbands deutscher Architekten- und Ingenieurvereine* (11 Apr. 1914), 129–130; Steponas Kolupaila, *Bibliography of Hydrometry* (Notre Dame, Ind., 1961), 12, 282, 326, 328–329; and Hunter Rouse and Simon Ince, *History of Hydraulics* (Ann Arbor, Mich., 1957), 134–136, 141.

ARTHUR H. FRAZIER

**WOOD, HORATIO C** (*b*. Philadelphia, Pennsylvania, 13 January 1841; *d*. Philadelphia, 3 January 1920), *pharmacology, therapeutics.*

Wood's father, Horatio Curtis Wood, was a successful Philadelphia businessman. His mother, Elizabeth Head Bacon Wood, was descended, like her husband, from English immigrants of the seventeenth century. Wood attended Quaker schools, then in 1862 graduated with an M.D. from the medical department of the University of Pennsylvania. After residencies in the Philadelphia Hospital (Blockley) and the Pennsylvania Hospital, followed by medical service with the Union army, he entered private practice in 1865 or 1866. In 1866 he assumed the chair of botany in the auxiliary faculty of medicine at the University of Pennsylvania. In the same year he married Elizabeth Longacre, by whom he had a daughter and three sons, two of whom became physicians.

Wood was a pioneer in experimental pharmacology and therapeutics, supplemented by other contributions to the field of materia medica. About fifty of his nearly three hundred publications dealt with pharmacology, experimental therapeutics, and physiology. A high proportion of this segment of his papers involved laboratory study of the physiological action of drugs in animals, still exceptional at the time. Moreover, Wood understood the import and potential of work by such contemporaries as Oswald Schmiedeberg, A. R. Cushny, Benjamin Ward Richardson, Alexander Crum Brown, Thomas R. Fraser, and Thomas Lauder Brunton. Thus Wood became an early American exponent of the study of the physiological action of drugs under laboratory conditions and of classifying medicines according to such actions, thereby supplanting the primacy of empirical clinical experience as the basic guide to progressive therapeutics.

At the age of twenty Wood published his first paper, "Contributions to the Carboniferous Flora of the United States" (1861). During the 1860's he published at least eleven papers on freshwater algae and fourteen on the myriopods, thereafter devoting himself increasingly to clinical pathology (especially neurology and psychiatry), experimental pharmacology, and therapeutics. In the latter field his first important experimental paper reported "On the Medical Activity of the Hemp Plant [Marijuana], as Grown in North America" (1869). Among his most important subsequent investigations, as Wood himself believed, were studies of the physiology and treatment of sunstroke, the mechanism and treatment of fever, the discovery of the physiological and therapeutic action of hyoscine, and the treatment of accidents of anesthesia. Wood appears more important as an American exponent of animal experimentation and of the applications of new findings and a new outlook to therapeutics than as an originator of new methods.

Wood's laboratory did not serve to train a new school of pharmacologists as did that of John J. Abel. The reasons, although never seriously assessed, may relate to their time, funding of the laboratories, and even the personalities of the two men. Abel told G. B. Roth that during the summer of 1884 he served in Wood's laboratory as "a research assistant, without pay," then left to study in Ludwig's laboratory at Leipzig.

Beyond his scientific papers Wood's strong national influence was mediated by prolific editorial work. His *Treatise on Therapeutics . . .* (1874), which went through thirteen editions, helped foster the transition from case-based therapeutics to what Wood considered an experiment-based "applied science." He published five other medical books. He served as senior editor of the ubiquitous *Dispensatory of the United States of America* for five editions (from the fifteenth edition of 1883), edited at least three medical journals at various times, and from 1866 edited American editions of the British *Manual of Materia Medica and Therapeutics* (Frederick J. Farre, Robert Bentley, and Robert Warington's updated abridgment of Jonathan Pereira's *Elements of Materia Medica and Therapeutics*).

*The Pharmacopeia of the United States*, which generates legally enforceable standards for drugs, had the benefit of Wood's services from 1890 to 1910 as president of the policy-setting U.S. Pharmacopeial Convention. In 1902 he and Frederick B. Power represented the United States government in Brussels at the International Conference for the Unification of the Formulae of Heroic Medicines.

In 1906 poor health forced Wood to retire from academic work; and he considered that the presidential address he sent in 1910 from his sickbed to the U.S. Pharmacopeial Convention brought his career to a close.

If Wood's professional work was more forward-looking than daring, it accorded with a personality basically conservative, although critically evaluative of the old empirical therapeutics. If the practical dominated the theoretical in his work, he offered in a transitional period a combination of originality, productivity, and literary skill that influenced the shift of American pharmacology and therapeutics toward experimental, quantifiable science.

*BIBLIOGRAPHY*

I. ORIGINAL WORKS. A "Bibliographic Record 1860–1911" of Wood's publications appears in *Transactions and Studies of the College of Physicians of Philadelphia*, 3rd ser., **42** (1920), 242–257, which lists seven books on aspects of clinical medicine and materia medica, and published papers that may be classified as 142 on clinical pathology, neurology, medicine, and therapeutics; fifty-four on experimental pharmacology, physiology, and pathology; forty-four published addresses and lectures; fifteen papers on botany; fourteen on entomology; thirteen on medical jurisprudence and toxicology; and ten articles primarily for the laity. Some MS material is in the library of the College of Physicians of Philadelphia. Wood's useful "Reminiscences . . .," written "toward the close of his life," were published in the *Transactions and Studies of the College of Physicians of Philadelphia*, 3rd ser., **42** (1920), 195–234, with nine topical sections. Most of his publications are likewise in the library of the College of Physicians, and a large majority of them also are in the National Library of Medicine. For orientation to Wood's level of work, thought, and style, see *A Treatise on Therapeutics, Comprising Materia Medica and Toxicology, with Especial Reference to the Application of the Physiological Action of Drugs to Clinical Medicine* (Philadelphia, 1874); "Hyoscine; Its Physiological and Therapeutic Action," in *Therapeutic Gazette*, **9** (1885), 1–10; and "On the Medical Activity of the Hemp Plant [Marijuana], as Grown in North America," in *Transactions of the American Philosophical Society*, **11** (1869), 226–232. Wood's first publication was "Contributions to the Carboniferous Flora of the United States," in *Proceedings of the Philadelphia Academy of Natural Sciences*, no. 1 (1860), 236–240, no. 2 (1860), 519–552.

II. SECONDARY LITERATURE. Roth explains that Horatio C Wood had no middle name, hence insisted that no period be used after the "C" of his name. The varying result in the literature is further aggravated by his father being named Horatio Curtis Wood and his son, Horatio Charles Wood, Jr.

There is no definitive biography of Wood. A reliable

article, emphasizing his professional life, is George B. Roth, "An Early American Pharmacologist: Horatio C Wood (1841–1920)," in *Isis*, **30** (1939), 37–45. More revealing of his personality are Hobart Amory Hare, "Horatio C. Wood, The Pioneer in American Pharmacology," in *Therapeutic Gazette*, **44** (1920), 322–324; and G. E. de Schweinitz, "Dr. H. C. Wood as a Medical Teacher," in *Transactions and Studies of the College of Physicians of Philadelphia*, 3rd ser., **42** (1920), 235–241. Of supplemental usefulness are G. E. de Schweinitz, "Memoir of Dr. H. C Wood," *ibid.*, pp. 155–165; F. X. Dercum, "Memoir of Dr. H. C Wood," *ibid.*, pp. 166–169; Charles K. Mills, "Reminiscences of Dr. Horatio C Wood," *ibid.*, pp. 175–186; Henry Beates, Jr., "Professor Horatio C. Wood," in *American Journal of Pharmacy*, **77** (1905), 376–379; Henry Beates, Jr., "Horatio C. Wood, M.D.," in *Medical Record*, **98** (1920), 393–396; and *Family Sketches, Compiled and Arranged by Julianna R. Wood* (Philadelphia, 1870).

GLENN SONNEDECKER

**WOOD, ROBERT WILLIAMS** (*b.* Concord, Massachusetts, 2 May 1868; *d.* Amityville, New York, 11 August 1955), *experimental physics*.

Wood's chief contributions to science lay in physical optics, particularly in spectroscopy, in which he obtained experimental results of great significance for the advance of atomic physics during the first third of the twentieth century. He was an extremely versatile laboratory worker, and his insatiable curiosity took him into many other scientific and technical fields, such as the photography of sound waves, properties of ultrasonic radiation, color photography, molecular physics, the manufacture of high-precision diffraction gratings, fluorescence, and scientific crime detection. His book *Physical Optics* (1905) became the classic treatise on the experimental aspects of the subject in its day, and went through three editions.

Wood did his undergraduate work at Harvard College, where in 1891 he received the B.A. degree with a major in chemistry. His academic record was undistinguished in the required fields of languages and mathematics, but he early showed enthusiasm for all aspects of science. His graduate work took him to Johns Hopkins, Chicago, Berlin, and the Massachusetts Institute of Technology. This graduate study never led to an earned doctorate, and Wood had to content himself with honorary degrees. Early in his career he shifted from chemistry to physics; and by the time he began teaching at the University of Wisconsin in 1897, he had definitely settled down to the life of a physicist. In 1901 Wood succeeded Henry A. Rowland

as professor of experimental physics at Johns Hopkins, where he remained for the rest of his life, retiring officially in 1938 but continuing in an honorary capacity until his death.

Before he assumed his professorial duties at Johns Hopkins, Wood had published more than thirty papers covering a wide range of investigations in physics and chemistry. This early work clearly indicated his zest for experimentation and his great ingenuity in devising relatively simple ways to exhibit spectacular effects. Color always fascinated him and entered vitally into much of his work. Zeal for mathematical symbolism seems to have been missing from his make-up. He preferred to express his experimental results in terms of physical pictures that he felt he (and many others) could understand better than mathematical equations, which he found rather boring. This trait, which persisted throughout his life, in no way interfered with the fundamental logic of his physical reasoning.

At Johns Hopkins Wood's teaching duties were light and he devoted himself mainly to research, which for over three decades was concentrated primarily on the optical properties of gases and vapors, a field in which he soon established himself as an internationally recognized authority. His work on sodium vapor was especially noteworthy. The extensive precision measurements of atomic spectra stimulated much similar work in this area, and all of it proved to be of the utmost importance in connection with the growing interest in atomic models during the early years of the twentieth century. The Bohr theory, in particular, leaned very heavily on spectroscopic data such as those provided by Wood and others whose work was suggested by him. This was particularly true of Wood's fundamental experimental work from 1903 to 1920 on fluorescence and resonance radiation of vapors and also the effect of electric and magnetic fields on spectrum lines. Wood also greatly stimulated research in optical spectroscopy by his improvements in the diffraction grating and his determination to ensure a steady supply of high-quality gratings to investigators throughout the world by keeping Rowland's ruling engines steadily at work.

Throughout his professional career Wood was continually on the lookout for interesting new phenomena to study, particularly those involving striking effects. During World War I and in the late 1920's he became interested in high-frequency sound waves and their physical and biological properties. Wood performed many experiments in collaboration with A. L. Loomis at the latter's Tuxedo Park laboratory. These experiments received considerable publicity through the Colver lectures at Brown University in 1937 and the book based on them, *Supersonics, the Science of Inaudible Sounds* (1939). This work, although popular in presentation, aroused great interest and undoubtedly stimulated research in the important field of acoustics now known as ultrasonics.

A master lecturer with highly developed showmanship, Wood much enjoyed talking to large audiences and demonstrating his ideas with graphic experiments—the more spectacular the better. His name on the program of a meeting of the American Physical Society always guaranteed the attendance of a large crowd to hear his paper. Much more confident in experimental results than in abstract, mathematical reasoning, Wood was never satisfied until an experiment showed with complete clarity the idea he was trying to communicate. He often carried his showmanship into the perpetration of practical jokes; this led to the invention of a host of stories about his exploits that have become legendary among American physicists.

In his teaching of optics, Wood early felt the need for a book that would emphasize, to a greater extent than available standard texts, the experimental aspects of twentieth-century research on light. His *Physical Optics* satisfied an existing need for more information about the kind of optical techniques he himself was introducing. A fourth edition was being prepared at the time of his death.

Inevitably, as a result of his zeal for experimentation, Wood made many inventions. He was usually too restless, however, to follow them through the development stage into practical, salable devices. He was more successful financially as a legal consultant in cases involving scientific and related technical matters, as well as with his delightful little book *How to Tell the Birds From the Flowers, and Other Woodcuts*. First published in 1917, it went through twenty editions. Written to amuse Wood's children, it entertained hosts of others who knew nothing of his scientific achievements. Also worthy of mention is his experimentation with humorous scientific verse, of which his "Contemptuary Science" (relativity and Michelson optics) is a good example.

Wood traveled widely both in the United States and abroad. He received many honors in recognition of his accomplishments. In addition to his membership in the National Academy of Sciences, he was one of the relatively few foreign members of the Royal Society. He also belonged to numerous other foreign academies and societies, and received six honorary degrees and numerous medals.

## BIBLIOGRAPHY

I. ORIGINAL WORKS. Wood's complete scientific bibliography includes 2 books and 227 articles. The complete list is in Dieke's memoir (below). The following is a selection intended to illustrate the breadth of his work.

His books are *Physical Optics* (New York–London, 1905; 2nd ed., 1911; 3rd ed., 1934) and *Supersonics, the Science of Inaudible Sounds* (Providence, R.I., 1939).

Wood's earliest articles are "The Kingdom of the Dream. Experience With Hasheesh," in New York *Sunday Herald* (23 Sept. 1888); "Effects of Pressure on Ice," in *American Journal of Science*, 3rd ser., **41** (1891), 30–33; "Eine einfache Methode, die Dauer von Torsions-schwingungen zu bestimmen," in Wiedemann's *Annalen der Physik und Chemie*, n.s. **56** (1895), 171–172; "Ueber eine neue Form der Quecksilber Luftpumpe und die Erhaltung eines guten Vacuums bei Röntgen'schen Versuchen," *ibid.*, **58** (1896), 205–208; "On the Absorption Spectrum of Solutions of Iodine and Bromine Above the Critical Temperature," in *Philosophical Magazine*, 5th ser., **41** (1896), 423–431; *Zeitschrift für physikalische Chemie*, **19** (1896), 689–695; "A New Form of Cathode Discharge and the Production of X-Rays, Together With Some Notes on Diffraction," in *Physical Review*, **5** (1897), 1–10; "Phase-Reversal Zone-Plates and Diffraction Telescope," in *Philosophical Magazine*, 5th ser., **45** (1898), 511–522; "The Anomalous Dispersion of Cyanin," *ibid.*, **46** (1898), 380–386; "An Application of the Diffraction Grating to Colour Photography," *ibid.*, **47** (1899), 368–372; and "Photography of Sound Waves by the 'Schlieren Methode,'" *ibid.*, **48** (1899), 218–227.

Papers written early in the twentieth century are "Zone Plate Photography," in *Photographic Journal*, **24** (1900), 248–250; "The Photography of Sound Waves and the Demonstration of the Evolutions of Reflected Wave Fronts With the Cinematograph," in *Philosophical Magazine*, 5th ser., **50** (1900), 148–157; *Chemical News*, **81** (1900), 103; *Proceedings of the Royal Society*, **A66** (1900), 283–290; *Report of the Board of Regents of the Smithsonian Institution* for 1900 (1901), 359; "An Application of the Method of Striae to the Illumination of Objects Under the Microscope," in *Philosophical Magazine*, 5th ser., **50** (1900), 347–349; "Vortex Rings," in *Nature*, **63** (1901), 418–420; "The Problem of the Daylight Observation of the Corona," in *Astrophysical Journal*, **12** (1901), 281–286; "The Nature of the Solar Corona," *ibid.*, **13** (1901), 68–79; "The Anomalous Dispersion of Carbon," in *Philosophical Magazine*, 6th ser., **1** (1901), 405–410; "On the Production of a Bright-Line Spectrum by Anomalous Dispersion and Its

Application to the 'Flash-Spectrum,'" *ibid.*, 551–555; *Naturwissenschaftliche Rundschau*, **16** (1901), 394; *Astrophysical Journal*, **13** (1901), 63–67; "Anomalous Dispersion of Sodium Vapour," in *Proceedings of the Royal Society*, **69** (1901), 157–171; "The Invisibility of Transparent Objects," in *Physical Review*, **15** (1902), 123–124; "Absorption, Dispersion, and Surface Colour of Selenium," in *Philosophical Magazine*, 6th ser., **3** (1902), 607–622; "On a Remarkable Case of Uneven Distribution of Light in a Diffraction Grating Spectrum," *ibid.*, **4** (1902), 396–402; and "The Kinetic Theory of the Expansion of Compressing Gas Into a Vacuum," in *Science*, **16** (1902), 908–909.

Also see "Screens Transparent Only to Ultra-Violet Light and Their Use in Spectrum Photography," in *Philosophical Magazine*, 6th ser., **5** (1903), 257–263; *Physikalische Zeitschrift*, **4** (1903), 337–338; and *Astrophysical Journal*, **17** (1903), 133–140; "On the Anomalous Dispersion, Absorption and Surface Colour of Nitroso Dimethyl Aniline With a Note on the Dispersion of Toluene," in *Philosophical Magazine*, 6th ser., **6** (1903), 96–112; *Records of the American Academy of Arts and Sciences*, **39** (1903), 51–66; "Electrical Resonance of Metal Particles for Light Waves. Third Communication," in *Philosophical Magazine*, 6th ser., **6** (1903), 259–266; "Fluorescence and Absorption Spectra of Sodium Vapour," *ibid.*, 362–374; and *Astrophysical Journal*, **18** (1903), 94–111; written with J. H. Moore; "The N-Rays (Letter Exposing Delusion)," in *Nature*, **70** (1904), 530–531; "Apparatus to Illustrate the Pressure of Sound Waves," in *Physical Review*, **20** (1905), 113–114; and *Physikalische Zeitschrift*, **6** (1905), 22; "The Magnetic Rotation of Sodium Vapour," in *Physical Review*, **21** (1905), 41–51, written with H. W. Springsteen; "The Magneto-Optics of Sodium Vapour and the Rotatory Dispersion Formula," in *Philosophical Magazine*, 6th ser., **10** (1905), 408–427; "The Fluorescence of Sodium Vapour and the Resonance Radiation of Electrons," *ibid.*, 513–525; "Abnormal Polarization and Colour of Light Scattered by Small Absorbing Particles," *ibid.*, **12** (1906), 147–149; "Die Temperaturstrahlung des Joddampfes," in *Physikalische Zeitschrift*, **8** (1907), 517; "Polarized Fluorescence of Metallic Vapors and the Solar Corona," in *Astrophysical Journal*, **28** (1908), 75–78; "An Extension of the Principal Series of the Sodium Spectrum," in *Philosophical Magazine*, 6th ser., **16** (1908), 945–947; "The Mercury Paraboloid as a Reflecting Telescope," in *Astrophysical Journal*, **29** (1909), 164–176; and "The Ultra-Violet Absorption, Fluorescence, and Magnetic Rotation of Sodium Vapour," in *Philosophical Magazine*, 6th ser., **18** (1909), 530–535.

During the second decade of the century, Wood wrote "Determination of Stellar Velocities With the Objective Prism," in *Astrophysical Journal*, **31** (1910), 376–377; "The Echelette Grating for the Infra-Red," in *Philosophical Magazine*, 6th ser., **20** (1910), 770–778; "The Resonance Spectra of Iodine," *ibid.*, **21** (1911), 261–265;

"Diffraction Gratings With Controlled Groove Form and Abnormal Distribution of Intensity," *ibid.*, **23** (1912), 310–317; and *Physikalische Zeitschrift*, **13** (1912), 261–264; "Selective Absorption of Light on the Moon's Surface and Lunar Petrography," in *Astrophysical Journal*, **36** (1912), 75–84; "Method of Obtaining Very Narrow Absorption Lines for Investigations in Magnetic Fields," in *Physikalische Zeitschrift*, **14** (1913), 405, written with P. Zeeman; "The Satellites of the Mercury Lines," in *Philosophical Magazine*, 6th ser., **25** (1913), 443–449; and *Physikalische Zeitschrift*, **14** (1913), 273–275; "The Effect of Electric and Magnetic Fields on the Emission Lines of Solids," in *Philosophical Magazine*, 6th ser., **30** (1915), 316–320, written with C. E. Mendenhall; "Monochromatic Photographs of Jupiter and Saturn," in *Astrophysical Journal*, **43** (1916), 310–319; and "Condensation and Reflection of Gas Molecules," in *Philosophical Magazine*, 6th ser., **32** (1916), 364–371.

In the 1920's Wood produced "Light Scattering by Air and the Blue Colour of the Sky," in *Philosophical Magazine*, 6th ser., **39** (1920), 423–433; "Extension of the Balmer Series of Hydrogen, and Spectroscopic Phenomena of Very Long Vacuum Tubes," in *Proceedings of the Royal Society*, A**97** (1920), 455–470; "On the Influence of Magnetic Fields on the Polarization of Resonance Radiation," *ibid.*, A**103** (1923), 396–403, written with A. Ellett; "Fine Structure, Absorption and Zeeman Effect of the 2536 Mercury Line," in *Philosophical Magazine*, 6th ser., **50** (1925), 761–774; and *Nature*, **115** (1925), 461; "Improved Grating for Vacuum Spectrographs," in *Philosophical Magazine*, 7th ser., **2** (1926), 310–312, written with T. Lyman; "The Physical and Biological Effects of High Frequency Sound Waves of Great Intensity," *ibid.*, **4** (1927), 417–436, written with A. L. Loomis; "Anti-Stokes Radiation of Fluorescent Liquids," *ibid.*, **6** (1928), 310–312; "Raman Spectra of Scattered Radiation," *ibid.*, 729–743; and "Improved Technique for the Raman Effect," in *Physical Review*, **33** (1929), 294, and **36** (1930), 1421–1430.

His last works were "Absorption Spectra of Salts in Liquid Ammonia," in *Physical Review*, **38** (1931), 1648–1650; "The Purple Gold of Tut-Ankhamun," in *Journal of Egyptian Archaeology*, **20** (1934), 62–65; "Fluorescence of Chlorophyll in Its Relation to Photochemical Processes in Plants and Organic Solutions," in *Journal of Chemical Physics*, **4** (1936), 551–560, written with J. Franck; and "Improved Diffraction Gratings and Replicas," in *Journal of the Optical Society of America*, **34** (1944), 509–516.

II. SECONDARY LITERATURE. See the biographical sketch by G. H. Dieke in *Biographical Memoirs of Fellows of the Royal Society*, **2** (1956), 327–345; and William Seabrook, *Doctor Wood—Modern Wizard of the Laboratory* (New York, 1941).

R. B. LINDSAY

**WOODHOUSE, ROBERT** (*b*. Norwich, England, 28 April 1773; *d*. Cambridge, England, 28 [23?] December 1827), *mathematics*.

Woodhouse was a critic and reformer. The son of Robert Woodhouse, a linen draper, and of the daughter of J. Alderson, a nonconformist minister, Woodhouse attended the grammar school at North Walsham. In 1790 he was admitted to Caius College, Cambridge, and four years later graduated with the B.A., as senior wrangler and first Smith's prizeman. In 1798 he received the M.A. from the university, and was successively fellow (1798–1823), Lucasian professor of mathematics (1820–1822), and Plumian professor of astronomy and experimental philosophy (1822–1827). Woodhouse also served as the first superintendent of the astronomical observatory at Cambridge. In 1802 he was elected a fellow of the Royal Society. He married Harriet Wilkens in 1823; they had one son, Robert.

Woodhouse was primarily interested in what was then called the metaphysics of mathematics; that is, he was concerned with questions such as the proper theoretical foundations of the calculus, the role of geometric and analytic methods, the importance of notation, and the nature of imaginary numbers. Many of these questions are discussed in his *Principles of Analytical Calculation* (1803), a polemic aimed primarily at the fellows and professors at Cambridge. In this work Woodhouse defended analytic methods, the differential notation, and a theory of calculus based, like that of Lagrange, on series expansions. It does not appear to have had much influence in the introduction of continental methods at Cambridge. His elementary text on trigonometry (1809), however, was widely used. George Peacock, who himself played a decisive role in the reform of mathematical studies at Cambridge, considered this work to be of major importance in achieving this goal. It was not polemical, but used analytic methods and the differential notation throughout.

Woodhouse's other writings include a history of the calculus of variations (1810), a treatise on astronomy (1812), and a work on the theory of gravitation, somewhat misnamed *Physical Astronomy* (1818). In all these works Woodhouse presented the results of continental research from the time of Newton up to his own time.

*BIBLIOGRAPHY*

I. ORIGINAL WORKS. Woodhouse's papers include "On the Necessary Truth of Certain Conclusions Ob-

tained by Means of Imaginary Quantities," in *Philosophical Transactions of the Royal Society*, **91** (1801), 89–119; and "On the Independence of the Analytical and Geometrical Methods of Investigation; and on the Advantages To Be Derived From Their Separation," *ibid.*, **92** (1809), 85–125. His books are *Principles of Analytical Calculation* (Cambridge, 1803); *A Treatise on Plane and Spherical Trigonometry* (Cambridge, 1809; 5th rev. ed., 1827); *A Treatise on Isoperimetrical Problems and the Calculus of Variations* (Cambridge, 1810), reprinted as *A History of the Calculus of Variations in the Eighteenth Century* (New York, n.d.); *Treatise on Astronomy* (Cambridge, 1812); and *Physical Astronomy* (Cambridge, 1818).

II. SECONDARY LITERATURE. The fullest account of Woodhouse's life and work is in Augustus DeMorgan, "Robert Woodhouse," in *Penny Cyclopaedia*, XXVII (London, 1843), 526–527. Woodhouse's influence is considered in Elaine Koppelman, *Calculus of Operations: French Influence in British Mathematics in the First Half of the Nineteenth Century* (Ph.D. diss., Johns Hopkins University, 1969).

ELAINE KOPPELMAN

**WOODWARD, JOHN** (*b*. Derbyshire, England, 1 May 1665; *d*. London, England, 25 April 1728), *geology*, *mineralogy*, *botany*.

Woodward was said to have been the son of a man of good family from Gloucestershire. He was educated at a country school, where he became proficient in Latin and Greek. About 1680, at the age of sixteen, he was apprenticed to a linen draper in London, but he abandoned this occupation to pursue a further course of study. A few years later he became acquainted with Peter Barwick, physician in ordinary to Charles II. Barwick was impressed by Woodward's ability and about 1684 took him into his household to study medicine; Woodward remained there about four years. During this period, while on a visit to Sherborne, in Gloucestershire, he studied botany in the surrounding country. While on these excursions he learned for the first time that rocks may contain fossil animal remains—they are particularly common in the Jurassic rocks in that neighborhood. These fossils greatly interested Woodward, and he resolved to investigate their occurrence in other parts of the country. This he undoubtedly did, although no detailed account of the course of his investigation has survived. Later in Oxford he made the acquaintance of two well-known naturalists, Robert Plot, keeper of the Ashmolean Museum, and his assistant, Edward Lhwyd, who also were interested in fossils. On this occasion he seems to have told Lhwyd that he had already formed a theory explaining the origin of fossils, then still a matter for debate. In 1690 Lhwyd wrote to a friend stating that Woodward seemed well informed for his age but that he doubted that he was sufficiently experienced to satisfy others on such a debatable matter. This visit to Gloucestershire, however, led Woodward to adopt the study of geology and mineralogy as one of his major interests for the rest of his life. Meanwhile he continued to study medicine and botany.

In 1692, at the age of twenty-seven, Woodward was appointed professor of physic at Gresham College, London. His candidature had been supported by Barwick and Plot, among others. Evidently his abilities had now become more widely known. Barwick stated in his testimonial that Woodward "had made the greatest advance not only in physick, anatomy, botany, . . . but likewise in all other useful learning of any man I ever knew of his age . . .," and that he was "very much respected upon this account by persons of the greatest judgement and learning." Not long after his appointment Woodward took up residence at Gresham College. He was elected fellow of the Royal Society in 1693, and in 1695 was awarded the degree of doctor of medicine by special dispensation of Thomas Tenison, archbishop of Canterbury. In 1696 Woodward was granted an M.D. by the University of Cambridge, and he was elected fellow of the College of Physicians in March 1703. As a lecturer in Gresham College his obligations were relatively light, and he established himself as a practicing physician at least as early as 1709. In 1718 he published his only medical work, *The State of Physick and of Diseases . . . More Particularly of the Smallpox*. The treatment he recommended contradicted the views of some eminent contemporary physicians, notably Richard Mead, and led to a duel between the latter and Woodward.

Woodward continued to reside at Gresham College until his death. He spent much time cataloging his geological and mineralogical specimens, and his museum was often visited by other naturalists, who have left accounts of it. Contemporary records show that, at least in later life, Woodward, although not without friends, was a man of unattractive character, conceited, quarrelsome, and dogmatic. He quarreled with the council of the Royal Society and made enemies of other naturalists. His contributions to science were nevertheless of considerable importance.

Woodward made a valuable contribution to bo-
tanical science as a result of a series of systematic experiments on plant nutrition carried out in 1691 and 1692, a detailed account of which was published by the Royal Society in 1699. The most important result of this investigation was a clear demonstration that the greater part of the water absorbed by a growing plant is exhaled through its pores into the atmosphere. This was the first demonstration of transpiration. Woodward also claimed that the food of plants is not water, but the mineral substances dissolved in the water.

Woodward is chiefly remembered for his contributions to the earth sciences. In his first contribution, *Essay Toward a Natural History of the Earth* (1695), which he claimed was based on his own observations, Woodward assumed that the earth formerly had been submerged beneath a universal deluge, the waters of which had originated in a central abyss within the earth. These waters had dissolved, or disintegrated and held in suspension, all the stony and mineral matter forming the outer crust of the earth. At the same time all the animals and plants then living were submerged in the waters but were not destroyed beyond recognition. From the confused mass that had formed, the matter in suspension, both organic and inorganic, subsided in an order determined, so far as was possible, by the specific gravity of the individual components. Thus a stratigraphic succession was formed in which the specific gravity of both the organic remains and the rock matrix in which they occurred decreased gradually in passing upward in the succession.

Woodward asserted unequivocally that the fossil organic remains that had been found in rocks were definitely the remains of living animals or plants, a view not universally held at that time. The term "fossil" was then widely used to denote anything that was dug out of the earth, whether mineral substances or organic remains. In Woodward's terminology stones and minerals were "native" fossils, and organic remains were "extraneous" fossils.

Woodward had observed that particular rock formations might contain a different assemblage of extraneous fossil forms to those occurring in beds above or below the formation. While he realized that this observation required explanation, it is perhaps not surprising that he failed to recognize the true explanation; and the one he offered was soon criticized.

Woodward's *Essay* was widely read both in Great Britain and, in translation, in other European countries. The great Swiss naturalist J. J. Scheuchzer was converted by the *Essay* to belief in the organic origin of animal remains in rocks; and he translated the *Essay* into Latin. The information contained in the *Essay* and in Woodward's later works also contributed toward establishing that strata throughout the world are, generally speaking, similar in character, a conclusion necessary before any acceptable theory of the origin of the rocks of the crust of the earth could be formulated.

In 1696 Woodward published an anonymous twenty-page pamphlet entitled *Brief Instructions for making Observations in All Parts of the World: as Also for Collecting, Preserving, and Sending Over Natural Things*. This work is of considerable interest, for even today it might, with little emendation, serve the purpose for which it was intended. Woodward circulated the work, and by this means and through correspondents in many countries ultimately formed a large collection of fossils and minerals. The value of this collection lay in the fact that he studied his specimens carefully, and later published pioneer attempts to classify both minerals and fossils systematically.

Woodward first discussed minerals in Section 4 of his *Essay*, where he admitted the difficulties in determining the nature of individual minerals, inevitable at that time, and made greater because he included rocks with his minerals. His first attempt at a classification appeared in 1704, under the head "Fossils," in John Harris' *Lexicon chemicum*. Here he divided minerals into six classes: "earths, stones, salts, bitumina, metallick minerals and metals." This was reprinted with little change, in his *Naturalis historia telluris* (1714). Later Woodward greatly enlarged this classification. His *Fossils of All Kinds Digested Into a Method* (1728) contains a large folding table setting out his mineral classification systematically. It retains the six major classes, but adds many more subdivisions. The text includes fifty-six pages in which some two hundred minerals are described, together with their mode of occurrence in some cases. Some specimens were examined under the microscope, and Woodward mentions the characteristics used in making his determinations.

Woodward's last work, published posthumously in 1729, was *An Attempt Towards a Natural History of the Fossils of England*. This was a detailed catalogue of his collection of both British and foreign minerals and fossils, some 4,000–5,000 in number, occupying about 600 pages of small print. Localities of specimens are given with, frequently, the names of correspondents who supplied them, and the use of some minerals is discussed.

In this catalogue Woodward enlarged his systematic classification of minerals to include eleven classes. He also classified animal and vegetable fossils, the former into fifteen classes, and the latter into five groups. His classification of fossils was more elaborate and rational than that used by Lhwyd in his *Lithophylacii Britannici ichnographia* (1699). Woodward's catalogue was used by geologists for almost a century after its publication. The specimens he collected are now preserved in the Sedgwick Museum, Cambridge, in their original cases.

Woodward's last contribution to the advancement of geological science was to leave in his will funds to establish at the University of Cambridge a lectureship bearing his name; this eventually evolved into the Woodwardian chair in geology, the earliest such post in the subject in any British university.

Woodward was the first British author to publish a systematic classification and description of minerals based on his own observations; and he emphasized the importance to his country of its mineral wealth. His classification of fossil organic remains was one of the earliest of its kind. While Woodward does not rank high as an original thinker, his contributions to the advancement of geology were important in their time, in relation to contemporary knowledge. The true value of his work can only be assessed by examining all of his geological publications. His works were widely read and must have done much to stimulate interest in the earth sciences.

*BIBLIOGRAPHY*

I. ORIGINAL WORKS. For a complete and annotated bibliography of Woodward's works, including translations, see V. A. Eyles, "John Woodward, F.R.S., F.R.C.P., M.D. (1665–1728): A Bio-bibliographical Account of His Life and Work," in *Journal of the Society for the Bibliography of Natural History*, **5** (1971), 399–427.

Woodward's books of geological and mineralogical interest are *Essay Toward a Natural History of the Earth* (London, 1695; 2nd ed.; 1702; 3rd ed., 1723); *Brief Instructions for Making Observations in All Parts of the World* (London, 1696; repr. with an introduction by V. A. Eyles, by the Society for the Bibliography of Natural History, London, 1973); *Naturalis historia telluris illustrata & aucta* (London, 1714); *Natural History of the Earth, Illustrated, Enlarged and Defended* (London, 1726), a translation by B. Holloway, of *Naturalis historia*, with some other papers by Woodward; *A Supplement and Continuation of the Essay Towards a*

*Natural History of the Earth* (London, 1726), which is identical with the previous work, except for the title; *Fossils of All Kinds Digested Into a Method* (London, 1728); and *An Attempt Towards a Natural History of the Fossils of England* . . . (London, 1729).

Woodward's botanical paper, "Some Thoughts and Experiments Concerning Vegetation," is in *Philosophical Transactions of the Royal Society*, **21** (1699), 193–227.

II. SECONDARY LITERATURE. The principal biographical source is J. Ward, *Lives of the Professors of Gresham College* (London, 1740), 283–301. See also J. W. Clark and T. McKenny Hughes, *Life and Letters of Adam Sedgwick . . . Woodwardian Professor of Geology*, I (Cambridge, 1890), 166–189, for the establishment of the Woodwardian chair in geology.

For contemporary commentaries on Woodward's *Essay*, see J. A[rbuthnot], *An Examination of Dr. Woodward's Account of the Deluge, &c.* (London, 1697), and J. Harris, *Remarks on Some Late Papers, Relating to the Universal Deluge: and to the Natural History of the Earth* (London, 1697). A critical commentary on Woodward's geological views in relation to those of his contemporaries and eighteenth-century successors is in K. B. Collier, *Cosmogonies of Our Fathers* (New York, 1934; repr. 1968).

Woodward's quarrel with the Royal Society is described by G. R. De Beer in *Sir Hans Sloane and the British Museum* (London, 1953), 90–91. His botanical work is discussed in H. H. Thomas, "Experimental Plant Biology in Pre-Linnean Times," in *Bulletin of the British Society for the History of Science*, **2** (1955), 20–21.

Unpublished correspondence and MSS of Woodward are preserved in the archives of the Royal Society of London, and in the British Museum and Bodleian libraries. His correspondence with Cotton Mather and other naturalists in North America is discussed by R. P. Stearns, in *Science in the British Colonies of America* (Urbana, 1970).

V. A. EYLES

**WOODWARD, ROBERT SIMPSON** (*b.* Rochester, Michigan, 21 July 1849; *d.* Washington, D.C., 29 June 1924), *applied mathematics, geophysics.*

Woodward was part of the tradition of mathematical physics that saw the earth as the great object of study. In 1904 he asserted, "The earth is thus at once the grandest of laboratories and the grandest of museums available to man." To this laboratory and museum Woodward brought a great skill in mathematics and an insistence on obtaining data of the highest precision in a form suitable for computation. The last point greatly influenced the young John Hayford, who worked with Woodward at the Coast and Geodetic Survey.

After receiving a degree in civil engineering in 1872 from the University of Michigan, Woodward worked for ten years with the Lake Survey of the U.S. Corps of Engineers. From 1882 to 1884 he was an astronomer with the U.S. Transit of Venus Commission. Woodward next served for six years with the U.S. Geological Survey, successively occupying the posts of astronomer, geographer, and chief geographer.

His most notable scientific contributions occurred during this period. For G. K. Gilbert he calculated the effects on shore lines of the removal of superficial masses by means of potential theory. In this work and his passing consideration of isostasy, Woodward considered thermal effects, clearly related to the concern with how heat influenced base bars and other instruments of precision. In a series of papers in 1887–1888, Woodward explored the cooling of homogeneous spheres and the diffusion of heat in rectangular masses. The findings were applied to Kelvin's work on the age of the earth. By 1889 Woodward criticized Kelvin for the "unverified assumption of an initial uniform temperature and a constant diffusivity." As the data for Kelvin's calculations were derived from observations of continental areas, Woodward felt the probabilities were against obtaining satisfactory numerical results for the entire earth. His position strengthened the opposition of many geologists, at least in America, to Kelvin's constriction of geological time.

From 1890 to 1893 Woodward was with the U.S. Coast and Geodetic Survey. In 1893 he became professor of mechanics and mathematical physics at Columbia University; and in 1895 he was named dean of the College of Pure Science. From 1904 through 1920 Woodward was president of the Carnegie Institution of Washington, succeeding D. C. Gilman. As chairman of two advisory committees, he had previously played a role in the development of the policies of the Institution. He was a strong administrator and largely responsible for the direction taken by the Carnegie Institution.

*BIBLIOGRAPHY*

F. E. Wright's memoir in *Biographical Memoirs. National Academy of Sciences*, **19** (1938), 1–24, has a good bibliography. The archives of the Carnegie Institution of Washington and the papers of many of his contemporaries contain manuscripts by or about Woodward. The correspondence of J. McK. Cattell in the Library of Congress and T. W. Richards in the Harvard

University Archives are valuable for his views on the policies of the Carnegie Institution. The correspondence of Presidents Low and Butler in the Office of the Secretary, Columbia University, contains a small number of interesting items.

NATHAN REINGOLD

**WOOLLEY, CHARLES LEONARD** (*b.* Upper Clapton, London, England, 17 April 1880; *d.* London, 20 February 1960), *archaeology.*

Woolley was the son of the Reverend George Herbert Woolley and Sarah Cathcart. He received a degree from New College, Oxford, and intended to become a schoolmaster. W. A. Spooner, warden of New College, decided, however, that Woolley was to be an archaeologist. Woolley therefore became assistant to Sir Arthur Evans at the Ashmolean Museum in 1905, and did his first fieldwork and digging at Corbridge, Northumberland. He wrote in his autobiography, *Spadework* (1953): "I know only too well that the work there would have scandalized, and rightly . . . any British archaeologist of today. It was however typical of what was done forty-five years ago, when field-archaeology was, comparatively speaking, in its infancy and few diggers in this country thought it necessary to follow the example of that great pioneer, Pitt Rivers."

Woolley's work in the Near East began in 1907, when he dug with D. Randall-MacIver in Nubia. In 1912 he was appointed to succeed Reginald Campbell Thompson as director of the British Museum expedition to Carchemish. He was accompanied by T. E. Lawrence, with whom, after a subsequent six-week archaeological reconnaissance, he wrote *The Wilderness of Zin* (1915). During World War I, Woolley served as an intelligence officer on the British General Staff in Egypt.

The war had ended excavation in the Middle East, but work was recommenced as soon as hostilities ceased. Even before the 1918 armistice Thompson began digging at Ur and Eridu, under the auspices of the British Museum. On the strength of his finds, the museum sent an expedition under H. R. Hall to dig at both sites. Hall also found al'Ubaid, a new site four miles west of Ur. In 1922 a joint expedition of the British Museum and the Museum of the University of Pennsylvania, directed by Woolley, continued Thompson and Hall's work. Woolley began at Ur, then transferred his attention to al'Ubaid, returning to Ur in 1926 and the following years. It was in 1926 that the great prehistoric cemetery at Ur, with its "royal

tombs," was discovered and excavated. The discovery of these tombs, with their splendid treasures of gold and lapis lazuli and their remarkable evidence of funerary ritual, caused a sensation comparable with Schliemann's discoveries at Mycenae and those of Lord Carnarvon and Howard Carter of Tutankhamen's tomb. Woolley dug at Ur, Eridu, and al'Ubaid for thirteen years, publishing preliminary reports in *Antiquaries Journal* and the full report in a series of volumes between 1928 and 1938.

At Ur, Woolley demonstrated his remarkable insight into the methods used by early craftsmen and builders. The joint expedition under Woolley not only inaugurated a brilliant revival of excavation in Mesopotamia in the 1920's and 1930's; it also was responsible for widespread popular interest in Mesopotamian archaeology and the origins of civilization there. In 1900 very few people had heard of the Sumerians, but by 1930 the Sumerians had been added to the collection of prehistoric peoples of whom almost everyone knew something. This was due in part to the sensational nature of the Ur excavations, but also to the clear and helpful popular accounts published by Woolley, notably *Ur of the Chaldees* (1929), *The Sumerians* (1930), *Abraham, Recent Discoveries and Hebrew Origins* (1936), and *Excavations at Ur: A Record of Twelve Years Work* (1954).

Like W. M. Flinders Petrie and A. H. Pitt-Rivers, Woolley believed passionately that the results of archaeology must be communicated to the general public in readable form. It has been said, in criticism of his work, that he ran ahead of what could reasonably be inferred; but he was always certain of what he was doing in the scholarly popularization of archaeology. As Sir Max Mallowan said, "If his imagination sometimes outran the facts, that to him was preferable to allowing knowledge to lie dormant and inconclusive." The freshness and relevance of his popularization can be seen not only in the books on Ur and the Sumerians but also in *Spadework*, written when he was in his seventies, and *Dead Towns and Living Men*, written in 1920.

His great work in Mesopotamia over, Woolley dug at al-Mina, near Antioch, and at Atchana during 1937–1939 and 1946–1949. Atchana-Alalakh was revealed as the ancient Hittite capital of the province of Hatay in Turkey (now the sanjak of Alexandretta): it was destroyed in 1200 B.C. but had nine periods of occupation dating back from the latter year to the twentieth century B.C. The results were published in a popular account, *A*

*Forgotten Kingdom* (1953), and in *The Alakh Excavations and Tell Atchana* (1958). These works again showed Woolley's strength and purpose: he always published his results in exemplary and scholarly form, and also communicated them to the general public. As Sir Max Mallowan said: "To have dug so much and left nothing unwritten was indeed a phenomenal record."

In 1938 Woolley was invited by the government of India to advise it on the development and organization of archaeology there; his plans, not implemented until the 1940's, were carried out by Sir Mortimer Wheeler, director general of archaeology for India. During World War II, Woolley was specially employed in the safeguarding of museums, libraries, archives, and art galleries. Knighted in 1935, he continued working in the last quarter-century of his life, producing with Jacquetta Hawkes the first volume of the UNESCO *History of Mankind* (1963).

Woolley married Katharine Elizabeth Keeling in 1927.

## BIBLIOGRAPHY

Woolley's principal works are mentioned in the text. In addition see article in *Dictionary of National Biography* and obituary in *The Times* (22 Feb. 1960).

GLYN DANIEL

**WORM, OLE** (or **OLAUS WORMIUS**) (*b.* Aarhus, Jutland, Denmark, 13 May 1588; *d.* Copenhagen, Denmark, 7 September 1654), *natural history.*

Worm was the son of the mayor of Aarhus and a descendant of refugees from religious persecution in Holland. He received his basic education in Aarhus, then attended schools and universities including Marburg, Montpellier, Strasbourg, and Padua and received the doctorate in medicine at Basel in 1611. He then practiced medicine in London until 1611, when he was appointed professor of humanities at the University of Copenhagen. In 1615 he became professor of Greek, and in 1624 professor of medicine, which chair he retained until his death thirty years later. He also was several times elected rector of the university. Worm continued to practice medicine throughout his life and was personal physician to King Christian V. He discovered and described the small bones that occasionally occur along the lambdoid suture of the human skull; they are still called Wormian bones.

A conscientious physician, Worm remained in Copenhagen to tend his patients during epidemics when many had fled the city; in the plague of 1654 he caught the disease and died of it.

A gifted polymath, Worm collected many types of objects, especially those of natural history and man-made artifacts, which he carefully arranged and classified, following a rigorous method; he also prepared a detailed catalog, published in 1655 by his son William as *Museum Wormianum*. His museum, which became one of the great attractions of Copenhagen, is illustrated in *Museum Wormianum*: an assortment of bizarre and exotic objects, antiques, and stuffed animals. It included the skull of a narwhal properly described; previously narwhal tusks had been supposed to be the horns of unicorns. There were many prehistoric stone implements, but Worm did not conclude that they belonged to a stone age and were artifacts; he labeled them "*Cerauniae*, so called because they are thought to fall to earth in flashes of lightning"—a belief widely held at that time. This is curious, because Worm recognized the tip of a stone harpoon point embedded in a marine animal found in Greenland, and also knew of stone tools and weapons from America. On his death, Worm's museum passed to King Frederik III and was installed in the old castle at Copenhagen. The king planned a new building for Worm's collections and library opposite Christiansborg Palace; but the second story, housing the museum, was not finished until after the king's death in 1680. It was open to the public on payment of an admission charge, and was one of the first such museums.

Worm was interested in Danish antiquities and published accounts of them in his *Monumenta Danica* and his *Fasti Danici* (1643). Particularly interested in runic inscriptions, he traveled extensively to visit runic sites, and collected information through correspondence. In 1626 he arranged for a royal circular to instruct all clergy to submit a report on any runic inscriptions, burial sites, or other historical remains known in their parishes. In 1639 a gold horn was discovered in Jutland; and Worm, with his great knowledge of runes and antiquities, was asked to describe and study it; he did so, publishing *De aureo cornu* in 1641. This gold horn, and another discovered a hundred years later, were stolen from the royal collections in 1802 and destroyed. Worm's account of the horn, and the runes and designs on it, are therefore of great importance.

GLYN DANIEL

505

**WORSAAE, JENS JACOB** (*b*. Vejle, Jutland, Denmark, 14 March 1821; *d*. Copenhagen, Denmark, 15 August 1885), *archaeology*.

Worsaae, the son of the county sheriff at Vejle, became an avid collector of antiquities while quite young. As a schoolboy he and a porter employed by a local merchant traveled the countryside, collecting pottery and bronzes and driving shafts into prehistoric barrows. By the time he entered school in Copenhagen, he was said to have the best and largest collection of antiquities from Jutland. In 1836, when he was only fifteen, Worsaae contacted Christian Jurgensen Thomsen, director of the Museum of Northern Antiquities, now the National Museum. Thomsen used him as an unpaid assistant; and soon Worsaae was cataloging artifacts, conducting groups through the museum, and helping Thomsen with his correspondence.

Worsaae was concerned with aspects of prehistoric archaeology that did not interest Thomsen, who was essentially a museum man. Worsaae was keenly interested in excavation. During the years 1836–1840 Worsaae spent his Sundays and half-holidays digging barrows north of Copenhagen; and in the vacations he did fieldwork and excavation in Jutland, where his parents paid two laborers to assist him. He drove broad trenches through the barrows and observed changes of structure and secondary burials; thus he became one of the first archaeologists to study and understand the stratigraphy of barrow construction. In 1840 Worsaae published an article on the grave mounds of Denmark, dividing them into those of the Stone Age, the Bronze Age, and the Iron Age. It was a revolutionary achievement, for he had taken Thomsen's three-age system, originally devised as a museum classification; had applied it to antiquities found in the field; and had shown, in barrows and in peat bogs, that Thomsen's theory of the three successive ages of the prehistoric past was supported by stratigraphy. This sequence was later demonstrated in the Swiss lake-dwellings. The Danish technological model of the past thus became a proven fact of prehistory.

In 1841, Christian VIII of Denmark gave Worsaae a travel grant to study antiquities in southern Sweden. The result was his book *Danmarks oldtid oplyst ved Oldsager og Gravhøje* (1843), which was also published in German and was translated into English as *The Primaeval Antiquities of England and Denmark* (1849). It is undoubtedly one of the half-dozen most important and influential books on archaeology published in the nineteenth century. Worsaae then traveled in England, Ireland, and Scotland, studying the national collections and lecturing to archaeologists on the Danish three-age system.

Upon returning to Denmark from his British tour, Worsaae was appointed to the specially created post of inspector of ancient monuments. In 1854 he was made professor of archaeology at the University of Copenhagen, and in 1865 he succeeded Thomsen as director of the National Museum, a post he held until his death. Worsaae traveled throughout Europe, attending international conferences and making and continuing friendships. He was both a representative of Scandinavian archaeology and one of the first pan-European archaeological travelers and scholars.

Worsaae recognized the truth and importance of the Danish three-age system stated by Thomsen, calling it "the first clear ray . . . shed across the Universal prehistoric gloom of the North and the World in general." His contribution was to confirm the truth of the system through his excavations and his careful stratigraphical observations. Worsaae was interested not only in the archaeological record of the past but also in the interpretation of that record in terms of human history. For instance, he wondered whether the succession of the Stone, Bronze, and Iron ages meant cultural evolution, or whether they were caused by the arrival of new people. In all his writings he was keenly aware of the issue of independent invention versus diffusion, which became highly controversial during the nineteenth and early twentieth centuries. Worsaae himself believed that the transition from Stone Age to Bronze Age must have meant the arrival in northern Europe of new people from southeastern Europe or the Near East; he argued, however, that the change from Bronze Age to Iron Age could have been effected by trade and the movement of small groups without an invasion of new people.

Worsaae has often been described as the first full-time professional archaeologist. Johannes Brøndsted, a mid-twentieth-century director of the National Museum at Copenhagen, described him as "the actual founder of antiquarian research as an independent science." A pioneer in excavation, interpretation, synthesis, and exposition, he was undoubtedly one of the great archaeologists of the nineteenth century.

*BIBLIOGRAPHY*

O. Klindt-Jensen, *A History of Scandinavian Archaeology* (London, 1975), has a complete bibliography of Worsaae's writings. See also G. Bibby, *The Testimo-*

*ny of the Spade* (London, 1957); G. E. Daniel, *A Hundred Years of Archaeology* (London, 1950); G. E. Daniel, *The Idea of Prehistory* (London, 1962); and G. E. Daniel, *The Origins and Growth of Archaeology* (London, 1967).

GLYN DANIEL

**WOTTON, EDWARD** (*b.* Oxford, England, 1492; *d.* London, England, 5 October 1555), *medicine, natural history.*

Wotton was the son of Richard Wotton, beadle of the University of Oxford. He was educated at "the Grammar School joining to Magdalen College" and, from 1506, at Magdalen College, graduating 9 February 1514 and becoming a fellow in 1516. In January 1521 he followed John Claymond to Corpus Christi College, becoming *socio compar* then (or, more probably, in 1523). He was later permitted to travel in Italy for from three to five years to "improve his learning, and chiefly to learn Greek." He also studied at the medical school of Padua, graduating M.D. in 1526. He was awarded the same degree at Oxford on his return later that year. Wotton subsequently moved to London. He was admitted fellow of the Royal College of Physicians on 8 February 1528 and was active in its administration, becoming president (1541–1543) and censor (1552–1553, 1555). As befitted his standing at the College of Physicians, he numbered among his patients the duke of Norfolk and Margaret Pole, countess of Salisbury; and he is said to have also been physician to Henry VIII.

Wotton's scientific reputation rests on *De differentiis animalium libri decem* (Paris, 1552). Each of the ten books in this work deals with a major topic. Books 1–3 are devoted to generalities—the parts of, functions of, and differences between animals; book 4 deals with man; book 5, with quadrupeds that bear live young; book 6, with quadrupeds that lay eggs; book 7, with birds; book 8, with fishes; book 9, with insects; and book 10, with crustaceans, squids, and mollusks. The entries in the index refer to page numbers and a letter. Each text page is lettered every eleven lines (A–D on recto; E–H on verso), a practical and advanced method of indexing, considering the date at which it was printed.

Wotton dedicated his book to King Edward VI, then in the last year of his six-year reign. In this dedication he explains his purpose in compiling the book and briefly describes its preparation, mentioning his practice of studying books of writers whose work could contribute to his knowledge of medicine and telling how he compiled commentaries on them. His discovery of the writings of the French botanist Jean Ruel (*De natura stirpium libri tres*, 1536) and of Agricola (*De natura fossilium*, 1546) came during his study of earlier authors; but feeling that he could not surpass their work in these fields, Wotton concentrated on zoology.

It is as a compilation that Wotton's *De differentiis animalium* must be viewed. C. E. Raven called it an "astonishing mosaic of extracts from every sort of Graeco-Roman writer . . .," but this should not necessarily be seen as criticism. The book is the production of a man whose education had been that of a classical scholar and whose professional ethos was firmly rooted in ancient writers. Nothing was more natural than for Wotton to produce virtually a pandect of the classical writers on zoology. In this work, as in his sources, he was reflecting the development of Renaissance science. The invention of printing had made well-produced, indexed, and often illustrated editions of the writings of the classical authorities widely available. This rendered the knowledge of classicists of Wotton's generation more precise and paved the way for the great Renaissance encyclopedists in the natural sciences. Wotton was the first of these writers (although Adam Lonicerus' *Naturalis historiae opus novum . . .* was published a year earlier, Wotton's work had been long in preparation), who include Konrad Gesner and Ulisse Aldrovandi. Modern naturalists may view Wotton's book, like Aldrovandi's and much of Gesner's, as overweighted with information from the literature and short on original observation. But the encyclopedists' purpose was to bring together the literature; and it was on their foundation that the earliest field naturalists, such as William Turner (*ca.* 1508–1568) and Pierre Belon, built.

*De differentiis animalium* had a considerable influence on later naturalists. Gesner praised it as a complete and clearly written digest of zoological knowledge, but its reputation was greatest in entomological circles. In book 9 Wotton discussed at some length the complexities of insect metamorphoses but was unable to reconcile them with his implicit belief in spontaneous generation (lice formed from human sweat, and caterpillars from plants). This book, in which he gave evidence for some original observation, was quoted—and in places relied upon—in Thomas Moffett's *Theatrum insectorum*, an elaborate and creditable work based partly on the manuscript of his friend and fellow physician Thomas Penny. Moffett's book, published posthumously in 1634 by Theodore Mayerne, was the first entomological book to appear in England. It was later translated into English by John Rowland and appeared in 1658 as the third volume of Edward Topsell's *History of Four-Footed Beasts and Serpents . . .*, a book that, because of its use of English and despite its inclusion of fabulous beasts, strongly influenced popular interest in natural history in England.

*BIBLIOGRAPHY*

See A. F. P[ollard], "Wotton, Edward," in *Dictionary of National Biography*, LXIII, 48–49; C. E. Raven, *English Naturalists From Neckam to Ray* (London, 1947); and G. Sarton, *The Appreciation of Ancient and Medieval Science During the Renaissance (1450–1600)* (Philadelphia, 1955).

ALWYNE WHEELER

**WOULFE, PETER** (*b.* Ireland [?], 1727 [?]; *d.* London, England, 1803), *chemistry.*

The familiar two-necked bottle generally known as a Woulfe's bottle has long been a standard item of equipment in most chemical laboratories. The apparatus has been traced back to J. R. Glauber, and its attribution to Woulfe seems to stem from his use of a vessel with two outlets in a series of distillation experiments described in 1767. His "new method" was designed to prevent the escape of fumes "very hurtful to the lungs" by passing them through a tube into water.

Woulfe's origins are obscure and little seems to be known of him before his election to the Royal Society in 1767, when he was described as a "Gentleman well skilled in Natural Philosophy and particularly Chymistry." He was then living at Clerkenwell, London, and apparently spent most summers in Paris. What little is known of Woulfe, apart from his published work, relates mainly to his eccentricities, which were described by W. T. Brande, who cited him as a belated believer in transmutation: "He had long vainly searched for the elixir, and attributed his repeated failures to the want of due preparation by pious and charitable acts." Humphry Davy, in his *Collected Works* (IX, 367), said that Woulfe attached prayers to his apparatus. A. N. von Scherer, writing in 1801 (*Allgemeines Journal der Chemie*, **5**, 128–129), hints at mental derangement "that must concern all friends of philosophy and natural knowledge"; and it seems probable that these aberrations were char-

acteristic of Woulfe's later years. His writings are lucid and show him to have been a competent chemist. Priestley frequently referred to him as a valued friend who lent him apparatus, offered guidance, and suggested experiments.

In the paper of 1767, Woulfe described the preparation of "marine ether" (ethyl chloride) by mixing alcohol vapor with that from the reaction of sulfuric acid with common salt (hydrogen chloride). He also made "nitrous ether" (ethyl nitrate) by distilling alcohol with nitric acid, and in a paper of 1784 he reported a better yield by what he claimed to be a hitherto untried method, using niter and sulfuric acid instead of nitric acid. In 1771 he investigated "mosaic gold" (stannic sulfide; see J. R. Partington, in *Isis*, **21** [1934], 203–206), and in the same paper he described the use of indigo. After mentioning the known method of making a blue solution of the dye in sulfuric acid, Woulfe described its solution in nitric acid. He claimed to have obtained a yellow substance that would dye wool and silk, the first recorded preparation of picric acid.

In December 1775 Woulfe was appointed to give the first lecture under the terms of the will of Henry Baker, who had bequeathed £100 to the Royal Society, the interest from which was to finance an annual discourse, provided the first was given within a year of payment. The Council accepted the bequest on 13 July 1775, and Woulfe delivered the first Bakerian lecture on 20 June 1776.

*BIBLIOGRAPHY*

I. ORIGINAL WORKS. Woulfe's main papers are "Experiments on the Distillation of Acids, Volatile Alkalies, &c. Shewing How They May Be Condensed Without Loss, & How Thereby We May Avoid Disagreeable and Noxious Fumes," in *Philosophical Transactions of the Royal Society*, **57** (1767), 517–536; "Experiments to Shew the Nature of Aurum Mosaicum," *ibid.*, **61** (1771), 114–130; "Experiments on a New Colouring Substance From the Island of Amsterdam in the South Sea," *ibid.*, **65** (1775), 91–93; "Experiments Made in Order to Ascertain the Nature of Some Mineral Substances; and, in Particular, to See How Far the Acids of Sea-Salt and of Vitriol Contribute to Mineralize Metallic and Other Substances," *ibid.*, **66** (1776), 605–623, the first Bakerian lecture; "Experiments on Some Mineral Substances," *ibid.*, **69** (1779), 11–34; and "A New Method of Making Nitrous Aether, by Which Means a Greater Quantity of the Aether Is Obtained With Less Expense and Trouble Than by Any Other Process Heretofore Described," read 5 Feb. 1784—the paper was not published in *Philosophical Transactions*, but the MS is in the Royal Society archives, *Letters & Papers*, decade VIII (vol. **73**), no. 57; a French trans. was published in *Observations sur la physique, sur l'histoire naturelle et sur les arts*, **25** (1784), 352–354. A few of Woulfe's later papers (of little importance) were published in the *Observations*.

II. SECONDARY LITERATURE. No adequate biography exists; what little material is available seems to depend on W. T. Brande's short account, based on hearsay, in the historical introduction to his *Manual of Chemistry*— for instance, 6th ed., I (London, 1848), xvii–xviii. P. J. Hartog, in *Dictionary of National Biography*, LXIII (1900), 63–64, gives some useful references; see also J. R. Partington, *History of Chemistry*, III (London, 1962), 300–301. The origin and history of "Woulfe's bottle" is discussed in W. A. Campbell, "Peter Woulfe and His Bottle," in *Chemistry and Industry* (1957), 1182–1183.

E. L. SCOTT

**WREN, CHRISTOPHER** (*b*. East Knoyle, Wiltshire, England, 20 October 1632; *d*. London, England, 25 February 1723), *mathematics, architecture*.

Wren came from a family with strong ecclesiastical traditions. His father, for whom he was named, was rector of East Knoyle, chaplain to Charles I, and later (1634) dean of Windsor. His uncle, Matthew Wren, was successively bishop of Hereford, Norwich, and Ely. Wren was frail as a child, yet even in his earliest years he manifested an interest in the construction of mechanical instruments that included a rain gauge and a "pneumatic engine." He was educated at Westminster School, whence he proceeded in 1649 to Wadham College, Oxford. There he became closely associated with John Wilkins, who was later bishop of Chester and a member of that distinguished group whose activities led to the formation of the Royal Society. At Wadham College, Wren's talent for mathematical and scientific pursuits soon attracted attention. He graduated B.A. in 1651, and three years later received the M.A. He was elected a fellow of All Souls College, Oxford, in 1653 and remained in residence there until 1657.

Wren's interest in astronomy appears to have manifested itself about that time, and it led to his appointment, as professor of astronomy at Gresham College in 1657. In his inaugural lecture, after mentioning the relation of astronomy to mathematics, to theology in the interpretation of the Scriptures, to medicine, and above all to navigation, he praised the new liberty in the study and observation of nature, and the rejection of the tyranny of ancient opinions. He retained this professorship until 1661, when he was appointed Savilian professor of astronomy at Oxford, a post he occupied until 1673.

Wren is best remembered as an architect. His fame as the most distinguished architect England has produced probably has obscured his accomplishments in other branches of science. He was perhaps the most accomplished man of his day. While at Oxford he ranked high in his knowledge of anatomy; and his abilities as a demonstrator in that subject were acknowledged with praise by Thomas Willis in his *Cerebri anatome*, for which Wren made all the drawings. Wren also is said to have been the pioneer in the physiological experiments of injecting various liquids into the veins of living animals (Weld, *History*, I, 273).

Wren made important contributions to mathematics; and Newton, in the second edition of his *Principia* (1713), classed him with John Wallis and Christiaan Huygens as the leading geometers of the day ("Christopherus Wrennus, eques auratus, geometrarum facile principes," p. 19). Chief among his contributions was his rectification of the cycloid. This curve, because of its singularly beautiful properties, had long been a favorite of geometers since its discovery early in the sixteenth century. Many of its properties had been discovered by Pascal; its rectification, the finding of a straight line equal to an arc of the curve, was effected by Wren in 1658 and also by Fermat.

In 1668 Oldenburg asked Wren, along with Wallis and Huygens, to inform the Royal Society of his research into the laws of impact. In a terse paper read on 17 December 1668 and published on 11 January 1669 in the *Philosophical Transactions*, Wren offered a theoretical solution based on the model of a balance beam on which the impacting bodies are suspended at distances from the point of impact proportional to their initial speeds. Equilibrium in the model corresponds to an impact situation in which bodies approach one another at speeds inversely proportional to their sizes and, Wren postulated as a "Law of Nature," rebound at their initial speeds, which Wren termed their "proper speeds." In cases in which the center of motion does not coincide with the center of gravity of the system, Wren postulated that impact shifts the center of motion to a point equidistant from the center of gravity on the opposite side. Employing the further postulate that the speed of approach equals the speed of separation, Wren set forth rules of calculation that yield the center of gravity from the known sizes and initial speeds of the bodies, and then use the speeds and the center of gravity to compute the final speeds. The close fit of these results with experiment seems to have been the basic source of Wren's confidence in his solution. Wren also made a number of pendulum experiments, and Wilkins declared that he was the first to suggest the determination of standard measure of length by means of the oscillation of the pendulum (Weld, *History*, I, 196).

Even as a boy Wren had shown that he had the capacity to become a draftsman of exceptional ability. He probably applied himself to the serious study of the subject when he was commissioned to submit plans for the building of the chapel of Pembroke College, Cambridge, which was completed in 1663. His next major achievement was the building of the Sheldonian Theatre, Oxford, a model of which was exhibited before the newly formed Royal Society in April 1663. It was completed in 1669, and in that year Charles II appointed Wren surveyor of the royal works, a post he retained for half a century.

Meanwhile, the Great Fire had given Wren a unique opportunity to display his skill as an architect. Much of the City of London had been destroyed in the conflagration, including the old St. Paul's. This building, ancient and ruinous, had long been in urgent need of repairs; and just before the fire Wren had been invited by the dean to prepare plans for the building of a new cathedral. Wren's original plans were not approved, so he prepared a second scheme, having meanwhile obtained the concession that he might make such alterations as he deemed advisable. This second scheme was accepted, and a warrant for the building of the cathedral was issued in 1675. The first stone was laid on 21 June 1675, and after many delays the cathedral was finished in 1710.

Much of the City having been destroyed, Wren was invited to submit plans for the rebuilding of some fifty churches consumed in the flames. (These are described in *Parentalia*, 309–318.) At Oxford he built, in addition to the Sheldonian Theatre, the Tom Tower of Christ Church and Queen's College Chapel. At Cambridge, besides the chapel at Pembroke College, he built the library of Trinity College.

Wren received many honors. The University of Oxford conferred upon him the degree of doctor of Civil Laws; Cambridge awarded him the LL.D. In 1673 he was knighted. Wren also represented many constituencies in Parliament at different periods. In 1669 he married Faith Coghill, of Blechingdon, Oxford, by whom he had two sons, one of whom survived him. On the death of Lady Wren he married Jane Fitzwilliam, by whom he had a son and a daughter.

Wren played a prominent part in the formation of the Royal Society of London, which arose out of the informal gatherings of the votaries of experimental science that took place about the middle of the seventeenth century. These gatherings doubtless were inspired by the growing desire for learning that had been stimulated by the writings of Francis Bacon, notably the *Novum Organum*; but they also owed much to the institution founded under the will of Sir Thomas Gresham, according to which seven professors were employed to lecture on successive days of the week on divinity, astronomy, geometry, physic, law, rhetoric, and music. Of those whose enthusiasm prompted them to associate themselves with the new venture, the best-known, besides Wren, were Robert Boyle, John Wilkins, John Wallis, John Evelyn, Robert Hooke, and William Petty. The meetings, held at Gresham College, were suspended during the troubled times that followed the Civil War. On the return of Charles II in May 1660, they were revived and the need for a more formal organization was at once recognized. Accordingly, on 28 November 1660 the following memorandum was drawn up: "These persons following . . . mett together at Gresham Colledge to heare Mr. Wren's lecture." At the end of Wren's lecture it was proposed that the meetings should continue weekly. A list was drawn up of those interested; and at a meeting held on 19 December 1660, it was ordered that subsequent meetings should be held at Gresham College.

The charter of incorporation passed the great seal on 15 July 1662 (which thus is the date of the formation of the Royal Society); Wren is said to have prepared its preamble. A Council was formed, with Wren as one of the members. He was the Society's third president, serving from 30 November 1680 to 30 November 1682. *The Record Book of the Royal Society of London* (1940, 18) pays tribute to Wren's zeal and encouragement despite the difficulties facing the young organization: "To him the Royal Society owes a deep debt of gratitude for the constant and loyal service which he rendered to it in its early days."

Wren also studied meteorology long before it had become an exact science through the work of Mariotte, Boyle, and Hooke. He was one of the earliest naturalists to investigate, by means of the microscope, the structure of insects; and his remarkable skill as a draftsman enabled him to make accurate drawings of what he saw.

Wren was largely instrumental in arranging for the (unauthorized) publication of Flamsteed's *Historia coelestis Britannica* (1712), which had been financed by Prince George, Queen Anne's consort, but had ceased with his death in 1708. When at length printing was resumed, many obstacles were placed in Flamsteed's way. Wren had been appointed a member of the committee to oversee the printing of the work; and despite much opposition, he gave Flamsteed great encouragement. Nevertheless, Flamsteed's wishes met with little response; and after the work eventually appeared under Halley's editorship, Flamsteed managed to secure three hundred of the four hundred copies printed and at once consigned them to the flames.

In 1718 Wren was superseded as surveyor of the royal works, after more than fifty years of active and laborious service to the crown and the public. He then retired to Hampton Court, where he spent the last five years of his life. He is buried in St. Paul's Cathedral, where a tablet to his memory has been erected.

*BIBLIOGRAPHY*

I. Original Works. Among Wren's papers that appeared in *Philosophical Transactions of the Royal Society* are "Lex collisionis corporum" (Mar. 1669); "Description of an Instrument Invented Divers Years Ago for Drawing the Out-line of Any Objective in Perspective" (1669); "The Generation of an Hyperbolical Cylindroid Demonstrated, and the Application Thereof to the Grinding of Hyperbolical Glasses" (June 1669); "A Description of Dr. Christopher Wren's Engin Designed for Grinding Hyperbolical Glasses" (Nov. 1669); and "On Finding a Straight Line Equal to That of a Cycloid and to the Parts Thereof" (Nov. 1673).

II. Secondary Literature. See Sir Harold Hartley, ed., *The Royal Society: Its Origins and Founders* (London, 1960); *Parentalia, or Memoirs of the Family of Wrens* (London, 1750), compiled by his son Christopher and published by his grandson Stephen; *Record Book of the Royal Society of London* (1940); and C. R. Weld, *History of the Royal Society*, 2 vols. (London, 1848).

For Wren's work on impact, see A. R. Hall and M. B. Hall, eds., *The Correspondence of Henry Oldenburg*, V (Madison, Wis., 1968), 117–118, 125, 134–135, 193, 263, 265, and in particular 319–320 (Wren's paper in the original Latin) and 320–321 (an English translation).

J. F. Scott

**WRIGHT, ALMROTH EDWARD** (*b.* Middleton Tyas, near Richmond, Yorkshire, England, 10 August 1861; *d.* Farnham Common, Buckingham-shire, England, 30 April 1947), *pathology, bacteriology, immunology.*

Wright was the second son of an Irish Presbyterian minister, Charles Henry Hamilton Wright, and Ebba Johanna Dorothea Almroth, daughter of a Swedish chemistry professor. While his father was a minister at Dresden, Germany (1863–1868); at Boulogne, France (1868–1874); and at Belfast, Ireland (1874–1885), Almroth was educated by his parents and tutors, and at Belfast Academical Institution. At age seventeen he entered Trinity College, Dublin, and earned a B.A. in modern literature in 1882 and a B.M. in medicine in 1883. On a traveling scholarship he studied medicine at the University of Leipzig.

Upon his return to London, Wright read law briefly, then became an Admiralty clerk with free time for medical research at the Brown Institution (University of London) in Wandsworth. Subsequently he was demonstrator of pathology at Cambridge University in 1887; and on a scholarship he studied pathological anatomy at Marburg and physiological chemistry at Strasbourg. Wright was demonstrator of physiology at the University of Sydney, Australia, in 1889–1891; and, back in England, he worked briefly in the laboratory of the College of Physicians and Surgeons, London, in the latter year.

In 1892 Wright was appointed professor of pathology at Army Medical School, Netley, where for ten years he did original work in blood coagulation and in bacteriology, achieving notable success in developing a vaccine against typhoid fever. The vaccine was tested on soldiers in India and Wright promoted it as a member of the India Plague Commission (1898–1900), for which he wrote the report. The War Office used it on a voluntary and poorly supervised basis during the Boer War, but the vaccine seemed effective; and Britain alone entered World War I with troops largely immunized against typhoid fever. Differences with the army caused Wright to resign and enabled him to undertake his major work as professor of pathology at St. Mary's Hospital, London (1902–1946).

At St. Mary's Hospital, Wright continued his pioneer work in immunization, aided by a remarkable team of research workers that included Alexander Fleming, who later discovered penicillin. Wright initially had a large private practice and told his research workers to do the same, partly because the laboratory pay was small but mainly because he believed it made one sensitive to the human aspects of the laboratory's work. Wright's enthusiasm inspired his staff, who willingly worked long hours on difficult problems. At frequent midnight teas in the laboratory, he dominated the robust discussion. Fond of quoting long passages of poetry, he was admired by colleagues and disciples, although others found him difficult.

By 1908 the laboratory had expanded into a considerable research institute that received important visitors, including Robert Koch, Paul Ehrlich, and Élie Metchnikoff. In 1911 Wright was invited to South Africa to help prevent pneumonia among Africans in the Rand gold mines. He introduced prophylactic inoculations that greatly reduced the pneumonia death rate. In 1913 Wright was offered, and accepted, the directorship of the department of bacteriology of the Medical Research Committee (later Council) laboratory at Hampstead. World War I intervened, however; and from 1914 to 1919 Wright served in France, heading a research laboratory concerned with wound infections. He locally applied a hypertonic salt solution as an osmotic agent to draw lymph into wounds and also provided scientific justification for the early closure of such wounds. Honors for his war work included the Le Conte Prize of the Académie des Sciences (1915), the Buchanan Medal of the Royal Society (1917), and a special medal of the Royal Society of Medicine (1920) "for the best medical work in connection with the war." For his previous achievements in typhoid vaccine, he had been knighted in 1906.

Rather than resume the government position interrupted by the war, Wright in 1919 returned to St. Mary's Hospital for more than a quarter-century of work in immunology, retiring as principal of the research institute in 1946. Although a prodigious worker in the years between the wars, his influence declined in the medical world, partly because his bluntly stated and unconventional views caused some antagonism. These views were not all on medical questions. He was vigorously antifeminist and wrote letters to the press and a book to show that women were biologically and psychologically inferior. George Bernard Shaw wrote a devastating reply to Wright's views on the subject; but despite this difference of views, Shaw admired Wright, praised the quality of his writings, and got the idea for his play *The Doctor's Dilemma* from discussions with Wright and his colleagues at St. Mary's Hospital. The play's leading character, Sir Colenso Ridgeon, is modeled on Wright. His biographer, Leonard Colebrook, attributes some of Wright's unorthodox views to his long seclusion in the laboratory and to the austeri-

ty of his scientific life. Nevertheless, he had a fairly regular home life, having married Jane Georgina Wilson in 1889. They had two sons and a daughter.

Wright's place in science as one of the founders of modern immunology is probably not far behind that of Pasteur, Ehrlich, and Metchnikoff. Working independently, Wright in England, and Richard F. J. Pfeiffer and Wilhelm Kolle in Germany, shared in the discovery of a successful typhoid vaccine (1896). Wright also originated vaccines against enteric tuberculosis and pneumonia; proved the worth of inoculating with dead microbes; and made valuable contributions to the study of opsonins, blood substances that help to overcome bacteria. Although typhoid vaccine was his best-known discovery, members of the research team he trained made important contributions, and his lifetime work in immunology was considerable.

## BIBLIOGRAPHY

I. ORIGINAL WORKS. Prominent among Wright's more than 150 scientific writings are *A Short Treatise on Anti-Typhoid Inoculation* (London, 1904); *Principles of Microscopy* (London, 1906); *Studies in Immunization* (London, 1909; 2nd ser., 1944); *Technique of the Teat and Capillary Glass Tube* (London, 1912, 2nd ed., 1921); *The Unexpurgated Case Against Woman Suffrage* (London, 1913); *Prolegomena to Logic Which Searches for the Truth* (1941), the first part of a larger philosophical work never completed but continued posthumously in *Alethetropic Logic* (London, 1953); *Pathology and Treatment of War Wounds* (London, 1942); and *On Induction* (London, 1943). Seventeen of his works are listed in an obituary, "Sir Almroth Wright," in *British Medical Journal*, no. 4506 (17 May 1947), 699–700.

II. SECONDARY LITERATURE. An evaluative sketch appears in M. Marquardt, "Pioneer in Vaccine Therapy," in *Life and Letters*, **50** (Sept. 1946), 127–130. A book-length biography is Leonard Colebrook, *Almroth Wright; Provocative Doctor and Thinker* (London, 1954); also see his "Almroth Edward Wright," in *Lancet*, **252**, no. 6454 (10 May 1947), 654–656; and "Wright, Sir Almroth Edward," in *Dictionary of National Biography 1941–1950*, 976–978. Other obituary accounts are in *Who Was Who 1941–50* (London, 1952), 1265; New York *Times* (1 May 1947), 25; *Times* of London (1, 3, 6, 9, 13 May 1947), all on 7; *Obituary Notices of Fellows of the Royal Society of London*, **17** (1948), 297–314; and R. T. Mummery, "Sir Almroth Edward Wright, 1861–1947," in *Nature*, **159** (31 May 1947), 731–732. Wright also is mentioned in L. J. Ludovici, *Fleming, Discoverer of Penicillin* (Bloomington, Ind., 1952); and André Maurois, *The Life of Sir Alexan-*

*der Fleming, Discoverer of Penicillin* (New York, 1959), esp. chs. 3, 4.

FRANKLIN PARKER

**WRIGHT, EDWARD** (*b.* Garveston, Norfolk, England, October 1561; *d.* London, England, November 1615), *mathematics, cartography.*

Details of Wright's life are unusually scanty and must be supplemented from facts about his relatives and friends. His father, Henry, was described as "mediocris fortunae, deceased" when an elder brother, Thomas, entered Gonville and Caius College, Cambridge, as a pensioner in 1574. Probably both boys were taught by John Hayward at a neighboring school in Hardingham. Edward joined his brother at Caius College, Cambridge, in December 1576; but Thomas' support for him was short-lived, since he died early in 1579. Wright's academic career closely paralleled that of John Fletcher: both graduated B.A. in 1581 and M.A. in 1584, and obtained their fellowships on Lady Day 1587. Fletcher had returned for his fellowship after teaching for a few years at Dronfield Grammar School, Derbyshire, so it is possible that Wright was also away from Cambridge in 1581–1584. Fletcher had a reputation as a medical writer, collaborator with Sir Christopher Heydon on his *Defence of Judiciall Astrologie* (1603), and as mathematics teacher to Henry Briggs. Contemporary with Briggs at St. John's College was Thomas Bernhere, later Wright's brother-in-law; both graduated M.A. in 1585, became fellows of their college, and were closely associated with Henry Alvey, one of the leaders of Cambridge Puritanism.[1]

In 1589 Wright received royal permission to absent himself from Cambridge in order to accompany George, earl of Cumberland, on an expedition to the Azores that was intended to acquire booty from Spanish ships. In 1599 Wright wrote that "the time of my first employment at sea" was "more than tenne yeares since." This suggests that he may have been to sea previously, possibly in 1581–1584. There seems little doubt that he had already acquired a reputation in mathematical navigation, and none at all that his 1589 voyage contributed greatly to his main achievements (described below). Wright returned to Cambridge at the end of 1589 and prepared a draft of his most important book, *Certaine Errors in Navigation*, in the next year or so. The 1599 printed version incorporates results obtained from observations made at London in the period May 1594–November 1597. It would seem that Wright had moved from Cambridge before the expiration of his fellowship in 1596, and that he had married the sister of Thomas Bernhere in 1595. Their only son, Samuel, entered his father's college after schooling in London but died before graduation, "a youth of much promise."

The succession of London mathematical lecturers is confused, but it is probable that Wright had some such employment after leaving Cambridge. These lecturers had been supported by Sir Thomas Smith and Sir John Wolstenholme, two rich city merchants closely connected with several trading companies. Thomas Hood was an early lecturer, and it has been suggested that Wright succeeded him. The position was complicated by the starting of Gresham College, where Henry Briggs was first professor of geometry.

There was, however, still a need for lecturers in navigation; Wright was serving in this capacity in 1614 when the East India Company took over the patronage and paid him an annual salary of £50. He may have held this post from 1612, the year of the death of Prince Henry, whom he had tutored in mathematics and whose librarianship he had been expecting. About the same time Wright was surveyor for the New River project, under Sir Hugh Myddleton, for bringing water to London.[2] During this London period he also wrote and published a number of mathematical tracts.

The publishing history of Wright's main work, *Certaine Errors in Navigation*, is complex. Wright himself outlined the impetus for the chief feature of this work, the justification of the so-called Mercator map projection, described as "the greatest advance ever made in marine cartography."[3] He criticized the usual sea charts as "like an inextricable labyrinth of error," offering as an instance his own experience in 1589: land was sighted "when by account of the ordinary chart we should have beene 50 leagues short of it." He admitted that his development had been prompted by Mercator's 1569 map of the world, but stated that neither Mercator nor anybody else had shown him how to do it. Wright's principle was very simple: to increase the distance apart of the parallels of latitude to match the exaggeration arising from the assumption that they were equally long. Since the lengths of the parallels varied according to a factor $\cos \lambda$, the correction factor was $\sec \lambda$ at any point. In order to plot the parallels on the new charts, Wright had effectively to perform the integration $\int_0^\lambda \sec \lambda\, d\lambda$. This was done numerically—in his own words, "by perpetual addition of the Secantes answerable to the latitudes of each point or parallel into the summe compounded of all the former secantes. . . ."

Wright's development of the Mercator projection was first published by others. *Thomas Blundevile His Exercises Containing Six Treatises* (1594) was an important navigation compilation, the first to describe the use of the sine, tangent, and secant trigonometric functions. The author was at a loss to explain the new (Mercator) arrangement, which had been constructed "by what rule I knowe not, unless it be by such a table, as my friende M. Wright of Caius College in Cambridge at my request sent me (I thanke him) not long since for that purpose, which table with his consent, I have here plainlie set down together with the use thereof as followeth." The table of meridional parts was given at degree intervals.[4]

Two years later, following his publication of a Dutch version of Emery Molyneux's globe, Jodocus Hondius published at Amsterdam the well-known "Christian-Knight" maps of the world and of the four continents. These were based on Wright's theory of Mercator's projection, but were issued without acknowledgment. It seems that when he was in England, Hondius had been allowed to see the manuscript of Wright's *Certaine Errors*. In 1598–1600 Richard Hakluyt published his *Principal Navigations*, which contains two world charts on the new projection, that of 1600 a revision of the first. Although there is no attribution, it is clear that Wright was a major collaborator; further revisions in Hakluyt's work were made for versions in the 1610 and 1657 editions of his *Certaine Errors*.

Before the Hakluyt maps, William Barlow had included in his *The Navigator's Supply* (1597) a demonstration of Wright's projection "obtained of a friend of mine of like profession unto myself." This evidence of interest in his work was brought home to Wright when the earl of Cumberland showed him a manuscript that had been found among the possessions of Abraham Kendall and was being prepared for the press. Wright was surprised to find it was a copy of his own *Certaine Errors*, an experience that convinced him it was time to publish the work himself.

Ultimately Wright included his "The Voyage of the Earl of Cumberland to the Azores," which had been printed in Hakluyt's second volume. With it was a chart of the Azores on the new projection, showing Cumberland's route; this has been judged to be more significant than the world charts, since

it was large enough to be used. *Certaine Errors* discussed other navigation problems, and was considerably extended in the second edition (1610), dedicated to Prince Henry. Wright also contributed to two seminal works. In 1600 he helped, particularly with a preface, to produce William Gilbert's *De magnete*. His translation of John Napier's *Mirifici logarithmorum canonis constructio*, *A Description of the Admirable Table of Logarithmes*, appeared posthumously. It was approved by Napier and brought out by his friend Henry Briggs after the death of Wright's son Samuel, who contributed the dedication to the East Indies Company. The book marks the lifelong collaboration between Briggs and Wright, and the latter's efforts to spread a better understanding of navigation.[5] Nobody had done more to "set the seal on the supremacy of the English in the theory and practice of the art of navigation at this time."

*NOTES*

1. The baptism at Garveston took place on 8 October 1561; the father's will, dated 17 January 1573, left his house to his wife, Margaret, and then to Edward. (This information was provided by the Norfolk and Norwich Record Office.) J. Venn, *Biographical History of Gonville and Caius College*, I (Cambridge, 1897), 88–89; "From the Library," in *Midland Medical Review*, 1 (1961), 185–187; H. C. Porter, *Reformation and Reaction in Tudor Cambridge* (Cambridge, 1958).
2. See J. E. C. Hill, *Intellectual Origins of the English Revolution*, 39–40; D. W. Waters, *The Art of Navigation . . .*, 239, 278. It is possible that Wright lectured at Trinity House, Deptford, since he dedicated his 1599 translation to its master, Richard Polter.
3. Waters, *op. cit.*, 121.
4. R. C. Archibald, in *Mathematical Tables and Other Aids to Computation*, 3 (1948), 223–225, ignores these earlier eds. of the table, as well as the (independent) MS calculations by Thomas Harriot, discussed by Waters.
5. The final quotation is from Waters (p. 219), who also mentions several mathematical instruments that Wright helped to develop.

*BIBLIOGRAPHY*

I. ORIGINAL WORKS. Wright's main work, *Certaine Errors in Navigation, Arising Either of the Ordinarie Erroneous Making or Using of the Sea Chart, Compasse, Crosse Staffe, and Tables of Declinations of the Sunne, and Fixed Starres Detected and Corrected* (London, 1599; 2nd ed., enl., 1610; 3rd ed., Joseph Moxon, ed., 1657), includes, at the end, "The Voyage of the . . . Earle of Cumberland to the Azores," also printed by Hakluyt (1599) and at Lisbon (1911). Other writings are *The Haven-Finding Art*, translated from the Dutch of Simon Stevin (London, 1599), repr. in *Certaine Errors* (1657) and, in part, by H. D. Harradon in *Territorial Magazine*, **50** (Mar. 1945); *Description and*

*Use of the Sphaere* (London, 1614; 1627); *A Short Treatise of Dialling: Shewing the Making of All Sorts of Sun-Dials* (London, 1614); and *A Description of the Admirable Tables of Logarithmes*, translated from the Latin of John Napier (London, 1616; 1618).

The MSS at Dublin are briefly listed by T. K. Abbott, *Catalogue of the Manuscripts in the Library of Trinity College* (Dublin, 1900).

II. Secondary Literature. See W. W. R. Ball, *A History of the Study of Mathematics at Cambridge* (Cambridge, 1889), 25–27; F. Cajori, "On an Integration Ante-dating the Integral Calculus," in *Bibliotheca mathematica*, 3rd ser., **14** (1914), 312–319; and "Algebra in Napier's Day and Alleged Prior Inventions," in C. G. Knott, ed., *Napier Tercentenary Memorial Volume* (Edinburgh, 1915), 93–109; J. E. C. Hill, *Intellectual Origins of the English Revolution* (Oxford, 1965); C. Hutton, *A Philosophical and Mathematical Dictionary*, new ed., II (London, 1815), 619–620; J. K. Laughton, *Dictionary of National Biography*, LXIII; E. J. S. Parsons and W. F. Morris, "Edward Wright and His Work," in *Imago mundi*, **3** (1939), 61–71; Helen M. Wallis, "The First English Globe: A Recent Discovery," in *Geographical Journal*, **108** (1951), 275–290; "Further Light on the Molyneux Globes," *ibid.*, **121** (1955), 304–311; and "World Map in Principal Navigations, 1599: Evidence to Suggest That Edward Wright was the Main Author," an unpublished note (1972); and D. W. Waters, *The Art of Navigation in England in Elizabethan and Early Stuart Times* (London, 1958).

P. J. WALLIS

**WRIGHT, FREDERICK EUGENE** (*b.* Marquette, Michigan, 16 October 1877; *d.* Sagastaweka Island, near Gananoque, Ontario, Canada, 25 August 1953), *petrology.*

Wright was the son of Charles Eugene Wright, pioneer geologist of Michigan, and Carolyn Alice Dox. He was awarded the Ph.D. by the University of Heidelberg in 1900 after work in petrology under Harry Rosenbusch and in crystallography under Victor Goldschmidt. On returning to America, he spent three years as instructor at the Michigan College of Mines, Houghton, Michigan. About 1905 Wright became associated with the United States Geological Survey and he retained a connection for a dozen years. He was appointed petrologist at the Geophysical Laboratory of the Carnegie Institution of Washington in 1906, working there until his retirement in 1944 and retaining an office at the Institution until his death.

Wright's primary scientific contributions were in the development of the petrographic microscope and its applications, improvement of the techniques for the manufacture of high-grade optical glass during World War I, design and construction of a torsion gravity meter of high precision for field use (with J. L. England), and the remote determination of the nature of materials on the surface of the moon by optical methods. His book *The Methods of Petrographic-Microscope Research* (1911) greatly influenced the promotion of quantitative measurement of the optical properties of crystals. Similarly, Wright's reports on the systematic measurement of the amount of plane polarization and the relative spectral intensities of the reflected rays from various regions of the moon's surface, from which the nature of the materials on the surface were deduced, were pioneer efforts.

Wright's petrological field studies were made in the Upper Peninsula of Michigan, Alaska, South Africa, and the Columbia River in Washington and Oregon. Gravity surveys were undertaken in collaboration with Vening Meinesz in the Caribbean by means of a submarine and in Guatemala, in an effort to determine the relationship between gravity anomalies and volcanism. Data for his lunar field studies were collected at the United States Naval Observatory in Washington, D. C., and the Mt. Wilson Observatory in California.

Service to the sciences was performed through Wright's administrative work in the National Academy of Sciences (elected 1923) as a vice-president (1927–1931) and as home secretary (1931–1951). He also held high offices in the American Mathematical Society, Geological Society of America, Mineralogical Society of America, and Optical Society of America.

*BIBLIOGRAPHY*

Optical studies by Wright are "On the Measurement of Extinction Angles in the Thin Section," in *American Journal of Science*, 4th ser., **26** (1908), 349–390; "The Methods of Petrographic-Microscopic Research: Their Relative Accuracy and Range of Application," *Publications. Carnegie Institution of Washington*, no. 158 (1911); "The Formation of Interference Figures: A Study of the Phenomena Exhibited by Transparent Inactive Crystal Plates in Convergent Polarized Light," in *Journal of the Optical Society of America*, **7** (1923), 779–817; and "Computation of the Optic Axial Angle From the Three Principal Refractive Indices," in *American Mineralogist*, **36** (1951), 543–556.

A work on the glass industry is *The Manufacture of Optical Glass and of Optical Systems: A War-time Problem*, Paper on Optical Glass no. 40, Ordnance Dept. Document no. 2037 (Washington, D.C., 1921).

Field studies include *Notes on the Rocks and Minerals of Michigan* (Houghton, Mich., 1905); "The Intrusive Rocks of Mount Bohemia, Michigan," in *Annual Report of the Michigan Geological Survey* (1908), 361–402; "The Ketchikan and Wrangel Mining Districts," *Bulletin of the United States Geological Survey* no. 347 (1908), written with C. W. Wright; and "The Hot Springs of Iceland," in *Journal of Geology,* **32** (1924), 462–464.

Works on mineralogy are "Quartz as a Geologic Thermometer," in *American Journal of Science,* 4th ser., **27** (1909), 421–447, written with E. S. Larsen; optical studies in G. A. Rankin, "The Ternary System CaO-$Al_2O_3$-$SiO_2$," *ibid.,* **39** (1915), 1–79; and "Afwillite, a New Hydrous Calcium Silicate, From Dutoitspan Mine, Kimberley, South Africa," in *Mineralogical Magazine,* **20** (1925), 277–286, written with J. Parry.

Lunar studies include "Polarization of Light Reflected From Rough Surfaces With Special Reference to Light Reflected by the Moon," in *Proceedings of the National Academy of Sciences of the United States of America,* **13** (1927), 535–540; and "The Surface of the Moon," *Publications. Carnegie Institution of Washington* no. 501 (1938), 59–74.

Writings on gravity are "The Gravity Measuring Cruise of the U. S. Submarine S-21," in *Publications of the United States Naval Observatory,* 2nd ser., no. 13 (1930), app. 1, written with F. A. Vening Meinesz; "An Improved Torsion Gravity Meter," in *American Journal of Science,* **35A** (1938), 373–383, written with J. L. England; and "Gravity Measurements in Guatemala," in *Transactions. American Geophysical Union,* **22** (1941), 512–515.

H. S. YODER, JR.

**WRIGHT, GEORGE FREDERICK** (*b.* Whitehall, New York, 22 January 1838; *d.* Oberlin, Ohio, 20 April 1921), *geology.*

Wright was the fifth of the six children of Walter Wright, a farmer, and Mary Peabody Colburn. The attraction of the Wright family to the New School Calvinism, with its emphasis on personal regeneration and humanitarian reform, led Walter Wright to send five of his children to Oberlin College. The election of Charles Grandison Finney, one of the leaders of the New School movement, to the presidency of the college in 1851 was a sign to the Wrights that Oberlin was sound. After preparation at Castleton Academy in Vermont, Wright entered Oberlin in 1855. After receiving the B.A. degree in 1859, he entered the Oberlin Theological Seminary. Although his studies were interrupted by Civil War service, Wright received the M.A. in 1862. Just after graduation he married Huldah Maria Day and took her to Bakersfield, Vermont, where he became pastor of the Congregational church. In 1872 he moved to Andover, Massachu-

setts, where he began a nine-year ministry in the Free (Congregational) Church. In 1904, five years after the death of his first wife, who had borne him four children, Wright married Florence Eleanor Bedford.

Wright's interest in geology began during his childhood and gradually transformed from avocation to profession. He was an avid reader; and before he was twelve, he had gone through John C. Frémont's *Report* of his Rocky Mountain expedition. Oberlin's classical education furnished Wright with more than a smattering of science courses. In each winter of his college years he taught at a district school, a task that allowed him to travel through various parts of Ohio searching for fossils and collecting rock specimens. At Bakersfield, Wright read Lyell's *Antiquity of Man* and Darwin's *Origin of Species.* He explored portions of the Green Mountains and became an authority on the effects of glaciation in the locality. His friend Charles H. Hitchcock, Dartmouth geologist and administrator of the New Hampshire Geological Survey, brought Wright's work to the attention of a number of naturalists.

While he was at Andover, Wright worked closely with several Harvard scientists. It was his insistence that persuaded Asa Gray to publish *Darwiniana* (1876). Receptive to Darwin's views, Wright was the foremost early champion of a Christian Darwinist theology. His initial religious and scientific interests in the problem of the antiquity of man continued to stimulate his geological research for the rest of his life. His theory was that Andover's "Indian Ridge" was of glacial rather than marine origin, and in 1875 he demonstrated that the formation was one of a series of prominent eskers in New England. Clarence King, who soon became first director of the United States Geological Survey, gave Wright's conclusions an endorsement that brought his published work to the attention of James Dwight Dana, William M. Davis, and other geologists, with whom Wright continued to be associated.

In 1880 Wright and Clarence King noted the existence of a glacial boundary south of the Massachusetts shoreline; and with Henry C. Lewis and Peter Lesley, Wright followed the line of morainic deposits through New Jersey. In 1881 he worked with Lewis as an assistant on the Second Geological Survey of Pennsylvania, under Lesley's direction. Late in that year Wright accepted a professorship at Oberlin, where he taught courses in theology and glacial geology for the next twenty-seven years, in 1892 becoming professor of the harmony of science and revelation. Soon he had identified the drift margin in Ohio, and as an assistant on the United States Geological Survey (1884–1892) he completed the work through Indiana and Illinois. Thus he had personally traced the drift margin from the Atlantic Ocean to the Mississippi River.

In the summer of 1886 Wright conducted a series of pioneer investigations at Glacier Bay, Alaska. A result of his extensive glacial investigations in North America was an invitation to lecture before the Lowell Institute in Boston in the winter of 1887–1888. The revised lectures were published in 1889 as *The Ice Age in North America and Its Bearings Upon the Antiquity of Man*. He was twice again a Lowell lecturer: in 1891–1892 and in 1896–1897.

In the last three decades of his life, Wright's scientific work consisted mostly of explanations and refinements of his earlier conclusions. He investigated Greenland glaciation in 1894, and between 1892 and 1908 he visited Europe four times to observe effects of the Pleistocene there. Although he retired from teaching in 1907, he remained a tireless worker. From 1883 until his death he was editor of *Bibliotheca sacra*, a major theological quarterly. He also aided his son, Frederick Bennett Wright, in the publication of the thirteen volumes of *Records of the Past*, a journal of archaeology. Wright was instrumental in the crusade to preserve the nation's prehistoric earthworks.

Wright brought amazing energy to his work. Dedicated to the necessity for firsthand observation, he realized a long-held ambition in 1900, when he went to China to begin an arduous journey through Manchuria and Siberia. Traveling by mule, river steamer, train, and even hundreds of miles by horse-drawn cart, he recorded observations of elevated shorelines, loess deposits, and other consequences of Pleistocene action from Vladivostok to the Black Sea.

Wright was a founder of the Geological Society of America and was active in many other organizations, such as the American Association for the Advancement of Science, the Boston Society of Natural History, the Essex Institute of Salem, the American Anthropological Association, and the Arctic Club. He was president of the Ohio State Archaeological and Historical Society from 1907 to 1918. In 1887 Wright received two honorary degrees: the D.D. from Brown University and the LL.D. from Drury College, Springfield, Missouri.

Wright belonged to a generation of American geologists whose endeavors laid the basis for modern glacial theory. He was the most vigorous propo-

nent of several hypotheses that glaciologists debated, sometimes heatedly. On the basis of his work at the Niagara gorge and elsewhere, Wright advocated the relatively late end of the Ice Age, approximately ten thousand years ago. Further, he contended that there had been only one Ice Age. According to Wright, the Ice Age did not consist of alternating periods during which much of the northern hemisphere was covered by glaciers, and intermittent periods in which there was no extraordinary glaciation—the multiple glaciation theory, which set the duration of the Ice Age at far over one hundred thousand years. Rather, he espoused a unitary theory: the Ice Age, he believed, consisted of the alternate ebbing and flowing of glaciers over a period of time not to exceed ninety thousand years. Wright conceded the existence of certain interglacial deposits, but argued that these represented merely local recessions, not distinct interglacial periods.

The most controversial of Wright's positions was his unqualified affirmation of the existence of man in North America during the Pleistocene. Thomas C. Chamberlin, W. J. McGee, and John W. Powell opposed him, thus setting off a heated debate that involved some of the major scientific societies and periodicals, the departments of geology of the University of Chicago and other schools, and the United States Geological Survey for over two years. The spark was the publication of Wright's *Man and the Glacial Period* (1892), a careful description of alleged evidences of glacial man. Wright's side was supported in whole or in part by Warren Upham, Newton H. and Alexander Winchell, Nathaniel S. Shaler, Frederic W. Putnam, James D. Dana, and other naturalists; but it was a later generation that achieved a fuller appreciation of his efforts to establish the relatively short period since the end of the Ice Age, and to substantiate the existence of Pleistocene man in North America.

*BIBLIOGRAPHY*

I. ORIGINAL WORKS. Among Wright's 16 books and almost 600 articles not cited in the text are "Some Remarkable Gravel Ridges in the Merrimack Valley," in *Proceedings of the Boston Society of Natural History*, **19** (1877), 47–63; "The Glacial Phenomena of North America and Their Relation to the Question of Man's Antiquity in the Valley of the Delaware," in *Bulletin of the Essex Institute*, **13** (1881), 65–72; "Recent Investigations Concerning the Southern Boundary of the Glaciated Area of Ohio," in *American Journal of Science*,

3rd ser., **26** (1883), 44–56; "The Niagara River and the Glacial Period," *ibid.*, **28** (1884), 32–35; "The Terminal Moraine in Ohio, Kentucky, and Indiana," in H. C. Lewis et al., *Report on the Terminal Moraine in Pennsylvania and Western New York*, Second Geological Survey of Pennsylvania, vol. Z (Harrisburg, Pa., 1884), 203–243; "The Muir Glacier," in *American Journal of Science*, 3rd ser., **33** (1887), 1–18; "The Glacial Boundary in Western Pennsylvania, Ohio, Kentucky, Indiana, and Illinois," *Bulletin of the United States Geological Survey* no. 58 (1890); "Prehistoric Man on the Pacific Coast," in *Atlantic Monthly*, **67** (1891), 501–513; "Excitement Over Glacial Theories," in *Science*, **20** (1892), 360–361; "Unity of the Glacial Epoch," in *American Journal of Science*, 3rd ser., **44** (1892), 351–373; "Continuity of the Glacial Period," *ibid.*, **47** (1894), 161–187; and *Greenland Icefields and Life in the North Atlantic: With a New Discussion of the Causes of the Ice Age* (New York, 1896), written with Warren Upham.

Other works are "Recent Geological Changes in Northern and Central Asia," in *Quarterly Journal of the Geological Society of London*, **57** (1901), 244–250; "Evidence of the Agency of Water in the Distribution of the Loess in the Missouri Valley," in *American Geologist*, **33** (1904), 205–222; "Postglacial Erosion and Oxidation," in *Bulletin of the Geological Society of America*, **23** (1912), 277–296; *Origin and Antiquity of Man* (Oberlin, Ohio, 1912); and *Story of My Life and Work* (Oberlin, Ohio, 1916). The 5th ed. (1911) of *Ice Age in North America* was a complete revision.

II. SECONDARY LITERATURE. See "George Frederick Wright: In Memoriam," in *Ohio Archaeological and Historical Society Quarterly*, **30** (1921), 162–175; and Warren Upham, "Memorial of George Frederick Wright," in *Bulletin of the Geological Society of America*, **33** (1922), 14–30. For an investigation of Wright's work with Asa Gray, see Michael McGiffert, "Christian Darwinism: The Partnership of Asa Gray and George Frederick Wright, 1874–1881" (Ph.D. diss., Yale University, 1958). The most extensive study of Wright is William J. Morison, "George Frederick Wright: In Defense of Darwinism and Fundamentalism, 1838–1921" (Ph.D. diss., Vanderbilt University, 1971), which is based on Wright's correspondence and other papers (some 15,000 items) in the Oberlin College Archives.

WILLIAM J. MORISON

**WRIGHT, THOMAS** (*b.* Byers Green, near Durham, England, 22 September 1711; *d.* Byers Green, 25 February 1786), *astronomy*.

Thomas Wright "of Durham" was the third son of John Wright, a yeoman and carpenter who had a small holding near Durham. His early schooling was cut short by an impediment of speech, and at the age of thirteen he was apprenticed to a clockmaker. He used his leisure time to study astronomy with such alarming dedication that his father burned his books in an effort to frustrate this enthusiasm. In 1729 Wright was involved in a scandal that forced him to flee from his master, and after some adventures he reached home and was released from his apprenticeship. Failing to find employment, he studied navigation and noted: "Reflecting almost upon every object, conseive may find Ideas of y$^e$ Deaty and Creation."

After sampling various occupations, Wright began to teach navigation in the seaport of Sunderland; but in the spring of 1731 he was unemployed, owing to the departure of the seamen. He was evidently a natural teacher; and he used his leisure to prepare mathematical and astronomical publications, often in the form of wall sheets or "schemes." One such sheet, covering twenty-four square feet and accompanied by a "key" in the form of a substantial quarto volume, *Clavis coelestis*, appeared in 1742. Wright also spent much of the 1730's surveying the estates of the aristocracy and giving private and public classes in the physical sciences. Evidently he achieved something of an international reputation, for in 1742 he was offered £300 a year to become professor of navigation at the Imperial Academy of Sciences at St. Petersburg. His journal notes that "His Proposals of £500 were sent to Russia," but nothing came of these negotiations.

In 1746 Wright went to Ireland for several months to assemble drawings of antiquities for his most successful work, *Louthiana*. (A sequel to *Louthiana* and a volume on the antiquities of England remain in manuscript.) In 1750 Wright published his most significant work, *An Original Theory or New Hypothesis of the Universe*. By 1755, when his *Universal Architecture* appeared, his thoughts were turning again to his birthplace, perhaps because his noble patrons were beginning to die off. The following year he laid the foundation of a house at Byers Green and in 1762 retired there, to "Prosicute my Studies." He died there in 1786, unmarried but survived by a daughter.

Wright's early reflections on "Ideas of y$^e$ Deaty and Creation" mark the beginning of his lifelong preoccupation with the reconciliation of his religious and scientific views of the universe. The telescope revealed to the observer the structure of our locality in the universe, but religion alone could provide the cosmological overview. In its simplest form this overview comprised a unique divine center, the abode of God and the angels; a "Region of Mortality," consisting of the sun and the other stars forming a spherical assemblage surrounding the divine center; and an outer darkness or other spatial realization of the punishment of the wicked.

Wright's first attempt to effect this reconciliation is found in a manuscript dated 1734 that appears to be the text of a lecture-sermon accompanying a vast visual aid, now lost. In this lecture the divine center (the center in the moral order) was also the gravitational center (the center in the physical order), and thus Wright required the sun and the other stars to be moving in orbit about this center in order to avoid gravitational collapse. He found evidence of this circulation among the stars in Halley's 1718 paper on proper motions (*Philosophical Transactions*, **30**, 736–738), the significance of which had escaped more powerful minds than Wright's.

In his efforts to bring home to his audience their precarious moral position, Wright in his visual aid portrayed a cross section of creation, one that passed through the divine center and the solar system. With artistic license he represented the visible portion of the universe as it actually appears to us, beginning with the sun and moon and extending to the Milky Way, which he considered to be the effect of innumerable distant stars in the plane of the cross section. It was only sometime after 1742 that Wright realized that his model of the universe would produce such a milky way in *any* of the possible cross sections, whereas the visible Milky Way is unique. In 1750 *An Original Theory* met this difficulty by making the shell of stars thin, so that the Milky Way is the plane tangent to the shell at the position occupied by the solar system; because the shell is thin, no milky effect is produced when the observer looks either inward or outward. Alternatively (but with the loss of spherical symmetry), Wright would permit the stars to form a flattened ring, like a large-scale Saturn's ring; the Milky Way was then in the plane of the ring. This latter version, in which the stars lie in a plane and orbit their center as the planets orbit the sun, appealed to Immanuel Kant, who, not realizing that the center of Wright's system was supernatural, credited Wright with originating a disk-shaped model of the galaxy.

In fact, *An Original Theory* proposes a multiplicity of star systems, each with its own supernatural center; and the punishment of the wicked is not provided for. These defects may have prompted Wright to compose *Second Thoughts*, which never reached publication in his lifetime. In this late manuscript the universe consists of an infinite sequence of concentric shells surrounding the divine center; our sky is one of these solid shells and, viewed from without, appears as a large version of the sun. Viewed from within, it is studded with volcanoes, which we see as the stars and the Milky Way. A good life is rewarded by promotion to a more spacious sphere for our next existence; an evil life is punished by demotion to a more cramped sphere that, although nearer the divine center in terms of miles, is still infinitely many spheres away from it.

With *Second Thoughts*, Wright achieved his reconciliation of science and religion: the observations had at last been fitted into a universe that had symmetry about the center and provision for rewards and punishments. *Second Thoughts*, with its solid sky in which the stars are volcanoes, appears retrograde to modern readers, but only because we have been accustomed to judge Wright on our terms rather than his.

*BIBLIOGRAPHY*

I. ORIGINAL WORKS. Wright's autobiographical notes (for the period ending 1746) are in British Museum, Add. 15627, most recently edited by Edward Hughes as "The Early Journal of Thomas Wright of Durham," in *Annals of Science*, **7** (1951), 1–24. His principal books are *Clavis coelestis* (London, 1742), facs. ed. by M. A. Hoskin (London, 1967); *Louthiana* (London, 1748, 1758); *An Original Theory or New Hypothesis of the Universe* (London, 1750), facs. ed. by M. A. Hoskin, with transcription of Wright's MS "A Theory of the Universe" (1734) (London, 1971); *Universal Architecture* (London, 1755); and *Second or Singular Thoughts Upon the Theory of the Universe*, edited from the MS by M. A. Hoskin (London, 1968). Eight vols. of Wright MSS are in the Central Library, Newcastle-upon-Tyne, and others are in the Royal Society, the Royal Astronomical Society, and Durham University; the Durham collection includes the unique copy of his *The Universal Vicissitude of Seasons* (1737) and other rarities. A broadsheet, "The Universal Vicissitude of Seasons," is in the possession of Harrison Horblit.

II. SECONDARY LITERATURE. A list of books and MSS by Wright and a bibliography of secondary literature is appended to "Thomas Wright of Durham and Immanuel Kant," in Herbert Dingle and G. R. Martin, eds., *Chemistry and Beyond. A Selection From the Writings of the Late Professor F. A. Paneth* (New York, 1964), 93–119; note that *Pannauticon* is not a book but an instrument, and that Paneth fundamentally misunderstands Wright's cosmology. For an account of the development of Wright's cosmology, see M. A. Hoskin, "The Cosmology of Thomas Wright of Durham," in *Journal for the History of Astronomy*, **1** (1970), 44–52; and the intros. to the modern eds. of his works.

MICHAEL A. HOSKIN

**WRIGHT, WILBUR** (*b.* Millville, Indiana, 16 April 1867; *d.* Dayton, Ohio, 30 May 1912), and **WRIGHT, ORVILLE** (*b.* Dayton, Ohio, 19 August 1871; *d.* Dayton, Ohio, 30 January 1948), *aeronautics.*

Wilbur and Orville Wright, the sons of Milton Wright, a bishop of the United Brethren Church, and Susan Catherine Koerner, had two older brothers, Reuchlin and Lorin, and a younger sister, Katharine. Their upbringing in a family where liberality of thought and individual initiative and expression were encouraged, contributed markedly to their later achievements. Although their formal education did not go beyond high school, they were widely read, especially in the technical literature of the day, and taught themselves mathematics and smatterings of French and German. Both were of medium stature, trim, and athletic, and from boyhood showed powers of physical endurance and mechanical skill and ingenuity. After youthful ventures in editing and printing small neighborhood newspapers, they set up the Wright Cycle Company in 1892 and for the next decade made their living by the design, manufacture, and sale of bicycles.

The death, on 10 August 1896, of German aviation pioneer Otto Lilienthal, from injuries suffered in a gliding accident, led the Wrights to the serious study of flight. By 1899 they had carried their theory of lateral balance (aileron control) to the point of a practical demonstration made by Wilbur, in August, using a five-foot-span biplane kite. Equilibrium was maintained and maneuver made possible by varying the air pressures at the wing tips through adjustment of the angles of attack on the two sides. With this action and an adjustable horizontal surface (elevator), later (1902) combined with the compensating action of a movable vertical rudder, they achieved control about the three axes of the airplane. The system was patented in 1906 and has been used on all airplanes ever since.

Discovering—from field experiments and tentative gliding trials at Kitty Hawk, North Carolina, in the summers of 1900 and 1901—that almost all existing aerodynamic data were erroneous, the Wrights designed a small wind tunnel in which, in the fall of 1901, they tested several hundred model airfoils and obtained reliable lift and drag measurements as well as many other essential aerodynamic data.

With this knowledge, in October 1902 they began the construction of a powered airplane. The all-up weight, including pilot, was 750 pounds. The engine and propellers were of their own design and manufacture, and the propellers were based entirely on theories they originated. With this machine four successful flights were made from the level sand near the Kill Devil Hills, North Carolina, on 17 December 1903. The final, longest flight lasted for fifty-nine seconds and covered a distance of 852 feet; this represented about half a mile through the air.

The Wrights devoted the next five years to improving both their invention and their skill as pilots. In 1905, with the airplane nearing the state of practical utility, they offered their patent and their scientific data to the United States War Department, which rejected the overture. Convinced that the first use of the airplane would be in war, the Wrights sought markets abroad. In 1908, after many rebuffs, they received purchase offers from a French syndicate and from the United States government.

Demonstration trials in the two countries took place concurrently, with Orville flying in the United States and Wilbur in France. All doubt of the Wrights' mastery of the air evaporated, and the honors and adulation of two continents were heaped upon them. In 1909 Wilbur flew at Rome and Orville at Berlin.

The culmination of the Wrights' achievements came with Wilbur's two flights at New York in 1909. On 29 September, taking off from and landing at Governors Island, he made a circuit of the Statue of Liberty; on 4 October he flew a twenty-one-mile course to Grant's Tomb and back.

After their triumph the brothers quietly turned to teaching others to fly and to directing the Wright Company. They now had many imitators and rivals, and were forced to defend their pioneer patent in the courts. Under the strain, Wilbur contracted typhoid fever and died suddenly on 30 May 1912. Having divested himself of his interest in the Wright Company in 1915, Orville, after World War I, confined his aviation activities mainly to research, including membership in the National Advisory Committee for Aeronautics. He survived his brother by nearly thirty-six years. On the twenty-fifth anniversary of the first flight he witnessed the laying of the cornerstone of the Wright Brothers National Memorial at Kill Devil Hills—the only United States national monument erected during the lifetime of a man so honored.

*BIBLIOGRAPHY*

The letters of the Wrights have been collected in *Miracle at Kitty Hawk; the Letters of Wilbur and Orville Wright*, Fred C. Kelly, ed. (New York, 1951); their papers in *The Papers of Wilbur and Orville Wright, Including the Chanute-Wright Letters and Other Papers of Octave Chanute*, M. W. McFarland, ed., 2 vols. (New York–Toronto–London, 1953). Orville Wright wrote *How We Invented the Aeroplane* (New York, 1953), edited with a commentary by F. C. Kelly. See also Wilbur Wright's first rebuttal deposition contained in the complainant's record in the case of Wright Company *v.* Herring Curtiss Company and Glenn H. Curtiss, U.S. District Court, Western District of New York, 1912, vol. 1.

A biography of the Wrights is F. C. Kelly, *The Wright Brothers: A Biography Authorized by Orville Wright* (New York, 1943). See also C. H. Gibbs-Smith, *The Invention of the Aeroplane (1799–1909)* (New York, 1966); W. Langewiesche, "What the Wrights Really Invented," in *Harper's Magazine*, **200** (June 1950), 102–105; and M. W. McFarland, "When the Airplane Was a Military Secret: A Study of National Attitudes Before 1914," in *U.S. Air Services*, **39** (Sept. 1954), 11, 14, 16; (Oct. 1954), 18, 20–22; and "The Fame of Wilbur Wright," *ibid.*, **40** (Dec. 1955), 4–6.

MARVIN W. MCFARLAND

**WRIGHT, WILLIAM HAMMOND** (*b.* San Francisco, California, 4 November 1871; *d.* San Jose, California, 16 May 1959), *astronomy.*

Wright was a skillful designer of astronomical equipment, which he used to photograph the spectra of stars and nebulae. He was also the first to use six-color photography in studying the planet Mars.

Wright's parents were Joanna Maynard Shaw and Selden Stuart Wright. After attending public schools in San Francisco, Wright went to the University of California, where he received a B.S. in civil engineering in 1893. He remained in Berkeley for two years of graduate study, specializing in astronomy, and then transferred for a year to the University of Chicago, where George Ellery Hale taught him the latest techniques for photographing spectra.

In 1897 Wright returned to California, as an assistant astronomer at the Lick observatory, to help W. W. Campbell in his studies of solar motion. For this purpose Wright photographed the spectra of many stars, to get line-of-sight velocities. In 1903 he was sent to Santiago, Chile, with a $36\frac{1}{2}$-inch telescope, which he installed on Cerro San Cristobal and used to acquire similar data for stars in the Southern hemisphere. He was accompanied by his wife, Elna Warren Leib, whom he had married in 1901. Wright remained in charge of this Southern station of Lick until 1906.

Back in California, Wright was promoted to astronomer in 1908, a post he held until 1944. In 1935 he was also appointed director of the Lick observatory, succeeding R. G. Aitken.

Wright investigated nebulae, particularly those called planetaries, and the high temperature stars that they surround. His data later helped I. S. Bowen to unravel the "nebulium" mystery.

Wright also continued work on novae, begun earlier with Campbell. His photographs of the spectrum of Nova Geminorum 1912, taken on every possible night during more than nineteen months, provided a wealth of details basic to the understanding of such complicated explosive events.

Beginning in 1924, while Mars was well situated for observation, Wright used the Crossley 36-inch reflector at Lick to photograph this planet (and also Jupiter, Saturn, and Venus) on suitably sensitized emulsions exposed through a series of filters, in colors ranging from ultraviolet through the visible to the infrared. The enhanced contrast, particularly for Mars in the infrared, revealed many unsuspected details.

Wright's final project was a set of about 1,300 large-scale celestial photographs, to be repeated for comparison after several decades and thus provide information on motions within our galaxy. Interrupted by World War II, it was finally begun in 1947 by C. D. Shane, who succeeded Wright as director of Lick.

The National Academy of Sciences elected Wright to membership in 1922, and awarded him its Draper Medal in 1928, the same year that he received the Janssen Medal of the Paris Academy of Sciences. He was elected a fellow of the Royal Astronomical Society (London) in 1927, and was awarded its Gold Medal in 1938. Wright's two advanced degrees were both honorary: a D.Sc. from Northwestern University (1929) and an LL.D. from the University of California (1944).

BIBLIOGRAPHY

I. ORIGINAL WORKS. An early paper by Wright on instrumentation, "The Auxiliary Apparatus of the Mills Spectrograph for Photographing the Comparison Spectrum," is in *Astrophysical Journal*, **12** (1900), 274–278. For a brief account of Wright's work in Chile, see "On Some Results Obtained by the D. O. Mills Expedition to the Southern Hemisphere," *ibid.*, **20** (1904), 140–145. His ideas concerning the central stars of planetary nebulae are described in "The Relation Between the Wolf-Rayet Stars and the Planetary Nebulae," *ibid.*, **40** (1914), 466–472. Wright's photographs of Mars and other planets are described and illustrated in his George Darwin Lecture, "On Photographs of the Brighter Planets by Light of Different Colours," in *Monthly Notices of the Royal Astronomical Society*, **88** (1928), 709–718, with 34 figs. on 3 plates.

"The Spectrum of Nova Geminorum (1912)" appears in *Publications of the Lick Observatory*, **14** (1940), 27–91.

II. SECONDARY LITERATURE. Contemporary appraisals of Wright's work include the address delivered by H. Spencer Jones when awarding the Gold Medal to Wright, in *Monthly Notices of the Royal Astronomical Society*, **98** (1938), 358–374. An obituary notice by Paul W. Merrill is in *Publications of the Astronomical Society of the Pacific*, **71** (1959), 305–306, with a photograph of Wright; another by C. D. Shane can be found in *American Philosophical Society Yearbook for 1959*, 150–153.

SALLY H. DIEKE

**WRÓBLEWSKI, ZYGMUNT FLORENTY VON** (*b.* Grodno, Lithuania, Russia, 28 October 1845; *d.* Cracow, Poland, 19 April 1888), *physics*.

The son of a lawyer, Wróblewski achieved his fame as an experimental physicist mainly through work on the liquefaction of gases that he did with K. S. Olszewski. After attending the Gymnasium in Grodno, he entered the University of Kiev in 1862 but was banished to Siberia in 1863 for participating in the January Revolution in Poland. He was amnestied in 1869 and allowed to travel to Berlin for treatment at the eye clinic run by Albrecht von Graefe. Wróblewski began to study natural science in Berlin and continued his studies at Heidelberg and then at Munich, where in 1874 he earned the Ph.D. and worked briefly as an assistant. In 1875–1876 he was an assistant at the University of Strasbourg, where he qualified as a lecturer. A stipend from the Cracow Academy of Sciences enabled Wróblewski to continue his training in Paris under Henri Sainte-Claire Deville and to visit London, Oxford, and Cambridge. He was named professor of physics at Jagiellonian University, Cracow, in 1882. In 1883 he became corresponding member of the Cracow Academy and, in 1887, of the Vienna Academy of Sciences, which awarded him the Baumgartner Prize for his work on the liquefaction of air.

At this time the problem of liquefying the "permanent" gases was attracting much attention.[1] Wróblewski did research in this field with Olszewski. Improving upon a method devised by L. P. Cailletet and using ethylene in a vacuum as the cooling agent, they reached the critical temperature of air, thereby becoming the first to obtain oxygen, nitrogen, and carbon monoxide as waterlike fluids. Wróblewski reported their results to the Vienna Academy on 12 April 1883. During their brief collaboration Wróblewski and Olszewski, stimulated by mutual competition, also liquefied hydrogen, at least in the dynamic state.

Wróblewski, who had first investigated electrical phenomena, found during his research on low temperatures that the electrical conductivity of copper displays "extremely remarkable properties" at such temperatures. He drew attention to the great importance of this phenomenon and specifically to the greatly increased conductivity.[2] This extremely promising research came to an abrupt end when Wróblewski suffered fatal burns after overturning his kerosine lamp.

*NOTES*

1. At this time the term "permanent" was applied to gases that could not be transformed into other states of matter—that is, gases the critical temperature of which had not yet been determined. Among these were air and its components. Gases that could be liquefied or produced by sublimation were called—in contradistinction to the "permanent" gases—"coercible."
2. The existence of this superconductivity was demonstrated in 1911 by Kamerlingh-Onnes.

BIBLIOGRAPHY

I. ORIGINAL WORKS. Wróblewski's numerous scientific papers include his doctoral dissertation, *Untersuchungen über die Erregung der Electricität durch mechanische Mittel* (Munich, 1874); *Die Diffusion der Gase durch absorbierende Substanzen* (Strasbourg, 1876), his *Habilitationsschrift*; "Ueber die Gesetze, nach welchen die Gase sich in flüssigen, festflüssigen und festen Körpern verbreiten," in *Annalen der Physik und Chemie*, n.s. **2** (1877), 481–513; "Ueber die Natur der Absorption der Gase," *ibid.*, **8** (1879), 29–52; "Untersuchungen über die Absorption der Gase durch

Flüssigkeiten unter hohen Drucken," *ibid.*, **17** (1882), 103–128; and **18** (1883), 290–308, on carbon monoxide; "Ueber die Verflüssigung des Sauerstoffs, Stickstoffs und Kohlenoxyds," *ibid.*, **20** (1883), 243–257, written with K. S. Olszewski; "Ueber das specifische Gewicht des Sauerstoffs," *ibid.*, 860–870; "Ueber den Gebrauch des siedenden Sauerstoffs, Stickstoffs, Kohlenoxyds, sowie der atmosphärischen Luft als Kältemittel," *ibid.*, **25** (1885), 371–407; "Ueber den electrischen Widerstand des Kupfers bei den höchsten Kältegraden," *ibid.*, **26** (1885), 27–31; "Ueber das Verhalten der flüssigen atmosphärischen Luft," *ibid.*, 134–144; and "Ueber die Darstellung des Zusammenhangs zwischen dem gasförmigen und flüssigen Zustand der Materie durch Isopyknen," *ibid.*, **29** (1886), 428–451. See also "Über den Gebrauch des siedenden Sauerstoffs etc.," in *Sitzungsberichte der Akademie der Wissenschaften in Wien*, Math.-phys. Kl., **91** (1885), pt. 2, 667–711; and "Über die Condensation der schwer coërciblen Gase," *ibid.*, **92** (1886), pt. 2, 639–651. Wroblewski also published many of his scientific papers in *Anzeiger der Akademie der Wissenschaften Krakau*.

Bibliographies are in Academy of Sciences, Cracow, *Katalog der akademischen Publikationen seit 1873 bis 1909* (Cracow, 1910); and Poggendorff, III, 1468; and IV, 1672.

II. SECONDARY LITERATURE. Writings in German include M. von Smoluchowski, "Karl Olszewski," in *Naturwissenschaften*, **5** (1917), 738–740, an obituary that includes a biographical note on Wróblewski; and E. Suess, "Siegesmund von Wroblewski," in *Almanach der Akademie der Wissenschaften in Wien*, **38** (1888), 190–192, an obituary.

Articles in Polish, details of which were supplied by Dr. I. Stroński, of Cracow, include T. Estreicher, "Zygmunt Wróblewski," in *Wszechświat* (1948), 215–219, which commemorates the 60th anniversary of Wróblewski's death; *Kronika Uniwersytetu Jagiellońskiego 1864–1887* (Cracow, 1887), 179–182; A. Pasternak, "Karol Olszewski (1846–1915) i Zygmunt Wróblewski (1845–1888)," in *Polscy badacze przyrody* ("Polish Investigators of Nature"; Warsaw, 1959), 174–203; and T. Piech, "Zarys historii katedr fizyki Uniwersytetu Jagiellońskiego" ("Compendium of the History of the Chairs of Physics at the Jagiellonian University"), in *Studia ad universitatis Iagellonicae Cracoviensis facultatis mathematicae, physicae, chemicae cathedrarum historiam pertinentia* (Cracow, 1964), 223–270.

Further biographical literature is listed in the *DSB* article on Olszewski, X, 206–207.

HANS-GÜNTHER KÖRBER

**WROŃSKI, JÓZEF MARIA.** For a detailed account of his life and work, see **Hoëné-Wroński (or Hoehne), Józef Maria**, in the Supplement.

**WU, HSIEN** (*b.* Foochow, Fukien, China, 24 November 1893; *d.* Boston, Massachusetts, 1 August 1959), *biochemistry, nutrition.*

Wu, the son of Hsiao-chien Wu and Liang Shih Wu, achieved worldwide recognition for his early studies in the United States and became China's foremost biochemist and nutrition scientist. His name is particularly associated with analytical procedures known as the Folin and Wu methods. Born to a scholarly family, he received tutorial training in the Chinese classics, starting at age six, advanced rapidly through high school, and received a scholarship in naval architecture at the Massachusetts Institute of Technology in 1911.

During his first summer vacation, on a farm in New England, Wu became fascinated by the new horizons in biology opened by T. H. Huxley's "On the Physical Basis of Life." He changed his major field to chemistry and biology while at M.I.T. and then transferred to Harvard in 1917 for graduate studies (Ph.D., 1919) in biochemistry with Otto Folin. His interest in architecture was transformed into a lifelong hobby in the field of art, and his background in mathematics, physics, and organic analysis furnished a sound basis for his new career.

In medical laboratories it had been customary to require large samples of blood for diagnostic testing and metabolic research—a practice with disadvantages for both the physician and the patient. In his doctoral dissertation, "A System of Blood Analysis," Wu developed techniques that permitted quantitative measurements of the major constituents of blood with only 10 ml. samples. The methods included a particularly good procedure for measuring the sugar content in blood or urine in a sample as small as one drop. Wu remained with Folin for a year of postdoctoral work and subsequently accepted an appointment at the Peking Union Medical College. By 1923 Wu had organized an outstanding teaching and research program in Peking, and was promoted to associate professor and head of the department of biochemistry in 1924. He retained a full professorship from 1928 until January 1942, when the college was taken over by the Japanese. At Shanghai on 20 December 1924, Wu married Daisy Yen, a graduate student in biochemistry. They traveled to New York, where he worked with Donald van Slyke at the Rockefeller Institute and Mrs. Wu resumed her studies with Henry C. Sherman at Columbia University.

Wu's more than 150 research papers included many contributions on the functions of electrolytes, immunochemistry, biochemical analysis, food composition, and the behavior of proteins in solution and the changes involved in protein denaturing, including the first suggestion that the change was characterized from a globular to an open structure.

After his return to Peking, Wu urged that greater attention be paid to the effects of food habits on health; and his nutritional research on experimental animals was accompanied with studies of eating habits of human beings. Wu served as a member of the National Committee on Standardization of Scientific Terminology of China (1921–1927). In 1926 he assisted in organizing the Chinese Physiological Society and later served as president and on the editorial board (1926–1941). He was elected adviser to the Institute of Physiology of the Academia Sinica in 1930, a member of the administrative committee that directed Peking Union Medical College in 1935–1937, and a fellow of the Academia Sinica.

Wu's growing international recognition brought him membership in the American Society of Biological Chemists, honorary membership in the Deutsche Akademie Naturforscher Leopoldina, the advisory board of *Biochemica et biophysica acta*, and the Standing Advisory Committee on Nutrition of the Food and Agriculture Organization of the United Nations (1948–1950).

During the first two years of the Japanese occupation of Peking, Wu lived in retirement at his home. In March 1944 the Chinese government, then at Chungking, invited him to organize the National Nutrition Institute there; he developed plans for the Institute and was appointed director. Some three months later the government sent him to the United States as nutrition expert for a commission to study postwar problems of rehabilitation and reconstruction. After a year of negotiating for equipment and for dried milk in food shipments, and economic study at the Brookings Institution, Wu returned to Chungking to report on his mission and to submit further plans for the Nutrition Institute.

In 1946 the government invited Wu to direct a branch of the National Institute of Health in Peking as well as to continue as director of the Nutrition Institute, which had been reestablished in Nanking. But an invitation from UNESCO to be one of the six Chinese delegates to the International Physiological Congress at Oxford in July 1947 permitted Wu to revisit the United States. His discussions with his friend T. P. Hou encouraged him to plan for an Institute of Human Biology in China. He gathered equipment for research, including a mass spectrometer and instruments for isotope research; and to familiarize himself with its use he served as visiting scholar for more than a year at the biochemistry department of the College of Physicians and Surgeons of Columbia University. He also assisted in the purchase of equipment and supplies for the National Institute of Health in Peking and shipped library materials for the projected Research Institute of Human Biology.

Meanwhile, in China the Communists had surrounded Peking. With extreme difficulty Mrs. Wu escaped with their five children in January 1949 and reached San Francisco six months later. In September of that year Wu was appointed visiting professor of biochemistry at the Medical College of the University of Alabama, where he continued his research, assisted by his wife.

In 1952 Wu suffered a heart attack that led to his retirement from Alabama in August 1953. He recovered almost completely and moved to Boston, where he continued to write. A second coronary thrombosis in April 1958 was followed by his death the following year.

## BIBLIOGRAPHY

Wu's books are *Principles of Nutrition* (Shanghai, 1929), in Chinese; and *Principles of Physical Biochemistry* (Peking, 1934), in English. Of his 157 scientific memoirs, the most representative are "A System of Blood Analysis," in *Journal of Biological Chemistry,* **38** (1919), 81–110, written with Otto Folin; "Studies of Gas and Electrolyte Equilibria in the Blood. V. Factors Controlling the Electrolyte and Water Distribution in the Blood," *ibid.,* **56** (1923), 765–849, written with D. D. van Slyke and F. C. McLean; "Composition of Antigen-precipitin Precipitate," in *Proceedings of the Society for Experimental Biology and Medicine,* **25** (1928), 853–855, written with L. H. Cheng and C. P. Li; and **26** (1929), 737–738, written with P. P. T. Sah and C. P. Li; "Studies on Denaturation of Proteins. XIII. A Theory of Denaturation," in *Chinese Journal of Physiology,* **5** (1931), 321–344; "Nutritional Deficiencies in China and Southeast Asia," in *Proceedings of the Fourth International Congress on Tropical Medicine and Malaria,* II (Washington, 1948), 1217–1223; and "Interpretation of Urinary $N^{15}$-Excretion Data Following Administration of an $N^{15}$-labeled Amino Acid," in *Journal of Applied Physiology,* **14** (1959), 11–21, written with Julius Sendroy, Jr., and Charles W. Bishop.

On his life and work, see Daisy Yen Wu, *Hsien Wu, 1893–1959, In Loving Memory* (Boston, 1959), which includes a complete bibliography of his writings and tributes from his colleagues.

C. G. KING

**WULFF, GEORG (Yuri Viktorovich)** (*b.* Nezhin, Russia, [now Ukrainian S.S.R.], 10 June 1863; *d.* Moscow, U.S.S.R., 25 December 1925), *crystallography.*

Wulff's father, Viktor Konstantinovich, was director of the boy's Gymnasium in Nezhin. Wulff received his secondary education in Warsaw and entered the natural sciences section of the Faculty of Physics and Mathematics at Warsaw in 1880, specializing in mineralogy and crystallography with A. E. Lagorio and N. G. Egorov. His interest in crystallography was reflected in two student publications, on the morphology (1883) and physical properties of crystals (1884); and he was awarded a gold medal by the university for his research on the physical properties of quartz. After graduating in 1885, he was retained to prepare for a professorship in the department of mineralogy.

Wulff's growing interest in physical crystallography and the structure of crystals led him to investigate the optical anomalies of crystals and the cause of rotation of the plane of polarization in crystals, as well as the piezoelectrical properties of quartz. From 1889 to 1892 he visited E. S. Fyodorov and V. I. Vernadsky at St. Petersburg, P. Groth at Munich, and M. A. Cornu at Paris, becoming acquainted with the most recent developments in crystallography. He was the first to win recognition outside of Russia for Fyodorov's classical research on the theory of the structure of crystals.

After defending his master's dissertation in 1892 at Warsaw, Wulff became lecturer in the department of mineralogy there. Four years later he defended his doctoral dissertation at the University of Odessa and was appointed professor of mineralogy at the University of Kazan, where he remained for three semesters. In 1898 he became head of the department of mineralogy at the University of Warsaw; and in 1908, at Vernadsky's invitation, he began teaching crystallography, crystal chemistry, and crystal optics at the University of Moscow. He transferred to the Shanyavsky University in 1911, heading the laboratory of crystallography, and in 1916 became director of the department of mineralogy and crystallography at the Moscow University for Women. From 1918 until his death he was professor at the University of Moscow. He started teaching and research in crystallography at the Faculty of Physics. His teaching chiefly concerned questions of geometrical crystallography, the growth of crystals and crystallophysics. He became a corresponding member of the Academy of Sciences of the U.S.S.R. in 1921, was president of the P. N. Lebedev Physical Society, and was a member of the All-Union Mineralogical Society.

Pierre Curie's discovery of piezoelectricity in quartz (1880) and his work on the equilibrium morphology of crystals (1885) stimulated Wulff to investigate false pyroelectrical quartz (1886) and the velocity of growth and dissolution of crystals (1896, 1901). The results of this work led to the formulation of the Curie-Wulff principle (1916). Curie had demonstrated an inverse proportion between the sizes of crystal faces and their specific surface energies ($K_i$). In his 1895 thesis Wulff showed that for a constant volume, total surface energy would be minimized when the specific surface energies for each face ($K_i$) were proportional to the perpendicular distances ($n_i$ or Wulff vectors) from a central point (the Wulff point) to each face—$K_1 : K_2 : K_3 : \cdots : = n_1 : n_2 : n_3 : \cdots$. In modern studies of crystal growth the equilibrium form derived from the theorem is known as the Wulff construction.

Wulff also conducted detailed studies of the influence of concentration currents on the morphology of growing crystals (1895), investigated liquid crystals (1909), and invented a rotating crystallizer that, by removing the influence of concentration currents, made possible the formation of perfectly formed crystals. Fyodorov's and Arthur Schönflies' theoretical investigations of crystal symmetry and structure were incorporated in Wulff's works on the theory of crystal habit (1908) and on the structure of quartz, and in optical research on pseudosymmetric crystals (1887–1890). One of the first to recognize the superiority of the Fyodorov-Goldschmidt theodolitic goniometry (the two-circle goniometer), Wulff developed methods of measuring and computing for it. In 1909 he proposed the Wulff net, the stereographic projection of a sphere with its meridians and parallels, oriented with polar axis horizontal; it is still widely used in optical, X-ray, and morphological crystallography. Wulff's goniometric research showed an essential deviation between ideal theory and the real crystal.

In 1896 Wulff presented crystal symmetry in an original manner, by using consecutive reflection only in planes, which was incorporated in his subsequent textbooks (1923, 1926). Laue's discovery of X-ray diffraction in 1912 drew Wulff's attention to X-ray structural research on crystals. Concurrently with W. H. and W. L. Bragg (1913), he independently developed the diffraction relationship $n\lambda = 2d \sin \theta$ (the Bragg-Wulff equation), the basis for the structural analysis of crystals. Wulff founded the first X-ray laboratory in Russia and conducted

X-ray diffraction research there on crystal structure.

Wulff's lectures on crystallography made extensive use of microprojection, which made possible the immediate reproduction and visual demonstration of phenomena arising in the growth and development of crystals. His students included Sigmund Weiberg, A. V. Shubnikov, E. E. Flint, A. B. Mlodseevsky, and S. T. Konobeevsky.

## BIBLIOGRAPHY

I. ORIGINAL WORKS. Some of Wulff's writings on crystallophysics and crystallography were collected as *Izbrannye raboty po kristallofizike i kristallografii* ("Selected Works in Crystallophysics and Crystallography"; Moscow, 1952). Separately published early works include "Opytnoe issledovanie elektricheskikh svoystv kvartsa" ("Experimental Investigation of the Electrical Properties of Quartz"), in *Varshavskia universitetskia izvestia*, no. 3 (1886), 1–17; "O stroenii kristallov kvartsa" ("On the Structure of Quartz Crystals"), in *Zapiski Imperatorskago mineralogicheskago obshchestva*, 2nd ser., 25 (1889), 341–342; "Ob uproshchenii kristallograficheskikh vychisleny" ("On the Simplification of Crystallographic Computation"), *ibid.*, 29 (1892), 58–64; "Svoystva nekotorykh psevdosimmetricheskikh kristallov v svyazi s teoriey kristallicheskogo stroenia veshchestva" ("Properties of Certain Pseudosymmetrical Crystals in Relation to the Theory of the Crystal Structure of Matter"), *ibid.*, 29 (1892), 65–130, his master's thesis; "K voprosu o skorostyakh rosta i rastvorenia kristallicheskikh graney" ("On the Question of the Velocity of Growth and Dissolution of Crystal Faces"), in *Varshavskia universitetskia izvestia*, 7 (1895), 1–40; 8 (1895), 41–56; n.s., 1 (1896), 57–88; 2 (1896), 89–122, his doctoral diss.; also in German, in *Zeitschrift für Kristallographie und Mineralogie*, 34 (1901), 449–530; "Die Symmetrieebene als Grundelement der Symmetrie," *ibid.*, 27 (1897), 556–558; "Untersuchungen im Gebiete der optischen Eigenschaften isomorpher Krystalle," *ibid.*, 36 (1902), 1–28; "Ein Beitrag zur Theodolithmethode," *ibid.*, 37 (1903), 50–56; and "Untersuchungen über die Genauigkeitsgrenzen der Gesetze der geometrischen Krystallographie," *ibid.*, 38 (1904), 1–57; and *Rukovodstvo po kristallografii* ("Guide to Crystallography"; Warsaw, 1904).

Subsequent works are *Simmetria i ee proyavlenia v prirode* ("Symmetry and Its Appearance in Nature"; Moscow, 1908); "Über die Krystallisation des Kaliumjodids auf dem Glimmer," in *Zeitschrift für Kristallographie und Mineralogie*, 45 (1908), 335–345; "Zur Theorie des Krystallhabitus," *ibid.*, 433–472; "Über die Natur 'flüssiger' und 'fliessender' Krystalle," *ibid.*, 46 (1909), 261–265; "Über die Kristallröntgenogramme," in *Physikalische Zeitschrift*, 14 (1913), 217–222; "O kapillyarnoy teorii formy kristallov" ("On the Capillary Theory of Crystal Forms"), in *Zhurnal Russkago fiziko-khimicheskago obshchestva pri Imperatorskom St-Peterburgskom universitete*, 48 (1916), 337–349; *Kristally, ikh obrazovanie, vid i stroenie* ("Crystals, Their Formation, Appearance, and Structure"; Moscow, 1917; 2nd ed., ed. and annotated by M. M. and S. Sabshnikov, 1926); *Zhizn crystallov* ("The Life of Crystals"; Moscow, 1918); *Osnovy kristallografii* ("Principles of Crystallography"; Moscow, 1923, 2nd ed., 1926); *Praktichesky kurs geometricheskoy kristallografii so stereograficheskoy setkoy* ("Practical Course in Geometrical Crystallography With a Stereographic Net"; Moscow, 1924); and "O molekulyarnoy strukture muskovita" ("On the Molecular Structure of Muscovite"), in *Trudy Instituta prikladnoi mineralogii i metallurgii*, 25 (1926), 22–29.

II. SECONDARY LITERATURE. On Wulff and his work, see G. G. Leleyn and G. A. Kirsanov, "Khronologichesky ukazatel trudov Y. V. Vulfa" ("Chronological Guide to the Works of Y. V. Vulf"), in *Trudy Instituta kristallografii. Akademiya nauk SSSR* (1951), no. 6, 15–24; and M. von Laue, "Der Wulffsche Satz für die Gleichgewichtsform von Kristallen," in *Zeitschrift für Kristallographie und Mineralogie*, 105 (1943), 124–133.

V. A. FRANK-KAMENETSKY

**WUNDT, WILHELM** (*b.* Neckarau, Baden, Germany, 16 August 1832; *d.* Gross Bothen, Germany, 31 August 1920), *psychology.*

Wundt described his father, a Lutheran pastor, as cheery and impractical, and his mother as more aggressive. His earliest memories were painful: falling down a flight of cellar stairs, and being roused from fantasy by a paternal box on the ear. Play with other children was rare; visits to sympathetic oldsters frequent; daydreaming a passion. Father, mother, and maternal grandfather (who resided at Heidelberg) all had a hand, not infrequently heavy, in his early education. At the age of eight he acquired as tutor a kindly young vicar with whom he shared a room, and to whom he was soon more attached than to his parents. When the vicar obtained his own parish, heartbroken Wundt, now twelve years of age, was permitted to go with him. At thirteen Wundt endured a traumatic year at a Catholic Gymnasium, where he was advised to seek some honorable calling—such as the postal service—which did not require an education. Transferred to Heidelberg, sharing a room with a much older brother and a cousin, he at last acquired friends and the effective work habits that were to distinguish his adult life.

Because his scholastic record remained too poor to qualify for a scholarship, Wundt's first university year was at Tübingen, where an uncle was brain anatomist. Thus accidentally he was pointed toward medicine. Completing his studies at the University of Heidelberg, he passed the state examinations with distinction. Apprehensive about medical practice, he spent six months as assistant at a hospital, then a semester at Berlin under Johannes Müller and du Bois-Reymond. In 1857 Wundt finally attained academic shelter as *Privatdozent* at Heidelberg, and the following year he published *Die Lehre von der Muskelbewegung*, begun under du Bois-Reymond. Ominously, the mentor to whom the work was dedicated did not even acknowledge it.

Also in 1858 Wundt published the first of six experimental reports on sensory perception, which became the *Beiträge* of 1862, and was appointed assistant to Helmholtz, just called to Heidelberg. Helmholtz largely ignored and evidently disdained his assistant, assigning him to supervise a routine laboratory course. In 1863 Wundt resigned the unrewarding post, started lecturing on psychology, and published the *Vorlesungen*. The following year he became *ausserordentlicher Professor*.

In the introduction to the *Beiträge* Wundt calls for an inductive psychology, but E. B. Titchener points out that in this he leans on Mill's *Logic*. Wundt mainly emphasizes social data — reflecting the influence of Steinthal and Lazarus, and current interest in moral statistics — but sees experiment as essential because unconscious determinants of thinking are not accessible to introspection (see Helmholtz on "unconscious inference"). Insistence that philosophy must reflect the findings of science foreshadows his later *Logik* and *Ethik*. Finally, there is the immodest claim to a great discovery revealed more fully in the *Vorlesungen*: experimental determination of the "natural unit of time" as the duration of the "swiftest thought," along with experimental demonstration of the unity of consciousness. Wundt found that an observer cannot precisely note the position of a moving pointer at the instant when a click is heard — a problem arising out of the concern of astronomers with errors in fixing the moment of transit for a star. (Later, without confession of error, Wundt wrote disdainfully of the outdated "needle's eye theory of consciousness.") It is problematic whether, by his bold interpretation, Wundt perhaps sought to place himself alongside Helmholtz, who had measured the speed of the nerve impulse, and Fechner, whose *Elemente der Psychophysik* (1860) opened the era of quantitative psychology.

Helmholtz left Heidelberg in 1871. Although Wundt had published prolifically (despite four years in the Baden legislature) and since 1867 had been lecturing on "physiological psychology," he was passed over in the selection of a successor. Soon, however, he was developing those lectures into his *magnum opus*, the *Grundzüge der physiologischen Psychologie*, which attempted "to define the limits of a new science." The preface of the work is dated March 1874, and in that month he was surprised by a call to Zurich as professor of inductive philosophy, offering an escape from his humiliating post at Heidelberg. Wundt had been recommended by Friedrich A. Lange, who had held the post previously, and whom he had met once long before at a conference on workers' education. (Lange must have read the first half of the *Grundzüge* when it appeared in 1873. He refers approvingly to it in his *Geschichte des Materialismus* [1874]; Wundt was not mentioned in the 1866 edition, which already contained the famous phrase "eine Psychologie ohne Seele," which is sometimes falsely attributed to Wundt.)

This election to a post in philosophy facilitated the more important call to Leipzig in 1875, which Wundt owed to the enthusiasm of Zöllner (later an adherent of the medium Henry Slade) and, as Wundt relates, to the readiness of an indifferent faculty to hire two obscure candidates for the price of one man of distinction. Thus did Wundt arrive at the post in which he would attain international renown.

The flow of books continued, and Wundt became the most popular lecturer of the University of Zurich. At forty-three, the ugly-duckling physiologist had become a resplendent swan philosopher. Wundt's fame, however, is rooted in what has been called the first psychology laboratory — the first, indeed, in which the instrumentation familiar to physiologists was domiciled in halls of philosophy, and called upon to monitor controlled introspections. It started as a demonstration laboratory, but in the winter semester of 1879–1880 a student, Max Friedrich, performed an experiment on "apperception time," which was reported in the first issue of Wundt's new journal, *Philosophische Studien*. It was the start of an avalanche. The immense influence of Wundt's laboratory can be traced in three ways: first, in successive revisions of the *Grundzüge* (1880, 1887, 1893, 1902, 1908–1911) which, as it fattened, provided more and more information, including detailed illustrations of experimental apparatus, constituting virtual manuals for those aspiring to found new centers of "brass instrument psychology"; second, in the increasingly cosmopolitan authorship of reports in the *Studien*, as Wundt attracted foreign, and most conspicuously American, students; and third, in the dozens of new laboratories, again especially in the United States, directed by his former students. In 1903 Cattell found eighteen Wundt students among fifty leading psychologists in the United States. Most would have subscribed to H. C. Warren's sentiment: "Coming to him as I did from an atmosphere of philosophical speculation, the spirit of his laboratory was a God-send. I owe much to Wundt for the change he wrought in my life-ideals" (*Psychological Review*, **28**, p. 169).

Not everyone admired Wundt. Carl Stumpf, who suffered some of Wundt's intolerant diatribes, deplored his influence in a letter to William James, who replied consolingly in 1887:

> He aims at being a sort of Napoleon of the intellectual world. Unfortunately he will never have a Waterloo, for he is a Napoleon without genius and no central idea. . . . Cut him up like a worm, and each fragment crawls; there is no *noeud vital* in his mental medulla oblongata, so that you can't kill him all at once. . . . He has utilized to the uttermost fibre every gift that Heaven endowed him with at his birth, and made of it all that mortal pertinacity could make. He is the finished example of how much mere *education* can do for a man [R. B. Perry, *The Thought and Character of William James*, II (Boston, 1935), 68f.].

The diffuseness of Wundt's thought, and his practice of changing his views without specific acknowledgement other than to warn against reliance on earlier editions, make it impossible to give a brief synopsis of his system. For example, in 1874 he wrote that physiological psychology "cannot sidestep" the question "how internal and external existence are ultimately related." In 1902, however, he dismissed this view as one which "has been mistakenly asserted," and declared that physiological psychology does not seek to "derive or explain the phenomena of mental life from those of physical life." Wundt also had little tolerance for results not conforming to his own theories. G. S. Hall wrote that Wundt "seems to wish to be the last in fields where he was the first, instead of taking pleasure in seeing successors arise who advance his lines still further" (*Founders of Modern Psychology*, p. 419). When L. Lange discovered in 1888 the important distinction between sensorial and motor attitudes in reaction time experiments, Wundt, still aspiring to measure by the "subtractive method" the duration of the supposed psychic component of a voluntary act, dictated an absurd interpretation in terms of "complete" and "incomplete" reactions, thus rejecting as invalid all research in which reactions were too fast. When Oswald Külpe and his Würzburg group made advances in experimental analysis of the thought process, Wundt rejected their work, and his own early commitment, to insist that these processes could be studied only in the history of social institutions. (The ten-volume "folk psychology," which Wundt devoted to this problem, is cited only as a monument to his industry.) Wundt's later views tended to alienate his followers. Ever faithful to the Wundtian method, Titchener could find no empirical basis for the tridimensional theory of feeling, and many rejected Wundt's theory of apperception as not merely mistaken, but as a betrayal of scientific principles.

At an opportune moment of history, Wundt proclaimed himself the commander of a crusade, and enthusiasts flocked to his banner. Socially shy and intellectually arrogant, he often confused the defense of his command with advancement of the cause. His name is linked to no significant finding, no theory that did not prove to be flagrant error, no problem freshly defined. Yet Wundt constituted an important rallying point for the generation of young men who saw experimental psychology as a new avenue to man's self-understanding.

## BIBLIOGRAPHY

I. ORIGINAL WORKS. For a complete bibliography of Wundt's writings, see Eleonore Wundt, ed., *Wilhelm Wundts Werk, ein Verzeichnis seiner sämtlichen Schriften* (Munich, 1927).

His early works include *Die Lehre von der Muskelbewegung* (Brunswick, 1858); *Beiträge zur Theorie der Sinneswahrnehmung* (Leipzig–Heidelberg, 1862); *Vorlesungen über die Menschen- und Thierseele*, 2 vols. (Leipzig, 1863; 6th ed., Leipzig, 1919); *Lehrbuch der Physiologie des Menschen* (Erlangen, 1865; 4th ed., Stuttgart, 1878); *Handbuch der medicinischen Physik* (Erlangen, 1867); *Untersuchungen zur Mechanik der Nerven und Nervencentren*, 2 vols. (Erlangen, 1871–1876); *Grundzüge der physiologischen Psychologie* (Leipzig, 1873–1874; 6th ed., 3 vols., Leipzig, 1908–1911); *Logik*, 2 vols. (Stuttgart, 1880–1883; 5th ed., 3 vols., 1923–1924); *Philosophische Studien*, 20 vols. (1881–1903); *Essays* (Leipzig, 1885; 2nd ed., Leipzig, 1906).

Subsequent writings include *Ethik* (Stuttgart, 1886; 4th ed., 3 vols., Stuttgart, 1912); *System der Philosophie* (Leipzig, 1889; 4th ed., 2 vols., 1919); *Grundriss der Psychologie* (Leipzig, 1896; 11th ed., Leipzig, 1913); *Völkerpsychologie* (Leipzig, 1900; 2 vols., 1904; 10 vols., 1911–1920); *Einleitung in die Philosophie* (Leipzig, 1901; 9th ed., Leipzig, 1922); *Einführung in die Psychologie* (Leipzig, 1911); *Elemente der Völker-psychologie* (Leipzig, 1912); *Reden und Aufsätze* (Leipzig, 1913); *Sinnliche und übersinnliche Welt* (Leipzig, 1914); *Die Nationen und ihre Philosophie* (Leipzig, 1915); and *Erlebtes und Erkanntes* (Stuttgart, 1920), his autobiography.

II. SECONDARY LITERATURE. On Wundt and his work, see E. G. Boring, *A History of Experimental Psychology*, 2nd ed. (New York, 1950), 316–347; R. Eisler, *Wundt's Philosophie und Psychologie* (Leipzig, 1902); G. S. Hall, *Founders of Modern Psychology* (New York–London, 1912), 311–458; A. Heussner, *Einführungen in Wilhelm Wundts Philosophie und Psychologie* (Göttingen, 1920); Arthur Hoffmann, ed., "Wilhelm Wundt, eine Würdigung," which is *Beiträge zur Philosophie des deutschen Idealismus,* **2,** nos. 3–4 (1922); E. König, *W. Wundt, seine Philosophie und Psychologie* (Stuttgart, 1901); Willi Nef, *Die Philosophie Wilhelm Wundts* (Leipzig, 1923); Peter Petersen, *Wilhelm Wundt und seine Zeit* (Stuttgart, 1925); E. B. Titchener, "Wilhelm Wundt," in *American Journal of Psychology,* **32** (1921), 161–178; W. Wirth, "Unserem grossen Lehrer Wilhelm Wundt in unauslöschlicher Dankbarkeit zum Gedächtnis," in *Archiv für die gesamte Psychologie,* **40** (1921), i–xvi; and "In Memory of Wilhelm Wundt," in *Psychological Review,* **28** (1921), 153–188, which includes reminiscences by seventeen of his American students.

SOLOMON DIAMOND

**WURTZ, CHARLES-ADOLPHE** (*b.* Wolfisheim, near Strasbourg, France, 26 November 1817; *d.* Paris, France, 12 May 1884), *chemistry.*

Wurtz spent the earliest years of his life in Wolfisheim, a small village near Strasbourg, where his father, Jean-Jacques Wurtz, was Lutheran pastor. He grew up in a rather modest but cultured home that was intellectually stimulating and part of a healthy agricultural community. His mother, the former Sophie Kreiss, came from a well-educated family and she appears to have enjoyed a more good-humored disposition than her husband. Their son was intelligent and gifted with an artistic nature; but he attended the Protestant school in Strasbourg, from July 1826, without showing exceptional promise. By the age of seventeen, however, he had developed a sufficiently strong interest in chemistry to offend his father with experiments in the house. The idea of a career in the ministry appealed less and less to young Wurtz, who eventually was allowed to embark on a medical course at the University of Strasbourg. This promised both security and an opportunity to cultivate his interest in chemistry.

Such was his preoccupation with chemistry that for his doctorate in medicine (1843) Wurtz wrote a thesis on fibrin and albumin, in which he described a method for the purification of soluble albumin and argued for a difference between albumin of blood and the albumin of an egg. After graduating from Strasbourg it was a natural step to move to Giessen, where he could study with Liebig and where he soon met A. W. Hofmann, who later complemented his work on the amines and became his biographer. At Giessen, Wurtz began his research with a study of hypophosphorous acid in an attempt to decide between the conflicting formulas of Dulong and Rose. He found time to translate Liebig's papers into French for the *Annales de chimie,* work that brought him into contact with the leading chemists in Paris. In 1844 he moved to that city, where he soon joined Dumas at the laboratory associated with the Faculty of Medicine.

It was there that Wurtz succeeded Dumas as lecturer in organic chemistry (1849), as professor (1853), and as dean (1866). In the last, more administrative, role he did much to improve the scientific education of medical students and to ensure that clinical professors in the hospitals had better laboratory facilities. From the Faculty of Medicine, Wurtz transferred to a chair of organic chemistry which had been specially created for him at the Sorbonne in 1874. Henceforth he could leave behind his heavy administrative responsibilities and enjoy his real vocation as a teacher.

Throughout his life Wurtz remained true to his Lutheran heritage. He displayed no trace of anticlericalism and found little difficulty in harmonizing his science with his faith. A staunch defender of the atomic theory against the skeptical positivism of Berthelot, he gave the theory a teleological interpretation in perfect accord with his natural theology. He was greatly respected for the diplomacy he demonstrated while dean of the Faculty of Medicine and for the liberalism that enabled him to defend his socialist colleagues, Alfred Naquet and Robin, with whom he had few political sympathies. His liberalism also manifested itself in his campaign for the admission of women students to the Faculty of Medicine. Intensely patriotic, he was deeply affected by the capture of his native Alsace during the Franco-Prussian War. He helped to found a society for the protection of the refugees who crowded into Paris from Alsace, and he was active when the capital fell under siege.

In 1852 Wurtz married a well-to-do childhood friend; they had four children, only one of whom pursued a scientific career. Wurtz became one of the most enthusiastic and outstanding teachers of his generation. There never was a school of chemists in France to compare with Liebig's school at Giessen, but Wurtz probably came closest to realizing one. Since he spoke French, German, and English, he was able to surround himself with the most distinguished chemists of the day. Both Couper and Butlerov—pioneers of structural organic chemistry—studied in his laboratory; around him, during the 1870's, there gathered such giants as Le Bel, van't Hoff, and Charles Friedel; and it was in his laboratory that Boisbaudran discovered gallium in 1875.

For twenty years, from 1852, Wurtz was responsible for the section devoted to foreign literature in the *Annales de chimie*. He became a member of the Academy of Medicine in 1856, vice-president in 1869, and president in 1871. He was elected a foreign member of the Royal Society in 1864 and subsequently won the Copley Medal. Twice he was awarded the Jecker Prize by the Institut de France; and after having been admitted to the chemical section of the Académie des Sciences in 1867, he was its president in 1881. Although the idea for the Société Chimique de France may not have originated with Wurtz, he became its secretary, its guiding spirit, and several times its president (1864, 1874, 1878). It was during his presidency (1864) that a number of separate publications, including Wurtz's own *Répertoire de chimie pure*, were amalgamated to produce the official bulletin of the society. Wurtz was equally active in establishing the Association Française pour l'Avancement des Sciences, a new organization designed to foster science in the provinces. Modeled on the British Association, with which Wurtz was impressed, the French Association held its first meeting at Bordeaux in 1872. When it met at Lille in 1874, Wurtz delivered the presidential address. He was greatly honored in public as well as in academic life; he was elected mayor of the seventh *arrondissement* of Paris, and a member of the Senate.

Wurtz began his career at a time of great crisis in organic chemistry. The dualistic approach of Berzelius appeared to be collapsing under the attacks of Dumas, Laurent, and Gerhardt, who favored a unitary conception of organic molecules based on their novel concepts of substitution and double decomposition. Wurtz had no hesitation in aligning himself with Laurent and Gerhardt; he was the first teacher in France to champion their ideas, and became the architect of a new chemical system that embraced their antidualist concepts as well as the emerging concepts of atomicity (valence) and chemical types.

Remarkable among Wurtz's earliest discoveries was his fulfillment of Liebig's prediction that there might be organic compounds analogous to ammonia and derivable from it by the replacement of hydrogen. Having prepared substituted ureas from derivatives of cyanogen, Wurtz investigated the action of potassium hydroxide on his products and thus obtained the primary amines (1849). This outstanding discovery was soon extended by his friend Hofmann, who demonstrated that the remaining two equivalents of hydrogen in ammonia could be replaced by alkyl groups. This provided support for the thesis that Gerhardt was developing: that it might be possible to regard all organic compounds as derivable from a small number of inorganic types, such as water or hydrogen chloride. The value of ammonia as a primitive type was now revealed:

$$
\begin{array}{cccc}
H & R^1 & R^1 & R^1 \\
\diagdown & \diagdown & \diagdown & \diagdown \\
H\!-\!N, & H\!-\!N, & R^2\!-\!N, & R^2\!-\!N. \\
\diagup & \diagup & \diagup & \diagup \\
H & H & H & R^3
\end{array}
$$

It was thus clear to Wurtz that organic radicals could replace hydrogen without destroying the basic structure or type. There remained, however, at least one serious bone of contention between the dualist school, now represented by Kolbe in Germany, and the new French school. Could the hydrocarbon radicals, postulated by the dualists as constituents of organic acids and alcohols, actually be isolated in the free state? Kolbe and the English chemist Frankland thought they had succeeded in isolating the methyl and ethyl radicals, thereby corroborating the conservative view that acetic acid, for example, contained the methyl radical, then written as $(C_4H_6)$, in precisely the same way that sulfuric acid contained sulfur:

$$(C_4H_6) \cdot O_3 + H_2O \text{ and } S \cdot O_3 + H_2O.$$

Laurent and Gerhardt, however, argued that the supposed verification was circular, and that what Kolbe and Frankland had isolated were dimers of the hypothetical radicals. The stability, vapor density, and boiling point of these controversial hydrocarbons favored the dimerization thesis, but a strictly chemical proof was required. It was Wurtz who provided this proof when he applied sodium to a mixture of alkyl iodides (1854). When the iodides were those of ethyl and butyl, he obtained some ethyl butyl; when they were those of butyl and amyl, he obtained some butyl amyl, thereby confirming that what was isolated contained two equivalents of the radicals, and was not a free radical itself.

Wurtz ingeniously had not only found a new method for synthesizing alkanes but also had embarrassed the dualism of Kolbe, with whom, as with Berthelot, he was frequently at loggerheads. Earlier in his career (1844), Wurtz had observed the curious fact that a hydride of copper, when treated with hydrochloric acid, generated a quantity of hydrogen double that contained by the hydride alone. This clearly suggested the possibility that each molecule of hydrogen might comprise two equivalents or atoms of hydrogen—one from the hydride and one from the acid. His work on the controversial hydrocarbons now endorsed this interpretation, which in turn ratified Avogadro's molecular hypothesis, so long neglected. Consequently, Wurtz became a leading advocate of the presuppositions underlying the atom-molecule distinction and, by examining the dissociation of anomalous vapors such as phosphorus pentachloride, he was able to rehabilitate the use of vapor density measurements for the determination of molecular weights.

One of Wurtz's most popular works was *La théorie atomique* (1879). Its title denoted more than the atomic-molecular theory of Avogadro or Ampère; it designated a theory that incorporated the idea of combining power or atomicity of the atoms—a new concept for which Wurtz had helped to clear the ground. He had done so by contributing to the notion of polyatomic organic radicals and by clarifying the distinctions between affinity, basicity, and atomicity. It was one of his outstanding contributions to chemistry that he succeeded in the preparation of the first dihydroxy alcohol, ethylene glycol, by the hydrolysis of ethylene diiodide (1856). It followed that the radicals of ethyl alcohol, glycol, and glycerin had ascending capacities of combination, and could be called monatomic, diatomic, and triatomic, respectively. This concept of characteristic combining power, when applied to the elements, precipitated the notion of valence, credit for which belongs to several of Wurtz's contemporaries as well as to him. The carbon—carbon bond eluded Wurtz—perhaps because of his conviction that the elements (including carbon) might exhibit more than one valence. Although he was justified in this belief, he differed from Kekulé, whose commitment to an exclusive tetravalence for carbon inexorably led to the vital carbon—carbon bond. The evidence suggests, moreover, that

Wurtz simply found the structural formulas of Kekulé and Couper too arbitrary and unnecessarily pretentious.

By dehydrating glycol, Wurtz procured ethylene oxide—a missing link that permitted him to construct a comprehensive series of analogies between organic and inorganic oxides that was based on the twin concepts of atomicity and type. Ethylene oxide was hailed as an analogue of the oxides of diatomic calcium and barium, just as glyceryl oxide could be represented as an analogue of the oxides of triatomic antimony and bismuth. On the basis of such analogical argument—and not, it should be noted, on the basis of organic synthesis—Wurtz proclaimed the unification of chemistry (1862).

Wurtz excelled as a practical chemist, and almost all his contributions were of lasting value. Among his many miscellaneous methods of synthesis were those for the production of phosphorous oxychloride, of neurine from ethylene oxide, of aldol from acetaldehyde, of phenol from benzene, and of esters from alkyl halides and the silver salts of acids.

### BIBLIOGRAPHY

I. ORIGINAL WORKS. Several of Wurtz's major works were translated into English and German. The following references are to the original French eds.: *Répertoire de chimie pure en France et à l'étranger*, 4 vols. (Paris, 1858–1862); *Chimie médicale* (Paris, 1864); *Leçons de chimie professées en 1863 par MM. A. Wurtz, A. Lamy, L. Grandeau* (Paris, 1864); *Leçons de philosophie chimique* (Paris, 1864); *Leçons élémentaires de chimie moderne* (Paris, 1867–1868); *Histoire des doctrines chimiques depuis Lavoisier* (Paris, 1868), the intro. to *Dictionnaire de chimie pure et appliquée*, 14 vols. (Paris, 1868–1878); English trans. by H. Watts, *A History of Chemical Theory* (London, 1869); *Les hautes études pratiques dans les universités allemandes* (Paris, 1870); *La théorie atomique* (Paris, 1879); and *Traité de chimie biologique* (Paris, 1880).

Besides these volumes, Wurtz published prolifically. His work included at least 140 papers, of which the following contain his most important contributions to the advance of chemistry:"Recherches sur la constitution de l'acide hypophosphoreux," in *Annales de chimie et de physique*, 3rd ser., **7** (1843), 35–50; "Sur l'hydrure de cuivre," *ibid.*, **11** (1844), 250–252; "Recherches sur les éthers cyaniques et leurs dérivés," in *Comptes rendus . . . de l'Académie des sciences*, **27** (1848), 241–243; "Sur une série d'alcalis organiques homologues avec l'ammoniaque," *ibid.*, **28** (1849), 223–226; "Recherches sur les urées composées," *ibid.*, **32** (1851), 414–419; "Sur l'alcool butylique," *ibid.*, **35** (1852), 310–312; "Sur la théorie des amides," *ibid.*, **37** (1853), 246–250 and

357–361; "Sur une nouvelle classe de radicaux organiques," in *Annales de chimie et de physique*, 3rd ser., **44** (1855), 275–313; "Sur le glycol ou alcool diatomique," in *Comptes rendus . . . de l'Académie des sciences*, **43** (1856), 199–204; "Sur l'acétal et sur les glycols," *ibid.*, 478–481; "Sur la formation artificielle de la glycérine," in *Annales de chimie et de physique*, 3rd ser., **51** (1857), 94–101; "Recherches sur l'acide lactique," in *Comptes rendus . . . de l'Académie des sciences*, **46** (1858), 1228–1232; and "Sur l'oxyde d'-éthylène," *ibid.*, **48** (1859), 101–105. Also see "Observations sur la théorie des types," in *Répertoire de chimie pure*, **2** (1860), 354–359; "On Oxide of Ethylene, Considered as a Link Between Organic and Mineral Chemistry," in *Journal of the Chemical Society*, **15** (1862), 387–406; "Sur l'oxyde d'éthylène et les alcools polyéthyléniques," in *Annales de chimie et de physique*, 3rd ser., **69** (1863), 317–355; "Nouveau mode de formation de quelques hydrogènes carbonés," in *Comptes rendus . . . de l'Académie des sciences*, **54** (1862), 387–390; "Sur l'atomicité des éléments," in *Bulletin de la Société chimique de Paris*, **2** (1864), 247–253; "Sur les densités de vapeur anomales," in *Comptes rendus . . . de l'Académie des sciences*, **60** (1865), 728–732, and **62** (1866), 1182–1186; "Transformation des carbures aromatiques en phénols," *ibid.*, **64** (1867), 749–751; "Synthèse de la névrine," *ibid.*, **65** (1867), 1015–1018; "Sur la densité de vapeur du perchlorure de phosphore," in *Comptes rendus de l'Association française pour l'avancement des sciences*, **1** (1872), 426–445; "Nouvelles recherches sur l'aldol," in *Comptes rendus . . . de l'Académie des sciences*, **76** (1873), 1165–1171; "Recherches sur la loi d'Avogadro et d'Ampère," *ibid.*, **84** (1877), 977–983; "Sur la notation atomique," *ibid.*, 1264–1268; "Sur les densités de vapeur," *ibid.*, 1347–1349; "Sur le ferment digestif du *Carica papaya*," *ibid.*, **89** (1879), 425–429; "Sur la papaïne; contribution à l'histoire des ferments solubles," *ibid.*, **90** (1880), 1379–1385; and "Sur la préparation de l'aldol," *ibid.*, **92** (1881), 1438–1439.

The above selection is taken and corrected from the bibliography appended to C. Friedel, "Notice sur la vie et les travaux de Charles-Adolphe Wurtz," in *Bulletin de la Société chimique*, **43** (1885), i–lxxx, which also was published in the introduction to the 1886 ed. of Wurtz's *La théorie atomique*.

II. Secondary Literature. Besides Friedel's, biographies include A. W. Hofmann, in *Berichte der Deutschen chemischen Gesellschaft*, **17**, no. 1 (1884), 1207–1211, and **20**, no. 3 (1887), 815–996; A. Gautier, in *Revue scientifique*, **55** (1917), 769–770; M. Tiffeneau *et al.*, *ibid.*, **59** (1921), 573–602; and A. Williamson, in *Proceedings of the Royal Society*, **38** (1885), xxiii–xxxiv.

The following works contain invaluable information for an accurate appraisal of Wurtz's contributions to chemistry: R. Anschütz, *August Kekulé* (Berlin, 1929); J. H. Brooke, "Organic Synthesis and the Unification of Chemistry— a Reappraisal," in *British Journal for the*

*History of Science*, **5** (1971), 363–392; G. V. Bykov and J. Jacques, "Deux pionniers de la chimie moderne, Adolphe Wurtz et Alexandre M. Boutlerov, d'après une correspondance inédite," in *Revue d'histoire des sciences*, **13** (1960), 115–134; E. Farber, "The Glycol Centenary," in *Journal of Chemical Education*, **33** (1956), 117; H. Hartley, *Studies in the History of Chemistry* (Oxford, 1971), ch. 8; D. Larder, "A Dialectical Consideration of Butlerov's Theory of Chemical Structure," in *Ambix*, **18** (1971), 26–48; A. Metz, "La notation atomique et la théorie atomique en France à la fin du XIX$^e$ siècle," in *Revue d'histoire des sciences*, **16** (1963), 233–239; J. R. Partington, "The Chemical Society of France, 1857–1957," in *Nature*, **180** (1957), 1165; and *A History of Chemistry*, IV (London, 1964), 477–488; C. A. Russell, *The History of Valency* (Leicester, 1971); and G. Urbain, "J. B. Dumas and C. A. Wurtz—leur rôle dans l'histoire des théories atomiques et moléculaires," in *Bulletin de la Société chimique*, 5th ser., **1** (1934), 1425–1447.

John Hedley Brooke

**WYMAN, JEFFRIES** (*b.* Chelmsford, Massachusetts, 11 August 1814; *d.* Bethlehem, New Hampshire, 4 September 1874), *anatomy, physiology.*

Wyman was almost a model of the nineteenth-century scientist who had no life independent of his calling. His father, Rufus Wyman, was a physician who named his son after John Jeffries of Boston, his medical teacher; Wyman's mother was Ann Morrill. An elder brother, Morrill Wyman, was known as the leading physician in nineteenth-century Cambridge. In 1818 Dr. Rufus Wyman became physician for the McLean Asylum for the Insane, then in Charlestown, Massachusetts, where Jeffries had his early schooling. After preparation at an academy in Chelmsford and at Phillips Academy at Andover, Wyman entered Harvard in 1829, graduating in 1833. Not a distinguished scholar in general, he continued while an undergraduate a very early interest in natural history and in sketching, major tools for a future anatomist. In his senior year Wyman contracted pneumonia, which continued as what Oliver Wendell Holmes called "the pulmonary affection that kept him an invalid, and ended by causing his death." This condition, from which he suffered for over forty years, set important limits and opened important opportunities for the entire span of his adult career, especially its requirement that he spend each winter in the South.

After graduating from Harvard College, Wyman apprenticed himself to a John C. Dalton in Chelmsford and attended the Harvard Medical

School in Boston. On receiving the M.D. in 1837, he failed to find a lucrative post in a country town and was thus forced to open a Boston office and to accept the poorly paid post of demonstrator of anatomy to John C. Warren, the Hersey professor at Harvard Medical School.

Wyman's turn from medicine to science was largely financed by the few wealthy men in Boston who figured in most scientific careers of the community at that time. John Amory Lowell made Wyman curator of the Lowell Institute, and in the winter of 1840–1841 he delivered a course of lectures on comparative anatomy and physiology. With the proceeds Wyman made a somewhat truncated tour of Europe, the standard preparation for an American career in science. He spent the summer of 1841 in Paris, attending lectures in human anatomy, comparative anatomy, physiology, and zoology. In London he worked on the Hunterian collections at the Royal College of Surgeons and became acquainted with Richard Owen before being called back by the death of his father.

On returning to Boston, Wyman took his place in the scientific community as a fellow of the American Academy of Arts and Sciences and curator of reptiles and fishes at the Boston Society of Natural History. For a living and as an excuse to go south, he was professor of anatomy and physiology at Hampden-Sydney Medical College in Richmond, Virginia, from 1843 to 1848. During that period he published some of the most significant papers of his career.

In 1847 Wyman's friends at Harvard made an arrangement that sufficed to give him a secure institutional base for the rest of his life and gave the university a markedly increased capability in zoology and anatomy. Wyman took the Hersey professorship, which hitherto had been at the medical school, to Cambridge, while Oliver Wendell Holmes occupied a new chair, the Parkman professorship, in Boston. Thus anatomy and physiology became subjects for undergraduates, not just for medical students, and Wyman had scope to work on species other than *Homo sapiens*. Since Asa Gray, the Fisher professor of natural history, wished to concentrate on botany, he expected Wyman to hold recitations in elementary zoology, especially when Gray was on leave—an arrangement that significantly advanced the differentiation of botany and zoology at Harvard. With the appointment, at essentially the same time, of Louis Agassiz to the Lawrence Scientific School, Wyman was able to confine himself largely to anatomy and physiology, and to undertake the development of a

museum of anatomical specimens that he continued to the end of his life.

Specialization was still in transition in the mid-nineteenth century, however, and Wyman was associated with his brother Morrill Wyman in a private medical school at Cambridge from 1857 to 1866. From 1856 to the end of his life he was the beneficiary of gifts from two wealthy Bostonians that made possible his winter research in warm climates. He often went to Europe or Florida. He traveled to Surinam in 1856; and despite the fever he contracted there, was ready by 1858 to go on the La Plata expedition of J. M. Forbes, which crossed the Andes and returned from Chile by way of Peru and the Isthmus of Panama. This type of invalid's rest played a part in Wyman's becoming professor of American archaeology and ethnology in 1866, and effectively the first director of the museum endowed by George Peabody. Thus in the last years of his life he built an archaeological museum alongside his anatomical museum in Boylston Hall at Harvard.

Wyman gained national recognition as president of the American Association for the Advancement of Science and an original member of the National Academy of Sciences, but he did not serve as the one and soon resigned from the other. He was married twice, in 1850 and 1861. His first wife died in 1855, leaving two daughters; the second died in 1864, leaving a son. The combination of delicate health and steady exertion remained constant until Wyman's last days in September 1874. He was on an annual visit to the White Mountains, to escape the autumnal catarrh, when he died suddenly of a hemorrhage from the lungs.

Of Wyman's 175 papers, mostly on anatomy, the ones that attracted most notice were a series on the gorilla. With the memoir (written with Thomas S. Savage) "Notice of the Characters, Habits, and Osteology of *Troglodytes gorilla*, a New Species of Ourang From the Gaboon River" (*Boston Journal of Natural History*, 5 [1845–1847], 417–442), Wyman established himself as the peer of Richard Owen in elaborating the anatomical features of the higher primates. In 1859 he worked on a large collection of gorilla skins and skeletons sent him by the explorer Paul Belloni du Chaillu.

Despite his pose of being above the fray in both scientific politics and intellectual controversy, Wyman followed with informed care the great issues of his day that swirled about the work of Charles Darwin and Louis Pasteur. In his study of the gorilla, he generalized only to the extent of saying that the

. . . difference between the cranium, the pelvis, and the conformation of the upper extremities in the negro and Caucasian sinks into comparative insignificance when compared with the vast difference that exists between the conformation of the same parts in the negro and the orang. Yet it cannot be denied, however wide the separation, that the negro and orang do afford the points where man and brute, when the totality of their organization is considered, most nearly approach each other [p. 441].

From 1860 to 1866 Wyman corresponded with Darwin, providing a number of examples of possible natural selection. One was the action of light favoring black pigs over white ones after they had eaten a Florida plant called paint-root (*Lachnanthes tinctoria*). Another concerned the perfection of cells formed by bees, on which Wyman made and published careful measurements. These cases appear in *Origin of Species*. Other examples provided by Wyman include blind fishes of Mammoth Cave, Natá cattle of South America, malformed codfish, and rattlesnakes. Wyman never expressed himself publicly on the *Origin of Species*; but clearly he seriously considered the problems set by Darwin, and the testimony of his friends indicates that he was privately pro-Darwin and not a vitalist (and equally privately a theist).

In 1862 Wyman began a series of experiments on spontaneous generation, paralleling those conducted by Pasteur and Pouchet. He reported the presence of infusoria even in flasks that had been boiled, under carefully controlled conditions, for four hours. When the flasks were boiled beyond five hours, no infusoria appeared. Yet Wyman did not press to any conclusion, either for or against spontaneous generation, being content to let his experiments stand as examples of logically conceived and elegantly executed laboratory exercises.

Wyman's influence lived on in a number of students. B. G. Wilder carried on his theories of symmetry and homology in limbs. S. Weir Mitchell paid tribute to his inspiration. Perhaps the most effective projector of Wyman's influence, even into the twentieth century, was the young man who as a student had come to respect him over Agassiz and who succeeded him in his course in anatomy and physiology at the time of his death—William James.

## BIBLIOGRAPHY

A collection of MSS long held by the Wyman family is at the Countway Library, Harvard Medical School. Biographical notices include Asa Gray, "Jeffries Wyman Memorial Meeting . . . October 7, 1874," in *Proceedings of the Boston Society of Natural History*, **17** (1875), 96–124; Oliver Wendell Holmes, "Memoir of Professor Jeffries Wyman," in *Proceedings of the Massachusetts Historical Society*, **14** (Apr. 1875), 4–24; and A. S. Packard, "Memoir of Jeffries Wyman, 1814–1874," in *Biographical Memoirs. National Academy of Sciences*, **2** (1886), 75–126, which includes a list of Wyman's works.

Also see R. N. Doesch, "Early American Experiments on 'Spontaneous Generation' by Jeffries Wyman (1814–1874)," in *Journal of the History of Medicine and Allied Sciences*, **17** (1962), 326–332; A. H. Dupree, ed., "Some Letters From Charles Darwin to Jeffries Wyman," in *Isis*, **42** (1951), 104–110; and "Jeffries Wyman's Views on Evolution," *ibid.*, **44** (1953), 243–246; and G. E. Gifford, ed., "Twelve Letters From Jeffries Wyman, M.D.: Hampden-Sydney Medical College, Richmond, Virginia, 1843–1848," in *Journal of the History of Medicine and Allied Sciences*, **20** (1965), 309–333; and "An American in Paris, 1841–1842: Four Letters From Jeffries Wyman," *ibid.*, **22** (1967), 274–285.

A. HUNTER DUPREE

**XENOCRATES OF CHALCEDON** (*b.* Chalcedon [now Kadiköy], Bithynia [now Turkey], 396/395 B.C.; *d.* Athens, 314/313 B.C.), *philosophy, mathematics.*

Xenocrates was a student of Plato and, as head of the Academy from 339 B.C. to 314/313 B.C., was one of the founders of the ancient Academic tradition. He entered the Academy (in 378 B.C. at the earliest or 373 B.C. at the latest) and about ten years later accompanied Plato to Syracuse, the latter's second or third voyage to that city.

After Plato's death, Xenocrates and Aristotle were invited to Assos, where they remained until the overthrow of Hermias of Atarneus, in 342 B.C. Plato's successor, his nephew Speusippus, headed the Academy until his death in 340/339 B.C. He sent for Xenocrates, who was not in Athens at this time, and designated him his successor. Nevertheless, an election was held, which Xenocrates won by only a few votes. The opposing candidates, Heraclitus Ponticus and Menedemus of Pyrrha, thereupon left the Academy. (Aristotle was not a candidate.)

In 322 B.C. Xenocrates was appointed to an Athenian legation sent to negotiate with Antipatrus of Macedonia, but it was compelled, instead, to acknowledge Athens' submission. Since Xenocrates was not a citizen of Athens, Antipatrus did not recognize his status as a legitimate ambassador. Both before and after this incident, Xenocrates refused to seek Athenian citizenship, since he disapproved of the city's close relations with Macedonia. On this point he was at odds with the political views of his predecessor Speusippus, who had supported Athens' pro-Macedonian policies. After Xenocrates' death, the leadership of the Academy passed to Polemo.

According to a number of less substantiated anecdotes about Xenocrates, he is depicted as good-natured, gentle, and considerate—but it is also quite clear that he lacked the *charis* ("graciousness") of his teacher Plato. Along with these traits, Xenocrates is reported to have displayed singular diligence. The list of his writings, which is entirely preserved in Diogenes Laërtius (IV, 11–14), contains about seventy titles. The biographical anecdotes state that he never left the Academy (where all his work was done) more than once a year.

None of Xenocrates' writings has survived. They presumably were never published—that is, copied; rather, the single copies in his own hand were deposited at the Academy. When Athens was stormed by Sulla's troops in March 86 B.C., the Academy, located in front of the western gate, was destroyed together with its priceless library.[1]

Unlike Aristotle, Xenocrates did not wish to develop philosophy in new ways but considered it his task to maintain Plato's theory as he had received and understood it. This motivation underlay his extensive literary activity, in which enterprise Xenocrates relied primarily upon his memory—recalling, in some instances, what he had learned as much as twenty-five years earlier. Curiously, Xenocrates did not respect an important request made by Plato, who considered language unreliable and conducive to misunderstanding. Plato apparently insisted that the contents of philosophical doctrines be communicated only to those who would strictly observe definite precautions, and consequently he often veiled his meaning through the use of metaphors and myths. Xenocrates, seeking to render Plato's theories teachable without recourse to such means, established a system of doctrinal propositions. Xenocrates' lifework consisted in producing a kind of codification—and thus, of necessity, a transformation—of Plato's philosophy. But it immediately became apparent that others, especially Aristotle, understood Plato in a wholly different way with respect to certain key questions. Crantor of Soli, for example—himself the pupil of Xenocrates—was to some extent justified in reproaching him for having taught

things that differed from elements of Plato's surviving written works. Although Xenocrates did not attribute to Plato anything that he had not actually taught, he did choose single aspects—often overly narrow ones—from among the many possible ways of presenting Plato's conceptions and raised them to the status of official doctrine.

Xenocrates probably found himself confronted with a difficult situation. After it had been decided to preserve Plato's teachings, everything that could not be encompassed in words—that is, everything that Plato had not wished to set forth in words—had to be abandoned in the interest of a clear and systematic presentation. In the process of achieving this sort of systematization, Xenocrates sacrificed Plato's dialectical approach.

Xenocrates was no more a dualist than Plato. Rather, he belongs to the long line of those who have attempted to overcome a type of dualism within the philosophical tradition. In particular, in his comprehensive outline, Xenocrates provided for a gradation of all the elements that make up ontology, physics, ethics, and epistemology. This scheme assumed major importance in the development of Neoplatonism. Xenocrates' real legacy lies in the conception he sketched of a hierarchy of all existing things that culminates in a single, highest point, the One.

*NOTES*

1. Reports of Xenocrates' teaching have survived only in the works of Aristotle and in Cicero and other Roman authors. The so-called fragments have been collected by Richard Heinze (see below). All knowledge of Xenocrates was probably based on an indirect tradition. Reports of his teaching are only rarely supported by mention of the title of one of his works (cf. Heinze, 157, 158). The only quotation that seems to bear the stamp of authenticity is in Themistius' (A.D. 317[?]–ca. 388) commentary on Aristotle's *De anima;* see *Commentaria in Aristotelem Graeca,* V, pt. 3, R. Heinze, ed. (Berlin, 1899); and Heinze, *Xenocrates,* frag. 61. In Themistius' reference to the fifth book of περὶ φύσεως, it is possible to glean an indication that Xenocrates may have introduced the definition of soul as number. In this instance it cannot be ruled out that περὶ φύσεως had been published either in whole or in part. But such a quotation may also have originated in Crantor's interpretation of the *Timaeus,* where he suddenly attacks Xenocrates' theory of the soul as number. On this point, see H. F. Cherniss, *Aristotle's Criticism of Plato and the Academy,* I (Baltimore, 1944; repr. New York, 1962), p. 399, n. 325.

*BIBLIOGRAPHY*

See H. F. Cherniss, *The Riddle of the Early Academy* (Berkeley, Calif., 1945; repr. New York, 1962), esp. 31–59; H. Dörrie, "Xenokrates," in Pauly-Wissowa, *Real Encyclopädie der classischen Altertumswiss-*

*enschaft*, 2nd ser., IX, 1512–1528; R. Heinze, *Xenocrates. Darstellung der Lehre und Sammlung der Fragmente* (Leipzig, 1892; repr., Hildesheim, 1965); S. Mekler, ed., *Academicorum philosophorum index Herculanensis* (Berlin, 1902), esp. 38–39; Diogenes Laërtius, *De vitis philosophorum*, IV, ch. 2–also in English, R. D. Hicks, trans., *Lives of Eminent Philosophers*, I (Cambridge, Mass.–London, 1966), 380–393; and U. von Wilamowitz-Moellendorff, *Platon, sein Leben und seine Werke*, 4th ed., I (Berlin, 1948), 579–581.

H. DÖRRIE

**XENOPHANES** (*b*. Colophon, Ionia, *ca*. 580–570 B.C.; *d. ca*. 478 B.C.), *theology, epistemology.*

It is generally believed that Xenophanes was born about 570 B.C. in Colophon, a Greek city in Asia Minor. He left Ionia after 545, the time of the Persian conquest, in order to live in the western part of the Greek world, in southern Italy and Sicily. He died after 478. If it is true, as has recently been suggested,[1] that Xenophanes did not leave Colophon at the time he left Asia but, rather, ten years earlier, then the date of his birth can be pushed back in accordance with the ancient chronology (580–577). On this hypothesis, he was banished from Colophon in 555, when the city came under a tyrannical regime (at that time it was still under the control of the kingdom of Lydia).

Xenophanes seems to have opposed this regime openly and to have been known after 555 as a poet fighting for the restoration of his native city's ancient civil liberties. It was probably toward this end that he devoted an epic to the origins of Colophon and wrote a poem in honor of Elea. He may have joined the Phocaeans who founded the latter city on the coast of southern Italy (540–535).

Xenophanes' deep personal involvement in political matters is inseparable from his intellectual activities. He profoundly influenced Greek thought in at least two respects, through his criticism of the anthropomorphic beliefs upheld by traditional religion and through his "monist" definition of God. The principal surviving fragments of his elegies clearly show that the intellectual and moral reform to which he dedicated himself had a political objective. He believed that the thinker, through his statements, should clear the way for a strengthening of communal life within the framework of the city-state.

To further this goal, Xenophanes extended his critique of anthropomorphism to all the attitudes and activities attributed to the gods, judging these incompatible with a just conception of divine reality. He rejected the picture of the divine world and its organization propagated by Homer and Hesiod; he objected to certain ritual practices; and he denied that the gods intervene physically either in divination or in meteorological phenomena. To this refutation of accepted views which he elaborated in his *Satires* (Σίλλοι) Xenophanes joined a description of the attributes of God. These are such, he asserted, as reason conceives them when it has cast off the hold of mythology and popular beliefs. Thus, starting from the notion of omnipotence, Xenophanes derived the concepts of God's unity (that is, unicity or wholeness) and eternity. God, he stated, is present everywhere and acts without intermediary and without displacement or movement, solely by means of His mind's will.

Did Xenophanes apply his ideas concerning the attributes of divine reality to the universe? Did he identify God with the cosmos, as has often been supposed?[2] It does not seem that he did. This pantheistic interpretation (given by Theophrastus and already proposed by Aristotle) appears incompatible—despite the opposing views of certain authors[3]—with the wording of the existing fragments. Still, these attributes endow Xenophanes' God with an ontological status remarkably similar to that later enunciated in certain propositions of Eleatic logic. According to tradition, Xenophanes was the teacher of Parmenides; and the latter could indeed have found in the conception of a unique, eternal, and omnipotent God the starting point for his deduction of the properties of being.

Xenophanes' monotheism did not entail a denigration of man. On the contrary, he affirmed man's autonomy in material progress and civilization. But he did make a distinction of great epistemological significance: God alone possesses complete knowledge, whereas man can attain genuine knowledge only within the limits assigned to the combined activity of his senses. That is, he can really know only particular objects or partial aspects of the world. With regard to the totality of things, the universe (and God himself), man must be satisfied with a probable knowledge, which is incapable of verifying the truth of what it grasps. This restriction has given rise to much discussion. Some authors, including a few modern ones, have claimed that Xenophanes meant to apply it to empirical knowledge itself, thus portraying him as an advocate of radical skepticism.[4] This view is incorrect. He thought that human knowledge was limited, not with respect to things but relative to God's omniscience.

Xenophanes did not conceive or set forth a

complete doctrine of the physical world,[5] although he occasionally touched on physical questions in his polemical writings—alluding, for example, to Thales, Anaximander, and Pythagoras. He was neither a philosopher of nature nor a "sage" in the primary sense of the word. Highly independent and curious about everything (something for which he was reproached by Heraclitus), Xenophanes was a poet and a thinker who played a major role in the intellectual adventure of his age. He stimulated the emancipation of reason in Greek ethical and religious discourse and thus contributed, although indirectly, to the triumph of systematic thinking in science and philosophical reflection.

## NOTES

1. See P. Steinmetz, "Xenophanesstudien," sec. entitled "Zur Datierung."
2. Most recently, by M. Untersteiner, *Senofane*, clxxxix–cciii; and W. K. C. Guthrie, *A History of Greek Philosophy*, 381–383. Those who disagree or reserve opinion include W. Jaeger, *The Theology of the Early Greek Philosophers*, 43 and n. 23; H. Fränkel, *Dichtung und Philosophie des frühen Griechentums*, 378; A. Lumpe, *Die Philosophie des Xenophanes von Kolophon*, 22–26; and G. S. Kirk, in Kirk and Raven, *The Presocratic Philosophers*, 171–172.
3. Especially Guthrie, *loc. cit.*,
4. Particularly E. Heitsch, who opposes Fränkel. Compare K. von Fritz, "Xenophanes," cols. 1557–1559.
5. Summaries of the controversy over the *De natura* attributed to him are in Untersteiner, *op. cit.*, ccxlii–ccl; and in Reale's note in E. Zeller and R. Mondolfo, *La filosofia dei Greci . . .*, 69–71. There are some perceptive remarks in Steinmetz, *op. cit.*, 54–68 ("Ein Lehrgedicht des Xenophanes?").

## BIBLIOGRAPHY

Fragments and testimonia are in H. Diels and W. Kranz, *Die Fragmente der Vorsokratiker*, 6th ed., I (Berlin, 1951), 113–139; the fragments alone are in E. Diehl, *Anthologia lyrica Graeca*, fasc. 1, *Poetae elegiaci*, 3rd ed. (Leipzig, 1949), 64–76; and M. L. West, *Iambi et Elegi Graeci ante Alexandrum cantati*, II (Oxford, 1972), 163–170. There is abundant information in M. Untersteiner, *Senofane, testimonianze e frammenti* (Florence, 1955); and E. Zeller and R. Mondolfo, *La filosofia dei Greci nel suo sviluppo storico*, pt. 1, *I Presocratici*, III, *Eleati*, G. Reale, ed. (Florence, 1967), 1–164.

Recent writings include H. Fränkel, *Dichtung und Philosophie des frühen Griechentums* (New York, 1951; 2nd ed., Munich, 1962), 371–384; K. von Fritz, "Xenophanes," in Pauly-Wissowa, *Real-Encyclopädie der classischen Altertumswissenschaft*, 2nd ser., IX (1967), cols. 1541–1562; W. K. C. Guthrie, *A History of Greek Philosophy*, I (Cambridge, 1962), 360–402; E. Heitsch, "Das Wissen des Xenophanes," in *Rheinisches Museum für Philologie*, 109 (1966), 193–235; H. Herter, "Das Symposion des Xenophanes," in *Wiener Studien*, 69 (1956), 33–48; W. Jaeger, *The Theology of the Early Greek Philosophers* (Oxford, 1947), 38–54; G. S. Kirk, in G. S. Kirk and J. E. Raven, *The Presocratic Philosophers* (Cambridge, 1957), 163–181; A. Lumpe, *Die Philosophie des Xenophanes von Kolophon* (Munich, 1952); A. Rivier, "Remarques sur les fragments 34 et 35 de Xénophane," in *Revue de philologie*, 3rd ser., 30 (1956), 37–61; P. Steinmetz, "Xenophanesstudien," in *Rheinisches Museum für Philologie*, 109 (1966), 13–73; and M. Untersteiner, intro. and commentary to his *Senofane* (see above).

ANDRÉ RIVIER

**YAḤYĀ IBN ABĪ MANṢŪR** (*d.* near Aleppo, Syria, 832), *astronomy.*

Yaḥyā was a member of an important family of Persian scientists. His father, Abū Manṣūr Abān, was an astrologer; his son ʿAlī bin Yaḥyā (*d.* 888) was eminent in Baghdad and had a great library in which Abū Maʿshar studied; his grandson, Hārūn ibn ʿAlī (*d.* 900), also was an astronomer.

Yaḥyā spent his life casting horoscopes (one is given by Ibn al-Qifṭī, *Taʾrīkh al-ḥukamāʾ*, pp. 358–359) and seeking methods to determine the positions of the stars with maximum precision. His first work as an astrologer was in the service of al-Faḍl ibn Sahl, vizier of Caliph al-Maʾmūn. After al-Faḍl's assassination in February 818, he entered the service of al-Maʾmūn and converted to Islam. We know that Yaḥyā was an official at *bayt al-ḥikma*, who may have controlled funds for astronomy. He taught the Banū Mūsā and died while accompanying the caliph on an expedition against Tarsus.

Yaḥyā was appointed director of the group of scholars who by order of al-Maʾmūn (828) established an observatory in the Shamāsiya quarter of Baghdad and the observatory at the monastery of Dayr Murrān in Damascus. These centers were intended to make observations that would improve and correct existing astronomical tables. The Damascus observatory was headed by Ḥabash al-Ḥāsib (*d.* 864/874), who sent the results obtained there to Baghdad for further elaboration. This would explain why the tables attributed to Ḥabash are closely connected with *Zīj al-mumtaḥan*.

Yaḥyā's team of scientists included al-Marwarrūdhī; al-Khwārizmī, who collaborated with Yaḥyā in 828; and Sanad ibn ʿAlī (*d. ca.* 864), who was in charge of improving the observational instruments, some of which were unusually large. Most of the instruments were graduated by the leading expert of the time, ʿAlī ibn ʿIsā al-Asṭurlābī, but were not very dependable. The group also included the Banū Mūsā and al-Jawharī; the latter corrected the data concerning the positions of the planets and of the sun and moon, incorporating the results into his own tables, on the margin of the *Zīj al-mumtaḥan*.

This same group measured one degree of the meridian by using two different processes: the measurement *in situ* of one degree on the earth's surface, and the corroboration of this value by means of a trigonometric process based on measuring the dip of the horizon, with an astrolabe, from a mountaintop. The latter method seems to have been used for the first time by Sanad ibn ʿAlī.

The numerical results of the observations were recorded in the *Zīj al-mumtaḥan* (*Tabulae probatae* in Latin). It should be noted that the words *mumtaḥan* and *probatae* are generic and indicate any table based on observation; thus the tables of Yahyā's group are not the only ones to be so designated. The observations terminated abruptly at the almost simultaneous deaths of the caliph and of Yahyā. A written copy of the completed work was deposited at the library of the palace at Baghdad. Only one manuscript (Escorial 927) is known to contain these tables, but it is badly bound and comprises many folios that are not from Yahyā's work and are explicitly attributed to astronomers of the tenth and eleventh centuries. Internal criticism seems to indicate that the first folios are by Yahyā's group and the later ones are intermingled with works written long afterward.

Because of this disorder the manuscript can be analyzed only by means of an arbitrary arrangement. It contains a full explanation of calendars (Coptic, Greek, Jewish, Muslim) and chronological eras, the majority of which are primitive. Many of the tables were compiled before those of Yahyā, the date being indicated at the top of each. It is difficult to state precisely to what extent they used all the trigonometric functions, as Habash did in his works. The elements for the calculation of ephemerides were generally primitive, as were two of the tables of star positions. The inferior planets are treated numerically (without theoretical explanations) as satellites of the sun—an approach equivalent to the system of Heraclides and Tycho Brahe. This model may have been suggested by an ancient text, perhaps one by Theon of Smyrna. The margins contain tables and rules that are very difficult to group and date because of their lack of unity.

Yahyā's tables exerted a great influence on astronomy: Thābit ibn Qurra (*d*. 901) wrote an introduction to them that drew on data supplied by Habash, and took these tables into consideration in his works on eclipses. Ibn Yūnus adapted them for use in Egypt; and al-Zarqālī derived from them the value of the inclination of the ecliptic and certain other values used in the calculation of ephemerides.

BIBLIOGRAPHY

See E. S. Kennedy, "A Survey of Islamic Astronomical Tables," in *Transactions of the American Philosophical Society*, n.s. **46**, no. 2 (1956), nos. 15, 51. MS Escorial 927 is analyzed by J. Vernet, in "Las 'Tabulae probatae,'" in *Homenaje a Millás-Vallicrosa*, II (Barcelona, 1956), 501–522. Vernet has also published partial studies of this MS: "Los símbolos planetarios rumíes," in *al-Andalus*, **16** (1951), 493; and "Un antiguo tratado sobre el calendario judío en las *Tabulae probatae*," in *Sefarad*, **14** (1954), 59–78.

The Arabic sources are listed in W. Hartner, "Habash al-Hāsib al-Marwazī," in *Encyclopedia of Islam*, new ed., III (Leiden–London, 1971), 8–9; Aydin Sayili, *The Observatory in Islam* (Ankara, 1960), 50–87 and index; and H. Suter, *Die Mathematiker und Astronomen der Araber und ihre Werke* (Leipzig, 1900), nos. 14, 22.

J. VERNET

**YAʿĪSH IBN IBRĀHĪM.** See **Al-Umawī, Abū ʿAbdallāh Yaʿīsh ibn Ibrāhīm ibn Yūsuf ibn Simāk al-Andalusī.**

**YANG HUI** (*fl.* China, *ca.* 1261–1275), *mathematics.*

The thirteenth century was perhaps the most significant period in the history of Chinese mathematics. It began with the appearance of Ch'in Chiu-shao's *Shu-shu chiu-chang* in 1247, and the following year Li Chih issued an equally important work, the *Ts'e-yüan hai-ching*. These two great algebraists were later joined by Yang Hui (literary name, Yang Ch'ien-kuang), whose publications far surpassed those of his predecessors, and of whom we have absolutely no knowledge. The golden age of Chinese mathematics came to an end after the appearance of Chu Shih-chieh's *Ssu-yüan yü-chien* in 1303. Of the works of these four great Chinese mathematicians, those by Yang Hui have, until very recently, been the least studied and analyzed.

Nothing is known about the life of Yang Hui,

except that he produced mathematical writings. From the prefaces to his works we learn that he was a native of Ch'ien-t'ang (now Hangchow). He seems to have been a civil servant, having served in T'ai-chou, and he had probably visited Su-chou (modern Soochow). His friends and acquaintances included Ch'en Chi-hsien, Liu Pi-chien, Ch'iu Hsü-chü, and Shih Chung-yung, the last having collaborated with him on one of his works; but we know nothing else about their personal history. Yang Hui also names as his teacher another mathematician, Liu I, a native of Chung-shan, of whom nothing is known.

In 1261 Yang Hui wrote *Hsiang-chieh chiu-chang suan-fa* ("Detailed Analysis of the Mathematical Rules in the Nine Chapters"), a commentary on the old Chinese mathematical classic *Chiu-chang suan-shu*, by Liu Hui. The present version of the *Hsiang-chieh chiu-chang suan-fa*, which is based on the edition in the *I-chia-t'ang ts'ung-shu* (1842) collection, is incomplete and consists of only five chapters; two additional chapters have been restored from the *Yung-lo ta-tien* encyclopedia. Besides the original nine chapters of the *Chiu-chang suan-shu*, Yang Hui's *Hsiang-chieh chiu-chang suan-fa* included three additional chapters, making a total of twelve. According to the preface written by Yang Hui, he had selected 80 of the 246 problems in the *Chiu-chang suan-shu* for detailed discussion. The now-lost introductory chapter of the *Hsiang-chieh chiu-chang suan-fa*, as we learn from the *shao-kuang* ("Diminishing Breadth") chapter of the text and from a quotation in another of Yang Hui's works, *Suan-fa t'ung-pien pen-mo*, contained diagrams and illustrations.

Chapter 1, according to what Yang Hui describes in *Suan-fa t'ung-pien pen-mo* and *Ch'eng-ch'u t'ung-pien suan-pao*, dealt with the ordinary methods of multiplication and division. This chapter is also lost, but two of its problems have been restored from the *Yung-lo ta-tien* encyclopedia by Li Yen; it was entitled *Chu-chia suan-fa*. Chapter 2, *Fang-t'ien* ("Surveying of Land"), is now lost. Chapter 3, *Su-mi* ("Millet and Rice") is also lost, but three problems have been restored from the *Yung-lo ta-tien* encyclopedia. Chapter 4, *Ts'ui-fen* ("Distribution by Progression"), is no longer extant; but eleven of its problems have been restored from the *Yung-lo ta-tien* encyclopedia. Chapter 5, *Shao-kuang* ("Diminishing Breadth"), also has been partially restored from the *Yung-lo ta-tien* encyclopedia. As for Chapter 6, *Shang-kung* ("Consultations on Engineering Works"), the *I-chia-t'ang ts'ung-shu* collection contains thirteen

problems (fifteen problems are missing). Chapter 7, *Chün-shu* ("Impartial Taxation"); chapter 8, *Ying-pu-tsu* ("Excess and Deficiency"); chapter 9, *Fang-ch'eng* ("Calculation by Tabulation"); chapter 10, *Kou-ku* ("Right Angles"); and chapter 11, *Tsuan-lei* ("Reclassifications") remain more or less intact in the *I-chia-t'ang ts'ung-shu* collection, except for one missing problem in chapter 7 and four in chapter 9.

In 1450 the Ming mathematician Wu Ching wrote the *Chiu-chang hsiang-chu pi-lei suan-fa* ("Comparative Detailed Analysis of the Mathematical Rules in the Nine Chapters"), in which the "old questions" (*ku-wen*) are referred to. Yen Tun-chieh has shown that Wu Ching's "old questions" were based on Yang Hui's *Hsiang-chieh chiu-chang suan-fa*, and he has been engaged in restoring this text. A substantial part of the *I-chia-t'ang ts'ung-shu* edition of the text has been rendered into English by Lam Lay Yong of the University of Singapore.

Yang Hui published his second mathematical work, the two-volume *Jih-yung suan-fa* ("Mathematical Rules in Common Use"), in 1262. This book is no longer extant. Some sections have, however, been restored by Li Yen from the *Chu-chia suan-fa* in the *Yung-lo ta-tien* encyclopedia. The book seems to be quite elementary.

In 1274 Yang Hui produced the *Ch'eng-ch'u t'ung-pien pen-mo* ("Fundamental Mutual Changes in Multiplications and Divisions") in three volumes. The first volume was originally known as the *Suan-fa t'ung-pien pen-mo* ("Fundamental Mutual Changes in Calculations"); the second as *Ch'eng-ch'u t'ung-pien suan-pao* ("Treasure of Mathematical Arts on the Mutual Changes in Multiplications and Divisions"); and the last volume, written in collaboration with Shih Chung-yung, was originally called *Fa-suan ch'ü-yung pen-mo* ("Fundamentals of the Applications of Mathematics"). The next year Yang Hui wrote the *T'ien-mou pi-lei ch'eng-ch'u chieh-fa* ("Practical Rules of Mathematics for Surveying") in two volumes. This was followed in the same year by the *Hsü-ku chai-ch'i suan-fa* ("Continuation of Ancient Mathematical Methods for Elucidating the Strange Properties of Numbers"), written after Yang Hui had been shown old mathematical documents by his friends Liu Pi-chien and Ch'iu Hsü-chü. Subsequently all seven volumes that Yang Hui wrote in 1274–1275 came to be known under a single title, *Yang Hui suan-fa* ("The Mathematical Arts of Yang Hui"). The work was first printed in 1378 by the Ch'in-te shu-t'ang Press and was reprinted in

Korea in 1433. A handwritten copy of the Korean reprint was made by the seventeenth-century Japanese mathematician Seki Takakazu. (A copy of the Korean reprint is in the Peking National Library.) Li Yen had Seki Takakazu's handwritten copy of the *Yang Hui suan-fa* dated 1661; it became the property of the Academia Sinica after his death in 1963. At the beginning of the seventeenth century Mao Chin (1598–1652) made a handwritten copy of the fourteenth-century edition of the *Yang Hui suan-fa.*

All of Yang Hui's writings, including the *Yang Hui suan-fa*, seem to have been forgotten during the eighteenth century. Efforts were made in 1810 to reconstruct the text from the *Yung-lo ta-tien* encyclopedia by Juan Yuan (1764–1849), but they were confined to a portion of the *Hsü-ku chai-ch'i suan-fa.* In 1776 Pao T'ing-po included a portion of the *Hsü-ku chai-ch'i suan-fa* in his *Chih-pu-tsu ts'ung-shu* collection that may have come from the restoration by Juan Yuan. In 1814 Huang P'ei-lieh discovered an incomplete and disarranged copy of the *Yang Hui suan-fa.* He and the mathematician Li Jui put the text in order. Lo Shih-lin had a handwritten copy made of this corrected text. This version of the *Yang Hui suan-fa*, consisting of only six volumes, was incorporated into the *I-chia-t'ang ts'ung-shu* collection by Yu Sung-nien (1842). Later reproduction of the text in the *Ts'ung-shu chi-ch'eng* collection (1936) is based on the version in the *I-chia-t'ang ts'ung-shu* collection. Some of the textual errors in the book have been corrected by Sung Ching-ch'ang in his *Yang Hui suan-fa cha-chi.* A full English translation and commentary of the *Yang Hui suan-fa* was made by Lam Lay Yong in 1966 for her doctoral dissertation at the University of Singapore.

The *Hsiang-chieh chiu-chang suan-fa* is perhaps the best-known, but certainly not the most interesting, of Yang Hui's writings. In it he explains the questions and problems in the *Chiu-chang suan-shu*, sometimes illustrating them with diagrams, and gives the detailed solutions. Problems of the same nature also are compared with each other. In the last chapter, the *Tsuan lei*, Yang Hui reclassifies all the 246 problems in the *Chiu-chang suan-shu* in order of progressive difficulty, for the benefit of students of mathematics. Some examples of algebraic series given by Yang Hui in this book are

$$m^2 + (m+1)^2 + \cdots + (m+n)^2 = \frac{m+1}{3}$$

$$\left\{ m^2 + (m+n)^2 + m(m+n) + \frac{1}{2}\left[(m+n) - m\right]\right\}$$

$$1 + 3 + 6 + \cdots + \frac{n(n+1)}{2} = \frac{1}{6}n(n+1)(n+2)$$

$$1^2 + 2^2 + 3^2 + \cdots + n^2 = \frac{1}{3}n\left(n + \frac{1}{2}\right)(n+1)$$

$$1^2 + (a+1)^2 + \cdots + (c-1)^2 + c^2$$
$$= \frac{1}{3}(c-a)\left(c^2 + a^2 + ca + \frac{c-a}{2}\right).$$

The portions restored from the *Yung-lo ta-tien* encyclopedia contain the earliest illustration of the "Pascal triangle." Yang Hui states that this diagram was derived from an earlier mathematical text, the *Shih-so suan-shu* of Chia Hsien (*fl. ca.* 1050). This diagram shows the coefficients of the expansion of $(x + a)^n$ up to the sixth power. Another diagram showing coefficients up to the eighth power was later found in the early fourteenth-century work *Ssu-yüan yü-chien* of Chu Shih-chieh. Other Chinese mathematicians using the Pascal triangle before Blaise Pascal were Wu Ching (1450), Chou Shu-hsüeh (1588), and Ch'eng Ta-wei (1592).

The *Tsuan-lei* also quotes a method of solving numerical equations higher than the second degree taken from Chia Hsien's *Shih-so suan-shu.* The method is similar to that rediscovered independently in the early nineteenth century, by Ruffini and Horner, for solving numerical equations of all orders by continuous approximation. A method called the *tseng-ch'eng k'ai-li-fang fa* for solving a cubic equation $x^3 - 1860867 = 0$ is given in detail below.

The number 1860867 is set up in the second row of a counting board in which five rows are used—the top row (*shang*) is for the root to be obtained, the second row (*shih*) is for the constant, the third row (*fang*) is for the coefficient of $x$, the fourth row (*lien*) is for the coefficient of $x^2$, and the last row (*hsia-fa*) is for the coefficient of $x^3$. Thus 1 is placed in the last row, and this coefficient is shifted to the left, moving two place values at a time until it comes in line with the number 1860867, at the extreme left in this case, as shown in Figure 1*a.*

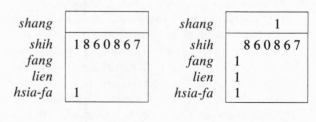

FIGURE 1*a*　　　　　　　FIGURE 1*b*

Since $x$ lies between 100 and 200, 1 is placed at the hundreds' place of the first row. Multiplying this number by the number in the last row yields 1, which is entered on the fourth row as the *lien*. Again, multiplying the number 1 on the top row by the *lien* gives 1, which is entered in the third row as the *fang*. The number in the *fang* row is subtracted from the number in the same column in the *shih* row. The result is shown in Figure 1*b*. The number on the last row is multiplied a second time by the number in the top row and the product is added to the *lien*. The number in the *lien* is multiplied by the number on the top row and added to the *fang*. The number on the last row is multiplied a third time by the number on the top row, and the product is added to the number in the fourth row. The result is shown in Figure 1*c*.

| *shang* | 1 | | *shang* | 1 |
|---|---|---|---|---|
| *shih* | 860867 | | *shih* | 860867 |
| *fang* | 3 | | *fang* | 3 |
| *lien* | 3 | | *lien* | 3 |
| *hsia-fa* | 1 | | *hsia-fa* | 1 |

FIGURE 1*c*             FIGURE 1*d*

The number in the third row (*fang*) is moved to the right by one place, that in the fourth row (*lien*) is moved to the right by two places, and that in the fifth row (*hsia-fa*) is moved to the right by three places, as in Figure 1*d*.

For the next approximation, $x$ is found to lie between 120 and 130. Hence 2 is placed in the upper row in the tens' place. The same process is repeated, using 2 as the multiplier. We have $2 \times 1 = 2$, which is then added to the *lien*, giving a sum 32; and $2 \times 32 = 64$, which, when added to the *fang*, gives 364. Then 364 is multiplied by 2, giving 728, which is subtracted from 860867 to give 132867, as shown in Figure 1*e*.

| *shang* | 12 | | *shang* | 12 |
|---|---|---|---|---|
| *shih* | 132867 | | *shih* | 132867 |
| *fang* | 364 | | *fang* | 364 |
| *lien* | 32 | | *lien* | 36 |
| *hsia-fa* | 1 | | *hsia-fa* | 1 |

FIGURE 1*e*             FIGURE 1*f*

Then the *hsia-fa* is multiplied a second time by 2 and added to the *lien*, giving a sum of 34, which again is multiplied by 2 and added to the *fang*, giv-

ing 432. The *hsia-fa* is multiplied a third time by 2 and added to the number 34 in the *lien* row to give 36, as shown in Figure 1*f*. The number in the *fang* row is now shifted one place, that in the *lien* row two places, and that in the *hsia-fa* row three places to the right, as shown in Figure 1*g*.

| *shang* | 12 | | *shang* | 123 |
|---|---|---|---|---|
| *shih* | 132867 | | *shih* | 0 |
| *fang* | 432 | | *fang* | 44289 |
| *lien* | 36 | | *lien* | 363 |
| *hsia-fa* | 1 | | *hsia-fa* | 1 |

FIGURE 1*g*             FIGURE 1*h*

The last digit of $x$ is found to be 3. This is placed on the top row in the units' column. Three times the *hsia-fa* gives 3, which, when added to the *lien*, gives 363. $3 \times 363 = 1089$, which, when added to the *fang*, gives 44289. Then $3 \times 44289 = 132867$, which, when subtracted from the *shih* row, leaves no remainder, as shown in Figure 1*h*. The root is therefore 123.

The *Hsiang-chieh chiu-chang suan-fa* also contains a method for solving quartic equations called the *tseng san-ch'eng k'ai-fang fa*. This involves the equation $x^4 - 1,336,336 = 0$. The method used is similar to that employed above for cubic equations. The solution is presented below in a slightly modified form, in order to show the resemblance to Horner's method.

$$x^4 - 1336336 = 0, \quad x = 34$$

$$
\begin{array}{l}
1(10)^4 + \quad 0 \times (10)^3 + \quad\quad 0 \times (10)^2 + \quad\quad 0 \times (10) - 1336336 \quad\underline{|30} \\
\quad\quad + \quad 30 \times (10)^3 + \quad 900 \times (10)^2 + \quad 27000 \times (10) + \quad 810000 \\
\hline
1(10)^4 + \quad 30 \times (10)^3 + \quad 900 \times (10)^2 + \quad 27000 \times (10) - \quad 526336 \\
\quad\quad + \quad 30 \times (10)^3 + 1800 \times (10)^2 + \quad 81000 \times (10) \\
\hline
1(10)^4 + \quad 60 \times (10)^3 + 2700 \times (10)^2 + 108000 \times (10) \\
\quad\quad + \quad 30 \times (10)^3 + 2700 \times (10)^2 \\
\hline
1(10)^4 + \quad 90 \times (10)^3 + 5400 \times (10)^2 \\
\quad\quad + \quad 30 \times (10)^3 \\
\hline
1(10)^4 + 120 \times (10)^3 \\
1(10)^4 + 120 \times (10)^3 + 5400 \times (10)^2 + 108000 \times (10) - 526336 \quad\underline{|4} \\
\quad\quad + \quad 4 \times (10)^3 + \quad 496 \times (10)^2 + \quad 23584 \times (10) + 526336 \\
\hline
1(10)^4 + 124 \times (10)^3 + 5896 \times (10)^2 + 131584 \times (10) + \quad\quad 0
\end{array}
$$

Both the few remaining problems of the *Jih-yung suan-fa* restored from the *Yung-lo ta-tien* encyclopedia and its title *Jih-yung*, meaning "daily or common use," suggest that the book must be of an elementary and practical nature, although we no longer have access to its entire text. Two examples follow:

a. A certain article actually weighs 112 pounds.

How much does it weigh on the provincial steelyard? Answer: 140 pounds. (Note that on the provincial steelyard 100 pounds would read 125 pounds.)

b. The weight of a certain article reads 391 pounds, 4 ounces, on a provincial steelyard. What is its actual weight? Answer: 313 pounds.

The first volume of the *Ch'eng-ch'u t'ung-pien pen-mo* (the *Suan-fa t'ung-pien pen-mo*) gives a syllabus or program of study for the beginner that is followed by a detailed explanation of variations in the methods of multiplication. In it Yang Hui shows how division can be conveniently replaced by multiplication by using the reciprocal of the divisor as the multiplier. For example, $2746 \div 25 = 27.46 \times 4$; $2746 \div 14.285 = 27.46 \times 7$; and $2746 \div 12.5 = 27.46 \times 8$. Sometimes he multiplies successively by the factors of the multiplier—for example, $274 \times 48 = 274 \times 6 \times 8$—and at other times he shows that the multiplier can be multiplied by the multiplicand—for example, $247 \times 7360 = 7360 \times 247$. Of special interest are the "additive" and "subtractive" methods that are applied to multiplication. These methods are quite conveniently used on the counting board, or even on an abacus, where the numbers are set up rather than written on a piece of paper. If the multiplier is 21, 31, 41, 51, 61, 71, 81, or 91, multiplication can be performed by multiplying only with the tens' digit and the result, shifted one decimal place to the left, is added to the multiplicand. Yang Hui gives a number of examples to illustrate this method, such as $232 \times 31 = 232 \times 30 + 232$; $234 \times 410 = 234 \times 400 + 2340$. In the "subtractive" method of multiplication, if the multiplier $x$ is a number of $n$ digits, the multiplicand $p$ is first multiplied by $10^n$, and from the result the product of the multiplicand and the difference between $10^n$ and the multiplier $x$ is subtracted, that is, $xp = 10^n p - (10^n - x)p$. Yang Hui gives the example $26410 \times 7 = 264100 - (2641 \times 3) = 1848700$. The book ends with an account of how division can be performed.

In the second volume of the *Ch'eng-ch'u t'ung-pien pen-mo* (the *Ch'eng-ch'u t'ung-pien suan-pao*), Yang Hui proceeds further in showing how division can be avoided by multiplying with the reciprocal of the divisor. He also elaborates on the "additive" and "subtractive" methods for multiplication. He states the rule that in division, the result remains unchanged if both the dividend and the divisor are multiplied or divided by the same quantity. The examples he gives include the following:

(a) $274 \div 6.25$
$= (274 \times 16) \div (6.25 \times 16)$
$= 2.74 \times 16$
$= 27.4 + (2.74 \times 6)$

(b) $342 \times 56$
$= \dfrac{342}{2} \times 112$
$= \frac{1}{2}[34200 + 3420 + (342 \times 2)]$

(c) $247 \times 1.95$
$= 247 \times 1.3 \times 1.5$
$= [247 + (247 \times 0.3)] \times 1.5$
$= [247 + (247 \times 0.3)]$
$\quad + [247 + (247 \times 0.3)] \times 0.5$

(d) $107 \times 10600 = 1070000 + (107 \times 600)$

(e) $19152 \div 56$
$= \dfrac{19152}{4} \div \dfrac{56}{4}$
$= 4788 \div 14$

(f) $9731 \div 37$
$= (9731 \times 3) \div (37 \times 3)$
$= 29193 \div 111$

The "subtractive" method for division is applied to cases (e) and (f). The steps for solving (e) are shown below:

```
            3 4 2
     14 | 4 7 8 8
        3 0
        1 7 8 8
        1 2
          5 8 8
          4 0
          1 8 8
          1 6
            2 8
            2 0
              8
              8
```

Yang Hui also states the rule that in multiplication, the result remains unchanged if the multiplicand is multiplied by a number and the multiplier by the reciprocal of the same number. Then he shows how to apply the rule to make the methods of "additive" and "subtractive" multiplication applicable. For example, $237 \times 56 = \dfrac{237}{2} \times (56 \times 2) = 118.5 \times 112 = 11850 + 1185 + (118.5 \times 2)$. The last part of the volume contains the division tables, the first instance of such tables in Chinese mathematical texts. They were later used by the Chinese in division operations involving the abacus.

The last volume of the *Ch'eng-ch'u t'ung-pien pen-mo* (the *Fa-suan ch'ü-yung pen-mo*) gives various rapid methods for multiplication and division for multipliers and divisors from 2 to 300 that are based on the rules described in the first two volumes. For example, when the multiplier is 228, Yang Hui and his collaborator Shih Chung-yung recommend the use of the factors 12 and 19 and the successive application of the "additive" method of multiplication; and when the multiplier is 125, they recommend shifting the multiplicand three places to the left and then halving it three times successively.

The *T'ien-mou pi-lei ch'eng-ch'u chieh-fa*, interesting mainly for its theory of equations, consists of two chapters. The first begins with a method for finding the area of a rectangular farm that is extended to problems involving other measures—weights, lengths, volumes, and money. These problems indicate that the length measurements for the sides of a rectangle can be employed as "dummy variables." Yang Hui was hence on the path leading to algebra, although neither he nor his Chinese contemporaries made extensive use of symbols. The text shows that Yang Hui had a highly developed conception of decimal places, simplified certain divisions by multiplication with reciprocals, and avoided the use of common fractions and showed his preference for decimal fractions. The words *chieh-fa* (literally, "shorter method") in the title must have referred to these and other simplified methods that he introduced. Three different values for the ratio of the circumference to the diameter of a circle are used: 3, 22/7, and 3.14. The rest of the first chapter deals with the area of the annulus, the isosceles triangle, and the trapezium; series; and arithmetic progressions exemplified by problems involving bundles of arrows with either square or circular cross sections.

The second chapter of the *T'ien-mou pi-lei ch'eng-ch'u chieh-fa* contains the earliest explanations of the Chinese methods for solving quadratic equations. For equations of the type $x^2 + 12x = 864$, Yang Hui recommends the *tai tsung k'ai fang* method, literally the method of extracting the root by attaching a side rectangle (*tsung*). The constant 864 is called *chi* ("total area"). If $x = 10x_1 + x_2$, $10x_1$ is called the *ch'u shang* ("first deliberation") and $x_2$ the *tz'u shang* ("second deliberation"), then $(10x_1)^2$ is the *fang fa*, $x_2^2$ the *yü*, and $10x_1x_2$ the *lien*. Also, $12x = 12(10x_1 + x_2)$, with $12(10x_1)$ being called *tsung fang* and $12x_2$ the *tsung*. Five rows on the counting board are used: *shang, chih, fang-fa, tsung-fang,* and *yü* or *yü suan*, in descending order. The constant 864 is first placed in the second row (*chih*), then the coefficient of $x$ on the fourth row (*tsung-fang*), and the coefficient for $x^2$

on the last row (*yü suan*). The coefficient of $x$ is moved one place to the left and that of $x^2$ two places to the left, as shown in Figure 2a. The value of $x$ lies between 20 and 30. The number 20, called the *ch'u shang*, is placed on the top row. Taking the number 2 of the *ch'u shang* as the multiplier, the product with the *yü suan* is 20. This is entered in the third row (*fang-fa*), as shown in Figure 2b. The number 2 of the *ch'u shang* is again used as the multiplier to find the products of the *fang-fa* and the *tsung-fang*. The sum of these two products (640) is subtracted from the *chih*, giving a remainder 224. The third row, now known as *lien*, and the fourth row, now known as *tsung*, are moved one place to the right, while the *yü suan* is moved by two places, as shown in Figure 2c.

| shang | | |
|---|---|---|
| chih | 8 6 | 4 |
| tsung-fang | 1 2 | |
| yü suan | 1 0 | |

FIGURE 2a

| shang | 2 | |
|---|---|---|
| chih | 8 6 | 4 |
| fang-fa | 2 0 | |
| tsung-fang | 1 2 | |
| yü suan | 1 0 | |

FIGURE 2b

| shang | 2 | |
|---|---|---|
| chih | 2 2 | 4 |
| lien | 4 | 0 |
| tsung | 1 | 2 |
| yü suan | | 1 |

FIGURE 2c

| shang | 2 4 | |
|---|---|---|
| chih | 2 2 | 4 |
| lien yü | 4 | 4 |
| tsung | 1 | 2 |
| yü suan | | 1 |

FIGURE 2d

The "second deliberation" (*tz'u shang*) is found to be 4. This is placed in the first row after the number 2. The product of the "second deliberation" and the *yü suan*, called *yü*, is added to the third row, which then becomes known as the *lien yü* (44 in this case). See Figure 2d. The sum of the products of the "second deliberation" and each of the *lien yü* and the *tsung* (224), when subtracted from the *chih*, leaves no remainder. Hence $x = 24$.

The solution is also illustrated by Yang Hui in a diagram as shown in Figure 3. If $x = (10x_1 + x_2)$, where $x_1 = 2$ and $x_2 = 4$, then from the equation $(10x_1 + x_2)^2 + 12(10x_1 + x_2) = 864$ we obtain $100x_1^2 + 20x_1x_2 + x_2^2 + 120x_1 + 12x_2 = 864$. Here the *fang-fa* is given by $100x_1^2$, the two *lien* by $20x_1x_2$, *yü* by $x_2^2$, *tsung-fang* by $120x_1$, *tsung* by $12x_2$, and the total *chih* by 864.

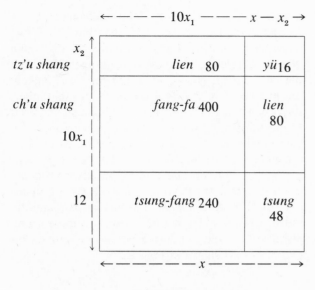

FIGURE 3

For equations of the type $x^2 - 12x = 864$, Yang Hui gives two different methods: the *i chi k'ai fang* (extracting the root by increasing the area) and the *chien ts'ung k'ai fang* (extracting the root by detaching a side rectangle, or *ts'ung*). For finding the smaller root of an equation of the type $-x^2 + 60x = 84$, Yang Hui recommends either of the two methods of *i yu* ("adding a corner square") and *chien ts'ung* ("detaching a side rectangle"). Finally, for finding the larger root of the same equation, he gives the *fan chi* ("inverted area") method. The geometrical illustrations of these methods suggest that means for solving quadratic equations may have been first derived geometrically by Yang Hui. Negative roots are also discussed, and the general solutions given are similar to Horner's method.

In the second chapter of his *T'ien-mou pi-lei ch'eng-ch'u chieh-fa*, Yang Hui also describes a method of solving equations of the type $x^4 = c$ as given by Liu I and Chia Hsien. There are also quadratic equations in which either the product and the difference of the two roots, or the product and the sum of the two roots, are given, such as an equation in the form

$$(x + y)^2 = (x - y)^2 + 4xy.$$

In addition he gives a general formula for the positive roots in the form

$$x = \frac{-b \pm \sqrt{(b^2 - 4ac)}}{2a}.$$

The methods used by Yang Hui for solving quadratic equations appear to be more flexible than those used in the West. He also demonstrated how to solve a biquadratic equation of the form

$$-5x^4 + 52x^3 + 128x^2 = 4096$$

by means of the *san-ch'eng-fang* ("quartic root") method, which is very similar to the method rediscovered in the early nineteenth century by Horner and Ruffini. The rest of the chapter deals with dissection of areas: a rectangle cut off from a larger isosceles triangle, a trapezium cut away from a larger trapezium, and an annulus cut off from a larger annulus.

The *Hsü-ku chai-ch'i suan-fa* consists of two chapters. The first has recently aroused considerable interest because of its magic squares. It is found only in the rare Sung edition and is missing from the *I-chia-t'ang ts'ung-shu* version, which is more commonly available. The *Hsü-ku chai-ch'i suan-fa* is the earliest Chinese text extant that gives magic squares higher than the third order and magic circles as well. In the preface Yang Hui disclaims originality in regard to its contents, saying that the material was among the old manuscripts and mathematical texts brought to him by his friends Liu Pi-chien and Ch'iu Hsü-chü. After Yang Hui, magic squares were discussed by Ch'eng Ta-wei in his *Suan-fa t'ung-tsung* (1593), by Fang Chung-t'ung in his *Shu-tu yen* (1661), by Chang Ch'ao in his *Hsin-chai tsa tsu* (ca. 1670), and by Pao Ch'i-shou in his *Pi-nai-shan-fang chi* (ca. 1880). In 1935 Li Yen published a paper on Chinese magic squares and reproduced the entire section on magic squares in Yang Hui's book, but with some misprints. In 1959 a subsection on magic squares was included in volume III of Joseph Needham's *Science and Civilisation in China*. Through the courtesy of Li Yen, a microfilm of his personal copy of the Sung edition of *Yang Hui suan-fa*, containing the full chapter on magic squares, was obtained for the preparation of Lam Lay Yong's doctoral dissertation. Some of Yang Hui's magic squares are shown in Figure 4a–4h.

④   ⑨   ②

③   ⑤   ⑦

⑧   ①   ⑥

| 2 | 16 | 13 | 3 |
|---|----|----|---|
| 11 | 5 | 8 | 10 |
| 7 | 9 | 12 | 6 |
| 14 | 4 | 1 | 15 |

FIGURE 4a. The *lo-shu*, magic square of order 3.

FIGURE 4b. One of the two magic squares of order 4.

| 12 | 27 | 33 | 23 | 10 |
|---|---|---|---|---|
| 28 | 18 | 13 | 26 | 20 |
| 11 | 25 | 21 | 17 | 31 |
| 22 | 16 | 29 | 24 | 14 |
| 32 | 19 | 9 | 15 | 30 |

FIGURE 4c. One of the two magic squares of order 5.

| 13 | 22 | 18 | 27 | 11 | 20 |
|---|---|---|---|---|---|
| 31 | 4 | 36 | 9 | 29 | 2 |
| 12 | 21 | 14 | 23 | 16 | 25 |
| 30 | 3 | 5 | 32 | 34 | 7 |
| 17 | 26 | 10 | 19 | 15 | 24 |
| 8 | 35 | 28 | 1 | 6 | 33 |

FIGURE 4d. One of the two magic squares of order 6.

| 1 | 20 | 21 | 40 | 41 | 60 | 61 | 80 | 81 | 100 |
|---|---|---|---|---|---|---|---|---|---|
| 99 | 82 | 79 | 62 | 59 | 42 | 29 | 22 | 19 | 2 |
| 3 | 18 | 23 | 38 | 43 | 58 | 63 | 78 | 83 | 98 |
| 97 | 84 | 77 | 64 | 57 | 44 | 37 | 24 | 17 | 4 |
| 5 | 16 | 25 | 36 | 45 | 56 | 65 | 76 | 85 | 96 |
| 95 | 86 | 75 | 66 | 55 | 46 | 35 | 26 | 15 | 6 |
| 14 | 7 | 34 | 27 | 54 | 47 | 74 | 67 | 94 | 87 |
| 88 | 93 | 68 | 73 | 48 | 53 | 28 | 33 | 8 | 13 |
| 12 | 9 | 32 | 29 | 52 | 49 | 72 | 69 | 92 | 89 |
| 91 | 90 | 71 | 70 | 51 | 50 | 31 | 30 | 11 | 10 |

FIGURE 4h. Magic square of order 10.

| 46 | 8 | 16 | 20 | 29 | 7 | 49 |
|---|---|---|---|---|---|---|
| 3 | 40 | 35 | 36 | 18 | 41 | 2 |
| 44 | 12 | 33 | 23 | 19 | 38 | 6 |
| 28 | 26 | 11 | 25 | 39 | 24 | 22 |
| 5 | 7 | 31 | 27 | 17 | 13 | 45 |
| 48 | 9 | 15 | 14 | 32 | 10 | 47 |
| 1 | 43 | 34 | 30 | 21 | 42 | 4 |

FIGURE 4e. One of the two magic squares of order 7.

| 61 | 3 | 2 | 64 | 57 | 7 | 6 | 60 |
|---|---|---|---|---|---|---|---|
| 12 | 54 | 55 | 9 | 16 | 50 | 51 | 13 |
| 20 | 46 | 47 | 17 | 24 | 42 | 43 | 21 |
| 37 | 27 | 26 | 40 | 33 | 31 | 30 | 36 |
| 29 | 35 | 34 | 32 | 25 | 39 | 38 | 28 |
| 44 | 22 | 23 | 41 | 48 | 18 | 19 | 45 |
| 52 | 14 | 15 | 49 | 56 | 10 | 11 | 53 |
| 5 | 59 | 58 | 8 | 1 | 63 | 62 | 4 |

FIGURE 4f. One of the two magic squares of order 8.

| 31 | 76 | 13 | 36 | 81 | 18 | 29 | 74 | 11 |
|---|---|---|---|---|---|---|---|---|
| 22 | 40 | 58 | 27 | 45 | 63 | 20 | 38 | 56 |
| 67 | 4 | 49 | 72 | 9 | 54 | 65 | 2 | 47 |
| 30 | 75 | 12 | 32 | 77 | 14 | 34 | 79 | 16 |
| 21 | 39 | 57 | 23 | 41 | 59 | 25 | 43 | 61 |
| 66 | 3 | 48 | 68 | 5 | 50 | 70 | 7 | 52 |
| 35 | 80 | 17 | 28 | 73 | 10 | 33 | 78 | 15 |
| 26 | 44 | 62 | 19 | 37 | 55 | 24 | 42 | 60 |
| 71 | 8 | 53 | 64 | 1 | 46 | 69 | 6 | 51 |

FIGURE 4g. Magic square of order 9 (the number 43 is incorrectly written in Seki Takakazu's copy as 42).

Besides magic squares and magic circles, the first chapter deals with problems on indeterminate analysis, calendar computation, geometrical progressions, and volumes and areas of objects of various regular shapes. For indeterminate analysis Yang Hui also gives the common names used in his time, such as *Ch'in Wang an tien ping* ("the Prince of Ch'in's secret method of counting soldiers"), *chien kuan shu* ("method of cutting lengths of tube"), and *fu shê chih shu* ("method of repeating trials"). (For further details on the Chinese method of indeterminate analysis, see "Ch'in Chiu-shao.")

The first problem of the second chapter reads: "A number of pheasants and rabbits are placed together in the same cage. Thirty-five heads and ninety-four feet are counted. Find the number of each." Besides simultaneous linear equations of two unknowns, this chapter deals with three unknowns. The chapter then considers miscellaneous examples taken from several mathematical texts, including Liu Hui's *Chiu-chang suan-shu* and *Hai-tao suan-ching*, the *Sun-tzu suan-ching*, the *Chang Ch'iu-chien suan-ching*, the *Ying-yung suan-fa*, the *Chih-nan suan-fa*, and the *Pien-ku t'ung-yuan*. The last three mathematical texts were printed during the eleventh and twelfth centuries in China, but are now lost. It is only through the works of Yang Hui that fragments of them and some of the other texts printed in the same era are extant. In the last problem of the chapter, Yang Hui gives a detailed analysis of the method employed by Liu Hui in his *Hai-tao suan-ching*. It is interesting that Yang Hui's first publication, the *Hsiang-chieh chiu-chang suan-fa*, is a study of Liu Hui's *Chiu-chang suan-shu*, which had been authoritative in China for about 1,000 years. Thus, with the last problem in his last publication, Yang Hui had completed a total analysis of Liu Hui's writings.

## BIBLIOGRAPHY

See Schuyler Cammann, "The Evolution of Magic Squares in China," in *Journal of the American Oriental Society*, **80**, no. 2 (1960), 116; and "Old Chinese Magic Squares," in *Sinologica*, 7, no. 1 (1962), 14; Ch'ien Pao-tsung, *Chung-kuo Shu-hsüeh-shih* (Peking, 1964); Ch'ien Pao-tsung et al., *Sung Yuan shu-hsüeh-shih lun-wen-chi* (Peking, 1966); Hsü Shun-fang, *Chung-suan-chia ti tai-shu-hsüeh yen chiu* (Peking, 1952); Lam Lay Yong, *The Yang Hui Suan Fa, a Thirteenth-Century Chinese Mathematical Treatise* (Singapore); Li Yen, "Chung-suan-shih lun-ts'ung," in *Gesammelte Ab-handlungen über die Geschichte der Chinesischen Mathematik*, II and III (Shanghai, 1935); and *Chung-kuo suan-hsüeh-shih* (Shanghai, 1937; rev. ed., 1955); Li Yen and Tu Shih-jan, *Chung-kuo ku-tai shu-hsüeh chien-shih*, II (Peking, 1964); Yoshio Mikami, *Mathematics in China and Japan* (1913; repr. New York, 1961); and Joseph Needham, *Science and Civilisation in China*, III (Cambridge, 1959).

HO PENG-YOKE

**IBN YA'QŪB.** See **Ibrāhīm ibn Ya'qūb al-Isrā'īlī al-Turtushi.**

**YA'QŪB IBN ISHĀQ.** See **Al-Kindī, Abū Yūsuf Ya'qūb ibn Ishāq al-Sabbāh.**

**YA'QŪB IBN TĀRIQ** (*fl.* Baghdad, second half of eighth century), *astronomy.*

Ya'qūb ibn Tāriq was the astronomer most closely connected with al-Fazārī in introducing the *Zīj al-Sindhind* to Islamic scientists; he seems, in fact, to have collaborated personally with the Indian astronomer who came to Baghdad with an embassy from Sind in 771 or 773. The most important of his works in this connection were *Zīj mahlūl fī al-Sindhind li daraja daraja* ("Astronomical Tables in the Sindhind Resolved for Every Degree"), *Tarkīb al-aflāk* ("Composition of the Spheres"), and *Kitāb al-'ilal* ("Book of Causes").

Evidently the most prominent feature of the *Zīj* was that the interval between the entries in the columns of arguments for the tables was one degree. Its basic parameters were very similar to those of the *Zīj al-Sindhind al-kabīr* of al-Fazārī, except that Ya'qūb completely accepted the equa-tions of the center from the *Zīj al-Shāh* while mixing in some equations of the anomaly from the *Zīj al-Arkand* (the *ārdharātrika* system; see essay in Supplement).

In the *Tarkīb al-aflāk*, Ya'qūb also drew upon the *Zīj al-Sindhind* and the *Zīj al-Arkand*, as well as on his conversations with the Indian astronomer. The subjects covered in this work, insofar as they can be determined, were the geocentric distances of the planetary orbits, geography, the computation of the *ahargaṇa*, and perhaps the geometric models of planetary motion. The *Kitāb al-'ilal* is known only from citations by al-Bīrūnī in his work *On Shadows*; the extant fragments deal exclusively with rules for employing the gnomon. Like al-Fazārī, Ya'qūb is inconsistent, adopting whatever formula comes to hand without regard for its relation to the other formulas in his books. Also like al-Fazārī, he is significant primarily for his role in the transmission of Indian science to Islam.

## BIBLIOGRAPHY

The fragments by Ya'qūb ibn Tāriq are collected and discussed in D. Pingree, "The Fragments of the Works of Ya'qūb ibn Tāriq," in *Journal of Near Eastern Studies*, **27** (1968), 97–125; and in E. S. Kennedy, "The Lunar Visibility Theory of Ya'qūb ibn Tāriq," *ibid.*, 126–132.

DAVID PINGREE

**YĀQŪT AL-HAMAWĪ AL-RŪMĪ, SHIHĀB AL-DĪN ABŪ 'ABDALLĀH YĀQŪT IBN 'ABD AL-LĀH** (*b.* Rūm, Byzantine empire [now Turkey], 1179; *d.* Aleppo, Syria, 20 August 1229), *transmission of knowledge, geography.*

Probably of Greek parentage, Yāqūt was taken prisoner as a young boy and was brought to Baghdad, where he was sold as a slave to a merchant named 'Askar ibn Ibrāhīm al-Hamawī (after whom Yāqūt was also called al-Hamawī; he assumed his other names later). When Yāqūt grew up, 'Askar gave him a little education; for being uneducated himself, he needed someone to assume the secretarial work of his trade. He subsequently engaged Yāqūt and sent him on commercial tours to what is now Qeys Island in the Persian Gulf and to Syria. In 1199, after a disagreement, Yāqūt was freed by his master; he then copied and sold manuscripts and studied Arabic language and grammar under al-'Ukbarī (*d.* 1219) and Ibn Ya'īsh (*d.* 1245). After a reconciliation, Yāqūt rejoined his former master in the latter's trade activities. After 'Askar's death, Yāqūt settled in Baghdad as a bookseller. He held strong Kharijite views that he expressed in Damascus (1215) during a public argument with a supporter of 'Alī ibn Abī Ṭālib. The crowd could not tolerate his attack on 'Alī and assaulted him. He later escaped from Aleppo; went to Mosul; and then, by way of Irbil, reached Marw, where he remained for two years, consulting the rich libraries and collecting material for his books. Toward the end of 1218, Yāqūt went to Khorezm; he encountered the invading Mongol armies in 1219–1220 and escaped to Khurāsān, leaving behind all his belongings. In 1220 he reached Mosul and in 1222 finally arrived in Aleppo, where he remained under the patronage of Abuʾl-Ḥasan 'Alī ibn Yūsuf al-Qifṭī (d. 1248) until his death. Yāqūt spent most of his life traveling in the Islamic world: Syria, Palestine, Egypt, Iran, Iraq, Khurāsān, and Khorezm.

Besides earning his livelihood as a bookseller, Yāqūt seems to have spent much time as an author. Only four of his several known works have been discovered: Muʿjam al-buldān ("Dictionary of the Lands"); Kitāb irshād al-arīb ilā maʿrifat al-adīb (or Irshād al-alibbāʾ ilā maʿrifat al-udabāʾ) known as Muʿjam al-udabā (or Ṭabaqāt al-udabāʾ) ("Dictionary of the Learned Men"); Kitāb al-mushtarik waḍʿan waʾl-mukhtalif ṣaqʿan, containing selections from Muʿjam al-buldān that list only the titles that applied to several places that had the same name; and Al-Muqtaḍab min kitāb jamharat al-nasab (on the genealogy of the Arabs). Among his other works are Kitāb al-mabdaʾ waʾl-maʾāl and Kitāb al-duʾal (both on history); Akhbār al-shuʿarāʾ al-mutaʾakhkhirīn waʾl-qudamāʾ, probably identical with Yāqūt's Muʿjam al-shuʿarāʾ, a biographical dictionary of poets in forty-two volumes; Kitāb Akhbār al-Mutanabbī, on the life of the poet al-Mutanabbī; Majmūʿ kalām Abī 'Alī al-Fārisī, a collection of the sayings of al-Fārisī (d. 987); and ʿUnwān kitāb al-aghānī, probably an introduction to the famous Book of Songs by Abuʾl-Faraj al-Iṣfahānī (d. 967).

In the absence of his works on history, it is difficult to judge Yāqūt's ability as a historian; but as a biographer he was one of the outstanding scholars of medieval Islam, possessing encyclopedic knowledge. Distinguishing a man of letters (adīb) from a scholar ('ālim), he quotes a saying: ". . . the man of letters selects the choicest from everything and then composes it, while a scholar selects a particular branch of knowledge and then improves upon it."[1] For Yāqūt the science of akhbār ("usages

of the Prophet") was the fountainhead of all knowledge and wisdom, and was superior to all other sciences. Quoting Abuʾl-Ḥasan 'Alī ibn al-Ḥasan, who quoted earlier writers on the subject, Yāqūt says that if scholars had not concerned themselves with akhbār and with the works of ʾāthār (usages of the companions of the Prophet), the beginnings of knowledge would have become corrupt and its ends would have perished. It had been said since ancient times, he points out, that nasab (genealogy) and akhbār were the sciences of the kings and the nobility.[2] With these precepts in mind, Yāqūt compiled his monumental Dictionary of the Learned Men, which covers the lives of men of letters, grammarians, linguists, genealogists, famous readers (of the Koran), historians, and secretaries, with preference given to poets; authors of prose whose poetry was of a secondary order came later. This work and Akhbār al-shuʿarāʾ covered, in Yāqūt's words, most of the information relating to men of letters, including scholars and poets.[3] The work, in more or less alphabetical order, reveals the author's deep interest in Arabic literature and his vast knowledge of the subject.

Equally concerned with geography, Yāqūt believed in its intrinsic relationship with history and emphasized the importance of orthography of place names. Arranged in alphabetical order, the Muʿjam al-buldān attempts to fix the spellings of place names and gives their geographical positions, boundaries, and coordinates. It covers cities and towns, rivers and valleys, mountains and deserts, and seas and islands. For each place Yāqūt gives information on eminent natives, including anecdotes and interesting facts. He was aware that earlier writers had not paid sufficient attention to the two important aspects of a place name: orthography and geographical position of the place. This earlier inattention often misled scholars and men of letters.[4] The inspiration to produce a geographical dictionary that would serve as a travel guide to Muslims, however, came from the teachings of the Koran and other religious works.[5] Yāqūt believed that such a work was essential not only for the traveler but also for the jurist, the theologian, the historian, the physician, the astrologer, and the savant.[6]

Besides utilizing a variety of sources for this work, including biographers, geographers, and historians, Yāqūt enhanced its value by adding his own experiences and observations gathered during his travels, as well as information acquired from those he met. An important aspect of the work is that Yāqūt preserved a number of passages from works that have only recently become available. That he was fully conversant with the various concepts of Muslim geographers relating to mathematical, physical, and regional geography is amply evident in the long introduction, which includes discussions of the geographical and legal terms used in the book.[7]

Ever since its publication more than seven centuries ago, the *Muʿjam* has been an important historical and geographical reference work for scholars in the Islamic world as well as for Orientalists in the West. Because of its size, an abridgment was prepared in the fourteenth century by ʿAbd al-Muʾmin ibn ʿAbd al-Ḥaqq, under the title *Marāṣid al-iṭṭilāʿ ʿalā asmāʾ al-amkina waʾl-biqāʿ*, that included only the geographical material.

Yāqūt represented an age when knowledge in medieval Islam had almost reached its zenith. It was a period of consolidation of the knowledge acquired during the preceding centuries by the Muslim scientists, and scholars like Yāqūt had begun producing comprehensive dictionaries, biographies, and general surveys in specific aspects of the arts and sciences. It was about this time that the center of Muslim academic and intellectual activity had shifted from Baghdad, which played its role for over four centuries, to places like Aleppo, Damascus, and Cairo. It is for this reason that we find in Yāqūt's works a variety of information, including ethnology, folklore, literature, and other features of medieval Islamic society. In this respect, Yāqūt may be considered one of the most outstanding transmitters of knowledge of the medieval period.

*NOTES*

1. See D. S. Margoliouth, *Yāqūt's Dictionary of the Learned Men*, I, 17.
2. *Ibid.*, 27–28.
3. *Ibid.*, 5–6.
4. See Wadie Jwaideh, *The Introductory Chapters of Yāqūt's Muʿjam al-buldān*, 3–4.
5. *Ibid.*, 1–3.
6. *Ibid.*, 4–9.
7. *Ibid.*, 19 f.

*BIBLIOGRAPHY*

I. Original Works. The *Kitāb al-mushtarik waḍʿan waʾl mukhtalif ṣaqʿan* was edited by F. Wüstenfeld as *Jacut's Moschtarik, das ist: Lexicon geographischer Homonyme* (Göttingen, 1846).

*Muʿjam al-buldān* was edited by F. Wüstenfeld as *Jacut's geographisches Wörterbuch, Kitāb Muʿjam al-buldān*, 6 vols. (Leipzig, 1866–1873); see also Sachin-dex zu Wüstenfeld's Ausgabe von Jaqut's Muʿǧam al-buldān (Stuttgart, 1928). Other eds. of the *Muʿjam* are F. J. Heer, *Die historischen und geographischen Quellen in Jāqūt's geographischem Wörterbuch* (Strasbourg, 1898); a version by Aḥmad Amīn al-Shanqīṭī, 8 vols. (Cairo, 1906), with a 2-vol. supp. by Muḥammad Amīn al-Khānjī (Cairo, 1907); and Wadie Jwaideh, *The Introductory Chapters of Yāqūt's Muʿjam al-buldān* (Leiden, 1959), an excellent analysis of the intro. The abridgment of this work, *Marāṣid al-iṭṭilāʿ ʿalā asmāʾ al-amkina waʾl-biqāʿ*, was edited by T. W. Juynboll, 6 vols. (Leiden, 1851–1864); other abridgments are listed in Jwaideh, ix–x.

*Kitāb irshād al-arīb ilā maʿrifat al-adīb (Muʿjam al-udabā)* was edited by D. S. Margoliouth as *Yāqūt's Dictionary of the Learned Men*, no. 6 in the E. J. W. Gibb Memorial Series, 6 vols. (Leiden, 1907–1931).

*Al-Muqtaḍab min kitāb jamharat al-nasab* is discussed in Fuat Sezgin, *Geschichte des arabischen Schrifttums*, I (Leiden, 1967), 269.

II. Secondary Literature. See R. Blachère, "Yāḳūt al-Rūmī," in *Encyclopaedia of Islam*, 1st ed., IV, pt. 2, 1153–1154; C. Brockelmann, *Geschichte der arabischen Literatur*, I (Leiden, 1943), 480, and *Supp.*, I (Leiden, 1937), 880; Ḥājjī Khalīfa, *Kashf al-ẓunūn*, I (Istanbul, 1941), 64, 363, and II (Istanbul, 1943), 1580, 1691–1692, 1733–1734, 1734–1735, 1793; *Ibn Khallikan's Biographical Dictionary*, translated by Baron MacGuckin de Slane, IV (Paris, 1871), 9–22; I. Y. Krachkovsky, *Arabskaya geograficheskaya literatura*, IV (Moscow–Leningrad, 1957), 330–342, Arabic trans. by Ṣalāḥ al-Dīn ʿUthmān Hāshim as *Taʾrīkh al-abab al-jughrāfī al-ʿArabī*, I (Cairo, 1963), 335–344; and Ibn al-Qifṭī, *Inbāh al-ruwāh*, facs. Arabic text concerning Yāqūt, published by Rudolf Sellheim in his "Neue Materialien zur Biographie des Yāqūt," in Wolfgang Voigt, ed., *Forschungen und Fortschritte der Katalogisierung der orientalischen Handschriften in Deutschland* (Wiesbaden, 1966), tables xvi–xxxiv.

S. Maqbul Ahmad

**YATIVṚṢABHA** (*fl.* India, sixth century), *cosmography, mathematics*.

Yativṛṣabha (in Prākrit, Jadivasaha) was a Jain author who studied under Ārya Mañkṣu and Nāgahastin, and compiled several works in Prākrit expounding Jain traditions. One of these, the *Tiloyapaṇṇattī*, a description of the universe and its parts, is of some importance to historians of Indian science because it incorporates formulas representative of developments in Jain mathematics between the older canonical works and the later texts of the ninth and following centuries. Unfortunately, almost nothing is known of Yativṛṣabha himself; his lifetime is fixed by the general character of his work, as well as by his references to the *Loyav-*

*ibhāga* (probably that written by Sarvanandin in 458) and by the reference to him by Jinabhadra Kṣamāśramaṇa (*fl.* 609). Yativṛṣabha's statement that the end of the Gupta dynasty occurred after 231 years of rule must refer to a contemporary event in Gupta Era 231 (A.D. 551).

## BIBLIOGRAPHY

The *Tiloyapaṇṇattī* was edited by Ādinātha Upādhyāya and Hīrālāla Jaina with a Hindi paraphrase by Balchandra, 2 vols. (Śolāpura, 1943–1951; I, 2nd ed., 1956). There is a study in Hindi of the mathematics of Yativṛṣabha by Lakṣmīcandra Jaina, *Tiloyapaṇṇattī kā gaṇita* (Śolāpura, 1958).

DAVID PINGREE

**YAVANEŚVARA** (*fl.* western India, 149/150), *astrology, astronomy.*

The word Yavaneśvara is a title (meaning "Lord of the Greeks"), not a proper name; it or its equivalent, Yavanarāja, was borne by several officials in western India during the rule of the Western Kṣatrapas (*ca.* 78–390), and perhaps earlier under Aśoka, in the middle of the third century B.C. Their function was evidently to act as leader of the Greek merchants settled in the area. The one in whom we are interested was responsible for the translation of a Greek text on astrology into Sanskrit prose in 149/150, during the reign of Rudradāman, the most powerful of the Western Kṣatrapas. The Greek original was composed in Egypt (probably at Alexandria) in the first half of the second century B.C., and therefore is one of the earliest Greek astrological texts known to us in a substantially complete form, although not in the original. Unfortunately, even Yavaneśvara's prose translation is no longer available, and we must be content with the versification of it made by Sphujidhvaja in 269/270.

In translating this text Yavaneśvara did his best to make it appeal to an Indian audience. He interpreted illustrations of the deities of the Decans and Horās that appeared in the Greek manuscript, for instance, in terms of Śaivite iconography; and he introduced the caste system and some elements of the older Indian astral-omen texts and of *āyurveda* into his work. Yavaneśvara also included a version of a Greek adaptation of Babylonian planetary theory, in an attempt to make it possible for Indians to become astrologers (see essay in Supplement). He was extremely successful, and the basic methodology of all of Indian horoscopy can be traced back to his translation and another, lost translation from the Greek that was known to Satya (in the third century?).

## BIBLIOGRAPHY

An ed. of the *Yavanajātaka* of Sphujidhvaja by D. Pingree, in the Harvard Oriental Series, will contain all available information about Yavaneśvara.

DAVID PINGREE

**YERKES, ROBERT MEARNS** (*b.* Breadysville, Pennsylvania, 26 May 1876; *d.* New Haven, Connecticut, 3 February 1956), *comparative psychology.*

Yerkes was the oldest child of Silas Marshall Yerkes and Susanna Addis Carrell Yerkes, members of well-established farm families residing north of Philadelphia. As a boy he lived close to nature, and his familiarity with domestic and wild animals eventually contributed to his vocational choice. He attended an ungraded rural school and at the age of fifteen entered the State Normal School at West Chester, transferring in 1892 to Ursinus College, first as a preparatory and then as a collegiate student (A.B., 1897). In 1897 Yerkes entered Harvard, where he was awarded an A.B. after one year and proceeded into graduate work without pause, working with Hugo Münsterberg. He received the A.M. in 1899 and the Ph.D., in psychology, in 1902. By the latter year he had already launched his scientific career with publications and was appointed instructor in psychology at Harvard.

Yerkes was one of the first of a new breed of comparative psychologists who worked with their animal subjects in a laboratory setting. He was preceded by only a few years by E. L. Thorndike (whom he assisted one summer at Woods Hole) and was a collaborator (mostly by mail) with a slightly younger man, John B. Watson. Thorndike's work led him into learning theory and educational psychology. Watson's researches led him into methodological reformism and antimentalism in general psychology. Yerkes, in contrast with these eminent peers, recognized the kinship of the animal psyche to that of man; but whatever his speculations on that kinship, in his research he studied animal behavior for its own sake, assuming that he was dealing with animal mentality as such. Relatively early in his career he was convinced that observing the animals with mental processes most like those of man, the apes, would be of great importance to psychology. He envisaged the founding of an institute in which these animals might be studied, but decades passed before he realized this project.

Yerkes became the most versatile psychologist of his generation, responding in large part to the stimulation of the Harvard environment in the years that he spent there as a faculty member, until 1917. Under the aegis of Harvard psychiatrist E. E. Southard, Yerkes spent half his time from 1913 to 1917 as psychologist to the Boston Psychopathic Hospital. Although he published relatively little based on that experience, he became deeply involved in mental testing as it was then practiced. As a result, from 1917 to 1919 Yerkes was in effect largely in charge of the psychological testing of U.S. Army personnel in World War I. The large-scale use of psychological devices at that time substantially established the profession of psychology in a way quite different from its tendency toward academic isolation before the war. Yerkes, through his promotional and organizing abilities, was one of the key figures responsible for the conception and execution of the program.

Although appointed chairman of the psychology department at the University of Minnesota in 1917, Yerkes never took up residence in Minneapolis. From 1919 to 1924 he stayed in Washington with the National Research Council and continued to exploit his ability to facilitate the work of others. He headed N.R.C. programs to explore the characteristics of various types of humans who migrate (with immigration-exclusion legislation in mind) and to encourage and support scientific investigation of sexuality. He also was elected president of the American Psychological Association for 1916–1917, while still an assistant professor at Harvard. Yerkes thus spent the period of the war and afterward in the heart of the American scientific establishment, helping to make policy and channel funds. Although he did not feel himself to be one of the scientist-politicians, he served on committees and advisory groups and exerted great influence on the institutions and programs of American science in the 1920's and 1930's.

Not until 1924 did Yerkes return to his career as comparative psychologist, when Yale offered him an opportunity to join its new Institute of Psychology and devote himself primarily to advanced work with nonhuman primates. By 1929 he had founded an experimental station near Orange Park, Florida, later named the Yerkes Laboratories of Primate Biology, which was the nucleus of the present Yerkes Regional Primate Research Center. As preparation for this work he and his wife, Ada Watterson Yerkes, published a monumental book, *The Great Apes: A Study of Anthropoid Life* (1929), which for decades remained the standard work on the biology and psychology of these mammals.

Yerkes had originally wanted to become a physician, but he was turned away from medicine by his interest in laboratory research. Nevertheless, throughout his life his basic approach to comparative psychology remained close to biology. Indeed, at Yale his appointment ultimately was in the department of physiology. In psychology, Yerkes' formal stance was very traditional—influenced, he said, by the structuralism of E. B. Titchener of Cornell. Yerkes' early research work, dealing with invertebrates, involved testing organic reactions to sensory input. He soon began working with vertebrates, giving attention not only to sensations but also to instinct, imitation, and learning. His classic study of the behavior of the dancing mouse (1907) did much to establish the rat and mouse as standard laboratory animals in psychology. Many of his most important publications in science involved new techniques for psychological investigation. With his wide-ranging interests, Yerkes also was responsible for contributions as diverse as (with S. Morgulis) publishing the first important American notice on Pavlov's work (1909) and a discussion of the application of psychological findings to illumination engineering (1911). In 1915 Yerkes spent half a year with G. V. Hamilton's primate colony in Santa Barbara, California; and after that period, except for the war and N.R.C. service, devoted himself largely to the monkeys and apes. The staff at the Orange Park laboratories employed both experimental and observational methods, mostly utilizing chimpanzees for subjects, and produced a prodigious number of publications. The topics covered involved not only thinking processes and adaptation but also physiology and even medicine.

Yerkes was a determined, persistent leader. A large part of his contribution to science consisted of organizing or directing it. He was, for example, a prime mover in the reform of the structure of the American Psychological Association in 1943. He was founding editor of the *Journal of Animal Behavior* in 1911 and held other important editorial positions. Yerkes felt that he had a limited amount of energy that was always overtaxed, so what resources he had were used efficiently. He retired as director of the Orange Park laboratories in 1941, and in 1944 retired from Yale. He continued to publish, although at a diminishing rate, and was still active in organizing psychology in the World War II defense effort.

*BIBLIOGRAPHY*

I. Original Works. The number of Yerkes' published works is very large. The most complete bibliography is in Ernest R. Hilgard, "Robert Mearns Yerkes, May 26, 1876–February 3, 1956," in *Biographical Memoirs. National Academy of Sciences*, **38** (1965), 412–425. Probably no bibliography will ever be complete, including all of the editorial material and book reviews contributed to various journals, especially those he edited. Yerkes published a short autobiography, "Robert Mearns Yerkes, Psychobiologist," in Carl Murchison, ed., *A History of Psychology in Autobiography*, II (Worcester, Mass., 1932), 381–407; and, posthumously, some reminiscences, "Creating a Chimpanzee Community," Roberta W. Yerkes, ed., in *Yale Journal of Biology and Medicine*, **36** (1963), 205–223.

The Yerkes Papers, in the Yale University Medical School Library, constitute one of the chief sources of the history of American psychology in the first half of the twentieth century. They include an unpublished autobiography, a bibliography, and a large number of letters and personal papers covering not only Yerkes and his career but also all of the activities in which he was interested.

II. Secondary Literature. The most authoritative account of Yerkes' life is Hilgard's (see above), 385–425. Also see E. G. Boring, "Robert Mearns Yerkes (1876–1956)," in *Yearbook. American Philosophical Society* (1956), 133–140; Leonard Carmichael, "Robert Mearns Yerkes, 1876–1956," in *Psychological Review*, **64** (1957), 1–7; and Richard M. Elliott, "Robert Mearns Yerkes (1876–1956)," in *American Journal of Psychology*, **69** (1956), 487–494.

John C. Burnham

**YERSIN, ALEXANDRE** (*b.* Aubonne, near Lausanne, Switzerland, 23 September 1863; *d.* Nha Trang, Annam, Vietnam, 1 March 1943), *medicine, bacteriology.*

Yersin received his secondary education in Lausanne before entering the Academy there; he subsequently attended the University of Marburg and the Paris Faculty of Medicine. Having cut himself while performing an autopsy on a patient who had died of rabies, Yersin immediately contacted Émile Roux, one of Pasteur's most brilliant pupils, who gave him an injection of a new therapeutic serum that saved his life. This incident brought Yersin into close contact with Roux, who hired him as his assistant in 1888 and with whom he conducted research on rabies. He then worked with Robert Koch, in Berlin, collaborating with the noted microbiologist in his research on the tubercle bacillus. Upon his return to Paris, Yersin began his own research with Roux, at the Institut Pasteur, on the toxic properties of the diphtheria bacillus. In 1889, however, he suddenly embarked as ship's doctor on a steamer bound for Saigon and Manila. He returned to Paris and left again for Indochina; and during three dangerous expeditions into the interior, he discovered the high plateau of Langbiang, where he founded a small colonial village. The area soon became a vacation center for Europeans, and the city of Dalat was developed there. In 1935 the municipal authorities established the Lycée Yersin at Dalat.

In 1894 Yersin became a medical officer in the French colonial service and conducted research on the bubonic plague epidemic that was sweeping through China, in order to determine the measures that should be taken to prevent its spread into Indochina. At a small bacteriological research laboratory, set up for him in Hong Kong, he discovered the plague bacterium, practically at the same time that Kitasato did so independently; and after much work he isolated an effective serum. In 1904 he was recalled to Paris and continued his research at the Institut Pasteur, of which Roux had become director. With Albert Calmette and Amédée Borrel he made the important observation that certain animals can be immunized against the plague through the injection of dead plague bacteria. He then returned to Nha Trang, where a branch of the Institut Pasteur had been established under his direction. There, in modest laboratories, Yersin perfected an antiplague serum that made it possible to reduce the death rate from 90 percent to about 7 percent.

With the assistance of Paul Doumer, then governor-general of Indochina, a medical school was founded at Hanoi; Yersin directed this center of study and research for many years. Through Yersin's work Indochina was able to control the epidemics that beset the country, especially malaria. In recognition of his medical achievements, the French government appointed Yersin honorary director of the Institut Pasteur.

Besides his activity in science and medicine in Indochina, Yersin conducted research in agronomy. His interest in the cultivation of grains and in soil conditions led him to initiate a series of ecological studies. He also reflected on the natural history of Indochina, having become fascinated by the flora and fauna of his adopted country. Yersin became deeply concerned over the needs of the sick and the poor and fought hard against the exploitation of the lower classes.

*BIBLIOGRAPHY*

I. ORIGINAL WORKS. Yersin's dissertation for the M.D. at Paris is *Sur le développement du tubercule expérimental* (Paris, 1888). Most of his papers were published in *Annales de l'Institut Pasteur*; they include "Contributions à l'étude de la diphtérie," **2** (1888), 629–661; **3** (1889), 273–288; and **4** (1890), 385–426, written with Émile Roux; "La peste bubonique à Hong-Kong," *ibid.*, **8** (1894), 662–667; and "Sur la peste bubonique: Sérothérapie," *ibid.*, **11** (1897), 81–93.

II. SECONDARY LITERATURE. See N. Bernard, "A. Yersin (1863–1943)," in *Annales de l'Institut Pasteur*, **69** (1943), 129–134, with portrait; N. Bernard, P. Hauduroy, and G. Olivier, *Yersin et la peste* (Lausanne, 1944); H. Buess, *Recherches, découvertes et inventions de médecins suisses* (Basel, 1946); and P. Hauduroy, "Les découvertes de Yersin et les méthodes pastoriennes," in *Schweizerische medizinische Wochenschrift*, **24** (1943), 750–751.

P. E. PILET

**YOUDEN, WILLIAM JOHN** (*b.* Townsville, Australia, 12 April 1900; *d.* Washington, D.C., 31 March 1971), *mathematical statistics.*

Youden was the eldest child of William John Youden, an English engineer, and Margaret Hamilton of Carluke, Scotland. In 1902 the family returned to the father's birthplace—Dover, England—and resided there until 1907, when they left for America. They lived for a while in Connecticut and at Niagara Falls, New York, where Youden attended public school, before moving to Rochester, New York, in 1916. Youden attended the University of Rochester from 1917 to 1921, except for three months in the U.S. Army in 1918, receiving a B.S. in chemical engineering in 1921. He began graduate work in September 1922 at Columbia University, earning an M.A. in chemistry in 1923 and a Ph.D. the following year.

Immediately after receiving his doctorate, Youden joined the Boyce Thompson Institute for Plant Research in Yonkers, New York, as a physical chemist. He held this post until May 1948, when he joined the National Bureau of Standards as assistant chief of the Statistical Engineering Laboratory, Applied Mathematics Division. Three years later he became a consultant on statistical design and analysis of experiments to the chief of this division, a position he retained until his retirement in 1965.

He was an honorary fellow of the Royal Statistical Society (1965), and was awarded the Medal of Freedom in 1964, the 1969 Samuel S. Wilks Memorial Medal of the American Statistical Association, and the 1969 Shewhart Medal of the American Society for Quality Control.

In 1922 Youden married Gladys Baxter of Rochester, New York; they had two sons, William Wallace (1925–1968) and Robert Hamilton, both of whom chose careers in the computer field. In 1938 he married Grethe Hartmann of Copenhagen, Denmark; they had one son, Julius Hartmann, now a teacher in Copenhagen. In 1957 Youden married Didi Stockfleth of the Norwegian Embassy staff in Washington, D.C. Survivors of his immediate family include his widow, Didi; two sons; and eight grandchildren. Youden is buried in the National Cemetery, Gettysburg National Military Park, Gettysburg, Pennsylvania, in deference to his expressed wishes to remain in his adopted country.

Youden began his professional career as a physical chemist. His first paper to exhibit any knowledge of statistical methods, "A Nomogram for Use in Connection With Gutzeit Arsenic Determinations on Apples" (September 1931), was expository in nature: he noted that the differences between repeated determinations of a physicochemical property of a particular biological material reflect not only the "probable error" of the method of chemical analysis but also the "probable error" of the technique of sampling the material under investigation, and then, with guidance from a 1926 paper of W. A. Shewhart, outlined the requisite theory, illustrated its application, furnished a nomogram to facilitate correct evaluation of the precision of a particular procedure, and pointed out statistical errors that marred a number of earlier publications on sampling of apples for determination of arsenical sprayed residue. This paper marks the beginning of Youden's "missionary" efforts to acquaint research workers with statistical methods of value in their work.

About 1928 Youden "obtained one of the 1050 copies . . . of the first edition" of R. A. Fisher's *Statistical Methods . . .* (1925). At that time he was "so discouraged by what was called 'measurement' in biology that [he] was on the point of resigning" his post at Boyce Thompson. "Fisher's book opened a ray of hope," however, and

Youden soon realized that at Boyce Thompson "he had the opportunity to perform agricultural experiments, both in the field and in the greenhouse, and to try out the early experiment designs" and Fisher's new small-sample methods of data analysis. The publicity for the visit of Fisher to Iowa State College in 1931 came to Youden's attention and aroused his curiosity, but he was unable to attend. When Fisher visited Cornell on his way home from Iowa, Youden "drove there . . . to show him an experimental arrangement."[1] During the academic year 1931–1932, he commuted to Columbia University to attend Harold Hotelling's lectures on statistical inference.[2] During the next few years he published a number of mathematical-statistical papers describing the application of statistical techniques to problems arising in studies of seeds, soils, apples, leaves, and trees.

During this period Youden devoted increasing attention to statistical design of experiments, in order to cope with the enormous variability of biological material; he found many of the standard experiment designs developed for agricultural field trials to be directly applicable in greenhouse work, a situation that led to vastly improved precision. Recognizing that the limited number of leaves per plant thwarted the use of Latin square designs to effect precise within-plant comparisons of a large number of proposed treatments for plant ailments, Youden devised new symmetrically balanced, incomplete block designs that had the characteristic "double control" of Latin square designs but not the restriction that each "treatment" (or "variety") must occur once, and only once, in each row and column. He brought these new designs to R. A. Fisher's attention in 1936 and subsequently completed "Use of Incomplete Block Replications in Estimating Tobacco Mosaic Virus" (1937), in which he presented and illustrated the application of four of the new rectangular experimental arrangements. In a subsequent paper (1940) he gave eight additional designs and, for six of these, the complementary designs. Youden's new rectangular experiment designs, called "Youden squares" by R. A. Fisher and F. Yates in the introduction to their *Statistical Tables* . . . (1938, p. 18), were immediately found to be of broad utility in biological and medical research generally; to be applicable but of less value in agricultural field trials; and, with the advent of World War II, to be of great value in the scientific and engineering experimentation connected with research and development. To gain further knowledge of statistical theory and methodology, Youden audited the courses on mathematical statistics and design of experiments, by Harold Hotelling and Gertrude M. Cox respectively, and took part in a number of statistical seminars at North Carolina State College in 1941.

Youden served as an operations analyst with the U.S. Army Air Force (1942–1945), first in Britain, where he directed a group of civilian scientists seeking to determine the controlling factor in bombing accuracy; in the latter part of the war, he conducted similar studies in India, China, and the Marianas, preparatory to the assault on Japan. He displayed exceptional skill in the invention of novel, and adaptation of standard, statistical tools of experiment design and analysis to cope with problems arising in the study of bombing accuracy.

In a lecture delivered at the National Bureau of Standards in 1947 Youden exposed the fallaciousness of the all-too-common belief that statistical methods—and a statistician—can be of no help unless one has a vast amount of data; demonstrated that one can obtain valuable information on the precision—and even on the accuracy—of a measurement process without making a large number of measurements on any single quantity; and showed how in routine work one can often obtain useful auxiliary information on personnel or equipment at little or no additional cost through skillful preliminary planning of the measurements to be taken.

On joining the National Bureau of Standards in 1948, Youden revealed the advantages of applying carefully selected statistical principles and techniques in the planning stages of the Bureau's experiments or tests. In the course of these demonstrations he noticed, and was one of the first to capitalize on, important differences between experimentation in the biological and agricultural sciences and in the physical and chemical sciences.[3]

Youden began to devise new forms of experimental arrangements, the first of which were his "linked blocks" (1951) and "chain blocks" (1953), developed to take advantage of special circumstances of spectrographic determinations of chemical elements carried out by comparing spectrum lines recorded on photographic plates.[4] In 1952 Youden and W. S. Connor began to exploit a special class of experiment designs having block size 2 in the thermometer, meter-bar and radium-standards calibration programs of the Bureau. The thermometer calibration application involved observation of the reading of each of the two thermometers forming a "block"; the meter-bar application involved observation of only the difference of the lengths of the two meter bars making up a block, and marked the start of the development of a system of "calibration designs" that Youden did not develop further and exploit as a special subclass until 1962; and the radium-standards application, observation of only ratios of pairs of standards. Meanwhile, Youden and J. S. Hunter had originated a class of designs that they termed "partially replicated Latin squares" (1955), to provide a means of checking whether the assumption of additivity of row, column, and treatment effects is valid. In an epochal 1956 address, "Randomization and Experimentation," Youden introduced a technique for constrained randomization that obviates "the difficult position of the statistician who rules against . . . a systematic sequence when advanced on the grounds of convenience and insists on it when it pops out of the hat" (p. 16).

In the early 1960's Youden exploited a class of selected experiment designs with the specific purpose of identifying and estimating the effects of sources of systematic error. "Systematic Errors in Physical Constants" (1961) contains his first "ruggedness test" based on the observation that some of the fractional factorial designs, developed a decade earlier for optimum multifactor experiments, were ready-made for testing the "ruggedness" (insensitivity) of a method of measurement with respect to recognized sources of systematic error and changes of conditions likely to be encountered in practice.

Youden also originated at least three new statistical techniques: an index for rating diagnostic tests (1950), the two-sample chart for graphical diagnosis of interlaboratory test results (1959), and an extreme rank sum test for outliers (1963), devised to test the statistical significance of outlier laboratories in interlaboratory collaborative tests. The two-sample chart has the same advantage as Shewhart's control chart: simplicity of construction, visual pinpointing of trouble spots, and comparative ease of more refined analysis.[5] Although developed in the setting of test methods for properties of materials, it has become a standard tool of the National Conference of Standard Laboratories in its nationwide program of searching for and rectifying systematic differences in the most accurate programs for instrument calibration.[6] This technique is now used in all measurement fields where interlaboratory agreement is important, and the term "Youden plot" specifies not only the plotting technique but also the experimental procedure for sampling the performance of each laboratory through the results obtained on paired test items.[7] In the case of the extreme rank sum test, Youden's

ideas had been anticipated by R. Doornbos and H. J. Prins (1958), but it was characteristic of Youden that he had independently conceived his test primarily as a device to dramatize and clarify the messages contained in experimental results, rather than as a contribution to distribution-free statistical methods.

By his publications and by his example, Youden contributed substantially to the achievement of objectivity in experimentation and to the establishment of more exact standards for drawing scientific conclusions. "Enduring Values," his address as retiring president of the Philosophical Society of Washington, is an exposition of schemes for incorporating investigations of systematic errors into experimental determinations of fundamental physical constants and a plea for efforts by scientists to accumulate objective evidence for the description of the precision and accuracy of their work. Shortly before his death Youden completed the manuscript of another "missionary" effort, *Risk, Choice and Prediction* (1974), formally intended to familiarize students in the seventh grade and above with basic statistical concepts but actually meant "for anyone . . . who wants to learn in a relatively painless way how the concept and techniques of statistics can help us better understand today's complex world" (p. vii).

*NOTES*

1. The first and last quotations are from W. J. Youden, "Memorial to Sir Ronald Aylmer Fisher," in *Journal of the American Statistical Association*, **57**, no. 300 (Dec. 1962), 727; the others, from Youden's "The Evolution of Designed Experiments," 59.

2. At this time Hotelling was the person in the United States most versed in the Student-Fisher theory of small samples.

3. Of paramount importance, he noted, is the difference in the magnitude of the errors of measurement: in agricultural and biological experimentation unavoidable variation is likely to be large, so the early experiment designs developed for application in these fields compensate by incorporating many determinations of the quantities of principal interest; physical measurements, in contrast, can often be made with high precision and the experimental material usually is comparatively homogeneous, so that the quantities of interest often can be determined with acceptably small standard errors from as few as two or three, or even from a single, indirect determination. Also, in many experimental situations in the physical sciences and engineering, a "block" and the "plots" within a block are sharply and naturally defined, and often are quite distinct; this is in marked contrast with the arbitrary division of a given land area into "blocks" in agricultural field trials, and the subdivision of a block into contiguous "plots." Consequently, various "interactions" commonly present in agricultural field trials are often absent or negligible in physical-science experimentation.

4. "Linked block" designs are incomplete block designs for which every pair of blocks has the same number of treat-

ments in common; they were subsequently shown to be special cases of partially balanced incomplete block designs with two associate classes of triangular type. "Chain block" designs were developed for situations in which the number of treatments considerably exceeds the block size while, within blocks, comparisons are of such high precision that at most two replications are needed, some treatments occurring only once. Chain block designs with two-way elimination of heterogeneity were subsequently devised by Mandel (1954).

5. See, for example, Acheson J. Duncan, *Quality Control and Industrial Statistics*, 3rd ed. (Homewood, Ill., 1965), pt. 4.

6. See *Proceedings of the 1966 Standards Laboratory Conference*, National Bureau of Standards Miscellaneous Publication 291 (Washington, D.C., 1967), 19, 20, 27–29, 42, 45, 48, 51, 61, 62.

7. "Graphical Diagnosis of Interlaboratory Test Results" (May 1959) is the basic reference on the "Youden plot." A condensed version appeared in *Technical News Bulletin. National Bureau of Standards*, **43**, no. 1 (Jan. 1959), 16–18; and its evolution can be followed in four columns in *Industrial and Engineering Chemistry*: "Presentation for Action," **50**, no. 8 (Aug. 1958), 83A–84A; "Product Specifications and Test Procedures," *ibid.*, no. 10 (Oct. 1958), 91A–92A; "Circumstances Alter Cases," *ibid.*, no. 12 (Dec. 1958), 77A–78A; and "What Is Measurement?" **51**, no. 2 (Feb. 1959), 81A–82A.

## BIBLIOGRAPHY

I. ORIGINAL WORKS. Brian L. Joiner and Roy H. Wampler, "Bibliography of W. J. Youden," in *Journal of Quality Technology (JQT)*, **4**, no. 1 (Jan. 1972), 62–66, lists 5 books and 110 papers (including book chapters, encyclopedia articles, editorials, and military documents, but excluding the 36 columns "Statistical Design" [see below], 9 book reviews, and a foreword to a book by another author). It appears to be complete and correct, except for omission of the 1969 and 1970 papers noted below, a premature date for his posthumous book, and the unfortunate substitution of "Quality" for the third word in the title "Simplified Statistical Quantity Control" (1963). Dedicated to Youden, this issue of *JQT* also contains a portrait; a biographical essay by Churchill Eisenhart; "Summary and Index for 'Statistical Design,'" prepared by Mary G. Natrella, which covers his column "Statistical Design," in *Industrial and Engineering Chemistry* (1954–1959); and reproductions of several papers and other materials.

Youden's doctoral dissertation, *A New Method for the Gravimetric Determination of Zirconium*, was privately printed (New York, 1924). As a member of the staff of the Boyce Thompson Institute, he published 15 research papers on chemical and biological studies and instrumentation pertinent to the work of the Institute in *Contributions From Boyce Thompson Institute*. The items below that are marked "repr. in *JQT*" were reprinted in *Journal of Quality Technology*, **4**, no. 1; and those marked "repr. in *SP 300-1*," in Harry H. Ku, ed., *Precision Measurement and Calibration: Selected Papers on Statistical Concepts and Procedures*, National Bureau of Standards Special Publication 300, vol. 1 (Washington, D.C., 1969).

Youden's earlier works include "A Nomogram for Use in Connection With Gutzeit Arsenic Determinations on Apples," in *Contributions From Boyce Thompson Institute*, **3**, no. 3 (Sept. 1931), 363–373; "Statistical Analysis of Seed Germination Data Through the Use of the Chi-Square Test," *ibid.*, **4**, no. 2 (June 1932), 219–232; "A Statistical Study of the Local Lesion Method for Estimating Tobacco Mosaic Virus," *ibid.*, **6**, no. 3 (July–Sept. 1934), 437–454, written with Helen P. Beale; "Relation of Virus Concentration to the Number of Lesions Produced," *ibid.*, **7**, no. 1 (Jan.–Mar. 1935), 37–53, written with H. P. Beale and J. D. Guthrie; "Field Trials With Fibre Pots," *ibid.*, **8**, no. 4 (Oct.–Dec. 1936), 317–331, written with P. W. Zimmerman; "Use of Incomplete Block Replications in Estimating Tobacco Mosaic Virus," *ibid.*, **9**, no. 1 (Nov. 1937), 41–48 (repr. in *JQT*), the paper in which the first four members of a new class of rectangular experimental arrangements, now called "Youden squares," appeared—the paper that catapulted him to fame; "Selection of Efficient Methods for Soil Sampling," *ibid.*, 59–70; "Experimental Designs to Increase the Accuracy of Greenhouse Studies," *ibid.*, **11**, no. 3 (Apr.–June 1940), 219–228; "Burette Experiment," part of the lecture "A Statistical Technique for Analytical Data," delivered at the National Bureau of Standards, 29 Apr. 1947, repr. in *JQT* from pp. 344–346, 350, of Churchill Eisenhart, "Some Canons of Sound Experimentation," in *Bulletin de l'Institut international de statistique*, **37**, no. 3 (1960), 339–350; and "Technique for Testing the Accuracy of Analytical Data," in *Analytical Chemistry*, **19**, no. 12 (Dec. 1947), 946–950.

Later works are "Index for Rating Diagnostic Tests," in *Cancer*, **3**, no. 1 (Jan. 1950), 32–35; "Linked Blocks: A New Class of Incomplete Block Designs" (abstract only), in *Biometrics*, **7**, no. 1 (Mar. 1951), 124; *Statistical Methods for Chemists* (New York, 1951); also in Italian (Genoa, 1964), his first book; "Statistical Aspects of Analytical Determinations," in *Analyst* (London), **77**, no. 921 (Dec. 1952), 874–878 (repr. in *JQT*); "The Chain Block Design," in *Biometrics*, **9**, no. 2 (June 1953), 127–140, written with W. S. Connor; "Sets of Three Measurements," in *Scientific Monthly*, **77**, no. 3 (Sept. 1953), 143–147 (repr. in *JQT*); "Making One Measurement Do the Work of Two," in *Chemical Engineering Progress*, **49**, no. 10 (Oct. 1953), 549–552 (repr. in *JQT*), written with W. S. Connor; "New Experimental Designs for Paired Observations," in *Journal of Research of the National Bureau of Standards*, **53**, no. 3 (Sept. 1954), 191–196 (repr. in *SP 300-1*), written with W. S. Connor; "Instrumental Drift," in *Science*, **120**, no. 3121 (22 Oct. 1954), 627–631 (repr. in *SP 300-1*); "Comparison of Four National Radium Standards: Part 2. Statistical Procedures and Survey," in *Journal of Research of the National Bureau of Standards*, **53**, no. 5 (Nov. 1954), 273–275 (repr. in *SP 300-1*), written with W. S. Connor; "Partially Replicated Latin Squares," in *Biometrics*, **11**, no. 4 (Dec. 1955), 399–405, written with J. S. Hunter; "Graphical Diagnosis of Interlaboratory Test Results," in *Industrial Quality Control*, **15**, no. 11 (May 1959), 24–28 (repr. in *JQT* and *SP 300-1*), the basic reference on Youden's two-sample procedure and diagram, collectively known as the "Youden Plot"; and "Measurements Made by Matching With Known Standards," in *Technometrics*, **1**, no. 2 (May 1959), 101–109, written with W. S. Connor and N. C. Severo.

See also *Statistical Design* (Washington, D.C., 1960), a collection of 36 articles published in a column with this title in *Industrial and Engineering Chemistry*, **46**, no. 2 (Feb. 1954)–**51**, no. 12 (Dec. 1959); "Physical Measurements and Experiment Design," in *Colloques internationaux du Centre national de la recherche scientifique* (Paris, 1961), no. 110, le Plan d'Expériences, 115–128 (repr. in *SP-300-1*); "Systematic Errors in Physical Constants," in *Physics Today*, **14**, no. 9 (Sept. 1961), 32–42, repr. in *Technometrics*, **4**, no. 1 [Feb. 1962], 111–123, and in *SP-300-1*; "Experimental Design and ASTM Committees," in *Materials Research and Standards*, **1**, no. 11 (Nov. 1961), 862–867 (repr. in *SP-300-1*); *Experimentation and Measurement* (New York, 1962); "Uncertainties in Calibration," in *I.R.E. Transactions on Instrumentation*, I-11, nos. 3–4 (Dec. 1962), 133–138 (repr. in *JQT* and *SP-300-1*); "Ranking Laboratories by Round-Robin Tests," in *Materials Research and Standards*, **3**, no. 1 (Jan. 1963), 9–13 (repr. in *SP-300-1*); "Measurement Agreement Comparisons," in *Proceedings of the 1962 Standards Laboratory Conference*, National Bureau of Standards Miscellaneous Publication 248 (Washington, D.C., 1963), 147–151 (repr. in *SP-300-1*), the paper that inspired the work of Bose and Cameron (1965, 1967) and Eicke and Cameron (1967) on "calibration designs." "The Collaborative Test," in *Journal of the Association of Official Agricultural Chemists*, **46**, no. 1 (Feb. 1963), 55–62 (repr. in *SP-300-1*); and "The Evolution of Designed Experiments," in *Proceedings of the [1963] IBM Scientific Computing Symposium on Statistics* (White Plains, N.Y., 1965), 59–67 (repr. in *JQT*).

Additional works are *Statistical Techniques for Collaborative Tests* (Washington, D.C., 1967); "How Mathematics Appraises Risks and Gambles," in T. L. Saaty and F. J. Weyl, eds., *The Spirit and Uses of Mathematics* (New York, 1969), 167–187; "A Revised Scheme for the Comparison of Quantitative Methods," in *American Journal of Clinical Pathology*, **54**, no. 3 (Sept. 1970), 454–462, written with R. N. Barnett; "Enduring Values," in *Technometrics*, **14**, no. 1 (Feb. 1972), 1–11; "Randomization and Experimentation," *ibid.*, 13–22; and *Risk, Choice and Prediction: An Introduction to Experimentation* (North Scituate, Mass., 1974).

Copies of all of Youden's journal articles and book reviews, and many of his book chapters, published in 1924–1965, are bound together, generally in chronological order, along with copies of his Air Force manuals, his patents, and his paperbound books *Statistical Design* and *Experimentation and Measurement*, in "W. J. Youden Publications," 2 vols., in the Historical Collection of the Library of the National Bureau of Standards at

Gaithersburg, Md. His publications of 1966–1972 have been assembled for a 3rd vol. There is also a vol. containing abstracts of his talks given during 1949–1965. In addition, among the records of the Bureau's Applied Mathematics Division are eight boxes of "Youdeniana" covering 1920–1971: personal records given by his widow in 1973, professional correspondence, reports, commendations, certificates of awards, photographs, handwritten notes and computations, and a considerable number of Youden's papers, lectures, and speeches.

II. SECONDARY LITERATURE. Youden's career and contributions to statistical theory and practice are summarized briefly in an unsigned obituary in *American Statistician*, **25**, no. 3 (June 1971), 51; and more fully by Churchill Eisenhart, in *Journal of Quality Technology*, **4**, no. 1 (Jan. 1972), 1–6. His contributions to the theory of statistical design and analysis of experiments are given special attention by Churchill Eisenhart and Joan R. Rosenblatt, in *Annals of Mathematical Statistics*, **43**, no. 4 (Aug. 1972), 1035–1040. A biography of Youden, with portrait, is scheduled for publication in *National Cyclopedia of American Biography*, LVI (1975), 99–100. A biographical essay on Youden's contributions to statistical theory, methodology, by Harry H. Ku is to appear in a volume tentatively titled *Statistics: Articles From the International Encyclopedia of the Social Sciences* (New York, 1976 or 1977).

Other publications are R. N. Barnett, "A Scheme for the Comparison of Quantitative Methods," in *American Journal of Clinical Pathology*, **43**, no. 6 (June 1965), 562–569; R. C. Bose and J. M. Cameron, "The Bridge Tournament Problem and Calibration Designs for Comparing Pairs of Objects," in *Journal of Research of the National Bureau of Standards*, **69B**, no. 4 (Oct.–Dec. 1965), 323–332; "Calibration Designs Based on Solutions to the Tournament Problem," *ibid.*, **71B**, no. 4 (Oct.–Dec. 1967), 149–160; Willard H. Clatworthy, *Tables of Two-Associate-Class Partially Balanced Designs*, National Bureau of Standards Applied Mathematics Series, no. 63 (Washington, D.C., 1973); W. G. Eicke and J. M. Cameron, *Designs for Surveillance of the Volt Maintained by a Small Group of Saturated Standard Cells*, National Bureau of Standards Technical Note 430 (Washington, D.C., 1967); R. A. Fisher, *Statistical Methods for Research Workers* (Edinburgh–London, 1925; 14th ed., Edinburgh–London–Darien, Conn., 1970); R. A. Fisher and F. Yates, *Statistical Tables for Biological, Agricultural, and Medical Research* (Edinburgh–London, 1938; 6th ed., London–New York, 1963); H. O. Halvorson and N. R. Ziegler, "Application of Statistics to Problems in Bacteriology. I. A Means of Determining Bacterial Population by the Dilution Method," in *Journal of Bacteriology*, **25**, no. 2 (Feb. 1933), 101–121; J. Mandel, "Chain Block Designs With Two-Way Elimination of Homogeneity," in *Biometrics* **10**, no. 2 (June 1954), 251–272; Benjamin L. Page, "Calibration of Meter Line Standards of Length at the National Bureau of Standards," in *Journal of Research of the National Bureau of Standards*, **54**, no. 1 (Jan. 1955), 1–14; Gary J. Sutter, George Zyskind, and Oscar Kempthorne, "Some Aspects of Constrained Randomization," *Aeronautical Research Laboratories Report 63-18* (Wright-Patterson Air Force Base, Ohio, 1963); and Walter A. Shewhart, "Correction of Data for Errors of Measurement," in *Bell System Technical Journal*, **5**, no. 1 (Jan. 1926), 11–26.

CHURCHILL EISENHART

[Contribution of the National Bureau of Standards, not subject to copyright.]

**YOUNG, CHARLES AUGUSTUS** (*b.* Hanover, New Hampshire, 15 December 1834; *d.* Hanover, 3 January 1908), *astronomy.*

The family into which Young was born had strong ties to Hanover, New Hampshire, the site of Dartmouth College. His mother was Eliza M. Adams, whose father, Ebenezer Adams, occupied the chair of mathematics and philosophy (later natural philosophy and astronomy) at Dartmouth from 1810 to 1833 and was succeeded by Ira Young, Charles's father, who held the post until 1858. Charles began his higher education at Dartmouth at the age of fourteen; four years later he graduated with distinction, first in a class of fifty. Upon graduation he took a post teaching classics at Phillips Academy, Andover, Massachusetts. He taught there full-time for two years and part-time for another year while he was enrolled in the Andover Theological Seminary.

Fortunately for astronomy, in 1856 Young changed his plans to become a missionary and instead took the post of professor of mathematics and natural philosophy at Western Reserve College in Hudson, Ohio. He began his duties there in January 1857 and the following August married Augusta S. Mixer, by whom he had three children.

In 1862 Young took four months from his teaching at Hudson in order to captain Company B, 85th Regiment, Ohio Volunteers. The duties of the command involved only the guarding of prisoners, yet he returned to civilian life with his health impaired.

Although offered a professorship of mathematics at Dartmouth, Young remained in Hudson until 1866, when he accepted the Appleton professorship at Dartmouth—the chair that had been held by his grandfather and father.

The promise of modern equipment and less classroom time induced Young to move to the College of New Jersey (now Princeton University) in 1877. He held that post until retiring to Hanover in 1905.

Young started serious research soon after taking his post at Dartmouth. The spectroscope was just beginning to become a powerful tool in astronomy, and the Appleton fund was sufficient to provide him with the equipment he requested. In 1869 he began publishing a series of "spectroscopic notes" in the *Journal of the Franklin Institute*. The nine papers dealt with spectra of the solar chromosphere and sunspots, design and use of equipment, and observations of prominences, including possibly the first photograph ever taken of one. During 1871–1872 he compiled a catalog of bright spectral lines in the sun; and in 1876, using the Doppler principle, he measured the rotational velocity of the sun. (Although Vogel had made a similar measurement in 1871, Young's results were more accurate.)

His interest in solar research naturally led Young to make many eclipse expeditions. While on the U.S. Naval Observatory expedition to Burlington, Iowa, 7 August 1869, he devised a method for using the spectroscope to observe first contact; he later suggested the application of this method for the transit of Venus in 1874. And during an expedition to Jerez, Spain, 22 December 1870, he found that the dark lines of the sun's spectrum are momentarily reversed just at totality; hence, he is credited with the important discovery of the "reversing layer." He led other expeditions to Colorado (July 1878), Russia (August 1887), and North Carolina (May 1900).

Although Young had a conspicuous career as a researcher, he was equally talented as a teacher. Besides teaching at Western Reserve, Dartmouth, and Princeton, he lectured at Mount Holyoke Female Seminary (now College) from 1868 to 1903, at Bradford Academy from 1872 to 1898, and at Williams College from 1873 to 1875; in addition, he gave numerous talks to the public.

In addition to teaching, Young wrote some of the most famous and widely read textbooks on astronomy of his era. These books aided the education of several generations of scientists and affected the writing of astronomy texts for the next half-century. *General Astronomy* (1888), which was widely adopted, sold over thirty thousand copies by 1910—an amazing accomplishment at that time. His *Elements of Astronomy*, a more basic text, appeared in 1890. A version for younger students, *Lessons in Astronomy* (1891), had sold sixty thousand copies by 1910. Finally, in 1902, he issued an intermediate-level text that became perhaps his most famous book—his *Manual of Astronomy*. (Incidentally, the renowned text by H. N. Russell, R. S. Dugan, and J. Q. Stewart [1926] was a revision of the *Manual*.) More than any other individual, Young profoundly influenced the nature of American texts in the field.

Young received many honorary degrees and awards; he was also a member and officer of leading astronomical and scientific societies in the United States and abroad.

*BIBLIOGRAPHY*

I. ORIGINAL WORKS. Young's books include *The Sun,* in International Science Series (New York, 1881; rev. ed., 1895); *A Text-book of General Astronomy for Colleges and Scientific Schools* (Boston, 1888; rev. ed., 1898); *Elements of Astronomy* (Boston, 1890); *Lessons in Astronomy* (Boston, 1891); and *Manual of Astronomy* (Boston, 1902). Some of his most important papers are "American Astronomy—Its History, Present State, Needs and Prospects," in *Proceedings of the American Association for Advancement of Science* (1876), 35–48; "Pending Problems in Astronomy," *ibid.* (1884), 1–27; "Ten Years' Progress in Astronomy, 1876–1886," in *Sidereal Messenger*, **6** (1887), 4–41; "Spectroscopic Notes," in *Journal of the Franklin Institute*, **58** (1869), 141–142, 287–288, 416–424; **60** (1870), 64–65, 232a–232b, 331–340, 349–351; **62** (1871), 348–360, 430; "On the Solar Corona," in *American Journal of Science*, 3rd ser., **1** (1871), 311–320; and "Observations on the Displacement of Lines in the Solar Spectrum Caused by the Sun's Rotation," *ibid.*, **12** (1876), 321–328.

II. SECONDARY LITERATURE. Obituaries and biographical sketches of Young are the following, listed chronologically: New York *Times* (5 Jan. 1908), pt. I, 11; Hector MacPherson, Jr., in *Observatory*, **31** (1908), 122–125; John M. Poor, in *Popular Astronomy*, **16** (1908), 218–230; Sidney D. Townley, in *Publications of the Astronomical Society of the Pacific*, **20** (1908), 46–47; Edwin B. Frost, in *Astrophysical Journal*, **30** (1909), 323–338, with portrait; Henry Norriss Russell, in *Monthly Notices of the Royal Astronomical Society*, **69** (1909), 257–260; and Edwin B. Frost, in *Biographical Memoirs. National Academy of Sciences*, **7** (1910), 89–114, with portrait and complete bibliography. Further background information can be found in Agnes M. Clerke, *A Popular History of Astronomy* (London, 1893); A. Pannekoek, *A History of Astronomy* (London, 1961); Otto Struve and Velta Zebergs, *Astronomy of the Twentieth Century* (New York, 1962); and Reginald L. Waterfield, *A Hundred Years of Astronomy* (New York, 1938).

RICHARD BERENDZEN
RICHARD HART

**YOUNG, JOHN RICHARDSON** (*b.* Hagerstown, Maryland, 1782 [?]; *d.* Hagerstown, 8 June 1804), *physiology*.

Young received his early education at the College of New Jersey (now Princeton), graduating in 1799. Before beginning his formal medical education at the University of Pennsylvania in November 1802, he evidently served as apprentice to his father, Dr. Samuel Young, a native of Ireland who is reported to have received his medical education in Edinburgh. Few other biographical facts are known about John Young or his family beyond the information on their gravestones. His mother, Ann Richardson Young, died at the age of thirty-one and two sisters at ages twenty-one and thirty. John himself died in his twenty-second year, after a two-month illness. There is a family tradition that he and his sisters died of tuberculosis. An obituary, describing Young's fatal illness in detail, suggests this disease. All were survived by the father, who lived to the age of 108, not dying until 1838.

Young's claim to historical notice rests on his inaugural dissertation for the M.D. degree, *An Experimental Inquiry, Into the Principles of Nutrition, and the Digestive Process* (Philadelphia, 1803). Dedicating this student effort to his father and to Dr. Benjamin Smith Barton, his professor of materia medica, Young argued that "acid" is not nutritious, and that digestion is a process whereby foodstuffs are dissolved in the stomach, are mixed with bile and pancreatic juices in the duodenum, and then converted into chyle by a secretory process in the ducts of the lacteals. He rejected the notion that digestion involves fermentation and supported the view that the gastric juice naturally contains phosphoric acid. His opinions were supported by a number of animal experiments.

A variety of claims have been made for Young's contributions to our understanding of gastric physiology and to our methods of experimentation. A study of the knowledge of his time and the work of other scientists and medical students, however, does not support the view that Young's work should be singled out for special acclaim. There is clear evidence, on the other hand, that even his contemporaries recognized in him a young man of "uncommon talents and great industry," and, in his work, "a very ingenious Thesis."

*BIBLIOGRAPHY*

I. ORIGINAL WORKS. Note reference in the text. This thesis was republished several times, and recently as facsimile reprint no. 1 in the history of science sponsored by the History of Science Society of the University of Illinois, with an introductory essay by William C. Rose (Urbana, 1959). His only other writings were two letters published posthumously: "A Case of Tetanus Cured by Mercury," in *Philadelphia Medical and Physical Journal*, **1** (1804), 47–51, and one on the use of Saccharum Saturni in three cases of uterine hemorrhage, *ibid.*, 145.

II. SECONDARY LITERATURE. See Howard A. Kelly, "John R. Young, Pioneer American Physiologist," in *Bulletin of The Johns Hopkins Hospital*, **29** (1918), 186–191; and *Dictionary of American Medical Biography* (New York–London, 1928), 1352. D. G. Bates, "American Therapeutics in 1804: the Case of John R. Young," in *Bulletin of the History of Medicine*, **38** (1964), 226–240, quotes in full the obituary notice of Young and the details of his last illness. In "The Background to John Young's Thesis on Digestion," *ibid.*, **36** (1962), 341–361, Bates evaluates Young's work in the light of the knowledge and research of his contemporaries.

DONALD G. BATES

**YOUNG, JOHN WESLEY** (*b.* Columbus, Ohio, 17 November 1879; *d.* Hanover, New Hampshire, 17 February 1932), *mathematics, education.*

Young's father, William Henry Young, a lieutenant colonel during the Civil War and professor of ancient languages at Ohio University, served as United States consul in Karlsruhe, Germany, from 1869 to 1876. His mother was Marie Widdenhorn.

After graduating from the Gymnasium in Baden-Baden, Young entered Ohio State University and earned a Ph.B. there in 1899. He received the A.M. (1901) and the Ph.D. (1904) from Cornell University. In 1907 he married Mary Louise Aston of Columbus. After teaching at Northwestern University (1903–1905), Princeton (preceptor, 1905–1908), the University of Illinois (1908–1910), the University of Kansas (head of the mathematics department, 1910–1911), and the University of Chicago (summer of 1911), he settled for the rest of his life at Dartmouth College, where he modernized and humanized the mathematics curriculum.

Young was influential in many learned societies, both in the United States and in Europe. He served as an editor of *Mathematics Teacher; Bulletin* and *Colloquium Publications, American Mathematical Society*; and *Carus Mathematical Monographs*. His active participation in the American Mathematical Society included membership on its Council (1907–1925) and vice-presidency

(1928–1930). He was also instrumental in the founding of the Mathematical Association of America, of which he was vice-president in 1918 and president in 1929–1931. As chairman of its Committee on Mathematical Requirements (1916–1924), he edited a 652-page report, *The Reorganization of Mathematics in Secondary Education* (1923), which circulated widely and profoundly influenced educational thought and practice.

Throughout his professional career three themes dominated Young's publications: the concept of generalization, the presentation of advanced mathematics from an elementary viewpoint, and, in conjunction with these, the "popularization" of mathematics. His *Lectures on the Fundamental Concepts of Algebra and Geometry* (1911) is excellently written and is still highly regarded. At Dartmouth his synoptic course gave the nonspecialist an understanding of topics in advanced mathematics.

In 1908, Young, with Oswald Veblen, created a set of postulates for projective geometry that embodied the first fully independent set of assumptions for that branch of geometry. This formulation served as the basis for the first volume of the classic *Projective Geometry* (1910), written with Veblen.

*BIBLIOGRAPHY*

I. ORIGINAL WORKS. Young's A.M. thesis, "On the Homomorphisms of a Group," in *Transactions of the American Mathematical Society*, **3** (1902), 186–191; and "On a Certain Group of Isomorphisms," in *American Journal of Mathematics*, **25** (1903), 206–212, were written under the direction of G. A. Miller. His Ph.D. dissertation, "On the Group of Sign (0, 3; 2,4,∞) and the Functions Belonging to It," in *Transactions of the American Mathematical Society*, **5** (1904), 81–104, used methods developed by Klein in treating the elliptic modular group. Other papers are "The Use of Hypercomplex Numbers in Certain Problems of the Modular Group," in *Bulletin of the American Mathematical Society*, **11** (1905), 363–367; "A Class of Discontinuous ζ-Groups Defined by the Normal Curves of the Fourth Order in a Space of Four Dimensions," in *Rendiconti del Circulo matematico di Palermo*, **23** (1907), 97–106; "A Fundamental Invariant of the Discontinuous ζ-Groups Defined by the Normal Curves of Order *n* in a Space of *n* Dimensions," in *Bulletin of the American Mathematical Society*, **14** (1908), 363–367; "A Set of Assumptions for Projective Geometry," in *American Journal of Mathematics*, **30** (1908), 347–380, written with O. Veblen; "The Discontinuous ζ-Groups Defined by Rational Normal Curves in a Space of *n* Dimensions," in *Bulletin of the American Mathematical Soci-*

*ety*, **16** (1910), 363–368; "The Geometries Associated With a Certain System of Cremona Groups," in *Transactions of the American Mathematical Society*, **17** (1916), 233–244, written with F. M. Morgan; and "A New Formulation for General Algebra," in *Annals of Mathematics*, 2nd ser., **29** (1921), 47–60.

*Lectures on the Fundamental Concepts of Algebra and Geometry* (New York, 1911) was translated into Italian by L. Pierro (Naples, 1919). *Projective Geometry* (Boston, 1910) consisted of 2 vols.: vol. I written with O. Veblen and vol. II, published under the names of Veblen and Young, but written by Veblen alone. *Projective Geometry* was Carus Mathematical Monograph no. 4 (Chicago, 1930). Young wrote a number of elementary mathematical textbooks, of which *Elementary Mathematical Analysis* (New York, 1918), written with F. M. Morgan, a pioneer text in the reorganization of freshman college courses, is structured around the unifying concept of function.

Other works are *The Reorganization of Mathematics in Secondary Education* (Oberlin, Ohio, 1923); "The Organization of College Courses in Mathematics for Freshmen," in *American Mathematical Monthly*, **30** (1923), 6–14; "Geometry," (in part) in *Encyclopaedia Britannica*, 14th ed. (1929), X, 174–178; and "The Adjustment Between Secondary School and College Work," in *Journal of Engineering Education*, **22** (1932), 586–595, his last paper, which is typical of a number of papers on collegiate mathematical teaching. Young's retiring presidential address, "Functions of the Mathematical Association of America," in *American Mathematical Monthly*, **39** (1932), 6–15, is an excellent example of the range of his interests and involvement in mathematics.

II. Secondary Literature. K. D. Beetle and C. E. Wilder, "John Wesley Young: In Memoriam," in *Bulletin of the American Mathematical Society*, **38** (1932), 603–610, is a good biography complete with bibliography. Another, by E. M. Hopkins, L. L. Silverman, and H. E. Slaught, is in *American Mathematical Monthly*, **39** (1932), 309–314. For additional material on Young's role in American mathematics and the work and impact of the National Committee on Mathematical Requirements, see K. O. May, ed., *The Mathematical Association of America: Its First Fifty Years* (1972), 26–30, 39–40, 44; and the *American Mathematical Monthly*, **23** (1916), 226, 283; **24** (1917), 463–464; **25** (1918), 56–59; **26** (1919), 223–234, 279–280, 439–440, 462–463; **27** (1920), 101–104, 145–146, 194, 341–342, 441–442; **28** (1921), 357–358; **29** (1922), 46; and **32** (1925), 157.

Henry S. Tropp

**YOUNG, SYDNEY** (*b.* Farnworth, near Widnes, Lancashire, England, 29 December 1857; *d.* Bristol, England, 8 April 1937), *physical chemistry*.

Young was a pioneer in the separation and spec-

ification of pure organic compounds, and clarified crucial thermodynamical relationships for solids and liquids. The third son of a merchant, he spent five years at a private school in Southport and two years at the Royal Institution School in Liverpool. After being in business for over two years, he entered Owens College, Manchester, in 1876, studying chemistry under Henry Roscoe and Carl Schorlemmer. In 1880 Young graduated B.Sc. of London University. He then became elected an associate of Owens College in 1881. Young spent the semester 1881–1882 at Strasbourg, where he was one of the first to assist Rudolph Fittig in an extended investigation "of the relations between lactones and the corresponding acids."[1] In 1883 he obtained the D.Sc. from London University and in 1893 he was elected fellow of the Royal Society.

Young had been appointed lecturer and demonstrator of chemistry at University College, Bristol, under William Ramsay in the autumn of 1882, and he succeeded to that professorship in 1887. Young married Grace M. Kimmins in 1896 and they had twin sons.

Young was stimulated by Thomas Carnelley's observation of "hot" ice in 1881. He proved that the volatilizing point of ice depended upon the pressure and showed "that the volatilising point-pressure curve is identical with the vapour pressure curve constructed from the data calculated on theoretical grounds by James Thomson and by Kirchhoff."[2] This result for ice, whereby the graph representing the vapor pressure at different temperatures also represents the volatilizing point as a function of pressure, was extended to other volatile solids as well as to substances such as benzene. Young and Ramsay in partnership at Bristol published an exhaustive series of researches concerning the vapor pressures of liquids, thereby clarifying the vexed question of whether Kopp's quantitative laws held at all pressures. In 1885 Ramsay and Young derived an empirical equation that relates the ratio of absolute temperature of two liquids at a given vapor pressure, say $T_a/T_b$, to the same at another vapor pressure, say $T_{a'}/T_{b'}$, so that

$$T_a/T_b = T_{a'}/T_{b'} + c(T_a - T_{a'}),$$

where $c$ is constant.

Showing that $c$ is very small or even negligible for two closely related chemical substances (they used chloro- and homobenzenes), one can say that $T_a/T_b = T_{a'}/T_{b'}$. The significance is that this ratio is constant at all vapor pressures and that the ratio of the boiling points of two similar substances is the same, no matter what the external pressure. Later, Young tested van der Waals' equation of state noting that it was "strictly true" only for closely related substances, such as the four halogen derivatives of benzene. In the case of non-associated substances "the ratio of the actual to the theoretical density at the critical point should be the same for all unassociated substances"[3], and van der Waals had determined the ratio $RT_c/p_cV_c$ = 2.67. The actual values of this ratio tend to range between 3 and 4 being much higher in the case of associated substances. Modifying the equation of state, Conrad Dieterici in 1899 succeeded in obtaining the theoretical ratio 3.695.[4] For this work Young devised a new method, improving upon the law of Cailletet and Mathias, for determining the critical densities of liquid and saturated vapor.

From 1885, the potential for extracting paraffin hydrocarbons from petroleum and a general need for substances in the purest possible state led Young to devise improved techniques of fractional distillation. He designed and constructed his own efficient still heads, having become an expert glassblower while at Strasbourg. He examined the vapor pressures, boiling points, and behavior on distillation of mixed liquids including azeotropic mixtures. He also developed a new method of dehydrating ethyl alcohol using benzene and made fundamental contributions concerning the separation and specification of the various hydrocarbons of petroleum.[5] In 1904 Young proposed that the difference in boiling points between two successive homologues of most unassociated compounds is not constant, as Kopp had maintained in 1842, but is a function of the absolute temperature, approximating the empirical formula

$$\Delta = 144.86/T^{0.0148\sqrt{T}},$$

where $T$ is the absolute boiling point of the lower member. Most of Young's publications appeared during his twenty-one years at Bristol. Succeeding James Emerson Reynolds at Trinity College, Dublin, in 1903, he assumed a post not conducive to continued research, but he did advance the development of the practical applications of his separation techniques.[6] Although Young established no "school," he was the first to prove that pure organic compounds are no less unique than inorganic elements; and through his techniques he exerted a profound, albeit often indirect, influence on all subsequent research concerning their purification.[7]

NOTES

1. E. von Meyer, *A History of Chemistry* (London, 1891), 410–411.
2. "On the Volatilisation of Solids," in A. Keitner, *Menschen und Menschenwerk*, II, 453.
3. *Ibid.*, 453–454.
4. A. Findlay, *Introduction to Physical Chemistry*, 3rd ed. (London, 1953), p. 85.
5. The industrial implications of this patented dehydration process using a third liquid seem first to have been appreciated and adopted by the firm of C. A. F. Kahlbaum, Chemische Fabrik, Berlin. Young received special recognition in 1933 from the Petroleum Division of the American Chemical Society, which expressed high appreciation of his work on distillation, on the composition of petroleum, and on the specification of numerous hydrocarbons.
6. Young elaborated a quantitative analysis of the process in *Fractional Distillation* (1903; 1918) and included industrial applications in *Distillation, Principles and Processes* (1922).
7. J. Timmermans, "Sydney Young," 13–14.


BIBLIOGRAPHY

I. ORIGINAL WORKS. Most of Young's more than 100 publications are listed in W. R. G. Atkins, "Sydney Young," in *Obituary Notices of Fellows of the Royal Society of London*, **2** (1938), 370–379, also abbreviated in *Dictionary of National Biography, 1931–1940*, 932–933. His books include *Fractional Distillation* (London, 1903); *Stoichiometry* (London, 1908; 2nd ed., 1918); and *Distillation, Principles and Processes* (London, 1922), written with Ernest Briggs, T. H. Butler, T. H. Durrans, F. R. Henley, James Kewley, and Joseph Reilly; 2nd ed. condensed and translated into German as *Theorie und Praxis der Destillation* (Berlin, 1932). His scientific "autobiography" is "On the Volatilisation of Solids and the Thermic Properties of Mixtures of Liquids," in A. Keitner, ed., *Menschen und Menschenwerke*, II (Vienna, 1925), 453–454, preceded by a German version, 451–453, and followed by a French version, 455–456. This is preceded by a brief autobiographical résumé, 450–451, in the three languages. Two autobiographical letters, dated 8 Nov. 1892 and 13 Feb. 1893, accompanied by his list of publications, are in the Krause *Album*, IV, held in the Sondersammlungen of the library of the Deutsches Museum, Munich.

II. SECONDARY LITERATURE. Young's successor at Bristol, F. Francis, considered his work in detail in *Journal of the Chemical Society* (1937), 1332–1336; and there is an anonymous obituary in *Nature*, **180** (1957), 1451. His work on critical constants is considered in W. Nernst, *Theoretische Chemie* (Stuttgart, 1921), 241–246. The importance of Young's research and influence on the purification of organic compounds is stressed in J. Timmermans, "Sydney Young," in *Endeavour*, **6** (1947), 11–14. A discussion of subsequent developments pertaining to the distillation of hydrocarbons at high pressures is in the article on M. Benedict in *Modern Men of Science*, I (New York, 1966), 31.

Young's research on boiling points in relation to the work of his contemporaries is considered in S. Smiles, *The Relations Between Chemical Constitution and Some Physical Properties* (London, 1910), ch. 7. The significance of Young's experimental results for theoretical chemistry is considered in H. Davies, "On Some Applications of the Law of the Rectilinear Diameter," in *Philosophical Magazine*, 6th ser., **24** (1912), 418–421; and G. Le Bas, "The Unit-Stere Theory," *ibid.*, **14** (1907), 340–346.

THADDEUS J. TRENN

**YOUNG, THOMAS** (*b.* Milverton, Somerset, England, 13 June 1773; *d.* London, England, 10 May 1829), *natural philosophy.*

Young made many discoveries in natural philosophy and physiological optics, and he was one of the first persons to translate Egyptian hieroglyphics. He is most famous, however, for his attempt to win acceptance for an undulatory theory of light. His scientific colleagues initially did not share his interest in that theory, nor were they ultimately convinced by his discoveries or arguments. Young's achievements, as well as his failures, must be understood in the context of his education, heterogeneous career, and personality as well as in terms of contemporary scientific evaluations of his theories.

The eldest son of Thomas Young, a mercer and banker, and of Sara Davis, Young was raised as a member of the Society of Friends and was largely self-educated in languages and natural philosophy.[1] He learned to read at age two; and by the time he was six, he had read twice through the Bible and had started the study of Latin. Between 1780 and 1786 he attended two boarding schools, where he learned elementary mathematics and gained a reading knowledge of Latin, Greek, French, and Italian. He also had begun independent study of natural history, natural philosophy, and fluxions, and had learned to make telescopes and microscopes. In 1786 Young began independent study of Hebrew, Chaldean, Syriac, Samaritan, Arabic, Persian, Turkish, and Ethiopic. Shortly thereafter he became tutor to his lifelong friend and biographer Hudson Gurney, who was a member of the Gurney banking family. By 1792 Young had become a proficient Greek and Latin scholar; had mastered the fluxionary calculus; and had read Newton's *Principia* and *Opticks*, Lavoisier's *Elements of Chemistry*, Joseph Black's manuscript lectures on chemistry, and Boerhaave's *Methodus studii medici*, in addition to plays, law, and politics.

Between 1792 and 1799 Young studied medicine at London, Edinburgh, and Göttingen (M.D. 1796). In January 1794 he was one of the assistants in experiments of the Society for Philosophical Experiments and Conversations organized by the chemist Bryan Higgins.[2] At the end of 1794 and in 1795, when he was at Edinburgh, Young began to enjoy music, dancing, and the theater, and in general to abandon the practices of the Society of Friends. Later in his life he formally became a member of the Church of England. In 1797–1803 he was enrolled at Emmanuel College, Cambridge (M.B. 1803; M.D. 1808), partly to fulfill the requirements of the Royal College of Physicians and partly to satisfy the desires of his maternal uncle, Dr. Richard Brocklesby, who sponsored Young's medical education and his election to the Royal Society (19 June 1794). Brocklesby also introduced Young to such influential men as Edmund Burke, the duke of Richmond, and William Herschel. When Brocklesby died in 1797, he left Young his London house, his library and paintings, and £10,000.

Young moved from Cambridge to London in 1800 and attempted to establish a medical practice. He was never very successful as a doctor, however, probably because he did not inspire confidence in his patients. Young's undemanding practice gave him the opportunity for regular attendance at meetings of the Royal Society. As a result he became known to the Society's president, Joseph Banks, and to Benjamin Thompson, Count Rumford, founder of the Royal Institution.

In the summer of 1801 Rumford was looking for a professor of natural philosophy. On Banks's and Rumford's recommendations, Young was employed on 3 August 1801 as "Professor of Natural Philosophy, Editor of the Journals, and Superintendent of the House" at an annual salary of £300. As professor his first task was to prepare popular lectures on natural philosophy and the mechanical arts for the Institution's members. Young delivered these lectures in 1802 and 1803, and published them in revised form in 1807.[3] These lectures were erudite and at times contained the results of his recent researches. They also were obscure, technical, and too detailed for a popular audience. At the same time, in contrast, his colleague Humphry Davy's lectures on chemistry were brilliantly successful. Rumford left England in May 1802, and Young seems to have become unpopular with the Institution's managers. They probably forced his resignation, which was effective 4 July 1803.

Young then resumed his medical practice in London and later, during the summers, in the fashionable resort of Worthing. On 4 June 1804 he married Eliza Maxwell, who was related to the Scottish aristocracy through the family of Sir William Maxwell of Calderwood.

In November 1808 Young gave the endowed Croonian lecture to the Royal Society, and he was elected to the Royal College of Physicians in December 1809. During that winter at the Middlesex Hospital, he delivered a course of lectures on physiology, chemistry, nosology and general practice, and materia medica that were published in 1813. In January 1811 Young at last obtained a lifetime professional position, being elected physician to St. George's Hospital. He was chosen to give the other endowed Croonian lecture, to the Royal College of Physicians, in 1822–1823; and in March 1824 he was appointed inspector of calculations and physician to the Palladium Insurance Company, at an annual salary of £500.[4]

During much of his life Young received a substantial income as an anonymous author of a wide variety of articles. In 1808 and 1809 he wrote for *Retrospect of Philosophical, Mechanical, Chemical, and Agricultural Discoveries*; in 1810, an article for the *London Review*; between 1809 and 1818, at least twenty-one articles for the *Quarterly Review*; and between 1816 and 1824, over sixty articles for the *Supplement* to the *Encyclopaedia Britannica*. These last works included biographies as well as many pieces on optics, mechanics, and the mechanical arts.[5]

Young held several public offices related to science. From 22 March 1804 until his death he was foreign secretary of the Royal Society, and after 1806 he was also a member of its Council.[6] He was at times a consultant to the Admiralty and was secretary to the Royal Commission on Weights and Measures from 1816 to 1821. Young was secretary of the Board of Longitude at an annual salary of £300, from 1818 until its abolition in 1828. He was also superintendent of the *Nautical Almanac*, at an additional salary of £100, from 1818 until his death. The last two posts were among the very few salaried scientific offices in England; and with Young's appointment to them, his combined income became commensurate with his social status. In 1827 Young's work in science received international recognition when he was elected a foreign associate of the French Academy of Sciences.

Young was a scholar with the scholar's love of knowledge and the search for truth, however esoteric. Shortly before his death he persisted, against

advice, in compiling his Egyptian dictionary and expressed great satisfaction that he had not yet spent an idle day in his life.[7] His self-education in many difficult fields shows that Young had the successful autodidact's persistence and self-confidence. He never seems, however, to have developed much sensitivity, in his professional relations, to other people's emotions or differing perspectives. In his professional life he seems to have been formal almost to coldness and self-assured almost to being cocksure. Young's writing was frequently both prolix and obscure; at other times it was concise almost to incomprehensibility. Despite these limitations, as his varied career continued to open new vistas of scholarship, his education and independent income gave him the opportunity to be an intellectual dilettante.

As a result of his uncle's influence and his marriage, Young's social position was high. He was fond of music, dancing, riding, and conversation; and he valued and sought friendship and acquaintance with persons of culture and social status. After abandoning his Quakerism he seems to have been impeccably conservative at a time when the English establishment was reacting conservatively to threats of radicalism at home and abroad. In sum, Young had the attitudes, personality, ability, money, and influence to be a gentleman scholar and to pursue careers as a physician, writer, administrator of science, and Egyptologist as well as a natural philosopher. Consequently his diverse writings are related to each other more by his love of scholarship and the accidents of his life than by any dominant research or theoretical concerns. But, unlike most gentlemen scholars, Young was exceptionally intelligent. As a result he often showed clear insight into problems and made several important discoveries.[8]

Young once remarked that, as a natural philosopher, ". . . acute suggestion was . . . always more in the line of my ambition than experimental illustration."[9] In the course of his very diverse writings Young did make many "acute suggestions," as well as many ingenious "experimental illustrations" in physiological optics, the theory of light, mechanics, and Egyptian linguistics. In none of these fields, however, did he systematically develop his discoveries, hypotheses, or suggestions. Nor did he fully confront their implications. His failure to do this, despite the importance of some of his discoveries, partly accounts for his limited influence in science.

From 1791 to 1801 Young published most of his experiments and theories in physiological optics.

In 1793, when he wrote his first important paper, "Observations on Vision," there was no consensus about the mechanism of the accommodation of the eye. Various earlier authors had argued that the eye adjusted its focus to different distances by changing either its length or the curvature of the cornea or the crystalline lens. Young conjectured that the lens is composed of muscle fibers. Nerve impulses are sent ". . . by the ciliary processes to the muscle of the crystalline [lens], which, by the contraction of its fibers, becomes more convex. . . ."[10] Measurements that he had made on the lens from an ox's eye indicated that the necessary changes in focal length could easily be achieved by the possible changes in the shape of the lens.[11] In 1796, in his doctoral dissertation, Young temporarily abandoned this hypothesis when he learned of investigations by Everard Home, John Hunter, and Jesse Ramsden that appeared to show that accommodation was achieved by changes in the curvature of the cornea and the length of the eyeball.[12] These researchers also had reported that persons who had had their lenses removed retained the ability to change the focus of their eyes.

Late in 1800, however, Young reaffirmed his first hypothesis after performing new experiments that refuted Home and Ramsden. In his paper "On the Mechanism of the Eye," he first derived a formula for the path of a ray refracted through a variable medium such as the crystalline lens.[13] Then he described his improvement of the optometer, analyzed the optics of the eye, made optometric measurements of its dimensions, and computed the change in focal length that would be required to accommodate for near and far vision.[14] Next Young determined the amount of change that would have to occur in the curvature of the cornea or the length of the eyeball, singly or jointly, for accommodation.[15] Then he made a series of observations that were sensitive enough to detect as little as one-fourth of the required change in the cornea. He found no change.[16] His most compelling experimental demonstration, however, involved immersing his eye in water, which eliminated refraction at the cornea. His power of accommodation was unchanged. This result eliminated any role for the cornea in accommodation.[17] Furthermore, Young could perceive no change in his ability to accommodate even when he made the length of his eye almost invariable by rotating it to the side and applying pressure.[18] Finally he reported that he had examined five persons without crystalline lenses. None of them had any power of accommodation.[19]

To show that changes in the shape of the lens do take place, Young made use of his own astigmatism. By viewing an out-of-focus point he first produced a "star" image on his retina; then, when he passed light from the point through horizontal or vertical slits, he observed straight-sided bands with a relaxed eye and curved bands when he accommodated. From this he concluded that the only way such curvature could be produced was by a change in the shape of the lens during accommodation. Young then formally readopted his opinion of 1793 that the lens changed shape because it was a muscle. His final conclusion was ". . . whether we call the lens a muscle or not, it seems demonstrable that such a change of figure takes place [in it] as can be produced by no external cause."[20] In this paper Young clearly demonstrated his ability to formulate a testable hypothesis, design and perform delicate experiments, and draw convincing conclusions that did not go beyond his evidence. Moreover, he was able to refute the opinions of persons as renowned as Home.

In 1801 Young also suggested that the retina responded to all colors in terms of variable amounts of three "principal colours." He believed that ". . . it is probable that the motion of the retina is rather of a vibratory than an undulatory nature. . . ." "Now as it is almost impossible to conceive each sensitive point of the retina to contain an infinite number of particles, each capable of vibrating in consonance with every possible undulation, it becomes necessary to suppose the number limited, for instance, to the three principal colours, red, yellow, and blue. . . ."[21] In 1807 he reaffirmed this hypothesis but eliminated any reference to undulatory theories:

> It is certain that the perfect sensations of yellow and blue are produced, respectively, by mixtures of red and green and of green and violet light, and there is reason to suspect that those sensations are always compounded of the separate sensations combined; at least, this supposition simplifies the theory of colours: it may, therefore, be adopted with advantage, until it is found to be inconsistent with any of the phenomena. . . ."[22]

Part of Young's "reason to suspect" presumably was based on John Dalton's blindness to red. Dalton thought it ". . . probable that [his] vitreous humour is of a deep blue tinge; but this has not been observed by anatomists, and it is much more simple to suppose the absence or paralysis of those fibres of the retina which are calculated to perceive red. . . ."[23] Young published nothing more than these "acute suggestions" on tricolor vision. Maxwell and Helmholtz later modified and extended his speculations into what has come to be called the Young-Helmholtz theory of color sensation.[24]

Young's most sustained interest in natural philosophy was his attempt to gain acceptance for an undulatory theory of light. His failure was partly the result of several hostile reviews of his first papers by Henry Brougham and partly the result of the inherent limitations of his work.[25] Young never worked out a detailed mathematical theory; nor were his suggestions, except possibly for the principle of interference, influential on the man who did, Augustin Fresnel. Young's colleagues, however, quickly acknowledged the principle of interference as a major discovery.

Young's interest in the nature of light probably began with his investigations on the formation of the human voice for his Göttingen dissertation and lecture. During the three years after his return to England from Göttingen he wrote an essay on the human voice. This led him to make theoretical and experimental investigations of vibrating strings, musical pipes, beats, and the motions of fluids.[26] During this work he was "forcibly impressed" with the probability of a very close "analogy" between the vibrations of a series of organ pipes and the colors of thin plates. This analogy was later dismissed by his biographer George Peacock as "fanciful and altogether unfounded," but it seems at least to have impressed Young with the need to reexamine the accepted theory of the nature of light.[27]

For many years before 1800, when Young published his first discussion of the nature of light, most men of science had affirmed that light is particulate. Newton had argued that if light were a vibration in a material medium, it ought to bend around corners; and the vibrations would have to have "sides" to account for polarization. Finally, Newton's arguments that the hypothetical Cartesian interplanetary vortices would cause the planets to spiral into the sun seemed to apply with equal force to an interplanetary ether.[28] In part, Newton was also writing against the opinions of Descartes that light was a "pression" in a fluid and the ideas of Hooke and Huygens that light was a random succession of pulses in a Cartesian plenum. During the middle of the eighteenth century Euler had argued that there was a strong analogy between light and sound, and that light must therefore be a vibratory motion.[29] In 1792 Abraham Bennet suggested to the Royal Society that light must be caused by vibrations in "the universally

diffused caloric or matter of heat or fluid of light."[30] Neither Euler nor Bennet attracted any large following, presumably because the same conclusive objections seemed to apply to their particular hypotheses that had to Descartes's, Hooke's, and Huygens'. In contrast, the emission theory did not seem to be plagued by similar difficulties. In fact, in 1796 and 1797 Brougham had shown how the emission theory could be extended to account for "inflection" and dispersion.[31]

In January 1800, in a paper he submitted to the Royal Society, Young reopened this old debate. He began by stating that ". . . some considerations may be brought forwards, which may tend to diminish the weight of objections to a theory similar to the Huygenian. There are also one or two difficulties in the Newtonian system, which have been little observed."[32] The difficulties were not new: light has a uniform velocity regardless of its origin; light is partially reflected from every refracting surface. In turn, one of the prime "objections" to the vibratory system was that it was founded on the supposed existence of some kind of "luminous ether." Young answered this objection by arguing that ". . . a medium resembling, in many properties, that which has been denominated ether, does really exist, is undeniably proved by the phaenomena of electricity. . . ."[33] Because the existence of the "electric medium" was manifest, Young argued, it was legitimate to assume the existence of an analogous medium for the transmission of light. He then went on to assume that, except for its medium and frequency, the undulations of light are the same as those of sound. Making these assumptions, Young was then able to "solve" the problems of the uniform motion of light that seemed to plague the emission system because ". . . all impressions are known to be transmitted through an elastic fluid with the same velocity."[34]

Earlier in this paper Young had shown that sound waves had very little tendency to diverge. Hence, he argued, ". . . in a medium so highly elastic as the luminous ether must be supposed to be, the tendency [for light] to diverge must be infinitely small, and the grand objection to the system of vibration will be removed."[35] By assuming that "all refracting media" contain the same mechanical ether composed of elastic particles of matter, but with different densities of ether of the same "elasticity," he then gave qualitative explanations of ". . . partial and total reflection, refraction, and inflection [diffraction]."[36] He concluded this discussion by asserting that the "colours of light consist in the different frequencies of vibration of the luminous ether. . . ." He based this statement on his supposed analogy between the sounds of organ pipes and the colors of thin plates.[37] There were no published scientific reactions to this article, perhaps because Young's arguments seemed familiar, speculative, and unsupported by any new experiments.

In May 1801 Young discovered his principle of interference ". . . by reflecting on the beautiful experiments of Newton. . . ."[38] By November he had completed what became his second Bakerian lecture, "On the Theory of Light and Colours," in which he partially announced this principle.[39] His statement, however, was entirely hypothetical and not at all experimental: "When two Undulations, from different Origins, coincide either perfectly or very nearly in Direction, their joint effect is a Combination of the Motions belonging to each."[40] He then went on to report an experiment that exhibited four orders of fringes produced by sunlight reflected from a set of parallel grooves in glass.[41] Using Newton's measurements of the spacing of ring colors and the principle of interference, Young calculated the wavelengths and frequencies of the visible spectrum and gave qualitative explanations of the colors of thin and thick plates, of color or blackness associated with total internal reflection, and of the colors produced by inflection.[42] On the basis of these reasonings he concluded: "Radiant Light consists in Undulations of the luminiferous Ether."[43]

In July 1802 Young made the first full announcement of his principle of interference: ". . . whenever two portions of the same light arrive at the eye by different routes, either exactly or very nearly in the same direction, the light becomes most intense when the difference of the routes is any multiple of a certain length, and least intense in the intermediate state of the interfering portions; and this length is different for light of different colours."[44] He then used the principle to explain the fringes produced by thin fibers and the "colours of mixed plates." In the case of the fibers, Young argued that the fringes were caused by the interference of one portion of light reflected from the fiber with another ". . . bending around its opposite side. . . ."[45] He then calculated the difference in path lengths for the two portions of red light that produced the first fringe. His measurements were crude, and his result was only within 11 percent of what he had expected on the basis of Newton's data.

Nonetheless, Young concluded that ". . . this coincidence, with only an error of one-ninth of so minute a quantity [is] sufficiently perfect to warrant completely the explanation of the phenomenon, and even to render a repetition of the experiment unnecessary. . . ."[46] Young was easily persuaded. He used the same "bending" explanation to account for the halos that can be seen when wool is held to the light and also for ". . . coloured atmospherical halos. . . ."[47] Young's suggestions about fringes appear to have been unknown to Fresnel, who, in 1818 or 1819, was the first to work out a physically and mathematically satisfactory explanation for the fringes that did not depend on the implausible (and nonexistent) reflecting and bending of rays.[48]

In this same paper Young's discussion of the colors of mixed plates is more persuasive than his discussion of fibers. First he showed that the diameter of the colored circles was inversely dependent on the "refractive density" of the interposed liquids. Next he asserted that this and other experiments necessarily implied that if light is an undulation, then its velocity increases as the medium becomes denser. Young then attempted to describe an experiment that would decide between the two theories. Although the results he obtained from this experiment were equivocal, he asserted that they confirmed his prediction.[49]

Young presented his first really convincing evidence that fringes are produced by interference in his third Bakerian lecture, "Experiments and Calculations Relative to Physical Optics" (November 1803). First he exposed a small piece of paper to sunlight diverging from a pinhole. The shadow exhibited not only fringes of color, but ". . . the shadow itself was divided by similar parallel fringes. . . ." Then, by inserting a small screen into either edge of the shadow, he was able to make the fringes disappear, ". . . although the light inflected on the other side was allowed to retain its course. . . . [Hence] these fringes were the joint effects of the portions of light passing on each side of the slip of card, and inflected . . . into the shadow."[50] In the next section of the paper Young compared the different "characteristic lengths" (wavelengths) that were implied by Newton's observations of fringes produced by knife edges and by a hair, and in his own similar experiments with the "analogous interval, deduced from the experiments of Newton on thin plates." These results were within about 13 percent of each other. Young optimistically concluded that "this appears to be a coincidence fully sufficient to authorise us to attribute these two classes of phenomena to the same cause."[51]

Young did not stop after presenting his evidence and conclusions. Rather, he applied his "principle" to the explanation of supernumerary rainbows, to the colors of natural bodies, and to an "Argumentative Inference respecting the Nature of Light."[52] Young's argument was that because the lengths and phenomena in his experiments on interference and in the colors of thin plates described by Newton were similar, they were the result of the same phenomenon: interference. Newton's experiments showed that the denser the medium, the smaller the intervals; but, according to the emission theory, they ought to be larger. Therefore light must move more slowly in the denser medium, which was contrary to the assumption made to explain refraction on the emission theory. Therefore light must be an undulation in the "luminous ether."[53]

Young summarized and completed this phase of work on his undulatory theory by 1807 for the published version of his lectures for the Royal Institution. To the published version he added a description of his two-slit experimental demonstration of interference. He also withdrew his speculation that the colors of halos were produced by interference.[54] At this time Young had convincingly demonstrated the fact of the interference of light, but he had by no means demonstrated that light was the longitudinal undulation of a mechanical, luminiferous ether.

By early 1810 Young had learned of Malus's discovery that, in addition to its being polarized by transmission through Iceland spar, light could be polarized by reflection.[55] This implied that light could acquire ". . . properties independent of its direction . . ., but exclusively relative to the sides of the . . . ray. . . ."[56] Young concluded that "the general tenor of these phenomena is such, as obviously to point to some property resembling polarity, which appears to be much more easily reconcileable with the Newtonian ideas than with those of Huygens."[57] Between 1811 and the early 1820's Arago, Biot, and Brewster had made many additional discoveries indicating that light must have some property very much like "sides" or "poles."[58] In January 1817 Young suggested to Arago that polarization might be accounted for by assuming that it was a minute transverse component added to the longitudinal undulation of the ether that he assumed to be light. "But its inconceivable minuteness suggests a doubt as to the possibility of its producing any sensible effects; in a physical sense it is almost an evanescent quantity, although not in a mathematical one."[59]

By September 1817, when he wrote his article "Chromatics" for the *Supplement* to the *Encyclopaedia Britannica*, Young had worked out a qualitative suggestion of how a small transverse component of vibration might explain the facts of partial reflection. He was not confident that it did, however, nor did he express any idea that the vibrations might be entirely transverse. All that he felt willing to suggest was ". . . a mathematical postulate, in the undulatory theory, without attempting to demonstrate its physical foundation, that a transverse motion might be propagated in a direct line . . . ." Rather than urge that this modification was true, Young was careful to emphasize the minuteness of this transverse component. As far as the discovery of the true theory of light was concerned, he continued to believe at this time that ". . . the general phenomena of polarisation . . . cannot be said to have been explained on any hypothesis respecting the nature of light."[60] Young's theory at this time also did not adequately predict the spacing of the exterior fringes of diffraction or the rectilinear propagation of light. Less than a year later Fresnel had completed a mathematical solution to both problems.

In July 1818 Fresnel reported his solution to the problem of explaining the exterior fringes. In it he demonstrated their production by a combination of the principles of interference and Huygens' principle that a wave front may be considered to consist of an infinite number of point sources of new waves. Fresnel calculated their combined effect by means of the integral calculus; and in passing he also derived a solution to the problem of the rectilinear propagation of light, which had been Newton's chief objection to an undulatory theory. Fresnel also designed and performed interference experiments to test his theory. The difference between the observed and calculated positions of the successive minima were never greater than 0.05 millimeter, or 7.4 percent, and they averaged about 0.006 millimeter, or about 0.9 percent. Probably independently of any knowledge of Young's work or any use of transverse undulations, Fresnel had given a far more persuasive argument than had Young that light was an undulation.[61]

As early as 1816, and before Young made his suggestion, Fresnel seems to have become convinced that polarization might be explained by some kind of transverse undulation.[62] From then until his death in 1827, he applied this assumption successfully to a detailed mathematical analysis of most known optical phenomena: reflection, diffraction, partial reflection, single and double refraction, and polarization. Only in the cases of dispersion, elliptical polarization by reflection from metals, and absorption did he fail to derive explanations and formulas the predictions of which were repeatedly confirmed by experiments. What Young had been unable to do, even conceptually, Fresnel did mathematically and experimentally—and probably with little or no assistance from Young's suggestions. Young claimed the priority of suggestion, and Fresnel agreed; but Fresnel disagreed with Young's contention that he had planted the tree and Fresnel had picked the apples: "I am personally convinced that the apple would have appeared without the tree, for the first explanations which occurred to me of the phenomena of the coloured rings, or of the laws of reflection and refraction, I have drawn from my own resources, without having read either [Young's] work or that of Huygens."[63] Nor was Fresnel plagued by doubt that light was indeed the transverse undulations of an elastic solid ether. In contrast, Young realized that if there were to be transverse undulations, the undulating particles had to have lateral adhesion. But, he concluded in 1823, if they did, ". . . it might be inferred that the luminiferous ether, pervading all space, and penetrating almost all substances is not only highly elastic, but absolutely solid!!!"[64]

Young's hesitation to affirm the existence of transverse undulations, which were now essential for the success of any undulatory theory, depended on his sense of the physical requirements they imposed on the ether. At this time there was no alternative to a mechanical ether. Young then abandoned his work on light and returned to some of his older lines of research at least in part because he had been unable to reduce the theory of light to propositions in mechanics.

In these investigations on light, Young based his hypotheses on physical analogies or comprehensible physical entities such as mechanical ethers and imponderable fluids. If such a hypothesis led to a plausible qualitative or semi-quantitative explanation, he was quick to make rather extravagant claims that his explanations were true. He had mathematical ingenuity; but he had taught himself fluxions, and he lacked skill in the use of differential and integral calculus. His discovery of interference convinced him that light must be at least periodic and probably an undulation; but his conviction that there must be some mechanical entity to undulate brought him to an impasse, for he was convinced that a mechanical luminiferous ether that would support transverse undulations had contradictory physical properties. Ironically, Young's faith in the use of mechanical analogies, which had led him to his discoveries, kept him from accepting their consequences. Perhaps this was because he lacked Fresnel's skill and faith in mathematics. Fresnel either solved or ignored the problems that checkmated Young. His skillful solutions were immensely persuasive to the scientific community that Young never persuaded. Young's work in mechanics had limited influence for some of these same reasons.

Young described many of his mechanical discoveries and "suggestions" in his first book, *A Course of Lectures on Natural Philosophy and the Mechanical Arts*. Its organization is typical of numerous popular "courses," "systems," and "syllabi" that were published frequently in eighteenth-century Britain. In it Young juxtaposed lectures on motion, forces, and "passive strength" with ones on drawing, writing, modeling, and engraving; lectures on hydrostatics, hydraulics, and the friction of fluids with ones on hydraulic and pneumatic machines such as pumps, steam engines, and firearms; and lectures on astronomy, the physics of matter, electricity, and magnetism with ones on the study of meteors, vegetation, and animals.

Unlike those of the typical "course," however, Young's arguments and illustrations were much more complicated and detailed, his prose much less easy to understand, and his scholarship intimidating. Moreover, the size of the work—two thick quarto volumes totaling more than 1,500 closely printed pages—made it a work of reference for a few persons rather than a popular text for many. Indeed, much of the second volume is devoted to a long index and to an annotated bibliography of about twenty thousand references on all the subjects in his lectures, as well as reprints of several of his papers. Anyone who had the patience and time to explore Young's *Course* might have found several "acute suggestions." At this time, however, several relatively new scientific journals had begun to supplant books as the means to announce discoveries that were not presented to the philosophical societies.[65]

In his lecture "On Collision," Young was probably the first person to suggest substituting the term "energy" for "living force" or *vis viva*. His use of the term, however, indicates that he did not generalize this concept. Rather, he used it only twice for what is now known as kinetic energy. As he stated it: "The term energy may be applied, with great propriety, to the product of the mass or weight of a body, into the square of the number expressing its velocity."[66] The word "energy" did not become widely used until after its revival in the early 1850's by Rankine and William Thomson in their writings on the conservation of energy.[67]

Young defined a "modulus of elasticity" in his lecture "Passive Strength and Friction." It is almost impossibly obscure: ". . . we may express the elasticity of any substance by the weight of a certain column of the same substance, which may be denominated the modulus of its elasticity, and of which the weight is such that any addition to it would increase it in the same proportion, as the weight added would shorten, by its pressure, a portion of the substance of equal diameter."[68] In 1867 Thomson and Tait reexpressed this modulus in its present form: the ratio between the stressing force and the resultant strain. They also pointed out that this is the modulus of elasticity of stretch and that there is an additional modulus of rigidity or shear modulus that is not the same as Young's.[69]

In his *Lectures*, Young also began developing his theory of the tides. His first discussion outlined how an analogy to a pendulum might be used to develop such a theory.[70] By 1811 he had completed its mathematical development; and he finally published it, anonymously, in 1813. His analysis used fluxions and was based on another analogy to a pendulum. The vibrating pendulum also had a vibrating suspension point, and it experienced resistance proportional to the first and second powers of the velocity. In this way Young attempted to account for the effects of friction on the times of the tides.[71] In 1824 he published his complete theory in the *Supplement* to the *Encyclopaedia Britannica*.[72] His theory was probably the most complete when it was published, but it was soon superseded by the work of Airy, which was published in 1842.[73] Airy appears not to have read any of Young's writings on the tides.[74]

As a result of his work on the tides and on the Commission on Weights and Measures, Young had a continuing interest in the pendulum. As secretary to the Commission, he wrote its report, which recommended that the standard of length be a "pendulum vibrating seconds of mean solar time in London, on the level of the sea, and in a vacuum."[75] Later he published articles on errors affecting this standard, on measurements of the resistance of the air, and reduction of pendulum lengths to sea level.[76]

After he ended his work on the theory of light, Young returned to his long-standing interest in languages.[77] In 1813 he had started his attempts to decipher the Egyptian hieroglyphics, and by the following year he had translated the "enchorial" or demotic running script of the Rosetta Stone and had concluded that the enchorial was derived from the hieroglyphic. He published very little at this time, and most of what did appear was published anonymously. During 1817 and 1818 Young returned to the subject in preparing his unsigned article "Egypt" for the *Supplement* to the *Britannica*. This article was published in December 1819. His other commitments for the *Britannica*, as well as the demands of his new duties with the Board of Longitude and the *Nautical Almanac*, seem to have prevented Young from doing much more on hieroglyphics than corresponding with other translators. In March 1823 he published, under his own name, a comparison of his and J. F. Champollion's alphabets, intending to assert his own priority. His final work was *Enchorial Egyptian Dictionary*, published in 1830.

Young's need to defend his priority as a translator of hieroglyphics, as well as his limited influence in natural philosophy (quite apart from the technical limitations of his work), were the results of his personality, his methods of communication, and his career. He left his "acute suggestions" for others to develop and complete. He published sporadically; often anonymously; frequently in obscure, unwieldy, or unlikely publications; and almost always using weak analogies, awkward prose, or inadequate mathematics. Young's frequent changes of occupation prevented sustained concentration and favored dilettantism. Late in his life, when he added the demands of two salaried scientific posts to his other activities, his principal avocation had become hieroglyphics. Young was a sporadically brilliant, gentleman natural philosopher who lived to see other men receive the credit and fame for completing what he had begun.

*NOTES*

1. Biographical details of Young's life are drawn from the accounts of François Arago, Hudson Gurney, George Peacock, Thomas Pettigrew, and Alexander Wood. Also see H. S. Rovell, "Thomas Young and Gottingen."
2. J. R. Partington, *History of Chemistry*, III, 728–729.
3. *The Archives of the Royal Institution of Great Britain in Facsimile*, II and III, *passim*. My account of Young's career at the Royal Institution is based on G. N. Cantor, "Thomas Young's Lectures at the Royal Institution." Also see Morris Berman, "The Early Years of the Royal Institution, 1799–1810: A Re-evaluation"; and Henry Bence Jones, *The Royal Institution*, 188–257.

4. William Munk, *The Roll of the Royal College of Physicians of London*, III, 80–88; and *Works of Sir Benjamin Collins Brodie*, I, 90–93.

5. Young's anonymous publications are listed in Hudson Gurney, *Memoir of the Life of Thomas Young*, 51–62. Hill Shine and Helen Shine, in *The Quarterly Review Under Gifford*, list a few other articles that may be by Young, *passim*.

6. *Record of the Royal Society of London* (1897), 208, and Sir Henry Lyons, *The Royal Society 1660–1940*, 220, 223, 227, 243, 245.

7. Gurney, *op. cit.*, 42.

8. G. N. Cantor's articles on Young have been very influential on my thinking, but I alone am responsible for this interpretation of Young's personality.

9. George Peacock, *Life of Thomas Young*, p. 397.

10. Young, "Observations on Vision," *Works*, I, 5.

11. *Ibid.*, 6.

12. Everard Home, "On the Mechanism Employed in Producing Muscular Motion," 1.

13. Young, *Works*, I, 20–21.

14. *Ibid.*, 21–36.

15. *Ibid.*, 37.

16. *Ibid.*, 37–40.

17. *Ibid.*, 41.

18. *Ibid.*, 41–43.

19. *Ibid.*, 46–48.

20. *Ibid.*, 51.

21. "On the Theory of Light and Colours," *ibid.*, 146, 147. "I use the word undulation, in preference to vibration, because vibration is generally understood as implying a motion which is continued alternately backwards and forwards, by a combination of the momentum of the body with an accelerating force, and which is naturally more or less permanent; but an undulation is supposed to consist in a vibratory motion, transmitted successively through different parts of a medium, without any tendency in each particle to continue its motion, except in consequence of the transmission of succeeding undulations, from a distinct vibrating body; as, in the air, the vibrations of a chord produce the undulations constituting sound" [p. 143].

22. *A Course of Lectures on Natural Philosophy and the Mechanical Arts*, I, 439.

23. *Ibid.*, II, 315.

24. Alexander Wood, *Thomas Young, Natural Philosopher 1773–1829*, 113. Also see James P. C. Southall, ed., *Helmholtz's Treatise on Physiological Optics*, II, 143–146.

25. For a discussion of Brougham's reviews, see the traditional accounts by Peacock and Wood in their biographies of Young. Their interpretation has recently been challenged by G. N. Cantor, "Henry Brougham and the Scottish Methodological Tradition"; and Edgar W. Morse, "Natural Philosophy, Hypotheses, and Impiety," ch. 2.

26. Peacock, *op. cit.*, 90–91; Andrew Dalzel, *History of the University of Edinburgh*, I, 144, 161; Young, *Works*, I, 199.

27. Young, *Works*, I, 199, 81, 81n.

28. Isaac Newton, *Opticks*, 362–370 (query 28). Also see A. W. Badcock, "Physical Optics at the Royal Society, 1660–1800." Badcock's article should be compared with the interpretation in Henry Steffens, "The Development of Newtonian Optics in England, 1738–1831." Steffens' thesis is one of the first systematic reinterpretations of the history of eighteenth-century optics. His conclusions are similar to mine.

29. Sir Edmund Whittaker, *A History of the Theories of Aether and Electricity*. I, *The Classical Theories*, 97–98.

30. Quoted in Badcock, *op. cit.*, 102.

31. Henry Brougham, "Experiments and Observations on the Inflection, Reflection, and Colours of Light"; and "Further Experiments and Observations on the Affections and Properties of Light."

32. "Outlines of Experiments and Inquiries Respecting Sound and Light," *Works*, I, 79.

33. *Ibid.*

34. *Ibid.*

35. *Ibid.*, 78–79.

36. *Ibid.*, 80.

37. *Ibid.*, 81.

38. "A Reply to the Animadversions of the Edinburgh Reviewers . . .," in *Works*, I, 202.

39. *Works*, I, 140–169.

40. *Ibid.*, p. 157. Original in italics.

41. *Ibid.*, 159.

42. *Ibid.*, 160–166.

43. *Ibid.*, 166.

44. "An Account of Some Cases of the Production of Colours not Hitherto Described," *ibid.*, 170.

45. *Ibid.*, 171.

46. *Ibid.*, 171–172.

47. *Ibid.*, 172–173. Young later designed an instrument, which he called an eriometer, that used these interference halos as a measure of the average size of the fibers in wool or particles suspended in a fluid. See Young, *Works*, I, 343, 172, 305.

48. Augustin Fresnel, "Mémoire sur la diffraction de la lumière," 282–364. Also see A. Rubinowica, "Thomas Young," which gives a different interpretation of Young's explanation. On the colors of the halos see Carl Boyer, *The Rainbow*, esp. 245–246. These halos are caused by refraction in ice crystals. The smaller halo was first explained by Mariotte in 1679 and the larger by Henry Cavendish in a conversation with Young. See Young, *Course of Lectures*, I, 443–444.

49. Young, *Works*, I, 174–175.

50. *Ibid.*, 180.

51. *Ibid.*, 181–184.

52. Supernumerary rainbows are the result of interference effects; the colors of natural bodies are not. See Boyer, *op. cit.*, *passim*, for a discussion of supernumerary rainbows.

53. Young, *Works*, I, 187–188.

54. Young, *Course of Lectures*, I, 457–471, 443–444.

55. Young, *Works*, I, 247–254.

56. "Popular Statement of the Beautiful Experiments of Malus . . .," 345.

57. Young, *Works*, I, 251.

58. Alexander Wood, *Thomas Young*, 181–183. Also see Morse, *loc cit.*

59. Young, *Works*, I, 383.

60. *Ibid.*, 332–334.

61. Augustin Fresnel, "Mémoire sur la diffraction de la lumière," 262–335.

62. Fresnel, "Mémoire sur l'influence de la polarisation," 394n.

63. Young, *Works*, I, 401–402. Translation in Alexander Wood, *Thomas Young*, 199.

64. Young, *Works*, I, 415.

65. S. Lilley, "'Nicholson's Journal' (1792–1813)." Also see David M. Knight, *Natural Science Books in English 1600–1900*, esp. ch. 11.

66. Young, *Course of Lectures*, I, 78.

67. The term used by Helmholtz and the other "discoverers" of the conservation of energy had been "conservation of force." Young's work seems to have been rooted in the *vis viva* controversies of the eighteenth century. Also see D. S. L. Cardwell, "Early Development of the Concepts of Power, Work, and Energy."

68. Young, *Course of Lectures*, I, 137. Also see Young, *Works*, II, 129.

69. W. Thomson and P. G. Tait, *Natural Philosophy*, secs. 686, 687; W. Thomson, "Elasticity," secs, 41, 42. Also see the discussion by Isaac Todhunter in *History of the Theory of Elasticity*, I, 82–83.

70. Young, *Course of Lectures*, I, 583–588. His principal innovation in the *Lectures* was to devise a map of the times

of simultaneous high water around the British Isles (I, pl. 38, fig. 21). He did not, however, discuss this concept or its potential for generalization. The term "cotidal map" now used was coined in 1833 by Whewell: "Essay Towards . . . a Map of Co-tidal Lines."

71. Young, *Works*, II, 262–290.
72. *Ibid.*, 291–335.
73. "Tides and Waves," in *Encyclopaedia metropolitana* (1842).
74. Young, *Works*, II, 262n.
75. *Supplement* to the *Encyclopaedia Britannica*, VI, 788.
76. Young, *Works*, II, 8–28, 93–98; 99–101; *Quarterly Journal of Science, Literature and the Arts*, **22** (1827), 365–367.
77. Wood, *Thomas Young*, chs. 9, 10. Young, *Works*, III, is devoted almost entirely to his writings on languages. It also includes correspondence related to his controversies about priorities.

## BIBLIOGRAPHY

I. ORIGINAL WORKS. Many of Young's writings are reprinted in *Miscellaneous Works of the Late Thomas Young, M.D., F.R.S., . . .*, George Peacock and John Leitch, eds., 3 vols. (London, 1855). An appendix in Alexander Wood and Frank Oldham, *Thomas Young, Natural Philosopher 1773–1829* (Cambridge, 1954), reproduces the bibliography of his articles that is given in the Royal Society *Catalogue of Scientific Papers*; it is limited, however, to articles published after 1799. An indispensable supplementary bibliography, probably taken from Young's own records, is given in Hudson Gurney, *Memoir of the Life of Thomas Young* (London, 1831). Young's articles for the *Supplement* to the *Encyclopaedia Britannica* are listed in Wood, *Young*, 258. (Wood's discussion implies that Young also wrote the article "Craniology." According to the signature on the article, however, it was written by Peter Mark Roget.) Some of Young's biographical articles are mentioned in Wood and reprinted in Young's *Works*. The full list is in Gurney's biography. The most complete list of Young's anonymous articles in the *Quarterly Review* is in Hill and Helen Shine, *The Quarterly Review Under Gifford. Identification of Contributors 1809–1824* (Chapel Hill, N.C., 1949).

With few exceptions Young's MSS are not in public ownership. Some of his correspondence on hieroglyphics is in the British Museum. A few letters, and his official papers as foreign secretary, are in the library of the Royal Society. Microfilms of the papers of the Board of Longitude (1714–1829) are in the National Maritime Museum, Greenwich.

Young's books include *A Course of Lectures on Natural Philosophy and the Mechanical Arts*, 2 vols. (London, 1807; facs. ed., New York, 1971); and *An Introduction to Medical Literature, Including a System of Practical Nosology* (London, 1813).

Among his articles are "Observations on Vision," in his *Works*, I, 1–11; "Bakerian Lecture on the Mechanism of the Eye," *ibid.*, 12–63; "Outlines of Experiments and Inquiries Respecting Sound and Light," *ibid.*, 64–98; "Bakerian Lecture on the Theory of Light and Colours," *ibid.*, 140–169; "An Account of Some Cases of Colours not Hitherto Described," *ibid.*, 170–178; "Experiments and Calculations Relative to Physical Optics," *ibid.*, 179–191; "A Reply to the Animadversions of the Edinburgh Reviewers," *ibid.*, 192–215; "Review of the Memoirs of Arcueil," *ibid.*, 234–259; "Chromatics," *ibid.*, 279–342; letter from Young to Arago, *ibid.*, 380–384; "Polarisation. Addendum," *ibid.*, 412–417; "Remarks on the Probabilities of Error in Physical Observations, and on the Density of the Earth, Considered With Regard to the Reduction of Experiments on the Pendulum," *ibid.*, II, 8–28; "On the Resistance of the Air. Determined From Captain Kater's Experiments on the Pendulum," *ibid.*, 93–98; "A Theory of Tides, Including the Consideration of Resistance," *ibid.*, 262–290; "Tides," *ibid.*, 291–335; "Weights and Measures," in *Supplement* to the *Encyclopaedia Britannica*, VI (1824), 785–796; and "Note on Professor Svanberg's Reduction of the Length of the Pendulum," in *Quarterly Journal of Science, Literature and the Arts*, **22** (1827), 365–367.

II. SECONDARY LITERATURE. Besides the biographies cited above, see François Arago, "Thomas Young," in *Biographies of Distinguished Scientific Men*, translated by W. H. Smith, Baden Powell, and Robert Grant (London, 1857), 472–518; George Peacock, *Life of Thomas Young, M.D., F.R.S., . . .* (London, 1855); and Thomas Pettigrew, "Thomas Young," in *Medical Portrait Gallery* (London, 1840).

Also see George Biddell Airy, "Tides and Waves," in *Encyclopaedia metropolitana* (1842); *The Works of Sir Benjamin Collins Brodie With an Autobiography*, collected and arranged by Charles Hawkins, 3 vols. (London, 1865); Henry Brougham, "Experiments and Observations on the Inflection, Reflection, and Colours of Light," in *Philosophical Transactions of the Royal Society*, **86** (1796), 227–277; and "Further Experiments and Observations on the Affections and Properties of Light," *ibid.*, **87** (1797), 352–385; Andrew Dalzel, *History of the University of Edinburgh From Its Foundation. With a Memoir of the Author*, 2 vols. (Edinburgh, 1862), I, 68, 118, 120, 137–140, 142–144, 148–150, 159–162, 191–193, 205–208, 212–214, 223–225; Augustin Fresnel, "Mémoire sur la diffraction de la lumière," in *Oeuvres complètes d'Augustin Fresnel*, I (Paris, 1866), 247–382; and "Mémoire sur l'influence de la polarisation dans l'action que les rayons lumineux exercent les uns sur les autres," *ibid.*, 385–409; Everard Home, "The Croonian Lecture. On the Mechanism Employed in Producing Muscular Motion," in *Philosophical Transactions of the Royal Society*, **85** (1795), 1; Sir Isaac Newton, *Opticks* (New York, 1952); "Popular Statement of the Beautiful Experiments of Malus, in Which He Has Developed a New Property of Light," in *Nicholson's Journal of Natural Philosophy*, **33** (1812), 344–348; *The Archives of the Royal Institution of Great Britain in Facsimile. Minutes of Managers' Meetings, 1799–1900*, 4 vols. in 3 (Menton, England, 1971–1973), II, 203, 205; III, 129, 148, 154; and William Whewell, "Essay Towards a First Approximation to a Map of Co-tidal Lines," in *Philosophical Transactions of the Royal Society*, **123** (1833), 147–236.

The standard histories of optics are Ernst Mach, *The Principles of Optics, an Historical and Philosophical Treatment* (New York, 1953); Vasco Ronchi, *Histoire de la lumière*, translated by Juliette Taton (Paris, 1956); and Sir Edmund Whittaker, *A History of the Theories of Aether and Electricity*, I, *The Classical Theories* (New York, 1960).

Other works that deal with aspects of Young's career include A. W. Badcock, "Physical Optics at the Royal Society, 1600–1800," in *British Journal for the History of Science*, **1** (1962), 99–116; Morris Berman, "The Early Years of the the Royal Institution, 1799–1810; A Re-evaluation," in *Science Studies*, **2** (1972), 205–240; Carl Boyer, *The Rainbow From Myth to Mathematics* (New York, 1959); Geoffrey N. Cantor, "The Changing Role of Young's Ether," in *British Journal for the History of Science*, **5** (1970), 44–62; "Thomas Young's Lectures at the Royal Institution," in *Notes and Records. Royal Society of London*, **25** (1970), 87–112; and "Henry Brougham and the Scottish Methodological Tradition," in *Studies in History and Philosophy of Science*, **2** (1971), 69–89; D. S. L. Cardwell, "Early Development of the Concepts of Power, Work, and Energy," in *British Journal for the History of Science*, **3** (1967), 209–224; *Helmholtz's Treatise on Physiological Optics*, James P. C. Southall, ed., 3 vols. in 2 (New York, 1962); Henry Bence Jones, *The Royal Institution: Its Founder and Its First Professors* (London, 1871), 188–257; David M. Knight, *Natural Science Books in English 1600–1900* (London, 1972); S. Lilley, " 'Nicholson's Journal' (1787–1813)," in *Annals of Science*, **6** (1948), 78–101; and Sir Henry Lyons, *The Royal Society 1660–1940; a History of Its Administration Under Its Charters* (New York, 1968), 220, 243.

Also see Edgar W. Morse, "Natural Philosophy, Hypotheses, and Impiety: Sir David Brewster Confronts the Undulatory Theory of Light" (Ph. D. diss., Univ. of California, Berkeley, 1972); William Munk, *Roll of the Royal College of Physicians of London*, III (London, 1878), 80–88; James R. Partington, *A History of Chemistry*, III (London, 1962), 728–729; *Record of the Royal Society of London* (London, 1897), 208, 251, 369; H. S. Rovell, "Thomas Young and Gottingen," in *Nature*, **88** (1912), 516; A. Rubinowica, "Thomas Young and the Theory of Diffraction," *ibid.*, **180** (1958), 160–162; Henry Steffens, "The Development of Newtonian Optics in England, 1738–1831" (M. A. thesis, Cornell Univ., 1965); Sir William Thomson, "Elasticity," in *Encyclopaedia Britannica*, 9th ed.; Sir William Thomson and Peter Guthrie Tait, *Treatise on Natural Philosophy* (Oxford, 1867); and Isaac Todhunter, *A History of the Theory of Elasticity and of the Strength of Materials From Galilei to the Present Time*, 2 vols. (Cambridge, 1886–1893), I, 82–83.

EDGAR W. MORSE

**YOUNG, WILLIAM HENRY** (*b*. London, England, 20 October 1863; *d*. Lausanne, Switzerland, 7 July 1942), *mathematics*.

Young was the eldest son of Henry Young and Hephzibah Jeal. The Young family had been bankers in the City for some generations. Young went to the City of London School, of which the headmaster, Edwin A. Abbott, author of the mathematical fantasy *Flatland*, recognized his flair for mathematics. Young entered Peterhouse, Cambridge, in 1881. In the mathematical tripos of 1884 he was expected to be senior wrangler but was placed fourth. In later years he related that he refused to restrict his interests (intellectual and athletic) to the intensive training in mathematics necessary for the highest place in the order of merit. The first books he borrowed from the College library were the works of Molière. Instead of writing a mathematical essay for a Smith's prize, he competed for and won a prize in theology. He was of Baptist stock and, at Cambridge, was baptized into the Church of England.

Young was a fellow of Peterhouse from 1886 to 1892, but he held no official position in the college or the university. It is surprising that between the ages of twenty-five and thirty-five he did not turn to research, but deliberately set himself to earn a large income and accumulate savings by private teaching of undergraduates from early morning until late at night.

In 1896 Young married Grace Emily, daughter of Henry W. Chisholm. She had taken the mathematical tripos and was ranked equal to a wrangler; as Grace Chisholm Young, she became a mathematician of international reputation. At the end of their first year together, she said, " . . . he proposed, and I eagerly agreed, to throw up lucre, go abroad, and devote ourselves to research." They lived mainly in Göttingen until 1908 and then in Switzerland, first in Geneva and later in Lausanne.

In striking contrast with most mathematicians, Young did hardly any research until he was over thirty-five, but between 1900 and 1924 he wrote more than two hundred papers. At the turn of the century, the theory of real functions was subject to artificial and unaesthetic restrictions. For instance, the standard process (Riemann's) of reconstructing an integral from its derivative required the continuity of the derivative. In the late 1890's the Paris school, led by Baire and Borel, laid the foundations of an essentially more powerful theory, based on the concept of the measure of a set of points. Lebesgue's famous thesis, "Intégrale, longueur, aire," appeared in 1902. Young, working independently, arrived at a definition of integration, different in form from, but essentially equivalent to, Lebesgue's. He was anticipated by about two years, and it must have been a heavy blow to one who had become conscious of his power to make fundamental discoveries; but he bore the disappointment magnanimously, and himself called the integral that of Lebesgue. Many aspects of the later development are Young's own, notably his method of monotone sequences as used in the Stieltjes integral.

Young showed supreme power in two other fields of analysis. The first is the theory of Fourier series. In 1912 he established the connection between the sum of the $q$th powers of the Fourier constants of a function $f$ and the integral of $f^p$, where $p$ and $q$ are conjugate indices and $q$ is an even integer. The completion for unrestricted $q$ was achieved after eleven years by Hausdorff. Young proved many other theorems, some of striking simplicity and beauty, about Fourier series and more general orthogonal series. The second field — in which lay what was probably Young's most far-reaching work — was the basic differential calculus of functions of more than one variable. The best tribute to it is that, since 1910, every author of an advanced calculus textbook has adopted Young's approach.

Every word and every movement of Young gave evidence of restless vitality. His appearance was striking; after his marriage he grew a beard — red in contrast with his dark hair — and wore it very long in later years. Of his three sons and three daughters, Professor Laurence Chisholm Young and Dr. Rosalind Cecily Tanner continued their parents' work in pure mathematics. The eldest son was killed flying in France in 1917.

Young held part-time chairs at Calcutta (1913–1916) and Liverpool (1913–1919), and he was professor at Aberystwyth from 1919 to 1923. More than once electors to a chair passed him over in favor of men less powerful as mathematicians but less exacting as colleagues. He was an honorary doctor of the universities of Calcutta, Geneva, and Strasbourg; and his honors included the Sylvester Medal of the Royal Society (1928). He was president of the International Union of Mathematicians in 1929–1936.

When France fell in 1940 he was at Lausanne, cut off from his family, and he had to remain there, unhappy and restive, for the last two years of his life.

## BIBLIOGRAPHY

I. ORIGINAL WORKS. Young wrote more than 200 papers; for a list of the most important of them see the obituary notices below. His books are *The First Book of Geometry* (London, 1905), written with Grace Chisholm Young, an excellent and original book doubtless composed for the education of their children; *The Theory of Sets of Points* (Cambridge, 1906), written with Grace Chisholm Young; and *The Fundamental Theorems of the Differential Calculus* (Cambridge, 1910).

II. SECONDARY LITERATURE. See *Obituary Notices of Fellows of the Royal Society of London*, **3** (1943), 307–323, with portrait; *Journal of the London Mathematical Society*, **17** (1942), 218–237; and *Dictionary of National Biography, 1941–1950* (1959), 984–985.

J. C. BURKILL

**YULE, GEORGE UDNY** (*b*. Morham, near Haddington, Scotland, 18 February 1871; *d*. Cambridge, England, 26 June 1951), *statistics*.

Yule was the son of Sir George Udny Yule and his wife, Henrietta Peach. Sir George was an administrator in the Indian Civil Service and a member of an old Scottish farming family with a history of some government, military, and literary distinction. In 1875 Sir George moved his family to London; and Yule was sent first to a day school there, and then to a preparatory school near Rugby. He was subsequently educated at Winchester College and University College, London, where, between 1887 and 1890, he read civil engineering but did not take a degree, there being none in the subject at the time. After two years' training in a small engineering works, however, Yule decided against engineering as a career and spent a year under Heinrich Hertz at Bonn, investigating the passage of electric waves through dielectrics. This was the subject of his first published paper.

Yule returned to London in 1893, at the invitation of Karl Pearson, to become demonstrator (lecturer) at University College. In 1896 he was promoted to assistant professor of applied mathematics. Three years later he married May Winifred Cummings, but the marriage was annulled in 1912. One consequence of his marriage was that Yule felt obliged to earn a higher salary, and he accepted a dreary administrative post at the City and Guilds of London Institute. Between 1902 and 1909 he held concurrently a lectureship in statistics at University College, delivering evening lectures that were the basis of his first book, *An Introduction to the Theory of Statistics* (1911). This was for long the only comprehensive textbook on the subject (the fourteenth edition, revised by M. G. Kendall, appeared in 1958). The *Introduction*, and his reputation as a lecturer, led to his being offered the newly created lectureship in statistics at Cambridge in 1912.

Yule soon had a range of practical statistical experience. He was statistician to the School of Agriculture at Cambridge while he was university lecturer; and during World War I he was statistician first to the director of army contracts, and later to the Ministry of Food. In 1922 Yule became a fellow of both St. John's College, Cambridge, and the Royal Society. He resigned his university position in 1931. The following year he obtained a pilot's license; but a serious heart ailment obliged him to spend most of his retirement in a quieter pursuit, a study of the statistical aspects of literary style.

Yule's principal achievements in statistical theory concern regression and correlation, association, time series, Mendelian inheritance, and epidemiology. His early memoirs on correlation (1897, 1907) and association (1900) have proved to be fundamental. In the first of these he introduced the concept of partial ("net") correlation, and in 1907 he demonstrated that the sampling distributions for partial correlation coefficients are of the same form as those for total correlation coefficients. In the paper of 1900, Yule presented the coefficient of association for the measurement of the degree of association in $2 \times 2$ contingency tables. His introduction of this coefficient led to a long controversy with his former mentor and friend Karl Pearson, who joined forces with David Heron in a protest that M. G. Kendall said was "remarkable for having missed the point over more pages (173) than perhaps any other memoir in statistical history" (*The Advanced Theory of Statistics*, I [1943], 322).

From 1912 Yule and Major M. Greenwood laid the foundations of the theory of accident distributions. In 1921 he wrote on time correlation and began work leading to a well-known paper on sunspots (1927) that marked the beginning of the modern theory of oscillatory time series.

Yule introduced many new ideas into statistical theory and corrected many errors, especially in biometrics. He made important studies of the mathematics of biological evolution and of the statistics of agricultural field trials. He was perhaps the first to consider (1902) whether the observed correlations between parents and offspring could be accounted for by multifactorial Mendelian inheritance, a problem taken up later by R. A. Fisher.

## BIBLIOGRAPHY

Yule wrote two books: *An Introduction to the Theory of Statistics* (London, 1911) and *The Statistical Study of Literary Vocabulary* (Cambridge, 1944). A bibliography of 71 scientific papers, plus 12 on other subjects, is in the notice by F. Yates, in *Obituary Notices of Fellows of the Royal Society of London*, **8** (1952), 309–323, with portrait.

J. D. NORTH

**IBN YŪNUS, ABUᵓL-ḤASAN ᶜALĪ IBN ᶜABD AL-RAḤMĀN IBN AḤMAD IBN YŪNUS AL-ṢADAFĪ** (*d.* Fusṭāṭ, Egypt, 1009), *astronomy, mathematics.*

Ibn Yūnus was one of the greatest astronomers of medieval Islam. He came from a respected family, his great-grandfather Yūnus having been a companion of the famous legal scholar al-Shāfiᶜī and his father, ᶜAbd al-Raḥmān, being a distinguished historian and scholar of *ḥadīth* (the sayings of Muḥammad). Besides being famous as an astronomer and astrologer, Ibn Yūnus was widely acclaimed as a poet, and some of his poems have been preserved. Unfortunately nothing of consequence is known about his early life or education.

We know that as a young man Ibn Yūnus witnessed the Fatimid conquest of Egypt and the foundation of Cairo in 969. In the period from 977 to 996, which corresponds roughly to the reign of Caliph al-ᶜAzīz, he made astronomical observations that were renewed by order of Caliph al-Ḥakim, who succeeded al-ᶜAzīz in 996 at the age of eleven and was much interested in astrology. Ibn Yūnus' recorded observations continued until 1003.

Ibn Yūnus' major work was *al-Zīj al-Ḥākimī al-kabīr*, *zīj* meaning an astronomical handbook with tables. It is a particularly fine representative of a class of astronomical handbooks, numbering perhaps 200, compiled in medieval Islam. The *Zīj* of Ibn Yūnus was dedicated to Caliph al-Ḥakim and was aptly named *al-kabīr* ("large"). The text of the first forty-four of the eighty-one chapters of the original work is twice the length of the text of the *Zīj* by al-Battānī and contains more than twice as many tables as the earlier work. The only extant chapters of the *Ḥakimī zīj* are in two unpublished manuscripts at Leiden and Oxford, comprising about three hundred folios. A manuscript in Paris contains an anonymous abridgment of part of the *Zīj* and is a source for some additional chapters up to chapter 57, and chapters 77–81.

The importance of Ibn Yūnus was realized in the West when the Leiden manuscript was first seriously studied. In 1804, Armand-Pierre Caussin de Perceval published the text of Ibn Yūnus' observational reports with a French translation. He also included the introduction to the *Zīj*, which contains the titles of the eighty-one chapters. J.-J. Sédillot's translation (now lost) of the Leiden and Paris manuscripts was summarized by Delambre in 1819. The German scholar Carl Schoy published several articles containing translations and analyses of individual chapters of the *Zīj* relating to spherical astronomy and sundial theory.

The *Ḥākimī zīj* deals with the standard topics of Islamic astronomy but is distinguished from all other extant *zījes* by beginning with a list of observations made by Ibn Yūnus and of observations made by some of his predecessors, quoted from their works. Despite the critical attitude of Ibn Yūnus toward these earlier scholars and his careful recording of their observations and some of his own, he completely neglects to describe the observations that he used in establishing his own planetary parameters—nor does he indicate whether he used any instruments for these observations. Indeed, the *Ḥākimī zīj* is a poor source of information about the instruments used by Ibn Yūnus. In his account of measurements of the latitude of Fusṭāṭ and of the obliquity of the ecliptic from solar meridian altitudes at the solstices, Ibn Yūnus states that he used an instrument provided by Caliph al-ʿAzīz and Caliph al-Ḥākim. Although he describes it only by mentioning that the divisions for each minute of arc were clearly visible on its scale, the instrument was probably a large meridian ring. His only other references to instruments used for simple observations are to an astrolabe and a gnomon.

In view of the paucity of this information, it is remarkable that the statement that Ibn Yūnus worked in a "well-equipped observatory" is often found in popular accounts of Islamic astronomy. A. Sayili, *The Observatory in Islam*, has shown how this notion gained acceptance in Western literature.

There are two sources, however, that might cast a little more light on the situation if their reliability could be established. First, the historian Ibn Ḥammād (*fl. ca.* 1200) mentions a copper instrument, resembling an astrolabe three cubits in diameter, that a contemporary of his had seen and associated with the Ḥākimī observations. Likewise the Yemenite Sultan al-Ashraf (*fl. ca.* 1290), who was an astronomer, records that al-Ḥākim had an armillary sphere consisting of nine rings, each of which weighed 2,000 pounds and was large enough

for a man to ride through on horseback. The possibility that this large instrument was that known to have been constructed in Cairo about 1125—over a century after the death of Ibn Yūnus—cannot yet be discounted.

There is evidence that al-Ḥākim had a house on the Muqaṭṭam hills overlooking Cairo, which may have contained astronomical instruments: Ibn Yūnus is known to have visited this house on one occasion to make observations of Venus. Nevertheless, al-Ḥākim's unsuccessful attempt to build an observatory in Cairo took place after Ibn Yūnus' death; and the only locations mentioned by Ibn Yūnus in his own accounts of his observations are the Mosque of Ibn Naṣr al-Maghribī at al-Qarāfa, and the house of his great-grandfather Yūnus, in nearby Fusṭāṭ. A note written in the fifteenth century on the title folio of the Leiden manuscript of the *Ḥākimī zīj* states that Ibn Yūnus' observations were made in the area of Birkat al-Ḥabash in Fusṭāṭ.

Ibn Yūnus explains in the introduction to his *Zīj* that the work is intended to replace the *Mumtaḥan zīj* of Yaḥyā ibn Abī Manṣūr, prepared for the Abbasid Caliph al-Maʾmūn in Baghdad almost 200 years earlier. Ibn Yūnus reports the observations of some astronomers before his own time, in which what was observed was at variance with what was calculated with the tables of the *Mumtaḥan zīj*. When reporting his own observations, Ibn Yūnus often compares what he observed with what he had computed with the *Mumtaḥan* tables.

From the introduction and chapters 4, 5, and 6 of the *Ḥākimī zīj*, which contain the observation accounts, it is clear that Ibn Yūnus was familiar with the *zījes* of Ḥabash al-Ḥāsib, al-Battānī, and al-Nayrīzī, as well as the *Mumtaḥan zīj*. The observations made by Ḥabash that Ibn Yūnus quotes are not in the two extant versions of Ḥabash's *Zīj*. Ibn Yūnus also records observations made by al-Māhānī, whose works are not extant. He lists the planetary parameters of the *Mumtaḥan zīj*, and this has enabled the positive identification of at least the planetary tables in the only extant manuscript of this early work, which contains considerable spurious material. Ibn Yūnus also quotes observations made by the Banū Amājūr family in Baghdad; their five *zījes* are not extant. Other works quoted by Ibn Yūnus, although not necessarily directly, are the *zījes* of al-Nihāwandī, Ibn al-Adamī, the Banū Mūsā, Abū Maʿshar, Ibn al-Aʿlam, al-Ṣūfī, and Muḥammad al-Samarqandī; none of these works is extant, and Ibn Yūnus' references provide valuable information about them.

The observations described by Ibn Yūnus are of conjunctions of planets with each other and with Regulus, solar and lunar eclipses, and equinoxes; he also records measurements of the obliquity of the ecliptic (chapter 11) and of the maximum lunar latitude (chapter 38). All of these accounts are notable for their lack of information on observational procedures. The following passage is a translation of one of Ibn Yūnus' accounts of a planetary conjunction that he had observed:

A conjunction of Venus and Mercury in Gemini, observed in the western sky: The two planets were in conjunction after sunset on the night whose morning was Monday, the thirteenth day of Jumādā II 390 Hegira era. The time was approximately eight equinoctial hours after midday on Sunday, which was the fifth day of Khardādh, 369 Yazdigird era. Mercury was north of Venus and their latitude difference was a third of a degree. According to the *Mumtaḥan Zīj* their longitude difference was four and a half degrees [A. P. Caussin de Perceval, "Le livre de la grande table Hakémite," in *Notices et extraits des manuscrits de la Bibliothèque nationale*, 7 (1804), p. 217].

The Sunday mentioned was 19 May 1000, and computation with modern tables confirms that there was a conjunction in longitude that evening and that Mercury was indeed one-third degree north of Venus. About forty such planetary conjunctions observed by Ibn Yūnus are described in the *Zīj*.

The following passage is a translation of Ibn Yūnus' account of the lunar eclipse that occurred on 22 April 981 (Oppolzer no. 3379):

This lunar eclipse was in the month of Shawwāl, 370 Hegira era, on the night whose morning was Friday, the third day of Urdibihisht, 350 Yazdigird era. We gathered to observe this eclipse at al-Qarāfa, in the Mosque of Ibn Naṣr al-Maghribī. We perceived first contact when the altitude of the moon was approximately 21°. About a quarter of the lunar diameter was eclipsed, and reemergence occurred about a quarter of an hour before sunrise [A. P. Caussin de Perceval, p. 187].

Some of the thirty eclipses reported by Ibn Yūnus were used by Simon Newcomb in his determination of the secular acceleration of the moon. More recently, other observations recorded in the *Ḥakimī zīj* have been used by R. Newton.

The first chapter of the *Zīj* is the longest of the extant chapters and deals with the Muslim, Coptic, Syrian, and Persian calendars. There are detailed instructions for converting a date in one calendar

to any of the other calendars, and extensive tables for that purpose. There are also tables for determining the dates of Lent and Easter in both the Syrian and the Coptic calendars. Such tables are found in several Islamic *zījes*.

Chapters 7 and 9, on planetary longitudes, contain instructions for determining true longitudes from the tables of mean motion and equations. No theory is described, but the theory underlying the instructions and tables is entirely Ptolemaic. The mean motions differ from those used by Ibn Yūnus' predecessors, and his values for the sun and moon were deemed sufficiently reliable by al-Ṭūsī to be used in the *Īlkhānī zīj* 250 years later. Ibn Yūnus' planetary tables are computed for both the Muslim and Persian calendars, and define the mean positions of the sun, moon, and planets, as well as the astrologically significant "comet" *al-kayd*, for over 2,700 Muslim and 1,800 Persian years from the respective epochs 622 and 632.

For the year 1003, Ibn Yūnus gives the solar apogee as Gemini 26;10° and the maximum solar equation as 2;0,30°, corresponding to a double eccentricity of 2;6,10° (where the solar deferent radius is 60). No solar observations made by Ibn Yūnus are recorded in the *Zīj*. He changes the values of the lunar epicyclic radius and the eccentricity from Ptolemy's 5;15° and 10;19°, also used in the *Mumtaḥan zīj*, to 5;1,14° and 11;7°, respectively (the latter is not used consistently), again without explanation. His planetary equation tables are identical with those of Ptolemy's *Handy Tables* and the *Mumtaḥan zīj* for Saturn, Jupiter, and Mars. For Venus, Ibn Yūnus assumes an eccentricity exactly half that of the sun and uses an epicyclic radius of 43;42 rather than Ptolemy's 43;10. For Mercury he adopts a maximum equation of 4;2°, an Indian parameter previously used in the *Zīj* of al-Khwārizmī, rather than Ptolemy's 3;2°. Ibn Yūnus' tables of equations for the moon, Venus, and Mercury contain the same inconsistencies as al-Battānī's tables for Venus, in that some of the columns are not adjusted for the new parameters; this is a fairly common feature in Islamic *zījes*. There is evidence that Ibn Yūnus was not altogether satisfied with his determination of the planetary apogees: the *Ḥakimī zīj* contains three different sets of values (chapters 6, 8, and 9).

In his discussion of solar and lunar distances (chapters 55, 56), Ibn Yūnus assumes a maximum solar parallax of 0;1,57°, instead of Ptolemy's value of 0;2,51°. Chapters 59–75, on parallax and eclipse theory and the associated tables, are not in the known manuscripts; and their recovery in other sources would be extremely valuable for the study of Islamic astronomy.

In chapter 38, on lunar and planetary latitudes, Ibn Yūnus states that he found the maximum lunar latitude to be 5;3°. Although he says that he measured it many times and repeatedly found this value, he does not say how the measurements were made. He did not pursue the suggestion of the Banū Amājūr that he quotes: that the maximum lunar latitude was not constant. His planetary latitude tables are derived from those in the *Almagest*, except in the case of Venus, for which he used values originally taken from the *Handy Tables*.

Ibn Yūnus measured the position of Regulus as Leo 15;55° in 1003. His value for the motion of the fixed stars is 1° in 70 1/4 Persian years (of 365 days) and apparently was computed by using his own observation of Regulus and that made by Hipparchus; it is the most accurate of all known Islamic values. He had information at his disposal from which he might have deduced that the motion of the planetary apogees was different from the motion of the fixed stars, but he chose to conclude that the apogees moved at the same rate as the stars (chapter 8).

The trigonometric functions used by Ibn Yūnus are functions of arcs rather than angles, and are computed for radius 60, as was standard in Islamic works. Chapter 10 of the *Zīj* contains a table of sines for each 0;10° of arc, computed to four significant sexagesimal digits. The values are seldom in error by more than ±2 in the fourth digit. Ibn Yūnus determined the sine of 1° to be 1;2,49,43,28 (to base 60), using a method equivalent to interpolating linearly between the values of $\sin x/x$ for $x = 15/16°$ and $9/8°$. He then improved this value by a rather dubious technique to obtain 1;2,49,43,4. The accurate value to this degree of precision is 1;2,49,43,11. Ibn Yūnus' younger contemporary al-Bīrūnī was able to calculate the chord of a unit circle subtended by an angle of 1° correctly to five significant sexagesimal digits. Although in chapter 11 of the *Zīj* Ibn Yūnus tabulates the cotangent function to three sexagesimal digits for each ten minutes of arc, he does not take full advantage of it. Many of the methods he suggests throughout the *Zīj* require divisions of sines by cosines; and he uses the cotangent function, which he calls the shadow, only when the argument is an altitude arc.

In spherical astronomy (chapters 12–54) Ibn Yūnus reached a very high level of sophistication. Although none of his formulas is explained, it seems probable that most of them were derived by means of orthogonal projections and analemma constructions, rather than by the application of the rules of spherical trigonometry that were being developed by Muslim scholars in Iraq and Persia. Altogether, there are several hundred formulas outlined in the *Zīj*, many of which are trivially equivalent. These are stated in words and without recourse to any symbols. For each method outlined, Ibn Yūnus generally gives at least one numerical example. The problems of spherical astronomy discussed in the *Ḥākimī zīj* are more varied than those in most major Islamic *zījes*, and the following examples are intended to illustrate the scope of the treatment.

Ibn Yūnus describes several methods for computing right and oblique ascensions (chapters 13, 14). He also computes both, the latter for each degree of the ecliptic and for each degree of terrestrial latitude from 1° to 48° (beyond which limit, according to Manṣūr ibn 'Irāq, "there is no one who studies this sort of thing or even thinks about it"). Ibn Yūnus discusses in great detail the determination of time and solar azimuth from solar altitude, and it will be clear from the tables mentioned below that he devoted much effort to these problems. Certain functions that he discusses in the text are also tabulated, such as the solar altitude in the prime vertical and the rising amplitude of the sun (that is, the distance of the rising sun from the east point). The problem of finding solar altitude from solar azimuth (chapter 24) is not so simple as the inverse problem; but Ibn Yūnus solves it in several ways, including the use of an algebraic method. He also tabulates the solar altitude for certain azimuths, such as that of the *qibla*, the direction of Mecca (chapter 28), and ten different azimuths (chapter 24), to be used for finding the meridian. Several geometric solutions to the problem of determining the *qibla*, a favorite of the Islamic astronomers, are also outlined. One of Ibn Yūnus' solutions is equivalent to successive applications of the cosine rule and sine rule for spherical triangles, but is derived by a projection method that was also used by the contemporary Egyptian scholar Ibn al-Haytham.

Particularly elegant solutions are presented for finding the meridian from three solar observations on the same day (chapter 23) and for finding the time between two solar observations on the same day (chapter 33). The latter problem is solved by a direct application of the cosine rule for plane triangles, the earliest attested use of this rule. Ibn Yūnus transforms ecliptic to equatorial coordinates (chapter 39) by a method equivalent to the cosine rule for spherical triangles but probably derived by means of an analemma construction. His sundial theory (chapters 26, 27, 35) is also of considerable sophistication. It deals with horizontal and vertical sundials, the latter oriented in the meridian, the prime vertical, or a general direction inclined to both. He proves geometrically that for a horizontal sundial the gnomon shadow measures the altitude of the upper rim of the solar disk, and stresses the precautions to be taken when setting the gnomon on a marble slab to ensure that it is aligned correctly.

The chapters of the *Zīj* dealing with astrological calculations (77–81), although partially extant in the anonymous abridgment of the work, have never been studied. Ibn Yūnus was famous as an astrologer and, according to his biographers, devoted much time to making astrological predictions. His *Kitāb bulūgh al-umniyya* ("On the Attainment of Desire") consists of twelve chapters devoted to the significance of the heliacal risings of Sirius when the moon is in any of the twelve zodiacal signs, and to predictions based on the day of the week on which the first day of the Coptic year falls.

In chapter 10 of the *Ḥakimī zīj* Ibn Yūnus states that he had prepared a shorter version of his major work; this, unfortunately, is no longer extant. There are, however, numerous later *zījes* compiled in Egypt, Persia, and Yemen that are extant and contain material ultimately due to Ibn Yūnus. For example, the thirteenth-century Egyptian *Muṣṭalaḥ zīj*, as well the *Īlkhānī zīj* of al-Ṭūsī and the *Zīj* of Muḥyi'l-Dīn al-Maghribī, both compiled at the observatory in Maragha, Persia, in the thirteenth century, relied on the *Ḥakimī zīj*. Likewise, the *Mukhtār zīj* by the thirteenth-century Yemenite astronomer Abu'l-'Uqūl is based mainly on a *zīj* by Ibn Yūnus other than the *Ḥakimī*; and an anonymous fourteenth-century Yemenite *zīj* is adapted from the *Ḥakimī zīj*.

There are other sets of tables preserved in the manuscript sources and attributed to Ibn Yūnus that are distinct from those in the *Ḥakimī zīj* but based on them. First, Ibn Yūnus appears to be the author of tables of the sine and tangent functions for each minute of arc, as well as tables of solar declination for each minute of solar longitude. These sine tables display values of the sine function to five sexagesimal digits, which is roughly equivalent to nine decimal digits. The values are often in error in the fourth sexagesimal digit, however, so that it was a premature undertaking. Indeed, over four centuries passed before the compilation of the trigonometric tables in the *Zīj* of Ulugh

Beg in Samarkand, in which values are also given to five sexagesimal digits for each minute of arc— but are generally correct. Second, it appears that Ibn Yūnus was the author of an extensive set of tables, called *al-Ta'dīl al-muḥkam*, that display the equations of the sun and moon; the latter are of particular interest. They are based on those in the *Ḥakimī zīj* but are arranged so as to facilitate computation of the lunar position: the equation is tabulated as a function of the double elongation and mean anomaly, both of which can be taken from the mean motion tables; thus there is no need to find the true anomaly. The table, which accurately defines the Ptolemaic lunar equation for Ibn Yūnus' parameters, contains over 34,000 entries.

Ibn Yūnus' second major work was part of the corpus of spherical astronomical tables for timekeeping used in Cairo until the nineteenth century. It is difficult to ascertain precisely how many tables in this corpus, which later became known as the *Kitāb ghayat al-intifa'* ("Very Useful Tables"), were actually computed by Ibn Yūnus. Some appear to have been compiled by the late thirteenth-century astronomer al-Maqsī. The corpus exists in numerous manuscript sources, each containing different arrangements of the tables or only selected sets of tables; and in its entirety the corpus consists of about 200 pages of tables, most of which contain 180 entries. The tables are generally rather accurately computed and are all based on Ibn Yūnus' values of 30;0° for the latitude of Cairo and 23;35° for the obliquity of the ecliptic.

The main tables in the corpus display the time since sunrise, the time remaining to midday, and the solar azimuth as functions of the solar altitude and solar longitude. Entries are tabulated for each degree of solar altitude and longitude, and each of the three sets contains over ten thousand entries. The remaining tables in the corpus are of spherical astronomical functions, some of which relate to the determination of the five daily prayers of Islam.

The times of Muslim prayer are defined with reference to the apparent daily motion of the sun across the sky and vary throughout the year. The prayers must be performed within certain intervals of time, which are variously defined. The following general definitions underlie the tables in the corpus. The day is considered to begin at sunset, and the evening prayer is performed between sunset and nightfall. The permitted interval for the night prayer begins at nightfall. The interval for the morning prayer begins at daybreak and the prayer must be completed by sunrise. The period for the noon prayer begins when the sun is on the meridian, and that for the afternoon prayer begins when the shadow of any object is equal to its midday shadow plus the length of the object.

Examples of functions relating to the prayer times, which are tabulated in the corpus for each degree of solar longitude, include the following:

1. The length of morning and evening twilights, defining the permitted times for the morning and evening prayers, based on the assumption that twilight appears or disappears when the sun reaches a particular angle of depression below the horizon. (The angles suggested by Ibn Yūnus in the Ḥākimī zīj are 18° for both phenomena, but in a later work he suggests 20° and 16° for morning and evening, respectively. The main twilight tables in the corpus are based on 19° and 17°.)

2. The time from nightfall to daybreak, defining the permitted interval for the night prayer.

3. The time from sunrise to midday.

4. The time from midday to the beginning of the time for the afternoon prayer, defining the interval for the noon prayer; and the time from the beginning of the afternoon prayer to sunset, defining the interval for the afternoon prayer.

5. Corrections to the semidiurnal arc for the effect of refraction at the horizon, apparently based on the assumption that the true horizon is about 2/3° below the visible horizon. (These corrections, which are specifically attributed to Ibn Yūnus, represent the earliest attested quantitative estimate of the effect of refraction on horizon phenomena.)

6. The solar altitude in the azimuth of Mecca, and the time when the sun has this azimuth. (Such tables were used to establish the direction of prayer and the orientation of miḥrābs in mosques.)

Virtually all later Egyptian prayer tables until the nineteenth century were based on those in this main corpus. In certain cases the original tables were well-disguised, the entries being written out in words for each day of the Coptic year or a given Muslim year. The impressive developments in astronomical timekeeping in thirteenth-century Yemen and fourteenth-century Syria, particularly the tables of Abu'l-ʿUqūl for Taʿizz and of al-Khalīlī for Damascus, also owe their inspiration to the main Cairo corpus.

It is clear from the biography of Ibn Yūnus by his contemporary al-Musabbiḥī, preserved in the writings of later authors, that Ibn Yūnus was an eccentric. Al-Musabbiḥī describes him as a careless and absent-minded man who dressed shabbily and had a comic appearance. One day, when he was in good health, he predicted his own death in seven days. He attended to his personal business, locked himself in his house, and washed the ink off his manuscripts. He then recited the Koran until he died—on the day he had predicted. According to his biographer, Ibn Yūnus' son was so stupid that he sold his father's papers by the pound in the soap market.

## BIBLIOGRAPHY

I. Original Works. Ibn Yūnus' works are the following:

1. *al-Zīj al-Ḥākimī al-kabīr*: MS Leiden Cod. Or. 143 contains chs. 1–22; MS Oxford Hunt. 331 contains chs. 21–44; MS Paris B.N. ar. 2496 is an anonymous abridgment containing some additional chs. up to 57 and chs. 77–81; MS Leiden Cod. Or. 2813 contains part of ch. 1. Extracts from Ibn Yūnus' mean motion tables are in numerous later sources, such as MS Princeton Yahuda 3475, fols. 16r–21r; and MS Cairo Dār al-Kutub, *mīqāt* 116M.

2. Other *zījes* are not extant. A treatise on the compilation of solar, lunar, and planetary ephemerides, which appears to be taken from a *zīj* by Ibn Yūnus other than the Ḥākimī, survives in MS Cairo Dār al-Kutub, *mīqāt* 116M, fols. 8v–9r; and probably in MS Berlin Ahlwardt no. 5742, pt. 2. A fragment of an Egyptian *zīj* containing tables due to Ibn Yūnus is MS Berlin Ahlwardt 5733. The late thirteenth-century Yemenite *Mukhtār zīj*, extant in MS British Museum 768 (Or. 3624), appears to be based on a *zīj* by Ibn Yūnus compiled prior to the Ḥākimī zīj.

The following *zījes* are incorrectly attributed to Ibn Yūnus on their title folios: MS Aleppo Awqāf 947; MS Cairo Ṭalʿat, *mīqāt* 138; MSS Paris B.N. ar. 2520 and 2513. The first two are quite unrelated to the Egyptian astronomer. The two Paris MSS are copies of the thirteenth-century Egyptian *Muṣṭalaḥ zīj* and a later recension: they both contain material due to Ibn Yūnus. Two treatises purporting to be commentaries on a *zīj* by Ibn Yūnus—MS Gotha Forschungsbibliothek A1401 and MS Cairo Dār al-Kutub, *mīqāt* 1106—are based on the *Muṣṭalaḥ zīj*.

Short notices on topics in spherical astronomy attributed to Ibn Yūnus are in MS Milan Ambrosiana 281e (C49) and MS Paris B.N. ar. 2506.

3. *Kitāb ghāyat al-intifāʿ* ("Very Useful Tables," a later title given to the corpus). The following sources contain most of the tables: MS Dublin Chester Beatty 3673 and MS Cairo Dār al-Kutub, *mīqāt* 108.

Ibn Yūnus' original solar azimuth tables, entitled *Kitāb al-samt*, are extant in MS Dublin Chester Beatty no. 3673, pt. 1; MS Gotha Forschungsbibliothek no. A1410, pt. 1; MS Cairo Dār al-Kutub, *mīqāt* 137M; and MS Cairo Azhar, *falak* no. 4382, pt. 2.

The tables of time since sunrise, entitled *Kitāb al-dāʾir* and associated with al-Maqsī (*fl.* 1275), are in

MS Gotha Forschungsbibliothek A1402. The hour-angle tables and numerous prayer tables in the version by Ibn al-Kattānī (*fl.* 1360) are preserved in MS Istanbul Kiliç Ali Paša 684. The hour-angle tables, entitled *Kitāb faḍl al-dāʾir*, are copied separately in MS Cairo Taymūriyya, *riyāḍiyyāt* 191; and MS Cairo Azhar, *falak* no. 4382, pt. 1; they are copied together with the tables of time since sunrise in MS Dublin Chester Beatty no. 3673, pt. 2; and MS Dublin Chester Beatty 4078. The edition of the corpus by al-Bakhāniqī (*fl.* 1350) is extant in MS Cairo Dār al-Kutub, *mīqāt* 53 and 108.

There are literally dozens of MSS that contain extracts from the corpus in varying degrees of confusion.

MSS Cairo Taymūriyya, *riyāḍiyyāt* 354; and Dār al-Kutub, *mīqāt* 1207, together constitute a corpus of tables for timekeeping computed for the latitude of Alexandria. In the first the tables are falsely attributed to Ibn Yūnus.

4. *Kitāb al-jayb* (sine tables) are extant in MS Berlin Ahlwardt no. 5752, pt. 1; and MS Damascus Ẓāhiriyya 3109.

5. *Kitāb al-ẓill* (cotangent tables) apparently are not extant. The tangent tables in MS Berlin Ahlwardt no. 5767, pt. 3, attributed to Ibn Yūnus are not based on the cotangent tables in the *Ḥākimī zīj*.

6. *Kitāb al-mayl* (solar declination tables) are MS Berlin Ahlwardt 5752,2.

7. *Kitāb al-taʿdīl al-muḥkam* (solar and lunar equation tables) are extant in MS Cairo Dār al-Kutub, *mīqāt* 29, which contains the complete set of lunar tables; MS Gotha Forschungsbibliothek no. A1410, pt. 2, which contains an incomplete set; and MS British Museum Or. 3624, fols. 111v–129r, 113v–151r, which contains the solar tables and a related set of lunar tables.

8. A short treatise on a candle clock is in MS Beirut St. Joseph, Arabe 223/12. This is attributed to Ibn Yūnus al-Miṣrī (the Egyptian) in the introduction but is attributed by the Syrian engineer al-Jazarī (*fl. ca.* 1200) to Yūnus al-Asṭurlābī (the astrolabe maker), who may not be identical with the celebrated Egyptian astronomer. On the clock itself, see E. S. Kennedy and W. Ukashah, "The Chandelier Clock of Ibn Yūnis," in *Isis*, **60** (1969), 543–545.

9. *Kitāb bulūgh al-umniyya fī mā yataʿallaq biṭulūʿ al-Shiʿrā l-yamāniyya* (astrological treatise) is in MS Manchester Mingana 927 (916); MS Gotha Forschungsbibliothek A1459; and MS Cairo Dār al-Kutub, *majāmīʿ* 289.

10. The poem on the times of prayer attributed to Ibn Yūnus in MS Cairo Dār al-Kutub, *mīqāt* 181M, fols. 46v–48r, also occurs in two corrupt versions attributed to the Imām al-Shāfiʿī in MSS Berlin Ahlwardt 5700, fol. 11r, and 5820, fol. 65r. Poems by Ibn Yūnus are found in several medieval Arabic anthologies.

II. Secondary Literature. Early studies of the *Ḥākimī zīj* are A. P. Caussin de Perceval, "Le livre de la grande table Hakémite," in *Notices et extraits des manuscrits de la Bibliothèque nationale*, **7** (1804),

16–240, on the observation accounts; and J.-B. Delambre, *Histoire de l'astronomie du moyen âge* (Paris, 1819, repr. New York–London, 1965), containing a summary of the contents of the *Zīj*. The major studies by Carl Schoy on Ibn Yūnus are his "Beiträge zur arabischen Trigonometrie," in *Isis*, **5** (1923), 364–399; *Gnomonik der Araber*, which is I, pt. 6, of E. von Bassermann-Jordan, ed., *Die Geschichte der Zeitmessung und der Uhren* (Berlin–Leipzig, 1923); and *Über den Gnomonschatten und die Schattentafeln der arabischen Astronomie* (Hannover, 1923). Articles by Schoy on individual chapters of the *Ḥākimī zīj* were published in *Annalen der Hydrographie und maritimen Meteorologie*, **48** (1920), 97–111; **49** (1921), 124–133; and **50** (1922), 3–20, 265–271. A more recent study of the spherical astronomy in the *Ḥākimī zīj* is D. A. King, "The Astronomical Works of Ibn Yūnus" (Ph.D. diss., Yale University, 1972). The tables entitled *Kitāb al-taʿdīl al-muḥkam* are discussed in D. A. King, "A Double-Argument Table for the Lunar Equation Attributed to Ibn Yūnus," in *Centaurus*, **18** (1974), 129–146.

On the observatories in medieval Cairo, see A. Sayili, *The Observatory in Islam* (Ankara, 1960), 130–156, 167–175.

For modern studies relying on data from Ibn Yūnus' observational accounts, see S. Newcomb, "Researches on the Motion of the Moon. Part I . . .," in *Washington Observations for 1875* (1878), app. 2; and R. Newton, *Ancient Astronomical Observations and the Acceleration of the Earth and Moon* (Baltimore, 1970).

On the corpus of spherical astronomical tables for Cairo attributed to Ibn Yūnus, see D. A. King, "Ibn Yūnus' *Very Useful Tables* for Reckoning Time by the Sun," in *Archive for History of Exact Sciences*, **10** (1973), 342–394. The problems of their attribution, and all other known medieval tables for regulating the times of prayer, are discussed in D. A. King, *Studies on Astronomical Timekeeping in Medieval Islam*, which is in preparation.

David A. King

**ZABARELLA, JACOPO** (*b.* Padua, Italy, 5 September 1533; *d.* Padua, 15 October 1589), *natural philosophy, scientific method.*

Zabarella was born into an old and noble Paduan family, the son of Giulio Zabarella, from whom, as firstborn son, he inherited the title of palatine count. After humanistic education he entered the University of Padua, where he studied logic with Bernardino Tomitano and natural philosophy with Marcantonio de' Passeri, among others, receiving a degree in 1553. In 1564 he succeeded Tomitano in the first chair of logic and four years later moved to the more prestigious and more lucrative chair of natural philosophy, a position he held for the remainder of his life.

Zabarella must be considered one of the major figures of the revival of Aristotelian philosophy in the sixteenth and seventeenth centuries. He is a prime representative of a specifically Italian form of Aristotelianism in which the teaching of philosophy was closely tied to the needs of medical education. Consequently, his writings epitomize a "naturalistic" approach to philosophy rather than the more theological and metaphysical orientation that had developed in the universities of northern Europe during the later Middle Ages. Both Zabarella's published writings and his teaching focused upon an interpretation of Aristotle's works on logic and natural philosophy. Especially in the latter subject he displayed a strongly empirical approach to understanding the physical and biological world. Observation and experience played an important role in his attempt to comprehend nature, although a very rudimentary "experimental method" was developed in his works. Like most philosophers of the period, Zabarella was more concerned to understand the organic, biological world of natural change than the more abstract realm of what later came to be called "physical science." Consequently, he gave little attention to the possible uses of mathematics as a tool for understanding the physical world.

According to most interpreters, Zabarella's lasting contribution lies in his work on logic and scientific method. It was also in this field that he gained an enormous and authoritative reputation during his lifetime and in the first half of the seventeenth century. Although he wrote on many aspects of logic, it was to methodological questions that he devoted his major effort and on which he wrote most penetratingly. Following an interpretation of Aristotle that goes back to the Greek commentators, Zabarella insisted that logic is not, strictly speaking, a part of philosophy itself but, rather, is an instrumental discipline (*instrumentum*) that furnishes a useful tool of inquiry for the arts and sciences. Expanding on and clarifying Aristotle's doctrine of scientific method, as found in the *Posterior Analytics*, he distinguished "demonstrative method" (*methodus demonstrativa*) from "resolutive method" (*methodus resolutiva*). Both of these are syllogistic in form. The former proceeds from causes to effects, and the latter from effects to causes.

These notions are analyzed in great detail in Zabarella's *De methodis*, one of the works in his *Opera logica* (1578). The same collection contains his *De regressu*, which attempts to work out a specific form of demonstration to be applied to the investigation of natural science. In it Zabarella explains his notion of "regress" (*regressus*), a concept that for many years had been discussed in writings on logic and natural philosophy by his Italian Aristotelian predecessors. "Regress" uses both demonstrative and resolutive methods. It is a technique by which one proceeds from a particular effect to its cause and then returns to a consideration of the effect, thereby having gained a fuller understanding of it and its relation to its cause. The procedure involves several distinct steps, including a careful intellectual analysis (*examen mentale*) of the situation and a final attempt to relate cause to effect in a fuller manner than was possible at the beginning of the analysis.

Although it has been suggested that Zabarella and the methodological tradition of Italian Aristotelianism that he represented were a major influence on the development of Galileo's scientific methodology, concrete evidence has not been adduced to establish a direct connection. In fact, the Aristotelian terminology and doctrines that Zabarella and Galileo share (for instance, Zabarella, *methodus resolutiva*; Galileo, *metodo resolutivo*) seem for the most part to have been commonplaces of late medieval and Renaissance thought, in mathematics and medicine as well as in logic and natural philosophy. Moreover, Zabarella's application of these methods was unwaveringly cast in a syllogistic form, whereas Galileo repeatedly rejected the use of the syllogism in scientific investigation. It must also be noted that—quite contrary to Galileo—Zabarella in no way suggested a systematic application of mathematics to the study of the natural world. On the other hand, it seems evident that the clarity of Zabarella's thought, the precision of his distinctions, and his sharp focus on problems of natural science contributed materially to the progressive clarification of the place of the sciences in the cultural complex of the seventeenth century.

In addition to his logical works, Zabarella wrote commentaries on several treatises of Aristotle (including *Posterior Analytics, De anima, De generatione et corruptione, Meteorology*, and several books of the *Physics*). An important and influential collection of short treatises on various topics of natural philosophy is in his *De rebus naturalibus* (1590). In it he treats many specific problems (including the motion of heavy and light bodies, reaction, the regions of the air, mixture, and elementary qualities), often showing the acuteness of the logical works, although he often relies on traditional solutions to the problems. This collection contains a typical late sixteenth-century approach to natural philosophy. Little attention is paid to the peculiarly medieval natural philosophy that had been dominant from the early fourteenth century until the early sixteenth century (such as the Merton and Paris schools), but much is devoted to a study of the Greek text of Aristotle and a consideration of the opinions of his Greek expositors. Zabarella was an excellent Greek scholar and devoted much effort to presenting what he considered to be the true meaning of Aristotle's text. He also drew extensively upon such Greek commentators as Alexander of Aphrodisias, Themistius, Olympiodorus, Philoponus, and Simplicius. Besides relying on earlier authorities, Zabarella occasionally displayed a strongly empirical bent that allowed him to utilize his personal experiences to reject traditional views. Throughout his writings the approach to natural philosophical problems is qualitative and bears little similarity to either that developed at Oxford and Paris during the fourteenth century or to that employed by Galileo and others in the seventeenth century.

The important collections of Zabarella's writings, especially the *Opera logica* and the *De rebus naturalibus*, began to exert influence throughout Europe soon after the initial publication. This lasted at least until the middle of the seventeenth century, when the dominant position of the Aristotelian tradition finally began to wane. Besides Italy, Zabarella was particularly influential in Germany, where his works were frequently reprinted, and in the British Isles, where the Scholastic revival of the early seventeenth century owed much to his writings. The full impact of Zabarella and the extent of his influence on later philosophy and science have yet to be worked out in detail.

## BIBLIOGRAPHY

I. ORIGINAL WORKS. The most important of Zabarella's logical writings are in the *Opera logica* (Venice, 1578; repr. Hildesheim, 1966; at least 14 later eds.) and *In duos Aristotelis libros posteriorum analyticorum commentarii* (Venice, 1582; repr. Frankfurt, 1966; several later eds.). *De rebus naturalibus* (Venice, 1590; repr. Frankfurt, 1966; at least 8 later eds.) contains 30 short works on natural philosophy. Among the commentaries on Aristotle are *In libros Aristotelis Physicorum commentarii* (Venice, 1601; Frankfurt, 1602), the latter ed. also containing commentaries on *De generatione et corruptione* and *Meteorology*, and *In tres Aristotelis libros De anima commentarii* (Venice, 1605; Frankfurt,

1606, 1619). For a more exhaustive listing of printed works and of MSS, see Edwards' dissertation (below). See also M. Dal Pra, "Una *oratio* programmatica di G. Zabarella," in *Rivista critica di storia della filosofia*, **21** (1966), 286–290.

II. SECONDARY LITERATURE. The most comprehensive studies of Zabarella are William F. Edwards, "The Logic of Iacopo Zabarella (1533–1589)," Ph.D. diss. Columbia University, 1960; summary in *Dissertation Abstracts*, **21** (1961), 2745–2746 (with an extensive bibliography of Zabarella's works and secondary literature published before 1960), and Antonino Poppi, *La dottrina della scienza in Giacomo Zabarella* (Padua, 1972). Other useful general treatments are Edwards' article in *Enciclopedia filosofica*, 2nd ed., VI (Florence, 1967), 1187–1189; Eugenio Garin, *Storia della filosofia italiana* (Turin, 1966), 548–558; and Giuseppe Saitta, *Il pensiero italiano nell'umanesimo e nel Rinascimento*, 2nd ed., II (Florence, 1960), 400–423.

Works more specifically oriented toward Zabarella's logic or methodology include F. Bottin, "La teoria del *regressus* in Giacomo Zabarella," in *Saggi e ricerche su Aristotele . . . Zabarella . . .* (Padua, 1972), 49–70; E. Cassirer, *Das Erkenntnisproblem*, 2nd ed., I (Berlin, 1911), 136–143; A. Corsano, "Per la storia del pensiero del tardo Rinascimento. X: Lo strumentalismo logico di I. Zabarella," in *Giornale critico della filosofia italiana*, **41** (1962), 507–517; A. Crescini, *Le origini del metodo analitico: Il Cinquecento* (Udine, 1965), 168–188; W. F. Edwards, "The Averroism of Iacopo Zabarella," in *Atti del XII Congresso internazionale di filosofia*, IX (Florence, 1960), 91–107; N. W. Gilbert, *Renaissance Concepts of Method* (New York, 1960), 167–176; and "Galileo and the School of Padua," in *Journal of the History of Philosophy*, **1** (1963), 223–231; P. Ragnisco, "Una polemica di logica nell'Università di Padova nelle scuole di B. Petrella e G. Zabarella," in *Atti del Istituto veneto di scienze, lettere ed arti*, 6th ser., **4** (1886), 463–502; and "La polemica tra Francesco Piccolomini e Giacomo Zabarella nell'Università di Padova," *ibid.*, 1217–1252; J. H. Randall, *The School of Padua and the Emergence of Modern Science* (Padua, 1961), 15–68; W. Risse, *Die Logik der Neuzeit*, I (Stuttgart–Bad Cannstatt, 1964), 278–290; C. B. Schmitt, "Experience and Experiment: A Comparison of Zabarella's View With Galileo's in *De motu*," in *Studies in the Renaissance*, **16** (1969), 80–138; and C. Vasoli, *Studi sulla cultura del Rinascimento* (Manduria, 1968), 308–342.

CHARLES B. SCHMITT

**ZACH, FRANZ XAVER VON** (*b*. Pest [now part of Budapest], Hungary, 4 June 1754; *d*. Paris, France, 2 September 1832), *surveying, astronomy*.

Zach came of a noble and distinguished family. His father was a well-known physician who practiced at Pressburg (now Bratislava), Czechoslova-kia, and later at Pest. Authorities disagree in which of these cities it was that Zach was born.

Although the transit of Venus in 1769 and the comet of the same year had awakened his interest in astronomy, Zach joined the Austrian army as an engineering officer but soon left to participate in the survey of Austria. He spent the next few years in Berlin and London as tutor to the children of Graf Moritz von Brühl, the ambassador of Saxony, who was an amateur astronomer and possessed a private observatory. In 1786 Zach entered the ser-vice of Duke Ernst II of Saxe-Coburg, with the ti-tle of "Oberst Wachtmeister." The duke erected an observatory for him on the Seeberg near Gotha, and Zach remained in charge of it until 1806. Upon the duke's death Zach became chief steward to the duchess and in this capacity traveled with her to Italy. Greatly troubled by kidney stones in his later years, he went to Paris to seek relief from this ailment and died there of cholera.

While on the Seeberg, Zach published a series of observations, as well as solar tables and star cata-logs. In 1798–1799 he and F. J. Bertuch edited *Geographische Ephemeriden*, in which the fore-most travelers of the period recounted their ex-periences. This led to the founding of *Monatliche Correspondenz zur Beförderung der Erd- und Him-melskunde* (1800), in which the latest astronomical news was published. Zach edited this publication until 1813 and later, while in Genoa, recommenced it in French, as *Correspondance astronomique, géographique, hydrographique et statistique* (1818–1826). Toward the end of the eighteenth century he formed an association of twenty-four astronomers, each of whom was assigned a celes-tial zone to be searched methodically, especially for new comets and planets, a project that culmi-nated in the discovery of the asteroids.

## BIBLIOGRAPHY

Among Zach's most important writings are *Explicatio et usus tabellarum solis, explicatio et usus catalogi stel-larum fixarum* (Gotha, 1792); *Novae et correctae tabu-lae motuum solis* (Gotha, 1792); *Nachricht von der preussische trigonometrische und astronomische Auf-nahme von Thüringen, usw.*, pt. I (Gotha, 1806); *Tabu-lae speciales aberrationis et nutationis . . .*, 2 vols. (Gotha, 1806–1807); and *L'attraction des montagnes et ses effets sur le fil à plomb* (Avignon, 1814). There is a complete list of his books and articles in Poggendorff, II, 1387–1389.

For biographical information, see the notice by Günther, in *Allgemeine deutsche Biographie*, XLIV (Leipzig, 1898), 613–615.

LETTIE S. MULTHAUF

**ZACUTO** (or **ZACUT**), **ABRAHAM BAR SAMUEL BAR ABRAHAM** (*b.* Salamanca, Spain, *ca.* 1450; *d.* Portugal, *ca.* 1522), *astrology, astronomy.*

Zacuto, a Jew, studied medicine and astrology at the University of Salamanca. He became a re-nowned astrologer, and several historians have claimed that he held a chair there; but no docu-ment has yet been found that can adequately sup-port this assertion. After the publication of the law requiring the conversion or expulsion of the Span-ish Jews, Zacuto went to Portugal, where he was welcomed by John II (1492). The king, who was interested in developing the art of navigation, quickly profited from Zacuto's presence to refine a number of rules pertaining to sailing.

Gaspar Correia (*Lendas da India*, I [Lisbon, 1858], 261) stated that Zacuto introduced the as-trolabe into Portugal and that he was the author of the quadrennial tables of solar declination. Al-though the first part of this claim is surely incorrect (the astrolabe had been known in Portugal since at least the twelfth century), Correia was right about the second. Zacuto was certainly the author of the tables prepared for the voyage of Vasco da Gama (for the period 1497–1500), fragments of which are preserved in Andre Pires' *Livro de marinharia* (edited by Luis de Albuquerque [Coimbra, 1963], 34–81). These tables were computed on the basis of elements taken from Zacuto's *Almanach perpe-tuum*. Two editions of this work were printed at Leiria in 1496; and in one of them the preliminary note, containing explanations of the use of the ta-bles, was translated into Spanish. Until 1537—the year of the publication of Pedro Nuñez Salaciense's tables—all solar tables for navigation prepared in Portugal were computed from the figures fur-nished by the *Almanach perpetuum*.

## BIBLIOGRAPHY

Zacuto's most important work, *Almanach perpetuum* (Leiria, 1496), was reprinted several times. His other writings, which deal primarily with astrology, include *Mixtapé ha' isteganin* ("Judgments of Astrology") and *Haajibbun hagadol* ("The Great Compilation"). *Trata-do de las ynfluencias del cielo* and *Dos eclipses del sol y la luna* were first published by Joaquim de Carvalho in *Estudos sobre a cultura portuguesa do século XVI*, I (Coimbra, 1947), 109–177, 177–183.

LUIS DE ALBUQUERQUE

**AL-ZAHRĀWĪ, ABUʾL-QĀSIM KHALAF IBN ʿABBĀS,** also known as **Abulcasis** (*b.* al-Zahrāʾ, near Córdoba, Spain, *ca.* 936; *d.* al-Zahrāʾ, *ca.* 1013), *medicine, pharmacology.*

The epithet al-Zahrāwī derives from the fact that he spent most of his life in his native city as a practicing physician-pharmacist-surgeon. Although references have been made to his contributions to theology and the natural sciences, none of his writings in these fields, if any, is known.

We know nothing about al-Zahrāwī's parentage except that his forebears were of the Anṣār, who presumably came from Arabia (al-Anṣār) with the Muslim armies that conquered and inhabited Spain, later forming the aristocracy in the larger Moorish cities and in the capital, Córdoba. Little is known of al-Zahrāwī himself, but his life-span coincided with the golden age of Moorish Spain, when intellectual activities, including the natural and mathematical sciences, reached their first peak. Córdoba and al-Zahrāʾ then formed a metropolitan area unmatched for excellence in Europe, except for Constantinople.

Al-Zahrāwī was first mentioned very briefly by Futuḥ al-Ḥumaydī, Ibn Ḥazm, and Ibn Abī Uṣaybiʿa. His only known literary contribution, *al-Taṣrīf li-man ʿajiza ʿan al-taʾlīf*, a medical encyclopedia in thirty treatises, sheds some additional light on his life and personality. He seems to have traveled very infrequently. His *Taṣrīf*, completed about A.D. 1000, was the result of almost fifty years of medical education and experience. In it he discussed not only medicine and surgery, but also midwifery, pharmaceutical and cosmetic preparations, materia medica, cookery and dietetics, weights and measures, technical terminology, medical chemistry, therapeutics, and psychotherapy.

Al-Zahrāwī attempted to separate medical practice from alchemy, theology, and philosophy, advocating specialization in the health professions: "Too much branching and specializing in many fields before perfecting one of them causes frustration and mental fatigue." He also called for upholding the high ethical standards of the healing art, the return to and reliance on nature, and recognition that "time plays an important part in the treatment and cure of diseases."

Al-Zahrāwī was the first to recommend surgical removal of a broken patella and the first to practice lithotomy on women. He introduced what is now known as the Walcher position in obstetrics and devised new obstetrical forceps. He gave original descriptions for manufacturing and using probes, surgical knives, scalpels, and hooks of various shapes and designs. He invented several types of true surgical scissors ending in recurved or ring extremities, as well as grasping forceps. He described lachrymal fistula and other eye operations in which he employed pointed blades, speculums, and hooks. For scaling teeth he used long-handled scrapers fluted for good grip. He was the first to describe accurately aural polyps as well as lithotomy using a special scoop and lancets. His illustrations of surgical instruments are the earliest known to be intended for use in teaching and for demonstration of the method of manufacture. Before Paré, he ligatured arteries and recommended several types of threads and catguts in suturing. Al-Zahrāwī applied plasters and bandages to ordinary fractures; described hydatid cysts, hemophilia, and the extraction of a polyp; and gave a very interesting explanation of a case of hydrocephaly resulting from a congenital defect caused by blocked drainage of cerebral fluid: "I have seen a baby boy whose head was abnormally enlarged with prominence of the forehead and sides to the point that the body became unable to hold it up." Al-Zahrāwī's surgery was the most advanced in the Middle Ages until the thirteenth century. Although its influence in Arab lands has been limited (Ibn al-Quff in the thirteenth century was an exception), his surgical and chemopharmaceutical writings were highly regarded in the West after they were translated into Latin by Gerard of Cremona, Rogerius Frugardi, Rolandus Parmensis, Arnald of Villanova, and others. His emphasis on the importance of human anatomy and physiology generated special interest in their study by later doctors. He observed, for example, that the brain includes the three functions of the intellect: imagination, thought, and memory.

Al-Zahrāwī was not only one of the greatest surgeons of medieval Islam, but a great educator and psychiatrist as well. He devoted a substantial section in the *Taṣrīf* to child education and behavior, table etiquette, school curriculum, and academic specialization. He encouraged the study of medicine by intelligent and gifted students after completion of their primary education in language, religion, grammar, poetry, mathematics, astronomy, logic, and philosophy. Following the Hippocratic tradition, he divided man's life-span into four stages: early age up to twenty years, youth up to forty, adulthood or maturity to sixty, and old age over sixty.

Al-Zahrāwī emphasized hygienic measures, special diets for the sick and the healthy, and effective, high-quality drugs for the benefit of patients. He promoted bedside clinical medicine and strong doctor-patient relationships: "Only by repeated visits to the patient's bedside can the physician follow the progress of his medical treatment."

As a natural scientist and applied chemist, al-Zahrāwī described Spanish fauna and flora and simples of plant, animal, and mineral origins, where they are found, their cultivation, and their preservation. He also discussed technical methods of preparing and of purifying for medicinal uses such chemical substances as litharge, ceruse (white lead), iron pyrite (crystalline marcasite), vitriols, and verdigris. He likewise recommended the use of minerals, elements, and precious stones—individually or compounded with other simples—for medical treatment. In his psychiatric treatment, al-Zahrāwī used drugs to induce hallucinations, thrills, and happiness. For example, he manufactured an opium-based remedy that he called "the bringer of joy and gladness, because it relaxes the soul, dispels bad thoughts and worries, moderates temperaments, and is useful against melancholy."

*BIBLIOGRAPHY*

I. ORIGINAL WORKS. Al-Zahrāwī's *al-Taṣrīf* exists in fragments in treatises, and in its entirety in numerous MSS. A list of most of these extant copies, with bibliography, can be found in Sami Hamarneh and Glenn Sonnedecker, *A Pharmaceutical View of Abulcasis al-Zahrāwī in Moorish Spain* (Leiden, 1963), 130–133, 137–151. There are partial translations in Spanish, Hebrew, and Latin (see bibliographies below). Another important ed. (although with numerous errors) is the Arabic-Latin copy of the surgical treatise by Johannes Channing, *Albucasis De chirurgia arabice et latine*, 2 vols. (Oxford, 1778). The French trans. by Lucien Leclerc, *La chirurgie d'Abulcasis* (Paris, 1861), with a useful intro., was very influential in making al-Zahrāwī's surgery better known to modern historians of science. The definitive ed. by M. S. Spink and G. L. Lewis, *Abulcasis on Surgery and Instruments* (Berkeley, Calif., 1973), includes the Arabic text with English trans. and commentary. There is also a rare lithographed copy of the surgical treatise (Lucknow, 1878). For details see also George Sarton, *Introduction to the History of Science*, I (Baltimore, 1927), 681–682; Carl Brockelmann, *Geschichte der arabischen Literatur*, I (Leiden, 1943), 276–277, and Supp., I (Leiden, 1937), 425; and Sami

Hamarneh, *Catalogue of Arabic Manuscripts on Medicine and Pharmacy at the British Library* (Cairo, 1975), 90–93.

II. SECONDARY LITERATURE. The first to write a separate biography of al-Zahrāwī was Muhammad ibn Futūḥ al-Ḥumaydī (1029–1095), *Jadhwat al-Muqtabis fī Dhikr Wulāt al-Andalus* (Cairo, 1952), 195. Abū Muḥammad Ibn Ḥazm (994–1064) of Córdoba, in his epistle defending the scholars of his native country, quoted by Aḥmad al-Maqqarī in the first part of his *Nafḥ al-Ṭīb*, mentions him in passing as a great surgeon-physician. Al-Ḍabbī and Ibn Bashkuwāl quote al-Ḥumaydī with no additional information. Ibn Abī Uṣaybiʿa, *ʿAyūn al-anbāʾ*, Būlāq ed., II (Cairo, 1882), 52, mentions al-Zahrāwī's interest in medical therapy and his knowledge of the materia medica.

For a thorough exposition of his general contributions see Lucien Leclerc, *Histoire de la médecine arabe*, I (Paris, 1876), 437–457; and Sami Hamarneh, *Ẓāhirīyah Index* (Damascus, 1969), 147–170. For his surgery, see Zaki Aly, "La chirurgie arabe en Espagne," in *Bulletin de la Société française d'histoire de la médecine*, **26** (1932), 236–243; George J. Fisher, "Abul-Casem . . . al-Zahravi," in *Annals of Anatomy and Surgery*, **8** (1883), 21–29, 74–82, 124–131; Ernst F. Gurlt, *Geschichte der Chirurgie und ihrer Ausübung*, I (Berlin, 1898), 620–649; Sami Hamarneh, "Drawings and Pharmacy in al-Zahrāwī's 10th Century Surgical Treatise," in *Contributions. Museum of History and Technology, United States National Museum*, no. 228 (1961), paper 22, 81–94; and Tewfick Makhluf, *L'oeuvre chirurgical d'Abul-Cassim . . . ez-Zahrawi* (Paris, 1930).

For his contribution to medicine and obstetrics, see M. S. Abu Ganimah, *Abul-Kasim ein Forscher der arabischen Medizin* (Berlin, 1929); Henri Paul J. Rénaud, "La prétendue 'hygiène d'Albucasis' et sa véritable origine," in *Petrus nonius* (Lisbon), **3** (1941), 171–179; and Martin S. Spink, "Arabian Gynaecology," in *Proceedings of the Royal Society of Medicine*, **30** (1937), 653–671.

For his contribution to weights and measures, cosmetology, materia medica, and chemotherapy, see Sami Hamarneh, "Climax of Chemical Therapy in 10th-Century Arabic Medicine," in *Islam* (Berlin), **38** (1963), 287–288; "The First Known Independent Treatise on Cosmetology in Spain," in *Bulletin of the History of Medicine*, **39** (1965), 309–325; and *A Pharmaceutical View of . . . al-Zahrāwī . . .* (Leiden, 1963), 37–126, written with Glenn Sonnedecker; and H. Sauvaire, "Traité sur les poids et mesures par ez-Zahrawy," in *Journal of the Royal Asiatic Society of Great Britain and Ireland*, n.s. **16** (1884), 495–524.

SAMI HAMARNEH


**ZAKARIYĀ IBN MUḤAMMAD IBN MAḤMŪD.** See **Al-Qazwīnī, Zakariyā ibn Muḥammad ibn Maḥmūd, Abū Yaḥyā.**

**ZALUŽANSKÝ ZE ZALUŽAN, ADAM** (*b*. Mnichovo Hradiště, Bohemia [now Czechoslovakia], *ca*. 1558; *d*. Prague, Bohemia, 8 December 1613), *botany, medicine*.

The son of a clerk, Zalužanský studied at Wittenberg and at the Charles University in Prague, where he received the bachelor's degree in 1581 and the M.A. in 1584; he was awarded the M.D. at Helmstedt in 1587. He subsequently became lecturer in the Greek classics at the Charles University; in 1591 he was elected dean of the Faculty of Philosophy and, in 1593, rector of the university. After his marriage the following year he was obliged to leave the university. He established a medical practice in Prague and died during the plague. Active in the medicine, pharmacy, poetry, politics, and religion of his time, Zalužanský was also instrumental in reforming the Charles University.

Zalužanský's three-volume botanical treatise, *Methodi herbariae*, represented an important departure from the customary practice of publishing herbals mainly to illustrate the herbs used in medicine. Zalužanský's work had a purely scientific purpose, like Cesalpino's *De plantis* (1583), and included no illustrations. Botany, he wrote, should be investigated as an independent branch of natural history.

In book I, "De aetiologia plantarum," Zalužanský included a chapter on the sexuality of plants, in which he drew on Aristotle, Theophrastus, and especially on Pliny's principles that all plants have sexuality—although most of them do not display sexual differentiation. Like the ancient writers, he was completely unaware of the functions of stamens and pistils, understanding sexuality as male and female principles inherent in the plant as a whole. His idea of sex connected in a single individual, however, was the first speculation about monoecism in plants.

In book II, "De historia plantarum," Zalužanský attempted to establish a natural system of plants. Beginning with the fungi and mosses, he progressed to grasses, herbs, and finally to species of wood. Since his method was primarily physiognomical, based on habitual features, he was rarely able to discern the natural groupings that he found in the Papilionaceae, Compositae, and Malvaceae, for example; his other groupings are considerably heterogeneous.

The last book, "De exercitio plantarum," deals with botanical methodology. Zalužanský termed the first phase of botanical investigation "analysis," believing that it should lead to the description of the plant under examination and to the determination of its name and properties. The second phase, "genesis," was based on the data thus obtained and would demonstrate the properties of plants that are useful to man.

Despite his emphasis on the study of all stages of plant evolution, Zalužanský frequently used the empirical findings of other authors, such as L'Obel, Dodoens, Mattioli, and even Pliny. His overall conception was still Aristotelian and Scholastic, rather than that of a natural historian seeking new knowledge. However, because he conceived of botany as an independent science and presented his treatise completely along these lines, he deserves to be considered one of the first researchers whose methodological concepts were capable of influencing the evolution of botany.

*BIBLIOGRAPHY*

I. ORIGINAL WORKS. Zalužanský's writings are *Rzad apathekařský* (Prague, 1592); *Methodi herbariae libri tres* (Prague, 1592; Frankfurt, 1604), facs. repr., K. Pejml, ed. (Prague, 1940); *Oratio pro anatomia et restauratione totius studii medici in inclyto regno Bohemiae* (Prague, 1600); and *Animadversionum medicarum in Galenum et Avicennam libri septem* (Frankfurt, 1604).

II. SECONDARY LITERATURE. On Zalužanský and his work, see L. Čelakovský, "Adam Zalužanský ze Zalužan ve svém poměru k nauce o pohlaví rostlin" ("Zalužanský in His Relation to the Theory of Sexuality in Plants"), in *Osvěta*, **6** (1876), 33–54; and K. Pejml, "Adam Zalužanský de Zalužany, sa personnalité et son oeuvre en tenant compte de son ouvrage *Methodi herbariae libri tres*," in *Summa dissertationum Facultati rerum naturalium Universitati Carolinae anno 1946*, no. 183 (Prague, 1948), 11–13.

VĚRA EISNEROVÁ

**ZAMBECCARI, GIUSEPPE** (*b*. Castelfranco di Sotto, Italy, 19 March 1655; *d*. Pisa, Italy, 13 December 1728), *medicine*.

At age eighteen Zambeccari was admitted to the Ducal College of Pisa (which later became the university), where he studied medicine. The college already had won renown as the producer of the previous centuries' most brilliant scientists, and among his professors was the anatomist Lorenzo Bellini.

After graduating in 1679, Zambeccari moved to Florence, where he continued his studies under Francesco Redi, who encouraged him to improve his clinical knowledge by working as an intern in the wards of the Hospital of Santa Maria Novella. According to the custom of the time, Zambeccari lodged in the house of his professor and there in 1680 conducted his most important experiments in physiology, which consisted in removing various internal organs from live animals (mainly dogs) in order to acquire a better understanding of what functions they performed in relation to the whole organism.

One of the first series of experiments dealt with the removal of the spleen; several of the animals operated upon survived, and a few months later they were killed and carefully examined in order to discover what anatomical, pathological, and physiological changes had been caused by the removal of the organ. Obviously, no conclusive results could be obtained from these experiments, because nothing was then known of the function of the spleen and there were no means of carrying the investigation further.

Turning to the study of other organs, Zambeccari performed unilateral nephrectomies and discovered that the animal apparently was not incommoded by the operation. In other experiments he tied the common bile duct and thus demonstrated that bile is not formed in the gall bladder, as was then the common belief. Encouraged by the results of his experiments, he not only removed the bile duct but also fragments of hepatic tissue, and even entire lobes of the liver, always finding that a good percentage of the animals survived the operation. Zambeccari performed a resection of the cecum and finally went so far as to remove the pancreas and to ligate the mesenteric veins. He also studied the eyes and noted that pricking the cornea of various animals rapidly leads to the reconstitution of the aqueous humor.

Despite their importance in the history of experimental physiology, Zambeccari's studies had no immediate impact on biology—in part because too little was known for them to be really useful. Nevertheless, the book in which he described his experiments was for a time rather successful and went through several editions; yet it does not appear to have inspired others to use the same approach. Later the work was forgotten completely, until Murri in the nineteenth century brought it to the attention of scientists.

After his period of experimentation in the house of Francesco Redi, Zambeccari returned to Pisa, where he was offered the chair of practical medicine and, in 1689, that of medicine proper. In 1704 he succeeded Bellini in the chair of anatomy.

Other works—manuscripts and letters by Zambeccari, some of which are of considerable interest—either are still unpublished or were discovered only long after his death. Among the most interesting is *Del sonno della vigilia e dell'uso dell'oppio*, written in 1665, but published, by C. Fedeli, only in 1914. An essay of deductive rather than experimental character, it deals with the physiology of nerve transmission and of muscle contraction, and is based on Galenic assumptions on anatomy and physiology, and on the iatromechanical concepts of Borelli and Galileo.

## BIBLIOGRAPHY

I. ORIGINAL WORKS. Zambeccari's writings include *Esperienze del Dottor Giuseppe Zambeccari intorno a diverse viscere tagliate a diversi animali viventi . . .* (Florence, 1680); *De sonno, della vigialia, e dell'uso dell'oppio* (Pisa, 1914); and *Breve trattato de'bagni di Pisa e di Lucca* (Padua, 1712).

II. SECONDARY LITERATURE. See U. Calamida, "Di un carteggio inedito di Giuseppe Zambeccari," in *Atti del III Congresso della Società italiana di storia delle scienze mediche e naturali* (Venice, 1925), 120–127; C. Fedeli, *Giuseppe Zambeccari, lettera sulle separazioni* (Pisa, 1927), reviewed by A. Corsini in *Rivista di storia critica delle scienze mediche e naturali*, **18** (1927), 320; P. Ferrari, *Giuseppe Zambeccari* (Pontremoli, 1925), reviewed by A. Corsini, *ibid.*, **17** (1926), 112–113; and S. Jarcho, "A Seventeenth-Century Pioneer in Experimental Physiology and Surgery," in *Bulletin of the History of Medicine*, **9** (1941), 144–176; and "Experiments of Doctor Joseph Zambeccari Concerning the Excision of Various Organs From Different Living Animals," *ibid.*, 311–331.

CARLO CASTELLANI

**ZAMBONINI, FERRUCCIO** (*b*. Rome, Italy, 17 December 1880; *d*. Naples, Italy, 12 January 1932), *chemistry, mineralogy*.

Zambonini was the son of Ersilia Zuccari and Gustavo Zambonini di Montebugnoli, descended from a noble Bolognese family reduced to near poverty by financial misfortunes. Obliged to work in order to continue his studies after his father's death, Ferruccio gave private lessons and copied documents for lawyers. His first scientific works were published in 1898, while he was still a student. Zambonini graduated in natural sciences from the University of Rome in 1903 and immediately became assistant in chemistry at the Turin Polytechnic, where he acquired a considerable knowledge of general analytical chemistry. In 1906 he worked at the University of Naples with Arcangelo Scacchi, the leading Italian mineralogist of the nineteenth century.

Zambonini became professor at the University of Sassari in 1909; in 1911 he moved to Palermo, and two years later to Turin. In 1923 he obtained the chair of general chemistry at the University of Naples, where he continued his mineralogical and chemical studies, and was twice elected vice-chancellor of the university.

Zambonini was the leading mineralogist in Italy during the first half of the twentieth century, a worthy successor of Scacchi and Quintino Sella. He contributed substantially to the knowledge of many minerals; one of his most important works, fundamental to the study of volcanic products, is "Mineralogia vesuviana" (1910), a collection of data on more than 250 minerals from Vesuvius and Monte Somma, with Zambonini's own minutely detailed descriptions and commentary. This work won him the annual award of the Royal Academy of Sciences of Naples. An appendix appeared in 1912; and in 1935, after his death, Emanuele Quercigh compiled a second edition that included all the new minerals discovered by Zambonini and his students during the last ten years of his life.

Zambonini extended knowledge of the dehydration of minerals by studying the role of water in hydrated silicates, especially zeolites, and interpreting it in the light of the most advanced theories of colloidal chemistry.

In general mineralogy, Zambonini's isomorphism anticipated modern theories of crystal chemistry. In the important "Sulle soluzioni solide dei composti di calcio . . . ," he demonstrated that the rare earths in trivalent rare-earth compounds could be replaced with alkaline earths and lead. He also studied their solubility limits in the solid state and applied the results to simplifying and clarifying the formulas of many minerals.

Zambonini gave a very interesting explanation of the concomitant replacement, in plagioclase, of part of the calcium by sodium, and silicon by aluminum. He attributed this substitution to the closeness of the ionic radii of sodium and calcium, and of aluminum and silicon. In Italy the possibility of isomorphism between ions of similar radii is called Zambonini's rule, thus indicating that the solid-state substitution of elements is a function of ionic radii, rather than of chemical properties.

Zambonini conducted pioneering research on the mixed crystals of the epidote-clinozoisite series. Through chemical analyses and a study of optical properties of the series, he discovered the existence of mixed stereoisomeric crystals, which have the same chemical composition but optical properties that vary according to whether it is the free aluminum or the aluminum bound to hydroxyls that is replaced by ferric iron.

While working on mixed crystals of molybdates and tungstates of calcium, barium, strontium, and lead, along with the analogous compounds of rare earths, Zambonini noticed that their angular values and optical properties did not vary regularly with the variation in composition of the mixed crystals; there are values not included among those of the two components. He observed the same phenomenon in pairs of artificial compounds and concluded that there are important exceptions to the principle that the optical properties of mixed crystals vary regularly with their composition. In 1922 Zambonini discovered the isomorphism between potassium fluoborate and permanganate, two compounds that are similar neither in their chemical composition nor even in the sum of their valences.

In 1924 Zambonini was one of the first to apply Bohr's atomic theory in order to explain the isomorphism of the trivalent rare earths with alkaline earths and with lead. Similarly, in 1911 he had been an innovator when he used the amount of lead and uranium in some minerals to date rocks, thus anticipating modern methods. For the calculations he used Rayleigh's formula.

In the last decade of his active life Zambonini contributed substantially to the chemistry of the rare earths. With collaborators he studied an isotherm of the binary systems of rare-earth sulfates and alkaline sulfates. He had obtained the lanthanides for this research through a long and difficult process of fractionation, carried out with very limited means at the Institute of Mineralogy in Turin.

For his scientific achievements Zambonini was elected a member of the Accademia Nazionale dei Lincei, the Royal Academy of Physical and Mathematical Sciences of Naples, the Academy of Sciences of Turin, and the Accademia dei Quaranta. He was president of the Geological Society of Italy, vice-chancellor of the University of Naples, and editor of *Zeitschrift für Kristallographie, Kristallgeometrie, Kristallphysik, Kristallchemie*, and was awarded the Wilde Prize of the Institut de France.

*BIBLIOGRAPHY*

A comprehensive bibliography of Zambonini's writings (162 works) is included with F. Giordani, "Commemorazione di Ferruccio Zambonini," in *Rendiconti dell'Accademia delle scienze fisiche e matematiche*, 4th ser., **3** (1933), 8–19, with portrait. "Mineralogia Vesuviana" was published as *Atti dell'Accademia delle scienze fisiche e matematiche*, 2nd ser., **14**, no. 6 (1910); 2nd ed., compiled by E. Quercigh, *ibid.*, supp. **20** (1935). "Sulle soluzioni solide dei composti de calcio, stronzio, bario e piombo con quelli delle 'terre rare' . . . ," appeared in *Rivista italiana di mineralogia*, **45** (1915), 1–185.

GUIDO CAROBBI

**ZANOTTI, EUSTACHIO** (*b.* Bologna, Italy, 27 November 1709; *d.* Bologna, 15 May 1782), *astronomy, geometry.*

Like the astronomer Eustachio Manfredi, his godfather, Zanotti belonged to a prominent family distinguished in the arts, letters, and sciences. The son of Gian Pietro Zanotti and Costanza Gambari, he was educated by the Jesuits and entered the University of Bologna, becoming Manfredi's assistant at the Institute of Sciences in 1729. He graduated in philosophy in 1730 and obtained his first university post, as reader in mechanics at Bologna, in 1738, after presenting his trial lecture on the Newtonian theory of light. The following year he succeeded Manfredi as director of the Institute observatory, a post to which he dedicated himself almost exclusively for the next forty years, never marrying and declining all offers from other universities. He began teaching hydraulics at the university in 1760, having been requested by the government to supervise works on rivers and waterways. His publications in this field include a work on the characteristics of riverbeds near the sea (1760) that remained in print for almost a century. Zanotti wrote the last part of Manfredi's *Elementi della geometria*, "according to the method of indivisibles"; and his lucid and informative *Trattato teorico-pratico di prospettiva* (1766) was intended for painters as well as mathematicians.

Zanotti established a reputation as an astronomer even before Manfredi's death, through the discovery of two comets, to the second of which (1739) he attributed a parabolic orbit. In 1741, under his direction, the new instruments that Manfredi had ordered from Sisson's were installed at the Bologna observatory: a mural quadrant 1.2 meters in radius and a transit instrument with a focal length of about one meter. In 1780 he added a movable equatorial telescope made by Dollond's. With the acquisition of Sisson's instruments, Zanotti's observatory became one of the finest in Europe. In 1748 and 1749, with his assistants G. Brunelli and Petronio Matteucci, he carried out repeated observations of the sun and planets, and compiled a catalog of 447 stars, all but thirty-three of them within the zodiac. The work was published with additions in 1750 as an appendix to the new edition of Manfredi's introductory volume to his ephemerides. Zanotti continued to publish the ephemerides with scrupulous care: three volumes covered the period 1751–1774, and a fourth was published posthumously by Matteucci in 1786.

Zanotti's principal observations and descriptions, including some on occultations of stars by the moon, concern six comets (1737, 1739, 1742, 1743–1744, Halley's comet of 1758, and 1769), four lunar eclipses (December 1739, January 1740, November 1745, June 1750), three solar eclipses (August 1738, July 1748, January 1750), the aurora borealis (December 1737, March 1739), and transits of Mercury (1743, 1753) and of Venus (1751) on the sun.

In 1750 Zanotti was invited by the Paris Academy of Sciences to participate in a major international research project, the main purpose of which was to measure the lunar parallax. His observations provided the program with some of its most accurate results.

Zanotti's accomplishments also included the restoration in 1776 of Gian Domenico Cassini's sundial in the church of San Petronio. The displaced perforated roofing slab forming the gnomon was raised slightly, restoring the instrument to its original height. The old deformed iron ship representing the meridian was removed and a solid foundation was laid as a base for new level marble slabs with the new brass meridian strip. Accurate geodetic and topographic measurements made in 1904 and 1925 have verified that the instrument has remained as Zanotti left it, that is, in the position that perfectly reproduces Cassini's original conditions of construction.

According to L. Palcani-Caccianemici, his collaborator and principal biographer, Zanotti was also a pioneer in the study of variable stars, a little-understood phenomenon that was then considered to represent an error of vision or an effect caused by the intervening atmosphere. Zanotti, however, maintained that changes of light occur even when the possibility of such causes is entirely ruled out. "If you observe with a telescope two stars extremely near to each other," he said, "you will see that one remains exactly the same and that the other, altered in intensity, no longer appears as before."

Unfortunately, no trace of these observations appears in Zanotti's published writings, possibly because he did not wish to seem to be questioning the incorruptibility and constancy of the heavens—a subject about which the Aristotelians who controlled the University of Bologna were particularly sensitive and uncompromising.

## BIBLIOGRAPHY

I. ORIGINAL WORKS. Most of Zanotti's astronomical memoirs appeared in the *Commentarii* of the Istituto e Accademia delle scienze di Bologna, beginning with **2**, pt. 1 (1745); the last one appeared in **7** (1791)—see index. There are also three papers, in English, in *Philosophical Transactions of the Royal Society*: on the aurora borealis, **41** (1741), 593–601; on the comet of 1739, *ibid.*, 809; and on the 1761 transit of Venus, **52** (1761), 399–414.

His most important separately published works are *Ephemerides motuum coelestium ex anno 1751 ad annum 1786*, 3 vols. (Bologna, 1750–1774); *Trattato teorico-pratico di prospettiva* (Bologna, 1766); and *La meridiana del tempio di San Petronio rinnovata l'anno 1776* (Bologna, 1779).

II. SECONDARY LITERATURE. See the following, listed chronologically: L. Palcani-Caccianemici, *De vita Eustachii Zanotti commentarius* (Bologna, 1782), translated into Italian by G. A. Maggi as "Elogio di Eustachio Zanotti" and prefixed, with a bibliography, to the new ed. of Zanotti's *Trattato teorico-pratico di prospettiva* (Milan, 1825); *Vita di Eustachio Zanotti* (n.p., n.d.), an extract from *Giornale dei letterati* (Pisa), **58** (1785), 175–197; G. Fantuzzi, *Notizie degli scrittori bolognesi*, VIII (Bologna, 1790; repr. 1965), 265–270; Noël Poudra, *Histoire de la perspective* (Paris, 1864), 529–533; and P. Riccardi, *Biblioteca matematica italiana*, II (Modena, 1873–1876; repr. Milan, 1952), 651–657.

More recent works include M. Rajna, "L'astronomia in Bologna," in *Memorie della Società degli spettroscopisti italiani*, **32** (1903), 241–250, esp. 245; Federigo Guarducci, *La meridiana di Gian Domenico Cassini nel tempio di San Petronio di Bologna riveduta nel 1904 e nel 1925* (Bologna, 1925); E. Bortolotti, *La storia della matematica nella Università di Bologna* (Bologna, 1947), 177–178; G. Horn d'Arturo, *Piccola enciclopedia astronomica*, II (Bologna, 1960), 364; and Anna Maria Matteucci, *Carlo Francesco Dotti e l'architettura bolognese del settecento*, 2nd ed. (Bologna, 1969), 44–49, *passim*.

GIORGIO TABARRONI

**ZARANKIEWICZ, KAZIMIERZ** (*b*. Czestochowa, Poland, 2 May 1902; *d*. London, England, 5 September 1959), *mathematics*.

Zarankiewicz's contributions to mathematics were in topology, the theory of graphs, the theory of complex functions, number theory, and mathematical education. In addition, he founded and for several years headed the Polish Astronautical Society.

Zarankiewicz was born and raised in a moderately well-to-do family. After obtaining his baccalaureate degree in 1919 in Bedzin, near Czestochowa, he studied mathematics at the University of Warsaw. He was awarded a Ph.D. there in 1923 for a dissertation (published in 1927) on the cut points in connected sets, and in 1924 he was made assistant to the professor of mathematics at the Warsaw Polytechnic. In 1929, following publication of his habilitation essay on a topological property of the plane (concerning the mutual cuttings of three regions and three continua), Zarankiewicz became *Dozent* in mathematics. He spent the academic year 1930–1931 working with Karl Menger at Vienna and with Richard von Mises at Berlin, where he collaborated with Stefan Bergman and other mathematicians. Upon returning to Warsaw, Zarankiewicz was assigned to teach a course in rational mechanics at the Polytechnic and courses in mathematics and statistics at the High Agricultural College. In 1936 he was invited to the University of Tomsk to lecture for a semester on conformal mappings, particularly on several problems that he had solved. He was named substitute for the professor at the Warsaw Polytechnic in 1937; but his nomination to the professorship (1939) was not confirmed until after the war.

During the German occupation of Poland, Zarankiewicz taught mathematics, clandestinely, to underground groups of high school and college students. In 1944 he was deported to a forced labor camp in Germany. Returning to the ruins of Warsaw in 1945, he resumed his courses at the Polytechnic and continued them for the rest of his life.

Zarankiewicz was appointed full professor in 1948 and spent several months of that year working at Harvard and at several other American universities. From 1949 to 1957 he supervised in Poland the Mathematical Olympics for high school students, remaining a member of its central board thereafter. At the same time he was a member of the editorial committees of *Applied Mechanics Reviews* and *Matematyka*, a Polish journal written primarily for secondary-school teachers. From 1948 to 1951 Zarankiewicz headed the Warsaw section of the Polish Mathematical Society. He maintained a long-standing active interest in astronautics and in the organization in Poland of a society founded in 1956 devoted to this field. Zarankiewicz died in London while presiding over a plenary session of the Tenth Congress of the International Astronautical Federation, of which he was vice-president. His funeral was held in Warsaw, and one of the city's streets is named for him. Zarankiewicz's topological writings deal mainly with cut points, that is, those points which disconnect (and locally disconnect) the continua, and with the continua that disconnect the spaces. In 1926 he showed, among other things, that if $C$ is a locally connected continuum (a continuous image of an interval), then the set $\tau(C)$ of all the cut points of $C$ possesses a special structure, which he characterized. In particular, the closures of the constituents of $\tau(C)$ are dendrites, that is, one-dimensional, acyclic, locally connected continua. In his doctoral dissertation Zarankiewicz introduced and investigated the important notion of the continua of convergence. He characterized the locally connected continua by the equivalence, for their closed subsets $F$, of the connectedness and of the semicontinuity of the set $C \backslash F$ between all the pairs of its points. He also characterized the dendrites $C$ by the structure of the set $C \backslash \tau(C)$ and—independently of Pavel Urysohn—the hereditarily locally connected continua by the absence, among their subsets, of continua of convergence (1927). In 1932 and in 1951 Zarankiewicz resumed and extended the study of the set $\tau(C)$ by a series of remarkable theorems. In particular, he gave a new definition of the cyclic element in G. T. Whyburn's sense, for the locally connected continua.

Zarankiewicz's studies of the cutting of spaces by continua were concerned especially with local cuttings of the plane or, which is topologically equivalent, of the sphere. In publications of 1927, 1929, and 1932, he established interesting topological characterizations of the circumference, of the straight line, and of several other lines with the aid of the number of their connectedness points, another notion that he originated. These theorems, which are more quantitative than qualitative, reflect Zarankiewicz's tendency to seek numerical solutions in every field of mathematics in which he worked. For example, generalizing R. L. Moore's theorem concerning triods in the plane, he showed that in Euclidean spaces of more than two dimensions, every family of disjoint continua each of which locally cuts the space at a point that cuts locally itself (*doppelt zerlegender Punkt*) is, at most, countable (1934).

Zarankiewicz's last publication in topology (1952), written with C. Kuratowski, deals with a problem that is still unsolved: Given $n$ disjoint regions in the plane (or on the sphere) with connected boundaries $R_1, R_2, \cdots, R_n$ and $k$ continua $C_1, C_2, \cdots, C_k$, each of which meets each of these regions, what is the minimum number $s_{k,n}$ of couples $i,j$ such that $C_i$ cuts $R_j$ (where $i = 1, 2, \cdots, k$ and $j = 1, 2, \cdots, n$)? Zarankiewicz's conjecture is that $s_{k,n} = (k - 2)(n - 2)$ for all integers $k \geq 2$ and $n \geq 2$. In 1928 he showed that $s_{3,3} = 1$ and, in the joint work of 1952, that the presumed formula holds for all $k \geq 4$ and $n \leq 4$.

In theory of graphs Zarankiewicz developed, among other topics, a criterion for the existence of a complete subgraph of highest possible order in every graph of a given order in which the minimum number of edges arising from a vertex is sufficiently high (1947). Later, Pál Turán improved this criterion and devoted an interesting study to it. Zarankiewicz, in publications of 1953 and 1954, solved, independently of K. Urbanik, a problem posed by Turán by showing that if $A$ and $B$ are finite sets of the plane, composed of $a$ and $b$ points, respectively, and if each point of $A$ is joined by a simple arc to all the points of $B$ in such a way that outside of $A$ and $B$ every point of intersection belongs to two arcs, then the number of these points of intersection is at least equal to

$$\mathrm{E}(\tfrac{1}{2}a) \cdot \mathrm{E}(\tfrac{1}{2}a - 1) \cdot \mathrm{E}(\tfrac{1}{2}b) \cdot \mathrm{E}(\tfrac{1}{2}b - 1),$$

and that this minimum is attained. In 1951 Zarankiewicz posed the problem of finding the least number $k_j(n)$ such that every set of $k_j(n)$ points of a plane net of $n^2$ points (where $n > 3$) contains $j^2$ points on $j$ lines and on $j$ columns. Several other authors have subsequently treated this problem.

Zarankiewicz's works on complex functions (1934, 1938, 1956) deal principally with the kernel (*Kernfunktion*) and its applications. Given a complete system $\{\phi_\nu(z)\}$, where $\nu = 1, 2, \cdots$, of orthonormal analytic functions in a domain $D$ of the complex plane of $z = x + iy$, the function $K_D(z,\bar{\zeta}) = \sum_{\nu=1}^{\infty} \phi_\nu(z) \overline{\phi_\nu(\zeta)}$ is called the kernel of the domain $D$. It is known that it exists for all $z$ and $\zeta$ of $D$ and depends only on $D$; that if $D$ is simply connected—that is, if the boundary of $D$ is connected—the function $W(z) = \int_0^z K_D(z,\bar{\zeta})dz$ transforms $D$ onto the interior of the circle $|W| < c$, where $c$ is a constant; that the function $K_D$ is a relative invariant—that is,

$$K_D(z,\bar{z}) = K_{D^*}(z^*[z], \overline{z^*[z]}) \cdot |dz^*(z)/dz|^2$$

for every analytic function $z^*z$ mapping the domain $D$ of the complex $z$-plane onto the domain $D^*$ of the complex $z^*$-plane—and, consequently, that the formula

$$ds_D^2(z) = K_D(z,\bar{z}) \cdot |dz|^2 =$$

$$K_{D^*}(z^*,\overline{z^*}) \cdot |dz^*|^2 = ds_{D^*}^2(z^*)$$

represents the square of the length of the line or element of an invariant metric; that the curvature of the metric

$$J_D(z,\bar{z}) = -\frac{2}{K_D(z,\bar{z})} \cdot \frac{d^2 \log K_D(z,\bar{z})}{dz d\bar{z}}$$

is an absolute invariant of the conformal mappings; and that if the boundary of $D$ is connected, $J_D(z,\bar{z})$ is a constant.

Zarankiewicz showed that when the boundary of $D$ is doubly connected—that is, has exactly two components—the function $J_D(z,\bar{z})$ is no longer constant; in this case he represented it by doubly periodic functions. He established a criterion for recognizing, with the aid of this representation, when it is that a boundary domain with two components can be transformed conformally into another domain of this type. (P. P. Kufarev determined the minimum domain, that is, into which every domain of which the boundary consists of two components is transformable by the function $W[z]$.) This Zarankiewicz result played an important role in the development of the theory of the kernel and its generalizations to several variables, notably to pseudo-conformal transformations in space of more than three dimensions.

In number theory Zarankiewicz devoted particular attention to what are called triangular numbers—that is, triplets of integers equal to the lengths of the sides of right triangles (1949). His ideas inspired a work by Sierpiński (1954), at the end of which the author reproduces an ingenious example, inspired by Zarankiewicz, of a decomposition of the set of natural numbers into two disjoint classes, neither of which contains a triplet of consecutive numbers or an infinite arithmetic progression.

*BIBLIOGRAPHY*

I. ORIGINAL WORKS. A list of Zarankiewicz's 45 publications is in *Colloquium mathematicum*, **12** (1964), 285–288. The most important are "Sur les points de division dans les ensembles connexes," in *Fundamenta mathematicae*, **9** (1927), 124–171; "Über eine topologische Eigenschaft der Ebene," *ibid.*, **11** (1928), 19–26; "Uber die lokale Zerschneidung der Ebene," in *Monatshefte für Mathematik und Physik*, **39** (1932), 43–45; "Sur la représentation conforme d'un domaine doublement connexe sur un anneau circulaire," in *Comptes rendus . . . de l'Académie des sciences*, **198** (1934), 1347–1349; "Über doppeltzerlegende Punkte," in *Fundamenta mathematicae*, **23** (1934), 166–171; "O liczbach trójkątowych" ("On Triangular Numbers"), in *Matematyka*, **2** (1949), nos. 4–5; "Sur un problème concernant les coupures des régions par des continus," in *Fundamenta mathematicae*, **39** (1952), 15–24, written with C. Kuratowski; and "On a Problem of P. Turán Concerning Graphs," *ibid.*, **41** (1954), 137–145.

II. SECONDARY LITERATURE. See S. Bergman, R. Duda, B. Knaster, Jan Mycielski, and A. Schinzel, "Kazimierz Zarankiewicz," in *Wiadomości matematyczne*, 2nd ser., **9** (1966), 175–184 (in Polish), also in *Colloquium mathematicum*, **12** (1964), 277–288 (in French), which contains a list of Zarankiewicz's works.

BRONISLAW KNASTER

**AL-ZARQĀLĪ** (or **AZARQUIEL**), **ABŪ ISḤĀQ IBRĀHĪM IBN YAḤYĀ AL-NAQQĀSH** (*d.* Córdoba, Spain, 15 October 1100),[1] *astronomy.*

During his lifetime al-Zarqālī was known in Spain as Azarquiel; the correct form of this word, al-Zarqiyāl, was preserved by Ibn al-Qifṭī.[2] The name is composed of the Arabic article *al*, the adjective *zarqāʾ* ("blue"; "the blue-eyed one"), and *ellus/el*, the diminutive form in Spain.

The few known facts of al-Zarqālī's life can be established from the autobiographical passages in his works. He must have been born in the first quarter of the eleventh century to a family of artisans.[3] His manual skill led him to enter the service of Cadi Ibn Ṣāʿid of Toledo[4] as a maker of the delicate instruments needed to continue the astronomical observations begun about 1060—possibly to emulate those carried out by Yaḥyā ibn Abī Manṣūr—perhaps by order of al-Maʾmūn of Toledo. Al-Zarqālī's intelligence encouraged his clients to supply him with the books he needed to educate himself; and around 1062 he became a member of the group of which he soon became director. He constructed the water clocks of Toledo, which al-Zuhrī[5] has described; and they must have aroused great admiration, for Moses ben ʿEzra (*d. ca.* 1135) dedicated a poem to them that begins: "Marble, work of Zarquiel." The clocks were in use until 1133, when Hamis ibn Zabara, having been given permission by Alfonso VII to try to discover how they worked, took them apart and could not reassemble them. They constituted a very precise lunar calendar and were, to some extent, the predecessors of the clocks or planetary calendar devices that became fashionable in seventeenth-century Europe.

Al-Zarqālī lived in Toledo until the insecurity of the city, repeatedly attacked by Alfonso VI, obliged him to move to Córdoba sometime after 1078. There he determined the longitude of Calbalazada (Regulus) in 1080 and the culmination of the planets a year later; in 1087 he carried out his last observations. This fact has led some writers to establish 1087 as the year of his death. Very little is known about his students, who included Muhammad ibn Ibrāhīm ibn Yahyā al-Sayyid (d. 1144). Considerably more is known about his indirect influence on such later authors as Ibn al-Kammād, al-Bitrūjī, Abu'l-Ḥasan ʿAlī, Ibn al-Bannāʾ, and Abraham IbnʿEzra.

We shall consider seven works definitely known to be by al-Zarqālī.[6] The first is the Toledan Tables. The original Arabic version has been lost, but two Latin versions have survived: one by Gerard of Cremona and one by an unknown author, perhaps John of Seville, who presents a shorter text than Gerard's. It deals only with a collective work directed by Cadi Ibn Sāʿid, in which al-Zarqālī participated and of which he wrote the definitive account. The Latin version, analyzed by Delambre in the nineteenth century and by Millás-Vallicrosa more recently, deals with a combination of processes and methods.[7] It follows the table of al-Khwārizmī in the determination of the right ascensions, and the equations of the sun and moon and of the planets; al-Battānī's table in the oblique ascension, ascendant, parallax, eclipses, and the setting of planets; Hermes' table in the equation of houses; and Thābit ibn Qurra's table in the theory of trepidation or accession and recession. Such Indian processes as the *kardaga* are used side by side with the sine, cosine, tangent, and cotangent. The table of stellar positions is apparently based on an older one corrected in precession.[8] The Toledan Tables were extraordinarily successful in the Latin world: the Marseilles Tables (*ca.* 1140) were based on them, and by the twelfth century they were used throughout Europe, ultimately displaced only by the Alfonsine Tables. They also influenced the Islamic West, in the works of Ibn al-Kammād, for example.

*Almanac* of Ammonius[9] was elaborated by al-Zarqālī in 1089, using material that predated 800, as M. Boutelle[10] has demonstrated. Millás-Vallicrosa identified the Aumenius Humeniz in various texts with Ammonius, son of Hermias, a disciple of Proclus, who restored the Platonic school of Alexandria in the late fifth and early sixth centuries. Study of the tabular values, unique in the medieval Arabic literature, shows that the *Almanac* deals with the combination of planetary values and Ptolemaic parameters with the Babylonian doctrine of the limit years, calculated according to the linear system A by Nabu-Rimannu, as van der Waerden[11] has demonstrated. Drawing on the works of Hipparchus and Ptolemy,[12] al-Zarqālī's *Almanac* was known in Europe as part of al-Bitrūjī's *corpus* until the fifteenth century.

The trigonometrical portion of the *Almanac* presents the same minglings of sources and contains tables of sines, cosines, versed sines, secants, and tangents. The work was translated into Latin (John of Pavia, 1154; William of Saint Cloud, 1296), Hebrew (Jacob ibn Tibbon, 1301), Portuguese, Catalan, and Castilian. Regiomontanus may be considered one of the last to express al-Zarqālī's views.

*Suma referente al movimiento del sol* has been lost.[13] Its subject is known, since the identically entitled work of Thābit ibn Qurra, written about two centuries earlier, is extant, and al-Zarqālī refers to the latter work in his *Tratado . . . de las estrellas fijas*. It is based on twenty-five years of observations in which he discovered the proper motion of the solar apogee, which he set as 1° every 299 common years (12.04″ annually) counted in the same direction as the zodiacal signs. This discovery is shown in the Marseilles Tables (*ca.* 1140), and Abu'l-Ḥasan ʿAlī (*fl.* 1260) attempted to explain it by means of an epicycle, which he sought to provide.[14]

*Tratado relativo al movimiento de las estrellas fijas* is preserved in the Hebrew translation by Samuel ben Yehuda (called Miles of Marseilles).[15] Known by Ibn Rushd,[16] the *Tratado* sought to demonstrate mathematically the trepidation theory according to which the movement of the sphere of the fixed stars is determined by the movement of a straight line that joins the center of the earth with a movable point on a base circle or epicycle. Comparing his observations with those of earlier authors, al-Zarqālī explained the trepidation theory according to three models that situate the epicycle (1) in a meridian plane, (2) in the plane of the ecliptic, and (3) with two equal epicycles centered in the mean equinoctial points normal to the equator. He always took the beginning of Aries as a movable point on the epicycle and referred its motion to the vernal equinox. He thus justified the accession and retrocession of the fixed stars, studied and calculated their longitudinal movement, and determined the dimensions of the epicycle (radius) and period of trepidation in the three models. Having critically studied the results to which the three models led him, al-Zarqālī concluded that the third conforms most to the observational data and, relying on it, he constructed tables of mean movement at the beginning of Aries in Christian, Arab, and Persian years. In the same work he studied the variation in the obliquity of the ecliptic by the action of two small circles, one concentric to an equator of 23°43' diameter and the other with its center in a point of the first, 10' in diameter.

*Tratado de la azafea*[17] concerns the *azafea*. Al-Zarqālī constructed one superior to the universal sheet of ʿAlī ibn Khalaf.[18] The latter, which exerted only limited influence in the Muslim world—and none in the Latin world—contained the stereographic projection of the sphere on a plane normal to the ecliptic that cuts it along the solstitial line Cancer–Capricorn. In his *Tratado de la azafea* (*al-ṣafīḥa*) al-Zarqālī presented the stereographic projections of the equatorial circle and of the circle of the ecliptic at the same time.

The construction of the apparatus and the formulation of the corresponding rules occurred in several stages. Before 1078 a draft of the *Tratado* was dedicated to al-Maʾmūn of Toledo (*azafea maʾmūniyya*); it was not transmitted to Alfonso X. The *azafea ʿabbādiyya* (dedicated to al-Muʿtamid ibn ʿAbbād) subsequently appeared in two versions: the major one, comprising 100 chapters, was translated into Castilian at the court of Alfonso X[19] and exerted little influence in the Latin world; the minor one, of sixty-one chapters, was transmitted through Jacob ibn Tibbon, Moshe Galino, and William the Englishman to influence Gemma Frisius, Juan de Rojas (*fl.* 1550), and Philippe de La Hire.[20]

The back of the copy of this instrument, at the Fabra Observatory of Barcelona,[21] presents the orthographical projection of the sphere and, in the fourth quadrant, a representation of sines that Millás-Vallicrosa called the quadrant *vetustísimo* ("very ancient"), which is believed to date from the mid-tenth century in the Iberian Peninsula.[22]

Arabic treatises on the *azafea* frequently contain a description of the *azafea shakāziyya*, which is not now known. It was the forerunner, however, of the *shakāzi*[23] quadrant invented by Ibn Tibūgā (1358–1447), who used the same projection system on its face as in al-Zarqālī's *azafea*, the only difference being the omission of the ecliptic projec-

tion and the major circles of longitude and the minor circles of latitude. Also, there was an alteration of the quadrant of the umbra, which was at the back of the *azafea* and was determined by an arc of extensive or convex umbras parallel to the arc of altitude. There was an ordinary zodiacal calendar on the back, another of right ascension, and the projection of the fixed stars that made it possible to determine, by means of the alidade, the equatorial coordinates of any fixed star through simple reading. The projection system used seems to be the polar stereographic one of the ordinary astrolabe.

*Tratado de la lámina de los siete planetas*, dedicated to al-Muʿtamid, was written in 1081 and surpasses the book on the sheets of the seven planets by Ibn al-Samh (*d.* 1035)[24]; it is a predecessor of the *Aequatorium planetarium* of the Renaissance. The importance of the Arabic text lies in its clarification of one of the most debated passages in medieval astronomy, for in the graphic representation included in the Castilian translation ordered by Alfonso X (The Wise) the orbit of Mercury is not circular.[25] On this basis it has been alleged that al-Zarqālī anticipated Kepler in stating that orbits—the orbit of Mercury in this case—are elliptical. Although the Arabic text merely states that an orbit is *bayḍī* ("oval"), it shows that al-Zarqālī treated Mercury in the same deductive way that Kepler dealt with Mars in his *Astronomia nova*. Before establishing his first law, Kepler considered the possibility of elliptical orbits; it is not known whether he knew al-Zarqālī's text.[26]

*Influencias y figuras de los planetas* is an astrological treatise of no particular importance.

## NOTES

1. Ibn al-Abbār, *Takmila*, Bel-Ben Cheneb, ed. (Algiers, 1920), no. 358, p. 169.
2. *Tarīkh al-ḥukamāʾ*, J. Lippert, ed. (Leipzig, 1903), 57.
3. Isḥāq Israeli, *Yesod ʿolam* (Berlin, 1848), IV, 7.
4. *Ṭabaqāt al-umam*, Luis Cheikho, ed. (Beirut, 1912), 74; French trans. by Régis Blachère (Paris, 1935), 138–139.
5. Castilian trans. by J. M. Millás-Vallicrosa, *Estudios sobre Azarquiel* (Madrid–Granada, 1943–1950), 6–9.
6. The order of the works is that of Millás-Vallicrosa, *op. cit.,* the fundamental work on the subject.
7. E. S. Kennedy, "A Survey of Islamic Astronomical Tables," in *Transactions of the American Philosophical Society*, n.s. **46**, no. 2 (1956), no. 24.
8. Analysis in Millás-Vallicrosa, *op. cit.,* 22–71.
9. Edition of the Arabic canons, Castilian trans., and corresponding tables, *ibid.,* 72–237.
10. M. Boutelle, "The Almanac of Azarquiel," in *Centaurus*, **12**, no. 1 (1967), 12–19.
11. "The Date of Invention of Babylonian Planetary Theory,"

in *Archive for History of Exact Sciences*, **5**, no. 1 (1968), 70–78.

12. *Almagest*, IX, 3.

13. See Millás-Vallicrosa, *op. cit.*, 239–247.

14. This discovery must have been made by al-Zarqālī. See Willy Hartner, "Al-Battānī," in *DSB*, I, 507–516.

15. Edition and Castilian trans. by Millás-Vallicrosa, *op. cit.*, 239–343.

16. See the Castilian trans. by Carlos Quirós Rodríguez, *Compendio de metafísica de Averroes* (Madrid, 1919); *Kitāb mā ba'd al-ṭabī'a* (Hyderabad, 1945), 135–136; and esp. O. Neugebauer, "Thâbit ben Qurra, 'On the Solar Year' and 'On the Motion of the Eighth Sphere,' " in *Proceedings of the American Philosophical Society*, **106**, no. 3 (1962), 264–299; B. R. Goldstein, "On the Theory of Trepidation," in *Centaurus*, **10** (1964), 232–247; and J. D. North, "Medieval Star Catalogues and the Movement of the Eighth Sphere," in *Archives internationales d'histoire des sciences*, **20** (1967), 71–83.

17. See Millás-Vallicrosa, *op. cit.*, 425–455.

18. The instructions for the construction and use of this instrument appear in *Los libros del saber de astronomía*, M. Rico y Sinobas, ed., III (Madrid, 1864), 1–132.

19. *Ibid.*, 135–237.

20. Jacob ibn Tibbon, *Tractat de l'assafea d'Azarquiel*, ed. of the Hebrew and Latin texts and Catalan trans. by J. M. Millás-Vallicrosa (Barcelona, 1933); E. Poulle, "Un instrument astronomique dans l'Occident latin: La 'saphea,' " in *A. Giuseppe Ermini* (Spoleto, 1970), 491–510; and F. Maddison, "Hugo Helt and the Rojas Astrolabe Projection," in *Revista da Faculdade de ciências, Universidade de Coimbra*, **39** (1966).

21. J. M. Millás-Vallicrosa, "Un ejemplar de azafea árabe de Azarquiel," in *al-Andalus*, **9**, no. 1 (1944), 111–119.

22. See J. Vernet, "La ciencia en el islam y occidente," in *XII Settimane di studio del centro italiano di studi sull'alto medioevo*, II (Spoleto, 1965), 555–556.

23. See Julio Samsó Moya, "Un instrumento astronómico de raigambre zarqalí: El cuadrante šakāzī de Ibn Ṭībugā, in *Memorias de la Real Academia de buenas letras de Barcelona*, **13** (1971–1975), 5–31.

24. See Millás-Vallicrosa, *op. cit.*, III, 241–271.

25. *Ibid.*, 272–284.

26. See Willy Hartner, *Oriens, Occidens* (Hildesheim, 1968), 474–478, 486.

J. VERNET

**ZAVADOVSKY, MIKHAIL MIKHAYLOVICH** (*b.* Pokrovka, Kherson guberniya [now Kirovograd], Russia, 29 July 1891; *d.* Moscow, U.S.S.R., 28 March 1957), *biology*.

Zavadovsky graduated in 1914 from the natural sciences section of the Faculty of Physics and Mathematics of Moscow University, with a dissertation on the lipoid semipermeable covering of the eggs of *Ascaris megalocephala*. From 1915 to 1918 he was assistant to N. K. Koltsov at the Moscow University for Women and, after receiving his master's degree in 1918, became privatdocent of experimental biology at Moscow University. He worked at the Askania Nova Zoo and at the University of the Crimea from 1919 to 1921, when he resumed teaching at Moscow University. From 1922 to 1924 he was professor at the Karl Liebknecht Institute of National Education in Moscow.

He assumed the post of head of the department of general biology at the Second Moscow State University (1924–1928) and from 1925 was director of the Moscow zoo, where he organized a laboratory of experimental biology. In 1929 he became head of the laboratory of the physiology of growth of the Institute of Livestock Breeding of the Lenin All-Union Academy of Agricultural Sciences, and from 1930 to 1948 he headed the department and laboratory of the dynamics of development at the First Moscow State University.

In his studies of the developmental conditions of parasitic worms (Ascaris, Enterobius, Trichostrongylidae) Zavadovsky paid special attention to the importance of external factors, such as oxygen and the chemical constitution of the environment, with the aim of developing measures to combat infection in man and domestic animals. He published about forty articles on experimental parasitology.

Zavadovsky also analyzed the development of sexual characteristics. Detailed studies of the effects of castration and the transplantation of sex glands in chickens led him to conclude that some of the secondary sexual characteristics depend on their development in the hormones of the sex glands and that some are independent of it. These results were confirmed in his studies of ducks, pheasants, antelopes, and horned cattle. The similarity of gelded males and spayed females testified to the equipotentiality of the soma of both sexes.

Zavadovsky established that the monosexuality of female birds and the bisexuality of the male—and the opposite among mammals and amphibians—correspond to the distribution of sex chromosomes: XY in female and XX in male birds, and the reverse among mammals and amphibians. Zavadovsky investigated the interrelationships between secondary sexual characteristics and the sex glands and studied the interaction of the endocrine glands. He concluded that a ± mutual influence exists: an organ that stimulates another also is inhibited by it. This was an important application to biology of the cybernetic principle of positive or negative feedback.

On the basis of his study of the sexual cycle of laboratory and farm animals, Zavadovsky suggested the possibility of hormonal stimulation of multiple pregnancy in sheep, by introducing the blood serum of a mare in foal. The applications of his proposal were especially important in the breeding of Karakul sheep.

## BIBLIOGRAPHY

I. ORIGINAL WORKS. Zavadovsky's writings include "O lipoidnoy polupronitsaemoy obolochke yaits *Ascaris megalocephala*" ("On the Lipoid Semipermeable Covering of the Eggs of *Ascaris megalocephala*"), in *Uchenye zapiski universiteta im. Shanyavskogo,* **1–2** (1914–1915); *Pol i razvitie ego priznakov. K analizu formoobrazovania u zhivotnykh* ("Sex and the Development of Its Signs. Toward an Analysis of Formation in Animals"; Moscow, 1922); *Pol zhivotnykh i ego prevrashchenie* ("Sex of Animals and Its Transformation"; Moscow, 1923); *Ravnopotentsialna li soma samtsa i samki u ptits i mlikopitayushchikh?* ("Are the Male and Female Soma Equipotent in Birds and Mammals?"; Moscow, 1923); "Hängt der Alterdimorphismus von der Geschlechtsdrüsen ab?" in *Biologia generalis,* **2** (1926), 631–638; "The Bisexual Nature of the Hen and Experimental Hermaphroditism in Hens," *ibid.,* **3** (1927); and "Priroda skorlupy yaits askarid raznykh vidov" ("The Nature of the Shells of the Eggs of Various Kinds of Ascarids"), in *Trudy Laboratorii eksperimentalnoi biologii Moskovskogo zooparka,* **4** (1928), 201–207; and *Vneshnie i vnutrennie faktory razvitia* ("External and Internal Factors of Development"; Moscow, 1928).

See also *Dinamika razvitia organizma* ("Dynamics of Development in the Organism"; Moscow, 1931); "Printsip ± vzaimodeystvia v razvitii osobi" ("Principle of ± Mutual Interaction in the Development of the Individual"), in *Uspekhi sovremennoi biologii,* **2** (1933), 86–103; "Upravlenie polovym tsiklom krolikov, ovets, i korov" ("Control of the Sexual Cycle of Rabbits, Sheep, and Cows"), in *Trudy po dinamike razvitiya,* **11** (1939), 15–24; "Opyt eksperimentalnogo mnogoplodia ovets" ("An Experimental Attempt at Multiple Pregnancy in Sheep"), *ibid.,* 94–112; *Estestvennoe i eksperimentalnoe mnogoplodie korov* ("Natural and Experimental Multiple Pregnancy in Cows"; Alma Ata, 1947): and *Teoria i praktika gormonalnogo metoda stimulyatsii mnogoplodia selskokhozyaystvennykh zhivotnykh* ("Theory and Practice of the Hormonal Method of Stimulating Multiple Pregnancy in Agricultural Animals"; Moscow, 1963).

II. SECONDARY LITERATURE. See N. I. Vavilov, "Prof. M. M. Zavadovskomu (Po povodu 20-letia ego nauchnoy deyatelnosti)" ("To Prof. M. M. Zavadovsky [On the 20th Anniversary of His Scientific Career]"), in *Trudy po dinamike razvitiya,* **10** (1935), 9–11.

L. J. BLACHER

**ZAVARZIN, ALEKSEY ALEKSEEVICH** (*b.* St. Petersburg, Russia [now Leningrad, U.S.S.R.], 25 March 1886; *d.* Leningrad, 25 July 1945), *histology, biology, embryology.*

Zavarzin completed his secondary studies at the technical high school in St. Petersburg in 1902 and graduated from the natural sciences section of the Faculty of Physics and Mathematics at St. Petersburg in 1907. Retained in the histology department of A. S. Dogel to prepare for a teaching career, he passed his master's examination in zoology and comparative anatomy in 1910 and defended his dissertation, on the structure of the sensory nervous system and the optical ganglia of insects, three years later. He was subsequently professor of histology and embryology at the University of Perm (1916–1922), at the Military Medical Academy in Leningrad (1922–1936), at the First Leningrad Medical Institute (1936–1945), and at the University of Tomsk (1941–1944). From 1932 to 1945 he headed the department of general morphology of the All-Union Institute of Experimental Medicine and in 1944–1945 was director of the Institute of Cytology, Histology, and Embryology of the U.S.S.R. Academy of Sciences.

In a series of works on the histology of the nervous system of insects (1911–1924) Zavarzin established the morphological similarity of the optical centers and of the trunk brain of systematically distant animals (mammals and insects) and formulated a theory of parallelism of histological structure that he subsequently stated in "Ob evolyutsionnoy dinamike tkaney" ("On the Evolutionary Dynamics of Tissues," 1934). In a two-part monograph devoted to the structure of blood cells and connective tissue (1945–1947) Zavarzin further developed the evolutionary trend in histology, transforming it from a purely descriptive into a dynamic discipline.

Zavarzin also worked on problems of general biology—the origin of multicelled organisms, the biological basis of inflammation, the theory of embryonic layers, the theory of the cellular structure of organisms, the significance of remote sensory organs in the formation of the encephalic section of the central nervous system, the relationship between form, function, and development as three aspects of a unified biological process, and the coordination of changes of histological structures in onto- and phylogenesis.

## BIBLIOGRAPHY

I. ORIGINAL WORKS. Zavarzin's textbooks, the fruit of almost thirty years' teaching, are *Kratkoe rukovodstvo po embriologii cheloveka i pozvonochnykh zhivotnykh* ("A Short Guide to the Embryology of Man and the Vertebrates"; Leningrad–Moscow, 1929; 4th ed.,

Leningrad, 1939); *Kurs mikroskopicheskoy anatomii* ("Course in Microscopic Anatomy"; Moscow–Leningrad, 1930); *Kurs obshchey gistologii* ("Course in General Histology"; Leningrad, 1932); *Kurs gistologii* ("Course in Histology"), 2 pts. (Moscow, 1933); *Kurs gistologii i mikroskopicheskoy anatomii* ("Course in Histology and Microscopic Anatomy"; 5th ed., Leningrad, 1939); *Kurs gistologii*, 6th ed. (Moscow, 1946), written with A. V. Rumyantsev; and *Isbrannye trudy* ("Selected Works"), 4 vols. (Moscow–Leningrad, 1950–1953).

Specialized works include "Histologische Studien über Insekten," in *Zeitschrift für wissenschaftliche Zoologie*, **97** (1911), 481–510; **100** (1912), 245–286, 447–458; **108** (1913), 175–257; and **122** (1924), 97–115, 323–424; and "Der Parallelismus der Strukturen als ein Grundprinzip der Morphologie," *ibid.*, **124** (1925), 118–212.

Among his monographs are *Gistologicheskie issledovania chuvstvitelnoy nervnoy sistemy i opticheskikh gangliev nasekomykh* ("Histological Research on the Sensory Nervous System and the Optical Ganglia of Insects"; St. Petersburg, 1913), his master's thesis; *Ocherki po evolyutsionnoy gistologii nervnoy sistemy* ("Sketches in the Evolutionary Histology of the Nervous System"; 1941); and *Ocherki po evolyutsionnoy gistologii krovi i soedinitelnoy tkani* ("Sketches in the Evolutionary Histology of the Blood and Connective Tissue"), 2 vols. (Moscow, 1945–1947).

II. SECONDARY LITERATURE. On Zavarzin and his work, see A. I. Abrikosov, "Aleksey Alekseevich Zavarzin," in *Vestnik Akademii meditsinskikh nauk SSSR* (1946), no. 1, 65–67, an obituary; D. N. Nasonov and A. A. Zavarzin (his son), *Aleksey Alekseevich Zavarzin* (Moscow, 1951), with bibliography; and G. A. Nevmyvaka; *Aleksey Alekseevich Zavarzin* (Leningrad, 1971).

L. J. BLACHER


**AL-ZAYYĀTĪ AL-GHARNĀTĪ, AL-ḤASAN IBN MUḤAMMAD AL-WAZZĀN.** See Leo the African.


**ZEEMAN, PIETER** (*b.* Zonnemaire, Zeeland, Netherlands, 25 May 1865; *d.* Amsterdam, Netherlands, 9 October 1943), *physics*.

Zeeman is best remembered for his observations in 1896 of the magneto-optic phenomenon that almost immediately was named the Zeeman effect. His experimental discovery was not fortuitous, but the fruition of theoretical views that had motivated attempts over a span of thirty-five years to detect some such interaction between magnetism and light. Zeeman's initial observations were beautifully comprehended by H. A. Lorentz' electromagnetic theory, which also served to guide Zeeman in

the very early refinement and extension of his discovery. As a result Zeeman and Lorentz shared the 1902 Nobel Prize for physics in recognition of their accomplishment and of the promise, since overwhelmingly fulfilled, of the Zeeman effect for contributing to the understanding of spectra and the particulate structure of matter.

Following his elementary education in the small village of Zonnemaire, Zeeman was sent by his parents—Catharinus Farandinus Zeeman, a Lutheran minister, and Wilhelmina Worst—to the secondary school at Zierikzee, five miles away. He subsequently studied classical languages for two years at the gymnasium in Delft in order to satisfy requirements for the university. His early scientific education seems to have been adequate, for he published an account of the aurora borealis from Zonnemaire and impressed Kamerlingh Onnes, whom he met at Delft, with his grasp of Maxwell's investigations on heat. Zeeman entered the University of Leiden in 1885 and spent nearly a dozen years there, working with Kamerlingh Onnes and Lorentz and becoming the latter's assistant in 1890. For his careful measurements of the Kerr effect, Zeeman won the gold medal of the Netherlands Scientific Society of Haarlem in 1892 and was awarded the doctorate in 1893. After a semester at the Kohlrausch Institute in Strasbourg, he returned to the University of Leiden as a *Privatdozent*. In 1895 he married Johanna Elisabeth Lebret; they had a son and three daughters.

From January 1897 until his retirement in 1935, Zeeman was associated with the University of Amsterdam. Appointed a lecturer, he was promoted to professor of physics in 1900, succeeded the retiring J. D. van der Waals as director of the Physical Institute in 1908; in 1923 he also became director of the new Laboratorium Physica, later renamed the Zeeman Laboratory. Zeeman the master experimentalist was most effective as a teacher in his regular informal discussions with advanced degree candidates concerning the progress and problems of their laboratory research. He received many awards and honors, including honorary degrees from at least ten universities; was a member of a number of academies; and was *associé étranger* of the Paris Academy of Sciences. He served as secretary of the Mathematics-Physics Section of the Royal Netherlands Academy of Sciences, Amsterdam, and was a knight of the Order of Orange-Nassau and commander of the Order of the Netherlands Lion.

Zeeman's was the third magneto-optic effect to be discovered. In 1845 Faraday had observed the first, which related magnetism and propagated light, and served as the experimental basis for subsequent attempts to discover a magnetic influence upon a source of light. The theoretical basis was provided by William Thomson (Lord Kelvin) and by Maxwell's establishment of the electromagnetic nature of light. Zeeman interrupted his measurements of the Kerr effect (the second magneto-optic effect to be discovered) to improvise an experiment, which proved unsuccessful, seeking some change in the spectrum of a sodium flame that was burning in a magnetic field. About a year later Zeeman learned that Faraday had attempted this experiment without success in 1862. His reaction was that if Faraday, whom he considered the greatest experimental genius of all time, had thought the experiment worth doing, then he could well afford to repeat it again, using the best spectroscopic apparatus and a specially designed electromagnet. Thus equipped, Zeeman observed that the D-lines of the sodium spectrum were decidedly broadened. Within a few weeks he obtained this broadening for other spectral lines and for the related absorption spectra, and convincingly demonstrated that the broadening was a direct effect of the magnetic field.

These results were presented to the Amsterdam Academy of Sciences on 31 October 1896. At the next meeting of the Academy, four weeks later, Zeeman reported that the Lorentz theory not only comprehended his initial findings but also had been used to predict that the light from the edges of the magnetically broadened lines should be polarized—and, further, that he had observed this polarization. The Lorentz theory also provided the equation

$$\frac{T'-T}{T} = \frac{e}{m} \cdot \frac{HT}{4\pi},$$

where $T$ is the natural period of vibration of an ion of charge $e$ and mass $m$, and $T'$ is its period in a magnetic field of strength $H$. This equation enabled Zeeman, from his measurements of $H$, $T$, and $T'$, to calculate the charge-to-mass ratio of the vibrating "ion" of the sodium atom. His next paper established that the "ion" was negatively charged.

In the spring of 1897, after his move to the University of Amsterdam, Zeeman resolved a magnetically "broadened" spectral line into the triplet of distinct polarized components that the Lorentz theory predicted for a sufficiently intense magnetic field. This in a very real sense was the peak of the Zeeman-Lorentz investigation of the Zeeman effect. For his more exacting measurements at this

time, Zeeman had to travel to the University of Groningen to use Hermann Haga's superior spectroscopic apparatus; and by the end of 1897, the limitations of his research facilities at Amsterdam proved decisive for Zeeman. The main deficiency, which persisted until the building of his own laboratory, was in the mountings of his spectroscope. The most interesting and demanding measurements required an isolated and rigid mounting system to ensure sharp definition in the photographs. Zeeman's attempts in this regard were usually spoiled (less than one photograph in thirty was usable) by vibrations due either to human movement on the same floor as his laboratory or to the traffic of Amsterdam—even in the middle of the night. After a promising but qualitative anticipation of a fundamental relationship between Zeeman effect patterns and the laws of spectral series (subsequently called Preston's law), Zeeman felt compelled to abandon this suggestive investigation and turn to less exacting studies of the Zeeman effect and related matters. For these researches, which fully engaged him over the next fifteen years, the magneto-optic theory of Woldemar Voigt performed the same roles that Lorentz' theory had for Zeeman's earlier investigations.

During World War I, Zeeman initiated a systematic redetermination of the velocity of propagation of light in moving transparent media. Early in the nineteenth century Fresnel's optical theory had required that light propagated longitudinally with respect to moving glass would suffer a velocity change of $\left(1 - \frac{1}{\mu^2}\right)v$, where the factor $\left(1 - \frac{1}{\mu^2}\right)$ was the Fresnel coefficient, $\mu$ was the index of refraction, and $v$ was the velocity of the glass. In the middle of the century Fizeau had used interference techniques to obtain experimental support for the Fresnel coefficient in the case of light traversing flowing water. Thirty-five years later Michelson and Morley repeated Fizeau's experiment, and with their more precise interferometer they obtained a value in closer agreement with the Fresnel coefficient. Zeeman's interest in this question was generated by the theoretical investigations that Lorentz conducted in 1895 and subsequently reconsidered in terms of relativity theory. By taking into account the dispersion of light in the medium, Lorentz deduced that the coefficient must be $\left(1 - \frac{1}{\mu^2} - \frac{\lambda}{\mu} \cdot \frac{d\mu}{d\lambda}\right)$, where $\lambda$ is the wavelength of light. In two papers of 1915 and 1916, Zeeman essentially repeated the Michelson-Morley experiment with water and showed that the experimental value of the coefficient *did* vary with the wavelength of the light used, and that within his limits of experimental error it confirmed the Lorentz rather than the Fresnel expression. In 1919 and 1920 Zeeman collaborated with others to communicate three additional papers dealing with the same measurements, but for quartz and glass rather than water. The use of rapidly moving solid substances imposed extraordinary experimental difficulties that Zeeman painstakingly surmounted in order to obtain experimental results further supporting the Lorentz refinement of the Fresnel coefficient.

In 1918 Zeeman published the results of another extremely meticulous set of experiments that also carried profound implications for relativity theory. These measurements, which Zeeman conducted at his country home after determining that they could not be made in the laboratory because of the ever-present vibrations, established an equality of the inertial and gravitational mass for certain crystals and radioactive substances to within one part in twenty or thirty million.

With the facilities of his new laboratory available after 1923, Zeeman, in collaboration with others, finally turned to experiments involving precision measurements of the Zeeman effect. Most notable were a series of investigations of the magnetic resolution of the spectral lines of certain noble gases and, in 1932, a detailed and beautifully presented study of the hyperfine structure and Zeeman effect of the strong spectral lines of rhenium, both of which confirmed the value of the nuclear moment of the two rhenium isotopes.

*BIBLIOGRAPHY*

I. ORIGINAL WORKS. Zeeman's main magneto-optic papers, written in the period 1896–1913, were collected and republished in the commemorative volume *Verhandelingen van Dr. P. Zeeman over magneto-optische Verschijnselen*, H. A. Lorentz, H. Kamerlingh Onnes, I. M. Graftdijk, J. J. Hallo, and H. R. Woltjer, eds. (Leiden, 1921). In *Researches in Magneto-Optics* (London, 1913) Zeeman discussed his own and others' contributions during this same period to Zeeman effect and closely related phenomena, and appended a very valuable bibliography. Nearly all of Zeeman's published papers are cataloged in Poggendorff, IV, 1682; V, 1404–1405; and VI, 2957–2958.

II. SECONDARY LITERATURE. For information on Zeeman see the "Biography" in *Nobel Lectures. Physics, 1901–1921* (Amsterdam, 1967), 41–44; Lord Rayleigh, "Pieter Zeeman 1865–1943," in *Obituary Notices of Fellows of the Royal Society of London*, **4** (1944), 591–595; and H. Kamerlingh Onnes, "Zeeman's Ont-

dekking van het naar hem genoemde Effect," in *Physica*, **1** (1921), 241–250.

JAMES BROOKES SPENCER

**ZEILLER, RENÉ CHARLES** (*b.* Nancy, France, 14 January 1847; *d.* Paris, France, 27 November 1915), *paleobotany.*

A number of Zeiller's ancestors were graduates of the École Polytechnique and his family environment was propitious to his intellectual development. He early developed an interest in botany through contact with his maternal grandfather, Charles Guibal, who took him on excursions through the Lorraine countryside. After attending the Lycée Bonaparte in Paris and then the *lycée* in Nancy, Zeiller studied at the École Polytechnique in Paris and at the École des Mines in Nancy, where he obtained his degree in 1870.

At the beginning of 1871 Zeiller was named engineer of the *sous-arrondissement* of Tours and assigned to supervise work on a portion of the Orléans railway. He returned to Paris in 1874, still working for the same administration and holding the same rank for ten years, until his promotion to chief engineer. In 1882 he transferred to the Service de Topographie Souterraine des Bassins Houillers de France. Rising steadily through the hierarchy of the Conseil Général des Mines, he ultimately became its president in 1911. Admired for his scrupulousness in fulfilling his duties, he was appointed, in addition, a member of the Commission des Appareils à Vapeur.

Zeiller's first publications dealt with technical subjects, namely with the application of geology to the detection of metal-bearing deposits. Although he faithfully executed all his administrative tasks, he still found time to pursue his interest in the study of fossil plants. In this research he was able to profit from his knowledge of both botany and geology and to draw conclusions useful in one or the other of these fields. In 1878 he was appointed *chargé de cours* of plant paleontology at the École des Mines in Paris. Named curator of the school's paleontology collections in 1881, he made such important additions to the collections that scientists came from all over the world to study them.

Zeiller studied fossil plants in order to determine their structures and relationships. At the same time he viewed them as constituents of large groups, the relative ages and geographic distribution of which he attempted to establish. His various memoirs in the series *Gîtes miñeraux de la France* (published by the Ministry of Public Works) are models of good scientific publications. In them he dealt also with purely botanical questions. For example, he investigated the mode of fructification of fossil ferns, a subject that long had held his attention. In the course of answering questions raised by leading scientists who held opposing views, Zeiller elaborated several brilliant demonstrations. He proved that *Sigillaria*, in spite of their centrifugal secondary wood and the composition of the vascular strands of their leaves, are cryptogams. This conclusion, a result of his discovery of cones, was in opposition to the French school of Brongniart but in accord with English authors. Through his study of carbonaceous impressions of *Sphenophyllum* fructifications, Zeiller arrived at the conclusion that these plants have no true relation with any living type. His description of several species of *Psaronius* constitutes a model of anatomical research.

Zeiller was especially interested in the Cycadofilicales, and his clear and precise account of the "Fougères à graines" is still worth reading. Finally, after his trenchant critique, the existence of a group of so-called proangiosperms (proposed by Gaston de Saporta) could no longer be accepted.

Zeiller did not restrict his numerous publications to material gathered in France. Through his study of the *Glossopteris* floras (he established that they come from the Permian-Triassic period, as the geologists held) and his attribution of different ages—and not always from the Carboniferous—to coals of varied origins (Tonkin, Chile, New Caledonia), he was the author of several revolutionary ideas.

Zeiller had an impressive capacity for work. Beyond his professional activities and personal research, he also wrote a remarkable treatise on paleobotany and regularly published bibliographic analyses containing abundant new critical commentary. In spite of an incurable disease, he retained his kindly manner until the very end.

### BIBLIOGRAPHY

On Zeiller and his work, see G. Bonnier, "René Zeiller," in *Revue générale de botanique*, **28** (1916), 354–367, with portrait, and *ibid.*, **29** (1917), 33–55, which lists his works; A. Carpentier, "René Zeiller (1847–1915). Son oeuvre paléobotanique," in *Bulletin. Société botanique de France*, **25**, 5th ser. (1928), 46–67, with portrait and list of Zeiller's works; and D. H. Scott, "Charles René Zeiller," in *Proceedings of the Linnean Society of London* (1916), 74–78.

F. STOCKMANS

**ZEISE, WILLIAM CHRISTOPHER** (*b*. Slagelse, Denmark, 15 October 1789; *d*. Copenhagen, Denmark, 12 November 1847), *chemistry*.

The son of Friedrich Zeise, a pharmacist, and Johanna Helena Hammond, Zeise developed an interest in the natural sciences while attending secondary school, which he left in 1805 without graduating. He then was admitted to a pharmacy in Copenhagen—the customary way in Denmark of beginning the study of the natural sciences; the pharmacist for whom he worked was extraordinary professor of chemistry at the University of Copenhagen. After a few months poor health obliged Zeise to return to the family pharmacy in Slagelse, where he continued his studies. The influence of Lavoisier's concepts was so great that by 1806 he had rearranged his father's pharmacy according to the antiphlogistic nomenclature, officially introduced in the Danish pharmacopoeia the previous year.

After returning to Copenhagen in 1806, Zeise lived with Oersted and his family. Oersted, who had recently become extraordinary professor of physics and chemistry at Copenhagen, appointed Zeise his lecture assistant. In 1809 he began the study of medicine, physics, and chemistry; and in 1815 he graduated with a degree in pharmacy. The following year he received his master's degree, and in 1817 he defended his doctoral dissertation, on the action of alkalies on organic substances.

Zeise visited chemical laboratories in Göttingen and Paris in 1818 and in 1819 returned to Copenhagen, where, under Oersted's influence, he established one of the first laboratories in Europe for analytical and organic chemistry. In 1822 he became extraordinary professor of chemistry at the University of Copenhagen and from 1829 until his death was professor of organic chemistry at the Polytechnic Institute of Copenhagen, which had been established on Oersted's initiative. In 1824 he was elected a member of the Royal Danish Academy of Sciences.

Zeise's investigation of organic sulfur compounds led to the discovery of a new class of organic compounds that he named xanthogenates (usually called xanthates), because they were isolated as yellow potassium salts in 1823. Other classes of sulfur compounds that he discovered include the thioalcohols (thiols), in 1833, for which he coined the name mercaptan because they form insoluble mercury salts (*corpus mercurium captans*), and the sulfides (thioethers), in 1836.

Zeise's work on organic platinum compounds in the early 1830's involved him in the controversy between Dumas and Liebig. Zeise believed that his own elemental analysis of these compounds supported Dumas's etherin theory and his rules of substitution, but Liebig considered Zeise's analysis to be incorrect. Vehemently objecting to Liebig's insinuations, Zeise repeated the analysis and completely verified the composition as first established. Curiously, his investigations of mercaptans and sulfides decided the dispute between Liebig and the French chemists in Liebig's favor.

Zeise belongs to the group of organic chemists who laid the foundations of scientific organic chemistry in the first half of the nineteenth century. He also studied the composition of the products obtained by the dry distillation of tobacco and tobacco smoke (1843) and undertook one of the earliest investigations of carotene (1846).

## BIBLIOGRAPHY

I. ORIGINAL WORKS. A complete bibliography of Zeise's writings is included in Veibel (see below); see also the Royal Society *Catalogue of Scientific Papers*, VI, 494–496. His books include *Udførlig Fremstilling af Chemiens Hovedlærdomme, såavel i theoretisk som i praktisk Henseende* (Copenhagen, 1829); and *Haandbog i de organiske Stoffers almindelige Chemie* (Copenhagen, 1847).

Among his memoirs are "Om Svovelkulstoffets Forbindelser med Æskene," in *Oversigt over det K. Danske Videnskabernes Selskabs Forhandlinger* (1821–1822), 12–13, and (1822–1823), 10–16; "Die Xanthogensäure nebst einigen Producten und Verbindungen derselben," in *Journal für Chemie und Physik*, **36** (1822), 1–67; "Forsøg over Virkningen mellem Chlorplatin og Viinaand," in *Oversigt . . . Forhandlinger* (1830–1831), 24–25; "Wirkung des Platinchlorids auf Alkohol und daraus hervorgehende Produkte," in *Journal für Chemie und Physik*, **62** (1831), 393–441, and **63** (1831), 121–135; also in *Annalen der Physik*, **21** (1831), 497–541; "Nye undersøgelser af Svovelforbindelser," in *Oversigt . . . Forhandlinger* (1833–1834), 9–16; "Über das Mercaptan," in *Annalen der Physik*, **31** (1834), 369–431; "Mercaptanet, med Bemærkninger over nogle andre nye Producter af Svovelvinsyresaltene," in *Kongelige Danske Videnskabernes Selskabs naturvidenskabelige og mathematiske Afhandlinger*, 4th ser., **6** (1837), 1–70; "Nye Undersøgelser over det brændbare Chlorplatin," *ibid.*, 333–356; "Undersøgelser over Producterne af Tobakkens tørre Destillation og om Tobaksrøgens chemiske Beskaffenhed," in *Oversigt . . . Forhandlinger* (1843), 13–17; "Über die Produkte der trockenen Destillation des Tabaks und die Bestandtheile des Tabakrauches," in *Journal für praktische Chemie*, **29** (1843), 383–395; and "Beretning om nogle Forsøg over Carotinet," in *Oversigt . . . Forhandlinger* (1847), 101–103.

II. SECONDARY LITERATURE. See the obituary in *Oversigt over det K. Danske Videnskabernes Selskabs Forhandlinger* (1848), 19–30; and Stig Veibel, *Kemien i Danmark*, 2 vols. (Copenhagen, 1939–1943), I, 155–160, 180–188, and II, 488–494, with complete bibliography.

STIG VEIBEL

**ZELINSKY, NIKOLAY DMITRIEVICH** (*b.* Tiraspol, Kherson province [now Moldavian S.S.R.], Russia, 6 February 1861; *d.* Moscow, U.S.S.R., 31 July 1953), *chemistry.*

After graduating from the University of Odessa in 1884, Zelinsky was sent in 1885 to Germany, where he worked with Johannes Wislicenus at Leipzig and Victor Meyer at Göttingen. While trying to obtain tetrahydrothiophene in Meyer's laboratory he synthesized di-(β-chloroethyl) sulfide (mustard gas)—and became its first victim, receiving serious burns. In 1889 at Odessa he defended his master's thesis, on isomers in the thiophene series, and, in 1891, his doctoral dissertation, on stereoisomers in the series of saturated carbon compounds. From 1893 to 1953 Zelinsky was professor at Moscow University, except for the period 1911–1917, when he headed the central laboratory of the Ministry of Finances in St. Petersburg and taught at the Polytechnical Institute.

In connection with the use of poison gases in World War I, Zelinsky in 1915 developed a method of obtaining activated charcoal and a universal gas mask that was used by the Russian and Allied armies. In 1918–1919 he devised a process for obtaining gasoline by cracking higher-boiling petroleum fractions in the presence of aluminum chloride. He was elected a corresponding member of the U.S.S.R. Academy of Sciences in 1926 and, in 1929, a full member. In 1934 he became department head at the Institute of Organic Chemistry (named for him in 1953) of the U.S.S.R. Academy of Sciences.

Zelinsky's most important work dealt with the chemistry of hydrocarbons and with organic catalysis. From 1895 to 1905 he was the first to synthesize many hydrocarbons of the cyclopentane and cyclohexane series, used as standards in the study of the composition of petroleum fractions. He subsequently synthesized other hydrocarbons, including cyclopropanes and cyclobutanes, as well as bicyclic spirane and bridged hydrocarbons, and studied their catalytic transformations, many of which are considered classical. In 1911 Zelinsky discovered the smooth dehydrogenation of cyclohexane (and its homologues) into benzene in the presence of platinum and palladium catalysts at 300°C. In the 1920's and 1930's he studied the selective character of this reaction, used it extensively to determine the content in gasoline of cyclohexane hydrocarbons and kerosene fractions, and proposed it as an industrial process for obtaining aromatic hydrocarbons from petroleum.

In the 1930's Zelinsky investigated the reaction (that he discovered in 1911) of the disproportionation of hydrogen in cyclohexene with the simultaneous formation of benzene and cyclohexane. This reaction, which he termed "irreversible catalysis" and which occurred at room temperature in the presence of platinum and palladium, is peculiar to cyclohexane hydrocarbons containing double bonds, including many terpenes. In 1934 Zelinsky discovered the hydrogenolysis of cyclopentane hydrocarbons with their transformation into alkanes in the presence of platinized carbon and hydrogen at 300–310°C.

Zelinsky showed the intermediate formation of methylene radicals in many heterogenous catalytic reactions: in the decomposition of cyclohexane, in the Fischer-Tropsch synthesis on a cobalt catalyst, in the hydrocondensation of olefins with carbon monoxide, and in the hydropolymerization of olefins in the presence of small quantities of carbon monoxide. A pioneer in the study of the reciprocal isomerization of cyclopentane and cyclohexane hydrocarbons in the presence of aluminum chloride and aluminum bromide, Zelinsky showed in 1939 that cyclohexene and its homologues are almost completely isomerized (in the presence of oxides of aluminum, beryllium, or silicon at 400–450°C.) into homologues of cyclopentene. As early as 1915 he used oxide catalysts in the cracking of petroleum, which led to a lowering of the temperature of the process and to an increase in the quantity of aromatic hydrocarbons formed. In 1915 he was the first to show that in the transformation of organic compounds the reason for the poisoning of the catalyst is that a layer of carbon is deposited on its surface. By oxidizing it, the catalyst can be regenerated. This method found wide application in connection with the extensive use twenty years later of oxide catalysts in the petroleum processing industry.

To confirm the organic theory of the origin of petroleum, Zelinsky in the 1920's and 1930's obtained artificial petroleum from plant and animal materials—cholesterol, fatty acids, beeswax, and abietic acid under the action of aluminum chloride. He developed the cyanohydrin method for obtaining alpha-amino acids and was the first to obtain a number of hydroxy amino acids. In 1912 Zelinsky achieved the hydrolysis of proteins using dilute acids and, in addition to amino acids, obtained their cyclic anhydrides, diketopiperazines. In connection with this he proposed the theory of the cyclic structure of protein molecules.

## BIBLIOGRAPHY

I. ORIGINAL WORKS. Zelinsky's writings were published as *Izbrannye trudy* ("Selected Works"), 2 vols. (Moscow–Leningrad, 1941); *Sobranie trudov* ("Collection of Works"), 4 vols. (Moscow–Leningrad, 1954–1957); and *Izbrannye trudy* ("Selected Works"; Moscow, 1968); all three eds. include biography, bibliography, and a sketch of his career.

II. SECONDARY LITERATURE. On Zelinsky and his work, see the following: A. A. Balandin, "Akademik Nikolay Dmitrievich Zelinsky," in *Vestnik Akademii nauk SSSR*, **16**, nos. 5–6 (1946), 80–90, published on his eighty-fifth birthday; N. A. Figurovsky, *Ocherk razvitia ugolnogo protivogaza* ("A Sketch of the Development of the Charcoal Gas Mask"; Moscow, 1952); and *Zamechatelnnoe russkoe izobretenie (k 40-letiyu izobretenia ugolnogo protivogaza N. D. Zelinskogo* ("A Remarkable Russian Invention [on the Fortieth Anniversary of the Invention of the Charcoal Gas Mask by Zelinsky"]; Moscow, 1956); B. A. Kazansky. "Raboty N. D. Zelinskogo i ego shkoly v oblasti kataliticheskikh prevrashcheny uglevodorodov" ("Work of Zelinsky and His School in the Field of Catalytic Transformations of Hydrocarbons"), in *Yubileyny sbornik, posvyashchenny tridtsatiletiyu Velikoy Oktyabrskoy sotsialisticheskoy revolyutsii* ("Jubilee Collection Dedicated to the Thirtieth Anniversary of the Great October Socialist Revolution"), pt. 1 (Moscow–Leningrad, 1947); and *Vydayushchysya sovetsky ucheny akademik Nikolay Dmitrievich Zelinsky* ("The Distinguished Soviet Scientist Academician . . ."; Moscow, 1951, published on his ninetieth birthday; B. A. Kazansky, A. N. Nesmeyanov, and A. F. Platé, "Raboty akademika N. D. Zelinskogo i ego shkoly v oblasti khimii uglevodorodov i organicheskogo kataliza" ("The Work of Academician Zelinsky and His School in the Field of the Chemistry of Hydrocarbons and Organic Catalysis"), in *Uchenye zapiski Moskovskogo gosudarstvennogo universiteta*, no. 175 (1956), 5–53; Y. G. Mamadaliev, *Akademik Nikolay Dmitrievich Zelinsky* (Baku, 1951); A. F. Platé, "N. D. Zelinsky i sovremennoe razvitie neftekhimii" ("Zelinsky and the Contemporary Development of Petrol Chemistry"), in *Neftekhimia*, **1** (1961), 7–14, published on the centenary of his birth; V. M. Rodionov, "Nikolay Dmitrievich Zelinsky (vospominania i vstrechi) (". . . [Reminiscences and Meetings"]), in *Soobshchenie o nauchnykh rabotakh chlenov Vsesoyuznogo Khimicheskogo obshchestva im. D. I. Mendeleeva*, no. 12 (1951; N. I. Shuykin, "Pamyati akademika Nikolaya Dmitrievicha Zelinskogo" ("Memories of

Academician . . ."), in *Zhurnal obshchei khimii*, **31** (1961), i–vii, published on the centenary of his birth; V. A. Volkov and A. N. Shamin, "Novye dokumenty o deyatelnosti N. D. Zelinskogo" ("New Documents on the Activities of Zelinsky"), in *Voprosy istorii estestvoznania i tekhniki* (1975), no. 1, 54–56; and Y. K. Yuriev and R. Y. Levina, *Zhizn i deyatelnost akademika Nikolaya Dmitrievicha Zelinskogo* ("Life and Activities of Academician Zelinsky"; Moscow, 1953), also in English (1958).

A. F. PLATÉ

**ZEMPLÉN, GÉZA** (*b*. Trencsén, Hungary [now Trenčín, Czechoslovakia], 26 October 1883; *d*. Budapest, Hungary, 24 July 1956), *organic chemistry*.

Zemplén was the son of János Zemplén, a postal employee, and of Janka Wittlin. His older brother Viktor was appointed professor of physics at the Technical University of Budapest in 1913 at the age of thirty-three, but his career was cut short three years later by his death in World War I. Zemplén's ability is reflected in his having been named professor at the Technical University in 1913—when he was only twenty-nine. With his appointment the university created the first institute for organic chemistry in Hungary.

After attending secondary school in Fiume, Zemplén studied chemistry, physics, and biology at the University of Budapest, earning the doctorate in physics in 1904. He then became an assistant in chemistry at the Mining and Forestry Academy of Selmec, where he conducted analytic studies of natural substances. In 1909 Zemplén obtained a three-year scholarship; and until 1912 he worked in Emil Fischer's laboratory in Berlin, then one of the most famous centers for the study of organic chemistry. He worked on the synthesis of amino acids and of the synthetic disaccharide cellobiose, publishing several papers on these topics in collaboration with Fischer.

Appointed professor in 1913, Zemplén began a period of intense, uninterrupted research and also trained many students who later achieved distinction as organic chemists. His principal field of research was the carbohydrates. His most important results were the deacetylation of sugar acetates with sodium methoxide (Zemplén's saponification) and the successive (Zemplén) degradation of sugars to derivatives containing increasingly less carbon—which at the time was considered the best method for establishing the structure of the disaccharides. Zemplén also devised the so-called mercury acetate catalytic method for the production of oligosaccharides. His contributions to organic chemistry were printed in more than 200 publications, most of which appeared in German in *Berichte der Deutschen chemischen Gesellschaft*.

Zemplén's successful career earned him membership in many scientific societies. His life was not, however, free from personal tragedy. Upon returning home from a year spent at the University of Washington (1947), he fell ill with cancer and spent his remaining years bedridden.

*BIBLIOGRAPHY*

A complete list of Zemplén's publications is in an obituary, in German, by R. Bognár, in *Acta chimica Academiae scientiarum hungaricae*, **19** (1959), 121. See also L. Mora, *Géza Zemplén, 1883–1956* (Budapest, 1974), with complete bibliography; "The Degradation of Sugars," in *Berichte der Deutschen chemischen Gesellschaft*, **59** (1926), 125; and "The Mercury Acetate Method," *ibid.*, **62** (1929), 990.

FERENC SZABADVÁRY

**ZENODORUS** (*b*. Athens [?]; *fl*. early second century B.C.), *mathematics*.

Zenodorus is known to have been the author of a treatise on isoperimetric figures—plane figures of equal perimeter but differing areas, and solid figures of equal surface but differing volumes.[1] This has not survived as such, but it is epitomized in Pappus' *Collection*, in the commentary by Theon of Alexandria on Ptolemy's *Almagest*, and in the anonymous *Introduction to the Almagest*.

Older writers placed the date of Zenodorus in the fifth century B.C., but this was through a mistaken identification with a Zenodorus who is said by Proclus to have belonged "to the succession of Oenopides."[2] From several references by Zenodorus to Archimedes, Nokk rightly concluded that he must have flourished after, say, 200 B.C.[3] Because Quintilian showed awareness of isoperimetry, F. Hultsch and M. Cantor conjectured a lower limit of A.D. 90 for his life; but Zenodorus made no claim to have been the only, or even the first, person to have written on the subject and the deduction is erroneous.[4] Until recently all that could be said with certainty was that he lived after Archimedes and before Pappus, say 200 B.C.–A.D. 300; but it is now established that he must have flourished in the early part of the second century B.C. A fragment from a biography of the Epicurean philosopher Philonides, found in the Herculaneum papyrus roll no. 1044, mentions among his acquaintances a Zenodorus at least once and perhaps twice. In publishing the fragment, W. Crönert identified him with the mathematician.[5] G. J. Toomer, in an elaborate study of occurrences of the name, concluded that unless Zenodorus was a Hellenized Semite (which is not impossible), the comparative rarity of the name confirms Crönert's identification.[6] This is made certain by the fact that in the Arabic translation of Diocles' treatise *On Burning Mirrors*, which has been discovered and edited by Toomer, Zenodorus is mentioned as having posed a problem to Diocles. Toomer's literal translation reads:

> The book of Diocles on burning mirrors. He said: Pythion the geometer, who was of the people of Thasos, wrote a letter to Conon in which he asked him how to find a mirror surface such that when it is placed facing the sun the rays reflected from it meet the circumference of a circle. And when Zenodorus the astronomer came down to Arcadia and was introduced [?] to us, he asked us how to find a mirror surface such that when it is placed facing the sun the rays reflected from it meet a point and thus cause burning. So we want to explain the answer to the problem posed by Pythion and to that posed by Zenodorus; in the course of this we shall make use of the premises established by our predecessors.[7]

It is no bar to the identification of this Zenodorus with the author of the isoperimetric propositions that he is here called an astronomer. There was considerable overlap between mathematics and astronomy—Euclid, Archimedes, and Apollonius are notable examples—and Zenodorus may well have written astronomical works of which we have no knowledge. A Vatican manuscript gives a catalog of astronomers—οἱ περὶ τοῦ πόλου συντάξαντες—which includes the name Zenodorus.[8] In accordance with the principle of not multiplying entities unnecessarily, it would seem that he, too, should be identified with the mathematician.

The Herculaneum fragments mention two visits by Zenodorus to Athens. On the onomastic evidence he could be from Cyrene, or Ptolemaic Egypt, or possibly from Chios or Erythrae. But the name is attested eight or nine times in Athens; and on the assumption that he was an Athenian, Toomer has plausibly identified him with a member of the Lamptrai family mentioned in an inscription that lists contributions for some unknown purpose during the archonship of Hermogenes (183–182 B.C.).[9]

It is only in Theon's commentary that the isoperimetric propositions are specifically attributed to Zenodorus, but the passages in Pappus' *Collection* and the *Introduction* are so similar that they also must be derived from him. They are not, however, simply lifted from Zenodorus: there are considerable differences in the order and wording of the propositions in the three sources, and the question which is nearest to the original has given rise to some discussion. In all probability Pappus, like Theon, reproduced the propositions of Zenodorus at the relevant point in his commentary on the first book of the *Almagest*, where Ptolemy says, "Among different figures having an equal perimeter, since that which has the more angles is greater, of plane figures the circle is the greatest and of solid figures the sphere."[10] If so, this may have been the most exact reproduction of Zenodorus' text, ascribed to him by name, as in Theon; when he came to compile his *Collection*, Pappus varied the presentation, added the proposition "Of all segments of a circle having equal circumferences, the semicircle is the greatest in area," and proceeded to a disquisition on the semiregular solids of Archimedes.[11] Theon would have drawn upon Pappus, and the anonymous author of the *Introduction* upon both.

It would appear that Zenodorus' treatise contained fourteen propositions. There is agreement in the three versions that the first was "Of regular polygons having the same perimeter, the greater is that which has the more angles." The final proposition, stated but not actually proved, was almost certainly "If a sphere and a regular polyhedron have the same surface [area], the sphere is the greater." In between came such propositions as the following:

"If a circle and a regular polygon have the same perimeter, the circle is the greater."

"If on the base of an isosceles triangle there be set up a non-isosceles triangle having the same perimeter, the isosceles triangle is the greater."

"Given two similar right-angled triangles, the square on the sum of the hypotenuses is equal to the sum of the squares on the corresponding sides taken together."

"If on unequal bases there be set up two similar isosceles triangles, and on the same bases there be set up two dissimilar isosceles triangles having together the same perimeter as the two similar triangles, the sum of the similar triangles is greater than the sum of the dissimilar triangles."

"Among polygons with an equal perimeter and an equal number of sides, the regular polygon is the greatest."

"If a regular polygon [with an even number of sides] revolves about one of the longest diagonals, there is generated a solid bounded by conical surfaces that is less than the sphere having the same surface."

"Each of the five regular solids is less than the sphere with equal surface."

There is no little subtlety in the reasoning; indeed, rigorous proofs of the isoperimetric properties of the circle and sphere had to wait until H. A. Schwarz provided them in 1884.[12]

## NOTES

1. The Greek title is given by Theon, *Commentaires de Pappus et de Théon d'Alexandrie sur l'Almageste*, A. Rome, ed. II, 355.4, as Περὶ ἰσοπεριμέτρων σχημάτων. The earlier editors had read ἰσομέτρων, but Rome showed that this was a variant reading in some MSS. "Isoperimetric" makes better sense than "isometric" and is confirmed by the comment of Simplicius in his *Commentarium in Aristotelis de caelo*, J. L. Heiberg, ed., in *Commentaria in Aristotelem Graeca*, VII (Berlin, 1894), 412; δέδεικται . . . παρὰ Ἀρχιμήδους καὶ παρὰ Ζηνοδώρου πλατύτερον, ὅτι τῶν ἰσοπεριμέτρων σχημάτων πολυχωρητότερός ἐστιν ἐν μὲν τοῖς ἐπιπέδοις ὁ κύκλος, ἐν δὲ τοῖς στερεοῖσιν ἡ σφαῖρα.
2. Proclus, *In primum Euclidis*, G. Friedlein, ed. (Leipzig, 1873; repr. Hildesheim, 1967), 80.15–16; English trans. by Glenn R. Morrow, *Proclus: A Commentary on the First Book of Euclid's Elements* (Princeton, 1970), 66. There is one genuine reference to Zenodorus in Proclus, Friedlein ed., 165.24, where it is asserted that there are four-sided triangles, called "barblike" by some but "hollow-angled" (κοιλογώνια) by Zenodorus. The reference is to a quadrilateral with one angle greater than two right angles, called a reentrant angle. It was formerly believed that this word occurred in Theon's version, and Nokk (see note 3) used this as an argument for believing Theon's text to be the nearest the original; but Rome, *op. cit.*, 371, has shown that the word is interpolated and may, indeed, have been interpolated before Proclus read Theon. It remains in the *Introduction to the Almagest: Pappi Alexandrini Collectionis quae supersunt . . .*, F. Hultsch, ed., III, 1194.12, 13, 16.
3. Nokk, *Zenodorus' Abhandlung über die isoperimetrischen Figuren*, 27–29.
4. Quintilian, *De institutione oratoria* (I.10, 39–45), L. Radermacher, ed. (Leipzig, 1907; 6th ed., enl. and corr. by V. Buchheit, 1971), I, 63.12–64.12; also M. Winterbottom, ed. (Oxford, 1970), I, 65.28–66.31. But B. L. van der Waerden, *Science Awakening*, 2nd English ed., 268, is in error in saying that Quintilian "mentions" Zenodorus. Also see F. Hultsch, *op. cit.*, III, 1190; and M. Cantor, *Vorlesungen über Geschichte der Mathematik*, 3rd ed., I (Leipzig, 1907), 549.
5. W. Crönert, "Der Epikureer Philonides." The name occurs in fr. 31, ll. 4–5 (Crönert, 953–954) and probably in fr. 34, l. 1 (Crönert, 954).
6. G. J. Toomer, "The Mathematician Zenodorus," 186.
7. *Ibid.*, 190–191. In both cases where the name occurs, Zenodorus is an emendation, but Toomer regards it as certain.
8. Vaticanus Graecus 381, published by Ernst Maass in *Hermes*, **16** (1881), 388, and more definitively in his *Aratea* (Berlin, 1892), 123. Maass himself identified the Zenodorus of the catalog with the mathematician.
9. Toomer, *op. cit.*, 187–190.
10. Ptolemy, *Syntaxis mathematica (Almagest)*, I.3: *Claudii Ptolemaei Opera quae exstant omnia*, J. L. Heiberg, ed., I (Leipzig, 1898), 13.16–19.
11. If Pappus in his commentary gave credit to Zenodorus, as Theon did, this would help to explain why Zenodorus is not mentioned in the *Collection*; there is no question of Pappus' trying to appropriate another's work as his own.
12. H. A. Schwarz, "Beweis des Satzes, dass die Kugel kleinere Oberfläche besitzt, als jeder andere Körper gleichen Volumens," in *Nachrichten von der Gesellschaft der Wissenschaften zu Göttingen* (1884), 1–13, repr. in Schwarz's *Gesammelte mathematische Abhandlungen*, II (Berlin, 1890), 327–340.

## BIBLIOGRAPHY

I. ORIGINAL WORKS. Zenodorus' one known work was entitled Περὶ ἰσοπεριμέτρων. It has not survived as such but is epitomized in three other works: Pappus, *Collection*, V. 3–19: *Pappi Alexandrini Collectionis quae supersunt*, F. Hultsch, ed., I (Berlin, 1876), 308.2–334.21; Theon of Alexandria, *Commentary on the Almagest* I.3: *Commentaires de Pappus et de Théon d'Alexandrie sur l'Almageste*, A. Rome, ed., II, *Théon d'Alexandrie* (Vatican City, 1936), 354.19–379.15, which was translated into Latin and collated with the passages in Pappus in Hultsch, *op. cit.*, III (Berlin, 1878), 1189–1211; and an anonymous work usually known as the *Introduction to the Almagest* and published in F. Hultsch, *op. cit.*, III, as "Anonymi commentarius de figuris planis isoperimetris," 1138–1165.

II. SECONDARY LITERATURE. See the following, listed chronologically: Nokk, *Zenodorus' Abhandlung über die isoperimetrischen Figuren nach den Auszügen welche uns die Alexandriner Theon und Pappus aus derselben überliefert haben* (Freiburg im Breisgau, 1860); James Gow, *A Short History of Greek Mathematics* (Cambridge, 1884), 271–272; W. Crönert, "Der Epikureer Philonides," in *Sitzungsberichte der Preussischen Akademie der Wissenschaften zu Berlin* (1900), 942–959; W. Schmidt, "Zur Geschichte der Isoperimetrie im Altertum," in *Bibliotheca mathematica*, 3rd ser., **2** (1901), 5–8; T. L. Heath, *A History of Greek Mathematics*, II (Oxford, 1921), 207–213; W. Müller, "Das isoperimetrische Problem im Altertum," in *Sudhoffs Archiv*, **37** (1953), 39–71, with a German trans. of Theon's epitome; B. L. van der Waerden, *Science Awakening*, English trans. of *Ontwakende Wetenschap* with author's additions, 2nd ed. (Groningen, n.d.), 268–269; and G. J. Toomer, "The Mathematician Zenodorus," in *Greek, Roman and Byzantine Studies*, **13** (1972), 177–192.

IVOR BULMER-THOMAS

**ZENO OF CITIUM** (*b.* Citium, Cyprus, *ca.* 335 B.C.; *d.* Athens, 263 B.C.), *philosophy.*

Cyprus was colonized by Greeks, but had many Phoenician inhabitants. Zeno's father was a merchant called Mnaseas, perhaps a Greek version of the Phoenician Manasse or Menahem; Zeno is commonly referred to as "the Phoenician" by ancient writers. His education, however, was Greek; he studied in Athens and eventually set up his own school there. The most important of his teachers were Polemo, then head of Plato's Academy; Stilpo the Megarian; and Crates the Cynic. He was well soaked in the Greek tradition of philosophy; and his own style of philosophizing, although strikingly original, shows clear traces of the influence of Heraclitus, Socrates, Plato, and Aristotle.

Zeno established his own school about 300 B.C., perhaps in deliberate opposition to the school of Epicurus, which had recently been founded. He taught in the Stoa Poikile, or "Painted Colonnade"; and the name "Stoics" supplanted "Zenonians" for his pupils. At the end of his life he was given public honors by the Athenians. The headship of the school passed first to Cleanthes of Assos, and then to Chrysippus of Soli: the individual contributions of the three to the school's doctrine are hard to disentangle, in the absence of any complete writings, and this article does not attempt the task. The school survived until at least A.D. 260.

The main emphasis of Stoic teaching was moral. Zeno preached a morality that could claim to be an interpretation of the message of Socrates. The peculiarity of his doctrine is his refusal to allow that there is anything good but the virtuous state of a man's soul, coupled with an "all or nothing" definition of virtue. Virtue is wisdom: the wise man is wholly good, and everything he does is good, whereas the rest of the world and all its doings are sunk in iniquity. The wisdom that constitutes virtue includes an understanding of nature —indeed, that is its most important component, since the wise man's goal is "to live in accordance with nature." A particular physics, a particular interpretation of the physical universe and man's place in it, is an essential part of Stoicism, just as the atomic world picture was an essential part of the rival Epicurean doctrine.

The Stoic world picture was the lineal descendant of Plato's *Timaeus* and Aristotle's *De caelo*, with some features of the Platonic-Aristotelian cosmology exaggerated or changed, perhaps in conscious opposition to Epicurus. It was a picture of the cosmos as a single material continuum. Outside the cosmos there is void space: this was a modification of Aristotelian doctrine, according to which there is nothing whatever outside the cosmos, not even void space.

The cosmos is regarded as a single whole sub-

stance. It is held together by an unexplained natural tendency of matter to contract upon its own center. Thus Aristotle's cosmology is altered in two respects. The center toward which matter tends to move is its own center, the center of the cosmic body, whereas in Aristotle's system it is the center of the universe; second, all matter in the Stoic system, including the two light, centrifugal elements of the Aristotelian cosmology, air and fire, tends toward the center. These two elements, according to the Stoics, are less heavy than earth and water; and for that reason they tend to stay outside the central spheres composed of the heavy elements. They are also characterized as the active elements: together they make up *pneuma*, which permeates the whole cosmos and sets up a tension ($\tau \acute{o} \nu o \varsigma$) in it. The elements are not chemically differentiated but are defined by the tension set up by these motions. In whatever region of the cosmic body, itself nothing but an undifferentiated medium, there is a strong motion toward the center, we can say that that is an earthy region; wherever there is a strong tendency to resist the centripetal motion, we can say there is fire; and so on.

Recent interpreters of Stoic physics (J. Christensen and S. Sambursky) have pointed out its similarity to a field theory. The whole cosmos is a field within which various motions occur, and within it one field can be distinguished from another according to the motions that occur there. The nature of the tension thus set up determines the properties possessed by the region in question. The Stoics lacked a language with which this idea could be expressed coherently, however, and their retention of expressions appropriate to a metaphysics of "substance" led to many paradoxes. In particular, since any region of the universe, in their theory, may contain motions of many different kinds; and since it is these motions that produce identifiable characters or "bodies," they had to say that many bodies could coexist in the same region. They were widely criticized in antiquity for this theory of "total mixture" ($\kappa \rho \hat{a} \sigma \iota \varsigma \delta \iota' \ \H{o} \lambda o \upsilon$).

Since the cosmos is a single continuous field, motions in one part of it may affect those in any other part: the Stoics used the term "sympathy" for this feature. Certain peculiarities of Stoicism follow from it. Astrology and divination, for example, are thus given a rationale; and they receive more emphasis than in any previous philosophical system. Moreover, the interconnection of all events in the cosmic continuum is referred to as fate. From an ideally complete description of the structure of the cosmos up to a given time, one can theoretically predict all subsequent events: all that happens is in accordance with fate. With regard to human actions, the Stoics held the position that since the individual's state of mind enters into the conditions that determine an action, human "freedom" is preserved despite the doctrine of universal fate (their Peripatetic opponents replied that in that case, a stone that is dropped also falls "freely"; and the distinction between "free" and "forced" is lost).

The active elements in the cosmos are also referred to collectively as "God." By this designation the Stoics attributed many characteristics to the cosmos. It is ever-living, in the sense that it will never cease to exist, although it undergoes the cyclical transformations described below. It is rational: that is, the structure of the cosmos is patterned on principles that the human mind, being endowed with reason (λόγος), can recognize. (The divine λόγος that permeates and directs the Stoic cosmos is referred to in the famous opening words of St. John's gospel.) Moreover, the structure of the cosmos, being determined by divine reason, is good. The Stoics exploited the argument from design to the full, and found evidences of divine craftsmanship everywhere in nature. Stoic ethics and physics are thus in full accord with one another: the good life for man is to be an assenting part of the cosmos, "to live in accordance with nature."

Periodically the cosmos loses all its differentiation and is wholly consumed by and assimilated to the divine fiery *pneuma*. After this ἐκπύρωσις, the cosmos is formed again. Since the structure is determined by the divine *pneuma*, which remains constant throughout the conflagration, the structure of the reborn cosmos is identical in every detail with that of the previous one; and every event is repeated in every cycle.

In logic the Stoics made important innovations (perhaps, however, these should be attributed not to Zeno but to Chrysippus). Aristotle's logic of predication was adapted to his view of science as demonstrating the connections between the properties of substances. The basic entities of Stoic philosophy are not substances but motions or events. Its logic, correspondingly, is a logic of propositions. The Stoics worked out five "indemonstrable" inference patterns, and tested the validity of other schemata by trying to reduce them to these five. They used ordinal numbers to stand for propositions, thus: "If the first, then the second; but the first, therefore, the second." "If the first, then the second; but not the second, therefore, not the first." We may conjecture that there is some

connection between this development of the logic of inference and the growth of experimental science in the Alexandrian schools, beginning in the third century B.C.

As a moral system, Stoicism had a wide acceptance in the Roman republic and the empire, Marcus Aurelius being the most notable follower. The physical system, however, soon became contaminated with elements of Platonism and Aristotelianism; Stoic ideas occur frequently but rather unsystematically in the work of Galen, the Neoplatonists, and the Peripatetic commentators. The unified and consistent world picture worked out by Zeno, which was in fact a remarkable achievement, lost its clear outlines and merged with the general amalgam of Aristotelianism, Neoplatonism, and Christianity that dominated the intellectual centers of late antiquity.

*BIBLIOGRAPHY*

There is no complete work by Zeno or any other of the old Stoics extant. The standard collection of fragments is J. von Arnim, *Stoicorum veterum fragmenta*, 4 vols. (Leipzig, 1905–1924). There is an ancient life of Zeno and other Stoics in Diogenes Laërtius, *Lives of Eminent Philosophers*, VII, text and trans. by R. D. Hicks in the Loeb Classical Library (London, 1953).

The fullest modern account of Stoicism is Max Pohlenz, *Die Stoa*, 2nd ed., 2 vols. (Göttingen, 1959). Johnny Christensen, *An Essay on the Unity of Stoic Philosophy* (Copenhagen, 1962), gives a short, original, and highly stimulating summary. S. Sambursky, *Physics of the Stoics* (London, 1959), translates selected texts into English and gives a comprehensive account of the cosmology, not altogether free from anachronism. The most important books on the logic are Benson Mates, *Stoic Logic* (Berkeley, 1953), and Michael Frede, *Die stoische Logik* (Göttingen, 1974). For epistemology and ethics, also see A. A. Long, ed., *Essays on Stoic Philosophy* (London, 1970). There is a recent monograph on Zeno, by Andreas Graeser, *Zenon von Kition* (Berlin, 1975).

DAVID J. FURLEY

**ZENO OF ELEA** (*b.* Elea, Lucania, *ca.* 490 B.C.; *d.* Elea, *ca.* 425 B.C.), *philosophy, mathematics.*

Zeno became a friend and disciple of Parmenides, with whom, according to Plato's dialogue *Parmenides*, he visited Athens in the middle of the fifth century B.C. Some later Greek authors, however, considered this visit an invention of Plato's. According to a widespread legend with many greatly differing versions, Zeno was tortured and killed by a tyrant of Elea or of Syracuse, against whom he had conspired.

Zeno's fame and importance both for philosophy and for the mathematical theory of the continuum rest on his famous paradoxes. There is, however, a tradition, preserved by Diogenes Laërtius (IX,5,29), that he also developed a cosmology, according to which there existed several "worlds" (κόσμοι), composed of "warm" and "cold," "dry" and "wet," but no empty space. Since it is difficult to find any direct connection between this cosmology and Zeno's paradoxes, that tradition has been questioned in recent times. The cosmology has some affinity, however, to certain medical doctrines of the fifth century B.C. There is at least the possibility that it was part of a theory of the phenomenal world analogous to Parmenides' theory of the world of belief (δόξα); and there is no other known Greek philosopher who held exactly these beliefs. Thus there is no compelling reason to reject the tradition.

According to Plato (*Parmenides*, 127 ff.), as a young man Zeno elaborated his paradoxes in defense of the philosophy of Parmenides but did not, like Parmenides, try to prove positively that there is nothing but the One and that plurality, change, and motion are mere illusions. He simply tried to show that if one assumes the existence of plurality and motion, no less strange consequences follow than if one denies their existence. In his commentary on Plato's *Parmenides* (127D), Proclus affirms that Zeno elaborated forty different paradoxes following from the assumption of plurality and motion, all of them apparently based on the difficulties deriving from an analysis of the continuum.

The best-known of the paradoxes is that of Achilles and the tortoise, according to which Achilles cannot overtake the tortoise. Though he always runs a hundred times faster than the tortoise, the latter will, before Achilles has reached the tortoise's starting point, have moved 1/100 of the original distance; and while Achilles traverses this second distance, the tortoise will have traversed 1/100 of the latter; and so on ad infinitum— so that Achilles can never catch the tortoise. Aristotle tried to refute this argument by pointing out that not only space but also time is infinitely divisible, so that the time particles, the sum of which is finite, correspond to the particles to be traversed and no difficulty arises for Achilles. At first sight this argument appears all the more convincing because in what seems to be the original formulation of the paradox, Achilles apparently finds it easy to traverse the distance between his starting point

and that of the tortoise and experiences difficulty only after the distance between him and the tortoise has become smaller. There is, however, a much more subtle form of the argument, according to which Achilles cannot even begin: Before he can traverse the distance between his starting point and that of the tortoise, he has first to traverse half of that distance, and before that one-quarter, before that one-eighth, and so on ad infinitum. Thus he never gets going.

That this difficulty cannot be overcome quite so easily by referring to the infinite divisibility of time is shown by the second famous paradox of Zeno, that of the flying arrow that cannot move. In its simplest form this paradox says that the arrow can move neither in the place where it is nor in a place where it is not. In a more elaborate form it says that at any given instant, the arrow occupies a space equal to its size. It can neither occupy a larger space nor be in two different places at the same time. Since there is nothing between one instant and the next, and since the arrow cannot move in an instant, it cannot move at all. Aristotle tried to refute this argument by pointing out that the "now" (νῦν), although it divides time into past and future, is not a part of time, since time is extensive and since any part of that which has extension must in its turn have extension. In other words, time is not composed of "nows" or instants.

In recent times interest in the problem has been so great that hardly a year has passed without the publication of one or more attempts at its solution. G. Vlastos very cleverly pointed out that if we use the mathematical formula for velocity $v = s/t$ and apply it to the instant, which is supposed to be extensionless, we obtain the value $v = 0/0$, which is no fixed value at all and certainly not the fixed value of 0, thus indicating that the arrow has no velocity but remains at rest. In order to obtain the result 0, $t$ must have a positive value: $v = 0/t = 0$. This is quite true. But Vlastos' further observation that the problem is similar to the problem of how a circle can be curved although it is supposed to be composed of points—and points are not curved— shows that what the mathematical formula reveals so clearly is still not quite realizable by human imagination.

The most thorough study of the problem from this latter point of view has been made by A. Grünbaum. He begins by distinguishing between two different concepts of time, one "mind-dependent" and one "mind-independent." The former is characterized by the experience of the fleeting "now," which—as in Aristotle's theory of time—

divides time into a constantly approaching future and into a constantly receding past into which what until "now" had been future sinks back, and in virtue of which things come into being and pass away. This kind of time, according to Grünbaum, can exist only in a mind consciously experiencing time. From it he distinguishes what he calls the "mind-independent" time of the physicist, within which one can clearly distinguish between an "earlier" and a "later" but within which, strictly speaking, there is no future, present, or past. In analogy to mind-dependent time, however, mind-independent time can be divided by "points of simultaneity," which can be assumed in any point of the time coordinate. These points of simultaneity can more strictly be considered as (extensionless) mathematical points than can the "now points" of mind-dependent time, which permits a kind of quasi-instantaneous awareness of succession—as, for instance, in the perception of the unity of a melody consisting of a succession of sounds.

By this distinction between two sorts of time, Grünbaum tries to eliminate from the discussion the result of observations made by William James and A. N. Whitehead, who tried to show that time cannot strictly be considered a continuum in the sense of Georg Cantor's theory of aggregates, since, as careful self-observation shows, human time-consciousness is not continuous, but discrete ("pulsating," not "punctual"). This, according to Grünbaum, is true of mind-dependent, but not of mind-independent, time. The latter is strictly a continuum with an absolute density of mathematical points. Within the context of this theory an attempt is then made to solve the Zenonian problem on the basis of the assumption that any extended magnitude or interval contains (in the sense of Cantor's theory of aggregates) an indenumerable or superdenumerable infinity of extensionless (or, as Grünbaum expresses it, degenerative) elements, which has extension although its elements do not. In other words, the theory, in contrast with that of Aristotle, who admitted only the "potential infinity" of unending division, postulates that any line or curve actually represents (or is composed of) a nondenumerable infinity of nonextended points that nevertheless has extension.

In a way, then, the paradox that the arrow cannot move in any given instant, but appears to move in a succession of instants, is "solved" by replacing it with the paradox that an infinite aggregate of nonextended points nevertheless has extension; that is, the paradox becomes connected with the intricacies of the modern theory of the continuum,

which is still hotly debated. Grünbaum unquestionably, however, drew attention to the psychological aspects of the problem—or, rather, to those aspects where it touches upon the theory of knowledge. As H. Fränkel pointed out, the paradoxes discussed really derive from the fact that

> The human mind, when trying to give itself an accurate account of motion, finds itself confronted with two aspects of the phenomenon. Both are inevitable but at the same time they are mutually exclusive. Either we look at the continuous flow of motion; then it will be impossible for us to think of the object in any particular position. Or we think of the object as occupying any of the positions through which its course is leading it; and while fixing our thought on that particular position we cannot help fixing the object itself and putting it at rest for one short instant ["Zeno of Elea's Attacks on Plurality," pp. 8–9].

The two main arguments against motion discussed so far have not survived in their original wording but appear in the ancient tradition in more or less refined formulations. Zeno's arguments against plurality, however, are—at least in part—quoted literally by Simplicius. These quotations are much less clearly and precisely formulated than the paradoxes of Achilles and the tortoise and the flying arrow. They show with what difficulties Zeno had to struggle when trying to express his thoughts, and they therefore require a good deal more interpretation. The difficulty is increased by the fact that Simplicius quotes only the second part of the argument literally and summarizes the first part. In his introduction he says that Zeno had first tried to prove that that which has no "magnitude" (extension [?]; μέγεθος) nor thickness (πάχος) nor body (ὄγκος) cannot exist. "For if it is added to something else, it will not make it bigger, and if it is subtracted, it will not make it smaller. But if it does not make a thing bigger when added to it nor smaller when subtracted from it, then it appears obvious that what was added or subtracted was nothing." The literal quotation then continues:

> If this is [so?], then it is necessary that the one must have a certain distance (ἀπέχειν) from the other, and this is also so with that which protrudes (περὶ τοῦ προέχοντος). For this also will have "magnitude" [extension] and something of it will protrude. And to say this once and to say it again and again is the same thing. For nothing of it in this way will be the outermost (τὸ ἔσχατον) and never will any of them be without proportion to the others. Therefore, if there are many things it is necessary that they are small and big: small to the extent of having no size [exten-

sion] at all and big to the extent of infinite extension [H. Diels and W. Kranz, *Die Fragmente der Vorsokratiker*, 7th ed., I, no. 29, p. 266].

The use of the word ἀπέχειν, which usually means "to be away from" or "to be at a distance from," has induced some commentators to interpret Zeno's argument in the following way: If there are many things, they must be distinguished from one another. If they are distinguished, they must be separate. If they are separate, there must be something between them. Since Zeno (according to his cosmology) denied the existence of empty space, what separates things must itself be a thing, which in its turn must be separated by another thing that separates it from the things that it separates from one another, and so on ad infinitum. But this interpretation is hardly reconcilable with what precedes and what follows in Simplicius' account. The argument as a whole is understandable only on the assumption that ἀπέχειν is used as a synonym of προέχειν, the term that is used in the remainder of the argument. The gist of the argument then appears to have been: What has size is divisible. What is divisible is not a real One, since it has parts. But any part that "lies beyond" or protrudes from a given part of something that has size, has size in its turn; hence it has parts, and so on ad infinitum, so that it becomes both small and big beyond all measure. If this is the meaning of the argument, we are back with the problem of the continuum.

Vlastos has claimed that in the last sentence of the fragment quoted, Zeno committed "a logical gaffe" by assuming that through infinitely continued division, one finally ends with particles "of no size!" But on closer inspection it seems clear that Zeno, at least in the first half of his last argument, committed no such logical error. Far from assuming that by infinitely continued division one finally comes to particles "of no size," his argument is based on the very opposite assumption: however far the division may have proceeded, what remains still always has size, hence is further divisible, hence has parts, hence is not really One. Therefore, in order to be really One (indivisible)—and this conclusion, if one starts from Zeno's assumption, is perfectly sound—it must be without size. But—and here the preliminary argument reported by Simplicius is brought in—what has no size does not make a thing to which it is added bigger, nor a thing from which it is subtracted smaller, and hence appears to be nothing.

This interpretation and analysis of the argument

is also in perfect agreement with a statement elsewhere attributed to Zeno, to the effect that if someone could really explain to him what the One is, then he would also be in a position to explain plurality. At the same time it shows that Plato was right when he reported that Zeno did not try to give direct support to Parmenides' doctrine that only the One exists, but merely tried to show that from the assumption of a plurality of things, no less strange conclusions could be drawn than from the assumption that there is nothing but the One.

Granting this, one may still contend that Zeno committed a "logical gaffe" in the second part of his last argument, where he speaks of an infinite number of parts that would make the size of the object composed of them grow beyond all measure; this statement appears to be at variance with one of the most elementary applications of the theory of convergent series: that the sum of the infinite series $1/2 + 1/4 + 1/8 + 1/16 + \cdots = 1$. But this mathematical formula is a convenient symbol for the fact that infinitely continued bisection of a unit cannot exceed the unit, a fact of which Zeno, as other fragments clearly show, was perfectly aware. What he obviously did try to point out is that it is not possible for the human mind to build up the sum of such an infinite series starting, so to speak, from the other end, the end with the "degenerative elements," as Grünbaum calls them. When building up a sum, one has always to start with elements that have size. The difficulty is essentially that which H. Fränkel so lucidly described in regard to motion.

The other paradoxes of Zeno that have been preserved by ancient tradition are not so profound and can be resolved completely. One of them is that of the falling millet: If a falling bushel of millet makes a noise, so must an individual grain; if the latter makes no noise, neither can the bushel of grain, for the size of the grain has a definite ratio to that of the heap. The same must then be true of the noises. The resolution here lies in the limitation of perception, which also plays a role in the modern discussion of the perception of time. Interestingly, Zeno argues on the basis of the mathematical argument that there must be a definite proportion.

Another is the paradox of the moving blocks: If four blocks *BBBB* of equal size move along four blocks *AAAA* of the same size which are at rest, and at the same time four blocks *CCCC*, again of the same size and the first two of which have arrived below the last two of the row *AAAA*, move with the same speed as *BBBB* in the opposite direction from *BBBB*, then *BBBB* will pass two blocks of *AAAA* in the same time in which they pass four blocks of *CCCC*. But since their speed remains the same, and yet time is measured by the distance traveled at the same time, half the time is equal to the double time.

Alexander of Aphrodisias made the following diagram to illustrate Zeno's moving blocks argument:

$$AAAA$$
$$BBBB \rightarrow$$
$$\leftarrow CCCC$$

It is interesting that this argument contains the first glimpse in ancient literature of an awareness of the relativity of motion. It is the only Zenonian paradox preserved that has nothing to do with the problem of the continuum, although there have been some attempts in modern times by Paul Tannery and R. E. Siegel to show that there is a connection.

Concerning Zeno's importance for the development of ancient Greek mathematics, the most various views have been held and are still held by modern historians of science. Tannery was the first to suggest that Zeno's relation to the philosophy of Parmenides may have been less close than ancient tradition affirms and that Zeno was much more deeply influenced by problems arising from the discovery of incommensurability by the Pythagoreans. On the basis of the same assumption, H. Hasse and H. Scholz tried to show that Zeno was the "man of destiny" of ancient mathematics. They attempted to prove that the Pythagoreans, after having discovered the incommensurability of the diameter of a square with its side, had tried to overcome the resultant difficulties by assuming the existence of infinitely small elementary lines (*lineae indivisibiles*). It was against this inaccurate handling of the infinitesimal that Zeno protested, thus forcing the next generation of Pythagorean mathematicians to give the theory a better and more accurate foundation.

Other scholars (W. Burkert, A. Szabó, J. A. Philip) contend that since, according to ancient tradition, the Pythagoreans engaged in a rather abstruse number mysticism such a profound mathematical discovery as that of incommensurability cannot have been made by them, but must have been made by "practical mathematicians" influenced by Zeno's paradoxes. But there is no direct road leading from Zeno's paradoxes to the proof of incommensurability in specific cases, whereas some of the speculations supporting the Pythagoreans (when carried through with the consistency char-

acteristic of the philosophers of the first century) must almost inevitably have led to the discovery, although we do not know exactly how it was first made; and there is no tradition concerning an effect of Zeno's speculations on the development of mathematics in the second half of the fifth century B.C. B. L. van der Waerden has shown that what we know of mathematical theories of the second half of the fifth century B.C.—when the discovery of incommensurability undoubtedly was made—is rather at variance with the assumption that Zeno had any considerable influence on the development of mathematics at that time.

This, however, does not necessarily mean that Zeno's name has to be stricken from the history of ancient Greek mathematics. In all likelihood he received the first impulse toward the invention of his paradoxes not from mathematics but, as attested by Plato, from the speculations of Parmenides, and did not immediately have a strong influence on the development of Greek mathematics. But it is hardly by chance that Plato wrote his dialogue *Parmenides*, in which he refers to Zeno's paradoxes, around the time that Eudoxus of Cnidus, who revised the theory of proportions in such a way as to enable him to handle the infinitesimal with an accuracy that has remained unsurpassed, spent some years at Athens and was a member of Plato's academy. Zeno's paradoxes can hardly have failed to have been thoroughly discussed then, and so Zeno may still have had some influence on Greek mathematics at that decisive point in its development.

*BIBLIOGRAPHY*

I. ORIGINAL WORKS. An extensive bibliography is in W. Totok, *Handbuch der Geschichte der Philosophie*, I, *Altertum* (Frankfurt, 1964), 123–124. The text ed. most convenient for English-speaking readers is H. D. P. Lee, *Zeno of Elea. A Text With Translation and Commentary* (Cambridge, 1936). In the secondary literature, however, the fragments are usually quoted according to H. Diels and W. Kranz, *Die Fragmente der Vorsokratiker*, 7th ed., I, no. 29, 247–258.

II. SECONDARY LITERATURE. See Guido Calogero, *Studi sull'Eleatismo* (Rome, 1932); and *Storia della logica antica*, I (Bari, 1967), 171–208; H. Fränkel, "Zeno of Elea's Attacks on Plurality," in *American Journal of Philology*, **63** (1942), 1–25, 193–206; Adolf Grünbaum, "A Consistent Conception of the Extended Linear Continuum as an Aggregate of Unextended Elements," in *Philosophy of Science*, **19** (1952), 288–305; "The Nature of Time," in *Frontiers of Science and Philosophy*, **1** (1962), 149–184; and *Modern Science and Zeno's Par-*

adoxes (Middletown, Conn., 1967); H. Hasse and H. Scholz, *Die Grundlagenkrisis der griechischen Mathematik* (Berlin–Charlottenburg, 1928); J. A. Philip, *Pythagoras and Early Pythagoreanism* (Toronto, 1966), 206–207; R. E. Siegel, "The Paradoxes of Zeno," in *Janus*, **48** (1959), 42 ff.; A. Szabó, *Anfänge der griechischen Mathematik* (Munich–Vienna, 1939), 333 ff.; P. Tannery, "Le concept scientifique du continu. Zénon d'Élée et Georg Cantor," in *Revue philosophique de la France et de l'étranger*, **20** (1885), 385–410, esp. 393–394; and *Pour l'histoire de la science hellène*, 2nd ed. (Paris, 1930), 248 ff.; B. L. van der Waerden, "Zenon und die Grundlagenkrise der griechischen Mathematik," in *Mathematische Annalen*, **117**, no. 2 (1940), 141–161, esp. 151 ff.; and G. Vlastos, "A Note on Zeno's Arrow," in *Phronesis*, **11** (1966), 3–18; and "Zeno's Race Course," in *Journal of the History of Philosophy*, **4** (1966), 95–108.

Concerning the influence of Zeno and of the methods developed by Eudoxus on the nineteenth-century attempts to give the calculus a more exact foundation, see M. Black, "Achilles and the Tortoise," in *Analysis*, **11** (1951), 91–101; J. M. Hinton and C. B. Martin, "Achilles and the Tortoise," *ibid.*, **14** (1953), 56–68; G. E. L. Owen, "Zeno and the Mathematicians," in *Proceedings of the Aristotelian Society*, n.s. **58** (1957–1958), 199–222; L. E. Thomas, "Achilles and the Tortoise," in *Analysis*, **12** (1952), 92–94; R. Taylor, "Mr. Black on Temporal Paradoxes," *ibid.*, 38–44; and J. O. Wisdom, "Achilles on a Physical Racecourse," *ibid.*, 67–72. There is also an especially instructive earlier paper by M. Dehn, "Raum, Zeit, Zahl bei Aristoteles vom mathematischen Standpunkt aus," in *Scientia*, **40** (1936), 12–21, 69–74, which deals with Aristotle's criticism of Zeno's paradoxes and its importance for modern mathematics.

Concerning the general problems underlying Zeno's paradoxes, see also P. Beisswanger, *Die Anfechtbarkeit der klassischen Mathematik* (Stuttgart, 1965); P. Bennacerraf, "What Numbers Could Not Be," in *Philosophical Review*, **74** (1965), 47–73; and Hermann Weyl, "Über die neue Grundlagenkrise der Mathematik," in *Mathematische Zeitschrift*, **10** (1921), 39–79.

KURT VON FRITZ

**ZENO OF SIDON** (*b.* Sidon, *ca.* 150 B.C.; *d.* Athens, *ca.* 70 B.C.), *philosophy, mathematics, logic.*

According to ancient tradition, Zeno of Sidon was a very prolific writer who discussed theory of knowledge, logic, various aspects of ancient atomic theory, the fundamental differences of the sexes (from which it follows that they have different diseases), problems of Epicurean ethics, literary criticism, style, oratory, poetry, and mathematics. Very little is known of the contents of these writings except those on mathematics and logic, which are of great interest.

Epicurus had been a very severe critic of mathematics as a science; but what he said about it is very superficial and shows that he did not understand what mathematics is. This is not at all the case with Zeno's criticism of Euclid's axiomatics. In his commentary on Euclid, Proclus says that Zeno attacked the first theorem of the *Elements* (the construction of an equilateral triangle) on the ground that it is valid only if one assumes that two straight lines cannot have more than one point in common, and that Euclid has not set this down as an axiom. On the same ground he attacked Euclid's fourth postulate, which asserts the equality of all right angles, observing that it presupposes the construction of a right angle, which is not given until I, 11. In addition, Proclus and Sextus Empiricus mention several criticisms of Euclid that they attribute to an unnamed Epicurean and that are similar to Zeno's criticisms: for instance, that there is no axiom establishing the infinite divisibility of curves, which is connected with a discussion of various consequences following from the assumption that curves are not infinitely divisible but, rather, are composed of the smallest units of indivisible lines. There is also a criticism anticipating Schopenhauer's of Euclid's method of superimposition, by which he proves the first theorem of congruence and a few other theorems: namely, that only matter can be moved in space.

On the basis of these criticisms of Euclid's axiomatics, E. M. Bruins has claimed that Zeno of Sidon was the first to discover the possibility of non-Euclidean geometry. This claim appears exaggerated, since there is not the slightest tradition indicating that Zeno elaborated his criticism in such a way as to show positively how a non-Euclidean geometrical system could be built up. Zeno's criticisms of Euclid are pertinent, however, and if any of the ancient philosophers and mathematicians who tried to refute them had been able to grasp their full implications, the development of mathematics might have taken a different turn.

Lengthy fragments of a treatise by the Epicurean philosopher Philodemus of Gadara have been found on a papyrus from Herculaneum (no. 1065), and most of those preserved contain a report on a controversy between Zeno and contemporary Stoics over the foundations of knowledge. In this dispute Zeno defended the old Epicurean doctrine that all human knowledge is derived exclusively from experience. What makes it interesting, however, is that he bases his defense on a theory that he calls "transition according to similarity" ($\mu\epsilon\tau\acute{\alpha}\beta\alpha\sigma\iota\varsigma$ $\kappa\alpha\vartheta$' $\dot{o}\mu o\iota\acute{o}\tau\eta\tau\alpha$) or "transition from the apparent to the not apparent" ($\mu\epsilon\tau\acute{\alpha}\beta\alpha\sigma\iota\varsigma$ $\dot{\alpha}\pi\dot{o}$ $\tau\tilde{\omega}\nu$ $\phi\alpha\iota\nu o\mu\acute{\epsilon}\nu\omega\nu$ $\dot{\epsilon}\varsigma$ $\tau\dot{\alpha}$ $\dot{\alpha}\phi\alpha\nu\tilde{\eta}$), but that is essentially an anticipation of John Stuart Mill's theory of induction.

In contrast to Aristotle's theory of induction, according to which the most certain kind of induction is that in which one case is sufficient to make it evident that the same must be true in all similar cases, and in opposition to the Stoic doctrine that no number of cases ever permits the conclusion that the same must be true in all cases, Zeno insisted that all knowledge is fundamentally derived by inference to all cases from a great many cases without observed counter-instance. He carried this principle to the extreme by asserting that the knowledge that the square with a side of length 4 is the only square in which the sum of the length of the sides (16) is equal to the contents ($4 \times 4 = 16$) was derived from measuring innumerable squares, although here it is evident that the result—insofar as it is correct, one-dimensional measures being equated with two-dimensional measures—can be derived from a simple deduction and that nobody will be so foolish as to "verify" it in innumerable squares. The recent proof by computers that the principle is not altogether applicable to mathematics and number theory shows that certain theorems of Pólya's that had been considered universally valid because they had been proved up to very high numbers were not valid beyond higher numbers unreachable by human calculation.

The details of the controversy between Zeno and the Stoics is extremely interesting because sometimes the positions become curiously reversed, and because it provides a kind of phenomenology of induction going beyond most modern works.

## BIBLIOGRAPHY

I. ORIGINAL WORKS. Extracts of Zeno's lectures are in T. Gomperz, *Herkulanische Studien*, I (Leipzig, 1865), 24–27; and P. H. and E. A. de Lacy, eds., *Philodemos: On Methods of Inference*, which is Philological Monographs of the American Philological Association, no. 10 (Philadelphia, 1941)—see index. (Pp. 22–66, columns Ia, 1–XIX, 4, are mostly extracts from Zeno's lectures, but it is not certain how far they are literal.)

II. SECONDARY LITERATURE. See Ludger Adam, "Das Wahrheits- und Hypothesenproblem bei Demokrit, Epikur und Zeno, dem Epikureer" (Ph.D. diss., Göttingen, 1947); E. M. Bruins, *La géométrie non-euclidienne dans l'antiquité*, Publications de l'Université de Paris, D121 (Paris, 1967); and G. Vlastos, "Zeno of Sidon as a Critic of Euclid," in *The Classical Tradition: Literary and Historical Studies in Honor of Harry Caplan* (New York, 1966), 148–159.

On problems arising in connection with Zeno's theory of induction, see C. B. Haselgrove, "A Disproof of a Conjecture of Pólya," in *Mathematica*, **5** (1958), 141; K. von Fritz, "Die $\dot{\epsilon}\pi\alpha\gamma\omega\gamma\acute{\eta}$ bei Aristoteles," in *Sitzungsberichte der Bayerischen Akademie der Wissenschaften zu München*, Phil.-hist. Kl. (1964), no. 3, 40 ff., 62 ff.; and R. Queneau, "Conjectures fausses en théorie des nombres," in *Mélanges Koyré*, I (Paris, 1964), 475 ff.

KURT VON FRITZ

**ZERMELO, ERNST FRIEDRICH FERDINAND** (*b.* Berlin, Germany, 27 July 1871; *d.* Freiburg im Breisgau, Germany, 21 May 1953), *mathematics*.

The son of Ferdinand Rudolf Theodor Zermelo, a college professor, and Maria Augusta Elisabeth Zieger, Zermelo received his secondary education at the Luisenstädtisches Gymnasium in Berlin, where he passed his final examination in 1889. He subsequently studied mathematics, physics, and philosophy at Berlin, Halle, and Freiburg, taking courses taught by Frobenius, Lazarus Fuchs, Planck, Erhard Schmidt, H. A. Schwarz, and Edmund Husserl. In 1894 he received the doctorate at Berlin with the dissertation *Untersuchungen zur Variationsrechnung*. Zermelo went to Göttingen and in 1899 was appointed *Privatdozent* after having submitted the *Habilitationsschrift* "Hydrodynamische Untersuchungen über die Wirbelbewegungen in einer Kugelfläche." In December 1905, shortly after his sensational proof of the well-ordering theorem (1904), Zermelo was named titular professor at Göttingen. In 1910 he accepted a professorship at Zurich, which poor health forced him to resign in 1916. A year after he had left Göttingen, 5000 marks from the interest of the Wolfskehl Fund was awarded him on the initiative of David Hilbert in recognition of his results in set theory (and to enable him to recover his health). After resigning his post at Zurich, Zermelo lived in the Black Forest until 1926, when he was appointed honorary professor at the University of Freiburg im Breisgau. He renounced connection with the university in 1935 because of his disapproval of the Hitler regime. After the war he requested reinstatement, which was granted him in 1946.

Zermelo had a lively interest in physics and a

keen sense for the application of mathematics to practical problems. He prepared German editions of Glazebrook's *Light* and Gibbs's *Elementary Principles in Statistical Mechanics*; and after having shown in "Ueber einen Satz der Dynamik" how application of Poincaré's recurrence theorem leads to the nonexistence of irreversible processes in the kinetic theory of gases, he had a penetrating discussion with Boltzmann on the explanation of irreversible processes.

In Zermelo's dissertation, which dealt with the calculus of variations, he extended Weierstrass' method for the extrema of integrals over a class of curves to the case of integrands depending on derivatives of arbitrarily high order, at the same time giving a careful definition of the notion of neighborhood in the space of curves. Throughout his life he was faithful to the calculus of variations, on which he often lectured and to which he contributed a report on its progress written with H. Hahn for the *Encyklopädie der mathematischen Wissenschaften* (1904) and the paper "Über die Navigation . . ." (1929).

Further examples of his original contributions to practical questions are his method for estimating the strength of participants in tournaments ("Die Berechnung der Turnier-Ergebnisse," 1929), which has been used in chess tournaments, and his investigation of the fracture of a cube of sugar ("Über die Bruchlinien zentrierter Ovale," 1933).

As an assistant at Göttingen, Zermelo lectured during the winter semester of 1900–1901 on set theory, to the development of which he was to contribute decisively. He had studied Cantor's work thoroughly, and his conversations with Erhard Schmidt led to his ingenious proof of the well-ordering theorem, which states that every set can be well-ordered; that is, in every set a relation $a \prec b$, to be read as "$a$ comes before $b$," can be introduced, such that (1) for any two elements $a$ and $b$, either $a = b$ or $a \prec b$ or $b \prec a$; (2) if for three elements $a$, $b$, $c$ we have $a \prec b$ and $b \prec c$, then $a \prec c$; (3) any nonvoid subset has a first element. In a commentary to his own proof, Zermelo pointed out the underlying hypothesis that for any infinite system of sets there always are relations under which every set corresponds to one of its elements. The proof stirred the mathematical world and produced a great deal of criticism—most of it unjustified—which Zermelo answered elegantly in "Neuer Beweis" (1908), where he also gave a second proof of the theorem. His answer to Poincaré's accusation of impredicativity is of some historical interest because he points out certain consequences and peculiarities of the predicative position that have played a role in the development of predicative mathematics.

Also in 1908 Zermelo set up an axiom system for Cantor's set theory that has proved of tremendous importance for the development of mathematics. It consists of seven axioms and uses only two technical terms: set and $\in$, the symbol for the "element of" relation. Zermelo emphasized the descriptive nature of the axioms, starting with a domain $B$ of objects and then specifying under what conditions (the axioms) an object is to be called a set. With the exception of the null set introduced in axiom 2, every set $a$ is an object of $B$ for which there is another object $b$ of $B$ such that $a \in b$.

Axiom 1 (extensionality): $m = n$ if and only if $a \in m$ is equivalent to $a \in n$.

Axiom 2 (elementary sets): There is a null set, having no element at all. Every object $a$ of $B$ determines a set $\{a\}$ with $a$ as its only element. Any two objects $a$, $b$ of $B$ determine a set $\{a,b\}$ with precisely $a$ and $b$ as elements.

Axiom 3 (separation): If a property $E$ is definite for the elements of a set $m$, then there is a subset $m_E$ of $m$ consisting of exactly those elements of $m$ for which $E$ holds.

Axiom 4 (power set): To any set $m$ there is a set $P(m)$ that has the subsets of $m$ for its elements.

Axiom 5 (union): To any set $m$ there is a set $\cup m$, the union of $m$, consisting of the elements of the elements of $m$.

Axiom 6 (axiom of choice): If $m$ is a set of disjoint nonvoid sets, then $\cup m$ contains a subset $n$ that contains exactly one element from every set of $m$.

Axiom 7 (infinity): There is a set $z$ that has the null set as an element and has the property that if $a$ is an element of $z$, then $\{a\}$ is also an element of $z$.

In order to avoid the paradoxes, particularly Russell's paradox, which would render the system useless, Zermelo restricted set formation by the condition of definiteness of the defining property of a subset. A property $E$ definite for set $m$ is explained as one for which the basic relations of $B$ permit one to decide whether or not $E$ holds for any element of $m$. Although this condition seemed to preclude contradictions in the system, Zermelo explicitly left aside the difficult questions of independence and consistency. This was a wise decision, as one may realize after having seen the solutions of the questions of relative consistency and independence of axiom 6 by Kurt Gödel (1938) and P. J. Cohen (1963), respectively.

Because of its generality the notion of definite property is very elegant. It is rather difficult to apply, however, because it does not yield a general method for proving a proposed property to be definite.

Although nonaxiomatic Cantorian set theory was then flourishing, particularly the branch that developed into point-set topology, there was no progress in axiomatic set theory until 1921, when A. Fraenkel, in his attempts to prove the independence of the axiom of choice, pointed out some defects in Zermelo's system. Fraenkel's objections were threefold. First, the axiom of infinity is too weak; second, the system is by no means categorical; and third, the notion of definite property is too vague to handle in proofs of independence and consistency. These remarks led Fraenkel to add the powerful axiom of replacement, which adds to any set $s$ its image under some function $F$, while the notion of function is introduced by definition. Another way of obtaining a similar result was achieved by T. Skolem, who specified a definite property as one expressible in first-order logic.

After having realized the importance of Fraenkel's and Skolem's remarks, Zermelo set out in "Über den Begriff der Definitheit in der Axiomatik" (1929) to axiomatize this notion by describing the set of definite properties as the smallest set containing the basic relations of the domain $B$ and satisfying certain closure conditions. He admitted that the reason for doing so was methodological: to keep to the "pure axiomatic" method, in avoidance of the genetic method and the use of the notion of finite number. Since there is no categoricity, an investigation of the structure of the possible domains $b$—models for axiomatic set theory—makes sense. In "Über Grenzzahlen und Mengenbereiche" (1930) Zermelo investigated the structure of models of an axiom system consisting of his earlier axioms 1, 4, 5, the last part of 2, the unrestricted form of 3, a liberal axiom of replacement, and an axiom of well-foundedness (with respect to $\in$) stating that every subdomain $T$ of domain $B$ contains at least one element $t_0$ that has no element $t$ in $T$.

Zermelo's fragmentary attempt, in "Grundlagen einer allgemeinen Theorie der mathematischen Satzsysteme" (1935), to abolish the limitations of proof theory has not been of great consequence because his conception of a proof as a system of theorems, well-founded with respect to the relation of consequence, seems too general to lead to results of sufficient interest.

## BIBLIOGRAPHY

I. ORIGINAL WORKS. Zermelo's writings include *Untersuchungen zur Variationsrechnung* (Berlin, 1894), his dissertation; "Ueber einen Satz der Dynamik und die mechanische Wärmetheorie," in *Annalen der Physik und Chemie*, n.s. **57** (1896), 485–494; "Ueber mechanische Erklärungen irreversibler Vorgänge. Eine Antwort auf Hrn. Boltzmann's 'Entgegnung,'" *ibid.*, **59** (1896), 793–801; *Das Licht. Grundriss der Optik für Studierende und Schüler*, his trans. of R. T. Glazebrook's *Light* (Berlin, 1897); "Ueber die Bewegung eines Punktsystemes bei Bedingungsungleichungen," in *Nachrichten von der K. Gesellschaft der Wissenschaften zu Göttingen*, math.-phys. Kl. (1899), 306–310; "Über die Anwendung der Wahrscheinlichkeitsrechnung auf dynamische Systeme," in *Physikalische Zeitschrift*, **1** (1899–1900), 317–320; "Ueber die Addition transfiniter Cardinalzahlen," in *Nachrichten von der K. Gesellschaft der Wissenschaften zu Göttingen*, math.-phys. Kl. (1901), 34–38; "Hydrodynamische Untersuchungen über die Wirbelbewegungen in einer Kugelfläche," in *Zeitschrift für Mathematik und Physik*, **47** (1902), 201–237, his *Habilitationsschrift*; and "Zur Theorie der kürzesten Linien," in *Jahresberichte der Deutschen Mathematikervereinigung*, **11** (1902), 184–187.

Further works are "Über die Herleitung der Differentialgleichung bei Variationsproblemen," in *Mathematische Annalen*, **58** (1904), 558–564; "Beweis, dass jede Menge wohlgeordnet werden kann," *ibid.*, **59** (1904), 514–516; "Weiterentwickelung der Variationsrechnung in den letzten Jahren," in *Encyklopädie der mathematischen Wissenschaften*, II, pt. 1 (Leipzig, 1904), 626–641, written with H. Hahn; *Elementare Grundlagen der statistischen Mechanik*, his trans. of Gibbs's work (Leipzig, 1905); "Neuer Beweis für die Möglichkeit einer Wohlordnung," in *Mathematische Annalen*, **65** (1908), 107–128; "Untersuchungen über die Grundlagen der Mengenlehre I," *ibid.*, 261–281; "Sur les ensembles finis et le principe de l'induction complète," in *Acta mathematica*, **32** (1909), 185–193; "Die Einstellung der Grenzkonzentrationen an der Trennungsfläche zweier Lösungsmittel," in *Physikalische Zeitschrift*, **10** (1909), 958–961, written with E. H. Riesenfeld; and "Ueber die Grundlagen der Arithmetik," in *Atti del IV Congresso internazionale dei matematici*, II (Rome, 1909), 8–11.

See also "Über eine Anwendung der Mengenlehre auf die Theorie des Schachspiels," in *Proceedings of the Fifth International Congress of Mathematicians*, II (Cambridge, 1913), 501–504; "Über ganze transzendente Zahlen," in *Mathematische Annalen*, **75** (1914), 434–442; "Ueber das Masz und die Diskrepanz von Punktmengen," in *Journal für die reine und angewandte Mathematik*, **158** (1927), 154–167; "Über den Begriff der Definitheit in der Axiomatik," in *Fundamenta mathematicae*, **14** (1929), 339–344; "Die Berechnung der Turnier-Ergebnisse als ein Maximumproblem der Wahrscheinlichkeitsrechnung," in *Mathematische Zeit-*

*schrift,* **29** (1929), 436–460; and "Über die Navigation in der Luft als Problem der Variationsrechnung," in *Jahresberichte der Deutschen Mathematikervereinigung,* **39** (1929), 44–48.

Additional works are "Über Grenzzahlen und Mengenbereiche. Neue Untersuchungen über die Grundlagen der Mengenlehre," in *Fundamenta mathematicae,* **16** (1930), 29–47; "Über die logische Form der mathematischen Theorien," in *Annales de la Société polonaise de mathématique,* **9** (1930), 187; "Über das Navigationsproblem bei ruhender oder veränderlicher Windverteilung," in *Zeitschrift für angewandte Mathematik und Mechanik,* **11** (1931), 114–124; "Über mathematische Systeme und die Logik des Unendlichen," in *Forschungen und Fortschritte,* **8** (1932), 6–7; "Über Stufen der Quantifikation und die Logik des Unendlichen," in *Jahresberichte der Deutschen Mathematikervereinigung,* **41** (1932), 85–88; "Über die Bruchlinien zentrierter Ovale. (Wie zerbricht ein Stück Zucker?)," in *Zeitschrift für angewandte Mathematik und Mechanik,* **13** (1933), 168–170; "Elementare Betrachtungen zur Theorie der Primzahlen," in *Nachrichten von der Gesellschaft der Wissenschaften zu Göttingen,* Fachgruppe 1, **1** (1934), 43–46; and "Grundlagen einer allgemeinen Theorie der mathematischen Satzsysteme. (Erste Mitteilung)," in *Fundamenta mathematicae,* **25** (1935), 136–146.

A collection of papers left by Zermelo is in the library of the University of Freiburg im Breisgau. A short description, furnished by H. Gericke, is as follows: a set of copies of articles by Zermelo and other mathematicians, a collection of letters and MSS and sketches of published papers, lecture notes in shorthand, parts of a translation of Homer in German verse, the second part of his *Habilitationsschrift,* and a sketch of a patent application "Kreisel zur Stabilisierung von Fahr- und Motorrädern" (gyroscope for stabilizing bicycles and motorcycles).

II. SECONDARY LITERATURE. Quite a number of relevant papers on set theory, including three memoirs by Zermelo, are reprinted in J. van Heijenoort, *From Frege to Gödel* (Cambridge, Mass., 1967), which also contains references to the literature up to 1966. See also P. J. Cohen, *Set Theory and the Continuum Hypothesis* (New York, 1966); S. Fefermann, "Systems of Predicative Analysis," in *Journal of Symbolic Logic,* **29** (1964), 1–30; A. Fraenkel, "Über die Zermelosche Begründung der Mengenlehre," in *Jahresberichte der Deutschen Mathematikervereinigung,* **30** (1921), 97–98; "Zu den Grundlagen der Cantor-Zermeloschen Mengenlehre," in *Mathematische Annalen,* **86** (1922), 230–237; "Der Begriff 'definit' und die Unabhängigkeit des Auswahlsaxioms," in *Sitzungsberichte der Preussischen Akademie der Wissenschaften zu Berlin* (1922), 253–257; and *Foundations of Set Theory* (Amsterdam, 1958), written with Y. Bar-Hillel; H. Gericke, *Beiträge zur Freiburger Wissenschafts- und universitätsgeschichte,* VII, *Zur Geschichte der Mathematik an der Universität Freiburg i.Br.,* J. Vincke, ed. (Freiburg im Breisgau, 1955), 72–73; K. Gödel, *The Consistency of the Continuum*

*Hypothesis* (Princeton, N.J., 1940); G. Kreisel and J. L. Krivine, *Elements of Mathematical Logic* (Amsterdam, 1967); M. Pinl, "Kollegen in einer dunklen Zeit," in *Jahresberichte der Deutsche Mathematikervereinigung,* **71** (1969), 167–228, esp. 221–222; C. Reid, *Hilbert* (Berlin, 1970); and J. Barkeley Rosser, *Simplified Independence Proofs* (New York, 1969).

Also see T. Skolem, "Logisch-kombinatorische Untersuchungen über die Erfüllbarkeit oder Beweisbarkeit mathematischer Sätze nebst einem Theoreme über dichte Mengen," in *Skrifter utgitt av Videnskapsselskapet i Kristiania,* I. Mat.-naturvid. kl. (1920), no. 4; "Einige Bemerkungen zur axiomatischen Begründung der Mengenlehre," in *Matematiker kongressen i Helsinfors den 4–7 Juli 1922* (Helsinki, 1923), 217–232; "Über einige Grundlagenfragen der Mathematik," in *Skrifter utgitt av det Norske videnskaps-akademi i Oslo,* I. Mat.-naturvid. kl. (1929), no. 4; and "Einige Bemerkungen zu der Abhandlung von E. Zermelo: 'Über die Definitheit in der Axiomatik,'" in *Fundamenta mathematicae,* **15** (1930), 337–341; and L. Zoretti and A. Rosenthal, "Die Punktmengen," in *Encyklopädie der mathematischen Wissenschaften,* II, pt. 3 (Leipzig, 1923), 855–1030.

B. VAN ROOTSELAAR

**ZERNIKE, FRITS** (*b.* Amsterdam, Netherlands, 16 July 1888; *d.* Naarden, near Amsterdam, 10 March 1966), *theoretical physics, technical physics.*

Zernike's father, headmaster of an elementary school, was well-known for his textbooks on arithmetic. While a chemistry student at Amsterdam University, Zernike won two gold medals for prize questions in mathematics and physics. In 1913 he became assistant to the astronomer J. C. Kapteyn at the University of Groningen, where he held various academic positions until his retirement at the age of seventy.

Zernike's dissertation, "L'opalescence critique, théorie et expériments" (Amsterdam, 1915), is still worth reading. In 1915 he succeeded L. S. Ornstein as lecturer in theoretical physics at Groningen; in 1920 he became full professor; and in 1941 his chair was extended to include mathematical and technical physics and theoretical mechanics. He became a member of the Royal Netherlands Academy of Sciences at Amsterdam in 1946, and seven years later he won the Nobel Prize in physics.

Widely read and wide-ranging in his work, Zernike paid especial interest to three main areas: statistical physics and fluctuation phenomena, the construction of instruments, and interference of light waves. He was an able speaker and possessed an extraordinary combination of mathematical and instrument-making skill, always using these abilities to bring out, in the simplest way, the essential physical principles of a problem or the characteristics of an instrument. Later his methods often found wider application.

For instance, in the wave theory of light he introduced the set of polynomials orthogonal on a circle that is widely used by mathematicians under the name of Zernike polynomials. In molecular statistics he introduced the concept of a radial distribution function $g(r)$ giving the mean number density of molecular centers around an arbitrary molecular center. Through Fourier inversion it leads to exact expressions for the scattering of light or the diffraction of X rays in liquids, and its use has been extended to other fields.

In constructing instruments Zernike always started from first principles and worked out the significant mathematical consequences. This procedure often led to unexpected results—for instance, the discovery that for a sensitive moving-coil galvanometer, the moment of inertia of the mirror has to be roughly three times that of the moving coil. The usual technique of instrument makers had been just the opposite: making the mirror quite small compared with the moving coil. He also worked on the ultracentrifuge and thermoelectrical devices.

Experimental and mathematical skill also formed the base of Zernike's best-known contribution, the method of phase contrast in wave theory. It is now generally used in microscopy but has a much wider application: it was used, for instance, in his study of errors in telescope mirrors and in the Groningen Rowland grating (in the winter of 1930–1931, the first application of phase contrast). It led Zernike to study the "degree of coherence" in light and to approach what is now called holography. The essential point is that in the "primary" diffraction pattern, already studied by Abbe, a phase difference between the central part and the wings of the pattern exists—and can be manipulated to increase the contrast in the image or to reconstruct the object in three dimensions.

It has rightly been said that the spirit of Zernike's work is reminiscent of Lord Rayleigh's, to whom Zernike often referred in his lectures.

BIBLIOGRAPHY

Lists of Zernike's writings are included in the obituaries by Tolansky and by Prins and Nijboer (see below). An autobiographical article is "How I Discovered Phase Contrast," in *Les prix Nobel en 1953* (Stockholm, 1953), 107–114.

See H. Brinkman, in *Nederlands tijdschrift voor natuurkunde*, **24** (1958), 139; J. A. Prins, in *Jaarboek der Koninklijke Nederlandsche akademie van wetenschappen* (1965–1966), 370–377; J. A. Prins and B. R. A. Nijboer, in *Nederlands tijdschrift voor natuurkunde*, **19** (1953), 314–328; S. Tolansky, in *Biographical Memoirs of Fellows of the Royal Society (London)*, **13** (1967), 393–402, with portrait; and N. G. van Kampen, in *Nature*, **211** (1966), 465—also see **172** (1953), 938.

J. A. PRINS

**ZEUNER, GUSTAV ANTON** (*b.* Chemnitz [now Karl-Marx-Stadt, German Democratic Republic], 30 November 1828; *d.* Dresden, Germany, 17 October 1907), *mechanical engineering, thermodynamics.*

The son of a cabinetmaker, Zeuner completed an apprenticeship in his father's trade (1846). At the local trade school and through private study he acquired the background to enter the mining academy at Freiberg, Saxony. Working closely with Julius Weisbach, professor of mechanics and mining machinery and a notable hydraulics engineer, he became interested in applied mathematics and mechanical engineering and decided upon a teaching career. In the first years after his graduation (1851–1855), Zeuner was unable to find permanent employment in his native Saxony because of his participation in the 1849 uprisings in Dresden. In 1851 he visited Paris, where he met Poncelet and Regnault. Impressed by Foucault's pendulum, he wrote a theoretical study of it, for which the University of Leipzig awarded him the Ph.D. in 1853. In 1854, with Weisbach and C. R. Bornemann, he founded the important journal *Der Civil-Ingenieur*, of which he was the first editor (until 1857) and a major contributor.

In 1855 Zeuner was appointed professor of mechanics and theory of machines, and head of the mechanical department of the Federal Polytechnicum at Zurich. His years in Zurich were his most productive; he served as deputy director (1859–1865, 1868–1871) and director (1865–1868) of the institution, and wrote his most important scientific works. In later years Zeuner was preoccupied with administrative duties, serving as director of the Freiberg Mining Academy from 1871 to 1875, and of the Dresden Polytechnical Institute from 1873 to 1890. He resigned the latter post in 1890, after reorganizing the school into an institute of technology, and retired from teaching in 1897.

Reflecting the influence of Weisbach, Zeuner's earliest publications dealt with problems of hydraulics and water turbines, a subject to which he returned in his later years. Most of his works, however, were devoted to theoretical aspects of the steam engine. In a book on steam-engine valve gears (1858) he proposed a graphical treatment of valve motion that was soon internationally accepted as the Zeuner diagram; other monographs dealt with steam injectors and the dynamic imbalances in the motion of locomotives. His main work, a comprehensive text on thermodynamics (1860), presented the first synthesis into a consistent system of the newly formulated first and second laws of thermodynamics and the improved understanding of the properties of steam (resulting from Regnault's experiments). This book, which had lasting international success, was distinguished by its emphasis upon theoretical principles and by its deductive approach. It was later criticized for its failure to do justice to certain practical problems of the steam engine.

Zeuner also made pioneer contributions to mathematical statistics and insurance mathematics, in which he had become interested through a study of miners' insurance systems done while he was a student.

Zeuner has been praised as a naturally gifted lecturer and teacher. Among his most prominent students were the engineers Carl von Linde and Hans Lorenz and the physicist Wilhelm Röntgen, whose doctoral dissertation (1869) he supervised.

## BIBLIOGRAPHY

I. ORIGINAL WORKS. Lists of Zeuner's publications are in Poggendorff, II, 1407–1408; III, 1481–1482; IV, 1689; and V, 1410. His books are *Die Schiebersteuerungen* (Freiberg, 1858; 6th ed., Leipzig, 1904), translated by J. F. Klein as *Treatise on Valve Gears* (London–New York, 1884) and by A. Debize and E. Merijot as *Traité des distributions par tiroir* (Paris, 1869); *Grundzüge der mechanischen Wärmetheorie* (Freiberg, 1860; 2nd ed., 1866), 3rd ed., enl., *Technische Thermodynamik*, 2 vols. (Leipzig, 1887–1890; 5th ed., 1905–1906), translated by Maurice Arnthal as *Théorie mécanique de la chaleur* (Paris, 1869) and by J. F. Klein as *Technical Thermodynamics* (New York, 1907); *Das Locomotiven-Blasrohr* (Stuttgart, 1863); *Abhandlungen aus der mathematischen Statistik* (Leipzig, 1869); and *Vorlesungen über Theorie der Turbinen* (Leipzig, 1899).

II. SECONDARY LITERATURE. Biographical information on Zeuner, listed chronologically, is A. Slaby *et al.*, "Gustav Zeuner," in *Zeitschrift des Vereins deutscher Ingenieure*, 51 (1907), 2049–2050; R. Mollier, "Gustav Zeuner," *ibid.*, 52 (1908), 1221–1224; Verein Deutscher Ingenieure, *Gustav Zeuner, sein Leben und Wirken* (Berlin, 1928); and Gustav Zeuner-Schnorf, "Als junger Professor an die Hochschule berufen," in *Neue Zürcher Zeitung*, no. 2812 (22 Oct. 1955); and "Röntgens Doktorvater in Zürich," in *Technische Rundschau* (1958).

OTTO MAYR

**ZEUTHEN, HIERONYMUS GEORG** (*b*. Grimstrup, West Jutland, Denmark, 15 February 1839; *d*. Copenhagen, Denmark, 6 January 1920), *mathematics, mechanics, history of mathematics.*

The son of a minister, Zeuthen received his earliest education in Grimstrup and at the age of ten entered the secondary school in Sorø, where his father had been transferred. From 1857 to 1862 he studied pure and applied mathematics at the University of Copenhagen. After passing the examination for a master's degree, he received a stipend in 1863 to travel to Paris for further study with Chasles. Having become familiar with his writings, Zeuthen followed Chasles's lead in his own work on enumerative methods in geometry and also in undertaking research on the history of mathematics.

Zeuthen found in enumerative methods in geometry ("number geometry") a fertile area for research. His first work on this subject was his doctoral dissertation at the University of Copenhagen, *Nyt Bidrag til Laeren on Systemer af Keglesnit* (1865), which was also published in French in *Nouvelles annales de mathématiques* (2nd ser., 5 [1866]) as "Nouvelle méthode pour déterminer les caractéristiques des systèmes de coniques." In this work Zeuthen adhered closely to Chasles's theory of the characteristics of conic systems but also presented new points of view: for the elementary systems under consideration, he first ascertained the numbers for point or line conics in order to employ them to determine the characteristics. Arthur Cayley presented a thorough discussion of the relationships and an exposition of the entire theory in "On the Curves Which Satisfy Given Conditions" (*Philosophical Transactions of the Royal Society*, 158 [1868], 75–143).

The first decade of Zeuthen's scientific activity was devoted entirely to enumerative methods in geometry, and his works were published in *Tidsskrift for Mathematik*, of which he was editor from 1871 to 1889; he was also a contributor to *Mathematische Annalen* and other European scientific journals. A summary of this work was presented in

*Lehrbuch der abzählenden Methoden der Geometrie* (1914); and as a leading expert in the field, he was chosen to write "Encyklopädiebericht über abzählende Methoden" for the *Encyklopädie der mathematischen Wissenschaften* (III, pt. 2 [1905], 257–312).

In 1871 Zeuthen became assistant professor and in 1886 full professor at the University of Copenhagen, where he remained until his death, serving as rector in 1896. While at the university he also taught at the nearby Polytechnic Academy and for many years was secretary of the Royal Danish Academy of Sciences.

After 1875, in addition to teaching, Zeuthen wrote on mechanics, geometry, and the history of mathematics. In his first major work on this subject, "Kegelsnitlaeren in Oltiden" (1885), he presented an exposition of Apollonius of Perga's theory of conic sections, in which he showed that Apollonius had employed oblique coordinates in deriving the properties of conics. Zeuthen also found in his work the projective production of the conics from two pencils of lines.

In a second, larger work (1896), Zeuthen traced the development of mathematics to the Middle Ages, presenting the influences of the Greek tradition that were transmitted to medieval mathematics through the Arabs and the rediscovery of the original works. He continued his historical studies in *Geschichte der Mathematik im 16. und 17. Jahrhundert* (1903), a large portion of which is devoted to Descartes and Viète, with regard not only to algebra and analytic geometry but also to the history of analysis, the development of which Zeuthen traced from its beginnings to Newton and Leibniz. Zeuthen also emphasized the importance of Barrow's works in the emergence of this discipline.

Although in these works Zeuthen naturally drew on the findings and references of other authors, his results were based essentially on careful study of original texts. Moreover, he strove to attune his thinking to the ancient forms of mathematics, in order to appraise the value of the resources and methods available in earlier periods. Although he was criticized for not providing full details concerning his sources, it is widely conceded that Zeuthen was the foremost historian of mathematics of his time, perhaps superior to Moritz Cantor and Siegmund Günther.

Zeuthen saw things intuitively: he constantly strove to attain an overall conception that would embrace the details of the subject under investigation and afford a way of seizing their significance. This approach characterized his historical research equally with his work on enumerative methods in geometry.

A *Festschrift* was dedicated to Zeuthen on his seventieth birthday, and in honor of his eightieth birthday a medal with his likeness was struck.

### BIBLIOGRAPHY

I. ORIGINAL WORKS. A list of Zeuthen's 161 published writings is in M. Noether, "Hieronymus Georg Zeuthen" (see below), 15–23. Among his most important monographs are *Grundriss einer elementargeometrischen Kegelschnittslehre* (Leipzig, 1882); "Kegelsnitlaeren in Oltiden," which is *Kongelige Danske Videnskabernes Selskabs Skrifter*, 6th ser., **3**, no. 1 (1885), 1–319, 2nd ed. by O. Neugebauer (Copenhagen, 1949); German trans. by R. Fischer-Benzon as *Die Lehre von den Kegelschnitten im Altertum* (Copenhagen, 1886), 2nd ed. by J. E. Hofmann (Hildesheim, 1966); *Forelaesning over Mathematikens Historie: Oldtig i Middelalder* (Copenhagen, 1893), German trans. as *Geschichte der Mathematik im Altertum und Mittelalter* (Copenhagen, 1896), French trans. by J. Mascart (Paris, 1902); *Geschichte der Mathematik im 16. und 17. Jahrhundert* (Copenhagen, 1903), also in German (Leipzig, 1903) and Russian (Moscow–Leningrad, 1933); and *Lehrbuch der abzählenden Methoden der Geometrie* (Leipzig–Berlin, 1914).

II. SECONDARY LITERATURE. See Johannes Hjelmslev, "Hieronymus Georg Zeuthen," in *Matematisk Tidsskrift*, ser. A (1939), 1–10; and Max Noether, "Hieronymus Georg Zeuthen," in *Mathematische Annalen*, **83** (1921), 1–23. Luigi Berzolari, "Bericht über die allgemeine Theorie der höheren ebenen algebraischen Kurven," in *Encyklopädie mathematischen Wissenschaften*, III, pt. 2 (Leipzig, 1906), 313–455, contains many references to Zeuthen's work and results.

KARLHEINZ HAAS

**ZHUKOVSKY, NIKOLAY EGOROVICH** (*b.* Orekhovo, Vladimir province, Russia, 17 January 1847; *d.* Moscow, U.S.S.R., 17 March 1921), *mechanics, mathematics.*

The son of a communications engineer, Zhukovsky completed his secondary education at the Fourth Gymnasium for Men in Moscow in 1864 and graduated in 1868 from the Faculty of Physics and Mathematics of the University of Moscow, having specialized in applied mathematics. In 1870 he began teaching at the Second Gymnasium for Women in Moscow, and at the beginning of 1872 he was invited to teach mathematics at the Moscow Technical School, at which he also lectured on theoretical mechanics from 1874. Two years later he defended a dissertation at the Technical School on the kinematics of a liquid and was awarded the degree of master of applied mathematics; a separate chair of mechanics was subsequently established for him at the school. In 1882 he defended his doctoral dissertation, on the stability of motion, at Moscow University and four years later became head of the department of mechanics there. In 1894 he was elected corresponding member of the St. Petersburg Academy of Sciences, and in 1900 he was promoted to member. Unwilling to leave his teaching posts in Moscow and undertake the requisite move to St. Petersburg, however, Zhukovsky withdrew his candidacy. A member of the Moscow Mathematical Society, he also served as vice-president from 1903 to 1905, and as president from 1905 until his death he proved to be an outstanding administrator.

Zhukovsky's approximately 200 publications in mechanics and its applications to technology reveal the wide range of his interests. Several works are devoted to the motion of a solid around a fixed point, in particular, to the case of Sonya Kovalevsky, for which he gave an elegant geometrical interpretation. He also wrote on the theory of ships, on the resistance of materials, and on practical mechanics. From the beginning of the twentieth century his interest focused primarily on aerodynamics and aviation, to which he devoted himself exclusively in his later years.

In his clear and well-organized lectures Zhukovsky made extensive use of geometric methods, which he valued highly. His lectures on hydrodynamics were standard works for many years, and his course on the theory of regulation of mechanical action (1908–1909) was the first rigorous presentation in Russian of the fundamentals of that subject. His lectures at the Moscow Technical School on the theoretical basis of aeronautics (1911–1912) were the world's first systematic course in aviation theory and were based largely on his own theoretical research and on experiments conducted in laboratories that he had established. During World War I Zhukovsky and his students taught special courses for pilots at the Technical School.

Instrumental in the development of Soviet aviation, Zhukovsky was named head of the Central Aerohydrodynamics Institute, established in 1918. The school of aviation that subsequently developed from it was based on his teaching and be-

came the N. E. Zhukovsky Academy of Military and Aeronautical Engineering in 1922.

Zhukovsky is considered the founder of Russian hydromechanics and aeromechanics. In his master's thesis (1876) he made extensive use of geometric, as well as analytic, methods to establish the kinematic laws of particles in a current. In 1885 he was awarded the N. D. Brashman Prize for a major theoretical work on the motion of a solid containing a homogeneous liquid. The methods that he developed in this memoir made it possible to solve certain problems of astronomy, concerning the laws of planetary rotation, and of ballistics, on the theory of projectiles having liquid cores. In a work dealing with a modification of the Kirchhoff method for determining the motion of a liquid in two dimensions with constant velocity and an unknown line of flow (1890), Zhukovsky used the theory of functions of a complex variable to elaborate a method for determining the resistance of a profile having any number of critical points. In addition to solving the problems studied by Kirchhoff, he resolved others, the solution of which had been extremely complicated with the use of existing methods. A memoir written with S. A. Chaplygin (1906) gave a precise solution to the problem of the motion of a lubricant between pin and bearings, and stimulated a number of other investigations.

In hydraulics, Zhukovsky in 1888 undertook theoretical research on the movement of subsurface water and studied the influence of pressure on water-permeated sand, establishing the relation between changes in the water level and changes in barometric pressure. Showing that the variation in the water level depends on the thickness of the water-bearing layer, he introduced formulas to determine the undergound water supply, using experimental data extensively. This research was summarized in a work on hydraulic shock in water pipes (1898), in which Zhukovsky established that the reason for damage to water mains was the sudden increase in pressure that followed the rapid closing of the valves. Extensive experiments enabled him to present the physical nature of hydraulic shock, to give a formula for determining the time needed for safe closing of the mains, and to elaborate a method for preserving them from damage effected by hydraulic shock. Zhukovsky acquired an international reputation for this theory, which has remained fundamental to problems of hydraulic shock.

Zhukovsky's other works in hydrodynamics

concern the formation of riverbeds (1914) and the selection of a river site for constructing dams and for withdrawing water used to cool machines at large power stations (1915).

Known as "the father of Russian aviation," Zhukovsky became interested in the late 1880's in flight in heavier-than-air machines, a basic problem of which was lift. The experimental data that had been obtained proved useful only in particular cases; attempts to determine lift on the basis of theoretical premises—especially existing theories of jet stream—yielded results that differed considerably from experimental findings.

Considering it necessary to first establish a physical picture of lift, Zhukovsky in 1890 considered the possibility that it can result from certain vortical motions caused by the viscosity of the surrounding medium. His subsequent experiments with disks rotating in an air current (1890–1891) anticipated his concept of bound vortices, the basis of his theory of lift. In 1891 Zhukovsky began studying the dynamics of flight in heavier-than-air machines, theoretically substantiating the possibility of complex motion of an airborne craft, in particular the existence of loops. In 1890–1891 Zhukovsky undertook experiments designed to study the changing position of the center of pressure of a wing with the simplest profile, a flat disk. By that time he had already turned his attention to the question of stability and was conducting tests of gliders and kites. In studying propeller thrust, Zhukovsky considered heavier-than-air craft powered by flapping wings, multipropellered helicopters, and screw propellors. In 1897 he presented a method of computing the most efficient angle of attack of a wing.

Zhukovsky's works on the motion of a substance in a liquid, published in the 1880's and 1890's, included a memoir on the paradox of Du Buat (1734–1809), for which he gave a physical explanation. In 1779 Du Buat had shown experimentally that the resistance of an immobile disk in a moving liquid is greater than the resistance of a disk moving at the same speed in a stationary liquid—a phenomenon that seemed to contradict the general laws of mechanics. Zhukovsky explained the discrepancy by the fact that, in practice, turbulence always occurs on the walls and the free surface of a liquid. To support his explanation he constructed a small device by means of which he showed that when there is no turbulence the pressure remains the same in both cases.

Zhukovsky established that lift results from the flow in an airstream of an immobile bound vortex (or system of vortices) by which the object can be replaced. From this starting point, he derived a formula for lift, equal to the product of the density of air, the circulation velocity of the surrounding airstream, and the velocity of the body. The theorem was confirmed in experiments with rotating oblong disks, conducted in 1905–1906 at the Aerodynamics Institute at Kuchino, near Moscow.

The formulation in 1910 of the Zhukovsky-Chaplygin postulate, concerning the determination of the rate of circulation around a wing, made it possible to solve the problem of lift, to determine its moment, and to develop a profile for airplane wings. Zhukovsky also investigated the profile of resistance of a wing and established the existence of resistance caused by the flow of turbulence from the wing's sharp leading edge.

In high-speed aerodynamics, Zhukovsky in 1919 presented a theory of the distribution of high-velocity plane and spherical waves, and demonstrated its possible application to determine the resistance of projectiles. His work in airplane stability included a major monograph (1918) in which he considered the construction of airplanes on the assumption that the longerons bear uniform loads arising from the weight of the wings and from the air pressure.

Zhukovsky initiated the study in Russia of the theory of bombing from airplanes. In 1915 he offered a method of determining the trajectory and bomb velocity when the air resistance is proportional to the square of the velocity; he provided a method of calculating the change of air density from a given altitude; and he examined various practical methods for using bombing and sighting apparatus.

S. A. Chaplygin was the most distinguished member of Zhukovsky's school, which included A. I. Nekrason, L. S. Leybenzon, V. P. Vetchinkin, B. N. Yuriev, and A. N. Tupolev.

*BIBLIOGRAPHY*

I. ORIGINAL WORKS. Zhukovsky's complete collected works were published as *Polnoe sobranie sochineny*, 9 vols. (Moscow–Leningrad, 1935–1937). Other collections are *Izbrannye sochinenia* ("Selected Works"), 2 vols. (Moscow–Leningrad, 1948); and *Sobranie sochineny* ("Collected Works"), 7 vols. (Moscow–Leningrad, 1948–1950).

II. SECONDARY LITERATURE. On Zhukovsky and his work, see V. A. Dombrovskaya, *Nikolay Egorovich*

*Zhukovsky* (Moscow–Leningrad, 1939), with bibliography of his writings; V. V. Golubev, *Nikolay Egorovich Zhukovsky* (Moscow, 1947); A. T. Grigorian, *Ocherki istorii mekhaniki v Rossii* ("Sketches of the History of Mechanics in Russia"; Moscow, 1961); "Vklad N. E. Zhukovskogo i S. A. Chaplygina v gidro-dinamiky i aerodinamiku" ("The Contribution of Zhukovsky and Chaplygin to Hydrodynamics and Aerodynamics"), in *Evolyutsia mekhaniki v Rossii* ("Evolution of Mechanics in Russia"; Moscow, 1967); and *Mekhanika ot antichnosti do nashikh dney* ("Mechanics From Antiquity to Our Time"; Moscow, 1971); A. A. Kosmodemyansky, "Nikolay Egorovich Zhukovsky," in *Lyudi russkoy nauki* ("Men of Russian Science"; Moscow, 1961), 169–177; and L. S. Leybenzon, *Nikolay Egorovich Zhukovsky* (Moscow–Leningrad, 1947).

A. T. GRIGORIAN

**ZININ, NIKOLAY NIKOLAEVICH** (*b.* Shusha, Transcaucasia [now Azerbaydzhan S.S.R.], Russia, 25 August 1812; *d.* St. Petersburg, Russia, 18 February 1880), *chemistry*.

After graduating from Kazan University in 1836, Zinin studied abroad from 1837 to 1840 and worked in Liebig's laboratory at Giessen for about a year. From 1841 to 1847 he was professor of technical chemistry at Kazan University and, from 1848 until his retirement in 1874, was professor of chemistry at the St. Petersburg Academy of Medicine and Surgery. In the mid-1860's Zinin worked mainly at the St. Petersburg Academy of Sciences, to which he had been elected in 1855. He was also the first president of the Russian Chemical Society. His students included Borodin and Butlerov.

Zinin's work in chemistry concerned the aromatic compounds. His doctoral dissertation, prepared in Liebig's laboratory and defended at St. Petersburg University in 1841, was devoted to obtaining benzoin by the condensation of benzaldehyde, and benzyl by the oxidation of benzoin; he returned to the study of these compounds in the 1850's. Zinin developed a method for the reduction of organic compounds using hydrogen at the moment of separation (acid + metal). In particular he studied the reduction of benzyl into benzoin and benzaldehyde into hydrobenzoin, obtaining numerous other reaction products by the use of these compounds.

Zinin is known primarily for his research on the reduction of nitro compounds into amino derivatives by the action of ammonium sulfide. In 1842 he described the reduction of nitrobenzene into aniline, and $\alpha$-nitronaphthalene into the corresponding aminonaphthalene; in 1845, by reducing azobenzene, he obtained benzidine. His discovery of the reaction for obtaining numerous representatives of the amino derivatives was later of great importance for the creation of the aniline dye industry.

Zinin also obtained valuable results in his research on allyl derivatives; he was the first to synthesize allyl alcohol, allyl mustard oil, and the allyl esters of a number of organic acids. During the Crimean War Zinin also studied nitroglycerine as an explosive substance.

*BIBLIOGRAPHY*

I. ORIGINAL WORKS. Zinin's writings include *O soedineniakh benzoila i ob otkrytykh novykh telakh, otnosyashchikhsya k benzoilovomu rodu* ("On the Compounds of Benzoyl and on the Discovery of New Bodies, Related to the Benzoyl Type"; St. Petersburg, 1840), his doctoral diss.; "Organische Salzbasen aus Nitronaphthalos und Nitrobenzid mittelst Schwefelwasserstoff entstehend," in *Annalen der Chemie und Pharmacie*, **44** (1842), 283–287; "Ueber die Einwirkung des ätherischen Senföhls auf die organischen Basen," *ibid.*, **84** (1852), 346–349; and "Ueber die Einführung von Wasserstoff in organische Verbindungen," *ibid.*, **119** (1861), 179–182. See also the Royal Society *Catalogue of Scientific Papers*, VI, 512; VIII, 1304; and XI, 890; which lists 34 memoirs by Zinin.

II. SECONDARY LITERATURE. On Zinin and his work, see A. M. Butlerov and A. P. Borodin, "Nicolaus Nicolajewitsch Zinin," in *Berichte der Deutschen chemischen Gesellschaft*, **14** (1881), 2887–2908; N. A. Figurovsky and Y. I. Soloviev, *Nikolay Nikolaevich Zinin. Biografichesky ocherk* (Moscow, 1957), with bibliography; A. W. von Hofmann's report (8 Mar. 1880), in *Berichte der Deutschen chemischen Gesellschaft*, **13** (1880), 449–450; H. M. Leicester, "N. N. Zinin, an Early Russian Chemist," in *Journal of Chemical Education*, **17** (1940), 303–306; and B. N. Menshutkin, *Nikolay Nikolaevich Zinin* (Berlin, 1921), in Russian.

G. V. BYKOV

**ZINSSER, HANS** (*b.* New York, N.Y., 17 November 1878; *d.* New York, 4 September 1940), *bacteriology, immunology*.

Zinsser was the youngest son of August Zinsser, a German immigrant who had founded a prosperous chemical products business. The household retained many Old World features, and German was Zinsser's primary language until he was ten years old. He was also steeped in French literature and culture from his childhood. His early education at the fashionable private school run by Julius Sachs was supplemented by frequent trips to Europe, as well as by a year of study at Wiesbaden, Germany.

In 1895, Zinsser entered Columbia College, where George Edward Woodberry, professor of comparative literature, cultivated his poetic imagination. His enthusiasm for science was the result of courses under Edmund B. Wilson and Bashford Dean. He never lost either enthusiasm, but science became his profession and poetry a seriously practiced avocation. Zinsser graduated from the College of Physicians and Surgeons of Columbia University in 1903, receiving both the M.D. and the M.A. He interned at Roosevelt Hospital from 1903 to 1905, and after three years of desultory medical practice accepted a full-time appointment at Columbia as instructor in bacteriology. From 1907 until 1910 he was also assistant pathologist at St. Luke's Hospital. In 1910 Zinsser went to Stanford University, where in 1911 he was appointed professor of bacteriology and immunology. He was recalled to a similar position at Columbia in 1913. From 1923 until his death Zinsser taught at the Harvard Medical School, becoming Charles Wilder professor of bacteriology and immunology in 1925.

In 1905 Zinsser married Ruby Handforth Kunz; they had a son and a daughter. He received numerous honors and awards, including honorary doctorates from Columbia, Western Reserve, Lehigh, Yale, and Harvard. He was decorated with the French Legion of Honor and the American Distinguished Service Medal, and served as president of both the American Association of Immunologists (1919) and the Society of American Bacteriologists (1926).

Zinsser's professional interests ranged from theoretical questions involving the physicochemical nature of the antigen-antibody reaction to practical problems of military sanitation and the epidemiology of infectious diseases. He visited Serbia in 1915 as a member of the American Red Cross Sanitary Commission and studied at first hand an outbreak of epidemic typhus. His field investigations of typhus later took him to the Soviet Union (1923), Mexico (1931), and China (1938). Zinsser described these experiences in two engaging books, *Rats, Lice and History* (1935) and *As I Remember Him* (1940). The former book, which he called a "biography of the life history of typhus," was a Rabelaisian mixture of history, wit, philosophy, and science that achieved instant popularity. *As I Remember Him*, although written in the third person, is autobiographical. Its subject—"R.S."—is Zinsser himself, those letters forming the pseudo-

nym under which he published poems in the *Atlantic Monthly* and other periodicals. In his autobiography Zinsser exhibited much of the playfulness and penchant for digression that characterized the earlier popular study of typhus. Writing the book while suffering from lymphocytic leukemia, he movingly recorded his subjective reactions to the disease that was causing his death.

Zinsser dedicated *Rats, Lice and History* to his friend Charles Nicolle, the French bacteriologist, novelist, and philosopher who received the 1928 Nobel Prize in medicine or physiology for his studies on the natural history of typhus. Nicolle and his colleagues had proved that epidemic typhus is louse-borne, and had infected monkeys and guinea pigs with the causative organism (*Rickettsia prowazekii*), thus providing convenient laboratory models for studying host response to the disease. The relationship of louse-borne epidemic typhus to the sporadic, endemic variety of the disease prevalent in the southeastern regions of the United States was poorly understood. Endemic typhus was generally grouped with another form of typhus first described in 1898 by N. E. Brill, who found it among immigrants in New York City. In the 1920's and 1930's Hermann Mooser and others proved that the etiologic agent of murine (endemic) typhus is another species of *Rickettsia* (since named *R. mooseri*). The rat flea, rather than the louse, serves as the principal vector in transmitting this variety of typhus. In the early 1930's Zinsser and his associates suggested that Brill's disease is clinically distinct from murine typhus. Zinsser then demonstrated that the causative organism in Brill's disease is *R. prowazekii* rather than *R. mooseri*. He hypothesized that Brill's disease represented recrudescent typhus in patients who have already recovered from a primary attack of epidemic typhus. His hypothesis has since been confirmed epidemiologically and serologically, and Brill's disease has been renamed Brill-Zinsser's disease.

Zinsser and his associates, who included M. Ruiz Castañeda, Harry Plotz, S. H. Zia, and J. F. Enders, also worked on the production of an effective vaccine against typhus. From these studies came important new tissue culture methods for growing *Rickettsia*. Zinsser and his associates also developed improved staining techniques for *Rickettsia* in both smears and tissue cultures.

Zinsser's name is thus intimately connected with the development of modern knowledge of rickettsial diseases, an association cemented by the popularity of *Rats, Lice and History*. Nevertheless, his typhus studies represent only a portion of his scientific output. Zinsser also did important work on the nature of the antigen-antibody reaction, the etiology of rheumatic fever, the phenomena of delayed hypersensitivity and allergy, the measurement of virus size, and the host response to syphilis.

His concern with the fundamental problems of immunology began about the time Zinsser went to Stanford (1910). He was convinced that physical chemistry would ultimately provide the means of understanding the reactions between antigens and antibodies. Accordingly, he attempted to rectify the deficiencies in his own mathematical and chemical competence. This conviction also led to his collaboration with Stewart Young, professor of colloid chemistry at Stanford, with whom he investigated colloidal aspects of the precipitin reaction. Zinsser's first work on the influence of heat on antigens also dates from his time at Stanford. From the solutions of bacteria and their metabolic products used to immunize laboratory animals, he identified various heat-resistant fractions with pronounced antigenic properties. Since proteins are denatured by heat (and acid), he thus showed that other classes of compounds besides proteins can be antigenic. Zinsser's studies of tuberculin hypersensitivity and allergy led him to stress the importance of nonprotein bacterial products in the immune response. He was the first to formulate clearly the distinction between the tuberculin type of allergic reaction and classic anaphylactic shock.

In addition to his work on immunologic aspects of tuberculosis, Zinsser studied various hyperimmune and allergic phenomena associated with streptococcal and pneumococcal infections. He was one of several scientists in the 1910's and 1920's to suggest that diseases such as rheumatic fever and glomerulonephritis result from hypersensitivity to toxins produced by certain strains of *Streptococci*.

Between 1926 and 1930 Zinsser published a number of papers on the herpes virus and on herpes encephalitis. He and Fei-fang Tang undertook to measure virus sizes by passing viruses through graded filters. They obtained good approximations, although more sensitive techniques have since been developed.

Zinsser's research interests thus covered a spectrum of bacteriological and immunological problems. He also produced two systematic treatises. *A Textbook of Bacteriology* was first published in 1910, in collaboration with Philip H. Hiss, Jr., a Columbia bacteriologist. This book passed through eight editions during Zinsser's lifetime and was translated into several foreign languages, including Chinese. After Hiss's death in 1913, Zinsser collaborated with Stanhope Bayne-Jones in the production of the seventh and eighth editions, and through Bayne-Jones and others, the *Textbook* reached the fourteenth edition (1968).

*Infection and Resistance* (1914) was Zinsser's other major book. His own contributions to immunology may be traced through the successive editions of this work, last published in 1939 in collaboration with John Enders and Henry D. Fothergill as *Immunity: Principles and Application in Medicine and Public Health*.

Literature, history, politics, education, art, music, and philosophy also came within Zinsser's ken. He played an active role in university life at Harvard in the 1920's and 1930's, and taught his pupils and research associates far more than the principles of bacteriology.

## BIBLIOGRAPHY

I. ORIGINAL WORKS. The various eds. of Zinsser's *Textbook of Bacteriology* (New York–London, 1910), written with Philip H. Hiss, Jr., and *Infection and Resistance* (New York, 1914) give good accounts of his own work in relation to the developing disciplines of bacteriology and immunology. The following papers deal with particular aspects in greater detail: "On the Possible Importance of Colloidal Protection in Certain Phases of the Precipitin Reaction," in *Journal of Experimental Medicine*, **17** (1913), 396–408, written with Stewart Young; "Studies on the Tuberculin Reaction and on Specific Hypersensitiveness in Bacterial Infection," *ibid.*, **34** (1921), 495–524; "On the Significance of Bacterial Allergy in Infectious Disease," in *Bulletin of the New York Academy of Medicine*, 2nd ser., **4** (1928), 351–383; "Studies in Ultrafiltration," in *Journal of Experimental Medicine*, **47** (1927), 357–378, written with Fei-fang Tang; "The Bacteriology of Rheumatic Fever and the Allergic Hypothesis," in *Archives of Internal Medicine*, **42** (1928), 301–309, written with H. Yu; and "Varieties of Typhus Fever and the Epidemiology of the American Form of European Typhus Fever (Brill's Disease)," in *American Journal of Hygiene*, **20** (1934), 513–532.

Books by Zinsser not mentioned in the text are *A Laboratory Course in Serum Study* (New York, 1916), written with J. G. Hopkins and Reuben Ottenburg; and *Spring, Summer and Autumn* (New York, 1942), a volume of poems.

A full bibliography of Zinsser's writings is appended to Simeon Burt Wolbach's memoir in *Biographical Memoirs. National Academy of Sciences*, **24** (1947), 323–360.

II. SECONDARY LITERATURE. In addition to the Wolbach memoir, other valuable obituaries include those of

S. Bayne-Jones, in *Archives of Pathology*, **31** (1941), 269–280; J. F. Enders, in *Harvard Medical Alumni Bulletin*, **15**, no. 1 (1940), supp., 1–15; J. H. Mueller, in *Journal of Bacteriology*, **40** (1940), 747–753. Zinsser's contributions to the study of typhus were summarized by P. K. Olitsky, "Hans Zinsser and His Studies on Typhus Fever," in *Journal of the American Medical Association*, **116** (1941), 907–912.

WILLIAM F. BYNUM

**ZIRKEL, FERDINAND** (*b.* Bonn, Germany, 20 May 1838; *d.* Bonn, 11 June 1912), *geology, petrography, mineralogy.*

Zirkel was the son of Joseph Zirkel, professor of mathematics at a Gymnasium in Bonn. He remained single all his life, taking care of his mother and widowed sister. He enrolled at the University of Bonn in 1855, studying geology, mineralogy, and chemistry to prepare for a career as a mining geologist. After several semesters of practical work in mines, he returned to graduate work at Bonn, mainly with C. G. Bischof, J. J. Nöggerath, and Gerhard vom Rath.

In 1860 Zirkel traveled to the Faeroes and Iceland and remained for a time in Scotland and England, visiting the major ore deposits. His collection of volcanic rocks from Iceland was the basis of his doctoral dissertation, for which he obtained his degree on 14 March 1861. With this work Zirkel abandoned his original intention of becoming a mining geologist, although his later position on the Board of the Mansfelder Kupferschiefer Company kept him in touch with economic geology.

Very important to Zirkel was his friendship with Henry Clifton Sorby, whom he met in England and who started him off in the work that made his reputation in a field of which he was a founder, petrographic microscopy. Zirkel spent two years in Vienna with Haidinger, working out a monograph on bournonite (1862) and a paper entitled "Mikroskopische Untersuchungen von Gesteinen und Mineralien" (1862), the latter amplifying Sorby's discovery of fluid inclusions in minerals.

On the basis of his early systematic work on microscopic petrography, Zirkel was appointed associate professor in Lemberg (now Lvov) in 1863 and full professor in 1865. He obtained a professorship in Kiel in 1868 and in Leipzig in 1870, as successor to K. F. Naumann. He remained at Leipzig until his retirement in 1909.

Zirkel's fame was established in 1873 with *Die mikroskopische Beschaffenheit der Mineralien und Gesteine.* His most influential work was *Lehrbuch der Petrographie* (1866).

In 1894–1895 Zirkel visited Ceylon and the United States. A member of many European academies of science, he received an honorary doctorate from Oxford in 1907. He served as rector of the University of Leipzig and was a member of the Sächsische Akademie der Wissenschaften.

BIBLIOGRAPHY

I. ORIGINAL WORKS. Zirkel's books include *De geognostica Islandiae constitutione observationes* (Bonn, 1861), his dissertation; *Reise nach Island* (Leipzig, 1862), written with W. Preyer; *Lehrbuch der Petrographie*, 2 vols. (Bonn, 1866; 2nd ed., 3 vols., Leipzig, 1893–1894); *Untersuchungen über die mikroskopische Zusammensetzung und Struktur der Basaltgesteine* (Bonn, 1870); *Die mikroskopische Beschaffenheit der Mineralien und Gesteine* (Leipzig, 1873); and his eds. of K. F. Naumann's *Elemente der Mineralogie* (10th ed., Leipzig, 1877; through the 15th ed., 1907).

Among his articles are "Die trachytischen Gesteine der Eifel," in *Zeitschrift der Deutschen geologischen Gesellschaft*, **11** (1859), 507–540; "Versuch einer Monographie des Bournonit," in *Sitzungsberichte der K. Akademie der Wissenschaften in Wien*, **45**, sec. 1 (1862), 431–466; "Über die mikroskopische Zusammensetzung der Phonolithe" in Poggendorff's *Annalen der Physik*, **131** (1867), 298–336; "Beiträge zur geologischen Kenntnis der Pyrenäen," in *Zeitschrift der Deutschen geologischen Gesellschaft*, **19** (1867), 68–215; "Mikroskopische Untersuchung über die glasigen und halbglasigen Gesteine," *ibid.*, 737–802; "Microscopical Petrography," in *United States Geological Exploration of the Fortieth Parallel* (Washington, D.C., 1876), also published in German as "Über die Krystallischen Gesteine längs des 40. Breitegrades in Nordwest-Amerika," in *Math. Phys. Ber.*, **29** (1877), 156–243; "Über Urausscheidungen in rheinischen Basalten," in *Abhandlungen der K. Sächsischen Gesellschaft der Wissenschaften*, math.-phys. Kl., **28**, no. 3 (1903), 103–198; and "Über die gegenseitigen Beziehungen zwischen der Petrographie und angrenzenden Wissenschaften," in *Journal of Geology*, **12**, no. 6 (1904), 485–500, in German.

II. SECONDARY LITERATURE. See R. Brauns, "Ferdinand Zirkel," in *Zentralblatt für Mineralogie, Geologie, und Paläontologie* (1912), 513–521; F. Rinne, "Nachruf auf F. Zirkel," in *Berichte über die Verhandlungen der Sächsischen Gesellschaft der Wissenschaften zu Leipzig*, math.-phys. Kl., **64** (1912), 501–508; and Felix Wahnschaffe, "Ferdinand Zirkel," in *Zeitschrift der Deutschen geologischen Gesellschaft*, B, *Monatsberichte*, **64**, no. 7 (1912), 353–363, the most complete and accurate obituary.

G. C. AMSTUTZ

**ZITTEL, KARL ALFRED VON** (*b.* Bahlingen, Baden, Germany, 25 September 1839; *d.* Munich, Germany, 5 January 1904), *paleontology, geology, history of geology.*

Zittel is recognized as the leading teacher of paleontology in the nineteenth century and as the only encyclopedist of the subject. The youngest son of Karl Zittel, a liberal and politically active Protestant minister, he grew up in an intellectually stimulating atmosphere. At the University of Heidelberg he studied under the geologist Carl Caesar von Leonhard, the mineralogist Johann Reinhard Blum, and the paleontologist Heinrich Georg Bronn. He also worked without pay in a shop that sold natural history specimens. After 1860 Zittel traveled in Scandinavia for three months before completing his training in Paris under Edmond Hébert.

In 1862 Zittel moved to Vienna, then a center of geological studies. At first he worked as a volunteer at the Geologische Reichsanstalt and participated in the mapping of Dalmatia. The following year he qualified as a lecturer at the University of Vienna, at which Eduard Suess had just begun to teach. Zittel declined an offer from the University of Lemberg (Lvov) in order to continue his studies of the extensive Viennese paleontological collections and to produce his first publications. From 1863 to 1866 he was professor of mineralogy, geognosy, and paleontology at the technical college in Karlsruhe.

In 1866 Zittel accepted a post at the University of Munich, attracted by its exceptionally rich paleontological collections. As successor to Albert Oppel, he dealt with a stage that the latter had established: the Tithonian or Portland stage of the Upper Jurassic. Aided by his students, Zittel not only described Tithonian fauna in terms of guide fossils but also presented a thorough biological (paleozoological) discussion of the material. While at Munich, Zittel devoted great energy to expanding the paleontological collections, thereby establishing the basis for his lifework: the creation of a systematics of the organic fossil record. The results of twenty years of almost superhuman effort were presented in *Handbuch der Palaeontologie.* The sole author of the four volumes on paleozoology, Zittel covered all forms of fossils, from the protozoans to the mammals.

In order to further his great project, Zittel undertook intensive research into inadequately examined areas, devoting particular attention to relationships between fossil and recent forms of life. He was the first to investigate fossil sponges by zoological methods—previously they had been described solely according to external characteristics. Zittel exposed their skeletons through cauterization and applied to siliceous sponges the distinction between Lithistida and Hexactinellida that Oscar Schmidt had discovered in 1870. Having initially found lithistid skeletal elements in the hexactinellid *Coeloptychium,* he first assumed on this evidence that both groups were of common origin. He soon learned, however, that these lithistic elements were drifted secondarily by water transportation and, therefore, Hexactinellida and Lithistida were distinctly separated in their fossilized state.

Under the influence of Darwin's work, Zittel became a pioneer of evolutionary paleontology. Nonetheless, his experience with the sponges made him very cautious with regard to all phylogenetic speculation. Although his writings obviously are based on the presupposition of the continuity of the evolutionary process in nature, he constantly stressed the lacunae in the evidence for this continuity. This cautious attitude, however, has endowed Zittel's work with lasting value.

Zittel's exposition of systematics in the *Handbuch* is characterized by unsurpassed clarity at every level, down to that of the individual taxonomic diagnoses. He sustained this lucidity although he knew that it is impossible to determine the relationships between fossil types with certainty and that, therefore, every attempt to establish boundaries between them is necessarily precarious: this constitutes his greatest achievement in the *Handbuch.* In this respect, Zittel profited from the pre-Darwinian heritage of his student years, when he learned to give precise linguistic expression to boundaries that supposedly were found fixed in nature. He respected the concepts of systematics as a historical validity and was aware that their ability to provide continuity and a synoptic view would be threatened if they were made to depend too heavily on changing phylogenetic interpretations. Zittel adhered to these principles in his two-volume *Grundzüge der Paläontologie,* which was translated into several foreign languages and earned him the title "Linnaeus of Paleontology." His primarily systematic treatment might appear one-sided to the modern paleontologist, accustomed to an increasingly differentiated discipline and a marked ecological orientation. Nevertheless, using this approach, Zittel endowed the subject with a firm basis that is still indispensable.

As a paleontologist, Zittel naturally took an interest in historical geology and also contributed to general and regional geology. For example, he was the first to investigate closely the evidence of the existence of diluvial moraines on the Bavarian plateau. Further, while participating in Gerhard Rohlf's expedition to the Libyan desert (1873–1874), he recognized that the desert sand was a product of wind erosion and did not originate in a Quaternary Sahara sea. (Some scientists had held that European Quaternary glaciation was influenced by the existence of such a sea.)

Zittel's mastery of geology and paleontology and of its history is reflected in his *Geschichte der Geologie und Paläontologie*. (As an encyclopedic historical survey it still remains an indispensable reference for the history of geology, being especially strong on Continental European developments of the nineteenth century. The English translation of 1901 is currently in print.) In this book he could proudly state that during his years at the University of Munich, it became "a center of paleontological and geological studies, where a considerable number of researchers from all parts of the world received their training."

Elected president of the Bavarian Academy of Sciences in 1899, Zittel was an honorary member of many scientific societies in Europe and elsewhere.

*BIBLIOGRAPHY*

I. Original Works. Zittel's writings include "Analyse des Arendaler Orthits," in *Annalen der Physik*, **108** (1859), his dissertation; "Die Bivalven der Gosaugebilde in den nordöstlichen Alpen," in *Denkschriften der Akademie der Wissenschaften* (Vienna), Math.-phys. Kl., **24** (1864), 105–177; and **25** (1866), 77–198; "Palaeontologische Studien über die Grenzschichten der Jura- und Kreideformation im Gebiete der Karpathen, Alpen und Apenninen. I. Die Cephalopoden der Stramberger Schichten," in *Palaeontologische Mitteilungen aus dem Museum des K. bayerischen Staates*, **2** (1868); II. "Die Fauna der älteren Cephalopoden führenden Tithonbildungen," in *Palaeontographica*, supp. 2, pts. 1 and 2 (1870); III. "Die Gastropoden der Stramberger Schichten," in *Palaeontologische Mitteilungen aus dem Museum des K. bayerischen Staates*, **2**, pt. 3 (1873), 311–491; *Aus der Urzeit* (Munich, 1872; 2nd ed., 1875); "Über Gletschererscheinungen in der bayerischen Hochebene," in *Sitzungsberichte der Bayerischen Akademie der Wissenschaften zu München*, Math.-phys. Kl., **4** (1874), 252–283; "Über *Coeloptychium*. Ein Beitrag zur Kenntnis der Organisation fossiler Spongien," in *Abhandlungen der Bayerischen Akademie der Wissenschaften*, Math.-phys. Kl., **12**, pt. 3 (1876), 1–80; and "Studien über fossile Spongien," *ibid.*, **13**, pts. 1 and 2 (1877–1878).

Additional works are "Über die Flugsaurier (Pterodactylen) aus dem lithographischen Schiefer Bayerns," in *Palaeontographica*, **29** (1882), 47–80; "Beiträge zur Geologie und Paläontologie der Libyschen Wüste und der angrenzenden Gebiete von Ägypten, I. Geologie," *ibid.*, **30** (1883), 1–153; *Handbuch der Palaeontologie*, pt. 1, 4 vols. (Munich–Leipzig, 1876–1893); pt. 2, *Palaeophytologie*, by W. P. Schimper and A. Schenk (Munich–Leipzig, 1890), French trans. by Charles Barrois as *Traité de paléontologie*, 5 vols. (Paris, 1883–1894), English trans. by Charles Eastman as *Text-book of Paleontology* (London, 1896; 2nd ed., 1913); "The Geological Development, Descent and Distribution of the Mammalia," in *Geological Magazine*, **30** (1893), 401–412, 455–468, 501–514; *Grundzüge der Paläontologie (Paläozoologie)*, 2 vols. (Munich–Leipzig–Berlin, 1895); "Ontogenie, Phylogenie und Systematik," in *Comptes rendus du Congrès international de géologie, 1894* (Lausanne, 1897), 134–136; *Geschichte der Geologie und Paläontologie bis Ende des 19. Jahrhunderts* (Munich–Leipzig, 1899), trans. by Maria M. Ogilvie-Gordon as *History of Geology and Paleontology* (London, 1901; repr. New York, 1962); and "Über wissenschaftliche Wahrheit," in *Festrede der Bayerischen Akademie der Wissenschaften* (1902).

II. Secondary Literature. See Charles Barrois, "Notice nécrologique sur K.-A. von Zittel," in *Bulletin de la Société géologique de France*, 4th ser., **4** (1904), 488–493; Wilhelm Branco, "Karl Alfred von Zittel," in *Monatsberichte der Deutschen geologischen Gesellschaft*, **56** (1904), 1–7; Wilhelm Deecke, "Karl Alfred von Zittel," in *Badische Biographien*, VI (Heidelberg, 1935), 380–387; Archibald Geikie, "Anniversary Address," in *Quarterly Journal of the Geological Society of London*, **60** (1904), 1v–1ix; Otto Jaekel, "K. A. von Zittel, Der Altmeister der Paläontologie," in *Naturwissenschaftliche Wochenschrift*, n.s. 3, no. 23 (1904), 1–7; F. L. Kitchin, "Professor Karl Alfred von Zittel," in *Geological Magazine*, **41** (1904), 90–96, with complete bibliography; J. F. Pompeckj, "Karl Alfred von Zittel . . .," in *Palaeontographica*, **50** (1903–1904), 3–28, with portrait; August Rothpletz, "Gedächtnisrede auf Karl Alfred von Zittel," in *Sitzungsberichte der Bayerischen Akademie der Wissenschaften zu München*, **35** (1905), 3–23; and Charles Schuchert, "Karl Alfred von Zittel," in *Annual Report of the Board of Regents of the Smithsonian Institution* for 1904 (1905), 779–786.

Helmut Hölder

**ZÖLLNER, JOHANN KARL FRIEDRICH** (*b.* Berlin, Germany, 8 November 1834; *d.* Leipzig, Germany, 25 April 1882), *astrophysics*.

Zöllner's father was a patternmaker and later a cotton printer. Although Zöllner had displayed outstanding talent for constructing instruments and conducting experiments by the age of sixteen, the death of his father (1853) obliged him to take over the direction of his factory. But Zöllner was not temperamentally suited to a business career; and shortly after assuming that post, he gave it up and resumed his education. He failed the final secondary-school examination, however, because of his poor marks in languages. In 1855 he began to study physics and other sciences at the University of Berlin, where his teachers included H. G. Magnus and H. W. Dove. While still a student Zöllner published "Photometrische Untersuchungen" in Poggendorff's *Annalen der Physik und Chemie*. He also worked on developing electric motors; but considering the great success later achieved in this area by Werner von Siemens, Zöllner's efforts proved to be of little significance.

Zöllner erected a small private observatory in the tower of his father's factory in Schöneweide (now part of Berlin), and thus was able to test his ideas concerning the photometry of celestial bodies. In 1857 Zöllner went to Basel, where his teachers included G. H. Wiedemann. He received the Ph.D. in 1859 for a work on photometric problems: "Photometrische Untersuchungen, insbesondere über die Lichtentwickelung galvanisch glühender Plantindrähte."

Exploiting a chance observation that he had made at Basel, Zöllner invented the astrophotometer, which was constructed in the Kern optical and mechanical workshop in Aarau. (The accompanying drawing illustrates the instrument's operating principle.) Using this instrument, he investigated fundamental problems of photometry, made critical comparisons of other photometers, and soon

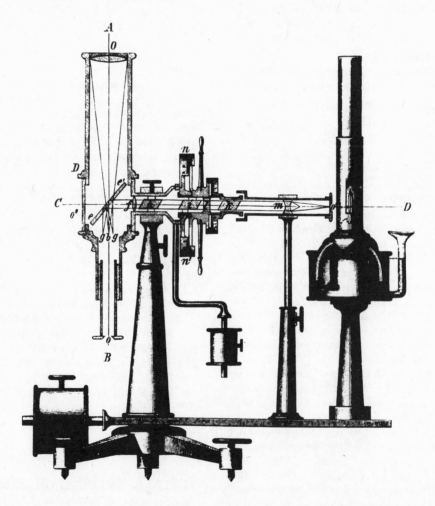

FIGURE 1. Operating principle of Zollner's astrophotometer. *AB*, axis of telescope; *CD*, axis of the arrangement for production of the artificial star; *m*, biconcave lens; *k*, Nicol prism; *l*, optical crystal; *i,k*, Nicol prisms; *f*, convex lens; *eé*, glass plate; *F*, petroleum lamp; *O*, objective; *o*, eyepiece; *b*, image of the star; *gg*, image of the artificial star. SOURCE: G. Müller, *Die Photometrie der Gestirne* (Leipzig, 1897), p. 247.

amassed a considerable body of material. On the advice of Mitscherlich and Wiedemann, Zöllner decided to compete for a prize offered by the Vienna Academy of Sciences. The jury found that Zöllner had not measured the brightness of enough stars to receive the prize. (The other two papers submitted were also found not to merit the prize, and thus none was awarded.) Zöllner's entry, which he published in 1861, is a classic of astrophysics. The photometer described in it far surpassed all its predecessors and, in a modified form, found wide application. The Potsdam observatory used it to obtain data of unsurpassed precision for its *Photometrische Durchmusterung des nördlichen Himmels*, the publication of which was begun at Zöllner's suggestion.

In 1862 Zöllner moved to Leipzig and published *Photometrische Studien mit besonderer Rücksicht auf die physische Beschaffenheit der Himmelskörper* (1865), which contains his *Habilitationsschrift*, "Theorie der relativen Lichtstärken der Mondphasen." With his appointment as professor at the University of Leipzig in 1866, Zöllner's financial situation was sufficiently improved for him to resume important experimental research.

Among Zöllner's main achievements was the design of the reversion spectroscope (1869), another instrument that demonstrates his experimental ingenuity. It is based on the principle of the heliometer: two beams of rays are conducted through two direct-vision prism systems arranged so that the dispersion within them occurs in mutually opposed directions. With this device Zöllner intended to improve the precision of measurements of Doppler shifts in the spectra of objects with velocities having a high radial component. Hermann Vogel used the instrument to determine the rotational velocity at the solar equator. The reversion spectroscope later lost its importance with the adoption of more exact methods.

Another important device designed by Zöllner is the horizontal pendulum, which in improved form was widely used in geophysical research. Inspired by the attempts of Janssen and Lockyer to observe solar protuberances, Zöllner devised the first method that made these phenomena easily amenable to study. These inventions, which make Zöllner a pioneer in astrophysics, brought him membership in the Saxon Academy of Sciences at Leipzig.

Zöllner also made an intensive study of theoretical questions, including solar theory, sunspots, and solar rotation, and Olber's paradox. One product of these rather speculative inquiries was especially important for the development of spectroscopy, the memoir "Über den Einfluss der Dichtigkeit und Temperatur auf die Spektra glühender Gase" (1870). Also of far-reaching significance was Zöllner's theory of comets, in which he correctly assumed that elements of the nucleus of a comet gradually vaporize as it nears the sun. Beyond this, the book on comets contains a wealth of penetrating remarks on the subject announced in the subtitle, *Beiträge zur Geschichte und Theorie der Erkenntnis*. This portion of the book is notable for a number of at least partly original ideas and critical comments. Attacking abuses in the scientific profession of his time, Zöllner lashed out with great vehemence against the vanity of scientists, ridiculing scientific careerism and contending that these vices are harmful to the progress of science.

Zöllner continued this polemic in such works as *Das deutsche Volk und seine Professoren. Eine Sammlung von Citaten ohne Kommentar* (Leipzig, 1880). The scientific community responded with counterattacks, and there began a long period of controversies that drove Zöllner into ever greater isolation. The excessive irony and somewhat biased approach of which he was guilty were, however, only partially responsible for this isolation. In 1875 Zöllner had met William Crookes in London and begun an intensive study of Spiritualism, to which he ultimately became a convert. In the following years some scientists did not hesitate to attribute Zöllner's views to an increasingly serious mental illness. Even sympathetic friends, such as Otto Struve, were much dismayed by his adherence to this doctrine, and W. Foerster termed this change in his life both remarkable and painful. Zöllner, however, refused to be dissuaded from pursuing his unscientific speculations; and he saw in his supposed proofs of the existence of a "transcendental world" a support for theology. In the last years of his life he produced little work of scientific significance. He died—presumably of a stroke—while preparing the preface to the third edition of his book on comets.

## BIBLIOGRAPHY

I. Original Works. A full list of Zöllner's major works can be found in F. Koerber, *Zöllner*, 106–107 (below). The papers by Zöllner in the *Astronomische Nachrichten* are cited in *Generalregister der Bände 41–80 der Astronomischen Nachrichten*, H. Kobold, ed. (Kiel 1938), col. 118; and in *Generalregister der Bände 81–120 der Astronomischen Nachrichten*, A. Krueger, ed. (Kiel, 1891), col. 132. Zöllner collected his most important shorter works as *Wissenschaftliche Abhandlungen*, 4 vols. (Leipzig, 1878–1881).

II. SECONDARY LITERATURE. See W. Foerster, *Lebenserinnerungen und Lebenshoffnungen* (Berlin, 1911), 95–98; D. B. Herrmann, "Karl Friedrich Zöllner und die 'Potsdamer Durchmusterung,'" in *Sterne*, **50** (1974), 170–180; and "Ein eigenhändiger Lebenslauf von Karl Friedrich Zöllner aus dem Jahre 1864," *Mitteilungen der Archenhold-Sternwarte Berlin-Trepton*, **97** (1974); R. Knott, "Zöllner," in *Allgemeine deutsche Biographie*, XLV (Leipzig, 1900), 426–428; F. Koerber, *Karl Friedrich Zöllner* (Berlin, 1899), no. 53 of Sammlung Populärer Schriften, edited by the Gesellschaft Urania, Berlin; S. (probably W. Scheibner), "Todes-Anzeige," in *Astronomische Nachrichten*, **102** (1882), cols. 175–176; and M. Wirth, *Friedrich Zöllner. Ein Vortrag mit Zöllners Bild und Handschrift* (Leipzig, 1882).

DIETER B. HERRMANN

**ZOLOTAREV, EGOR IVANOVICH** (*b.* St. Petersburg, Russia [now Leningrad, U.S.S.R.], 12 April 1847; *d.* St. Petersburg, 19 July 1878), *mathematics*.

Zolotarev was the son of a watchmaker. After graduating in 1863 with a silver medal from the Gymnasium, he enrolled at the Faculty of Physics and Mathematics of St. Petersburg, where he attended the lectures of Chebyshev and his student A. N. Korkin. He graduated with the candidate's degree in 1867 and the following year became assistant professor there. In 1869 he defended his master's dissertation, on an indeterminate third-degree equation; his doctoral dissertation (1874) was devoted to the theory of algebraic integers. In 1876 he was appointed professor of mathematics at St. Petersburg and junior assistant of applied mathematics at the St. Petersburg Academy of Sciences.

On two trips abroad Zolotarev attended the lectures of Kummer and Weierstrass, and met with Hermite. He shared his impressions of noted scholars and discussed mathematical problems with Korkin, whose collaborator he subsequently became. Zolotarev died at the age of thirty-one, of blood poisoning, after having fallen under a train.

The most gifted member of the St. Petersburg school of mathematics, Zolotarev produced fundamental works on mathematical analysis and the theory of numbers during his eleven-year career. Independent of Dedekind and Kronecker, he constructed a theory of divisibility for the whole numbers of any field of algebraic numbers, working along the lines developed by Kummer and elaborating the ideas and methods that now comprise the core of local algebra. He operated with the

numbers of the local ring $Z_p$ and its full closure in the field $Q(\theta)$ and, in essence, brought under examination the semilocal ring $O_p$. In modern terminology Zolotarev's results consisted in proving that (1) the ring $O_p$ is a finite type of $Z_p$-modulus and (2) $O_p$ is a ring of principal ideals. In his local approach to the concept of a number of the field $Q(\theta)$ Zolotarev demonstrated that the ring $O$ of the whole numbers in $Q(\theta)$ is the intersection of all semilocal rings $O_p$. Zolotarev defined ideal numbers in $O$ as essentially valuations and found the simple elements of $O_p$ with the aid of a lemma that is the analog of the theory of expansion into Puiseux series.

Zolotarev employed a theory that he had constructed for determining, with a finite number of operations, the possibility of selecting a number, $A$, such that the second-order elliptical differential $(x + A)\, dx\, /\sqrt{R(x)}$, where $R(x)$ is a fourth-degree polynomial with real coefficients, can be integrated in logarithms. Abel demonstrated that for an affirmative solution it is necessary and sufficient that $\sqrt{R(x)}$ be expandable into a periodic continuous fraction; but because he did not give an evaluation of the length of the period, his solution was ineffective. Zolotarev provided the required evaluation, applying the equation of the division of elliptic functions.

With Korkin, Zolotarev worked on the problem posed by Hermite of determining the minima of positive quadratic forms of $n$ variables having real coefficients; they gave exhaustive solutions for the cases $n = 4$ and $n = 5$.

Among Zolotarev's other works are an original proof of the law of quadratic reciprocity, based on the group-theoretic lemma that Frobenius had called "the most interesting," as well as solutions of difficult individual questions in the theory of the optimal approximation of functions. Thus, Zolotarev found the $n$th-degree polynomial, the first coefficient of which is equal to unity and the second coefficient of which is fixed, that deviates least from zero.

*BIBLIOGRAPHY*

I. ORIGINAL WORKS. Zolotarev's complete writings were published by the V. A. Steklov Institute of Physics and Mathematics as *Polnoe sobranie sochineny*, 2 vols. (Leningrad, 1931–1932); see esp. II, 72–129; and "Sur la théorie des nombres complexes," in *Journal de mathématiques pures et appliquées*, 3rd ser., **6** (1880), 51–84, 129–166.

II. SECONDARY LITERATURE. On Zolotarev's life and

work, see I. G. Bashmakova, "Obosnovanie teorii delimosti v trudakh E. I. Zolotareva" ("Foundation of the Theory of Divisibility in Zolotarev's Works"), in *Istoriko-matematicheskie issledovaniya*, **2** (1949), 231–351; N. G. Chebotarev, "Ob osnovanii teorii idealov po Zolotarevu" ("On the Foundation of the Theory of Ideals According to Zolotarev"), in *Uspekhi matematicheskikh nauk*, **2**, no. 6 (1947), 52–67; B. N. Delone, *Peterburgskaya shkola teorii chisel* ("The St. Petersburg School of the Theory of Numbers"; Moscow–Leningrad, 1947); R. O. Kuzmin, "Zhizn i nauchnaya deyatelnost Egora Ivanovicha Zolotareva" ("Zolotarev's Life and Scientific Activity"), in *Uspekhi matematicheskikh nauk*, **2**, no. 6 (1947), 21–51; and E. P. Ozhigova, *Egor Ivanovich Zolotarev* (Moscow–Leningrad, 1966).

I. G. Bashmakova

**ZOSIMUS OF PANOPOLIS** (*b.* Panopolis [now Akhmīm], Egypt; *d.* Alexandria, Egypt; *fl. ca.* A.D. 300), *alchemy.*

Zosimus appears to be the earliest genuine historical figure mentioned as an author in the Greek alchemical texts. Almost nothing is known about his life. That he came from Panopolis, in the Thebaid (Upper Egypt), is known from the extant texts, as well as from two of the three nonalchemical authors who mention him: Photius (ninth century) and Georgius Syncellus (eighth–ninth century). The third source, the *Suda* (formerly called the *Suidas*, about 950), refers to him as Alexandrian, but this undoubtedly means that he later lived in Alexandria. No source gives his dates. He is generally thought to have lived somewhat earlier than the alchemist Synesius, whose dates have been established by his having sent a book to Dioscorus, the high priest of the Serapeum in Alexandria, which was destroyed in 389. Accordingly, Zosimus is presumed to have lived around A.D. 300.

Books in which the author's name is given as Zosimus are preserved in Greek, Syriac, and Arabic. Syncellus mentions the book *Imuth* and cites from it a story (known from the Book of Enoch, chapters 6–8) in which alchemy, along with other arts, is revealed to mortal women by the fallen angels, who seek to win their favor in this way. This story is repeated in one of the Syriac texts by Zosimus, and the title *Imuth* occurs in various places in the Syriac texts (see *La chimie au moyen âge*, II, 238). The citations in the latter are inconsistent, however, and it is therefore impossible to infer anything with certainty about the nature of this book.

The *Suda* mentions a much more famous work, the twenty-eight books addressed to Zosimus' (spiritual) sister Theosebeia, each of which is supposedly designated by a different letter of the alphabet. The book *Omega* is found among the surviving Greek texts; and it, along with the books called *Kappa* and *Sigma*, is cited in certain Greek texts. In various books Theosebeia is addressed by name and by the phrase "O woman." Her name also appears in the Syriac texts, as does the second-person feminine form of address. Since the Greek alphabet contains only twenty-four letters, the designation of four of the books remains problematic.

Also unclear is the relationship between these twenty-eight books and the thirty-five chapters addressed to Eusebius, which are cited in the list of alchemical writings in *Codex Marcianus* 299. This list, which obviously records the contents of the codex (the oldest one preserved—it dates from the eleventh century) as it existed at an earlier date, mentions several works of Zosimus that are preserved. Among these are the book *On "Arete"* (outstanding quality or, perhaps, peculiarity), *On the Composition of Waters*, and fifteen chapters addressed to Theodorus, known as *On Tools and Ovens*. Another extant work in the list is the commentary by Olympiodorus on Zosimus' κατ' ἐνέργειαν, but it cannot be determined from the commentary how this title ought to be translated. Berthelot classified the book among the "traités démocritains."

The grouping of texts in Berthelot's *Collection des anciens alchimistes grecs* does not give a clear idea of which texts were really written by Zosimus. Among those under the name "Zosimus," several contain only citations from Zosimus; and for others not even this much is true. On the other hand, many of the texts attributed to Zosimus include citations from later authors. Further, Berthelot did not collect the citations from Zosimus that appeared in other books not published under his name, nor did he carry out a systematic comparison of the Syriac and Greek texts. Finally, the Syriac texts are given only in a French abridgment, not in the original.

As a result, it is not clear which texts can rightly be attributed to Zosimus. And the incomprehensibility of many of the writings makes textual criticism all the more difficult.

Of the approximately twenty Arabic book titles that F. Sezgin has assigned to Zosimus, some sound as if they might be translations from the Greek, while others appear to be Arabic forgeries. Something is known about the contents of only one of these books—thanks to H. E. Stapleton; the assertion found in this book that it was translated in the year A.H. 38 (A.D. 659) does not fit its context and is obviously false. Many citations from Zosimus can be found in published Arabic texts or in their Latin translation, sometimes with his name and sometimes, as in the *Turba philosophorum*, without it. The citations in the latter book are mentioned by J. Ruska in his notes to the translation. Sezgin's remarks on the individual titles require more careful examination.

Given the absence of a critical monographic study of Zosimus, it is scarcely possible to present an accurate account of his teachings. His alchemical statements sometimes take the form of visions, in which chemical apparatus is represented as a temple and the metals are personified (for example, as "lead man" and "copper man"). The alchemical operation itself is viewed as a sacrificial act. Elsewhere, his remarks bear the stamp of a kind of natural philosophy but are confined to general discussions. In any case, because of Zosimus' frequently allegorical style, it is not evident whether his subject is alchemy or religion. On the whole, his works seem to be the expression of a mystic religion that is almost never entirely eliminated even in the seemingly technical sections. He warns Theosebeia about deceitful prophets and against according the art too high a value. He advises her to cool her passion and to resist desire (for gold). Genuine and natural change of color is obtained by public worship. In this connection he cites two treatises from the *Corpus Hermeticum*: the *Poimandres* (I) and the *Crater* (IV).

Despite this attitude, Zosimus fulfills Theosebeia's wish and describes the apparatus and the ovens used in alchemical work. He warns her, however, to beware of persons who have misled her into adopting a contrary method of alchemical practice—people who love gold more than reason. He derides a priest named Nilus and is especially pleased with his lack of success.

Zosimus, who in the later texts is called "the Old One," "the Divine," and "the Most Learned," shows in all his writings a great reverence for the ancient masters of the art: Hermes, Agathodaemon, Zoroaster, Democritus, Ostanes, and Maria. On the whole, he gives the impression of having been a pagan, and E. Riess is certainly correct in ascribing the Christian passages in his books to later writers. Zosimus calls himself unoriginal, simply a compiler and commentator; but this is not necessarily sincere. He may have been seeking to win more confidence in his writings or perhaps was following an established literary practice.

Zosimus' works have attracted the interest of a number of historians of religion, who have investigated his relations to Gnosticism and especially to the Hermetic tradition (for example, R. Reitzenstein, W. Scott, H. Jonas, and A. J. Festugière). Ruska has been particularly concerned with the Hermetic tendencies in Zosimus' thought; he and Festugière have edited and translated some of his works, making many improvements in Berthelot's texts. The extensive use of pseudonyms in these writings makes it impossible to give an account of Zosimus' own chemical theories until further progress is made in the study of the entire corpus of Greek alchemical texts. Only then will scholars be able to judge the originality of Zosimus' ideas—a problem that has been studied especially by I. Hammer Jensen.

## BIBLIOGRAPHY

See M. Berthelot, *Les origines de l'alchimie* (Paris, 1885); *Collection des anciens alchimistes grecs* (Paris, 1888; repr. London, 1963); and *La chimie au moyen âge*, II and III (Paris, 1893); *Catalogue des manuscrits alchimiques grecs*, II (Brussels, 1927); A. J. Festugière, "Alchymia," in *Antiquité classique*, **8** (1939), 71 ff.; and *La révélation d'Hermès Trismégiste*, I (Paris, 1944; 2nd ed., 1950); W. Gundel, "Alchemie," in *Real-Lexikon für Antike und Christentum*, I (1950); I. Hammer Jensen, *Die älteste Alchymie* (Copenhagen, 1921); H. Jonas, *Gnosis und spätantiker Geist* (Göttingen, 1934–1964); E. O. von Lippmann, *Entstehung und Ausbreitung der Alchemie* (Berlin, 1919), 75–92; A. D. Nock and A. J. Festugière, eds. and trans., *Corpus Hermeticum*, IV (Paris, 1954), 117–121; R. Reitzenstein, *Poimandres* (Leipzig, 1904); E. Riess, "Alchemie," in *Real-Encyclopädie der classischen Altertumswissenschaft*, I (1894); J. Ruska, *Tabula smaragdina* (Heidelberg, 1926); "Zosimos," in G. Bugge, ed., *Das Buch der grossen Chemiker* (Berlin, 1929); and *Turba philosophorum* (Berlin, 1931); W. Scott, *Hermetica*, IV (Oxford, 1936); F. Sezgin, *Geschichte des arabischen Schrifttums*, IV (Leiden, 1971), 73–77; and H. E. Stapleton and R. F. Azo, "An Alchemical Compilation of the Thirteenth Century A.D.," in *Memoirs of the Asiatic Society of Bengal*, **3**, no. 2 (1910).

M. PLESSNER

---

**ZSIGMONDY, RICHARD ADOLF** (*b.* Vienna, Austria, 1 April 1865; *d.* Göttingen, Germany, 24 September 1929), *colloidal chemistry*.

Zsigmondy was a figure of paramount importance on colloid chemistry during the first quarter of the twentieth century. His receipt of the Nobel Prize in 1925, for invention of the ultramicroscope and his work on colloids, was the first time this fledgling science had been so honored. In 1926 work by J. B. Perrin and Theodor Svedberg that followed directly from Zsigmondy's achievement was recognized by the Nobel Prizes in physics and in chemistry, respectively. No Nobel Prize since then has been awarded for work solely in colloid chemistry.

Zsigmondy was the son of Adolf Zsigmondy, a dentist, and Irma von Szakmáry. He spent his childhood, his school years, and his first years as a university student in Vienna. He took his Ph.D. in organic chemistry at the University of Munich in 1890. With this, his activity in organic chemistry ended. Neither was he influenced by the great schools of physical chemistry developing in the Netherlands under van't Hoff and at Leipzig under Ostwald. At Berlin, Zsigmondy worked on inorganic inclusions in glass with the physicist A. A. Kundt (1891–1892) and then, at Graz, as a lecturer on chemical technology at the Technische Hochschule until 1897, when he joined the Schott Glass Manufacturing Company in Jena. There he was concerned with colored and turbid glasses, and invented the famous Jena milk glass. Zsigmondy left industrial work in 1900 to pursue private research that led to the invention of the ultramicroscope and his classic studies on gold sols. His achievements during this period led to his being called to Göttingen as professor of inorganic chemistry in 1907.

Zsigmondy became interested in colloids through work with glasses that owed their color and opacity to colloidal inclusions. He soon recognized that the red fluids first prepared by Faraday through reduction of gold salts are largely analogues of ruby glasses, and he developed techniques for preparing them reproducibly. These gold sols became the model systems used in much of his work.

The presence of colloidal particles is apparent from the cone of scattered light known as the Tyndall beam. Zsigmondy's great contribution was the invention of the ultramicroscope, which rendered the individual particles visible. In the ultramicroscope, ordinary illumination along the microscope's axis is replaced by illumination perpendicular to the axis. With such dark-field illumination the individual particles are rendered luminous by the scattered light that reaches the eye of the observer, in much the same fashion that moving dust particles are illuminated in a sunbeam. This achievement had been rejected for particles much smaller than the resolving power of the microscope. Certainly the exaltation Zsigmondy experienced could hardly have been less than that of any other intrepid explorer who reveals a new universe. "A swarm of dancing gnats in a sunbeam will give one an idea of the motion of the gold particles in the hydrosol of gold. They hop, dance, jump, dash together, and fly away from each other, so that it is difficult in the whirl to get one's bearings."

Although dark-field illumination had long been a recognized procedure in microscopy, many difficult technical problems remained. Zsigmondy was assisted by H. F. W. Siedentopf, a physicist with the Zeiss Company of Jena, in the design and construction of the apparatus. The company's director, Ernst Abbe, placed the facilities of the Zeiss plant at their disposal even though Zsigmondy was not associated with the company. Indeed, this activity came at a time in his career when he had no professional attachment.

Much of Zsigmondy's research was devoted to the investigation of gold sols and particularly purple of Cassius. Although it had been investigated by a number of noted chemists, no decision had been reached whether this peculiar preparation, valued as a glass paint, is a mixture or a compound. In 1898, Zsigmondy was able to show that it is a mixture of very small gold and stannic acid particles, and later directly confirmed the correctness of this finding with his ultramicroscope.

Zsigmondy investigated the color changes that occur in gold sols upon the addition of salts and studied the inhibition of these effects upon the addition of such protective agents as gelatin and gum arabic. With the aid of the ultramicroscope, he demonstrated that the color changes reflected alteration of particle size due to coagulation and that the protective agents acted so as to inhibit the coagulation.

At Göttingen, Zsigmondy was occupied with ultrafiltration, which he developed as another useful tool for the investigation of colloidal systems. He explored a broad range of substances, especially silica gels and soap gels.

A lover of nature and an avid mountain climber, Zsigmondy acquired an estate near Terlano, in the southern Tirol, to which he retreated frequently. He married Laura Luise Müller, the daughter of Wilhelm Müller, in 1903; they had two daughters.

## BIBLIOGRAPHY

Zsigmondy's books include *Zur Erkenntnis der Kolloide* (Jena, 1905), translated by Jerome Alexander as *Colloids and the Ultramicroscope* (New York, 1909);

*Kolloidchemie; ein Lehrbuch* (Leipzig, 1912), 5th ed., 2 vols. (Leipzig, 1925–1927), translated by E. B. Spear as *The Chemistry of Colloids* (New York, 1917); and *Das kolloide Gold* (Leipzig, 1925), written with P. A. Thiessen.

His memoirs and other writings are listed in Poggendorff, IV, 1695–1696; V, 1414; and VI, 2971; for a comprehensive bibliography of secondary literature, see VIIa supp., 796.

MILTON KERKER

**ZUBOV, NIKOLAY NIKOLAEVICH** (*b.* Izmail, Russia [now Ukrainian S.S.R.], 23 May 1885; *d.* Moscow, U.S.S.R., 11 November 1960), *oceanography*.

The son of an officer, Zubov followed family tradition and enrolled in the Naval Cadet Corps, from which he graduated in 1904. He then attended the Naval Academy, where his interest turned to hydrography. After graduating in 1910, Zubov served as navigator and commander of a torpedo boat. In 1912, on a cruise in the Barents Sea aboard the messenger ship *Bakan*, Zubov carried out his first scientific work, a plane-table and hydrographic survey of Matyushikha Inlet, on Novaya Zemlya, and of the lower course and mouth of the Pesha River, at the Cheshska Gulf. The following year he entered civil service as hydrographer in the office of commercial ports of the Ministry of Trade and Industry. Soon afterward he participated in the scientific expedition to the Baltic Sea of the schooner *Utro*, and in 1914 he was sent to Norway to continue his education at the geophysics institute at Bergen.

World War I interrupted Zubov's studies and he returned to military service as commander of the torpedo boat *Burny*; after the war he served at naval headquarters. Zubov was one of the first members of the Floating Marine Scientific Institute (later the State Institute of Oceanography), founded in 1921 to study the Soviet Union's northern seas; he was also director of the hydrological section. In 1923 the institute acquired its own expedition ship, the *Persia*, which, with Zubov's participation, completed four hydrographic sections of the southwest Barents Sea by 1928, using only modest equipment (two bathometers, each containing a thermometer, and two rotors). Zubov presented his scientific conclusions in a series of articles (1929–1932) that were later generalized in a fundamental memoir (1932); this work deals with the three major problems that retained his interest

throughout his life: the vertical mixing of seawater, ocean currents, and sea ice.

Zubov explained the origin of intermediate layers of warm and cold seawater and gave a theoretical basis and practical method for estimating the intensity of the vertical circulation during the winter. His findings were immediately applied to explain the degree of aeration of deep-sea layers, data needed in estimating fish reserves and their food resources. His subsequently elaborated concept of the index of freezing was important in compiling forecasts of sea ice.

Zubov also reexamined and reinterpreted the theoretical basis of Wilhelm Bjerknes' indirect method of determining the elements of ocean currents. Whereas Bjerknes believed the heterogeneity of density to be the cause of currents, Zubov considered it, to a much greater extent, a consequence of them. Zubov demonstrated that Bjerknes' method failed to reckon fully with density currents (or "convection currents" as they were then known) and, in general, with stationary currents of any origin. Zubov called his method of calculating currents according to the distribution of density the "dynamic method of processing oceanologic observations." His practical handbook on the subject (1935) led to a series of "dynamic maps" of the Soviet Union's northern seas that gave the first sufficiently accurate picture of their currents.

In his 1932 memoir Zubov also included his theory of climatic changes of currents, described their influence on sea ice, and gave the basis for forecasting ice in the polar seas. Internal waves and high tides were also considered; the latter subject was also dealt with in an important monograph (1933) that includes a rigorous exposition of the modern theory of high tides.

As secretary of the Soviet committee of the Second International Polar Year (1932–1933), Zubov was responsible for introducing into the program Soviet studies of the Arctic Ocean and of its northern seas, from the Greenland to the Chukchi seas, as well as the Bering and Okhotsk seas and the Sea of Japan. During the summer of 1932 he participated in a cruise aboard the small sail-and-motor-powered trawler, the *N. M. Knipovich*. The excursion confirmed the accuracy of Zubov's forecast that ice conditions would be extremely light in the Barents Sea, even at the highest latitudes; and the *Knipovich*—although completely unfit for high-latitude navigation—attained the latitude of 82°05' and was the first ship ever to circumnavigate Franz Joseph Land.

In 1935 Zubov headed the scientific section of the first Soviet high-latitude expedition of the icebreaker *Sadko*, which explored the upper latitudes of the Greenland, Barents, and Kara seas, and charted the paths of the deep northern currents that penetrate the warm waters of the Atlantic in the Kara Sea.

He also engaged in aerial reconnaissance of Arctic ice, proposing early spring surveys of separate regions and reconnaissance of an entire route "with only the naked eye." He completed his last flight over the Arctic practically on the eve of his seventieth birthday. Like the others it yielded new information used to maintain navigation through the northern sea routes.

Having returned to naval service at the beginning of World War II, Zubov was sent to Arkhangelsk, charged with maintaining an open passage through the ice at the mouth of the Northern Dvina River for the White Sea military flotilla. In an original work on the subject (1942) Zubov started from the assumption that in certain cases ice may be considered not as an elastic, but as a plastic, body. His formula based on this proposition for determining the flexure of ice under a given load was subsequently confirmed in practice. In his important monograph on Arctic ice (1945) Zubov presented the laws of the origin, growth, movement and hummocking, weakening, and melting of the Arctic ice cover. Central to the work is his conception of the unity of the "air-ice-water" system, of the close interdependence of phenomena in these areas, and of the continually changing condition of the ice. Of special importance to navigation were his method for predicting the depth of ice, his rule correlating the drift of ice with isobars, and his method of calculating the winter vertical circulation of water and the index of freezing. Certain conclusions that were not based on direct observation at the time they were formulated have subsequently been fully confirmed. For example, beginning with his general laws of ice drift, Zubov determined the presence, in that sector of the central polar basin bordering the Pacific Ocean, of an anticyclonic system of ice drift along a gigantic and, in some instances, closed curve. The presence of this circular motion was established over a decade later by the drifting of Soviet and American stations at the North Pole.

Zubov harbored a lifelong dislike of the term "oceanography," considering it equivalent only to a descriptive study of the sea. He considered himself an "oceanologist," who attempted to penetrate the very essence of the processes that he studied. In 1931 he created the world's first department of oceanology at the Hydrometeorological Center of the U.S.S.R. From 1949 to 1960 he was professor of oceanology at the University of Moscow.

Zubov's abiding concern with observation was expressed in his more than 200 publications. In September 1959, a year before his death, the results of his last two studies were presented to the First International Oceanographic Congress in New York. They dealt with the relation between barometric relief and sea level, and condensation as a result of the intermingling of seawater (written with K. D. Sabinin).

### BIBLIOGRAPHY

I. Original Works. An edition of Zubov's selected works on oceanology was published on his seventieth birthday as *Izbrannye trudy po okeanologii* (Moscow, 1955). His earlier writings include "Gidrologischeskie raboty Plavuchevo morskogo nauchnogo instituta v yugo-zapadnoy chasti Barentseva morya letom 1928 g. na e/s *Persey*" ("Hydrological Work of the Floating Marine Scientific Institute in the Southwest Part of the Barents Sea in the Summer of 1928 Aboard the Expedition Ship *Persia*"), in *Trudy Gosudarstvennogo okeanograficheskogo instituta*, **2**, no. 4 (1932); *Elementarnoe uchenie o prilivakh v more* ("An Elementary Study of High Tides"; Moscow, 1933); *Okeanograficheskie tablitsy* ("Oceanographic Tables"; Moscow, 1931), based on Knudsen's *Hydrographische Tabellen*; 2nd ed., enl., as *Okeanologicheskie tablitsy* ("Oceanographic Tables"; 1940), with supplementary *Okeanologicheskie grafiky* ("Oceanologic Graphs"; 1941), written with K. M. Sirotov; 3rd ed., rev. and enl. (Moscow–Leningrad, 1957); *Dinamichesky metod obrabotki okeanologicheskikh nablyudeny* ("The Dynamic Method of Processing Oceanologic Observations"; Moscow, 1935); *Morskie vody i ldy* ("Seawater and Sea Ice"; Moscow, 1938); *Morya zemnogo shara* ("Seas of the Terrestrial Globe"), appendix to the index of geographic names in the *Great Soviet World Atlas* (Moscow, 1940), written with A. V. Everling; *Ldy Arktiki* ("Arctic Ice"; Moscow–Leningrad, 1945); also in English trans. (San Diego, Calif., n.d. [1963]); *Dinamicheskaya okeanologia* ("Dynamic Oceanology"; Moscow–Leningrad, 1947); *V tsentre Arktiki* ("In the Middle of the Arctic"; Moscow–Leningrad, 1948); *Otechestvennye moreplavateliissledovateli morey i okeanov* ("Native Navigator-Investigators of the Seas and Oceans"; Moscow, 1954); *Dinamichesky metod vychislenia elementov morskikh techeny* ("Dynamic Method of Calculating the Elements of Ocean Currents"; Leningrad, 1956); *Osnovy uchenia o prolivakh Mirovogo okeana* ("Basic Study of Straits of the World's Oceans";

Moscow, 1956); and *Uplotnenie pri smeshenii morskikh vod raznoy temperatury i solenosti* ("Condensation as a Result of Mixing Seawater of Different Temperatures and Salinity"; Leningrad, 1957).

II. SECONDARY LITERATURE. On Zubov and his work, see A. D. Dobrovolsky, "N. N. Zubov—Okeanolog" ("N N. Zubov—Oceanologist"), in Zubov's *Izbrannye trudy* (see above), 5–11; and "N. N. Zubov—odin iz krupneyshikh sovetskikh okeanologov" (". . . One of the Most Outstanding Soviet Oceanologists"), in *Okeanologia*, **1** no. 2 (1961), 355–359; and B. L. Lagutin, A. M. Muromtsev, and A. A. Yushchak, "Pamyati Nikolaya Nikolaevicha Zubova" ("In Memory of . . ."), in *Meteorologia i gidrologia* (1961), no. 5, 59–60.

A. F. PLAKHOTNIK

**ZUBOV, VASILY PAVLOVICH** (*b.* Aleksandrov, Ivanovo province [now Ivanovskaya oblast], Russia, 1 August 1899; *d.* Moscow, U.S.S.R., 8 April 1963), *history of science.*

The son of a professor of chemistry at the University of Moscow, Zubov graduated in 1922 from the Faculty of History and Philology at Moscow; he subsequently worked at the Academy of Artistic Sciences and, from 1935 to 1945, at the Academy of Architecture. His main interest, the artistic, technical, and architectural ideas of the Middle Ages and the Renaissance, was focused on Alberti, Barbaro, and Leonardo da Vinci, whose works he helped to publish in Russian. He received the doctorate of art in 1946 for his research on Alberti's theory of architecture.

Zubov's interest had gradually turned to the scientific and philosophical literature of that time, and in 1945 he transferred to the Institute of the History of Sciences and Technology of the U.S.S.R. Academy of Sciences. In December 1946 he presented a critique of Duhem's concept of medieval science and proposed a program of further work in this area. In carrying it out, he conducted many investigations in the history of atomic theory and in the development of mathematics, physics, and mechanics. Related to these studies were his specialized work on the development of philosophical thought in Russia from the eleventh to the seventeenth centuries and a number of general investigations of the physics of antiquity, the Middle Ages, and the Renaissance. His extensive editorial activity included his work as editor of a three-volume history of the natural sciences in Russia (1957–1962).

Zubov was elected corresponding member of the International Academy of the History of Science in 1958 and became an active member two years later. In 1963 he was posthumously awarded the George Sarton Medal of the History of Science Society.

*BIBLIOGRAPHY*

I. ORIGINAL WORKS. Zubov's more than 200 writings include *Istoriografia estestvennykh nauk v Rossii* ("Historiography of the Natural Sciences in Russia"; Moscow, 1956); *Ocherki razvitia osnovnykh fizicheskikh idey* ("Sketches of the Development of Basic Physical Ideas"; Moscow, 1959); *Leonardo da Vinci* (Leningrad, 1961), English trans. by D. H. Kraus (Cambridge, Mass., 1968); *Ocherki razvitia osnovnykh ponyaty mekhaniki* ("Sketches in the Development of Basic Concepts of Mechanics"; Moscow, 1962), written with A. T. Grigorian; *Aristotle* (Moscow, 1963); and *Razvitie atomisticheskikh predstavleny do nachala XIX veka* ("Development of Atomic Ideas to the Beginning of the Nineteenth Century"; Moscow, 1965), with a detailed bibliography of Zubov's works, 360–370.

II. SECONDARY LITERATURE. On Zubov and his work, see A. T. Grigorian, B. G. Kuznetsov, and A. P. Youschkevitch, "Vassili Pavlovitch Zoubov," in *Archives internationales d'histoire des sciences*, **16** (1963), 305–306; C. Maccagni, "Vasilij Pavlovic' Zubov, 1899–1963," in *Physics*, **5** (1963), 333–339; and A. P. Youschkevitch, "Vassili Zoubov, homme et savant," in *Actes del' XIe Congrès international d'histoire des sciences*, I (Wrocław–Warsaw–Cracow, 1968), 34–40.

A. T. GRIGORIAN
A. P. YOUSCHKEVITCH

**ZUCCHI, NICCOLÒ** (*b.* Parma, Italy, 6 December 1586; *d.* Rome, Italy, 21 May 1670), *mathematics, theology.*

Zucchi taught rhetoric, and later theology and mathematics, at the Jesuits' Roman College, of which he was also rector and from which he moved to the one in Ravenna. Returning to Rome, he held the office of preacher in the Apostolic Palace for at least seven years and was in charge of his religious order's mother house. Because of the esteem in which he was held, he was a member of the retinue of the papal legate sent to the court of the Emperor Ferdinand II, where he met Kepler; Zucchi considered this event one of the most important in his life.

Zucchi is remembered today for his research, "partly the fruit of experiment and partly of reasoning," in optics. In 1616 (or perhaps 1608) he had constructed an apparatus in which an ocular lens was used to observe the image produced by reflection from a concave metal mirror. This was one of the earliest reflecting telescopes, in which the enlargement is obtained by the interaction of mirrors and lenses.

Later, in *Optica philosophia* . . ., Zucchi described the apparatus, from which, wittingly or not, the most improved models of a slightly later date were derived (those of Gregory and Newton, for instance).

This apparatus enabled Zucchi to make a more thorough examination of the spots on Mars (1640), observed four years earlier by F. Fontana, and thus to supply material for Cassini's discovery of the rotation of that planet (1666).

Zucchi worked in a period of contradictory thought and scientific investigation. Alongside the clarity of Galileo's ideas were beliefs at once highly ingenuous and abstruse, as well as extravagant errors.

Hence, Zucchi accepted strange astronomical theories, which he expounded with the utmost certainty in his sermons. In the cathedral of Pisa (Galileo's native city) he asserted in 1638 that the sun is further from the earth during the summer than in winter and that this is proved by the need to alter the length of the telescope in those seasons in order to be able to observe sunspots. But this was not enough: he stated that Venus is nearer the sun than Mercury is, because the former represents beauty and the latter skill. Such statements elicited laughter in some circles but were simultaneously accepted in others as a sign of profound doctrine.

*BIBLIOGRAPHY*

Zucchi's main work is *Optica philosophia experimentalis et ratione a fundamentis constituta* . . ., 2 vols. (Leiden, 1652–1656). He was also author of *Nova de machinis philosophia* (Rome, 1649).

LUIGI CAMPEDELLI

**IBN ZUHR, ABŪ MARWĀN ʿABD AL-MALIK IBN ABIʾL-ʿALĀʾ** (Latin, **ABHOMERON** or **AVENZOAR**) (*b.* Seville, Spain, *ca.* 1092; *d.* Seville, 1162), *medicine, toxicology, medical botany, theology.*

Ibn Zuhr was the patronymic of a family of famous scholars and physicians from the Arabian tribe of Iyād who had settled in Moorish Spain in the tenth century, if not earlier. Most important and influential among them was the physician Abū Marwān ibn Zuhr. He first studied medicine under his father, Abuʾl-ʿAlāʾ Zuhr, and excelled at an early age. Like his father, Ibn Zuhr served the Murābiṭ dynasty (Almoravids, 1090–1147) in Spain and was well received in their courts. He was then called to serve in the palace of his patron, ʿAlī ibn Tashfīn (reigned 1106–1143) at Marrakesh, Morocco.

Apparently as the result of a misunderstanding, his patron insulted Ibn Zuhr, removed him from his office about 1141, and threw him in prison. As a result of the many indignities he suffered, Ibn Zuhr retained both physical scars and bad feelings after his eventual pardon and release. Therefore, as he said in his later writings, it was not difficult, after the fall of the Murābiṭs, to establish friendships with their enemies, the Muwaḥḥids (Almohads). The new ruler, Abū Muḥammad ʿAbd al-Muʾmin (*d.* 1163), welcomed Ibn Zuhr and appointed him not only as his court physician but also as a counseling vizier. Ibn Zuhr dedicated two works to him: his treatise on theriaca, *al-Tiryāq al-sabʿīnī*, and one on diet, *al-Aghdhiya*.

During this later period, Ibn Zuhr accumulated much prestige and wealth and became a very close friend of Ibn Rushd, to whom he dedicated his best-known book, *al-Taysīr*. Ibn Rushd had asked Ibn Zuhr to write this book on the treatment of particular diseases of the organs of the body and methods of therapy. He personally compiled and wrote his *al-Kulliyāt*, on the generalities of medicine, as a supplement to *al-Taysīr*, as he explained in the introduction.

Ibn Zuhr's daughter became one of the better-known midwives in Islam, and a son became a physician, poet, and man of letters. On one occasion, when Ibn Zuhr was away from his office, the son treated patients. In recognition of the son's excellent performance and to encourage him, Ibn Zuhr dedicated to him *al-Tadhkira*, a book on therapeutics, fevers, and the careful use of laxatives—which he considered to be poisons when abused.

After a career in medical teaching, practice, and writing, Ibn Zuhr died of a malignant tumor and was buried outside the victory gate in Seville. He exerted a considerable influence on Western as well as Arabic medicine, after his works were translated and widely circulated in Latin and Hebrew. Although a true follower of Hippocrates and Galen, he developed numerous original ideas through his medical experimentation and observation. Ibn Zuhr wrote on the therapeutic value of good diets and on antidotes against poisons, and cautioned against deliberate uses of purgatives in treating the sick, who needed curing medications, not "poisons." He urged physicians to use mild drugs and to watch the reactions of the patient, especially for the first three days; if the drug was found useful, a larger dose could then be administered. He explained that drugs mixed with honey or sugar were carried to the liver, which reacted to these substances.

Ibn Zuhr described in more detail than his predecessors mediastinal tumors and the appearance of abscesses on the pericardium, paralysis of the pharynx, scabies, inflammation of the middle ear, and intestinal erosions. He also recommended tracheotomy, first described and illustrated by Abulcasis al-Zahrāwī, almost a century and a half earlier, artificial feeding through the gullet or the rectum, and the use of cold water to reduce fevers. Ibn Zuhr realized the noxiousness of air coming from marshes and, like Ḥunayn ibn Isḥāq (d. 877), Galen's competent translator, he emphasized the importance of clean, "good" air for health. As a clinician and medical therapist, he was one of the best Muslim physicians in Moorish Spain; and his influence on medicine in the West continued until the Renaissance.

*BIBLIOGRAPHY*

I. ORIGINAL WORKS. All of Ibn Zuhr's nine known works, which were widely circulated in the twelfth century and after, were medical. A century later Ibn Abī Uṣaybiʿa, in ʿAyūn al-anbāʾ, Būlāq ed., II (Cairo, 1882), 66–67, mentioned only seven:

1. al-Tiryāq al-sabʿīnī. This apparently lost work is on theriaca, which incorporates 70 drugs, and its abstraction into seven and/or ten ingredients, known also as al-Antala theriaca. He prepared this antidote for his patron, ʿAbd al-Muʾmin, as a safeguard against poisoning by his enemies.

2. Fī al-Zīna. Little is known about this lost work, except that the title suggests recipes for beautification, cosmetics, and skin medication. He wrote it during his early life as a medical author and practitioner and was ashamed of some of its contents when he matured in experience and knowledge.

3. al-Aghdhiya. Ibn Zuhr wrote this work on diet at the request of his patron, ʿAbd al-Muʾmin, to provide information on accessible foods and their therapeutic advantages. The writer of this article consulted a 14th-century MS of it in Istanbul (Ahmad III Library at the Suleimaniye Library) in 58 fols. Other copies of this dietetic text are also extant.

4. Fī ʿIlal al-kilā. Lost treatise on kidney diseases that Ibn Zuhr wrote at the request of colleagues in Seville.

5. Fī ʿIllatay al-Baras waʾl-ʾbahaq. A lost treatise on leprosy and vitiligo (known also as piebald skin and leukoderma), how they differ, and their treatment.

6. al-Tadhkira. A thesaurus for his son, then a young doctor, concerning the treatment of diseases. Studied by Gabriel Colin in his Avenzoar, sa vie et ses oeuvres (Paris, 1911).

7. al-Taysīr fiʾl-mudāwāt waʾl-ʾtadbīr (Latin, Alteisirʾ [or Teissir], scilicet regiminis et medelae), Ibn Zuhr's best-known medical text in 30 treatises, written at the instigation of Ibn Rushd, who copied it. A few copies exist in Arabic and several more survive in Latin and Hebrew, an indication of its wide circulation in Europe. See the list in Ludwig Choulant, Handbuch der Bücherkunde für dir ältere Medicin (Leipzig, 1841), 375–376. Copies examined by the author were in the National Library, Rabat (Q159), and the Royal Library, Rabat (no. 1538). In it Ibn Zuhr, as was the practice of the time, mixed astrology with pharmacological and experimental observations, and superstitions with rational and objective reasoning. The book was highly praised by Ibn Rushd as the best available on particulars in medicine and therapeutics. See Kitāb al-Kulliyyāt (Larache, Morocco, 1939), 230. Nonetheless, Ibn Zuhr was definitely influenced by the works of such predecessors as Ḥunayn ibn Isḥāq, al-Rāzī, and al-Zahrāwī.

8. al-Iqtiṣād fī Iṣlāḥ al-Anfus waʾl-ajsād. This work ("On the Ecology of the Treatment and Healing of Body and Soul") is not mentioned by Ibn Uṣaybiʿa. It was written for the Murābiṭ Prince Ibrāhīm ibn Yūsuf ibn Tashfīn after he moved to Morocco in 1121. It discusses therapeutics and hygiene and was written for the lay reader. At least in spirit and in title this work followed a similar one for treatment of body and soul, Kitāb al Irshād li-maṣāliḥ al-Anfus waʾl-ajsād, by the Egyptian Jewish physician Ḥibat Allāh ibn Jumayʿ (d. 1198). Two extant copies of al-Iqtiṣād are mentioned in Carl Brockelmann, Geschichte der arabischen Literatur, I (Leiden, 1943), 642, and Supp. I (Leiden, 1937), 890. It was studied by H. P. J. Renaud in "Trois études . . .," in Hespéris, 12 (1931), 91–105; and 20 (1935), 87.

9. Jāmiʿ Asrār al-Ṭibb. The other book not mentioned by Ibn Uṣaybiʿa, a copy of which is in the National Library, Rabat (D 532), is a compendium ("The Comprehensive Text on the Mystery or Secrets of the Healing Art"). It discusses human physiology especially in regards to the digestive system, physical therapy, and dietetics. It also describes the functions of other bodily organs including the liver, spleen, bladder, as well as general diseases such as fevers, gout, and hemorrhoids. It further includes a formulary on syrups, electuaries, and other pharmaceutical preparations, which erroneously was thought to be composed as an appendix to al-Taysīr and of which other copies are extant. Upon a thorough examination of the text this author discovered that it was the contribution of his father Abū al-ʿAlāʾ ibn Zuhr, who died in Cordoba, 525/1131. This same Rabat copy includes another text entitled al-Shāfī min al-Amrāḍ waʾl-ʿIlal ("The Healer of All Diseases")

on the diagnosis and treatment of diseases. It was dedicated, and most probably by the father, Abū al-'Alā' ibn Zuhr, to the Murābiṭ prince al-Manṣūr Abū al-'Abbās Aḥmad, divided into forty discourses with frequent quotations from ancient sages and religious sayings.

II. SECONDARY LITERATURE. Ibn Abī Uṣaybi'a's contemporary, Muḥammad Ibn al-Abbār (1199–1260), gave one of the earliest brief biographies of Ibn Zuhr and other members of his family in *Takmilat al-ṣila*, edited by F. Codera in *Bibliotheca arabico-hispana*, II (Madrid, 1889), 616. He was also mentioned in Abu'l-Falāḥ ibn al-'Imād (*d.* 1679), *Shadharāt al-dhahab*, IV (Cairo, 1350 A.H.), 179; and his *Taysīr* and *Jāmi'* are listed in Ḥājjī Khalīfa's *Kashf al-ẓunūn*, I (Cairo, 1892), 354, and (Istanbul, 1941) 520. The most useful and reliable later references are the following, listed chronologically: F. Wüstenfeld, *Geschichte der arabischen Aerzte und Naturforscher* (Göttingen, 1840), 90–91; L. Leclerc, *Histoire de la médecine arabe*, II (Paris, 1876), 86–93; Gabriel Colin, "Ibn Zuhr," in *Encyclopaedia of Islam*, II (Leiden, 1927), 430–431; George Sarton, *Introduction to the History of Science*, II (Baltimore, 1931), 231–234; Aldo Mieli, *La science arabe et son rôle dans l'évolution scientifique mondiale*, 2nd ed. (Leiden, 1966), 188–215; R. Arnaldes, "Ibn Zuhr," in *Encyclopaedia of Islam*, new ed., III (Leiden, 1969), 976–979; Sami Hamarneh, *Index of Mss. in the Ẓāhiriyyah* (Damascus, 1969), 174–176, in Arabic; and the commemorative volume, *Al-Ṭabib Ibn Zuhr* (Aleppo, 1972), esp. Michael Khoury, "Banu Zuhr," pp. 159–203.

SAMI HAMARNEH

**ZWELFER, JOHANN** (*b.* Rhenish Palatinate, 1618; *d.* Vienna, Austria [?], 1668), *pharmacy, chemistry.*

After sixteen years as a pharmacist in his native region, Zwelfer went to Padua to study medicine. Upon receiving the M.D. degree he went to Vienna, where he apparently spent the rest of his life. Statements that he taught chemistry and was physician to the court are undocumented. He is first mentioned as the author of a book of corrections to the standard German pharmacopoeia and of an original pharmacopoeia, both published in 1652.

Zwelfer has been credited with a few minor chemical innovations: the "purification" of calomel (mercurous chloride) by use of a water wash to remove the violently poisonous mercuric chloride, and the preparation of a pure form of iron oxide (*crocus martis*) by igniting ferrous nitrate. His outstanding contribution, however, was his general influence in reform of the pharmacopoeia. He was the first to write a commentary on a pharmacopoeia—the standard official German work of that

genre, the *Pharmacopoeia Augustana*, which had appeared under the auspices of the Collegium Medicum of Augsburg and was used in Vienna. Like other works of this kind, it was an uncritical compilation of recipes, many of them ancient. The principal controversy involved in the compilation of these works had been whether the new chemical remedies associated with Paracelsus should be included; but this question had been settled, with their inclusion, by the time Zwelfer became active. The next issue was the improvement of the recipes, and he may have been the first to raise it.

In this commentary Zwelfer reveals a bellicose nature in the tradition of Paracelsus. Objections (*animadversiones*) are made to almost every recipe—and in a tone of sarcasm and invective that aroused not only the Collegium Medicum of Augsburg, but almost everyone mentioned in the book, in cities from Montpellier to Venice. In Venice, Otto Tachenius was inspired by Zwelfer's criticism of his "volatile viperine salt" to write his *Hippocrates chimicus*, a more famous book than any Zwelfer ever wrote. The Augsburg Collegium was still sufficiently aroused sixteen years after Zwelfer's death to issue, with him in mind, a "renovated and augmented" *Pharmacopoeia Augustana*.

Zwelfer was indeed intemperate, as Lucas Schröck charges in the preface to the renovated *Pharmacopoeia* and as is still evident to the reader of these books. "Stupid" was his word for the *Pharmacopoeia*'s recipe for the preparation of "water of lead oxide" (*aqua lithargyri*) by distillation, and it was a typical comment. But it seems to have been Zwelfer's choice of words that was at fault, for this recipe is absent from the renovated *Pharmacopoeia*. As for Tachenius, he was indignant that "Reformer" (as he called Zwelfer) had called him a "cheat" in his commentary on the *Pharmacopoeia*'s recipe for viperine salt. But Tachenius went on to admit that there was some truth in the remark, for although he personally instructed Zwelfer in the preparation of the salt, he did so only "metaphorically," feeling it best not to reveal the recipe.

*BIBLIOGRAPHY*

I. ORIGINAL WORKS. Zwelfer's works are *Animadversiones in Pharmacopoeia Augustana* (Vienna, 1652) and *Pharmacopoeia regia* (Vienna, 1652).

II. SECONDARY LITERATURE. Zwelfer is said to have died unlamented, a situation apparently reflected in the standard German and Austrian national biographical dictionaries, in which he is not mentioned. The brief account in C. G. Jöcher, *Allgemeines Gelehrten-Lexicon*, IV (Leipzig, 1751), 2141, has served as the source for most later accounts. J. R. Partington, *A History of Chemistry*, II (London, 1961), 292, 296–297, has a little on his chemistry.

R. P. MULTHAUF

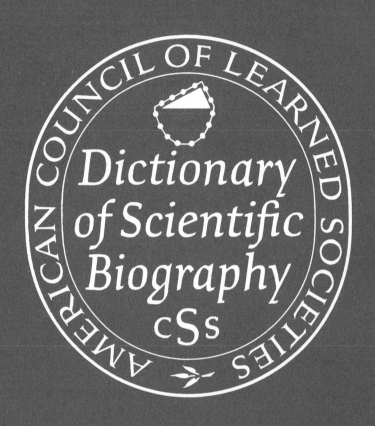

*Dictionary
of Scientific
Biography*

AMERICAN COUNCIL OF LEARNED SOCIETIES

cSs